human sexuality

in a world of diversity

Vice-President and Editorial Director: Gary Bennett
Editor-in-Chief: Michelle Sartor
Acquisitions Editor: Matthew Christian
Sponsoring Editor: Carolin Sweig
Marketing Manager: Lisa Gillis
Senior Developmental Editor: Patti Altridge
Project Manager: Jessica Hellen
Manufacturing Manager: Susan Johnson
Production Editor: Katrina Wilbur, Element LLC
Copy Editor: Anne Brennan
Proofreaders: Sheila Joyce and Marne Evans
Compositor: Element LLC
Photo and Permissions Researcher: Monika Schurmann
Art Director: Julia Hall
Cover and Interior Designer: Miriam Blier
Cover Image: Shannon Fagan/Getty Images

Credits and acknowledgments of material borrowed from other sources and reproduced,
with permission, in this textbook appear on the appropriate pages within the text and on page 549.

Original edition published by Pearson Education, Inc., Upper Saddle River, New Jersey, USA.
Copyright © 2011 Pearson Education, Inc. This edition is authorized for sale only in Canada.

If you purchased this book outside the United States or Canada, you should be aware that it has been
imported without the approval of the publisher or the authors.

10 9 8 7 6 5 4 3 CKV

Library and Archives Canada Cataloguing in Publication

   Human sexuality in a world of diversity/Spencer A. Rathus . . . [et al.].—4th Canadian ed.

Includes bibliographical references and index.

ISBN 978-0-205-01576-4

   1. Sex—Textbooks.   2. Sex customs—Canada—Textbooks.   I. Rathus, Spencer A.

HQ21.H84 2012   306.7   C2011-906793-5

ISBN 978-0-205-01576-4

human sexuality

in a world of diversity

fourth canadian edition

Spencer A. Rathus

The College of New Jersey

Jeffrey S. Nevid

St. John's University

Lois Fichner-Rathus

The College of New Jersey

Edward S. Herold

University of Guelph

Alexander McKay

Sex Information and Education Council of Canada

Chang School of Continuing Education, Ryerson University

PEARSON

Toronto

Dedicated with love to our children Taylor Lane Rathus and Michael Zev Nevid, who were born at the time the first edition of this book was written.

—S.A.R., L.F.-R., J.S.N.

Dedicated with love to my wife Yvette and our daughter Malia.

—E.S.H.

Dedicated to my parents Janet and Gerald McKay.

—A.G.M.

Brief Contents

Contents

x   Contents

Preface

Canada in the twenty-first century is rapidly evolving with respect to human sexuality. Underlying this change is a wide and profound diversity, as our sexuality is shaped by both human biology and an array of sociocultural factors. The approach that separates *Human Sexuality in a World of Diversity* from other human sexuality textbooks is its full embrace and affirmation of this diversity in general, and of the diversity of human sexuality within Canadian society in particular.

Before writing this edition, we searched extensively for new Canadian materials from a number of sources, including Canadian researchers themselves. We've added many new Canadian references to each chapter. In addition integrating up-to-date Canadian research and statistics, we've addressed key issues in human sexuality within the uniquely Canadian context. In the first chapter, we've detailed various theories used to explain sexual attitudes and behaviours. We've illustrated these theories in almost every other chapter, demonstrating the usefulness of theory in guiding our understanding of diverse aspects of human sexuality.

This fourth Canadian edition is more concise than most other human sexuality textbooks, because we're aware that many enthusiastic users find other textbooks too long or unnecessarily complex for their courses. We have sought to combine clarity with a high standard of scholastic rigour, and to emphasize theory and research as well as practical applications that are relevant to students' lives.

New to the Fourth Canadian Edition

Pearson Canada is pleased to introduce a new Canadian author, Alexander McKay, PhD, who joins Ed Herold for this edition. Dr. McKay is the research coordinator of the Sex Information and Education Council of Canada (SIECCAN) and associate editor of *The Canadian Journal of Human Sexuality*. He teaches CFNF 400: *The Social Context of Human Sexuality* at the G. Raymond Chang School of Continuing Education at Ryerson University.

The fourth Canadian edition of *Human Sexuality in a World of Diversity* embodies many exciting changes that reflect rapid developments in the behavioural and social sciences, biology, and medicine. These include:

- Expanded coverage of sexual-health education in Canada (Chapter 12).
- Highlights examining the impact of new information technologies on human sexuality (throughout the book).
- A greater focus on diversity (throughout the book).

New features include:

- Critical-thinking questions in the margins that stimulate students' interest in the subject matter and encourage them to critically assess their own perspectives on key issues.
- *MySearchLab* and *Pearson eText*.

Chapter-by-Chapter Changes

We've added hundreds of new references that reflect the newest research in the field of human sexuality. No part of the textbook has been untouched by change. Following are just a few of the topics we've added, substantially revised, or updated.

Chapter 1

■ Thinking critically about human sexuality.
■ Thinking critically about sexual advice on the internet.
■ Sexuality and values.
■ Social and political differences between Canada and the United States with respect to sexuality.
■ The influence of feminism on thinking about sexuality.

Chapter 2

■ Qualitative research methods.
■ The Canadian Community Health Survey.
■ Canadian contraception studies.

Chapter 3

■ Female genital cutting/mutilation.
■ Male circumcision.
■ Penis size.
■ Cervical, uterine/endometrial, ovarian, breast, testicular, and prostate cancer.

Chapter 4

■ Effects of recreational drugs on sexual response.
■ Effects of aphrodisiacs and psychoactive drugs on sexual response.
■ The placebo effect.
■ Comparing models of female sexual response.
■ Sexuality and disability.

Chapter 5

■ Variations in gender identity among boys and girls.
■ Gender differences in sexual attitudes and behaviours.

Chapter 6

■ Partner preferences in different relationship contexts.
■ Evolutionary perspectives on mate preferences.

Chapter 7

■ The ABCDE model of romantic relationships.
■ Sexting and Canadian youth.
■ Dating in the era of new communication technologies.
■ Sexual self-disclosure within couple relationships.
■ Initiation of sexual activity within relationships.

Chapter 8

■ Theoretical perspectives on sexual-fantasy content.
■ Survey data on masturbation among males and females at different ages.
■ Survey data on giving and receiving oral sex among males and females at different ages.

Chapter 9

■ Queer, questioning, transgendered, and two-spirited people.
■ Harassment of LGBTQ youth in Canada.
■ Self-acceptance among gay, lesbian, and bisexual youth.

Chapter 10

- Reproductive technologies.
- Sexual activity during pregnancy.
- Teen pregnancy in Canada.

Chapter 11

- Contraceptive use among Canadian women.
- Effectiveness of different methods of contraception.
- Emergency contraception.
- Canadian attitudes toward abortion.
- Canadian abortion rates.
- Women who have repeat abortions.

Chapter 12

- Development of sexuality in childhood.
- Developmental tasks of adolescent sexuality.
- "Hooking up" and "friends with benefits."
- Obstacles faced by sexual-minority youth.
- Developmental tasks of adult sexuality.
- Canadian attitudes toward sexual-health education.
- *Canadian Guidelines for Sexual Health Education.*
- Key ingredients of effective sexual-health education.

Chapter 13

- Prevalence of sexual problems and dysfunctions in the Canadian population.
- Biological and psychosocial causes of sexual problems and dysfunctions.
- Sexual problems within relationships.
- The PLISSIT model.
- Optimal sexuality—a portrait of great sex.

Chapter 14

- Sexually transmitted infections in Canada.
- Epidemiology of STIs and HIV—biological, psychological, and social factors.
- Reducing your risk of STIs and HIV.

Chapter 15

- Normal versus deviant sexual behavior.
- Sexual addiction, compulsive sexual behaviour, and hypersexuality.

Chapter 16

- Incidence of sexual assault in Canada.
- Female sex offenders.
- Treatment of pedophilia.

Chapter 17

- Challenges to Canada's prostitution laws.
- Canadian attitudes toward prostitution.
- Types of sex work.
- Advocacy for sex workers.
- Perspectives on pornography.
- Sexually explicit material (SEM) and Canadian law.

Themes in this Edition

The fourth Canadian edition of *Human Sexuality* in *a World of Diversity* builds upon the strong themes for which previous editions have become known. Four themes are woven throughout the text:

- Human diversity.
- Critical thinking.
- Responsible sexual decision-making.
- Sexual health.

Human Diversity

Colleges and universities undertake the mission of broadening students' perspectives, encouraging them to tolerate and appreciate human diversity. Canada is a nation of hundreds of ethnic and religious groups, many of which endorse culturally distinct beliefs about appropriate gender roles for men and women, as well as distinctive sexual practices and customs. Diversity is even greater within the global village of the world's nearly 200 nations and their subcultures.

Human Sexuality in a World of Diversity incorporates a multicultural, multi-ethnic perspective that reflects the diversity of sexual experience in Canadian society and around the world. Discussion of diversity encourages respect for people who hold diverse beliefs and attitudes.

Critical Thinking

Colleges and universities also encourage students to become critical thinkers. Today's students are so inundated with information about gender and sexuality that it can be difficult to sort truth from fiction. Critical thinking requires thoughtful analysis and probing of others' claims and arguments in light of evidence. Moreover, it requires a willingness to challenge conventional wisdom and the common knowledge many of us take for granted. Throughout this book we raise issues that call for critical thinking.

Responsible Sexual Decision-Making

We encourage students to make responsible sexual decisions on the basis of accurate information. Responsible decision-making is based not only on acquiring accurate information, but also on carefully evaluating this information in light of your own values.

Sexual Health

Human Sexuality in a World of Diversity emphasizes issues that affect sexual health, with extensive coverage of such topics as HIV/AIDS and other STIs, innovations in contraception and reproductive technologies, breast cancer, menstrual distress, sex and disabilities, and diseases that affect the reproductive tract. The textbook encourages students to take an active—in fact, a proactive—role in health promotion.

Feature Boxes and Additional Learning Aids

This fourth Canadian edition of *Human Sexuality in a World of Diversity* continues to use a variety of features to stimulate interest and enhance understanding.

"Innovative Canadian Research" boxes emphasize significant new research contributions by Canadian scholars.

"A World of Diversity" boxes highlight the rich variety of human sexual customs and practices, in Canadian society and around the world. They also include opinions that are contrary to commonly held beliefs.

"Applied Knowledge" boxes assist students with personal decisions, providing information and advice.

"A Closer Look" boxes provide in-depth discussions of societal issues and research.

Each chapter begins with an outline that organizes the subject matter. Key terms appear in boldface within the paragraphs, while a running glossary provides definitions in the margins, close to where the key terms appear. At the end of each chapter, a "Summing Up" section organizes and reviews the subject matter according to the headings within the chapter.

The "Test Yourself" section at the end of each chapter contains multiple-choice and critical-thinking questions to facilitate individual study and promote class discussion. "Answer Key," at the end of the book, contains answers to the "Test Yourself" questions.

Student Supplements

MySearchLab

MySearchLab is a website that offers extensive help with writing and research projects, and provides round-the-clock access to credible, reliable source material.

Research

Content on *MySearchLab* includes immediate access to thousands of full-text articles from leading Canadian and international academic journals, as well as daily news feeds from the Associated Press. Articles contain the full downloadable text, including abstract and citation information, and can be cut, pasted, emailed, and saved for later use.

Writing

MySearchLab contains a step-by-step tutorial on writing a research paper. It includes sections on planning a research assignment, finding a topic, creating effective notes, and finding source material.

Our exclusive online handbook provides grammar and usage support.

Pearson SourceCheck™ offers an easy way to detect accidental plagiarism issues, and our exclusive tutorials teach students how to avoid such issues.

MySearchLab also contains *AutoCite*, which helps students correctly cite sources using the Modern Language Association (MLA), American Psychological Association (APA), Chicago Manual of Style (CMOS), and Council of Biology Editors (CBE) documentation styles for both endnotes and bibliographies.

Take a tour at www.mysearchlab.com.

Pearson eText

Pearson eText provides access to the textbook whenever and wherever you have access to the internet. eText pages look exactly like the printed textbook, offering powerful new functionality for both students and instructors. Users can create notes, highlight passages in different colours, create bookmarks, zoom in and out, click on hyperlinked words and phrases to view definitions, and view the material in single- and double-page views.

CourseSmart for Students

CourseSmart provides instant online access to the textbooks and course materials you need, at an average savings of 60%. With instant access from any computer and the ability to search the textbook, you'll quickly find the content you need, no matter where you are. And with online tools such as highlighting and note-taking, you can save time and study efficiently. See all of the benefits at www.coursesmart.com/students.

Instructor Supplements
Instructor's Resource Manual

This manual includes a variety of resources, including chapter-at-a-glance tables (which correlate chapter topics and learning objectives with the offered resources), teaching tips, activities, additional lecture material, and recommended readings, videos, and websites.

Test Item File

This test bank in Microsoft Word format includes approximately 2000 multiple-choice, true-or-false, and essay questions. This test bank is also available in *MyTest* format (see below).

PowerPoint Presentations

Chapter-by-chapter presentations highlight the key points from the text, supported by diagrams and visuals.

The preceding instructor supplements are available for download from a password-protected section of Pearson Canada's online catalogue (http://vig.pearsoned.ca). Navigate to your book's catalogue page to view a list of available supplements. See your local sales representative for details and access.

MyTest

Pearson Canada's MyTest is a powerful assessment-generation program that helps instructors easily create and print quizzes, tests, exams, and homework and practice handouts. Questions and tests can be created online, allowing instructors ultimate flexibility and the ability to efficiently manage assessments at any time, from anywhere. *MyTest* for *Human Sexuality in A World of Diversity* includes more than 2000 questions in multiple-choice, true-or-false, and essay formats. These questions are also available in Microsoft Word format in the online catalogue.

peerScholar

Firmly grounded in published research, *peerScholar* is a powerful online pedagogical tool that helps develop students' critical and creative thinking skills through creation, evaluation, and reflection. Working in stages, students begin by submitting written assignments. *peerScholar* then circulates their work for others to review, a process that can be anonymous or not, depending on instructors' preferences. Students immediately receive peer feedback and evaluations, reinforcing their learning and driving development of higher-order thinking skills. Students can then re-submit revised work, again depending on instructors' preferences.

Contact your Pearson representative to learn more about *peerScholar* and the research behind it.

CourseSmart for Instructors

CourseSmart provides instant online access to the textbooks and course materials you need, at a lower cost for students. And as students save money, you can save time and hassle with a digital eTextbook that allows you to search for the most relevant content at the moment you need it. Whether it's evaluating textbooks or creating lecture notes to help students with difficult concepts, CourseSmart can make life a little easier. See how by visiting www.coursesmart.com/instructors.

Technology Specialists

Pearson's technology specialists work with faculty and course designers to ensure that Pearson technology products, assessment tools, and online course materials are tailored to your specific needs. By assisting with the integration of a variety of instructional materials and media formats, this highly qualified team helps schools take full advantage of a wide range of educational resources. Your local Pearson Canada sales representative can provide more details about this service program.

Pearson Custom Library

For enrolments of at least 25 students, you can create your own textbook by choosing the chapters that best suit your course needs. To begin building your custom textbook, visit www.pearsoncustomlibrary.com. You can also work with a dedicated Pearson custom editor to create your ideal textbook, publishing your own original content or mixing and matching Pearson content.

Contact your local Pearson representative to get started.

VideoWorkshop for Human Sexuality

VideoWorkshop for Human Sexuality contains 18 observational video segments specially selected to illustrate many of the theories and concepts discussed in any course on human sexuality.

The accompanying *VideoWorkshop for Human Sexuality: Instructor's Teaching Guide with CD-ROM* and *VideoWorkshop for Human Sexuality: Student Learning Guide with CD-ROM* are designed to help instructors and students make the most of this video resource, correlating it with the material in *Human Sexuality in a World of Diversity*. The guide encourages students to think critically about various aspects of human sexuality, and provides questions to test their understanding of the material, as well as related websites that extend exploration of each topic.

Acknowledgments

The authors owe a great debt of gratitude to the many researchers and scholars whose contributions to the body of knowledge of human sexuality are represented in these pages. Underscoring the interdisciplinary nature of this area of study, we've drawn upon the work of scholars in such fields as psychology, sociology, medicine, anthropology, theology, and philosophy, to name a few. We're also indebted to the many researchers who have generously allowed us to quote from their work and reprint tabular material representing their findings.

The authors and publishers wish to thank the many professional colleagues who have provided feedback on this book at various stages in its development. The following people reviewed the previous edition and/or manuscript chapters:

Madeleine Côté, Dawson College
Shaniff Esmail, University of Alberta
Michelle Everest, King's University College
Judith Grad, Concordia University
Corey R. Isaacs, The University of Western Ontario
Robin Milhausen, University of Guelph
Stephanie Mitelman, McGill University
Matthew Numer, Dalhousie University
Jennifer M. Ostovich, McMaster University
B. J. Rye, University of Waterloo
Monika Stelzl, St. Thomas University

I'd like to thank Edward S. Herold for setting a standard of excellence in revising previous Canadian editions. His contributions to this textbook remain one of its greatest strengths.

I also wish to thank Mary Bissell of the Sex Information and Education Council of Canada, whose research expertise and critical insights in human sexuality have been invaluable. I appreciate her contributions to the development of this fourth edition. Thanks also to obstetrician/gynaecologist Jonathan Huber for his helpful suggestions about Chapter 10.

I'm grateful to the many people at Pearson Canada for their valuable assistance with this revision. Sponsoring editor Carolin Sweig helped guide significant changes to the new edition, using faculty reviews to develop a detailed revision plan. I'm especially indebted to senior developmental editor Patti Altridge, who's been exceptionally supportive of a first-time textbook author. I very much appreciate her constructive guidance, feedback, and calming influence. And Anne Brennan has been extremely detailed and thorough in her copy editing.

~ Alexander McKay, PhD

human sexuality

in a world of diversity

CHAPTER ONE

What Is Human Sexuality?

We're about to embark on the study of human sexuality. But why study human sexuality? Isn't sex something to do, rather than something to talk about? Isn't sex a natural function? Don't we learn what we need to know from personal experience, or from our parents or our friends?

Yes. And no. Personal experience teaches us how our bodies respond to sexual stimulation—what turns us on and what turns us off. It teaches us little, however, about the biological processes that bring about sexual response and orgasm. Experience does not inform us about the variations in sexual behaviour that exist around the world, or even in our own neighbourhoods. Nor does experience prepare us to recognize the signs of sexually transmitted infections (STIs), or to evaluate the risks of pregnancy. It does not help us deal with most sexual problems, or dysfunctions. What many of us learned about sex from our parents can probably be summarized in a single word: "don't." The information we received from our friends was probably riddled with exaggeration, or completely false.

Many young people now receive some form of sexual health education at school, but they are usually taught only about STIs and contraception, not about sexual techniques or the emotional aspects of sexuality and relationships.

You may know more about human sexuality than your parents or grandparents did at your age—perhaps more than they do today. But how much do you really know? What causes erection or vaginal lubrication? What factors determine sexual orientation? What are sexual dysfunctions, and what causes them? What leads one person to be sexually attracted to another? How do our sexual responsiveness and interests change as we age? Can you contract a sexually transmitted disease and not know it? These are just a few of the issues we explore in this book.

While you will likely find much of the information in this textbook interesting and useful in your own life, our primary objective is to introduce you to the multidisciplinary academic study of human sexuality. Attaining a knowledge and understanding of human sexuality informed by authoritative research from Canada and around the world is an important academic pursuit that can broaden and enhance our understanding of the world we live in.

Choices, Information, and Decision Making

Although sex is a natural function, and our sexuality can be influenced by biological factors, how we voluntarily express our sexuality is a matter of personal choice. We choose how, where, and with whom to become sexually involved. We face a wide array of sexual decisions. Whom should I date? When should my partner and I become sexually intimate? Should I initiate sexual relations, or wait for my partner to approach me? Should my partner and I practise contraception? If so, which method? Should I use a condom to protect against sexually transmitted infections (or insist that my partner do this)? Should I be tested for HIV? Should I insist that my partner be tested for HIV before we engage in sexual relations?

Many aspects of human sexuality are viewed as moral issues, involving questions of right and wrong. Issues such as premarital and extramarital sex, contraception, and abortion, for example, are often subject to moral debate. No single value system defines us all. Each of us has a unique set of moral values—as a Canadian, as a member of one of Canada's hundreds of cultural groups, as an individual. The world of diversity in which we live is a mosaic of different moral codes and cultural traditions and beliefs. Gathering information and weighing the scientific evidence will alert you to what is possible in the contemporary world, but only you can determine which of your options are compatible with your own moral values.

Making decisions involves choosing among various courses of action. The act of not making a formal decision may itself be a tacit decision. For example, we may vacillate about whether to use a particular form of birth control, but continue to engage in unprotected sex. Is this because we haven't made a decision, or because we've decided to accept whatever happens?

Gathering information helps us predict the outcomes of the decisions we make. This textbook provides you with a broad database concerning scientific developments and ways of relating to other people—including people who come from other cultures. We also encourage you to try to understand other people's sexual beliefs and values in light of their cultural backgrounds. Understanding is an essential milestone on the pathway to respect, and respect is vital to resolving conflicts and establishing healthy relationships.

Spelling it Out.
In this artistic photo by Hamilton photographer Melanie Gillis, nude people are arranged so their bodies form the word "SEX."

What Is Human Sexuality?

This is not a trick question. Consider the various meanings of the word "sex." One use of the term refers whether we're anatomically male or female. The words "sex" and "sexual" also refer to the anatomical structures, called sex organs or sexual organs, that play a role in reproduction and sexual pleasure. We may also speak of sex when referring to physical activities involving our sex organs for purposes of reproduction or pleasure, as in "having sex." Sex also relates to **erotic** feelings, experiences, or desires, such as sexual fantasies and thoughts, sexual urges, and feelings of sexual attraction.

Many researchers reserve the word "sex" for anatomical or biological categories, preferring the word **"gender"** to refer to social or cultural categories. For example, one might say that "reproductive anatomy appears to depend on the sex [not the gender] of the individual, but in so-called traditional societies, **gender roles** [not sex roles] are often seen as polar opposites."

The term **"human sexuality"** refers to the ways we experience and express ourselves as sexual beings. Our awareness of ourselves as females or males is part of our sexuality, as is the capacity we have for erotic experiences and responses. Our knowledge of the gender roles in our culture also has a profound influence on us.

Sex as Leisure

Researchers Meaney and Rye (2007), at St. Jerome's University at the University of Waterloo, have conceptualized sex as a fun, healthy activity that can be considered leisure when it is voluntary, is not seen as work, and serves some personal need. According to their definition, sex is not a leisure activity when it is not voluntary, is viewed as work, or is seen as an obligation.

At its most basic level, sex provides physical pleasure. It's a fun activity that can be enjoyed alone or with others. Sexuality can also be a key component of personality development, as we discover which sexual activities are enjoyable, and with whom. Sexuality is an important part of identity. This is certainly true for gay, lesbian, bisexual, or transgendered people. It's also true for people who engage in certain sexual variations, such as sadomasochism. Meaney and Rye (2007) argue that learning about one's

CRITICAL THINKING QUESTIONS

Some people don't consider oral-genital contact to be "having sex." What's your opinion?

Erotic Arousing sexual feelings or desires.

Gender One's personal, social, and legal status as a male or female.

Gender roles Complex clusters of the ways males and females are expected to behave within a given culture.

Human sexuality The ways we experience and express ourselves as sexual beings.

Innovative Canadian Research

WHAT IS THIS THING CALLED SEX?

New Brunswick researchers Hilary Randall and Sandra Byers (2003) asked university students to indicate which behaviours they would define as "having sex" with someone if they were the ones engaging in those behaviours. The only behaviours most students defined as sex were penile-vaginal intercourse and penile-anal intercourse. Only about one-fifth defined oral-genital contact as sex, and even fewer (10%) defined the touching of genitals leading to orgasm as sex. Interestingly, there was a slight increase in the percentage of students who defined each behaviour as sex if it resulted in orgasm.

When the researchers modified the question, however, far more students indicated that they would define someone as their "sexual partner" if that person were engaging in those behaviours with the respondent. For example, about two-thirds considered anyone with whom they had oral-genital contact to be a sexual partner, and about one-half considered touching of genitals as an indicator of partnership.

University of Calgary researchers Eileah Trotter and Kevin Alderson (2007) asked university students to define "loss of virginity." The students' definition of "loss of virginity" was more narrow than their definition of "having sex." For example, only about half thought penile-anal intercourse qualified as loss of virginity. Almost all accepted penile-vaginal intercourse as the marker for virginity loss. However, a small percentage indicated that orgasm had to be experienced with penile-vaginal intercourse for it to count as loss of virginity.

The researchers also presented students with a list of behaviours and asked them to define each behaviour as sexual if it was performed by an opposite-sex couple and if it was performed by a same-sex couple. Students were more likely to define most of the behaviours as sexual for opposite-sex couples than for same-sex couples. An exception was oral-genital sex: slightly more of the students classified this behaviour as "having sex" if the couple was same sexed than if it was opposite sexed (Trotter & Alderson, 2007).

sexual likes and dislikes through experimentation can lead to sexual self-actualization, a state in which a person is comfortable with his or her sexuality.

Clearly, sex is a common leisure activity for many Canadians. Yet sex is typically not listed as an option when researchers study the types of leisure activities Canadians engage in.

The Study of Human Sexuality

The study of human sexuality draws upon the scientific expertise of anthropologists, biologists, medical researchers, sociologists, and psychologists, to name but a few of the professionals involved in the field. These disciplines all make contributions because sexual behaviour reflects our biological capabilities, psychological characteristics, and social and cultural influences. Biologists inform us about the physiological mechanisms of sexual arousal and response. Medical science teaches us about sexually transmitted diseases and the biological bases of sexual dysfunction. Psychologists examine how our sexual behaviours and attitudes are shaped by perception, learning, thought, motivation, emotion, and personality. Sociologists consider the sociocultural contexts of sexual behaviour. For example, they examine relationships between sexual behaviour and religion, race, and social class. Anthropologists focus on cross-cultural similarities and differences in sexual behaviour. Scientists from many disciplines explore parallels between the sexual behaviours of humans and those of other animals.

A number of organizations promote sex research and sex education. In Canada, leading organizations include the Sex Information and Education Council of Canada (SIECCAN), which publishes *The Canadian Journal of Human Sexuality*, and the Canadian Sex Research Forum (CSRF). Two major international organizations are the Society for the Scientific Study of Sexuality (SSSS), which publishes *The Journal of Sex Research*, and the World Association for Sexual Health (WAS).

Canadian Society and Sexuality

To understand the complexity of factors influencing sexual attitudes and behaviours in Canada, it's important to be aware of the diverse nature of Canadians. Particularly today, immigration patterns are changing the landscape of Canadian society. One in five members of the population was born outside of Canada, with the majority of immigrants (63%) moving to the cities of Toronto, Vancouver, and Montreal. Immigrants constitute 20% of Canadian society and nearly 50% of Toronto's population (Statistics Canada, 2009a). Of course, prior to the European discovery of North America, Canada was inhabited by First Nations people. Currently, 4% of Canada's population is made up of First Nations people (Bailey, 2008).

The first European explorers in the region were mainly French and British, and for many years those two have been the dominant ethnic groups in Canada. In the latter half of the twentieth century, an increasing number of immigrants came from non-European countries. According to the 2006 Census, 59% of immigrants are from Asia and less than one-fifth from Europe. As a result, Canadians of French and British ancestry today make up only about half of the population (Statistics Canada, 2008a).

The most notable change in the Canadian mosaic has been the dramatic increase in the proportion of visible minorities. In 2006, 16% of Canadians (5 million) were members of visible minorities, with South Asian Canadians surpassing Chinese Canadians as the largest group (Statistics Canada, 2008a).

The **values** of immigrants often differ from those of people born in Canada. In South Asian communities, for example, arranged marriages are still fairly common. Some immigrants from Muslim countries maintain the practice of female circumcision, a procedure usually performed on young girls that involves surgical removal of the clitoris and in some cases parts of the labia. This practice, often referred to as "genital mutilation," is contrary to Canadian values. (The Canadian and American governments have declared female circumcision illegal. Within some immigrant communities, however, the procedure is still done.) Parents in some groups use gender-selection techniques, such as abortion, to ensure that they have boys rather than girls. In many cultures, sex is a taboo subject, not discussed openly between parents and their children.

For the most part, sexual attitudes and behaviours are more conservative among immigrants than among the rest of Canadian society. This is particularly pronounced in relation to the age of first intercourse. About three-quarters of 20- to 24-year-olds born in Canada report having had sexual intercourse before age 20, compared with less than half of 20- to 24-year-olds born outside of Canada (Maticka-Tyndale et al., 2001).

Children of immigrant parents often get caught in a culture clash between the traditional values of their parents and the more permissive values of Canadian society. A Manitoba study of ethno-racial minority youth found that since sex was a taboo subject within the family setting, young people felt they could not communicate their real thoughts and questions to their parents (Migliardi, 2007). Research also indicates, however, that most bicultural young people successfully adapt to Canadian culture, while still maintaining ties to the cultural identities of their families. Negotiating conflicting cultural norms may prove to be a challenge, especially for issues pertaining to sexuality and relationships,

Values The beliefs and qualities in life that are deemed important or unimportant, right or wrong, desirable or undesirable.

Sexual Appetites at the Burlesque Ball.
The Burlesque Ball in Montreal, organized by a group called Monde Osé, is meant to encourage people to explore their sexuality. In general, people in Quebec tend to have more permissive sexual attitudes than people in other provinces.

Innovative Canadian Research

ETHNOCULTURAL COMMUNITIES AND SEXUALITY

There has been relatively little research on the sexuality of Canadian ethnic minority groups. Fortunately, some Canadian researchers have begun to study these under-examined groups.

Concerned over the spread of HIV/AIDS, in 1996, Health Canada sponsored a study of diverse ethnic groups in Canada. The study, entitled "Ethnocultural Communities Facing AIDS," was conducted in consultation with representatives of five ethnic communities in Canada: South Asian, Chinese, South African, Caribbean, Latin American, and Arabic.

Most participants reported a double standard for sexual behaviour, with women expected to be virgins before marriage and monogamous after marriage, and men allowed to be sexually permissive before and to some extent after marriage. In the South Asian community, girls were not even allowed to date. In all five communities, many respondents took it for granted that at least some men would have sex with prostitutes and/or women outside their ethnic groups. Homosexuality was treated as if it didn't exist in their communities, and homosexuals were made to feel ashamed. Gender roles were rigidly prescribed, with men considered "bosses" in their families. Women weren't expected to have much interest in or knowledge of sex, and they lacked the power to ask their husbands to use condoms.

Researchers in Vancouver and Montreal, led by Lori A. Brotto of the University of British Columbia, compared the sexuality of Canadian university students from European-Canadian and Asian backgrounds. The Asian students had more conservative sexual attitudes and less sexual experience than the European-Canadian students. The European-Canadian women reported higher rates of sexual desire, arousal, receptivity, and pleasure. The Asian men reported higher rates of erectile dysfunction and less sexual satisfaction than the European-Canadian men.

Brotto et al. (2005) found that degree of acculturation to mainstream Canadian society was significantly related to sexual attitudes and experiences, but that length of residence in Canada was not. In other words, Asian students who kept the strongest ties to their cultural heritage had the most conservative sexual attitudes and experiences. Similarly, a study by Woo and Brotto (2008)

found that Asians in Vancouver who identified less with Canadian culture had higher rates of sexual problems and less communication with their partners about sexual issues. They were also more likely to avoid sexual contact, and when they did engage in sexual relations, their encounters were less sensual in nature.

Eleanor Maticka-Tyndale at the University of Windsor and two visiting researchers from Iran, Khosro Refaie Shirpak and Maryam Chinichian, conducted research with Iranian immigrants (2007). Like the Health Canada researchers, they found that maintaining virginity prior to marriage was considered essential for girls, to maintain good reputations and the honour of their families. The Iranian adults were fearful of having their children exposed to sexuality from the broader Canadian society, especially by the media. Based on images they saw on Canadian television, the Iranian immigrants believed most Canadian adolescents began having sexual intercourse by age 13 or 14. They also perceived that Canadians didn't seem to care about marital loyalty, and engaged in extramarital relationships. The women worried that their husbands would be tempted to engage in affairs, because of the sexual freedoms in Canada. The men worried that in Canada it would be too easy for their wives to walk out of their marriages. Respondents also believed that sex education in Canadian schools emphasized the use of condoms rather than abstinence before marriage.

Maticka-Tyndale et al. (2007) also studied the sexual health needs of immigrants from Iran. Some of the women expressed concerns that their husbands might want to engage in sexual practices, such as oral sex, that were commonplace in Canada but not acceptable in traditional Muslim culture. The immigrants acknowledged that their own lack of sex education resulted in embarrassment when discussing sexual-health topics with medical professionals. Women who had male physicians avoided having Pap smears taken because of embarrassment. Some women felt it was inappropriate to have Pap smears before marriage, because they worried the procedure might affect their virginity. Both males and females reported that modesty and shyness prevented them from discussing sexual problems and asking questions about sex when talking to health professionals. Maticka-Tyndale et al. recommended that health professionals be more culturally sensitive when interacting with immigrants, especially when talking about sexual-health issues.

but many young people find a workable balance between the expectations of each culture (Giguère, Lalonde, & Lou, 2010).

COMPARING CANADA WITH OTHER COUNTRIES   Tremendous variation in sexual attitudes and behaviours is found among the different countries of the world. Many of these variations are presented throughout this textbook. For example, Laumann et al. (2006) surveyed 27 500 men and women over age 40 from 29 countries, asking about their levels of sexual satisfaction. In general, men reported higher levels of satisfaction than women. Western countries with higher gender equality, such as Canada, had the highest rates of sexual satisfaction. The lowest levels of satisfaction were in Indonesia and Japan. According to Laumann et al., in societies that have greater gender equality, sexual pleasure is considered as important for women as it is for men. However, in male-centred cultures where sex is more reproduction-focused, sexual pleasure for women is not considered important. Not surprisingly, many women in those cultures view sex as a marital duty.

There are also many cross-cultural differences in adolescent sexuality. Eleanor Maticka-Tyndale at the University of Windsor has conducted a groundbreaking study of adolescent sexual practices in Kenya (see "A World of Diversity: Sexual Scripts of Young People in Kenya"). This study shows a sexual "script" for adolescent sexuality that diverges from the scripts with which most Canadians are familiar.

When it comes to sexuality, there are many cultural variations. Consider the issue of women going topless at the beach. In Australia and many European countries, it's commonplace to see topless women at public beaches. In Canada, however, this is not the case. Until a few years ago, in fact, it was illegal in Canada for women to go topless.

On a hot summer day in 1991, University of Guelph student Gwen Jacob caused a sensation in downtown Guelph when she removed her shirt and exposed her breasts. She was arrested and convicted of committing an indecent act in a public place. Jacob brought her case to the Ontario Court of Appeal, arguing that because men had the right to go topless, she had a constitutional right to go topless as well. In 1996, the Ontario Court of Appeal overturned the conviction, stating that her act was not degrading or dehumanizing and that it carried no sexual connotation.

This ruling brought out the central issue in the debate over toplessness: is it or is it not a sexual act? In a study of university students in Australia, Herold, Corbesi, and Collins (1994) found that women who had gone topless at the beach believed this was a "natural" rather than a sexual act when done at the beach. Conversely, women who had never gone topless argued that it was indeed sexual and a type of exhibitionism. Despite the court ruling, few women in Canada are willing to go topless in public, even at the beach.

CRITICAL THINKING QUESTIONS

In some cultures, women going topless is seen as sexually provocative and exhibitionist, while in other cultures, it's seen as natural and nonsexual. Can you think of other cultural differences related to human sexuality?

Go Topless Day.
At this event in Toronto, topless women march in protest against the city of Toronto. Toronto denied a group of women to bare their breast and hold a demonstration in a public park, while going topless in the street of Toronto is legal. The event was organized in 2011, in an effort to help women feel comfortable about going topless in public. Many Canadian women are still uncomfortable about going topless.

A World of Diversity

SEXUAL SCRIPTS OF YOUNG PEOPLE IN KENYA

While most Canadian researchers study the attitudes and behaviours of Canadians, some are conducting important research in other countries. Eleanor Maticka-Tyndale at the University of Windsor has studied sexual practices in a number of countries around the world. Most recently, she conducted several studies in African countries. Her groundbreaking research on the sexual scripts of adolescents in Kenya

(Maticka-Tyndale et al., 2005) illustrates the powerful role of culture in influencing sexual behaviour.

A key cultural belief in Kenya is that once puberty is reached, the male sex drive requires release and the female is ready for sex. There is also the belief that delaying the age of engaging in sex has negative consequences. If the male waits to a later age to experience sex, it is believed he may lose the capacity to impregnate his wife and become unable to produce children. Females are concerned that if intercourse

is delayed to a later age, their vaginas will become blocked, leaving them unable to engage in sex.

Both boys and girls feel pressure from peer groups to engage in sex at a young age. Having intercourse is referred to as "playing sex." Boys assume girls are easily available for sex. A girl may indicate an interest in a particular boy by acting in a sexually suggestive manner, such as by opening her legs when he looks at her. The actual initiation of a sexual relationship, however, begins with the male.

COMPARING CANADA AND THE UNITED STATES   Although there are many similarities between Canadians and Americans, there are also many differences. For example, a much higher proportion of the American population than of the Canadian population comes from a Spanish or African background. Consequently, ethnic comparisons in the United States are often based on three categories: African Americans, Latin Americans, and European Americans. This typology is far too narrow to describe Canada. The more than 5 million Canadians who are members of visible minority groups include significant numbers of South Asians, Chinese, Africans, Filipinos, Latin Americans, Arabs, Southeast Asians, West Asians, Koreans, and Japanese, as well as many who are members of more than one group (Statistics Canada, 2009b). It's important to be aware of social and demographic differences between Canada and the United States, because they account for some major differences in sexual attitudes and behaviours.

The birth rate in Canada is lower than that in the United States, especially for women in their twenties. The teenage pregnancy rate is also much higher in the United States (McKay & Barrett, 2010). Population growth in Canada depends more on immigration from other countries than it does in the United States.

The American population (which is about 10 times as large as Canada's) is widely spread throughout the various regions of the United States, whereas two out of three Canadians live near the United States border. And since most new immigrants to Canada choose to live in these populated areas, they also have the highest rates of population growth. Canada's population is especially concentrated in southern Ontario, Montreal, the Vancouver region, and the Calgary–Edmonton corridor (Statistics Canada, 2011). Almost two-thirds of Canada's more than 34 million people live in the two largest provinces, Ontario and Quebec.

More Canadians (49%) than Americans (40%) complete some form of post-secondary education. In the United States, income plays a larger role in determining whether someone attends university, with 63% of Americans from the top income quartile attending university, compared with only 15% of those from the bottom income quartile. In Canada, this income gap is lower, with 45% of those from the top income quartile attending university, compared with 24% of those from the bottom income quartile (Statistics Canada, 2005a).

The boy asks someone who knows the girl he's interested in to tell her he's attracted to her. He gives the go-between a material gift and/or money to give to the chosen girl, to indicate the sincerity of his interest. Along with the gift, the boy may send word that he loves her. Expressions of love don't have the emotional meaning they do in Canada, however; they refer to having sex. Both boys and girls are uncomfortable with talking openly about sex, so much of their communication is nonverbal.

If the girl accepts the gift, she signals that she is open to a dating relationship with the boy. Dating and sex are linked—when a boy and girl begin dating, they also engage in playing sex (having intercourse). There is no intermediate stage, as there is in Canada, where adolescents gradually proceed from kissing and petting to intercourse.

In Kenya, the sexual encounter generally consists of a brief episode of intercourse. Sexual pleasure for the girl is not expected. Rather, sex is seen as something to finish quickly. The objective is to satisfy a basic need for the male. This is an exchange process whereby girls provide sex to obtain material goods.

The girl may delay accepting the boy's advances if she feels the initial material gift is not large enough. Indeed, girls discuss strategies for obtaining more money and more expensive gifts. Many girls prefer to obtain gifts from adult men, because adults can provide more material goods than can younger boys.

Typically, a girl initially refuses to engage in sex. This strategy helps preserve her reputation as a "good" girl and encourages the boy to provide more gifts. If the girl continues to say no to sex, however, it's common practice for the boy to force her to have sex, especially if he feels the amount of his gift is sufficient.

According to a global Gallup poll of 123 countries, more Americans (65%) than Canadians (45%) view religion as an important part of their daily lives (Crabtree & Pelham, 2009). An Ipsos (2010) poll found that 65% of Americans but only 36% of Canadians agreed with the statement "Religion provides the common values and ethical foundations that diverse societies need to thrive in the twenty-first century." These American–Canadian differences are important, because they may help us understand differences between the two countries that relate to sexuality.

Since 1971, Canada has maintained an official policy of multiculturalism. According to this policy, Canadian society is openly accepting of differing cultural attitudes and traditions as espoused by diverse immigrant groups. The United States, on the other hand, has adhered to the "melting pot" theory, which encourages immigrants to adapt to American ways of thinking and acting. A recent Angus Reid (2010a) poll of Canadians on multiculturalism, however, points to a possible shift in opinion. While 55% of those surveyed agreed that multiculturalism has been good for Canada, 54% of Canadians preferred the concept of the melting pot, while only 33% preferred multiculturalism.

Recently, many Canadians have questioned how far we should go in accommodating immigrant values that conflict with basic Canadian values. In 2007, the Quebec government established a commission to examine the issue of "reasonable accommodation." People expressed a wide range of opinions to the commission. The most heated reactions were to the wearing of the hijab, or head scarf, by some Muslim women (Patriquin, 2007). A 2007 national survey conducted by the Institute for Research on Public Policy found that the majority of Canadians wanted limits to the "reasonable accommodation" of immigrants. Quebeckers by far had the strongest feelings on this issue, as many believed Quebec's culture to be threatened by various immigrant and minority groups (Patriquin, 2007).

When it comes to sexuality, Canadians are somewhat more liberal than Americans. For example, more Canadians (80%) than Americans (64%) are accepting of premarital sex (Bibby, 2006). Angus Reid (2010b) polls have found that more Canadians (61%) than Americans (36%) are accepting of same-sex marriage. In other chapters of this textbook, we'll present more comparisons of American and Canadian attitudes and behaviours.

POLITICS AND SEX IN CANADA AND THE UNITED STATES   Christian fundamentalists, known as the "religious right," have a greater presence in the United States than in Canada. They therefore have a much stronger voice in persuading American governments to take a conservative stance on the regulation of sexual values. Since the 1990s, for example, conservative politicians in the United States Congress have voted to spend hundreds of millions of dollars on education programs that teach abstinence from sex but do not teach contraceptive methods to adolescents. In the first two years of his presidency, Barack Obama reduced but did not eliminate federal government spending on abstinence-only programs, though he did provide relatively more funding for teen pregnancy programs that included contraception.

In general, Canadian governments have taken a more balanced approach to supporting sexual health education for youth. The provincial and territorial ministries of education tend to follow the broadly based approach to providing sexual health information recommended in the Public Health Agency of Canada's (2008) *Canadian Guidelines for Sexual Health Education.* We'll discuss this in Chapter 12.

In general, Canadian politicians have maintained a separation between religion and the state. The Canadian Charter of Rights and Freedoms has helped maintain this separation, giving individual rights precedence over religious values. This has been shown in judicial decisions regarding same-sex marriage. Despite protests from various religious groups, Canadian courts have consistently decided that disallowing same-sex marriage is a violation of the individual rights of gays and lesbians. Former Canadian Prime Minister Paul Martin adopted a similar position. Although he was a practising Roman Catholic and received intense pressure from Catholic Church officials to oppose same-sex marriage, Martin stated that his own religious values should not override personal freedoms. While current American President Barack Obama has defended the rights of gay and lesbian couples to form civil unions, he has stopped short of supporting gay marriage, and espouses the traditional definition of marriage as a union between a man and a woman.

In 2005, Canada became the fourth country in the world to legalize same-sex marriage. The main political opposition to this legislation came from the Conservative Party of Canada and the Progressive Conservative Alliance of Alberta. Federal Conservative leader Stephen Harper indicated that if his party were to form government, he would hold another vote in the House of Commons to overturn the law. Here Harper was going against public opinion. A survey conducted by the Strategic Counsel after the passage of same-sex legislation found that 55% of Canadians wanted the next government to leave the legislation in place, and only 39% wanted the law repealed. Shortly after the Conservative Party formed a minority government in 2006, it did introduce a motion to overturn the same-sex law. The motion was defeated by the other parties, which constituted the majority of Parliament.

Despite the fears of some Canadian religious groups that they would be forced to sanctify same-sex marriages, Bill C-38 governing same-sex marriage specifically states that the legislation is binding only on city officials, and not on religious organizations.

After the Progressive Conservative Party of Canada united with the more socially conservative Canadian Reform Conservative Alliance Party, the new party hinted at introducing restrictive legislation in other areas of sexuality. In 2008, the Harper Conservatives were able to pass legislation that raised the legal age of consent from 14 to 16. Previously, the Progressive Conservatives had followed a middle-of-the-road approach. It was, in fact, the Progressive Conservative government of Brian Mulroney that had lowered the age of sexual consent from 18 to 14 in 1987.

In 2010, Stephen Harper's Conservatives introduced a program to promote maternal health in developing countries, but refused to allow any of the money to fund abortion services. This was widely criticized in Canada and other countries as endangering the health of women in developing countries and being at odds with the goals of the G8 initiative on maternal and child health.

These examples show that it's not easy to generalize about trends related to sex and politics. While Canada is generally regarded as more liberal than the United States, recent initiatives by the Harper government (e.g., raising the age of consent, restricting funding for abortion in developing countries) may reflect a Canadian governmental shift toward more conservative values concerning sexuality.

Sexuality and Values

Our society is pluralistic with respect to sexuality. Collectively, we embrace a wide range of sexual attitudes and values. Some readers may be liberal in their sexual views and behaviours. Others may be conservative or traditional. Some are staunchly pro-choice on abortion, and others adamantly pro-life. Some approve of sex for couples who are dating casually, others hold the line at emotional commitment, and still others believe people should wait until marriage. While Canadian society has evolved considerably with regard to the rights of gay, lesbian, bisexual, and transgendered people, there is still a plurality of views about sexual orientation.

Perhaps one of the defining characteristics of Canadian society is our acceptance of diversity on many levels, including diversity of opinions and values related to sexuality. This acceptance gives us the freedom to adhere to our own distinct values and traditions, while also recognizing that we all have an obligation to respect the rights of others whose beliefs, perspectives, and behaviours are different from our own. The Canadian constitutional framework, particularly the Canadian Charter of Rights and Freedoms, creates an environment in which diverse communities can coexist and flourish, and this acceptance of diversity can and should apply to values and behaviours related to sexuality. The extent to which these ideals actually reflect the current reality in Canada is very much an open question.

People's sexual attitudes, experiences, and behaviours are to a large extent shaped by their cultural traditions and beliefs. Because the world consists of diverse peoples and cultures, the study of human sexuality is really the study of human sexualities. In this book we'll highlight the many ways people experience their sexuality.

Sexuality and Ethics

Some sexual choices can have negative consequences for individuals and society. All societies therefore have restrictions on certain kinds of sex-related behaviours. Sexual ethics govern what societies consider unacceptable sexual behaviours. Glenn Meaney and B. J. Rye (2007) at St. Jerome's University at the University of Waterloo have analyzed three distinct ethical frameworks: the ethics of divinity, community, and autonomy.

The ethics of divinity (which generally have religious roots) are based on a fundamental belief in a natural law of right and wrong. Those who break the law are viewed as sinners. The belief that sex should only occur within marriage is an example of the ethics of divinity, as all major religions consider this belief to be a fundamental value that should not be questioned.

The ethics of community are based on what is perceived as the greater good for the community. Although different societies vary widely in terms of which sexual behaviours they consider acceptable, they all find some behaviours unethical and intolerable. Laws against sexual assault, for example, are based on the community ethic that no one should force someone else to engage in sex against his or her will.

The ethics of autonomy value the rights and freedoms of individuals. People are allowed to satisfy their own sexual needs, as long as they do not impede the

CRITICAL THINKING QUESTIONS

Many of us take pride in the idea that Canadian society welcomes diversity with respect to ethnicity and religion. To what extent do you think Canadian society welcomes diversity when it comes to sexuality?

rights of others. The belief that same-sex relationships are acceptable because they cause no harm to others is an example of the ethics of autonomy.

Meaney and Rye's (2007) framework helps us understand the relationship between various ethical positions and sexual decision making. There are, however, many other approaches to understanding this topic. For example, in their national survey of Americans, Laumann et al. (1994) categorized their respondents' moral values into the three categories of traditional, relational, and recreational. These categories overlap with those of Meaney and Rye.

Ethics and Sexual Rights

Recent movements based on the ethics of autonomy have been promoting sexual rights and freedoms around the world. The World Association for Sexual Health (WAS) has been at the forefront in promoting sexual rights. At the 2005 World Congress of Sexology meeting in Montreal, participants agreed to urge governments and international agencies to move forward in promoting sexual health, with an emphasis on sexual rights.

To achieve this goal, WAS (2008) issued a declaration consisting of sexual health-related goals for the global community:

- Recognize, promote, ensure, and protect sexual rights for all.
- Advance toward gender equality and equity.
- Condemn, combat, and reduce all forms of sexuality-related violence.
- Provide universal access to comprehensive sexuality education and information.
- Ensure that reproductive health programs recognize the centrality of sexual health.
- Halt and reverse the spread of HIV/AIDS and other sexually transmitted infections (STI).
- Identify, address, and treat sexual concerns, dysfunctions, and disorders.
- Achieve recognition of sexual pleasure as a component of holistic health and well-being.

The validity of these goals may seem self-evident to many Canadians. Some, however, may not be embraced by people from non-Western cultures or some Western religious perspectives. Eleanor Maticka-Tyndale and Lisa Smylie (2008) at the University of Windsor note that the concept of sexual rights is contentious, particularly in cultures with different perspectives toward sexuality. They argue that the goal of sexual rights for all is more likely to be achieved by focusing on broader international human-rights commitments such as the United Nations' Universal Declaration of Human Rights than by trying to convince people from different cultural and religious perspectives to agree on sexual rights per se. Maticka-Tyndale and Smylie also make the case that a more consensus-building approach is needed before global agreements to promote sexual health can be reached.

Sexuality and Spirituality

While researchers have paid considerable attention to the role of religion as a predictor of sexual attitudes and behaviours, research into the spiritual aspects of sexuality has been limited. Peggy Kleinplatz, a researcher and therapist at the University of Ottawa, and Stanley Krippner, a researcher in Israel, believe sexual relationships can be more fulfilling when they extend beyond the purely physical aspects of sex, such as the techniques emphasized in many sex manuals (Kleinplatz & Krippner, 2007). They argue that many people want to transform their sex routines into spiritual experiences that make them "feel utterly alive. . . . Sharing such moments with one's partner feels like a sacred destiny fulfilled" (p. 306). Tantric sex, for example, which is based on tantric yoga that stems from religious practices in India, emphasizes prolonged sexual union as a way to achieve heightened consciousness and enlightenment.

To meet the desire of couples who wish to have spiritually based sexual relationships, workshops on tantric sex are given in many Canadian cities. Kleinplatz and Krippner (2007) are critical of tantric teachers who focus on the sexual techniques but neglect the spiritual foundations of this approach to sexual relationships.

Thinking Critically About Human Sexuality

We're flooded with so much information about sex that it's difficult to separate truth from fiction. Newspapers, television shows, books, magazines, and the internet contain one feature after another about sex. Many of them contradict one another, contain half-truths, or draw misleading or unsubstantiated conclusions. Taking a scientific approach to human sexuality includes thinking critically about claims and findings that are presented to us as fact or truth.

We tend to assume that information provided by influential or authoritative figures such as television psychologists or government officials must be accurate and valid. But critical thinkers never say, "This is true simply because so-and-so says it's true."

To arrive at a well thought out, independently developed point of view, we need to think critically. That is, we need to evaluate the strengths and weaknesses of various claims, arguments, and widely held beliefs. The core of critical thinking is skepticism—not taking things for granted. It means being skeptical of things that are presented in print, uttered by authority figures or celebrities, or passed along by friends. Another aspect of critical thinking is thoughtful analysis and probing of claims and arguments. Critical thinking means scrutinizing definitions of terms, and evaluating the premises and logic of arguments. It means basing our own beliefs on careful reasoning, rather than simply accepting what we're told. When we think critically, we maintain open minds. We reach conclusions only after we have obtained and evaluated the evidence.

Principles of Critical Thinking

Following are some suggestions for critical thinking.

- **Be skeptical.** Politicians, religious leaders, and other authority figures attempt to convince you of their points of view. Even researchers and authors may hold certain biases. Accept no opinion as fact—until you have personally weighed the evidence.
- **Examine definitions of terms.** Some statements are true when a term is defined one way, but not true when it's defined another way. Consider the statement "love is blind," for instance. If love is defined as head-over-heels infatuation, there may be substance to the statement. Infatuated people tend to idealize and overlook the faults of their loved ones. If, however, love is defined as deep caring and commitment involving a more realistic (if still somewhat slanted) appraisal of the loved one, then love is not so much blind as a bit nearsighted.
- **Examine the assumptions or premises underlying arguments.** For example, consider the statement "abortion is murder." *Webster's New World Dictionary* defines murder as "the unlawful and malicious or premeditated killing of one human being by another." The statement can be true, according to this definition, only if the victim is held to be a human being (and if the act is unlawful and either malicious or premeditated). Most pro-life advocates argue that embryos and fetuses are human beings. Most

pro-choice advocates claim that they are not. Hence the argument that abortion is murder would rest in part on the assumption that the embryo or fetus is a human being.

■ **Be cautious in drawing conclusions from evidence.** Recent research has found that teenagers who listen to rap, hip hop, pop, and rock music with lyrics that are sexually explicit or that refer to women as sex objects are more likely to initiate sexual activity at an early age (Martino et al., 2006). The popular media seem obsessed with the idea that sexually explicit songs lead to sex, and lots of it. However, teens who choose to dwell on these songs may have different values than those who don't, leading them not only to spend hours with their iPods blasting sexual lyrics into their ears, but also to choose to have sex at an earlier age. The evidence of a connection between listening to this music and having sex is open to various interpretations . . . which brings us to our next principle of critical thinking.

■ **Consider alternative interpretations of research evidence.** For example, teens who dwell on sexual song lyrics may also be more open to sexual activity because they are less traditional than teens who (literally) turn off these songs. This example shows that correlations between events do not necessarily reveal cause and effect. Also consider the kinds of evidence upon which conclusions are based. Some conclusions, even seemingly "scientific" conclusions, are based on anecdotes or poorly designed studies. Beware of writers who "cherry pick" research by only mentioning studies that support their own point of view but ignore studies that don't.

■ **Consider the strengths and weaknesses of different perspectives on sexuality, even ones you don't agree with.** Why do people with other opinions hold their beliefs? Evaluating the strengths and weaknesses of various perspectives can help us arrive at well thought out conclusions and effectively communicate our beliefs to others.

■ **Don't oversimplify.** Consider the statement "homosexuality is inborn." There is some evidence that sexual orientation may involve inborn predispositions, such as genetic influences. However, biology is not destiny in human sexuality. Gay, lesbian, and heterosexual sexual orientations appear to develop as a result of complex interactions of biological and environmental factors.

■ **Don't overgeneralize.** Consider the belief that gay men are effeminate and lesbians are masculine. Yes, some gays and lesbians fit these stereotypes, but many do not. Overgeneralizing makes us vulnerable to accepting stereotypes.

Perspectives on Human Sexuality

Human sexuality is a complex topic. No single theory or perspective can capture all of its nuances. In this book, we explore human sexuality from many perspectives. In this section, we introduce a number of perspectives that we'll draw on in subsequent chapters.

The Historical Perspective

History places our sexual behaviour in context. It tells us whether our sexual behaviours reflect trends that have been with us through the millennia, or are customs of a particular culture and era. History shows little evidence of universal sexual trends. Attitudes and behaviours vary extensively from one time and place to another. Contemporary Canadian society may appear permissive when compared with the Victorian and post-World War II eras, yet it looks staid when compared with the sexual norms and customs of some ancient societies. History also shows how religion has been a major influence on sexual values and behaviours.

Applied Knowledge

THINKING CRITICALLY ABOUT SEXUALITY INFORMATION ON THE INTERNET

Every day, people surf the internet in the hope of finding websites that will answer their questions about sexuality and sex-related problems. How can we evaluate the credibility and accuracy of a website?

There are no easy answers. Many of us believe the things we see posted. Anecdotes about how Tyrone increased the size of his penis by 30% and how Maria learned to reach orgasm "every time" can have a powerful allure. Be on guard, because the sexuality information on some websites can do more harm than good.

A price we pay for freedom of speech is that nearly anything can be posted on a website or appear in print. Authors can make extravagant, distorted, or false claims with little fear of punishment. They can lie about the effectiveness of a new sexual cure-all as easily as they can lie about sightings of Elvis Presley or UFOs.

How can you protect yourself?

- In this instance, do judge the book by its cover. Does the website look well organized? Do the links within the web pages work? A credible website will look professional and well maintained.
- Ignore websites that make extravagant claims. If it sounds too good to be true, it probably is. No method helps everyone who tries it. Very few methods work overnight. Extravagant claims are clues to look elsewhere.
- Check the credentials of the people who post the information. Be suspicious if the author's title is "Dr." and is placed before the name. The degree could be a phony doctorate bought through the mail. It's better if the "doctor" has a PhD, PsyD, MD, or EdD after her or his name.
- Check authors' affiliations. Helping professionals who are affiliated with colleges, universities, clinics, and hospitals may have more to offer than those who are not.

Are They Buying It?
Critical thinkers carefully consider the premises of an argument, weigh all the evidence, and arrive at their own conclusions. Critical thinking is important in matters of human sexuality, and valuable in all areas of life.

- Check out who is responsible for creating the website. Is it a professional association of health care providers or a respected nonprofit organization? Or is it someone with something to sell?
- Check the evidence reported on the website. Unscientific websites (and books) usually make extensive use of anecdotes. Anecdotes are unsupported stories or case studies about fantastic results with one or a few individuals. Responsible helping professionals check the effectiveness of techniques with large numbers of people. They carefully measure the outcomes.
- Check the reference citations for the evidence. Legitimate research is reported in the journals and websites you'll find in the References section of this book. These journals report research methods and outcomes that are more likely be scientifically valid. If there are no links to reference citations on the website, or if the list of references looks suspicious, you should be suspicious, too.

- Peer-reviewed academic journals are the gold standard for research on sexuality and other topics. "Peer-reviewed" means the research has been carefully reviewed by experts in the field. Peer-reviewed journals related to sexuality include *Archives of Sexual Behavior, Journal of Sex Research, The Canadian Journal of Human Sexuality, The Journal of Sexual Medicine, Journal of Sex and Marital Therapy, Perspectives on Sexual and Reproductive Health,* and *Culture, Health & Sexuality.* Students at most colleges and universities can access peer-reviewed sexuality journals online through their schools' libraries or library websites. (Hint: Instructors are more likely to be impressed by student assignments that reference peer-reviewed journals than by assignments that reference whatever websites the students have found simply by entering their topics into internet search engines.)

Let's examine some historical changes in attitudes toward sexuality. We'll begin by turning the clock back 20000 to 30000 years, to the days before written records were kept—that is, to prehistory.

SEXUALITY AND ART IN PREHISTORY AND ANTIQUITY   Information about life among our Stone Age ancestors is obtained largely from cave drawings, stone artifacts, and the customs of modern-day preliterate peoples whose existence may have changed little over the millennia.

Art produced in the Stone Age, some 20 000 years ago, suggests the worship of women's ability to bear children and perpetuate the species (Fichner-Rathus, 2010). Primitive statues and cave drawings portray women with large, pendulous breasts, rounded hips, and prominent sex organs. Most theorists regard the figurines as fertility symbols. Emphasis on the female reproductive role may also signify ignorance of the male's contribution to reproduction.

As the ice sheets of the last ice age retreated (about 11000 BCE) and the climate warmed, human societies turned agrarian. Hunters and gatherers became farmers and herders. As people became aware of the male role in reproduction, **phallic worship** sprang into being. Knowledge of paternity is believed to have developed around 9000 BCE, which is about the time people shifted from hunting and gathering to farming and shepherding. The penis was glorified in art as a plough, an axe, or a sword.

Phallic symbols figured in religious ceremonies in ancient Egypt. The ancient Greeks created art that suggests they revered phalluses, rendering them sometimes as rings and sometimes as necklaces. Some phalluses were given wings, suggesting the power ascribed to them. In ancient Rome, a large phallus was carried like a float in a parade honouring Venus, the goddess of love.

The **incest taboo** that discourages sexual intercourse between close blood relatives may have been the first taboo. All human societies apparently have some form of incest taboo, though its strictness may vary from one culture to another. Brother–sister marriages were permitted among the presumably divine rulers of ancient Egypt and the royal families of the Incas and the Hawaiians, even though they were generally prohibited among commoners. Incestuous relationships in these royal bloodlines may have kept wealth, power, and "divinity" in the family.

THE ANCIENT HEBREWS   The ancient Hebrews viewed sex—within marriage, at least—as a fulfilling experience intended to satisfy the divine injunction to "be fruitful and multiply" (Browning et al., 2006). Male–male and female–female sexual behaviours were strongly condemned, because they were thought to threaten perpetuation of the family. Adultery, too, was condemned—at least for women. Although the Hebrew Bible (the Old Testament in the Christian faith) permitted **polygamy**, the vast majority of the Hebrews practised **monogamy**.

The ancient Hebrews approved of sex within marriage not simply for procreation, but also for mutual pleasure and fulfillment. They believed the expression of sexual needs and desires helped strengthen marital bonds and solidify families. (These points are noteworthy because many people, both Jewish and non-Jewish, believe the traditional Jewish religion held mainly negative attitudes about sexual pleasure. David Ribner at Bar-Ilan University in Israel and Peggy Kleinplatz at the University of Ottawa provide a thorough analysis of myths regarding sexuality and Judaism [2007].)

Among the ancient Hebrews, a wife was considered her husband's property. If she offended him, she could be divorced on a whim. A wife could be stoned to death for adultery. She might also have to share her husband with his secondary wives and concubines. Men who committed adultery by consorting with the wives of other men were considered to have violated the latter's property rights. Although they were subject to harsh penalties for violation of property rights, male adulterers were not put to death.

Phallic worship Veneration of the penis as a symbol of generative power.

Phallic symbol An object that represents the penis.

Incest taboo The prohibition against intercourse with close blood relatives.

Polygamy The practice of having two or more spouses at the same time.

Monogamy The practice of having only one spouse.

Male Sexuality in Ancient Greece.
Many ancient Greek ceramics depict male–male sexual activity. The Greeks believed males were bisexual. In Homer's Iliad, brought to the silver screen in 2004 as Troy, Achilles is spurred to battle by the killing of his lover, Patroclus. The film glossed over this motive, however, emphasizing the pair's family relationship.

THE ANCIENT GREEKS The classical or golden age of ancient Greece lasted about 200 years, from approximately 500 to 300 BCE. Within this relatively short span lived the philosophers Socrates, Plato, and Aristotle. Like the Hebrews, the Greeks valued family life. Greek men admired the well-developed male body, and enjoyed nude wrestling among men in the arena. Erotic encounters and off-colour jokes characterized the works of Aristophanes and other playwrights.

The Greeks viewed their gods—Zeus, god of gods; Apollo, who inspired art and music; Aphrodite, the goddess of carnal love, whose name is the basis of the word *aphrodisiac*; and others—as voracious seekers of sexual variety. Not only were they believed to have sexual adventures among themselves, they were also thought to seduce mortals.

Three aspects of Greek sexuality are of particular interest to our study of sexual practices in the ancient world: male–male adult sexual behaviour, **pederasty**, and prostitution. The Greeks viewed men and women as **bisexual**. Male–male adult sex was deemed normal, and tolerated so long as it did not threaten the institution of the family.

"Pederasty" means love of boys. Sex between men and prepubescent boys was illegal, but families were generally pleased if their adolescent sons attracted socially prominent mentors. Men in Greece might take on an adolescent male as a lover and pupil. Pederasty did not impede the boy's future male–female functioning, because the pederast himself was usually married, and the Greeks believed people equally capable of male–female and male–male sexual activity.

Prostitution flourished at every level of society. Prostitutes ranged from refined **courtesans** to **concubines**, who were usually slaves. Courtesans could play musical instruments, dance, engage in witty repartee, and discuss the latest political crises. They were also skilled in the arts of love. No social stigma was attached to visiting a courtesan. At the lower rungs of society were streetwalkers and prostitutes who lived in tawdry brothels.

The women of Athens had no more legal or political rights than slaves. They were subject to the authority of their male next-of-kin before marriage, and of their husbands afterward. They received no formal education, and were consigned most of the time to women's quarters in their homes. They were chaperoned when they

Pederasty Sexual love between a man and a boy.

Bisexual Sexually responsive to either gender.

Courtesan A prostitute, especially the mistress of a noble or wealthy man.

Concubine A secondary wife, usually of inferior legal and social status.

ventured out of doors. A husband could divorce his wife without cause, and was obligated to do so if she committed adultery.

THE ANCIENT ROMANS   Much is made of the sexual excesses of the Roman emperors and ruling families. Emperors such as Caligula sponsored orgies at which guests engaged in a wide variety of sexual practices. These sexual excesses were found more often among the upper classes of palace society than among average Romans.

Unlike their counterparts in ancient Greece, Romans viewed male–male sexual behaviour as a threat to the integrity of the Roman family and to the position of the Roman woman. The family was viewed as the source of the Roman Empire's strength. Although Roman women were more likely than their Greek counterparts to share their husbands' social lives, they were still considered their husbands' property.

Western society traces the roots of many of its sexual terms to Roman culture, as indicated by their Latin roots. "Fellatio," for example, derives from the Latin *fellare*, meaning "to suck." "Cunnilingus" derives from *cunnus*, meaning "vulva," and *lingere*, "to lick." "Fornication" derives from *fornix*, an arch or vault; the term stems from Roman streetwalkers' practice of serving their customers in the shadows of archways near public buildings such as stadiums and theaters.

THE EARLY CHRISTIANS   Christianity emerged within the Roman Empire during the centuries following the death of Jesus. Early Christian views on sexuality were largely shaped by Saint Paul and the Church fathers in the first century and by Saint Augustine in the latter part of the fourth century. Adultery and fornication were rampant among the upper classes of Rome at the time, and early Christian leaders began to associate sexuality with sin (Browning et al., 2006).

In replacing the pagan values of Rome, the early Christians, like the Hebrews, sought to restrict sex to marriage. They saw temptations of the flesh as distractions from spiritual devotion. Paul preached that celibacy was closer than marriage to the Christian ideal. He recognized that not everyone could achieve celibacy, however, so he said it was "better to marry than to burn" (with passion, that is).

Christians, like Jews before them, demanded virginity of their brides (Newman, 2006). Prostitution was condemned. Christians taught that men should love their wives with restraint, not with passion (Browning et al., 2006). The goal of procreation should govern sexual behavior—the spirit should rule the flesh. Divorce was outlawed. Unhappiness with one's spouse might reflect sexual—thus sinful—restlessness. Dissolving a marriage might also jeopardize the social structure that supported the Church. Masturbation, male–male sexual behavior, female–female sexual behavior, oral–genital contact, and anal intercourse were viewed as abominations in the eyes of God (Browning et al., 2006).

Saint Augustine (353–430 CE) associated sexual lust with the original sin of Adam and Eve in the Garden of Eden. Lust and shame were passed down through the generations. Lust made any sexual expression inherently evil, even within marriage. According to Augustine, only through celibacy could men and women attain a state of grace.

THE MUSLIMS   Now the dominant religion in the Middle East, across North Africa, and into parts of southern Asia, Islam was founded by the prophet Muhammad, who was born in about 570 CE in what is now Saudi Arabia. The Islamic tradition treasures marriage and sexual fulfillment in marriage. Premarital sex invites shame and social condemnation—and, in some fundamentalist Islamic states, harsh penalties.

The family is the backbone of Islamic society (Browning et al., 2006). Muhammad decreed that marriage represented the road to virtue. Islamic tradition permits a sexual double standard, however. Men under most circumstances may take up to four wives, but women are permitted only one husband. Public social interactions between men and women are severely restricted in conservative Islamic societies. Women are expected to keep their heads and faces veiled in public, and to avoid all contact with men other than their husbands.

THE HINDUS   Perhaps no culture has cultivated sexual pleasure as a spiritual ideal to the same extent as the ancient Hindus of India did. Temples from the fifth century CE onward show sculptures of gods, nymphs, and ordinary people in erotic poses. Hindu sexual practices were codified in a sex manual, the *Kama Sutra*, which illustrated sexual positions, some of which would challenge a contortionist. It also held recipes for alleged aphrodisiacs. This manual is believed to have been written by the Hindu sage Vatsyayana sometime between the third and fifth centuries CE, at about the time Christianity was ascending in the West.

In its graphic representations of sexual positions and practices, the *Kama Sutra* reflected the Hindu belief that sex was a religious duty, not a source of shame or guilt. Hindu deities were often portrayed as engaging in same-sex as well as male–female sexual activities. In the Hindu doctrine of karma (the passage of souls from one place to another), sexual fulfillment was regarded as one way to become reincarnated at a higher level of existence. Indian society grew more restrictive toward sexuality after about 1000 CE.

An Illustration from the Kama Sutra.
Believed to have been written sometime between the third and fifth centuries CE, the Kama Sutra is an Indian sex manual containing graphic illustrations of sexual techniques and practices.

THE TAOISTS   In the cultures of the Far East, sexuality was akin to spirituality. To the Taoist masters of China, who influenced Chinese culture for millennia, sex was a sacred duty—a form of worship that led toward harmony with nature and immortality.

The Chinese culture was the first to produce a detailed sex manual, which came into use about 200 years before the birth of Jesus. The man was expected to extend intercourse as long as possible, to absorb more of his wife's natural essence, or yin, which enhanced his own masculine essence, or yang. Moreover, he was to help bring his partner to orgasm, so as to increase the flow of energy he might absorb.

Taoists believed it was wasteful for a man to "spill his seed." Masturbation, acceptable for women, was ruled out for men. Sexual practices such as anal intercourse and oral–genital contact (fellatio and cunnilingus) were permissible, so long as the man did not squander yang through wasteful ejaculation.

Same-sex activity was not prohibited by Taoist holy writings, though some Taoists frowned on exclusive homosexuality. A parallel to Western cultures was the role accorded women in traditional Chinese society. The "good wife," like her Western counterpart, was limited to a domestic role.

THE MEDIEVAL CHRISTIANS   The Middle Ages spanned the millennium of Western history from about 476 to 1450 CE. The attitudes of the Roman Catholic Church toward sexuality, largely unchanged since the time of Augustine, dominated medieval thought (Browning et al., 2006).

Yet some currents of change in the social standing of women crept across medieval Europe. The Church had long regarded all women as tainted by the sin of Eve. But in the Eastern Church of Constantinople, the cult of the Virgin Mary flourished. The ideal of womanhood was the image of Mary: good, gracious, loving, and saintly. Imported by the Crusaders and others who returned from the East, the cult of the Virgin Mary swept European Christendom and helped elevate the status of women (Newman, 2006).

THE PROTESTANT REFORMERS During the Reformation, Martin Luther (1483–1546) and other Christian reformers such as John Calvin (1509–1564) split off from the Roman Catholic Church and formed their own sects, which led to the development of the modern Protestant denominations of Western Europe (and later, the New World).

Luther disputed many Roman Catholic doctrines on sexuality. He believed priests should be allowed to marry and rear children. To Luther, marriage was as much a part of human nature as eating or drinking. Calvin rejected the Roman Catholic Church's position that sex in marriage was permissible only for the purpose of procreation. He believed sexual expression in marriage fulfilled other legitimate roles, such as strengthening the marriage bond and helping to relieve the stresses of everyday life. Extramarital and premarital sex, however, remained taboo.

THE VICTORIANS The middle and later parts of the nineteenth century are generally called the Victorian period, after Queen Victoria of England. Victoria assumed the throne in 1837 and ruled until her death in 1901. Her name has become virtually synonymous with sexual repression.

Victorian society in Europe and North America, on the surface at least, was prim and proper (Horowitz, 2002). Sex was not discussed in polite society. Many women viewed sex as a marital duty, to be performed for procreation or to satisfy their husbands' cravings. Consider the following often-cited quotation, attributed to Alice, Lady Hillingdon, wife of the second Baron Hillingdon:

> I am happy now that Charles calls on my bed chamber less frequently than of old. As it is, I now endure but two calls a week, and when I hear his steps outside my door, I lie down on my bed, close my eyes, open my legs, and think of England.

Women were assumed not to experience sexual desires or pleasures. "I would say," observed Dr. William Acton (1813–1875), an influential English physician, in 1857, "that the majority of women (happily for them) are not much troubled with sexual feeling of any kind."

It was widely believed among medical authorities that sex drained the man of his natural vitality. Physicians thus recommended that intercourse be practised infrequently. The Reverend Sylvester Graham (1794–1851) preached that ejaculation deprived men of the "vital fluids" they needed to maintain health and vitality. Graham preached against "wasting the seed" by masturbation or frequent marital intercourse (Laqueur, 2003). How frequent was frequent? In Graham's view, intercourse more than once a month could dangerously deplete the man's vital energies. He recommended that young men control their sexual appetites by a diet of simple foods based on whole-grain flours. He invented what we now call the Graham cracker for this purpose.

But the behaviour of Victorians was not as repressed as advertised. Despite Acton's beliefs, Victorian women did experience sexual pleasure and orgasm. Consider an early sex survey conducted in 1892 by a female physician, Clelia Duel Mosher. Although her sample was small and nonrandom, 35 of the 44 women who responded admitted to desiring sexual intercourse. And 34 of them reported experiencing orgasm. Women's diaries of the time also contained accounts of passionate and sexually fulfilling love affairs (Gay, 1984).

Prostitution flourished during the Victorian era. Men apparently thought they were doing their wives a favour by looking elsewhere. Accurate statistics are hard to come by, but there may have been as many as 1 prostitute for every 12 men in London during the nineteenth century; in Vienna, there was perhaps 1 woman for every 7 men.

Same-sex sexual behaviour was considered indecent in Victorian society. The celebrated gay Anglo–Irish novelist and playwright Oscar Wilde—author of *The Picture of Dorian Gray*, *An Ideal Husband*, and *The Importance of Being Earnest*—was imprisoned after being convicted of gross indecency.

THE SCIENTIFIC STUDY OF SEXUALITY   It was against this backdrop of sexual repression that scientists and scholars first began to approach sexuality as an area of legitimate scientific study. An important early contributor to the science of human sexuality was the English physician Havelock Ellis (1859–1939). Ellis compiled a veritable encyclopedia of sexuality—a series of volumes published between 1897 and 1910 entitled *Studies in the Psychology of Sex*. Ellis drew information from various sources, including case histories, anthropological findings, and medical knowledge. He challenged the prevailing view, arguing that sexual desires in women were natural and healthful. He promoted the idea that many sexual problems had psychological rather than physical causes. He also argued that a homosexual orientation was a naturally occurring variation within the spectrum of normal sexuality, not an aberration. Ellis treated homosexual orientations as inborn dispositions, rather than vices or character flaws.

Another influential **sexologist**, the German psychiatrist Richard von Krafft-Ebing (1840–1902), described more than 200 case histories of individuals with various sexual deviations in his book *Psychopathia Sexualis: With Especial Reference to the Antipathic Sexual Instinct: A Medico-Forensic Study* (1886). His writings contain vivid descriptions of deviations ranging from sadomasochism (sexual gratification through inflicting or receiving pain) and bestiality (sex with animals) to necrophilia (intercourse with dead people). Krafft-Ebing viewed sexual deviations as mental diseases that could be studied and perhaps treated by medical science.

Sexologist A scientist who studies sexual behaviour.

At about the same time, a Viennese physician, Sigmund Freud (1856–1939), was developing a theory of personality that was to have an enormous influence on modern culture and science. Freud believed the sex drive was our principal motivating force.

Alfred Kinsey (1894–1956), an Indiana University zoologist, conducted the first large-scale studies of sexual behaviour in the 1930s and 1940s. It was then that sex research became recognized as a field of scientific study in its own right. In 1938, Kinsey had been asked to teach a course on marriage. While researching the subject, he had discovered that little was known about sexual practices in American society. He soon embarked on an ambitious research project, conducting detailed personal interviews with nearly 12 000 people across the United States. His survey results were published in two volumes, *Sexual Behavior in the Human Male* (1948) and *Sexual Behavior in the Human Female* (1953). These books represented the first scientific attempts to provide a comprehensive picture of sexual behaviour in the United States.

Filled with statistical tables rather than racy pictures or vignettes, Kinsey's books made for rather dry reading. Nevertheless, they became bestsellers. They exploded on a public that hadn't yet learned to discuss sex openly. Their publication—especially the book on female sexuality—was met with intense criticism. Kinsey's research suffered from methodological flaws (especially by today's standards for scientific research), but much of the criticism branded it immoral and obscene. *The New York Times* refused to run advertisements for the 1948 volume

Generational Change.
Are today's young people more or less liberal than people of earlier generations in their expression of sexuality? Today the threat of HIV/AIDS hangs over every sexual encounter. While many young people are selective in their choices of partners, and take precautions to make sex safer, more teenagers are engaging in sexual activity—and at younger ages—than in previous generations. (Models for illustrative purposes only.)

on male sexuality. Many newspapers refused to report the results of his survey on female sexuality. A congressional committee in the 1950s went so far as to claim that Kinsey's work undermined the moral fibre of the nation, rendering it more vulnerable to a Communist takeover (Gebhard, 1976).

Despite the controversy, Kinsey and his colleagues made sex research a scientifically respectable field of study. They helped lay the groundwork for future generations of sexuality researchers and, on a broader societal level, prompted a greater openness to discussing sexual matters among the general public.

THE SEXUAL REVOLUTION   The period of the mid-1960s to the mid-1970s is often referred to as the sexual revolution. Dramatic changes occurred in sexual attitudes and practices during the "swinging sixties." Our society was on the threshold of major social upheaval, not only in sexual behaviour, but also in science, politics, fashion, music, art, and cinema. The so-called Woodstock generation, disheartened by commercialism and the Vietnam War, tuned in (to rock music on the radio), turned on (to drugs), and dropped out (of mainstream society). Films became sexually explicit. Critics seriously contemplated whether the pornography classic *Deep Throat* had profound social implications. Hard rock music bellowed the message of rebellion and revolution.

No single event marked the onset of the sexual revolution. Social movements often gain momentum from timely interplays of scientific, social, political, and economic forces. The Vietnam War, fear of the nuclear bomb, introduction of the birth-control pill, and television were four such forces in the 1960s. The pill greatly reduced the risk of unwanted pregnancy. It permitted young people to engage in recreational or casual sex, rather than procreative sex. Pop psychology movements such as the human-potential movement of the 1960s and 1970s (the latter known as the "Me Decade") spread the message that people should get in touch with and express their genuine feelings, including their sexual feelings. "Do your own thing" became one catchphrase; "If it feels good, do it" became another. Canadian Justice Minister Pierre Trudeau declared in 1967 that "there's no place for the state in the bedrooms of the nation." This often repeated quote is symbolic of a fundamental change taking place in Canadian society. Consensual sexual behaviour was now primarily a matter of personal choice, in the hands of the individual.

The sexual revolution was tied to social permissiveness and political liberalism. In part reflecting the times, in part acting as catalyst, the media dealt openly with sex. Popular books encouraged people to explore their sexuality. Film scenes of lovemaking became so commonplace that the movie rating system was introduced, to alert parents. Protests against the Vietnam War and racial discrimination spilled over into broader protests against conventional morality and hypocrisy.

FEMINISM   In some respects, the sexual revolution and the feminist movement were intertwined. Although modern feminism traces its roots to the nineteenth century, the 1960s and '70s were periods of significant advancement toward equal

A World of Diversity

THE HISTORY OF DESIRE

Much of the historical analysis of sexual practices over various time periods has focused on the roles of religious and cultural traditions. University of Toronto professor Edward Shorter, in his book *Written in the Flesh: A History of Desire* (2005), has also analyzed the role of other influences on sexual behaviour. He argues that past constraints suppressed not only the amount of sex people had, but also the variety of sexual behaviours they experienced.

According to Shorter, features of everyday life—such as poor hygiene, inadequate diet, periods of hunger, rampant disease, including plagues and sexually transmitted infections, plus lice and scabies infestation—put a damper on sexual desire and decreased the sexual attractiveness of potential partners.

For most people, there was also a lack of privacy. They lived in crowded conditions, children often sleeping in the same rooms as their parents. Sex was often engaged in quickly, in the dark and under the bedcovers. And since death in childbirth was common, women's fears made many want to avoid sex. Add religious prohibitions against sex for pleasure added to these constraints, and it's not surprising that historically, for most people, sex was not seen as a source of adventure.

rights for women in the social, political, and economic spheres. While the sexual revolution preached sexual freedom more generally, feminism instilled the principle that women were as entitled as men to sexual pleasure and satisfaction. Feminist writers such as Betty Friedan (*The Feminine Mystique*, 1963) and Germaine Greer (*The Female Eunuch*, 1970) wrote bestselling books describing the alienation and repression of the contemporary Western woman, each placing some level of emphasis on sexuality.

The 1976 publication of *The Hite Report: A Nationwide Study of Female Sexuality* provoked an ongoing public discussion and re-examination of stereotypes about female sexual desire and pleasure. Although many questioned author Shere Hite's sampling techniques (just as many had earlier critiqued Kinsey's research methods), the study provided a forum for women to write anonymously about their sexual fantasies, likes, and dislikes in a frank, explicit manner. Among the findings that emerged was the fact that most of the women did not reach orgasm through penile–vaginal intercourse, requiring instead some form of clitoral stimulation. While this observation may seem self-evident in the twenty-first century, public and media discussion of female orgasm and how it was best achieved was highly provocative in the mid-1970s.

The feminist movement played a pivotal role in reconfiguring Western society's conceptualization of female sexuality and the sexual dimensions of the relationship between the sexes.

GAY ACTIVISM   Some say gay activism began in 1969, with the gay "rebellion" against police discrimination at a Manhattan gay bar called the Stonewall Inn. Gay activism mushroomed during the sexual revolution. Gays not only became more vocal in demanding equal rights, they also began staging gay pride parades in major cities. Examples include the annual pride parades in San Francisco, New York's Greenwich Village, Toronto, Montreal, and Vancouver, as well as in many smaller communities.

In the early 1980s, gay people built social institutions to tackle the problem of acquired immunodeficiency syndrome (AIDS), which disproportionately affected gay men in Western societies. The gay community adopted the motto "Silence equals death." Many gay men publicly identified their sexual orientation and spoke up to spur medical research.

CRITICAL THINKING QUESTIONS

How have the feminist and gay rights movements transformed the ways we think about sexuality?

The rise of gay activism is an important development in the modern history of sexuality. It not only spurred a grassroots movement that continues to help society progress toward equal rights for gays, lesbians, and bisexuals, it also set an example for sexual minorities in general to speak out for recognition, protection against discrimination, and equal rights in a society that often still thinks of "normal" sexual behaviour as male–female intercourse.

The Biological Perspective

The biological perspective focuses on the roles of genes, hormones, the nervous system, and other physiological factors in human sexuality. We're biologically endowed with anatomical structures and physiological capabilities that make sexual behaviour possible and, for most people, pleasurable.

Study of the biology of sex acquaints us with the mechanisms of reproduction. It informs us of the physiological mechanisms of sexual arousal and response. Biology teaches us that erection occurs when the penis becomes engorged with blood. We learn that vaginal lubrication is the result of a "sweating" action of the vaginal walls. We learn that orgasm is a spinal reflex, as well as a psychological event. Researchers have discovered that some sexual dysfunctions originate in anatomical abnormalities or biological processes. In other words, advancements in the scientific understanding of biology have furthered our understanding of sexuality and our ability to help people overcome sexual problems.

The Evolutionary Perspective

Species vary not only in their physical characteristics, but also in their social behaviours, including their mating behaviours. Scientists look to the process of evolution to help explain such variability (Buss, 2009).

Evolution The development of a species by means of many small, cumulative adaptations to its environment.

Natural selection The evolutionary process by which adaptive traits enable members of a species to survive long enough to reproduce and transmit these traits to their offspring.

The English naturalist Charles Darwin (1809–1882), who proposed the modern theory of **evolution**, believed that animal and plant species were not created independently, but evolved from other life forms. According to Darwin's theory, the mechanism by which species evolve is **natural selection**, or, in the vernacular, survival of the fittest. Some individuals of every species are better adapted to their environments than others. Better-adapted members are more likely to survive to reproduce, and therefore are more likely to transmit their traits to their offspring. As the generations pass, an increasing proportion of the population carries the traits of the fittest members. Over time, natural selection favours traits that contribute to survival and reproduction. When environmental conditions change, natural selection favours those members of the species who possess traits that help them adapt to the new conditions.

Some scientists suggest that there is a genetic basis to human and animal social behaviour, including sexual behaviour (Buss, 2009). If so, we may carry traits that helped our prehistoric ancestors survive and reproduce.

Does biology govern sexual behaviour? Although the sexuality of other species is largely governed by biological processes, culture and experience play vital roles in human sexuality (Plomin & Asbury, 2005). Human sexuality involves a complex web of biological, psychological, and cultural factors.

EVOLUTIONARY PERSPECTIVE AND EROTIC PLASTICITY   Erotic plasticity is the degree to which human sexuality is affected by sociocultural and situational factors. Roy Baumeister of Case Western Reserve University in Cleveland reports evidence (2000) that women show greater erotic plasticity than men. Individual women show greater variation in sexual behaviour over time, for example, and more responsiveness to most specific cultural factors, such as cultural permissiveness and restraint. Men's sexual behaviour, on the other hand, is more consistent with their own sexual attitudes. Baumeister concludes that evolutionary, biological forces may be important determinants in women's greater erotic plasticity.

Some **evolutionary psychologists** argue that men are naturally more promiscuous because they are the genetic heirs of ancestors whose reproductive success was related to the number of women they could impregnate (Buss, 2005; Jonason et al., 2009). Women, by contrast, can produce only a few offspring in their lifetimes. Thus, the theory goes, they have to be more selective with respect to their mating partners. Women's reproductive success is enhanced by mating with the fittest males, not with any Tom, Dick, or Harry who happens by. From this perspective, the male's roving eye and the female's selectivity are embedded in their genes.

Genes govern the biological processes of sexual maturation and the production of sex hormones. Hormones, in turn, are largely responsible for regulating sexual behaviour in all animal species. Extending evolutionary psychology to human behaviour sparks considerable controversy. While few evolutionary psychologists would argue that natural selection drives all human behaviour, critics of evolutionary psychology contend that learning, personal choice, and sociocultural factors are likely to be the most important determinants of human behaviour (Shibley-Hyde & Durik, 2000).

The Cross-Species Perspective

The study of other animal species places human behaviour in a broader context. A surprising variety of sexual behaviours exist among animals. There are animal examples, or **analogues,** of human male–male sexual behaviour, female–female sexual behaviour, oral–genital contact, and oral–oral behaviour (kissing). Foreplay is also well known in the animal world. Turtles massage their mates' heads with their claws. Male mice nibble at their partners' necks. Most mammals use only a rear-entry position for **copulation,** but some animals, such as apes, use a variety of coital positions.

Cross-species research reveals an interesting pattern. Sexual behaviour among higher mammals such as primates is less directly controlled by instinct than it is among other species, such as birds, fish, and lower mammals. Experience and learning play more important roles in sexuality as we travel up the evolutionary ladder.

Sociological and Anthropological Perspectives

Sociological and anthropological perspectives, like the historical perspective, provide insight into how cultural beliefs affect sexual behaviour and morality. Interest in cross-cultural perspectives on sexuality was spurred by the early-twentieth-century work of anthropologists Margaret Mead (1901–1978) and Bronisław Malinowski (1884–1942).

In *Sex and Temperament in Three Primitive Societies* (1935), Mead laid the groundwork for later psychological and sociological research challenging gender-role stereotypes. In most cultures characterized by divisions of labour by gender, men typically go to business or to the hunt, and—when necessary—to war. In such cultures, men are perceived as strong, active, independent, and logical. Women are viewed as passive, dependent, nurturant, and emotional. Mead concluded that these stereotypes are not inherent in our genetic heritage. Rather, they are acquired through cultural expectations and socialization. Men and women learn to behave in ways that are expected of them within their particular cultures.

Malinowski lived on the Trobriand Island of Boyowa in the South Pacific during World War I. There he gathered data on two societies of the South Pacific, the Trobrianders and the Amphlett Islanders. The Amphlett Islanders maintained strict

CRITICAL THINKING QUESTIONS

The evolutionary and sociological/anthropological perspectives examine human sexuality in different ways. In your opinion, are these perspectives equally valid for explaining human sexual behaviour?

Evolutionary psychology The theory that a disposition toward a behaviour pattern that enhances reproductive success may be genetically transmitted.

Analogue Something that is similar or comparable to something else.

Copulation Sexual intercourse.

Sexuality in the South Pacific. Likely the inhabitants didn't wear coconut shells, but in the past, sexual norms on Mangaia in the Cook Islands were more permissive than today. In other places and at other times, sex has been seen as a necessary evil, required in order to obey God's command to "be fruitful and multiply."

sexual prohibitions, whereas the Trobriand Islanders enjoyed greater freedom. Trobrianders, for example, encouraged their children to masturbate. Boys and girls were expected to engage in intercourse when they were biologically old enough. Adolescents were expected to have multiple sex partners until they married. Malinowski found the Trobrianders less anxiety-ridden than the Amphlett Islanders. He attributed this difference to their sexual freedom, thus making an early plea to relax prohibitions in Western societies.

In 1951, anthropologist Clellan S. Ford and psychologist Frank A. Beach reviewed studies of sexual behaviour in preliterate societies around the world. They found great variety in sexual customs and beliefs among the almost 200 societies they studied. They also found some common threads.

Kissing was quite common across the cultures they studied, though not universal. The Thonga of Africa were one group that did not practise kissing. Upon witnessing two European visitors kissing one another, members of the tribe commented that they could not understand why Europeans "ate" one another's saliva and dirt. The frequency of sexual intercourse also varied from culture to culture, but intercourse was relatively more frequent among younger than older people everywhere. Attitudes toward public nudity varied across cultures. Ford and Beach found that where public nudity was accepted, it was not considered sexual. Societies also differed in their attitudes toward childhood masturbation. The Hopi of the southwest United States ignored it, for example, whereas Trobrianders encouraged children to stimulate themselves. Other societies condemned it.

People around the world differ widely in their sexual attitudes, customs, and practices. Members of all human societies, however, share the same anatomical structures and physiological capacities for sexual pleasure. The same hormones flow in their bloodstreams. Yet their sexual practices, and the pleasures they reap or fail to attain, may set some apart from others. Were human sexuality completely or predominantly determined by biology, we would not find such diversity.

Psychological Perspectives

Psychological perspectives focus on the many psychological influences—perception, learning, motivation, emotion, personality, and so on—that affect our sexual

A World of Diversity

NUDITY AND SEXUALITY DON'T ALWAYS GO TOGETHER

In Canada, nudity is associated with sexuality, and public nudity is usually illegal. Thousands of Canadians, however, including entire families, participate in naturism, or nudism.

Naturist organizations promote nudity as natural and freeing for the body, and prohibit sexual touching or gazing in public. Given the focus on naturism rather than sexuality, men seldom get erections in the naturist setting.

There are more than 30 private naturist sites in Canada, as well as a small number of public sites that allow nudity. Nudity also occurs in some secluded areas in summer, of course, such as during the practice of "skinny-dipping." You'll find information about the Federation of Canadian Naturists at www.fcn.ca.

Back to Nature.
This photo from the Canadian magazine Going Natural/Au Naturel *illustrates naturism's non-sexualized nudity, as well as its acceptance of bodies of every age, shape, size, and condition.*

behaviour and our experience of ourselves as female or male. Some psychological theorists, such as Sigmund Freud, focus on the motivational role of sex in human personality. Others focus on how our experiences and mental representations of the world affect our sexual behaviour.

SIGMUND FREUD AND PSYCHOANALYTIC THEORY   Sigmund Freud, a Viennese physician, formulated a grand theory of personality termed **psychoanalysis**. Freud believed that we're all born with biologically based sex drives. These drives must be channelled through socially approved outlets if family and social life are to carry on without undue conflict. Freud proposed that the mind operates on conscious and unconscious levels. The conscious level corresponds to our state of present awareness. The **unconscious mind** consists of the darker reaches of the mind that lie outside of our direct awareness. The **ego** shields the conscious mind from awareness of our baser sexual and aggressive urges, using **defence mechanisms** such as **repression**, the motivated forgetting of traumatic experiences.

Freud introduced controversial new ideas about people as sexual beings. For example, he originated the concept of **erogenous zones**—the idea that many parts of the body, not just the genitals, are responsive to sexual stimulation.

One of Freud's most controversial beliefs was that children normally harbour erotic interests. He believed that the suckling of the infant in the oral stage is an erotic act. So, too, is anal experimentation, through which children learn to experience pleasure in the control of their sphincter muscles and the processes of elimination. He theorized that it's normal for children to progress through stages of development in which the erotic interest shifts from one erogenous zone to another, such as from the mouth or oral cavity to the anal cavity. According to his theory of **psychosexual development**, children undergo five stages of development, named for the predominant erogenous zones of each stage: oral, anal, phallic, latency, and

Psychoanalysis The theory of personality originated by Sigmund Freud, which proposes that human behaviour represents the outcome of clashing inner forces.

Unconscious mind Those parts or contents of the mind that lie outside of conscious awareness.

Ego In psychoanalytic theory, the part of the mind that mediates between the id and the superego and that deals with external reality.

Defence mechanisms In psychoanalytic theory, automatic processes that protect the ego from anxiety by disguising or ejecting unacceptable ideas and urges.

Repression The automatic ejection of anxiety-evoking ideas from consciousness.

Erogenous zones Parts of the body, including but not limited to the sex organs, that are responsive to sexual stimulation.

Psychosexual development In psychoanalytic theory, the process by which sexual feelings shift from one erogenous zone to another.

Fixation In psychoanalytic theory, arrested development that includes attachment to traits and sexual preferences characteristic of an earlier stage of psychosexual development.

Oedipus complex A complex of emotions raised in a young child, especially a boy, by a subconscious sexual desire for the parent of the opposite gender.

Behaviourists Learning theorists who argue that a scientific approach to understanding behaviour must refer only to observable and measurable behaviours, and who emphasize the importance of rewards and punishments in the learning process.

Coitus Sexual intercourse.

Modelling Acquiring knowledge and skills by observing others.

Social-cognitive theory A cognitively oriented learning theory in which observational learning, values, and expectations play key roles in determining behaviour.

genital. Each stage gives rise to certain kinds of conflicts. Inadequate or excessive gratification in any stage can lead to **fixation** in that stage, and to development of traits and sexual preferences characteristic of that stage.

Freud believed it's normal for a child to develop erotic feelings toward the parent of the other gender during the phallic stage. These incestuous urges lead to conflict with the parent of the same gender. In later chapters, we'll see that these developments, which Freud termed the **Oedipus complex**, have profound implications for the assumption of gender roles and sexual orientation.

LEARNING THEORY   To what extent does sexual behaviour reflect experience? Would you hold the same sexual attitudes and do the same things if you'd been reared in another culture? We think not. Even within the same society, family and personal experiences can shape unique sexual attitudes and behaviours. Whereas psychoanalysts plumb the depths of the unconscious, learning theorists focus on environmental factors that shape behaviour.

Behaviourists such as John B. Watson (1878–1958) and B. F. Skinner (1904–1990) emphasized the importance of rewards and punishments in the learning process. Skinner used the term "reinforcement" for any event that increases the frequency or likelihood of a behaviour. Children left to explore their bodies without parental condemnation will learn what feels good, and tend to repeat it. The Trobriand child who is rewarded for masturbation and premarital **coitus** through parental praise and encouragement will be more likely to repeat these behaviours than a child in a more sexually restrictive culture, who is punished for the same behaviour. When sexual behaviour (such as masturbation) feels good but parents connect it with feelings of guilt and shame, the child is placed in conflict, and may vacillate between masturbating and swearing off the practice.

If young children are severely punished for sexual exploration, they may come to associate sexual stimulation in general with feelings of guilt or anxiety. Such early learning experiences can set the stage for sexual dysfunctions in adulthood.

COGNITIVE VIEWS   Cognitive psychologists differ from behaviourists in emphasizing the importance of cognitive activity—problem solving, decision making, expectations, and so on. Cognitive psychologists focus more on how individuals' choices are affected by their internal thoughts, rather than on how individuals may be merely responding to external rewards. They recognize that people learn intentionally and by observing others.

Observational learning, or **modelling**, refers to acquiring knowledge and skills by observing others. Observational learning involves more than direct observation of other people. It includes seeing models in films and on television, hearing about them, and reading about them. According to **social-cognitive theory**, children acquire the gender roles deemed appropriate in their society through reinforcement of gender-appropriate behaviour and through observing the gender-role behaviours of their parents, their peers, and other models on television, in films, in books, and so on.

In Chapter 5, we'll explore the nature of masculine and feminine gender roles, and why most males enact masculine roles and most females enact feminine roles. We'll see that the acquisition of gender roles is likely to involve a complex interaction of psychological, biological, and social factors.

Feminist Theory

The Greek philosopher Aristotle is said to have described a female as a deformed male. We can only guess at the number of objectionable beliefs expressed in this description, such as seeing the male as the ideal, focusing on the differences rather

Innovative Canadian Research

CANADIAN SEXUALITY, GENDER, AND OTHER SOCIAL VARIABLES

Gender differences are often analyzed in studies of sexuality. Other social variables are usually not considered.

Researchers at the University of Guelph–Dayna Fischstein, Ed Herold, and Serge Demarais (2007)–collected data from a national survey of 1 479 Canadian adults over the age of 18 to determine whether gender differences still exist when we take into account other social variables. The researchers examined how gender, age, marital status, education, religiosity, and geographic region affect the sexuality variables of frequency of sexual thoughts, oral sex, age at first intercourse, number of sexual partners, and intentions to engage in casual sex.

The researchers found that the men were more sexually permissive and more sexually active than the women. Some of the gender differences were small or moderate, however, which suggests that the gender gap for differences in sexuality may be narrowing.

Other demographic variables were also significant predictors of sexual attitudes and behaviours. Generally, survey participants who were younger, had more education, or did not attend religious services had more permissive attitudes.

The findings illustrate the value of taking into account other social variables when analyzing gender differences in sexuality.

The most substantial gender differences were seen with intention to engage in casual sex. None of the women reported that they would definitely engage in casual sex, and few reported that they would probably engage in casual sex. Most men, however, reported they would engage in casual sex if given the opportunity.

These findings may be explained by the sexual double standard, which allows greater sexual freedom for men than for women. The strength of the gender effect was demonstrated by the fact that the other social factors were relatively weak predictors of intentions to engage in casual sex. Interestingly, people living in Quebec were more likely than participants from all other regions to report an interest in casual sex.

This study is important because it illuminates the role of gender in relation to social variables in accounting for differences in sexuality among adult Canadians. The survey findings point to the need for large-scale national surveys that use heterogeneous samples, rather than samples of convenience such as university populations.

than the similarities between men and women, and the implicit right of men to hold power over women.

Feminism and feminist theory were born of protest against ideas such as Aristotle's—ideas that remain with us today in many (if not most) parts of the world (Chesler, 2006). Definitions of "feminism" and "feminist theory" are controversial, but it's clear enough that feminist theory focuses on the subordination of women to men. Feminist theory analyzes the relationships among sexism, heterosexism (prejudice or discrimination against homosexuals by heterosexuals), racism, and class oppression, and explores various means of individual and societal resistance (Butler, 1993, 2003).

Among other things, feminist theory challenges:

- Traditional views of men as breadwinners and women as homemakers.
- Traditional views of men as political policymakers, especially because those policies affect women and children.
- Traditional views of men as sexual aggressors and women as sexual "gatekeepers."
- Traditional gender roles that view men as objective and rational, and women as emotional and irrational.

Some feminists challenge the very concepts of femininity and masculinity, arguing that such concepts suggest some sort of biological or "actual" basis to the distinction (Squier & Littlefield, 2004; Wood, 2005). They argue, instead, that femininity and masculinity might be purely social constructions that have the effect of giving women second-class citizenship—or, in many historic periods and parts of the world, no citizenship whatsoever.

When it comes to sexuality, feminists assert that men have no right to control women's bodies. They argue that abortion is a woman's personal choice, that women have as much right as men to decide whether—and with whom—to engage in sexual activity, that few if any sex differences exist in terms of mental abilities, such as those used in math and science, and that most medical research has been conducted by men for men, with men as subjects.

Although the extent and nature of sex differences remain controversial, we can note that many traditions that subjugate women are falling by the wayside, at least in developed nations. Most Western women, for example, are now in the workforce. As a result, many men now share the child rearing and housekeeping with their female partners. In the United States, as many women as men are pursuing careers in traditionally male domains such as business, law, and medicine (Stamback & Miriam, 2005). Many women feel free to initiate sex and relationships.

Queer Theory

Queer theory A theory that challenges heteronormativity and heterosexism.

The word "queer" was initially used as an insult for homosexuals. After approximately two centuries, it was gradually replaced by the word "gay" (Bhugra, 2005). Homosexual people have recently reappropriated "queer" as a sign of pride, however, as shown by the title of the popular TV show *Queer Eye for the Straight Guy*. As one result of this reappropriation, a widely cited theory of the psychology and sociology of gender roles and sexual orientation is termed **queer theory** (Alexander, 2006; Valocchi, 2005).

Queer theory challenges a number of commonly held assumptions about gender and sexuality, such as the assumption that heterosexuality is "normal" and superior to homosexuality (Lovaas, et al., 2007). Queer theory also challenges the assumption that people are naturally divided into heterosexuals and homosexuals (Halpern, 2003; Hird, 2004).

Queer theory argues that the concepts of heterosexuality and homosexuality are social constructs that ignore commonly experienced mismatches among people's anatomic sex, society's gender roles, and individuals' sexual desires (Schlichter, 2004). Queer theory asserts that human sexuality has always been more varied than those in power—particularly male heterosexuals—are willing to admit. They point to historical examples such as ancient Greek bisexuality and the current **homophobia** as evidence.

Homophobia Hatred of homosexuals (even though the root "phobia" means "fear," not "hatred").

We'll revisit queer theory in later chapters, particularly those dealing with gender and sexual orientation.

Multiple Perspectives on Human Sexuality

Given the complexity and range of human sexual behaviour, we need to consider multiple perspectives to understand sexuality. Each perspective has something to offer in this enterprise. Let's venture a few conclusions based on our overview of these perspectives.

First, human sexuality appears to reflect a combination of biological, social, cultural, sociocultural, and psychological factors that interact in complex ways, perhaps in combinations that are unique for each individual. Second, there are few universal patterns of sexual behaviour, and views on what's right and wrong show great diversity. Third, although our own cultural values and beliefs may be deeply meaningful to us, they may not necessarily indicate what sexual behaviours are common, natural, or moral.

The complexity of human sexuality—complexity that causes it to remain somewhat baffling to scientists—adds to the wonder and richness of our own uniqueness as individual sexual beings.

Summing Up

Human sexuality concerns the ways we experience and express ourselves as sexual beings. The study of human sexuality draws upon the expertise of anthropologists, biologists, medical researchers, sociologists, psychologists, and other scientists.

Our values and our knowledge about human sexuality inform our sexual decisions.

Critical thinking is a skeptical approach to evaluating arguments, widely held beliefs, and evidence. Critical thinkers examine definitions of terms and premises of arguments, and are cautious in drawing conclusions from evidence.

The historical perspective suggests that there are few universal sexual trends.

The biological perspective focuses on biological sexual processes such as genetic, hormonal, and neural factors.

Evolutionary theory suggests that social behaviours that enhance reproductive success may be subject to natural selection.

The cross-species perspective reveals the variety of sexual behaviours among nonhumans.

The sociological perspective shows how cultural beliefs affect sexual behaviours and attitudes.

The psychological perspectives focus on the ways gender and sexual behaviour are affected by personality, emotion, learning, motivation, and perception. Freud formulated the theory of psychoanalysis, which proposes that biologically based sex drives conflict with social codes. Learning theory focuses on the roles of rewards and punishment. Social-cognitive theory views people as decision makers and emphasizes the role of observational learning.

Feminist theory challenges traditional gender roles and male oppression of females.

Queer theory challenges heteronormativity—the view that heterosexuality is "normal"—and as evidence points out mismatches among anatomic sex, gender roles, and sexual desires.

Test Yourself

Multiple-Choice Questions

1. According to a 2003 study, most students at a Canadian university said they were "having sex" when the behaviour was:
   (a) Oral-genital contact.
   (b) Penile-vaginal intercourse.
   (c) Manual stimulation of the genitals.
   (d) All of the above.

2. Historically, _____ was most likely the first sexual taboo.
   (a) incest
   (b) sex before marriage
   (c) male homosexuality
   (d) masturbation

3. Critical thinking includes all of the following except:
   (a) Skepticism.
   (b) Getting in touch with our feelings.
   (c) Evaluating the strengths and weaknesses of different perspectives.
   (d) Avoiding oversimplification.

4. A Freudian belief is that:
   (a) Children normally harbour erotic interests.
   (b) Children normally ignore unacceptable impulses.
   (c) Children are not interested in sexuality.
   (d) Children seek pain and avoid pleasure.

5. The ancient _____ were the first to produce a detailed sex manual.
   (a) Greeks
   (b) Romans
   (c) Chinese
   (d) Indians

6. Which of the following is not part of the ethical framework presented by Meaney and Rye?
   (a) Autonomy.
   (b) Community.
   (c) Divinity.
   (d) Authority.

continued

7. In a series of volumes published between 1897 and 1910, the physician _____ challenged the prevailing view by arguing that sexual desire in women was natural and healthy.

(a) Sylvester Graham
(b) Sigmund Freud
(c) Havelock Ellis
(d) Richard von Krafft-Ebing

8. Ford and Beach's research on preliterate societies found:

(a) A wide variety of sexual customs and beliefs.
(b) That intercourse was more common among older than younger people.
(c) That childhood masturbation was discouraged in all of the societies they studied.
(d) Kissing in all of the societies they studied.

9. According to _____ theory, children acquire the gender roles deemed appropriate in their society through reinforcement and observational learning.

(a) evolutionary
(b) social-cognitive
(c) feminist
(d) psychoanalytic

10. According to queer theory,

(a) There is no such thing as homosexuality.
(b) All heterosexuals are prejudiced.
(c) Everybody is bisexual.
(d) Current categories of sexual orientation do not adequately describe all people.

You'll find answers to the "Test Yourself" questions on page 495.

Questions for Critical Thinking

1. What are your goals for this course on human sexuality? Do you think what you'll learn here will help you later in life? Why or why not?

2. Religions have historically been major factors influencing human sexual behaviour. Do you think this is still true in Canada today? Why or why not?

3. A friend of yours insists that something is true because she found it on the internet. As a critical thinker, do you accept your friend's argument as proof? If not, what would you do to determine the truth or falsity of your friend's claim?

MySearchLab

MySearchLab offers extensive help to students with their writing and research project and provides round-the-clock access to credible and reliable source material. Take a tour at www.mysearchlab.com.

CHAPTER TWO

Research Methods

Empirical Derived from or based on observation and experimentation.

In this chapter, we look at how scientists conduct research into human sexuality. In addition to looking at different research methods, we discuss ethical issues involved in sexuality research.

Let's begin by briefly exploring the scientific method for conducting research. Because sexuality is so often misunderstood or subject to biased thinking, it's important to use sound research methods.

A Scientific Approach to Human Sexuality

Scientists and researchers who study human sexuality take an **empirical** approach. That is, they base their knowledge on research evidence, rather than on intuition, faith, or superstition. Scientists and other people may use intuition or religious beliefs to come up with topics for scientific study, but once they've selected those topics, they use the scientific method to seek answers to their questions.

The Scientific Method

Critical thinking and the scientific approach share the hallmark of skepticism. As skeptics, scientists question prevailing assumptions and theories about sexual behaviour. They are willing to dispute the assertions of authority figures such as political and religious leaders—and even other scientists. Scientists also recognize that they cannot gain perfect knowledge. One era's truths may become another era's ancient myths and fallacies. Scientists are involved in the quest for truth, but they recognize that this search is a continuous process, and that a set of final truths, especially those regarding human behaviour, will likely remain elusive.

The scientific method is a systematic way of gathering scientific evidence and testing assumptions through research. It has a number of elements:

1. **Formulating a research question.** Does alcohol inspire or impair sexual response? A scientist formulates a research question on the basis of observation and theory about an event or behaviour. S/he then conducts empirical research to answer these questions.
2. **Framing the research question in the form of a hypothesis.** Experiments are usually undertaken with a **hypothesis** in mind—a precise prediction about behaviour that is often derived from theory. A hypothesis is tested through research. For instance, the scientist might theorize that alcohol enhances sexual responsiveness by directly stimulating sexual response or by reducing feelings of guilt associated with sex. S/he might then hypothesize that an intervention (called, in experimental terms, a treatment), such as drinking alcohol in a laboratory setting, will lead to heightened sexual arousal in the presence of erotic stimuli, such as sexually explicit videos.
3. **Testing the hypothesis.** The scientist then tests the hypothesis through carefully controlled observation and experimentation. A specific hypothesis about alcohol and sexual arousal—that alcohol either increases or decreases sexual responsiveness—might be tested by administering a certain amount of alcohol to one group of people, exposing them to specific types of sexual stimulation (such as sexually explicit videos), and comparing their levels of sexual arousal to those of another group of people who have been shown the videos but not given alcohol (a control group).
4. **Drawing conclusions.** The scientist then analyzes the results of the test and draws conclusions, or inferences, about whether the hypothesis is correct. If the results of a well-designed research study fail to support a certain hypothesis, the scientist can revise the theory s/he has used served as the framework for the hypothesis. Research findings often lead scientists to modify their theories and, in turn, generate new hypotheses that can be tested with further research.

GOALS OF THE SCIENCE OF HUMAN SEXUALITY The goals of the science of human sexuality are congruent with those of other sciences—to describe, explain, predict, and control the events of interest (in this case, sexual behaviours). Let's discuss some of the general goals of science, and how they relate to the study of human sexuality.

Description is a basic objective of science. To understand a sexual behaviour, for example, we must first be able to describe it. Description precedes understanding. Scientists attempt to be clear, unbiased, and precise in their descriptions of events and behaviours. The scientific approach to human sexuality examines sexual behaviours through techniques as varied as the field study, the survey, the individual case study, and the laboratory experiment.

Researchers attempt to relate their observations to specific factors, or **variables**, that can help explain the observations. For example, researchers may attempt to explain variations in the frequency of different types of sexual behaviours by correlating the behaviours with **demographic** variables such as age, religious or social background, and cultural expectation. The variables that are commonly used to explain sexual behaviour are biological (e.g., age, sex, health status), psychological (e.g., anxiety, self-confidence, knowledge, skills), and demographic or sociological (e.g., educational level, socioeconomic status, ethnicity).

Theories provide frameworks within which scientists can explain and make predictions about what they observe. It's not sufficient for theories to explain only past events. Theories must also enable us to make predictions about what will happen in the future. Some sex researchers study factors that may predict the occurrence of specific sexual behaviours (e.g., oral sex, masturbation) or sexuality-related outcomes (e.g., improved sexual functioning, condom use).

The purpose of scientific research into human sexuality is not to dictate to people how they ought to behave. Rather, at its best, it can provide information or insights that people can use to better understand themselves and make decisions about their own behaviours. Sexuality research helps educators, social workers, psychologists, therapists, nurses, doctors, and other professionals improve the sexual health and well-being of individuals and communities. Research will continue to illuminate the many ways gender, sexual identity, sexual orientation, and other factors affect the diversity of human sexuality.

Variables Quantities or qualities that vary or that may vary.

Demographic Concerning the vital statistics of a human population (e.g., density, race, age, education).

Quantitative Research Methods
Populations and Samples: Representing the World of Diversity

Researchers try to learn about **populations**. A population is a complete group, such as everyone who lives in Canada. Other researchers focus on specific groups, such as First Nations people or transgendered people or women or adolescents. These are termed the *populations of interest*, or *target populations*.

These target populations are all sizable. It would be expensive, difficult, and all but impossible to study every individual. A scientist therefore selects individuals from the population and studies them. The individuals who participate in the research are collectively called a **sample**. To truly learn about a population of interest, the scientist must ensure that the sample accurately represents the population. A *representative sample* is a research sample of participants who accurately represent the population of interest.

If the sample does not represent the target population, the scientist cannot extend, or **generalize**, the results of his or her research to the population of interest. If we wished to study the sexual behaviour of Asian Canadians, for example,

Population A complete group of organisms or events.

Sample Part of a population selected for study.

Generalize Use information from a particular case or sample to draw conclusions about a larger phenomenon or population.

our population would consist of *all* Asian Canadians. If we used only Asian-Canadian college students as our sample, we could not generalize our findings to all Asian Canadians.

Including everyone in Canada in a study of sexual behaviour would be impossible. The government cannot even *find* everyone in Canada when it conducts the census. And incorporating sexuality research into the census would undoubtedly cause many more people to refuse to participate. Sampling a part of a target population makes research possible and practical—if imperfect.

Sampling Methods

Now and then, magazine editors boast that they've surveyed samples of 20 000 or 30 000 readers—but size alone doesn't mean a sample is representative. *Psychology Today* and *Glamour* regularly poll readers, but their readers don't represent the general population. Readers of *Psychology Today* are biased in that they tend to be better educated and more liberal than the population at large (*Psychology Today*, 2006). Readers of *Glamour* are biased in that they're also better educated than the average North American, and more likely to be concerned about their appearances and about optimizing their sex lives.

Random sample A sample in which every member of a population has an equal chance of participating.

Stratified random sample A random sample in which known subgroups of a population are represented in proportion to their numbers within the population.

Volunteer bias A slanting of research data caused by the characteristics of individuals who volunteer to participate (e.g., their willingness to discuss intimate behaviour).

One way of acquiring a representative sample is random sampling. A **random sample** is one in which every member of the target population has an equal chance of participating. Researchers overcome biased sampling by drawing random or **stratified random samples** of populations. In a stratified random sample, known subgroups of a population are represented in proportion to their numbers within the population. For instance, about 51% of the Canadian population is female. Researchers could therefore decide that 51% of their sample must be female if the sample is to represent everyone in Canada. The randomness of the sample would be preserved, because the subgroup members would be selected randomly from their particular subgroups.

Another problem is that sexual research is almost invariably conducted with people who volunteer to participate. Volunteers may differ from people who refuse to participate. For example, volunteers may tend to be more open about their sexuality than the general population.

The problem of **volunteer bias** is a thorny one for sex researchers, because the refusal of people who have been randomly selected to participate in the survey can ruin the representativeness of the sample. It would be unethical to coerce people to participate in a study on sexual behaviour (or in any other type of study), so researchers must use samples of volunteers, rather than truly random samples. A low response rate to a voluntary survey is an indication that the responses probably don't represent everyone the survey has been sent to.

In some cases, samples are samples of convenience. They consist of individuals who happen to be available to the researcher and who share some characteristics with the target population—perhaps religious background or sexual orientation. They may not truly represent the target group. Convenience samples often consist of European-Canadian, middle-class university students who volunteer for studies conducted at their schools.

Populations and Samples.
To what populations do you belong? College students? Returning students? What is your gender? What about your ethnic background? How do researchers obtain samples that represent populations such as these? What problems do they encounter in attempting to do so?

Methods of Observation

Once scientists have chosen who they'll study, they observe these people. They use several methods of observation: the case study, the survey, naturalistic observation, ethnographic observation, participant observation, and laboratory observation.

The Case Study Method

A **case study** is a carefully drawn, in-depth biography of an individual or a small group. The focus is on understanding one or several individuals as fully as possible by unravelling the interplay of various factors in the individual's or group's background. In most case studies, the researcher comes to know the person or group through interviews or other contacts conducted over a prolonged period. The interviewing pattern tends to build upon itself with a good deal of freedom, in contrast to the one-shot, standardized set of questions used in a survey questionnaire.

Reports of innovative treatments for sexual dysfunctions sometimes appear as well-described case studies. A clinician typically reports the client's background in depth, describes the treatment, reports the apparent outcome(s), and suggests factors that might have contributed to the treatment's success or failure. In writing a treatment case study, the therapist tries to provide information that may be helpful to other therapists who treat clients with similar problems. Case studies or multiple-case studies (reports concerning a few individuals) that hold promise may lead to controlled investigations—ideally, to experimental studies involving treatment groups and control (non-treatment) groups.

Despite the richness of material that may be derived from a case study, it is not as rigorous a research design as an experiment. People often have gaps in memory, especially concerning childhood events. The potential for observer bias is also a prominent concern. Clinicians and interviewers may unintentionally guide people into saying what they expect to hear. Then, too, researchers may inadvertently colour people's reports when they write them down—shaping them subtly in ways that reflect their own views.

Case study   A carefully drawn, in-depth biography of an individual or a small group of individuals. This information may be obtained through interviews, questionnaires, and historical records.

The Survey Method

Surveys typically gather information about behaviour through questionnaires or interviews. Researchers may interview or administer questionnaires to thousands of people from particular population groups to learn about their sexual behaviours and attitudes. Interviews such as those used by Kinsey and his colleagues (1948, 1953) have the advantages of allowing face-to-face contact and giving the interviewer the opportunity to probe—that is, to follow up on answers that seem to lead toward useful information. A skilled interviewer may be able to set a respondent at ease and establish a sense of trust, or rapport, that encourages self-disclosure.

University of Alberta researcher Melanie Beres (2006) interviewed seasonal workers in Jasper, Alberta, to study casual sex experiences and how the workers perceived potential partners' willingness to engage in casual sex. The interviews were unstructured, allowing the participants to talk about their experiences from their own perspectives, rather than that of the researcher. (Findings from this study are presented in Chapter 7.)

Survey   A detailed study of a sample obtained through such methods as interviews and questionnaires.

Research Interview.
Interviewing is a commonly used survey method. Questionnaires are also used.

Questionnaires can be administered to many people at once, and respondents can return them unsigned. Anonymity may encourage respondents to disclose intimate information. Of course, questionnaires can be used only by people who can read and record their responses. Interviews can be used even with people who can't read or write.

Most surveys contribute something to our understanding of human sexuality, but some are more methodologically sound than others. None, however, fully represent the Canadian population at large. Most people think of their sexuality as one of the most intimate, private aspects of their lives. People who willingly agree to be polled about their political preferences may refuse to participate in surveys about their sexual behaviour. It's therefore difficult if not impossible to recruit a truly representative sample of the population. Survey results provide, at best, approximations of the sexual attitudes, beliefs, and behaviours of the Canadian population.

Surveys are increasingly conducted through the internet. An Ontario survey found that research participants were more likely to fully complete an online survey than an equivalent traditional paper-and-pencil survey (Wood et al., 2006).

Let's review the sampling techniques used in some large-scale Canadian and American studies of human sexuality. Throughout this book, we'll reconsider the findings of these surveys.

Large-Scale Canadian and American Studies

THE KINSEY REPORTS Alfred Kinsey and his colleagues (1948, 1953) interviewed 5300 men and 5940 women in the United States between 1938 and 1949. They asked a wide array of questions about various types of sexual experience, including masturbation, oral sex, and coitus—before, during, and outside of marriage. Kinsey adopted a group sampling approach. He recruited study participants from organizations and community groups such as college fraternities and sororities. He contacted representatives of groups in diverse communities, and tried to persuade them to get their fellow group members to cooperate.

Kinsey's samples did not represent the general population. People of colour, people in rural areas, older people, the poor, Catholics, and Jews were all underrepresented in his samples. Statisticians who have reviewed Kinsey's methods have concluded that his sampling methods contained systematic biases, but that it would have been impossible to obtain a true probability sample from the general population (see, for example, Cochran et al., 1953). There is thus no way of knowing whether Kinsey's results accurately mirrored the practices of the American population at the time. His estimate that 37% of the male population had reached orgasm at least once through male–male sexual activity was probably too high. But the relationships Kinsey uncovered, such as the positive link between level of education and participation in oral sex, may be more generalizable.

To his credit, Kinsey took measures to encourage candour in the people he interviewed. He assured study participants that their responses were confidential. He trained his interviewers to ask questions in an objective, matter-of-fact style. To reduce the tendency to slant responses in socially desirable directions, interviewers reassured participants that they would not pass judgment on anything they said. Interviewers were trained to hide any emotional reactions their subjects might interpret as disapproving.

Alfred Kinsey.
Kinsey and his colleagues conducted the first large-scale scientific study of sexual behaviour in the United States.

Kinsey also checked the **reliability** of his data by evaluating the consistency of the responses given by several hundred interviewees who were re-examined after at least 18 months. Their reports of the **incidence** of various sexual activities (for example, whether they had ever engaged in premarital or extramarital coitus) were highly reliable. That is, participants tended to give the same answers on both occasions. Kinsey recognized, however, that consistency of responses across time—or retakes, as he called them—did not guarantee their **validity**. That is, the retakes did not show whether the reported behaviours had some basis in fact. One indirect measure was comparison of the reports of husbands and wives—for example, with respect to the incidence of oral–genital sex or the frequency of intercourse. There was a remarkable consistency in the reports of 706 pairs of spouses, lending support to the view that their self-reports were accurate.

The 2004 Hollywood film *Kinsey* gives a realistic portrayal of the interview techniques Kinsey and his colleagues used. As portrayed in the film, many research participants experienced emotional relief by discussing—for the first time in their lives—intimate behaviours they had felt anxious and guilty about. Most important, Kinsey's interviewers' nonjudgmental responses reassured participants that they were "normal."

THE NHSLS STUDY The National Health and Social Life Survey (NHSLS) was intended to provide general information about sexual behaviour in the United States, as well as specific information that might be used to predict and prevent the spread of AIDS. It was conducted by Edward O. Laumann of the University of Chicago and three colleagues—John H. Gagnon, Robert T. Michael, and Stuart Michaels—in the 1990s, and its findings were published in 1994 as *The Social Organization of Sexuality: Sexual Practices in the United States.* The NHSLS study was originally to be supported by government funds, but Republican Senator Jesse Helms of North Carolina blocked federal financing on the grounds that it was inappropriate for the government to support sex research (Bronner, 1998). The research team obtained private funding, but had to cut back the scope of the project.

The sample included 3432 people who were 18 to 59 years old. Of this number, 3159 lived in English-speaking households (rather than in dormitories, prisons, or other forms of housing). The other 273 were obtained by purposely over-sampling English-speaking African-American, Latino-American, and Latina-American households, so more information could be obtained about these ethnic groups.

The researchers sampled households by address in geographic areas, not by name. They sent a letter to each household, describing the study's purpose and methods, then an interviewer visited each household a week later. The people targeted were assured that the purposes of the study were important and their identities would be kept confidential. Incentives of up to $100 were offered for cooperating. A high completion rate of close to 80% was achieved this way.

THE CANADIAN YOUTH, SEXUAL HEALTH, AND HIV/AIDS STUDIES Two national surveys have focused on the sexual health of Canadian adolescents. The first, known as the Canada Youth and AIDS Study (CYAS), was conducted in 1988 (King et al., 1989). The second, known as the Canadian Youth, Sexual Health, and HIV/AIDS Study (CYSHHAS), was conducted in 2002 and 2003 (Boyce et al., 2003).

Reliability   The consistency or accuracy of a measure.

Incidence   A measure of an event's occurrence.

Validity   The degree to which a test measures what it purports to measure.

The Canadian Journal of Human Sexuality

VOLUME 14 - NUMBER 1-2

PUBLISHED BY SIECCAN
THE SEX INFORMATION & EDUCATION COUNCIL OF CANADA
http://www.sieccan.org

The Canadian Journal of Human Sexuality.
Published by the Sex Information and Education Council of Canada, this is the major journal focusing on Canadian sexuality research. It also covers American research.

The main objective of these studies was to understand the determinants of adolescent sexuality and sexual health for different age groups. Involving students in grades 7, 9, and 11 from all provinces and territories except Nunavut, the studies were coordinated by education ministers from across Canada and funded by Health Canada. Although the study samples were not nationally representative, they were large enough to provide information about the sexual health of a large number of Canadian adolescents.

THE CANADIAN COMMUNITY HEALTH SURVEY The Canadian Community Health Survey (CCHS) is repeatedly conducted by Statistics Canada over one- and two-year cycles. The aim of the survey is to provide data on the health status of Canadians who are aged 12 and up. The sample size for each cycle of the survey is more than 100 000.

The survey contains questions related to sexuality, such as sexual identity (gay, lesbian, bisexual), age of first intercourse, number of sexual partners in the prior 12 months, and condom use at last intercourse. The CCHS has been a key source of data about sexual behaviour and condom use among Canadian youth (Rotermann, 2005, 2008), and about condom use among 20- to 34-year-old single Canadians (Rotermann & McKay, 2009).

THE CANADIAN CONTRACEPTION STUDIES Beginning in the 1990s, four national surveys on contraceptive use were sponsored by the pharmaceutical company Janssen-Ortho. The 2002 study sampled 15- to 44-year-old women from across Canada (Fisher, Boroditsky, & Morris, 2004). Of 3345 questionnaires mailed out, 1582 were returned.

The surveys looked at contraception awareness, attitudes, and behaviours among a representative sample of Canadian women of childbearing age. They included questions about sexual behaviours, such as whether respondents had ever experienced sexual intercourse, or had experienced sexual intercourse in the previous six months. One of the unique features of these studies was that they also asked whether participants had experienced sexual difficulties, such as diminished sexual desire or pain during intercourse.

More recently, the Society of Obstetricians and Gynaecologists of Canada funded a national study of contraceptive choices and use among Canadian women (Black et al., 2009).

THE COMPAS SURVEY In 1998, the COMPAS survey organization, on behalf of the Sun newspaper chain, conducted one of the more comprehensive national surveys about relationships and sexuality (Compas, 1998). There were 1479 respondents in this survey. Their demographic characteristics, such as age and education, were proportionally similar to those of the Canadian population. The survey asked about sexual orientation, age at first intercourse, number of intercourse partners, sexual frequency, oral sex, sexual communication, sexual problems, sex and the workplace, attitudes toward casual sex, and attitudes toward toplessness and prostitution.

More than 95% of those who took part in the survey responded to the sexuality questions. The highest non-response rate was for the question on oral sex, which 15% of the females and 5% of the males declined to answer.

LIMITATIONS OF CANADIAN NATIONAL SURVEYS ON SEXUALITY Most national surveys on sexuality conducted in Canada have been limited in scope. They have focused mainly on issues such as age of first intercourse, number of sexual partners, condom use for prevention of sexually transmitted infections, and contraceptive use. Few methodologically sound recent national studies in Canada have investigated broader aspects of sexuality, such as the variables associated with sexual satisfaction and pleasure. Few national studies have adequately sampled sexual minorities, such as transgendered people. Smaller-scale studies that have sampled fewer people, and are therefore not representative of the wider population, remain our best source of data on various aspects of sexuality.

A new research initiative, currently in the development stage, may considerably broaden the focus of national research on sexuality. The project is a partnership between the Public Health Agency of Canada and a number of university and community-based researchers across the country. The survey instrument, which has been pilot-tested for use with 16- to 24-year-olds, includes scales to measure sexual assertiveness, sexual functioning and satisfaction, and sexual coercion, as well as more traditional measures of sexual health (Smylie et al., 2011).

RELIABILITY OF THE SURVEY METHOD How do we know whether respondents are telling the truth when they take part in sex surveys? We can determine their reliability by checking for consistency in their responses.

In a study of gay males in Toronto, for example, reliability was determined by giving the same interviews to the men 72 hours apart (Coates et al., 1986). The high degree of response consistency between the two interviews indicated that the data were reliable. Another Toronto study looked at men with AIDS or AIDS-related conditions and their male partners, and found a high degree of agreement between the pairs regarding details about their sexual encounters (Coates et al., 1988). Reliability of responses was very high for behaviours such as anal intercourse, but somewhat less so for less risky behaviours such as anal finger insertion.

McGill University researchers Eric Ochs and Yitzchak Binik (1999) obtained data concerning 68 sexual behaviours from 70 heterosexual couples, to determine the degree of consistency in the partners' responses. On individually completed questionnaires, they found that both partners within the couples gave similar responses, suggesting high reliability. And in a study of university students in British Columbia, only a few gave responses that were biased in a socially desirable direction (Meston, Heiman, Trapnell, & Paulhus, 1998).

Some surveys are less reliable than others. Those conducted by Statistics Canada and other government agencies tend to be more reliable than those sponsored by private companies, whose purpose may be to sell a product or to persuade the public to a point of view. It's important to evaluate a survey's methodology when assessing the accuracy of its findings.

LIMITATIONS OF THE SURVEY METHOD Many people refuse to participate in surveys. Samples are therefore biased by the inclusion of large numbers of volunteers, who are generally willing to take time to participate. Volunteers for sex surveys also tend to be more sexually permissive and liberal-minded than nonvolunteers. At an Ontario university, for example, students who volunteered for a study on human sexuality were more sexually experienced, more interested in sexual variety, and more permissive in their attitudes toward sexuality than were students who did not volunteer (Bogaert, 1996).

Many of the Canadian researchers who study sexuality are based in university social science departments, and for the sake of convenience they frequently obtain samples from students in their departments. Since relatively few men enroll in many social science courses, however, it's difficult to make adequate gender comparisons. Researchers at an Ontario university found that fewer males than females volunteered to take part in a sexuality study, which of course exacerbated the gender-ratio problem (Senn & Demarais, 2001). Interestingly, more students volunteered to take part in the sexuality study than in a study on memory.

Respondents may recall their behaviour inaccurately, or may purposely misrepresent it. People may not recall the age at which they first engaged in petting or masturbated to orgasm. People may have difficulty remembering or calculating the frequencies of certain behaviours, such as the weekly frequency of marital intercourse.

CRITICAL THINKING QUESTIONS

One study conducted at a university found that fewer male than female students volunteered for a sexuality study. Can you think of any reasons to explain this finding?

A World of Diversity

STUDYING THE SEXUAL BEHAVIOURS OF DIVERSE POPULATIONS

Ontario's First Nations

More than one million Canadians identify themselves as First Nations people. Rates of sexually transmitted infections (STIs) are much higher among First Nations people than among the general population, yet a notable lack of sex research has been conducted with this ethnic group.

Concern about the spread of HIV/AIDS, however, led to the development of the Ontario First Nations AIDS and Healthy Lifestyle Survey by researchers at the University of Toronto and representatives of Ontario's First Nations (Myers et al., 1993). Eleven reserve communities took part in the study, with participants randomly selected from the lists of on-reserve members. Almost all (87%) of those selected agreed to be interviewed.

Interviews were conducted face to face by trained First Nations interviewers. The questions were about sexuality and alcohol use. Each participant was given an answer booklet, which listed several possible answers for each question. The interviewer read each question from the interview schedule, and the respondent checked off the answers in the answer book, then sealed the book in an envelope. At the beginning of the sexual questions, each respondent was given the choice of hearing the sexual acts described in slang terms or in technical terms.

Of those who'd had sex in the previous year, 58% reported having had only one sex partner, 30% reported two to four partners, and 12% reported five or more partners (Calzavara et al., 1999). Almost all of those who'd experienced sex in the previous 12 months had engaged in sexual intercourse, 53% had experienced oral sex, and 13% had experienced anal intercourse. Individuals who'd engaged in sex with partners from both inside and outside of the community were more likely to experience oral and anal sex than were respondents who'd had sex only with partners from inside or from outside the community (Calzavara et al., 1999). Only 9% of those who'd engaged in vaginal intercourse reported always using condoms, and only 11% of those who'd engaged in anal sex always used condoms. Alcohol use was not related to condom use (Myers et al., 1997).

Asian Canadians

University of British Columbia researcher Lori A. Brotto and her colleagues compared samples of European-Canadian and Asian female students ((Brotto et al., 2005) and European-Canadian and Asian male students (Brotto et al., 2006). The Asian students had more conservative sexual attitudes and fewer sexual experiences than did the European Canadians.

Most cross-cultural researchers have focused only on ethnic group comparisons or length of residency as predictors of sexual attitudes and behaviours. Brotto et al. (2006, 2007) also considered acculturation to Western society, and found that acculturation was much more powerful than length of residence for predicting sexual attitudes, experiences, and responses.

Gay and Bisexual Men

Until the 1980s, limited research was focused on men who have sex with men. With the advent of the AIDS epidemic, however, the Canadian government targeted millions of dollars for research into the prevention and treatment of HIV/AIDS. Because HIV/AIDS affected gay males far more than any other group in Canada, several research projects were funded to analyze sexual behaviours and condom use among gay and bisexual men.

The first national survey of men who have sex with men was a joint project involving researchers from the University of Toronto, Université Laval, and the Université de Montréal (Myers, Orr, Locker, & Jackson, 1993). The project was designed by the researchers, the Canadian AIDS Society, and AIDS organizations from across Canada.

A sample of 4803 men ranging in age from 16 to 75 was obtained from gay bars, bathhouses, and community dances in 35 Canadian cities. Data were obtained by questionnaires. The response rate was very high, with 86% of those who were approached agreeing to take part in the survey; response rates were higher in bars and at dances than in the bathhouses. More than half (57%) attended bars at least once

Social desirability A response bias caused by a subject's tendency to provide a socially acceptable answer to a questionnaire or interview question.

("Well, let's see. This week I think it was four times, but last week only two times, and I can't remember the week before that.") Kinsey and Hunt speculated that people who desire more frequent sex tend to underestimate how often they have it, whereas people who prefer less frequent sex tend to overestimate how often they have it.

Even people who agree to participate in surveys of sexual behaviour may feel pressured to answer questions in the direction of **social desirability**. That is, they give responses they think are socially acceptable. For example, a survey participant who believes masturbation is viewed as a deviant or unacceptable practice may indicate on a week, but only 7% attended bathhouses once a week or more.

Respondents were asked whether, in the previous three months, they had engaged in deep-tongue kissing, mutual masturbation, receptive or insertive oral-anal sex, receptive or insertive oral sex with or without semen in the mouth, or receptive or insertive anal intercourse with or without a condom. They were also asked whether they'd been tested for HIV, and whether—to their knowledge—they were HIV-positive.

Twenty-three percent of the men reported at least one experience of unprotected anal intercourse in the previous three months. Two-thirds had been tested at least once for HIV, and 12% reported that they knew they were HIV-positive (Myers et al., 1996).

The second major Canadian survey of gay and bisexual men was conducted by University of Toronto researchers in 2002, using a sample of 5080 men in Ontario (Myers et al., 2004). Again, the researchers consulted extensively with AIDS service organizations while developing their research design.

The study recruited a more diverse sample than the previous national survey had. In particular, the researchers purposely recruited a higher proportion of men who were under the age of 20 or over the age of 50, or who had lower levels of education. Most important, the study recruited the largest number of non-Caucasian gay and bisexual men that had ever been surveyed in Canada. Compared with the previous national survey, this one had notably more gay men who were meeting partners on the internet.

A key finding of this study was an increase in the number of gay and bisexual men who reported at least one episode of unprotected anal intercourse (Myers et al., 2004).

Sex Workers

Frances Shaver at Concordia University in Montreal is one of Canada's leading experts on sex work. She has conducted three major surveys on this topic. In the first study, she interviewed male, female, and transgendered workers in Montreal and San Francisco. In the second study, she compared female and male sex workers with hospital workers in Montreal and Toronto, asking about working conditions, experiences, and stresses. Her third study, done in Montreal and Toronto, focused on different types of sex work—massage, exotic dancing, escorting, and domination.

Shaver (2005) outlined three main challenges in researching groups who are stigmatized by society, such as sex workers. The first difficulty is obtaining a representative sample. Researchers have typically sampled sex workers only on the street, because that's where they're most visible. However, those who work on the streets differ in many ways from those who work indoors. The second challenge arises because people whose work is illegal or stigmatized are less willing to be interviewed, and may be less honest in their responses. The third challenge is the traditional stereotype that sex workers are inherently exploited victims, rather than autonomous individuals who freely choose their occupations. Accompanying this stereotype is the belief that sex workers are all basically alike, rather than being diverse individuals.

To overcome these challenges, Shaver relied on a number of strategies. She asked an advisory group of sex workers for advice on what types of questions to ask and how to obtain research data. It was essential to convince sex workers that the researchers would be nonjudgmental and respectful of them and their privacy. The researchers also needed to distinguish themselves from other professionals, such as police officers and social workers.

One of Shaver's findings challenged the traditional wisdom that most sex workers work for pimps. We'll explore more of her findings in Chapter 17, when we discuss commercial sex.

Clients of Sex Workers

In Canada, the sexual behaviour of sex workers has been widely researched, but the behaviour of the male clients of female sex workers has not. Researchers find it difficult to make contact with these clients, because of the stigma attached to paying for sex. In British Columbia, researchers conducted an exploratory study to determine the feasibility of contacting and studying male clients (Kline at al., 2007). A total of 27 men replied to advertisements requesting the cooperation of male clients in a study aimed at improving their sexual health. However, only 9 of the men agreed to take part in a focus group. The men indicated that their fears about social disgrace, identity disclosure, and personal safety made them reluctant to take part in the study.

a survey that he doesn't masturbate, when in fact he does. A married survey respondent who perceives that extramarital sex is looked upon by society with disapproval may be less likely to report that she has engaged in extramarital sex. It's very likely that in the past, when Western culture was more homophobic than it is today, some gay, lesbian, and bisexual people failed to accurately report their sexual orientations when participating in sexuality research. These are all examples of social desirability bias.

It's important to understand that study participants whose are influenced by social desirability bias may be responding this way unconsciously, rather than on purpose.

Some respondents may consciously or unconsciously exaggerate their sexual behaviour in what they perceive to be socially desirable directions. For example, men may tend to exaggerate their levels of sexual activity, and women may tend to minimize theirs, in accordance with societal expectations (Ferraro, 2004; Nanda & Warms, 2004).

The Naturalistic Observation Method

Naturalistic observation A study method in which organisms are observed in their natural environments.

In **naturalistic observation**, also called the field study, scientists directly observe behaviour where it happens. Anthropologists, for example, live among preliterate societies and report on their social and sexual customs. Scientists in other disciplines also adopt methods of naturalistic observation in their research on human sexuality. For example, sociologists observe the street lives of prostitutes, and psychologists observe patterns of nonverbal communication and body language used by couples in dating situations.

The Ethnographic Observation Method

Ethnographic observation A study method in which behaviours and customs are observed within a group's native environment.

Ethnographic observation provides data about sexual behaviours and customs within various ethnic groups. This includes groups that are found in many cultures, as well as groups that are limited to one or a few cultures. Anthropologists are the specialists who typically engage in ethnographic research. They live among societies in the four corners of the earth, observing and studying human diversity. Margaret Mead (1935) reported on the social and sexual customs of various peoples of New Guinea. Bronisław Malinowski (1929) studied the Trobriand Islanders, among others.

Even so, ethnographic observation has its limits for the study of sexual behaviour. Sexual activities are most commonly performed away from the watchful gaze of others, especially visitors from other cultures. Ethnographers may therefore have to rely on indirect methods such as interviewing. Alean Al-Krenawi of Memorial University and John Graham (1999) of the University of Calgary used ethnographic methods to study the coping strategies of six women who were married to the same man in an Arab village in Israel.

The Participant Observation Method

Participant observation A study method in which observers interact with their subjects as they collect data.

In **participant observation,** the investigators learn about people's behaviour by directly interacting with them. Male–male sexual behaviour and mate swapping has been studied this way. As a graduate student in anthropology, Katherine Frank worked as a stripper at several clubs in a southeastern American city, "both as a means of earning extra cash for graduate school and as part of a feminism theory project investigating female objectification and body image" (Steinberg, 2004). In reports of her experiences, Frank (2002, 2003) notes that many men told her they attend the clubs because they "just want to relax." She writes that male customers may encounter some stigma for visiting the clubs, but not as much as the strippers do.

Katherine Frank.
Frank worked as a stripper in graduate school, both to augment her income and to learn about men who frequent strip clubs.

The Focus Group Method

Focus group research involves bringing together a group of people to determine their attitudes regarding a specific topic. The researcher guides the discussion by asking questions that are general in nature, with the intent of encouraging interaction and the free flow of ideas.

Focus groups are especially valuable in exploratory research, where there has been limited research on a particular topic. Researchers at the University of Guelph (Humphreys & Herold, 2007) used focus groups in developing scales to measure attitudes and behaviours pertaining to sexual consent. We'll discuss this study in Chapter 7.

The Laboratory Observation Method

With the 1966 publication of *Human Sexual Response*, William H. Masters and Virginia E. Johnson became some of the first scientists to report direct laboratory observations of individuals and couples engaged in sexual acts.

In all, 694 people (312 men and 382 women) participated in the research. The women ranged in age from 18 to 78, the men from 21 to 80. There were 276 married couples, 106 single women, and 36 single men.

The married couples engaged in intercourse and other forms of mutual stimulation, such as manual and oral stimulation of the genitals. The unmarried people participated in studies that did not require intercourse, such as measurement of female sexual arousal in response to the insertion of a penis-shaped probe, and male ejaculation during masturbation. Masters and Johnson made similar laboratory observations of sexual response among gay people for their 1979 book *Homosexuality in Perspective*.

Their methods offered the first reliable set of data on what happens to the body during sexual response. Their instruments permitted them to directly measure **vasocongestion** (blood flow to the genitals), myotonia (muscle tension), and other physiological responses.

Using a transparent artificial penis outfitted with photographic equipment, they were able to study changes in women's internal sex organs as the women became aroused. From these studies, Masters and Johnson observed that sexual response can be divided into four stages, which they called the sexual response cycle. We'll discuss this cycle in Chapter 4.

A methodological concern about the Masters and Johnson approach is the possibility that people engaged in sexual activities will alter their responses under observation. People may not respond publicly the same way they do in private. The physiological monitoring equipment may also alter the subjects' natural responses.

Correlation

What are the relationships between ethnicity and age of coming out among gay, lesbian, and bisexual people? What's the connection between socioeconomic status and teen pregnancy? In each case, we're relating two variables to one another—ethnicity and age of coming out, and socioeconomic status and rate of teen pregnancy. Correlational research describes the relationship between variables such as these.

A **correlation** is a statistical measure of the relationship between two variables. In a correlational study, two or more variables are related, or linked, to one another by statistical means. The strength and direction of the relationship between two variables are expressed with a statistic called a **correlation coefficient**. Correlations can be positive or negative. Two variables are positively correlated if one increases as the other increases, or one decreases as the other decreases. A negative correlation occurs when an opposite relationship exists, such as when one variable increases and the other decreases.

Research has shown relationships (correlations) between sexual satisfaction and a host of variables, including communication skills, marital satisfaction, and general health (see Figure 2.1) Although such research may give us an idea of the factors associated with sexual satisfaction, the experimenters have not manipulated the variables of interest. For this reason, we cannot say which—if any—of the factors is causally related to sexual happiness.

CRITICAL THINKING QUESTIONS

Which strikes you as the more important measure of sexual arousal—the person's subjective report of arousal or the level of arousal indicated by an instrument such as a vaginal photoplethysmograph?

Vasocongestion   Congestion resulting from the flow of blood.

Correlation   A statistical measure of the relationship between two variables.

Correlation coefficient   A statistic that expresses the strength and direction (positive or negative) of the relationship between two variables.

A Closer Look

MEASURING SEXUAL AROUSAL

What sexually excites a man? What sexually excites a woman? Research using a variety of methods suggests that men's sexual responses are more predictable, and that what goes on in men's bodies is more likely to correlate with what they're thinking.

Consider the research of Canadian investigator Meredith Chivers and her colleagues (Chivers & Bailey, 2007; Chivers et al., 2007). She showed erotic videos to men and women, straight and gay. The videos portrayed male-female sex, male-male sex, female-female sex, a man masturbating, a woman masturbating, a muscled man walking nude on a beach, and a well-toned nude woman doing calisthenics. The subjects watched the videos while Chivers measured their arousal objectively and subjectively. The objective measures were made possible by plethysmographs connected to the viewers' genitals. Men wore an apparatus on the penis that gauged its swelling (erection). Women inserted a tampon-shaped probe in the vagina that bounced light off the vaginal walls, providing a gauge of genital blood flow. In men, genital engorgement with blood produces erection; in women, it spurs lubrication. The participants used a keypad to rate their subjective feelings of arousal.

Self-labelled heterosexual men achieved erection while watching male-female sex, female-female sex, and masturbating and exercising women. They were generally unresponsive when they watched male-male sex and a masturbating man. Gay males showed the opposite pattern of arousal.

Subjective ratings by both the straight and the gay males matched the numbers provided by the plethysmograph. The men's thoughts were congruent with their body's responses.

Not so with the women. Regardless of whether the women labelled themselves straight or lesbian, they responded with

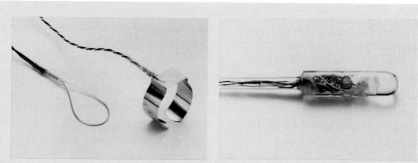

The penile strain gauge (left) and the vaginal photoplethysmograph (right) are used to measure physiological responses to sexual stimuli.

genital arousal when they viewed male-male sex, female-female sex, and male-female sex. Their genitals were more responsive to the exercising woman than to the nude man.

Their self-reported arousal rates, however, did not particularly match their bodies' responses. Heterosexual women reported less arousal than their bodies indicated when they watched female-female sex and male-male sex. They reported more arousal than their bodies showed when they watched male-female sex. Lesbians showed objective and subjective arousal in response to female-female sex, but reported less arousal than their bodies showed when they viewed male-male sex.

Chivers (in Bergner, 2009) suggests that women are genitally aroused by a wider range of stimuli than men, and that these differences might reflect innate, evolutionary forces. Could female sexuality be divided into two systems, one physiological and the other subjective? According to this view, feminine lust would be a subjective phenomenon, and physiological genital arousal would not tell us much about desire. That is, what a woman cognitively "wants" might not always be the same as what her body responds to.

In the Chivers studies, both heterosexual and lesbian women showed greater sexual arousal in response to stimuli depicting female than male targets. One possibility is that the female observers identified with the depicted female targets, imagining them-selves in the place of the women receiving pleasure, whereas the men were more likely to attend to the physical attributes of the actors.

Sexologist Lisa M. Diamond suggests that the response of women to a wider range of sexual stimuli allows for quite a bit of plasticity in sexual response. She begins her 2008 book *Sexual Fluidity: Understanding Women's Love and Desire* by noting that ". . . the actress Anne Heche began a widely publicized romantic relationship with the openly lesbian comedian Ellen DeGeneres after having had no prior same-sex attractions or relationships. The relationship with DeGeneres ended after two years, and Heche went on to marry a man." Diamond also notes that Julie Cypher left a heterosexual marriage for musician Melissa Etheridge. When they separated, 12 years later, Cypher returned to heterosexual relationships. Diamond speculates that for many women, desire may be dictated more by intimacy or emotional connection than by the attractiveness—or even the sex—of a partner.

Penile strain gauge A device for measuring a man's sexual arousal in terms of changes in penis circumference.

Vaginal photoplethysmograph A tampon-shaped probe that is inserted into the vagina to measure the light reflected from the vaginal walls, thereby determining the level of vasocongestion.

Innovative Canadian Research

USING A THERMOGRAPHIC CAMERA TO MEASURE SEXUAL AROUSAL

Researchers at McGill University (Kukkonen et al., 2007) have an alternative method for measuring sexual arousal. In a controlled laboratory experiment, they first showed men and women a neutral film, then randomly assigned the participants to watch either a sexually explicit film, a humorous film, or a neutral film. The researchers used a thermographic camera to measure changes in genital and thigh temperature.

The camera detected significant genital temperature changes during the showing of the erotic film, but not during the showing of the other two films. There were no changes in thigh temperature during the showing of the sex film, indicating that temperature changes during sexual arousal were specific to the genital region.

There was no difference between men and women in the amount of time it took to reach peak genital temperature. For both men and women, there was a high correlation between temperature change and subjective sexual arousal.

The findings indicate that a thermographic camera is a reliable and useful instrument for measuring sexual arousal. This method is less intrusive than other measures of sexual arousal, and can be used with both men and women. Thermography makes it possible to determine whether gender differences in arousal found in previous research are true differences or are results of measurement or instrumentation error.

The Experimental Method

The best method (though not always a feasible method) for studying cause-and-effect relationships is the **experiment**. Experiments permit scientists to draw conclusions about cause-and-effect relationships, because the experimenters are able to directly manipulate the factors or variables of interest, and observe the effects of this manipulation.

Aspects of the Experimental Method

In an experiment on the effects of alcohol on sexual arousal, for example, a group of participants would receive an intervention, called a **treatment**, such as a dose of alcohol. (In other experiments, the intervention or treatment might involve the administration of a drug, exposure to violent sexual material, or a program of sex

Experiment A scientific method that seeks to confirm cause-and-effect relationships by manipulating independent variables and observing their effects on dependent variables.

Treatment An experimental intervention (such as a test, drug, or sex education program) that's administered to participants so its effects can be observed.

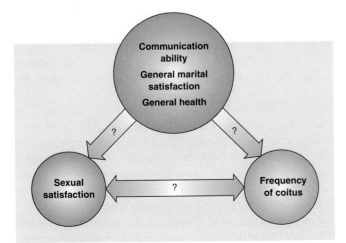

Figure 2.1 What's the relationship between frequency of intercourse and sexual satisfaction?
Married couples who engage in more frequent sexual relations report higher levels of sexual satisfaction . . . but why? Because researchers have not manipulated the variables, we cannot conclude that sexual satisfaction causes high coital frequency. Nor can we say that frequent coitus causes greater sexual satisfaction. Perhaps both variables are affected by other factors, such as communication skills, general marital satisfaction, and general health.

education.) They would then be carefully observed to learn whether that treatment made a difference in their behaviour—in this case, their sexual arousal.

In an experiment, the variable (treatment) that's hypothesized to have a causal effect is manipulated or controlled by the researcher. Consider an experiment designed to determine whether alcohol stimulates sexual arousal. The design might involve giving one group of participants a specified amount of alcohol and then measuring its effects on the participants' sexual arousal. In such an experiment, the dose of alcohol—whose presence and quantity are manipulated by the researchers—is considered the **independent variable**. As they manipulate the independent variable, they watch for changes in the **dependent variable**, which is believed to be affected by (dependent on) the independent variable. In this experiment, the dependent variable is sexual arousal. Changes in the dependent variable are observed and measured, but not manipulated by the researchers. Sexual arousal might be measured in terms of physiological change (gauging the degree of penile erection in the male, for example) or self-report (asking participants to rate their sexual arousal on a given scale).

In a study of the effects of sex education on teenage pregnancy, sex education would be the independent variable. The incidence of teenage pregnancy would be the dependent variable. Researchers would administer the experimental treatment (sex education) and track the participants for a time to determine their pregnancy rates. Ideally, the incidence of pregnancy among these subjects would be compared with that for subjects who do not receive sex education but who are similar to the subjects in all other respects.

Experimental and Control Groups

In a well-designed experiment, participants are randomly assigned to the experimental and control groups. Participants in the **experimental group** receive the treatment. Participants in the **control group** do not. Every effort is made to hold all other conditions constant for both groups. By using random assignment and holding other conditions constant, researchers can be reasonably confident that the independent variable (the treatment) has brought about the results, and extraneous factors (e.g., the temperature of the room in which the treatment is administered, or differences between the participants in the experimental and control groups) have not.

Why do experimenters try to assign individuals to experimental and control groups at random? Consider a study about the effects of alcohol on sexual arousal in response to sexually explicit films. If we permit study participants to choose whether they'll drink alcohol, we might not know whether it's the alcohol itself that accounts for the results. Some other factor, called a **selection factor**, might discriminate between people who do and people who do not choose to drink alcohol. Perhaps people who chose to drink have more permissive attitudes toward sexually explicit material. Their permissiveness, rather than the alcohol, might affect their sexual responsiveness to the stimuli. If this is the case, the experimental outcomes might reflect the effects of the selection factor, rather than the alcohol.

Ottawa researchers John M. W. Bradford and Anne Pawlak conducted an experiment to determine the effectiveness of cyproterone acetate (CPA), an antiandrogen, in treating men convicted of sex crimes. The 19 men who were studied were randomly assigned to receive either CPA or a placebo for three months. The study was double blind, meaning neither the men nor the researchers who administered the drugs knew which of the men were receiving CPA and which the placebo. (The double-blind approach controls for the placebo effect that can occur when people take any kind of medication, and eliminates the possibility that the researchers' own biases will distort their findings.) As predicted by the researchers,

Independent variable A condition in a scientific study that is manipulated so its effects can be observed.

Dependent variable The condition in a scientific study that is believed to be affected by the independent variable(s). The results of the study are assessed by measuring changes in the dependent variable.

Experimental group A group of study participants who receive the experimental treatment.

Control group A group of study participants who do not receive the experimental treatment. All other conditions are kept the same for the control group as for the experimental group.

Selection factor A research bias that may operate when people are allowed to determine whether they will receive an experimental treatment.

the CPA drug was associated with a significant reduction in aspects of sex behaviour, especially deviant fantasies such as having sex with children (Bradford & Pawlak, 1993).

Qualitative Research Methods

Most large-scale sexuality studies employ a **quantitative methodology**. Study participants fill out questionnaires that typically consist of multiple-choice questions with a range of answers devised by the researchers. The researchers then determine what percentage of the sample has chosen each of the responses available for each question. Findings from this type of study are presented as statistics. A number of statistical tests can be used to determine whether the results are statistically significant.

A **qualitative methodology** takes a different approach. Rather than forcing them to choose between a set of responses on a multiple-choice questionnaire, a qualitative study uses interviews, focus groups, diaries, or other methods that allow participants to express their thoughts, feelings, emotions, and opinions in their own words and in more detail (Denzin & Lincoln, 2005). Take, for example, the following quote from a male participant in a study investigating the components of "great sex":

> In normal good sex or good relationships, I think there's always some maybe small but detectable barriers, some things held back. In great sex, I think those, for me, disappear, and so that one is quite transparent to the other person, and therefore quite vulnerable, but it feels, it goes with an intensely erotic and good feeling, rather than a scary thing (Kleinplatz et al., 2009, p. 9).

In this example, through a structured interview, the study participant is able to express what "great sex" means for him. It's unlikely that this nuanced understanding would emerge by having him fill out a multiple-choice questionnaire. Because people's attitudes, feelings, and experiences pertaining to sexuality are often very complex and dependent on social context, qualitative research methods can increase our understanding of sexuality in ways quantitative methods can't.

In general, quantitative research methods are well suited to testing hypotheses and providing research findings that are generalizable to larger populations. Qualitative research methods, on the other hand, are well suited to revealing the ways individuals or specific groups experience their sexuality in more detail. Both approaches are indispensible to a comprehensive, research-based understanding of human sexuality.

Ethics in Sex Research

Sex researchers are required to protect the people they study. This ensures that subjects participate of their own free will and are not subjected to physical or psychological harm. In colleges, universities, hospitals, and research institutions, ethics-review committees examine proposed studies in light of ethical guidelines, and help researchers weigh the potential harm of administering the independent variables. If a committee finds fault with a proposal, it may advise the researcher about how to modify the research design so it complies with ethical standards, and may withhold approval until the proposal has been modified.

Let's consider a number of ethical issues:

- **Exposing participants to harm.** Individuals may be harmed if they're exposed to pain or placed in stressful situations. For this reason, researchers do not expose children to erotic materials in order to determine their effects. Nor

CRITICAL THINKING QUESTIONS

Can you think of a sexuality research question that might be effectively answered using quantitative research methods? What about using qualitative research methods?

Quantitative methodology
The collection of numerical data (e.g., percentages) to produce statistics.

Qualitative methodology
The use of interviews, focus groups, diaries, or other methods to record people's attitudes and experiences.

do researchers expose human fetuses to male or female sex hormones to learn whether they create predispositions toward tomboyishness, gay or lesbian sexual orientation, or other variables of interest.

- **Confidentiality.** Researchers can do many things to ensure confidentiality for participants. They can make questionnaires anonymous. They can withhold subjects' identities from interviewers. In their research reports, they can provide enough information about participants' backgrounds (size of city of origin, region of country, religion, age group, race, educational level, and so on) to make the studies useful without divulging participants' identities. Once the need for follow-up has passed and the results have been fully analyzed, researchers can destroy the participants' records, including names and addresses.

- **Informed consent.** The principle of **informed consent** requires that people freely agree to participate after being given enough information about the procedures and purposes of the research—and its risks and benefits—to make an informed decision. Once the study has begun, participants must be free to withdraw at any time without penalty.

- **The use of deception.** Ethical conflicts may emerge when experiments require that participants not know all about their purposes and methods. For example, in an experiment on the effects of violent pornography on aggression against women, participants may be misled into believing they're administering electric shocks to women (who are actually confederates of the experimenter), even though no shocks are actually delivered. The experimenter wants to determine participants' willingness to hurt other women after they've been exposed to aggressive erotic films. Such studies can't be carried out if participants know the shocks are not actually delivered.

Research is the backbone of human sexuality as a science. This textbook focuses on scientific findings that can expand our understanding of human sexuality in all of its varied dimensions.

Informed consent   Agreement to participate in research after receiving adequate information about the purposes and nature of the study and about its potential risks and benefits.

Innovative Canadian Research

DO RESEARCH CONSENT FORMS AFFECT FINDINGS?

Over the years, research-ethics requirements have become more stringent at universities and other institutions in Canada. Researchers at the University of Windsor and the University of Guelph (Senn & Desmarais, 2006) conducted two studies to determine whether these requirements were affecting findings in sexuality research.

Each participant was given one of three types of consent form. The first described only the research process. The second also described the study's sexuality content. The third form also included a warning about the possible negative effects of involvement in the study.

The first study involved female university students who were randomly assigned to watch one of three types of sexually explicit slides: erotica, nonviolent pornography, and violent pornography.

In the second study, a community sample was asked about sexual experiences, abuse, and assault.

There were no significant differences in the findings for the three different types of consent forms, except for one major difference in the study involving sexually explicit slides. There, the participants who were given detailed information about the explicit slides and the participants who were also warned about possible harm evaluated the slides significantly more negatively than those who were told only about the research process.

A surprising finding in both studies was that students who were given more detail about the content of the studies and warnings about possible harm did not feel they were better informed than those who were told only about the research process. The results raise the question of how best to adequately inform participants about a research study, while at the same time minimizing the possibility that the type of consent form will bias the findings.

Summing Up

The scientific method is a systematic means of gathering scientific evidence and testing assumptions through empirical research. It entails formulating a research question, framing a hypothesis, testing the hypothesis, and drawing conclusions about the hypothesis.

The goals of the science of human sexuality are to describe, explain, and predict sexual behaviours.

Research samples should accurately represent the populations of interest. Representative samples are usually obtained through random sampling.

Case studies are carefully drawn biographies of individuals or small groups that focus on unravelling the interplay of various factors in individuals' backgrounds.

Surveys typically gather information about behaviour through interviews or questionnaires administered to large samples of people.

In naturalistic observation, scientists directly observe the behaviour of animals and humans where it happens—in the "field." The scientists remain unobtrusive.

Ethnographic research provides data about sexual behaviours and customs that occur widely across cultures.

In participant observation, investigators learn about people's behaviour by interacting with them.

In the laboratory observation method, people engage in the behaviour under study within a laboratory setting.

Correlational studies reveal the strength and direction of relationships between variables. They do not show cause and effect.

Experiments allow scientists to draw conclusions about cause-and-effect relationships, because the scientists directly control or manipulate the variables of interest and observe their effects. Well-designed experiments randomly assign individuals to experimental and control groups.

Ethics concerns the ways researchers protect their research subjects from harm.

Ethical standards require that research be conducted only when the expected benefits of the research outweigh the anticipated risks to participants and experimenters attempt to minimize the expected risks.

Sex researchers keep participants' identities and responses confidential, to protect them from embarrassment and other sources of potential harm.

The principle of informed consent requires that people agree to participate in research only after being given enough information about the purposes, procedures, risks, and benefits to make informed decisions.

Some research cannot be conducted without deceiving people as to its purposes and procedures. In such cases, the potential harm and benefits of the proposed research are weighed carefully.

Test Yourself

Multiple-Choice Questions

1. Researchers use _____ that are often based on theory to predict behaviour.
   (a) hypotheses
   (b) operational definitions
   (c) research questions
   (d) research methods

2. A representative sample:
   (a) Consists of at least 75 males and 75 females.
   (b) Is a group of people who volunteer to participate in the study.
   (c) Is a sample that accurately reflects the composition of the population.
   (d) Is a sample in which each member of the population has an equal chance of participating in the study.

3. A random sample:
   (a) Consists of at least 75 males and 75 females.
   (b) Is a group of people who volunteer to participate in the study.
   (c) Is a sample that accurately reflects the composition of the population.
   (d) Is a sample in which each member of the population has an equal chance of participating in the study.

4. Structured interviews, focus groups, and diaries are examples of _____ research methods.
   (a) survey
   (b) qualitative
   (c) experimental
   (d) quantitative

continued

5. One problem with much of the research on human sexual behaviour is:
(a) Religious bias.
(b) Commercial bias.
(c) Volunteer bias.
(d) Sexual bias.

6. Masters and Johnson's research on sexual response is an example of:
(a) Participant observation of sexual behaviour.
(b) Laboratory observation of sexual behaviour.
(c) Correlational research on sexual behaviour.
(d) Experimental research on sexual behaviour.

7. Correlational studies provide information about:
(a) Whether a change in one variable causes a change in another.
(b) Statistical relationships between two variables.
(c) The margin of error due to a variable.
(d) The degree of bias in a sample.

8. If you wish to answer questions about cause-and-effect relationships, the best research method to use is the:
(a) Interview.
(b) Questionnaire.
(c) Laboratory observation.
(d) Experiment.

9. Concerns about the anonymity and confidentiality of sexual information are examples of _____ issues.
(a) ethical
(b) religious
(c) political
(d) commercial

10. A basic ethical requirement for all research on human sexuality is the provision of:
(a) Adequate compensation.
(b) Legal permission.
(c) Informed consent.
(d) Parental approval.

You'll find answers to the "Test Yourself" questions on page 495.

Critical Thinking

1. Have you ever responded to a survey on sexual behaviour, either in a magazine or on the internet? Looking back on it, do you think your responses were influenced by social desirability bias? Did you answer truthfully? Why or why not?

2. If you were to conduct a sexuality research study, what sexuality topic would you most like to investigate?

3. If you were to conduct a study on the psychological impact of sexual assault on its victims, what are some of the ethical issues you would need to take into account?

MySearchLab

MySearchLab offers extensive help to students with their writing and research project and provides round-the-clock access to credible and reliable source material. Take a tour at www.mysearchlab.com.

CHAPTER THREE

Female and Male Anatomy and Physiology

Female Anatomy and Physiology

The French have a saying: *Vive la différence!* (Long live the difference!) It celebrates the differences between men and women. Given the exclusive female possession of a clitoris, some might assert that women in particular have much to celebrate. Only women possess a sex organ—the clitoris—that's solely devoted to producing pleasurable sensations.

In the past, girls have commonly been taught to regard their genitals with a sense of shame. As women, they have tended to hold negative attitudes about their genitals and sexuality. Even today, children may be reprimanded for expressing curiosity about their own anatomy. They may be told to keep their hands off their private parts. This is unfortunate, because knowledge of one's own sexual anatomy contributes to sexual health and pleasure. For young women, a basic understanding of sexuality and how their genitals function is a prerequisite for sexual satisfaction.

The External Female Sex Organs

Taken collectively, the external sexual structures of the female are termed the **vulva**. The vulva consists of the **mons veneris**, the **labia majora** and **labia minora** (major lips and minor lips), the **clitoris**, and the vaginal opening. (See Figure 3.1.) Figure 3.2 shows variations in the appearance of women's genitals. If you're a female looking at Figure 3.2 and thinking your vulva doesn't look like the ones in the picture, don't be concerned. Each woman is unique, and there are endless variations in the size and appearance of different parts of the vulva.

The Mons Veneris

The mons veneris consists of fatty tissue that covers the public bone, which is the joining of the pelvic bones at the front of the body, below the abdomen and above the clitoris. At puberty the mons becomes covered with pubic hair, which is often thick and curly, but varies from person to person in waviness, texture, and colour.

The mons cushions a woman's body during sexual intercourse, protecting her and her partner from pressure against the pubic bone caused by thrusting motions. There's an ample supply of nerve endings in the mons, so caressing the area can produce pleasurable sexual sensations.

The Labia Majora

The labia majora are large folds of skin that run downward from the mons along the sides of the vulva. The labia majora are thick and bulging in some women, and thinner, flatter, and less noticeable in others. When close together, the labia majora shield the labia minora and the urethral and vaginal openings.

The outer surfaces of the labia majora, next to the thighs, are covered with pubic hair. They're darker than the skin of the thighs and the labia minora. The inner surfaces of the labia majora are hairless and lighter in colour. They're amply supplied with nerve endings that respond to stimulation and can produce sensations of sexual pleasure.

Vulva The external sexual structures of the female.

Mons veneris A mound of fatty tissue that covers the pubic bone (the joining of the pelvic bones at the front of the body, below the abdomen and above the clitoris). The mons veneris is also known as the mons pubis, or simply the mons.

Labia majora Large folds of skin that run downward from the mons along the sides of the vulva.

Labia minora Hairless, light-coloured membranes located between the labia majora.

Clitoris A female sex organ consisting of a shaft and a glans, located above the urethral opening. It's extremely sensitive to sexual sensation.

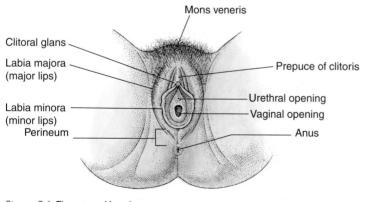

Figure 3.1 The external female sex organs.
This figure shows the vulva with the labia opened to reveal the urethral and vaginal openings.

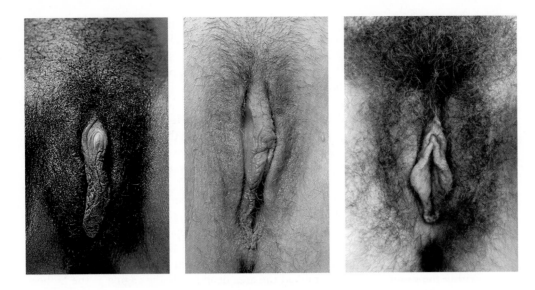

Figure 3.2 Typical variations in the vulva. The features of the vulva show a great deal of variation. A woman's attitude toward her genitals is likely to reflect her general self-concept and early childhood messages, rather than the appearance of her vulva.

It's increasingly common for women in Western cultures, including Canada, to remove some or all of their pubic hair. There are different methods of hair removal, including waxing, shaving, electrolysis, and laser removal. A recent study in British Columbia found that women's top reasons for removing some or all of their pubic hair included appearance in a bathing suit, feeling attractive, and the idea that pubic hair removal is cleaner (Riddell, Varto, & Hodgson, 2010).

The Labia Minora

The labia minora are two hairless, light-coloured membranes located between the major lips. They surround the urethral and vaginal openings. The outer surfaces of the labia minora merge with the major lips. At the top they join at the prepuce (hood) of the clitoris.

The labia minora differ markedly in appearance from woman to woman. The labia minora of some women form protruding flower shapes that are greatly valued in some cultures, such as the Khoikhoi of Africa. In fact, Khoikhoi women purposely elongate their labia minora by tugging at them.

Rich in blood vessels and nerve endings, the labia minora are highly sensitive to sexual stimulation. When stimulated, they darken and swell, indicating engorgement with blood.

The Clitoris

The clitoris is the female sex organ most sensitive to sexual sensation. It's known by many names around the world, from *bijou* (French for "jewel") to *pokhotnik* (Russian for "lust"). The word "clitoris" derives from the Greek word *kleitoris*, meaning "hill" or "slope." It received its name from the manner in which it slopes upward in the shaft and forms a mound of spongy tissue at the glans. (See Figure 3.1.)

The body of the clitoris, termed the clitoral shaft, is about 2.5 centimetres long and 0.5 centimetres wide. It consists of erectile tissue, which contains two spongy masses, called **corpora cavernosa** ("cavernous bodies"), that become engorged (filled with blood) and erect in response to sexual stimulation. The stiffening of the clitoris is less apparent than the erection of the penis, because the clitoris does not swing free from the body, as the penis does. The clitoral shaft is covered by the **prepuce** (meaning "before a swelling"), or hood, a sheath of skin formed by the upper part of the labia minora.

Corpora cavernosa Masses of spongy tissue in the clitoral shaft that become engorged with blood and stiffen in response to sexual stimulation.

Prepuce The fold of skin covering the glans of the clitoris (or of the penis, in a male).

The clitoral glans is a smooth, round knob or lump of tissue. It resembles a button and is situated above the urethral opening. The clitoral glans may be covered by the clitoral hood, but it's readily revealed by gently separating the labia minora and retracting the hood. It's highly sensitive to touch, because of its rich supply of nerve endings. Women thus usually prefer to be stroked or stimulated on the mons or the clitoral hood, rather than directly on the glans.

The glans, hood, and shaft of the clitoris are visible from the outside. The clitoral structure, however, extends into the body along the sides of the vagina. The size of the clitoris varies from woman to woman, just as the size of the penis varies from man to man. There is no known connection between clitoris size and sensitivity to sexual stimulation.

In a recent study, women were asked to rank the areas of their vulva which gave them the most sexual pleasure (Meyer-Bahlburg et al., 2007). The clitoris was ranked highest, followed by the area around the vaginal opening, the sides of the clitoris, the area below the clitoris, the area above the clitoris, the labia majora, and the area around the anus. When the women were asked to rank sources of pleasure within the vagina itself, they ranked the area deep inside the vagina as the highest, followed by the areas just inside and around the opening.

The clitoris and the penis develop from the same embryonic tissue, which makes them similar in structure, or **homologous**. They are not, however, fully similar in function, or **analogous**. Both organs receive and transmit sexual sensations, but the penis is directly involved in reproduction and excretion, serving as a conduit for sperm and urine, respectively.

It's ironic that many cultures—including Victorian culture—have viewed women as unresponsive to sexual stimulation. Women, not men, possess the only human sex organ whose only known function is the experiencing of pleasure. The clitoris is the woman's most erotically charged organ, which is why they most often masturbate through clitoral stimulation, not through vaginal insertion.

Surgical removal of the clitoral hood is common among Muslims in the Middle East and Africa. As we'll see in "A World of Diversity: Female Genital Cutting/Mutilation," this rite of passage to womanhood leaves many scars, both physical and emotional.

Homologous Similar in structure; developing from the same embryonic tissue.

Analogous Similar in function.

Urethral opening The opening through which urine passes from the female's body.

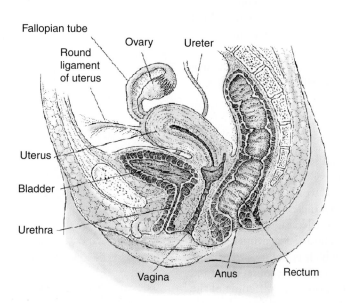

Figure 3.3 The female reproductive system.
This cross-section shows the locations of many of the internal sex organs that constitute the female reproductive system. Note that the uterus is normally tipped forward.

Labels: Fallopian tube, Round ligament of uterus, Ovary, Ureter, Uterus, Bladder, Urethra, Vagina, Anus, Rectum

The Vestibule

The word "vestibule" refers to the area within the labia minora that contains the openings to the vagina and the urethra. Richly supplied with nerve endings, the vestibule is very sensitive to tactile and other sexual stimulation.

The Urethral Opening

Urine passes from the female's body through the **urethral opening** (see Figure 3.1), which is connected by a short tube called the urethra to the bladder, where urine collects (see Figure 3.3). The urethral opening lies behind the clitoral glans and in front of the vaginal opening.

The proximity of the urethral opening to the external sex organs may pose hygienic problems for sexually active women. The urinary tract, which includes the urethra, bladder, and kidneys, may become infected by bacteria that are transmitted from the vagina or rectum.

A World of Diversity

FEMALE GENITAL CUTTING/ MUTILATION

Approximately 130 million girls and women worldwide have undergone genital cutting. Many people feel this practice is more accurately described as genital mutilation. Feminists and many others view the practice as attempts by patriarchal societies to control women's bodies and behaviour.

Some groups in Egypt and the Sudan perform **clitoridectomies** (removal of the clitoris) as an unchallenged social custom (Missailidis & Gebre-Medhin, 2000). Because women tend to adopt the values of the cultures in which they live, women who have undergone the process themselves usually carry out the genital cutting (Nour, 2000). Some perceive it as part of their submission to Islam. There is, however, no support for this practice in the Quran (Nour, 2000).

What effects does genital cutting have on women? A study of 250 female patients in maternal and childhood centres in Ismailia, Egypt, found that those who had experienced genital cutting were 80% more likely to complain of painful menstruation, 49% more likely to complain of vaginal dryness during intercourse, 45% more likely to lack sexual desire, 49% less likely to be pleased by sex, and 61% more likely to have difficulty reaching orgasm (El-Defrawi et al., 2001). Medical complications can include infection, bleeding, tissue scarring, painful menstruation, and obstructed labour.

A more radical form of clitoridectomy, called excision, is practiced widely in the Sudan, Ethiopia, and some other African countries (Eltahawy, 2003). Excision is the removal of the clitoris, the labia minora, and the labia majora. Only a tiny opening is left to allow the passage of urine and menstrual discharge. The sewing together of the vulva is intended to ensure chastity until marriage. Medical complications, including menstrual and urinary problems, are common; even deaths have occurred. After marriage, the opening is enlarged to permit intercourse. Hemorrhaging and tearing of surrounding tissues are common.

Some African countries, including Egypt and Kenya, have outlawed clitoridectomies, although such laws often go unenforced.

More than 100 million women in Africa and the Middle East have undergone excision. Clitoridectomies remain routine in nearly 30 countries in Africa, the Middle East, and parts of Malaysia, Yeman, Oman, Indonesia, and the India-Pakistan subcontinent. A sizable number of girls and women who immigrate to Canada from countries where clitoridectomy and excision are practised undergo the procedures before leaving their countries of origin.

Pulitzer Prize-winning novelist Alice Walker drew attention to the practice of female genital cutting in her bestselling novel *Possessing the Secret of Joy,* and called for its abolition in the book and film *Warrior Marks.*

The Canadian government has outlawed ritual genital mutilation. Calls from Westerners to ban the practice in parts of Africa and the Middle East have sparked arguments that people in one culture should not dictate the cultural traditions of another. For Alice Walker, however, "torture is not culture."

Infectious microscopic organisms may pass from the male's sex organs to the female's urethral opening during sexual intercourse. Manual stimulation of the vulva with dirty hands may also transmit bacteria through the urethral opening to the bladder. Anal intercourse followed by vaginal intercourse may transfer microscopic organisms from the rectum to the bladder and cause infection. For similar reasons, women should wipe from front to back, wiping first the vulva and then the anus, when using the bathroom.

Cystitis is a bladder inflammation that may stem from any of these sources. Its primary symptoms are burning and frequent urination (also called urinary urgency). Pus or a bloody discharge is common, and there may be an intermittent or persistent ache just above the pubic bone. These symptoms may disappear after several days, but consultation with a physician is recommended, because untreated cystitis can lead to serious kidney infection.

So-called honeymoon cystitis is caused by the tugging on the bladder and urethral wall that occurs during vaginal intercourse. It may occur upon beginning coital activity (though not necessarily on one's honeymoon) or upon resuming coital activity after lengthy abstinence. Figure 3.3 shows the close proximity of the urethra and the vagina.

Clitoridectomy Surgical removal of the clitoris.

Cystitis An inflammation of the urinary bladder.

The following precautions may help women prevent serious inflammation of the bladder:

- Drink two litres of water a day, to flush the bladder.
- Drink orange or cranberry juice, to maintain an acidic environment that discourages the growth of infectious organisms.
- Reduce the intake of alcohol and caffeine (from coffee, tea, and cola drinks), which may irritate the bladder.
- Wash hands prior to masturbation or self-examination.
- Wash partner's and own genitals before and after intercourse.
- Prevent objects that have touched the anus (fingers, penis, toilet tissue) from subsequently coming into contact with the vulva.
- Cover sex toys with condoms, to prevent possible infection.
- Urinate soon after intercourse, to help wash away bacteria.

The Vaginal Opening

Introitus The vaginal opening.

When we part the labia minora, we see the vaginal opening, or **introitus**, rather than the entire vagina. The introitus lies behind the smaller urethral opening. Across the vaginal opening, a fold of tissue called the **hymen** is usually present at birth. The hymen may remain at least partly intact until a woman engages in coitus. For this reason, it has been called the "maidenhead," and its presence has been taken as proof of virginity—and its absence as evidence of coitus. Some females are born with incomplete hymens, however, and other girls' hymens are accidentally torn during such activities as horseback riding, strenuous exercise, gymnastics, and cycling. A punctured hymen therefore doesn't necessarily indicate coital experience. And a flexible hymen may withstand many coital experiences, so its presence is not necessarily proof of virginity. Prior to marriage, some European Muslim women have hymenoplasties—operations that restore their hymens—to provide the illusion of virginity for their wedding nights (Sciolino & Mekhennet, 2008).

Hymen A fold of tissue across the vaginal opening that's usually present at birth and remains at least partly intact until a woman engages in sexual intercourse.

Figure 3.4 illustrates various vaginal openings. The first three show hymen shapes that are frequently found among women who have not had coitus. Now and then a hymen consists of tough, fibrous tissue and is closed, or imperforate, as in the fourth drawing. An imperforate hymen may not be discovered until after puberty, when menstrual discharges begin to accumulate in the vagina. In these rare cases, a simple surgical incision is used to perforate the hymen. The fifth drawing shows a parous ("passed through") vaginal opening, typical of women who have delivered babies.

Perineum The skin and underlying tissue that lies between the vaginal opening and the anus.

The skin and underlying tissue between the vaginal opening and the anus (or between the scrotum and the anus, in a male) is called the **perineum**. Because

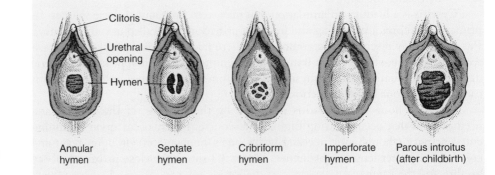

Figure 3.4 Typical variations in the hymen.
Before first coitus, the hymen can look different in different women. The illustration at far right shows how the introitus generally appears after childbirth.

Applied Knowledge

SELF-EXAMINATION OF THE GENITALS

If you've seen the film *Fried Green Tomatoes*, you may recall the scene where a group of women are encouraged to bring mirrors to one of their meetings in order to examine their genitals.

Female readers may wish to try this while following the text and the illustrations in this chapter. You may discover some new anatomic features. You will see that your own genitals can resemble those in the illustrations, yet also be unique.

There are still many women in our society who have never examined their own genitals. This is a reflection of the negative attitudes some women have about their genitals, and accounts for the fact that masturbation rates are lower for women than for men.

If you'd like to examine your genitals, here are suggested steps for doing so:

■ Choose a time when you're relaxed, such as after a bath.
■ Choose a private, comfortable space, such as your bedroom.
■ Use a mirror, and make sure there's sufficient lighting.
■ Begin by looking at the larger outer lips (labia majora). These are covered with pubic hair. The colour and hair texture varies from woman to woman.
■ The inner lips (labia minora) are just inside the outer lips. Their size varies considerably from one woman to another. Some labia minora extend beyond the labia majora.
■ The inner lips meet above the clitoris, where they form the clitoral hood.
■ Separate the inner lips at the top of the vulva, to examine the clitoris. The size and shape of the clitoris varies from woman to woman.
■ Behind the clitoris is the urinary opening (meatus).
■ Behind the urinary opening is the vaginal opening.
■ Just inside the vaginal opening is the vaginal ring, where the pubococcygeus (PC) muscle is located. The hymen is also located here; it may or may not be visible.
■ Use your finger to explore further inside the vagina. You may notice that the inside of your vagina feels similar to the inside of your mouth—both are mucous membranes, soft and sensitive to the touch. Pressing on the front wall of the vagina and up about five centimetres, you'll feel the area where the G spot is purported to exist. (The G spot is discussed later in this chapter.)
■ Between the vagina and the anus is a smooth area of skin called the perineum.

In conducting this examination, it's important to appreciate the uniqueness of your genital area with regard to shape and size. Some women may feel abnormal if

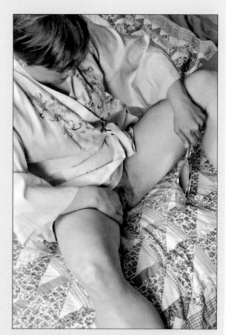

Genital Self-Examination.
For both health and pleasure reasons, women are encouraged to examine their own genitals.

the appearance of their genitals doesn't match that in pictures they may have seen of other women's genitals. Familiarity with the appearance of your own genitals can make it easier to become aware of potential health issues that may require medical attention, such as rashes or warts. Self-examination can also be useful in discovering the various pleasurable sensations provided by stimulation of different parts of the genitals.

---

the perineum is rich in nerve endings, stimulating this area may heighten sexual arousal. During labour, many physicians make a routine perineal incision, called an **episiotomy**, to facilitate childbirth.

Structures That Underlie the External Sex Organs

Figure 3.5 shows what lies beneath the skin of the vulva. The vestibular bulbs and Bartholin's glands are active during sexual arousal and are found on both sides (shown on the right in Figure 3.5). Muscular rings (**sphincters**) that constrict bodily openings, such as the vaginal and anal openings, are also found on both sides.

Episiotomy   A surgical incision in the perineum that may be made during childbirth, to protect the vagina from tearing.

Sphincters   Ring-shaped muscles that surround body openings, which they open or close by expanding or contracting.

Figure 3.5 The structures that underlie the external female sex organs.
If we could see beneath the vulva, we would find muscle fibres that constrict the various body openings, plus the crura ("legs") of the clitoris, the vestibular bulbs, and Bartholin's glands.

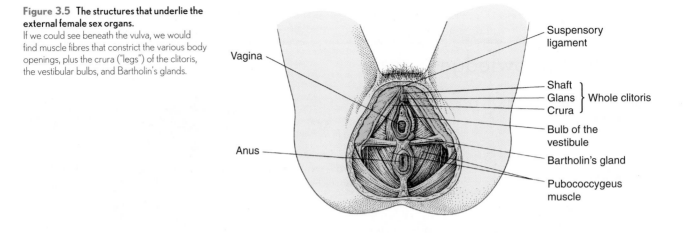

Vagina

Anus

Suspensory ligament

Shaft
Glans } Whole clitoris
Crura

Bulb of the vestibule

Bartholin's gland

Pubococcygeus muscle

Crura Anatomic structures resembling legs that attach the clitoris to the pubic bone. The singular is "crus."

Vestibular bulbs Cavernous structures that extend downward along the sides of the introitus and swell during sexual arousal.

Vagina The tubular female sex organ that contains the penis during sexual intercourse and through which a baby is born.

Bartholin's glands Glands that lie just inside the minor lips and secrete fluid just before orgasm.

Pubococcygeus muscle The muscle that encircles the entrance to the vagina.

The clitoral **crura** are wing-shaped, leg-like structures that attach the clitoris to the pubic bone beneath. The crura contain corpora cavernosa, which engorge with blood and stiffen during sexual arousal.

The **vestibular bulbs** are attached to the clitoris at the top and extend downward along the sides of the vaginal opening. Blood congests them during sexual arousal, swelling the vulva and lengthening the **vagina**. This swelling contributes to coital sensations for both partners.

Bartholin's glands lie just inside the minor lips, on each side of the vaginal opening. They secrete a couple of drops of lubrication just before orgasm. This lubrication is not essential for coitus. If the glands become infected and clogged, a woman may notice swelling and local irritation. It's wise to consult a gynecologist if these symptoms don't fade within a few days. It was once believed that Bartholin's glands were the source of the vaginal lubrication, or wetness, that women experience during sexual arousal. It's now known that engorgement of vaginal tissues during sexual excitement results in a form of "sweating" by the lining of the vaginal wall. During sexual arousal, the pressure from this engorgement causes moisture from the many small blood vessels that lie in the vaginal wall to be forced out and to pass through the vaginal lining, forming the basis of the lubrication. In less time than it takes to read this sentence (generally within 10 to 30 seconds), beads of vaginal lubrication, or "sweat," appear along the interior lining of the vagina in response to sexual stimulation, in much the same way that rising temperature causes water to pass through the skin as perspiration.

Pelvic floor muscles permit women to constrict their vaginal and anal openings. These are the muscles that are used to control urination. They contract automatically, or involuntarily, during orgasm, and toning them may contribute to increased sensation during sexual activity. Repeatedly contracting and relaxing the **pubococcygeal muscle** (these are referred to as Kegel exercises) is sometimes recommended for women who experience sexual response problems.

The Internal Female Sex Organs

The internal sex organs of the female include the innermost parts of the vagina, the cervix, the uterus, and two ovaries, each connected to the uterus by a fallopian tube. (See Figures 3.3 and 3.6.) These structures make up the female reproductive system.

The Vagina

The **vagina** extends back and up from the vaginal opening. (See Figure 3.3.) It's usually 7.5 to 12.5 centimetres long when at rest. Menstrual flow and babies pass from the uterus to the outer world through the vagina. During coitus, the vagina contains the penis.

The vagina is commonly pictured as a canal or barrel, but when at rest, it's like a collapsed muscular tube whose walls touch. The vagina expands in length and width during sexual arousal. It can also expand to allow insertion of a tampon, as well as passage of a baby's head and shoulders during childbirth.

The vaginal walls have three layers. The inner lining, or vaginal mucosa, can be seen by opening the labia minora. It's a mucous membrane similar to the skin that lines the inside of the mouth. It feels fleshy, soft, and corrugated. It may vary from very dry (especially if the woman is anxious about something, such as exams) to very wet. The middle layer of the vaginal wall is muscular. The outer or deeper layer is a fibrous covering that connects the vagina to other pelvic structures.

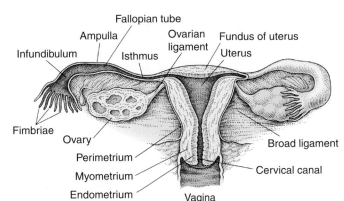
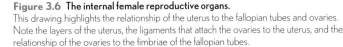

Figure 3.6 The internal female reproductive organs.
This drawing highlights the relationship of the uterus to the fallopian tubes and ovaries. Note the layers of the uterus, the ligaments that attach the ovaries to the uterus, and the relationship of the ovaries to the fimbriae of the fallopian tubes.

The vaginal walls are rich with blood vessels, but poorly supplied with nerve endings. Unlike the sensitive outer one-third of the vaginal barrel, the inner two-thirds are insensitive to touch. The entire vaginal barrel is sensitive to pressure, however, which may be experienced as sexually pleasurable.

The vaginal walls secrete substances that help maintain the vagina's normal acidity (pH 4.0 to 5.0). The secretions normally taste salty, but their odour and taste may vary during the menstrual cycle. Although the evidence is not clear, the secretions are thought to contain substances that may act as sexual attractants. Women who frequently **douche** or use feminine deodorant sprays may thus remove or mask substances that may arouse sex partners. Douching or spraying may also alter the natural chemical balance of the vagina, which can increase the risk of vaginal infections. Feminine deodorant sprays can also irritate the vagina and evoke allergic reactions. The normal, healthy vagina cleanses itself through regular chemical secretions that are evidenced by a mild white or yellowish discharge.

Vaginitis refers to any vaginal inflammation, whether it's caused by an infection, birth control pills, antibiotics that alter natural body chemistry, an allergic reaction, chemical irritation, or lowered resistance due to fatigue or poor diet. Changes in the natural body chemistry or lowered resistance may permit microscopic organisms normally found in the vagina to multiply to infectious levels. Vaginitis may be recognized by abnormal discharge, itching, burning of the vulva, and urinary urgency. Women with vaginitis are advised to seek medical attention.

The following suggestions may help prevent vaginitis:

- Wash your vulva and anus regularly with mild soap. Pat dry, taking care not to touch the vulva after dabbing the anus.
- Wear cotton panties. Nylon underwear retains heat and moisture, which causes harmful bacteria to flourish.
- Avoid pants that are tight in the crotch.
- Be certain your sex partners are well washed. Condoms may also reduce the spread of infection from your partner.
- Use a sterile, water-soluble gel if artificial lubrication is needed for intercourse. Do not use Vaseline. Avoid using flavoured lubricants that contain sugar products, as these can activate yeast infections. Birth-control jellies can be used for lubrication.

Douche Application of a jet of liquid to the vagina as a rinse. From the Italian *doccia*, which means "shower bath."

Vaginitis Vaginal inflammation.

Speaking of Vaginas.
The Vagina Monologues, *a celebrated play that presents the diversity of emotions women have about their vaginas, has been popular with audiences in Canada. A key objective of the play is to provide women with ownership and empowerment over their sexuality in general, and their genitals specifically.*

- Avoid intercourse that's painful or abrasive to the vagina.
- Avoid diets high in sugar and refined carbohydrates, because they alter the vagina's normal acidity.
- If you're prone to vaginal infections, you may find it helpful to douche occasionally with plain water, a solution of one or two tablespoons of vinegar in a quart of warm water, or a solution of baking soda and water. Douches consisting of unpasteurized plain (unflavoured) yogourt may help replenish the beneficial bacteria that are normally found in the vagina and that may be destroyed by antibiotics. Be careful when douching, and don't douche if you're pregnant or suspect you may be pregnant. Consult your doctor before deciding to douche or to apply any preparation to the vagina.
- Watch your general health. A poor diet and insufficient rest will reduce your resistance to infection.

The G Spot and Female Ejaculation: Sexual Realities or Gynecological Myths?

The Gräfenberg spot, or G spot, is a part of the vagina—a bean-shaped area in the anterior (front) wall that may have special erotic significance. The G spot is believed to lie about 2.5 to 5 centimetres from the vaginal entrance and to consist of a soft mass of tissue that swells from the size of a dime to a that of a loonie when stimulated. (See Figure 3.7.) It's named after gynecologist Ernst Gräfenberg, who first suggested the area's possible erotic importance.

The spot can be directly stimulated by the woman's or her partner's fingers or by penile thrusting in the rear-entry or the female-superior position. It can also be stimulated with a vibrator. Some researchers suggest that stimulation of the spot produces intense erotic sensations, and that prolonged stimulation results in a distinct form of orgasm characterized by intense pleasure and, in some cases, a biological event formerly thought to be exclusively male—ejaculation (Geddes, 2008; Jannini et al., 2008). These claims have been steeped in controversy.

In a laboratory experiment, Zaviacic and his colleagues (1988a, 1988b) found evidence of an ejaculate in 10 of the 27 women studied. Some researchers believe this fluid is urine released involuntarily during orgasm. Others believe it differs from urine (Zaviacic & Whipple, 1993). The nature of this fluid and its source remain unclear, but Zaviacic and Whipple (1993) suggest that it may represent a fluid that's released during sex by a "female prostate," a system of ducts and glands called Skene's glands, in much the same way as semen is released by the prostate gland in men. Zaviacic and Whipple suggest that "many women who felt that they may be urinating during sex . . . [may be helped by] the knowledge that the fluid they expel may be different from urine and a normal phenomenon that occurs during sexual response" (p. 149). Some women, however, may expel urine during sex, perhaps because of urinary stress incontinence (Zaviacic & Whipple, 1993). Zaviacic and Whipple also suggest that stimulation of the G spot may cause some women to ejaculate, but not others.

Even supporters of the existence of the G spot admit that it's difficult to locate, because it's not apparent to the eye or to the touch (Geddes, 2008; Jannini et al., 2008). Terence Hines (2001) summarizes criticisms of the research into the G spot by noting that

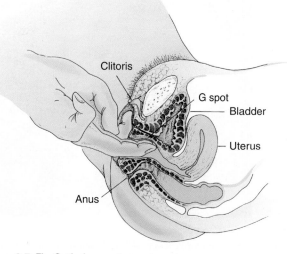

Figure 3.7 The Gräfenberg spot.
It's theorized that the G spot can be stimulated by fingers or by intercourse in the rear-entry or the female-superior position. Does stimulation of the G spot produce intense erotic sensations and a distinct form of orgasm?

it's based on anecdotes and case studies with small numbers of subjects. Hines characterizes the evidence for the existence of the G spot as weak and unsupported by more rigorous anatomic and biochemical research. He dubs the G spot a "modern gynecological myth."

Contemporary sexologists seem to agree on a number of points concerning the G spot and female ejaculation. First, they note that most if not all of the anterior wall of the vagina—and not just one area—is richly supplied with nerve endings and may be sensitive to erotic stimulation (Jannini et al., 2008; Levin, 2003a). However, it hasn't been adequately demonstrated that any particular zone of the anterior wall functions as a discrete sex organ; the area or areas that are exquisitely sensitive may vary from woman to woman (Maaita et al., 2002). Second, many females may exude a fluid through the urethra at about the time of orgasm. It's not clear what such fluid might be, though, and it's even less clear that it might correspond in some way to male ejaculation (Alzate & Hoch, 1986; Hines, 2001). And third, many sexologists wonder why other sexologists are so sensitive about this issue, and why it's become so politicized (Alzate & Hoch, 1986).

The Cervix

The **cervix** is the lower end of the uterus. Its walls, like those of the vagina, produce secretions that contribute to the chemical balance of the vagina. The opening in the middle of the cervix, called the **os**, is typically about the width of a straw, although it expands to permit passage of a baby from the uterus to the vagina during childbirth. Sperm passes from the vagina to the **uterus** through the cervical canal.

CERVICAL CANCER   The incidence of cervical cancer has declined dramatically in Canada since the early 1970s, largely because most women have regular Pap tests. In 2010, there were an estimated 1300 cases of cervical cancer and 370 deaths in Canada resulting from this disease (Canadian Cancer Society, 2010a). Cervical cancer is more common among women who've had many sex partners, women who become sexually active at a relatively early age, women of lower socioeconomic status, and women who smoke. All women, however, are at risk.

Canadian researchers (Franco et al., 2003) have ascertained that the greatest risk factor for cervical cancer is infection by the sexually transmitted human papillomavirus (HPV). As we'll discuss in Chapter 14, HPV is extremely common, and in most cases the infection resolves without causing damage. When the cervix is infected with certain strains of HPV, however, the infection can progress to cervical cancer. A vaccine to protect women against HPV infection has been successfully tested and approved by the Canadian government. Some provincial governments pay for vaccinations for girls and young women.

If detected early, most cases of cervical cancer can be successfully treated by surgery and **radiotherapy**. Cervical cancer can also be prevented if precancerous changes are detected by a **Pap test**. A Pap test involves smearing a sample of cervical cells on a slide to screen for cervical cancer and other abnormalities. The Canadian Cancer Society (2010a) recommends that once they become sexually active, women should have Pap tests every one to three years, depending on their previous test results and the screening guidelines for their provinces or territories. Most Canadian women (86%) have had Pap tests. It's estimated that half were screened for cervical cancer in 2005 (Statistics Canada, 2006b).

Women who are uncomfortable with the Pap test are less likely to be tested. Canadian research has found ethnocultural differences in rates of Pap testing. Brotto, Chou, Singh, and Woo (2008) found that Euro-Canadian women were significantly more likely to have ever had Pap tests than Indo-Canadian or East Asian-Canadian women. Amankwah, Ngwakongnwi, and Quan (2009) found that visible-minority women in Canada were less than half as likely to have had a Pap test.

Cervix   The lower end of the uterus.

Os   The opening in the middle of the cervix.

Uterus   The hollow, muscular, pear-shaped organ in which a fertilized ovum implants and develops until birth.

Radiotherapy   Treatment of a disease by X-rays or by emissions from a radioactive substance.

Pap test   Examination of a sample of cervical cells for cervical cancer and other abnormalities. Named after the originator of the technique, George Papanicolaou.

The Uterus

Ovum   Egg cell. The plural is "ova."

The uterus, or womb (see Figures 3.3 and 3.6), is the organ in which a fertilized **ovum** implants and develops until birth. The uterus usually slants forward (i.e., it's antroverted), although about 10% of women have uteruses that tip backward (i.e., they're retroverted). In most instances a retroverted uterus causes no problems, but some women with retroverted uteruses find coitus in certain positions painful. (A couple can quickly learn more comfortable positions by trial and error.) The uterus expands to house a fetus during pregnancy and shrinks after pregnancy, although not to its original size. A retroverted uterus normally tips forward during pregnancy.

Endometrium   The innermost layer of the uterus.

Like the vagina, the uterus has three layers (also shown in Figure 3.6). The innermost layer, or **endometrium**, is richly supplied with blood vessels and glands. Its structure varies according to a woman's age and the phase of the menstrual cycle. Endometrial tissue is discharged through the cervix and vagina at menstruation. For reasons not entirely understood, in some women endometrial tissue may also grow in the abdominal cavity or elsewhere in the reproductive system. This condition is called **endometriosis**, and its most common symptom is menstrual pain. If left untreated, endometriosis may lead to infertility.

Endometriosis   A condition caused by the growth of endometrial tissue in the abdominal cavity, or elsewhere outside the uterus, and characterized by menstrual pain.

UTERINE/ENDOMETRIAL CANCER   It's estimated that 4500 new cases of uterine cancer were diagnosed in Canada in 2010, and that 790 women died from it that year (Canadian Cancer Society, 2010b). One of the most common forms of uterine cancer is cancer of the endometrial lining. Risk factors for endometrial cancer include high exposure to estrogen, which is usually the result of early menarche, late menopause, or estrogen replacement therapy. For women who undergo hormone replacement therapy (HRT), combining estrogen with progestin lessens the risk of endometrial cancer. Not having children places a woman at risk, whereas pregnancy and hormonal contraceptives appear to lessen the risk.

Endometrial cancer is symptomized by abnormal uterine staining or bleeding, especially after menopause. The most common treatment is surgery (American Cancer Society, 2009). The five-year survival rate for endometrial cancer is up to 92% if it's discovered early and limited to the endometrium. (Endometrial cancer is usually diagnosed early because women tend to quickly report postmenopausal bleeding to their doctors.) The survival rate drops when the cancer invades surrounding tissues, or metastasizes.

Hysterectomy   Surgical removal of the uterus.

HYSTERECTOMY   A **hysterectomy** may be performed when women develop cancer of the uterus, ovaries, or cervix or have other diseases that cause pain or excessive uterine bleeding. An estimated 1.8 million Canadian women have had hysterectomies (Canadian Women's Health Network, 2010). A hysterectomy may be partial or complete. A **complete hysterectomy** involves surgical removal of the ovaries, fallopian tubes, cervix, and uterus. It's usually performed to reduce the risk of cancer's spreading throughout the reproductive system. A partial hysterectomy removes the uterus but not the ovaries and fallopian tubes. Sparing the ovaries allows the woman to continue to ovulate and produce adequate quantities of female sex hormones.

Complete hysterectomy   Surgical removal of the ovaries, fallopian tubes, cervix, and uterus.

The hysterectomy has become steeped in controversy. The operation can relieve symptoms associated with various gynecological disorders, improving quality of life for many women (Kjerulff et al., 2000). Many gynecologists, however, believe hysterectomy is often recommended inappropriately, before necessary diagnostic steps are taken or when less radical medical interventions might successfully treat the problems (Broder et al., 2000; Canadian Women's Health Network, 2010).

Brotto et al. (2008) have conducted research on the sexual difficulties women experience after hysterectomy. About half of those studied reported significant sexual difficulties, and most were highly distressed about these issues. Brotto has developed a brief educational program that is effective in improving the sexual functioning and enjoyment of women who have had hysterectomies.

The Fallopian Tubes

The two uterine tubes, called **fallopian tubes**, are about 10 centimetres in length and extend from the upper end of the uterus toward the ovaries. (See Figure 3.6.)

Ova pass through the fallopian tubes on their way to the uterus. The fallopian tubes are not inert passageways; they help nourish and conduct ova. The form of sterilization called tubal ligation ties off the fallopian tubes so ova cannot pass through them to become fertilized.

In an **ectopic pregnancy**, the fertilized ovum implants outside the uterus, most often in the fallopian tube, where fertilization has occurred. Ectopic pregnancies can eventually burst fallopian tubes, causing hemorrhaging and death. Ectopic pregnancies are thus terminated before the tube ruptures. They are not easily recognized, however, because their symptoms—a missed menstrual period, abdominal pain, and irregular bleeding—suggest many conditions. Any of these symptoms is an excellent reason to consult a gynecologist.

The Ovaries

The two **ovaries** are almond-shaped organs about four centimetres long. They lie on either side of the uterus, which they're attached to by ovarian ligaments. The ovaries produce ova (egg cells) and the female sex hormones **estrogen** and **progesterone**. Estrogen is a generic term for several hormones (such as estradiol, estriol, and estrone) that promote the changes of puberty and regulate the menstrual cycle. Progesterone, too, has multiple functions, including regulation of the menstrual cycle and preparation of the uterus for pregnancy by stimulating development of the endometrium (uterine lining). Estrogen and progesterone levels vary with the phases of the menstrual cycle.

The human female is born with all the ova she will ever have—about two million—but they're immature in form. About 400 000 of these survive into puberty, each contained in the ovary within a thin capsule, or **follicle**. During a woman's reproductive years, from puberty to menopause, only 400 or so ripened ova, typically one per month, are released by their rupturing follicles for possible fertilization.

OVARIAN CANCER   In 2010, about 2600 cases of ovarian cancer and 1750 deaths resulting from it occurred in Canada (Canadian Cancer Society, 2010c). Ovarian cancer most often strikes women between the ages of 40 and 70. It ranks as the fourth leading cancer killer of women, behind lung cancer, breast cancer, and colon cancer. Women most at risk are those whose blood relatives, especially first-degree relatives (mothers, sisters, daughters), have had ovarian or breast cancer. Other risk factors are high body weight and never having given birth.

Early detection is the key to fighting ovarian cancer. When it's detected before it spreads beyond the ovary, 94% of its victims survive. However, the overall five-year survival rate is only about 44% (American Cancer Society, 2009). Unfortunately, ovarian cancer is often silent in its early stages, showing no obvious signs or symptoms. The most common sign is enlargement of the abdomen, which is caused by the accumulation of fluid. Periodic, complete pelvic examinations are important. The Pap test, which is useful in detecting cervical cancer, does not reveal ovarian cancer.

Surgery, radiation therapy, and drug therapy are treatment options. Surgery usually includes the removal of one or both ovaries, the uterus, and the fallopian tubes.

Fallopian tubes   Tubes that extend from the upper uterus toward the ovaries, conducting ova to the uterus. Named after the Italian anatomist Gabriel Fallopius, who is credited with their discovery.

Ectopic pregnancy   A pregnancy in which the fertilized ovum implants outside the uterus, usually in the fallopian tube.

Ovaries   Almond-shaped organs that produce ova and the hormones estrogen and progesterone. These hormones are part of the endocrine system.

Estrogen   A generic term for female sex hormones (including estradiol, estriol, estrone, and others) or synthetic compounds that promote the development of female sex characteristics and regulate the menstrual cycle.

Progesterone   A steroid hormone that stimulates proliferation of the endometrium and is involved in regulation of the menstrual cycle. Progesterone is secreted by the corpus luteum or prepared synthetically.

Follicle   A capsule within an ovary, containing an ovum.

Figure 3.8 Use of the speculum and spatula during a pelvic examination.
The speculum is used to hold the vaginal walls apart, while the spatula is used to gently scrape cells from the cervix. The Pap test screens for cervical cancer and other abnormalities.

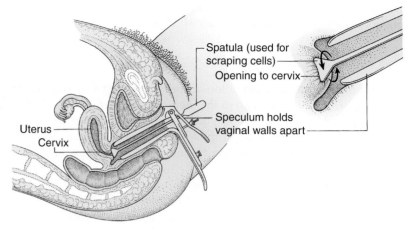

Spatula (used for scraping cells)

Opening to cervix

Uterus

Cervix

Speculum holds vaginal walls apart

The Pelvic Examination

During a pelvic examination, the physician first examines the woman externally for irritations, swellings, abnormal vaginal discharges, and clitoral adhesions. The physician normally inserts a speculum to help inspect the cervix and vaginal walls for discharges (which can be signs of infection), discolouration, lesions, or growths. This examination is typically followed by a Pap test, to look for cervical cancer. A sample of vaginal discharge may also be taken to test for the sexually transmitted infection gonorrhea.

To take a Pap smear, the physician holds the vaginal walls open with a plastic or (prewarmed!) metal speculum, then scrapes a sample of cells (a "smear") from the cervix with a wooden spatula. (See Figure 3.8.) A woman should not douche prior to a Pap test or schedule a test during menstruation, because douche and blood confound analysis of the smear.

The speculum exam is normally followed by a bimanual vaginal exam, in which the physician inserts the index and middle fingers of one hand into the vagina and palpates (touches) the lower part of the abdomen with the other hand from the outside. The physician uses this technique to examine the location, shape, size, and movability of the internal sex organs, searching for abnormal growths and symptoms of other problems. Palpation may be somewhat uncomfortable, but physical discomfort is usually mild. Severe pain is a sign that something is wrong. A woman should not try to be brave and hide such discomfort from the examiner.

It's normal for a woman to be anxious if she's never had a pelvic exam or she's visiting a new doctor. Talking about it with the examiner often relieves psychological discomfort. If the doctor isn't reassuring, the woman should feel free to consult another doctor. She should not forgo the pelvic examination itself—it's essential for early detection of problems.

CRITICAL THINKING QUESTIONS

Some men and women are uncomfortable with the prospect of having a doctor examine their genitals. What are the reasons for this discomfort?

The Female Breasts

Some college women recall:

I was very excited about my breast development. It was a big competition to see who was wearing a bra in elementary school. When I began wearing one, I also liked wearing see-through blouses so everyone would know. . . .

My breasts were very late in developing. This brought me a lot of grief from my male peers. I just dreaded situations like going to the beach or showering in the locker room. . . .

A World of Diversity

THE STRONG BREAST REVOLUTION

There's a fascination with female breasts in Canadian society. Among the two most viewed episodes of Discovery Channel Canada's series *The Sex Files* were those on female breasts.

Under the direction of drama professor Kim Renders, female University of Guelph students collectively created a play, largely based on their own experiences, designed to educate and entertain. *The Strong Breast Revolution* explored breastfeeding, breast cancer, breasts and sexuality, and women's anxieties about their breasts, as well as the pleasure they give.

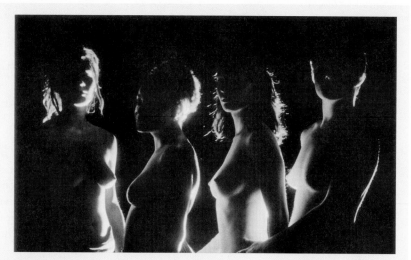

The Strong Breast Revolution.
In a play written by female University of Guelph students, actors went topless to show that women should feel proud of their breasts.

All through junior high and high school I felt unhappy about being over-endowed. I felt just too uncomfortable in sweaters—there was so much to reveal, and I was always sure that the only reason boys liked me was because of my bustline. . . .

—Morrison et al., 1980, pp. 66–70

In some cultures, the breasts are viewed merely as biological instruments for feeding infants. In our culture, however, breasts have taken on such erotic significance that a woman's self-esteem may become linked to her bustline.

The breasts are **secondary sex characteristics**. That is, like the rounding of the hips, they distinguish women from men but are not directly involved in reproduction. Each breast contains 15 to 20 clusters of milk-producing **mammary glands**. (See Figure 3.9.) Each gland opens through its own duct at the nipple. The mammary glands are separated by soft, fatty tissue. It's the amount of this fatty tissue—not the amount of glandular tissue—that largely determines breast size. Women vary little in their amount of glandular tissue, so breast size does not determine how much milk they can produce.

The nipple, which lies in the centre of the **areola**, contains smooth muscle fibres that contract to make the nipple erect. The areola, or area surrounding the nipple, darkens during pregnancy and remains darker after delivery. Oil-producing glands in the areola help lubricate the nipple during breastfeeding. Milk ducts conduct milk from the mammary glands through the nipple. The nipple is richly endowed with nerve endings, so stimulation heightens sexual arousal for many women.

Secondary sex characteristics Traits that distinguish women from men but are not directly involved in reproduction.

Mammary glands Milk-secreting glands.

Areola The dark ring on the breast that encircles the nipple.

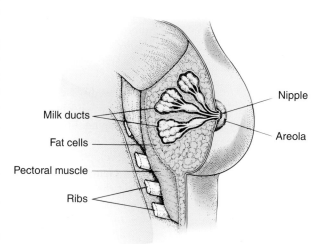

Figure 3.9 The breast of an adult woman.
This drawing reveals the structures underlying the breast, including milk ducts and fat cells.

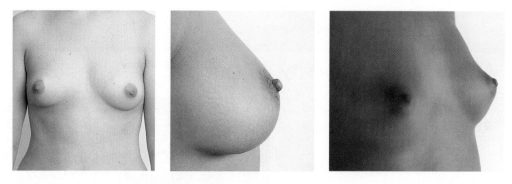

Figure 3.10 Typical variations in adult female breasts. Breast size and shape have little bearing on ability to produce milk or on sensitivity to sexual stimulation. Breasts have become highly eroticized in our culture.

CRITICAL THINKING QUESTIONS

The biological function of female breasts is to feed infants. Why do breasts carry such a high degree of erotic significance in Western culture?

Figure 3.10 shows typical variations in the size and shape of the adult female breast. The sensitivity of the breasts to sexual stimulation is unrelated to their size. Small breasts may have as many nerve endings as large breasts, but they're more densely packed. The breasts vary in sensitivity with the phases of the menstrual cycle. Some women appear less responsive to breast stimulation than others, though they may learn to enjoy breast stimulation during sexual activity in a relaxed atmosphere.

Breast Cancer

Among Canadian women, breast cancer is the most commonly diagnosed cancer and the second-leading cause of cancer-related death (Canadian Cancer Society, 2010d). In 2010, there were an estimated 23200 new cases of breast cancer and 5300 deaths among women in Canada (Canadian Cancer Society, 2010d). The five-year survival rate for women whose breast cancers have not spread beyond the breast is about 98%, up from nearly 80% in the 1950s (American Cancer Society, 2009). The five-year survival rate drops to about 80% if the cancer has spread to the surrounding region, and drops further to about 26% if it has spread to more distant sites.

RISK FACTORS   Breast cancer is rare in women under the age of 25. The risk increases sharply with age. About four out of five cases develop in women over the age of 50. The risk of developing breast cancer is about 1 in 229 for women aged 30 to 39 (National Cancer Institute, 2009), and it increases with each decade of life.

Genetic factors are involved in breast cancer, particularly among women with family histories of the disease and those who inherit the genetic mutations BRCA1 and BRCA2, which are associated with breast cancer (American Cancer Society, 2009). A study of more than 100 000 female nurses showed that those with mothers or sisters who'd had breast cancer were nearly twice as likely to develop the disease themselves (Colditz & Rosner, 2000). Those with both a mother and a sister who'd had the disease were two to three times as likely to get breast cancer themselves. Women who inherit BRCA1 or BRCA2 mutations have a 50 to 85% chance of developing breast cancer (American Cancer Society, 2009), compared with one woman in eight or nine in the general population. They also have an increased risk of developing ovarian cancer.

Genes for breast cancer appear to predict not only whether women will contract the disease, but also how deadly it will be. Health professionals can test the genomes of women with breast cancer, to help determine how aggressively they should treat the disease by such means as chemotherapy and radiation after they've surgically removed the tumors (American Cancer Society, 2009).

A key risk factor in breast cancer is prolonged exposure to estrogen, which stimulates both breast development in young women and proliferation of breast cancer cells (Colditz et al., 2004; Tamini et al., 2006). Exposure to estrogen—and therefore the risk of breast cancer—is heightened by early onset of menstruation (before age 14), late menopause (after age 55), delayed childbearing (after age 30), and never giving birth (American Cancer Society, 2009).

Heavy drinking of alcohol heightens the risk of breast cancer (American Cancer Society, 2009; Stein & Colditz, 2004). So do high amounts of fatty tissue in the body, since fat is connected with higher levels of estrogen production (American Cancer Society, 2006; Stein & Colditz, 2004). Exercise may reduce the risk of breast cancer by decreasing the amount of fatty tissue in the body. However, a study of nearly 49 000 50- to 79-year-old women whose health was tracked for 8 years showed that those who were assigned low-fat diets did not significantly differ in their breast cancer rates from women who ate as they wished (Prentice et al., 2006).

DETECTION AND TREATMENT   Women with breast cancer have lumps in the breast, but most lumps in the breasts are not cancerous. Most are either **cysts** or **benign** tumours. Breast cancer involves lumps in the breast that are **malignant**.

Breast cancer may be detected in various ways, including breast self-examination, physical examination by a doctor, mammography, and magnetic resonance imaging (MRI). **Mammography** allows the detection—and treatment—of tiny, highly curable cancers before they can be felt by touch. Mammography and MRI combined is a kind of X-ray technique that detects cancerous lumps in the breast. In Ontario, 92% of women aged 50 and older have had at least one mammogram in their lives (Pollard, 2006). There is some debate on the value of mammography, but all women should discuss it with their doctors. The Canadian Cancer Society (2010) recommends that all 50- to 69-year-old women should have mammograms every two years. Younger and older women should ask their doctors whether this schedule is appropriate for them.

The practice of breast self-examination is also controversial. After reviewing the results of teaching about self-examination, the Canadian Task Force on Preventive Health Care concluded in 2001 that there was no evidence that self-examination benefits women. Based on the task force's recommendations, Cancer Care Ontario, through its Ontario Breast Screening Program, ended its promotion of breast self-examinations (although it still provides instruction to women who wish to be taught). As of 2007, the Canadian Cancer Society no longer recommended that women conduct monthly breast self-examinations. Given the fact that the medical community is divided on this issue, women will have to decide, in consultation with their doctors, whether they wish to examine their own breasts.

Early detection and treatment reduce the risk of mortality. The sooner cancer is detected, the less likely it is to spread to critical organs. Smaller cancerous lumps can often be removed by **lumpectomy**, which spares the breast. More advanced cancers are likely to be treated by **mastectomy**, which is complete or partial removal of the breast.

Many drugs are used to treat breast cancer, and others are in the research pipeline. Tamoxifen, for example, locks into the estrogen receptors of breast cancer cells, blocking estrogen's stimulation of the cells to grow and proliferate. Tamoxifen also increases the risks of uterine cancer and of blood clots in the lungs, however, and has other side effects, especially among women over 50. Raloxifene is another drug that's been shown to reduce the risk of breast cancer (Cummings et al., 1999), but apparently without the side effects associated with tamoxifen.

Many women who undergo mastectomies have surgical breast implants to replace their missing tissue. Others have breast implants to augment their breast sizes. In 2006, after conducting a thorough review of the research evidence, Health Canada concluded that silicone gel implants were safe, and approved their use. These implants had previously been restricted, because of safety concerns. The issue remains controversial.

Cysts Saclike structures filled with fluid or diseased material.

Benign Doing little or no harm.

Malignant Lethal; causing or likely to cause death.

Mammography A special type of X-ray test that detects cancerous lumps in the breast.

Lumpectomy Surgical removal of a (usually cancerous) lump from the breast.

Mastectomy Surgical removal of all or part of a breast.

The Menstrual Cycle

Menstruation is the bleeding that results from the shedding of the uterine lining (endometrium) when a reproductive cycle has not led to fertilization of an ovum. The human menstrual cycle averages 28 days in length.

The cycle is regulated by the hormones estrogen and progesterone. It can be divided into four phases. The first phase, the proliferative phase, follows menstruation. During this phase, estrogen levels increase, causing the ripening of perhaps 10 to 20 ova (egg cells) within their follicles and the proliferation of endometrial tissue in the uterus. During the second phase of the cycle, estrogen reaches peak blood levels, and **ovulation** occurs. Normally only one ovum reaches maturity and is released by an ovary during ovulation.

The third phase of the cycle—the secretory, or luteal, phase—begins right after ovulation, and continues through the beginning of the next cycle. The term "luteal phase" derives from "corpus luteum," the name given to a follicle that has released an ovum. The **corpus luteum** functions as an **endocrine gland**, producing large amounts of progesterone and estrogen. Progesterone causes the endometrium to thicken, so it can support an embryo if fertilization occurs. If the ovum goes unfertilized, the estrogen and progesterone levels plummet. These falloffs trigger the fourth phase, the menstrual phase, which leads to the beginning of a new cycle.

Ovulation may not occur in every menstrual cycle. Anovulatory ("without ovulation") cycles are most common in the years just after **menarche**. They may become frequent again in the years prior to menopause, but they may also occur irregularly among women in their twenties and thirties.

Although the menstrual cycle averages 28 days, variations are common from woman to woman, and from month to month in the same woman. Girls' cycles are often irregular for a few years after menarche, but later assume reasonably regular patterns. Variations from cycle to cycle tend to occur during the proliferative phase that precedes ovulation. That is, menstruation tends to follow ovulation reliably by about 14 days. Variations of more than two days in the post-ovulation period are rare.

Although hormones regulate the menstrual cycle, psychological factors can influence the secretion of hormones. Stress can delay or halt menstruation. Age of menarche is related to a number of health problems. Girls who menstruate at very young ages are at greater risk for such problems as breast and endometrial cancer. Koo et al. (2002) at the University of Toronto have studied factors related to age of menarche. They've found that girls with higher intakes of dietary fibre or lower intakes of monounsaturated fat begin menstruating later.

Regulation of the Menstrual Cycle

The menstrual cycle involves finely tuned relationships between structures in the brain—the **hypothalamus** and the **pituitary gland**—and the ovaries and uterus. All of these structures are parts of the endocrine system, which means they secrete chemicals called **hormones** directly into the bloodstream.

Several hormones play important roles in sexual and reproductive functions. The gonads—the **testes** (or testicles) in the male and the ovaries in the female—secrete sex hormones directly into the bloodstream. The female gonads produce the sex hormones estrogen and progesterone. The male gonads produce the male sex hormone **testosterone**. Males and females also produce sex hormones characteristic of the other sex, but in relatively small amounts.

The hypothalamus is a pea-sized structure in the front part of the brain. It's involved in regulating many states of motivation, including hunger, thirst, aggression, and sex. The pituitary gland lies below the hypothalamus, at the base of the brain. Because many pituitary secretions regulate other endocrine glands, the pituitary has also been called the master gland. The pituitary gland produces

---

Ovulation The process by which a mature ovarian follicle ruptures and releases an ovum.

Corpus luteum An ovarian follicle that has released an ovum. The corpus luteum remains in existence only if pregnancy begins.

Endocrine gland A gland that secretes a hormone directly into the blood, rather than through a duct. Examples include the thyroid, adrenal, and pituitary glands, as well as the ovaries and testes.

Menarche ("men-AR-kee") The first menstrual period.

Hypothalamus A bundle of neural cell bodies involved in regulating body temperature, motivation, and emotion. It's located near the centre of the brain.

Pituitary gland The gland that secretes growth hormone, prolactin, oxytocin, and other hormones.

Hormone A substance secreted by an endocrine gland to regulate various body functions.

Testes The male gonads.

Testosterone The male sex hormone that fosters development of male sex characteristics and is connected with the sex drive.

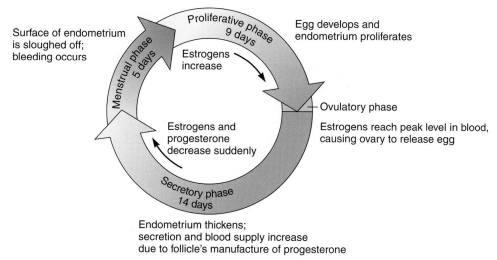

Surface of endometrium
is sloughed off;
bleeding occurs

Menstrual phase
5 days

Proliferative phase
9 days

Estrogens
increase

Egg develops and
endometrium proliferates

Ovulatory phase

Estrogens reach peak level in blood,
causing ovary to release egg

Estrogens and
progesterone
decrease suddenly

Secretory phase
14 days

Endometrium thickens;
secretion and blood supply increase
due to follicle's manufacture of progesterone

Figure 3.11 The four phases of the menstrual cycle.
The menstrual cycle consists of the proliferative, ovulatory, secretory (luteal), and menstrual phases.

gonadotropins (literally, "that which feeds the gonads"), called follicle-stimulating hormone (FSH) and luteinizing hormone (LH), which stimulate the ovaries and play a key role in regulating the menstrual cycle.

Phases of the Menstrual Cycle

As we've noted, the menstrual cycle has four phases—the proliferative, ovulatory, secretory, and menstrual stages. (See Figure 3.11.) It might seem logical that a new cycle begins with the first day of menstrual flow, since this is the most clearly identifiable event of the cycle. Many women begin to count the days of the menstrual cycle at the onset of menstruation. Biologically speaking, however, menstruation is really the culmination of the cycle. In fact, the cycle begins with the end of menstruation and the initiation of a series of biological events that lead to maturation of an immature ovum in preparation for ovulation and possible fertilization.

THE PROLIFERATIVE PHASE   The first phase, the **proliferative phase**, begins with the end of menstruation and lasts for about 9 or 10 days of an average 28-day cycle. (See Figure 3.11.) During this phase the endometrium develops, or proliferates. This phase is also known as the pre-ovulatory or follicular phase, because it's when certain ovarian follicles mature and the ovaries prepare for ovulation.

THE OVULATORY PHASE   During ovulation, or the **ovulatory phase**, a **Graafian follicle** ruptures and releases a mature ovum near (but not into) a fallopian tube. The other ripening follicles degenerate and are harmlessly reabsorbed by the body. Occasionally, two ova mature and are released during ovulation, and if both are fertilized, fraternal (non-identical) twins develop. Identical twins develop when one fertilized ovum divides into two separate **zygotes**.

Ovulation is set into motion when estrogen production reaches a critical level. A woman's basal body temperature, measured by oral or rectal thermometer, dips slightly at ovulation and rises by about 0.5°C on the day following ovulation. Many women use this information to help them conceive or avoid conceiving.

THE SECRETORY PHASE   The phase following ovulation is called the post-ovulatory or **secretory phase**. Some people refer to it as the luteal phase, which reflects the name given to the ruptured Graafian follicle—the corpus luteum.

Levels of progesterone and estrogen peak at around the twentieth or twenty-first day of an average cycle. These hormones cause the glands in the endometrium to secrete nutrients that will sustain a fertilized ovum implanted in the uterine wall.

Proliferative phase   The first phase of the menstrual cycle, which begins with the end of menstruation and lasts about 9 or 10 days. During this phase, the endometrium proliferates.

Ovulatory phase   The second stage of the menstrual cycle. This is when a follicle ruptures and releases a mature ovum.

Graafian follicle   A mature ovarian follicle that ruptures to discharge an ovum.

Zygote   A fertilized ovum (egg cell).

Secretory phase   The third phase of the menstrual cycle, following the ovulatory phase. Also referred to as the luteal phase, after the corpus luteum, which begins to secrete large amounts of progesterone and estrogen after ovulation.

If implantation does not occur, the corpus luteum decomposes. After its decomposition, levels of estrogen and progesterone fall precipitously.

Menstrual phase The fourth phase of the menstrual cycle, when the endometrium is sloughed off in the menstrual flow.

THE MENSTRUAL PHASE   During the **menstrual phase,** the uterine lining (endometrium) is sloughed off into a menstrual flow. This occurs when estrogen and progesterone levels decline to the point where they can no longer sustain the uterine lining, and the lining disintegrates. Menstruation itself is the passing of the lining through the cervix and vagina. Extremely heavy or prolonged (more than a week) menstrual bleeding may reflect health problems, and should be discussed with a health-care provider.

Tampon A cylindrical plug of cotton that's inserted into the vagina and left in place to absorb menstrual fluid. From a French word meaning "plug."

Prior to 1933, women generally used external sanitary napkins or pads to absorb the menstrual flow. In that year, **tampons** were introduced, altering the habits of millions of women. When they use tampons while menstruating, women can swim without concern, wear more revealing or comfortable apparel, and feel generally less burdened. Questions have arisen about whether tampons cause or exacerbate infections such as toxic shock syndrome (TSS), which is sometimes fatal. Signs of TSS include fever, headache, sore throat, vomiting, diarrhea, muscle aches, rash, and dizziness. Peeling skin, disorientation, and a plunge in blood pressure may follow. Toxic shock syndrome is caused by the *Staphylococcus aureus* ("staph") bacterium, which is most likely to overbreed when highly absorbent tampons are left in place for many hours. As a result, many women now use regular rather than superabsorbent tampons. Others change their tampons three or four times a day, or alternate them with sanitary napkins.

Sex During Menstruation

Many couples continue to engage in coitus during menstruation, but others abstain (Schneiderwind-Skibbe et al., 2007). Some people abstain because of religious prohibitions. Others express concern about the "fuss" or the "mess" of the menstrual flow. Despite traditional attitudes that associate menstruation with uncleanliness, there is no evidence that coitus during menstruation is physically harmful to either partner. Ironically, menstrual coitus may be helpful to the woman. The uterine contractions that occur during orgasm may help relieve cramping by dispelling blood congestion. Orgasm achieved through masturbation may have the same effect.

Women may be sexually aroused at any time during the menstrual cycle. The preponderance of the research evidence, however, points to a peak in sexual desire in women around the time of ovulation.

Human coital patterns during the phases of the menstrual cycle seem to reflect personal decisions, not hormone fluctuations (although it may be argued that hormonal fluctuations influence sexual decision making). Some couples decide to increase their frequency of coitus at ovulation, to optimize their chances of conceiving; others may abstain during menstruation, because of religious beliefs or beliefs

Innovative Canadian Research

MENSTRUAL SEX

Among female students at the University of Waterloo, being comfortable with one's sexuality in general was associated with being comfortable with menstruation. Women who engaged in coital sex during menstruation were more likely also to be aroused by a wide diversity of sexual activities such as group sex and spanking. This indicates that women who engage in menstrual sex are more willing to push the boundaries of what is considered to be conventional sex (Rempel & Baumgartner, 2003).

linking menses with uncleanliness. Some may also increase their coital activity preceding menstruation, to compensate for anticipated abstinence during menses, or increase coital activity afterward, to make up for deprivation.

Menopause

Menopause, or the "change of life," is the cessation of menstruation. Menopause is a process that most commonly occurs between the ages of 46 and 50 and lasts for about two years, though it may begin at any time between the ages of 35 and 60. There's at least one case of a woman who became pregnant at 61. **Perimenopause** refers to the beginning of menopause and is usually characterized by 3 to 11 months of amenorrhea (lack of menstruation) or irregular periods. Perimenopause ends with menopause.

Menopause is a specific event in a long-term process known as the **climacteric** ("critical period"), the gradual decline in the reproductive capacity of the ovaries. The climacteric generally lasts for about 15 years, from ages 45 to 60 or so. Beginning around the age of 35, many women's menstrual cycles shorten from an average of 28 days to about 25 days by age 40, and to about 23 days by their mid-forties. By the end of their forties, many women experience erratic cycles, with some periods close together and others missed.

In menopause, the pituitary gland continues to pour normal levels of FSH and LH into the bloodstream, but for reasons that aren't well understood, the ovaries gradually lose their capacity to respond. They no longer ripen egg cells or produce the sex hormones estrogen and progesterone.

The deficit in estrogen may lead to a number of unpleasant perimenopausal sensations, including night sweats, hot flashes (suddenly feeling hot), and hot flushes (suddenly looking reddened) (Bastian et al., 2003; Tuomikoski et al., 2009). Hot flashes and flushes may alternate with cold sweats, during which a woman feels suddenly cold and clammy. Anyone who has experienced cold feet or hands as a result of anxiety or fear will understand how dramatic the shifting patterns of blood flow can be. Hot flashes and flushes stem largely from waves of blood vessel dilation across the face and upper body. These sensations reflect vasomotor instability, or disruptions in the body mechanisms that dilate and constrict the blood vessels to maintain an even body temperature.

Additional signs of estrogen deficiency include dizziness, headache, joint pain, tingling in the hands or feet, burning or itchy skin, and heart palpitation. The skin usually becomes drier. There's some loss of breast tissue, as well as a decrease in vaginal lubrication during sexual arousal. Women may also encounter sleep problems, such as awakening more frequently at night and having difficulty falling back to sleep. Many perimenopausal women also experience migraine headaches (MacGregor, 2009).

HORMONE REPLACEMENT THERAPY (HRT)   Some women who experience severe physical symptoms are helped by **hormone replacement therapy (HRT)**, which typically consists of synthetic (but occasionally naturally sourced) estrogen and progesterone. These synthetic hormones are used to offset the loss of their naturally occurring counterparts. HRT may help reduce the hot flushes and other symptoms brought about by hormonal deficiencies during menopause (den Tonkelaar & Oddens, 2000).

In 2002, a major controversy over the use of HRT erupted in Canada and many other countries when researchers conducting the Women's Health Initiative study in the United States ended the project after three years instead of eight (the intended length of the study) because they'd found an increase in the incidence of breast cancer among women taking HRT. Currently, the Canadian Cancer Society (2009) recommends that women avoid taking HRT unless they're experiencing severe

Menopause The cessation of menstruation.

Perimenopause The years leading up to menopause, between the beginning of the climacteric and the cessation of menstruation.

Climacteric A long-term process, including menopause, that involves the gradual decline in the reproductive capacity of the ovaries.

Hormone replacement therapy (HRT) Post-menopausal replacement of naturally occurring estrogen or estrogen and progesterone with synthetic (or sometimes natural) equivalents.

menopausal symptoms that haven't responded to other treatment. And the Society of Obstetricians and Gynaecologists of Canada (SOGC, 2006) indicates that for women with severe symptoms, short-term use of HRT for one or two years is safe.

Because of the overall increased health risks, many women may decide not to use HRT. Despite the risks, though, some women use HRT because they feel their quality of life is better, with fewer menopausal symptoms such as hot flashes, night sweats, and vaginal dryness. Women with severe symptoms are therefore advised to explore the health benefits and risks of HRT with their doctors.

Women might also consider alternatives. Breast cancer specialist Larry Norton (cited in Duenwald, 2002) notes that progestin alone prevents or lessens hot flashes in about 70% of women. Selective serotonin reuptake inhibitors (SSRIs) such as Effexor, Paxil, and Prozac may also help (Stearns et al., 2003). Women using SSRIs to treat hot flashes usually take half the dose used to treat depression, which is their main use. Vaginal dryness can be treated with estrogens that are used locally—that is, placed in the vagina rather than into the bloodstream, as hormones usually are. Creams (e.g., Estrace), suppositories (e.g., Vagifem), and plastic rings (e.g., Estring) are available for this purpose.

It's important to put the symptoms of menopause into a balanced perspective. Most women cope quite well with menopause, and discover ways of minimizing unpleasant symptoms. Many are quite relieved that they no longer have to worry about the possibility of unplanned pregnancy. Not worrying about contraception can make sexual relationships more enjoyable, and most women continue to have active and pleasurable sex lives after menopause.

Menstrual Difficulties

Although menstruation is a natural biological process, 50 to 75% of women experience some discomfort prior to or during menstruation (Sommerfeld, 2000). About 30% of Canadian women report that they usually experience extremely painful menstrual periods (Fisher, Boroditsky, & Morris, 2004b). The menstrual difficulties we explore in this section include dysmenorrhea, amenorrhea, and premenstrual syndrome (PMS).

Dysmenorrhea

Dysmenorrhea Pain or discomfort during menstruation.

Primary dysmenorrhea Menstrual pain or discomfort that occurs in the absence of known organic problems.

Secondary dysmenorrhea Menstrual pain or discomfort caused by identified organic problems.

Prostaglandins Hormones that cause muscle fibres in the uterine wall to contract, as during labour.

Pain or discomfort during menstruation, known as **dysmenorrhea**, is the most common type of menstrual difficulty. Most women at some time have at least mild menstrual pain or discomfort. Pelvic cramps are the most common manifestation of dysmenorrhea. They may be accompanied by headache, backache, nausea, and a bloated feeling. Women who develop severe cases usually do so within a few years of menarche. **Primary dysmenorrhea** is menstrual pain or discomfort in the absence of known organic pathology. **Secondary dysmenorrhea** is menstrual difficulty caused by (or secondary to) an identified organic problem. Endometriosis, pelvic inflammatory disease, and ovarian cysts are just a few of the organic disorders that can give rise to secondary dysmenorrhea.

Menstrual cramps appear to result from uterine spasms that may be brought about by copious secretion of hormones called **prostaglandins**. Prostaglandins apparently cause muscle fibres in the uterine wall to contract, as during labour. Most contractions go unnoticed, but powerful, persistent contractions are not only discomfiting in themselves, they may temporarily deprive the uterus of oxygen, which is another source of distress. Women with more intense menstrual discomfort apparently produce higher quantities of prostaglandins than other women. Prostaglandin-inhibiting drugs such as ibuprofen, indomethacin, and aspirin are often helpful. Menstrual pain may also be secondary to endometriosis.

Applied Knowledge

HOW TO HANDLE MENSTRUAL DISCOMFORT

Menstrual problems were once erroneously attributed to women's "hysterical" nature. This is nonsense. Menstrual problems largely appear to reflect hormonal variations or chemical fluctuations in the brain during the menstrual cycle. Researchers have not yet fully identified all of the causal elements and patterns, but their lack of knowledge does not mean women who have menstrual problems are "hysterical." Most women experience some degree of menstrual discomfort.

If you experience persistent menstrual distress, you may profit from the suggestions listed below. Researchers are exploring the effectiveness of these techniques in controlled studies. For now, you might consider running a personal experiment. Adopt the techniques that sound right for you—all of them, if you wish.

- Keep a menstrual calendar, so you can systematically track your menstrual symptoms and identify patterns.
- Develop strategies for dealing with days when you experience the greatest distress—strategies that enhance your pleasure and minimize the stress you feel. Activities that distract you from your menstrual discomfort may be helpful. Go see a movie or get into that novel you've been meaning to read.
- Ask yourself whether you harbour any self-defeating attitudes toward menstruation that might be compounding your distress. Do close relatives or friends see menstruation as an illness, a time of "pollution," a "dirty thing"? Have you adopted any of these attitudes—if not verbally, then in ways that affect your behaviour, such as by restricting your social activities during your period?

- See a gynecologist about your concerns, especially if you have severe symptoms. Severe menstrual symptoms are often secondary to medical disorders such as endometriosis and pelvic inflammatory disease (PID). Check it out.
- Develop healthful eating habits and continue them throughout your entire cycle (that means always). Consider limiting your intake of alcohol, caffeine, fats, salt, and sweets, especially during the days preceding menstruation. Research suggests that a low-fat, vegetarian diet reduces the duration of premenstrual symptoms and the duration and intensity of menstrual pain (Barnard et al., 2000).
- Eat several smaller meals (or nutritious snacks) throughout the day, rather than a few highly filling meals.
- Try some vigorous exercise, such as jogging, swimming, bicycling, fast walking, dancing, skating, or even jumping rope. Many women find that vigorous exercise helps relieve premenstrual and menstrual discomfort. Evidence suggests that exercise relieves and possibly prevents menstrual discomfort (Daley, 2009).
- Check with your doctor about vitamin and mineral supplements such as calcium and magnesium. Vitamin B6 appears to help some women (Chavez & Spritzer, 2002).
- Try ibuprofen (marketed as Medipren, Advil, and Motrin, for example) and other over-the-counter medicines for cramping. Prescription drugs such as anti-anxiety medications (e.g., alprazolam) and antidepressants (selective serotonin reuptake inhibitors) may also help (Stearns et al., 2003).

Seasonale.
Women who use Seasonale contraceptives have just four periods per year.

Antidepressants affect neurotransmitter levels in a way that can be helpful for women with PMS. Their benefits do not mean women with PMS are depressed. Ask your doctor for a recommendation.

- Consider using oral contraceptives that reduce the number of menstrual periods. In 2007, Health Canada approved the use of Seasonale, an oral contraceptive that reduces the number of periods to four per year. Lybrel, another oral contraceptive, ends menstruation when taken every day, thereby eliminating PMS symptoms. (Menstruation returns once you stop taking the medication.) Lybrel has not been approved for use by Health Canada. The idea of eliminating menstruation is very controversial, and many health professionals are worried about the possibility that it may cause unknown long-term health problems.

Pelvic pressure and bloating may be traced to pelvic edema—the congestion of fluid in the pelvic region. Fluid retention can lead to a gain of several pounds, sensations of heaviness, and **mastalgia**, a swelling of the breasts that sometimes causes premenstrual discomfort. Orgasm (through coitus or masturbation) can help relieve menstrual discomfort by reducing the pelvic congestion that spawns bloating and pressure. Orgasm may also increase the menstrual flow and shorten this phase of the cycle.

Amenorrhea

Amenorrhea, the absence of menstruation, is a primary sign of infertility. **Primary amenorrhea** is the absence of menstruation in a woman who has not menstruated at all by about the age of 16 or 17. **Secondary amenorrhea** is delayed or absent menstruation in a woman who's had regular periods in the past.

Amenorrhea has various causes, including abnormalities in the structures of the reproductive system, hormonal abnormalities, growths such as cysts and tumours, and psychological problems such as stress. Amenorrhea is normal during pregnancy and following menopause. Amenorrhea is also a symptom of the eating disorder **anorexia nervosa**.

Premenstrual Syndrome (PMS)

Premenstrual syndrome (PMS) is the combination of biological and psychological symptoms that may affect a woman during the four- to six-day interval that precedes her menses each month. For many women, premenstrual symptoms persist during menstruation. The great majority of cases involve mild to moderate levels of discomfort. PMS is not unique to our culture.

Although 61% of Canadian women experience premenstrual syndrome (Fisher, Boroditsky, & Morris, 2004b), research on PMS has been limited, and concerned only with its psychological aspects. Only a generation ago, PMS was seen as something a woman had to put up with. No longer. Today there are many options to reduce the effects of PMS. These include exercise, dietary control (e.g., eating several small meals a day, rather than two or three large meals, limiting salt and sugar, and taking vitamin supplements), hormone treatments (usually progesterone), and medications that reduce anxiety or increase the amount of serotonin in the nervous system.

Some feminists have objected to the view that PMS and menopause are problems that require medical treatment. Leonore Tiefer (2001), in particular, argues that pharmaceutical companies have overly medicalized various aspects of female sexuality, such as PMS and menopause, for the sake of increasing profits.

Male Anatomy and Physiology

From the earliest foundations of Western civilization, male-dominated societies have elevated men and exalted male genitalia. The ancient Greeks carried oversized images of fish as **phallic symbols** in their Dionysian processions, which celebrated the wilder and more frenzied aspects of human sexuality. In the murky predawn light of Western civilization, humankind engaged in phallic worship.

Men held their own genitals in such high esteem that it was common courtroom practice in ancient Rome for them to swear to tell the truth with their hands on their genitals—as we swear to tell the truth in the name of God or by placing our hands on the Bible or other document. The words "**testes**" and "**testicles**" derive from the same Latin word as "testify."

Even today, we see evidence of pride in—indeed, veneration of—the male genitalia. Men with large genitals are accorded respect from their male peers, and

Mastalgia A swelling of the breasts that sometimes causes premenstrual discomfort.

Amenorrhea Absence of menstruation.

Primary amenorrhea Absence of menstruation in a woman who has never menstruated.

Secondary amenorrhea Absence of menstruation in a woman who has previously menstruated.

Anorexia nervosa A psychological disorder characterized by a desire to lose weight by refusing to eat.

Premenstrual syndrome (PMS) A combination of physical and psychological symptoms (such as anxiety, depression, irritability, weight gain from fluid retention, and abdominal discomfort) that regularly afflicts many women during the four- to six-day interval that precedes their menses each month.

Phallic symbols Images of the penis that are usually suggestive of generative power.

Testes The male sex glands, suspended in the scrotum. They produce sperm cells and male sex hormones. The singular of "testes" is "testis."

Testicles Testes.

sometimes adoration from female admirers. Slang describes men with large genitals as "well hung" or "hung like a bull" (or stallion).

Given these cultural attitudes, it's not surprising that some men belittle themselves if they feel, as many do, that they're small—that is, that their penises do not measure up to some ideal. In examining male sexual anatomy and physiology, we'll attempt to sort truth from fiction.

The External Male Sex Organs

The external male sex organs include the penis and the scrotum. (See Figure 3.12.)

The Penis

At first glance, the **penis** may seem rather simple and obvious in its structures, particularly when compared with female organs. Yet, as Figure 3.12 shows, the apparent simplicity of the penis is misleading. Much goes on below the surface.

The penis, like the vagina, is the sex organ used in sexual intercourse. Unlike the vagina, however, the penis also serves as a conduit for urine. Both semen and urine pass out of the penis through the urethral opening. The opening is called the urethral meatus (pronounced me-ATE-us), which means "passage."

Many mammals, including dogs, have penile bones that stiffen their penises to facilitate copulation. Despite the slang term "boner," the human penis contains no bones. Nor, despite another slang term, "muscle," does the penis contain muscle tissue. However, muscles at the base of the penis, like the muscles surrounding the urethral and vaginal openings in the female, are involved in controlling urination and ejaculation.

Rather than bone or muscle, three cylinders of spongy material run the length of the penis. The two larger cylinders, the **corpora cavernosa**, lie side by side and function like the cavernous bodies in the clitoris, filling with blood and stiffening during sexual arousal. The third cylinder, the **corpus spongiosum** (spongy body), runs along the lower (ventral) surface of the penis. It contains the penile urethra,

Penis   The male organ of sexual intercourse.

Corpora cavernosa   Two cylinders of spongy tissue in the penis that become congested with blood and stiffen during sexual arousal.

Corpus spongiosum   The spongy body that runs along the bottom of the penis, contains the penile urethra, and enlarges at the tip of the penis to form the glans.

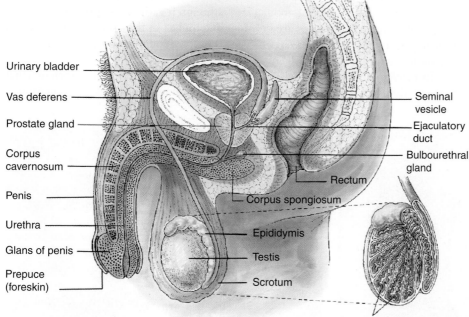

Urinary bladder
Vas deferens
Prostate gland
Corpus cavernosum
Penis
Urethra
Glans of penis
Prepuce (foreskin)
Seminal vesicle
Ejaculatory duct
Bulbourethral gland
Rectum
Corpus spongiosum
Epididymis
Testis
Scrotum
Seminiferous tubules

Figure 3.12 The male reproductive system.
The external male sex organs include the penis and the scrotum.

which conducts urine through the penis to the urinary opening (urethral meatus) at the tip, where the spongy body enlarges to become the glans, or head, of the penis. All three cylinders consist of spongy tissue that swells (becomes engorged) with blood during sexual arousal, resulting in erection.

The urethra is connected to the bladder, which is unrelated to reproduction and to those parts of the reproductive system that transport semen.

The glans of the penis, like the clitoral glans, is extremely sensitive to sexual stimulation. Direct, prolonged stimulation can become irritating, even painful. Some men prefer to masturbate by stroking the shaft of the penis rather than the glans. The **corona**, or coronal ridge, separates the glans from the body of the penis. After the glans, the parts of the penis men tend to find most sensitive are the corona and an area on the underside of the penis called the **frenulum**. The frenulum is a thin strip of tissue that connects the underside of the glans to the shaft. Most men find the top part of the penis to be the most sensitive part.

The base of the penis, called the **root**, extends into the pelvis. It's attached to the pelvic bones by leg-like structures, called crura, similar to those that anchor the female's clitoris. The body of the penis is called the penile **shaft**. Unlike the clitoral shaft, the penile shaft is free-swinging. Thus, when sexual excitement engorges the penis with blood, the result—erection—is obvious.

The skin of the penis is hairless and loose, allowing expansion during erection, and fixed to the penile shaft just behind the glans. In an uncircumcised male, some of the skin, like the labia minora in the female, folds over to cover part or all of the glans, just as the clitoral prepuce (hood) covers the clitoral shaft. Known as the prepuce, or **foreskin**, this penile covering consists of loose skin that freely moves over the glans. Smegma—a cheese-like, foul-smelling secretion—may accumulate below the prepuce, causing the foreskin to adhere to the glans.

CIRCUMCISION   Male **circumcision** is the surgical removal of the prepuce. (See Figure 3.13.) It has a long history as a religious rite. Jews traditionally carry out male circumcision shortly after a baby is born. Circumcision is performed as a sign of the covenant between God and the people of Abraham. Muslims also circumcise for religious reasons, although they do so some years after birth. Circumcision became widespread in North America, beginning in the second quarter of the twentieth century, because of its perceived medical benefits.

The circumcision rate for boys in Canada has declined significantly since the 1970s, and currently stands at about 17%, although it varies from province to province. Male circumcision rates are considerably higher in the United States than in Canada. The world's highest circumcision rates are found in countries where the population is largely or exclusively Muslim.

In a 1996 report on circumcision, the Canadian Paediatric Society concluded that the procedure is not medically necessary, and recommended against circumcision as

Corona   The ridge that separates the glans from the body of the penis.

Frenulum   The sensitive strip of tissue that connects the underside of the penile glans to the shaft.

Root   The base of the penis, which extends into the pelvis.

Shaft   The body of the penis, which expands as a result of vasocongestion.

Foreskin   The loose skin that covers the penile glans in an uncircumcised male. It's also referred to as the "prepuce."

Circumcision   Surgical removal of the foreskin of the penis.

CRITICAL THINKING QUESTIONS

Who understand their reproductive anatomy better—men or women?

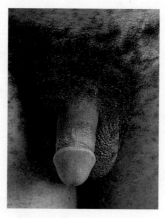
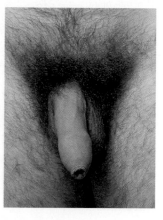

Figure 3.13 Typical variations in male genitalia. The penis and scrotum vary a good deal from one man to another. The penis in the photo on the right is uncircumcised.

A World of Diversity

A FEMALE PERSPECTIVE ON PENIS SIZE

The belief that the size of the man's penis determines his sexual prowess is based on the assumption that men with bigger penises are better equipped to satisfy a woman sexually.

Even though the inner vagina is relatively insensitive to touch, some women find the pressure of deeper penetration sexually pleasurable. Others, however, find deeper penetration uncomfortable or painful, especially if the thrusting is vigorous.

There has been a notable lack of research into women's preferences regarding penis size. In a 1998 national survey of Canadian women, the Compas polling organization asked, "What is the ideal penis size?" Most women preferred either an average-sized (37%) or somewhat larger than average penis (45%). Hardly any preferred a much larger than average (3%) or a somewhat smaller than average penis (4%). Twelve percent of the women expressed no preference.

---

a routine practice. Still, the Society took the view that parents should have the right to decide whether to have their infants circumcised. In light of recent research on the possible medical benefits of circumcision, the Canadian Pediatric Society began a review of its policy on male circumcision in 2009. As of mid-2011, the new policy had not yet been issued.

Some medical research suggests that circumcision lessens the risk of urinary tract infection (Muckherjee et al., 2009), HPV, HIV/AIDS (Tobian et al., 2009), and cancer of the penis. One study compared the incidence of HIV infection in two African cities that had high rates of circumcision and two African cities that had low rates of circumcision (White et al., 2008). In Yaoundé, Cameroon, and Cotonou, Benin, where 99% of the men were circumcised, the prevalence of HIV among sexually active men was about 4 to 5%. In Kisumu, Kenya, and Ndola, Zambia, where circumcision rates were much lower, the rates of HIV infection among sexually active men were about 26 to 27%. The protective effects of circumcision are likely to reflect a lower incidence of local inflammation and genital ulceration, which both provide ports of entry for HIV, as well as removal of cells in the foreskin (Langerhans cells) that are receptive to HIV infection (Gray et al., 2009).

Some people firmly oppose male circumcision, arguing that the procedure is painful and the child has not consented to it. From this perspective, circumcision is a violation of the infant boy's human rights. The Circumcision Information Resource Centre, a Montreal-based lobby group, seeks to ban male circumcision on infants and children in Canada, in the same way female circumcision has been made illegal. Some men are so upset over having been circumcised that they've made efforts to have their foreskins restored.

The perception that circumcised men experience less sexual sensation than uncircumcised men is controversial. One study by Canadian and American researchers (Payne et al., 2007) found no difference between these groups in terms of penile sensation. However, the uncircumcised men experienced larger increases in penile temperature with sexual arousal. In Australia, Richters et al. (2006) found that uncircumcised men were more likely to experience occasional physical pain during intercourse.

Physicians once agreed that circumcision was the treatment of choice for **phimosis**, a condition in which it's difficult to retract the foreskin from the glans. Today, only a small minority of males with phimosis are treated with circumcision (Rickwood et al., 2000).

Phimosis   An abnormal condition in which the foreskin is so tight that it cannot be withdrawn from the glans.

PENIS SIZE   In our culture, penis size is sometimes seen as a measure of a man's masculinity and ability to please a sex partner. The attitudes of Canadian women toward penis size are presented in "A World of Diversity: A Female Perspective on Penis Size."

Wylie and Eardley (2007) reviewed 12 studies measuring penis size, and found that the average flaccid (non-erect) penis was 9 to 10 centimetres in both length and girth, and that the average erect penis ranged from 14 to 16 centimetres in length and 12 to 13 centimetres in girth. There appears to be little relationship between the size of a given penis when flaccid and when erect. Penises that are small when flaccid tend to gain more size when they become erect. Larger flaccid penises gain relatively less size (Jamison & Gebhard, 1988).

Even when flaccid, the same penis can vary in size. Factors such as cold air, cold water, fear, and anxiety can cause the penis (along with the scrotum and testicles) to draw closer to the body, reducing its size.

Some men, particularly younger men, may feel inadequate after watching pornography that often features male actors with abnormally large penises. Some may go so far as to order pills after seeing internet and magazine ads that claim these products will cause the penis to grow substantially in size. There's no medical evidence that these products work.

The Scrotum

The **scrotum** is a pouch of loose skin that becomes lightly covered with hair at puberty. The scrotum consists of two compartments that hold the testes. Each testicle is held in place by a **spermatic cord**, a structure that contains the **vas deferens**, blood vessels, nerves, and the **cremaster muscle**. The cremaster muscle raises and lowers the testicle within the scrotum in response to temperature change and sexual stimulation. The testes are drawn closer to the body during sexual arousal.

Sperm production is optimal at a temperature slightly lower than the 37°C that's desirable for most of the body. Typical scrotal temperature is a few degrees lower than body temperature. The scrotum is loose-hanging and flexible. It permits the testes and nearby structures to escape the higher body heat, especially in warm weather. Tightening or constricting of the skin surface helps retain heat and gives the scrotum a wrinkled appearance in the cold.

The scrotum is developed from the same embryonic tissue that becomes the labia majora of the female. Thus, like the labia majora, the scrotum is quite sensitive to sexual stimulation. It's somewhat more sensitive than the top side of the penis, but less sensitive than other areas of the penis.

The Internal Male Sex Organs

The internal male sex organs consist of the testes, which manufacture sperm and testosterone, the system of tubes and ducts that conduct sperm through the male reproductive system, and the organs that help nourish, activate, and enable sperm to neutralize some of the acidity found in the vagina.

The Testes

The testes are the male gonads. In slang, the testes are frequently referred to as "balls" or "nuts." These terms are considered vulgar, but they are reasonably descriptive, and they make it easier for many people to refer to the testes in informal conversation.

The testes serve two functions analogous to those of the ovaries: they secrete sex hormones and they produce mature **germ cells**. The germ cells produced by the testes are called **sperm**, or **spermatozoa**, and the sex hormones are called **androgens**. The most important androgen is **testosterone**.

Scrotum   The pouch of loose skin that contains the testes. It comes from the same linguistic root as the word "shred," which means "a long, narrow strip," probably referring to the long furrows on the scrotal sac.

Spermatic cord   The cord that suspends a testicle within the scrotum and contains a vas deferens, blood vessels, nerves, and the cremaster muscle.

Vas deferens   A tube that conducts sperm from the testicle to the ejaculatory duct of the penis. The plural is "vas deferentia."

Cremaster muscle   The muscle that raises and lowers the testicle in response to temperature change and sexual stimulation.

Germ cell   A cell from which a new organism develops.

Sperm   The male germ cell, which fertilizes the ovum. It's also called "spermatozoon" (singular) and "spermatozoa" (plural).

Spermatozoa   Mature male germ cells, which fertilize the ova. The singular is "spermatozoon."

Androgens   The male sex hormones.

Testosterone   A male steroid sex hormone.

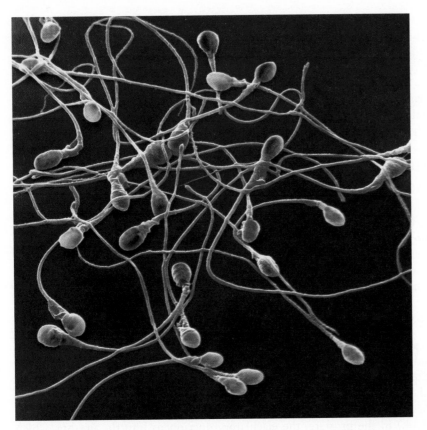

Human Sperm Cells.
This photo shows several spermatozoa, magnified many times. They're actually about 50 microns (0.0005 centimetres) long.

TESTOSTERONE   Testosterone stimulates the prenatal differentiation of male sex organs, the production of sperm, and the development of **secondary sex characteristics** such as the beard, deep voice, and growth of muscle mass.

Secondary sex characteristics Traits that distinguish the genders but are not directly involved in reproduction.

In men, several endocrine glands—the hypothalamus, the pituitary gland, and the testes—keep blood testosterone levels at a more or less even level. This contrasts with the peaks and valleys in female sex hormone levels experienced by women during the phases of the menstrual cycle. Testosterone levels vary slightly with stress, time of day or month, and other factors, but a feedback loop among the endocrine glands keeps them relatively stable.

The testes usually range between 2.5 and 4.5 centimetres in length. The left testicle usually hangs lower, because the left spermatic cord tends to be somewhat longer.

SPERM   Each testicle is divided into many lobes. The lobes are filled with winding **seminiferous tubules**. (See Figure 3.12.) Although packed into a tiny space, these tubules, if placed end to end, would span the length of several football fields. Through a process called **spermatogenesis**, these threadlike structures produce and store hundreds of billions of sperm cells through the course of a man's lifetime.

Seminiferous tubule A tiny, winding, sperm-producing tube located within the lobe of the testis.

Spermatogenesis The process by which sperm cells are produced and developed.

Sperm cells develop through several stages. It takes about 72 days for the testes to manufacture a mature sperm cell. Each sperm cell is about 50 microns (0.0005 centimetres) long, making it one of the smallest cells in the body.

During fertilization, the 23 chromosomes from the father's sperm cell combine with the 23 chromosomes from the mother's ovum, furnishing the standard ensemble of 46 chromosomes in the offspring. Among the 23 chromosomes borne by sperm cells is one sex chromosome—an X sex chromosome or a Y sex chromosome.

Ova contain only X sex chromosomes. The union of an X chromosome and a Y chromosome leads to the development of a male offspring. Two X chromosomes

Epididymis A tube that lies against the back wall of the testicle and serves as a storage facility for the sperm.

Vasectomy A sterilization operation in which the vas deferentia are severed.

Seminal vesicle A small gland that lies behind the bladder and secretes a fluid that combines with sperm in the ejaculatory duct.

Ejaculatory duct A duct formed by the convergence of a vas deferens and a seminal vesicle. Sperm travels via the ejaculatory duct through the prostate gland and into the urethra.

Andropause The so-called male menopause.

Potent Capable of sexual erection and orgasm.

Human Growth Hormone (HGH) A hormone that helps maintain muscle strength and that may help prevent fat buildup.

combine to yield a female offspring. Thus, whether the father contributes an X or a Y chromosome determines the baby's gender.

The testes are veritable dynamos of manufacturing power, churning out about 1000 sperm per second, or about 30 billion—yes, *billion*—per year. Mathematically speaking, 10 to 20 ejaculations hold enough sperm to populate the earth.

Sperm proceed from the seminiferous tubules through an intricate maze of ducts that converge in a single tube called the **epididymis**. The epididymis lies against the back wall of the testicle and serves as a storage facility for the sperm.

The Vas Deferentia

Each epididymis empties into a vas deferens. The vas is a thin, cylindrical tube, about 40 centimetres long, that serves as a conduit for mature sperm. In the scrotum, the vas deferens lies near the skin surface within the spermatic cord. A **vasectomy**, an operation in which the right and left vas deferentia are severed, is therefore a convenient means of sterilization. The vas deferens leaves the scrotum and follows a circuitous path up into the abdominal cavity, then it loops back along the rear surface of the bladder. (See Figure 3.14.)

The Seminal Vesicles

The two **seminal vesicles** are small glands, each about five centimetres long. They lie behind the bladder and open into the **ejaculatory ducts**, where the fluids they secrete combine with sperm. (See Figure 3.14.)

At the base of the bladder, each vas deferens joins a seminal vesicle to form a short ejaculatory duct that runs through the middle of the prostate gland. (See Figure 3.14.) In the prostate, the ejaculatory duct opens into the urethra, which leads to the tip of the penis.

Is There a Male Menopause?

The scientific jury is still out on the existence of a "male menopause," also known as **andropause**. Women encounter relatively sudden age-related declines in sex hormones and fertility during menopause. Men experience gradual declines in testosterone levels as they age, but nothing like the rapid estrogen drops women experience during menopause. Testosterone levels in men begin to fall at about age 30, and continue to decline thereafter.

The drop in testosterone may be connected to a variety of age-related symptoms, including reduced muscle mass and strength, increased body fat, reduced energy levels, lowered fertility, and reduced erectile ability. Despite these testosterone declines, most men remain **potent** throughout their lives. Little is known about the critical levels of testosterone needed to maintain erectile ability. Certain age-related changes, such as reduced muscle mass and strength and increased body fat, may be due not to declining testosterone production, but to other factors associated with aging, such as a gradual loss of **human growth hormone (HGH)**, a hormone that helps maintain muscle strength and that may help prevent fat buildup.

Some experts believe testosterone replacement can help avert problems with sex drive, bone loss, and frailty, in much the same way as estrogen replacement benefits postmenopausal women.

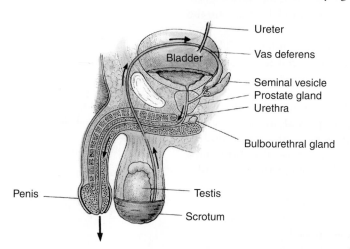

Figure 3.14 Passage of spermatozoa.
Each testicle is divided into lobes that contain threadlike seminiferous tubules. Through spermatogenesis, the tubules produce and store hundreds of billions of sperm over the course of a man's lifetime. During ejaculation, sperm cells travel through the vas deferens, up and over the bladder, into the ejaculatory duct, and through the urethra. Secretions from the seminal vesicles and the bulbourethral glands join with sperm to compose semen.

However, testosterone replacement in men increases the risk of prostate cancer and cardiovascular disease (American Cancer Society, 2009).

The Prostate Gland

The **prostate gland** lies beneath the bladder and is approximately the shape and size of a chestnut (about two centimetres in diameter). It contains muscle fibres and glandular tissue that secrete prostatic fluid. Milky and alkaline, prostatic fluid provides the texture and odour characteristic of the seminal fluid. The alkalinity neutralizes some of the acidity of the vaginal tract, prolonging the lifespan of the sperm as the seminal fluid spreads through the female reproductive system. The prostate is continually active in mature males, though sexual arousal further stimulates secretions. These secretions are conveyed by a sieve-like duct system into the urethra, where they combine with sperm and fluid from the seminal vesicles.

Stimulation of the prostate can heighten sexual arousal and pleasure, making orgasm more intense for some men. Because the prostate is stimulated through the anus, however, many men and their partners are uncomfortable with it.

A vasectomy prevents sperm from reaching the urethra, but does not cut off fluids from the seminal vesicles or the prostate gland. A man who's had a vasectomy emits an ejaculate that appears normal but contains no sperm.

Prostate gland The gland that lies beneath the bladder and secretes prostatic fluid, which gives semen its characteristic odour and texture.

The Cowper's Glands

The **Cowper's glands** lie below the prostate and empty their secretions into the urethra. During sexual arousal, they secrete one or more drops of clear, slippery fluid that appears at the urethral opening.

The functions of this fluid are not entirely understood. It may help buffer the acidity of the male's urethra and lubricate the urethral passageway, easing the passage of seminal fluid. The fluid is not produced in sufficient amounts to play a significant role in lubricating the vagina during intercourse.

Cowper's gland A structure that lies below the prostate and empties its secretions into the urethra during sexual arousal.

Semen

Sperm and the fluids contributed by the seminal vesicles, the prostate gland, and the Cowper's glands make up **semen**, the whitish seminal fluid that is expelled through the tip of the penis during ejaculation. The seminal vesicles secrete about 70% of the fluid that constitutes the ejaculate. The remaining 30% consists of sperm and fluids produced by the prostate gland and the Cowper's glands. Sperm itself accounts for only about 1% of semen volume. This is why men with vasectomies continue to ejaculate about as much semen as before, although their ejaculates are devoid of sperm.

Semen is the medium that carries sperm through much of the male's reproductive system and the female's reproductive tract. Semen contains water, mucus, sugar (fructose), acids, and bases. It activates and nourishes sperm, and the bases help shield sperm from vaginal acidity. The typical ejaculate contains 200 to 400 million sperm cells and ranges from 3 to 5 millilitres in volume. The quantity of semen decreases with age and frequency of ejaculation.

Semen The whitish fluid that constitutes the ejaculate, consisting of sperm and secretions from the seminal vesicles, prostate gland, and Cowper's glands.

Diseases of the Male Urogenital System

Because the organs that make up the urinary and reproductive systems are near one another and share some "piping," they're referred to as the urinogenital or urogenital system. A number of diseases affect the urogenital system. The type of physician who specializes in their diagnosis and treatment is a **urologist**.

Urologist A physician who specializes in the diagnosis and treatment of diseases of the urogenital system.

Urethritis

Urethritis An inflammation of the bladder or urethra.

Men, like women, are subject to bladder and urethral inflammations, which are generally referred to as **urethritis**. The symptoms include frequent urination (urinary frequency), a strong need to urinate (urinary urgency), burning during urination, and a penile discharge. People with symptoms of urinary frequency and urinary urgency feel the pressing need to urinate repeatedly, even though they may have just done so and have but another drop or two to expel.

Preventive measures for urethritis parallel those suggested for cystitis (bladder infection): drinking more water, drinking cranberry juice (125 millilitres 2 or 3 times a day), and lowering intakes of alcohol and caffeine. Cranberry juice is highly acidic, and acid tends to eliminate many of the bacteria that can give rise to urethritis.

Testicular Cancer

Cryptorchidism A condition in which at least one of the testicles fails to descend from the abdomen into the scrotum.

Cancer of the testicles remains a relatively rare form of cancer. In Canada in 2006, there were 844 new cases of testicular cancer, and in 2005, there were 43 deaths as a result of the disease (Canadian Cancer Society, 2010e). Yet it's the most common form of solid-tumour cancer to strike men between the ages of 20 and 34. There's no evidence that testicular cancer results from sexual overactivity or masturbation. Men who had **cryptorchidism** as children (a condition in which at least one testicle fails to descend from the abdomen into the scrotum) stand about a 40 times greater chance of contracting testicular cancer than do men whose testicles descended in childhood.

Although testicular cancer was generally fatal in earlier years, the prognosis today is quite favourable, especially for cases that are detected early. The survival rate among cases detected before the cancer has spread beyond the testes is about 99% (American Cancer Society, 2009). Treatments include surgical removal of the diseased testis, radiation, and chemotherapy.

The surgical removal of a testicle may have profound psychological implications. Some men who have lost a testicle feel less "manly." One option is testicular replacement surgery, which involves implanting a prosthetic testicle into the scrotum. Fears related to sexual performance can engender sexual dysfunctions. From a physiological standpoint, sexual functioning should remain unimpaired, because adequate quantities of testosterone are produced by the remaining testis.

Prostate Disorders

The prostate gland is tiny at birth and grows rapidly at puberty. It may shrink during adulthood, but usually becomes enlarged after age 50.

Benign prostatic hyperplasia (BPH) Enlargement of the prostate gland, due to hormonal changes associated with aging. It's characterized by urinary frequency, urinary urgency, and difficulty starting the flow of urine.

BENIGN PROSTATIC HYPERPLASIA   The prostate gland becomes enlarged in about half of men older than 50, and in 80% of men who reach age 80 (ProstateCare.com, 2006). **Benign prostatic hyperplasia (BPH)** is a noncancerous enlargement of the prostate gland resulting from hormonal changes associated with aging, rather than from other causes such as inflammation due to STIs.

Because the prostate surrounds the upper part of the urethra (see Figure 3.12), enlargement constricts the urethra, causing urinary frequency (including increased frequency of nocturnal urination), urinary urgency, and difficulty starting the flow of urine. Several treatments are available to relieve the pressure on the urethra and increase the flow of urine.

Two types of drug are helpful: 5-ARIs (5-alpha reductase inhibitors) and alpha blockers. An 5-ARI drug inhibits the production of the hormone DHT (a form of testosterone), which causes enlargement of the prostate. By shrinking the

Applied Knowledge

SELF-EXAMINATION OF THE TESTES

Self-examination (see Figure 3.15) is best performed shortly after a warm shower or bath, when the skin of the scrotum is most relaxed. Examine the scrotum for evidence of pea-sized lumps. Gently roll each testicle between your thumb and fingers. Lumps are generally found on the side or front of the testicle.

The presence of a lump is not necessarily a sign of cancer, but it should be promptly reported to a physician for further evaluation. Watch for these warning signals:

- A slight enlargement of one of the testicles.
- A change in the consistency of a testicle.
- A dull ache in the lower abdomen or groin. (Pain may be absent in cancer of the testes, however.)
- A sensation of dragging and heaviness in a testicle.
- A lump on a testicle.

Because early detection is crucial to survival, you should examine yourself monthly following puberty and have regular medical checkups.

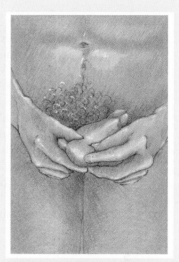

Figure 3.15 Self-examination of the testes.
Gently roll each testicle between your thumb and fingers, examining the scrotum for evidence of pea-shaped lumps.

prostate, a 5-ARI provides long-term improvement of symptoms and reduces the risk of severe urinary retention and the need for surgery. An alpha blocker acts by relaxing the muscles of the bladder, which improves the flow of urine and provides symptom relief.

Part of the prostate is also sometimes surgically removed (ProstateCare.com, 2006).

CANCER OF THE PROSTATE   Prostate cancer is a serious, life-threatening problem among Canadian men. One in 7 men will develop prostate cancer during their lifetimes—most after age 70—and 1 in 27 will die from it. About 24 600 Canadian men were diagnosed with prostate cancer in 2010, and an estimated 3000 men died from the disease (Canadian Cancer Society, 2010e). Prostate cancer involves the growth of malignant prostate tumours that can metastasize to bones and lymph nodes if not detected and treated early.

Men whose diets are rich in animal fats have a substantially higher chance of developing advanced prostate cancer than do men with low intakes of animal fat. The incidence of prostate cancer also increases with age (Tarone et al., 2000). More than 80% of cases of prostate cancer are diagnosed in men who are 65 or older (American Cancer Society, 2009). Genetic factors are also apparently involved. Moreover, testosterone spurs the development of prostate cancer (American Cancer Society, 2009).

The early symptoms of cancer of the prostate may mimic those of benign prostate enlargement—frequency and difficulty with urination. Later symptoms include blood in the urine, pain or burning during urination, and pain in the lower back, pelvis, or upper thighs (American Cancer Society, 2009). Most cases do not have noticeable symptoms in the early stages.

The Canadian Cancer Society (2010e) recommends that men over age 50 talk with their doctors about the potential benefits and risks of testing for prostate cancer. This type of cancer is the second most common cause of cancer death among Canadian men. Men at higher risk, especially those with family backgrounds of prostate cancer or African ancestry, should consider being tested earlier.

To test for prostate cancer, the physician inserts a finger into the rectum and feels for abnormalities in the prostate gland. Unfortunately, many men are reluctant to undergo rectal examinations. Avoidance of—or ignorance of the need for—regular exams is a major contributor to the prostate cancer death rate.

When a cancerous growth is suspected on the basis of a rectal examination or a PSA blood test, further testing is usually done via additional blood tests, ultrasound, or biopsy. Prostate-specific antigen (PSA) is a protein that helps transform a gel-like substance in the prostate gland into a liquid that transports sperm when it's ejaculated. In the diseased or enlarged prostate, PSA seeps into the blood at higher levels, giving higher test readings. Early detection is important, because treatment is most effective before the cancer has spread. About half of Canadian men aged 40 and over have had PSA tests (Gibbons & Waters, 2003).

There is controversy about the benefit of PSA screening for prostate cancer within the general population. Although a PSA test can detect evidence of prostate cancer even among men whose prostates feel normal upon physical examination (Tarone et al., 2000), the overall benefit of PSA testing has been questioned. Two recent studies have suggested that the aggressive treatments that may follow a positive PSA test may do more damage than the cancer itself among older men who are likely to die from other causes if the prostate cancer is left alone (Andriole et al, 2009; Schröder et al., 2009). It's important that every man talk to his doctor about the potential risks and benefits of PSA testing.

The most widely used treatment for prostate cancer is surgical removal of the prostate gland. This may damage surrounding nerves, however, leading to problems with urinary and sexual functioning. Recently introduced surgical techniques tend to spare the surrounding nerves and reduce—but not eliminate—the risk of complications.

Other treatments include radiation, hormone treatment, and anticancer drugs. Androgen-suppression (testosterone–suppression) therapy and anticancer drugs

Innovative Canadian Research

CONCERNS ABOUT PROSTATE SURGERY

For men considering prostate surgery, a major fear is that the surgery will lead to erectile dysfunction. An interview survey in Toronto concluded that "preservation of manhood" was a central concern for men who had experienced sexual dysfunction after prostate surgery (Fergus et al., 2002). The men were concerned about five major issues:

- The need to choose a type of surgery that would increase their chances of survival while minimizing the extent of sexual dysfunction.

- The belief that sexual dysfunction meant loss of their manhood.

- The fear that sexual dysfunction would lead to loss of status, especially among peers.

- Pressure to continue to focus on a high level of giving and receiving sexual pleasure, despite a loss of erectile functioning.

- The need to work to overcome the sexual loss, typically by acknowledging the value of being alive as more important than sexual pleasure. Some men refocused their sexual expression away from penile-vaginal intercourse to other kinds of sexual activities, and toward more intimate emotional relationships with their partners.

may shrink the tumour and relieve pain for long periods. One study found that the combination of radiation and androgen-suppression therapy was more effective than radiation therapy alone (D'Amico et al., 2000).

Men whose prostate glands have been removed are more likely to experience urinary incontinence (loss of control over urination) and sexual dysfunction (trouble attaining erection) than men whose tumours have been treated with radiation (Potosky et al., 2000). In a large-scale study of men who'd had prostate surgery in Quebec, 75% were found to experience erectile dysfunction and 6.6% to experience severe problems with urination (Karakiewicz et al., 2004). After prostate surgery, many men still feel uncomfortable about seeking help for sexual problems. Those with the highest feelings of distress over their loss of erectile function are most likely to seek medical assistance for this problem (Schover et al., 2004).

Because of the side effects of prostate surgery, some physicians recommend a period of watchful waiting involving regular PSA tests, rather than aggressive treatment. Toronto urologist Laurence Klotz found in a trial study that only 25% of prostate cancer patients required radical surgery (Dalby, 2007). A large American study found that with watchful waiting, the great majority of prostate cancer patients were more likely to die from other causes than prostate cancer (Marchione, 2008).

Ross Gray and his colleagues (2000) at the Sunnybrook Health Sciences Centre in Toronto have studied how couples cope when the male partners are diagnosed with prostate cancer. They've found that overall, the couples tend to minimize the impact of the disease, focusing as much as possible on normal living. Over time, as they become more knowledgeable, the couples develop coping strategies to deal with the situation.

Several prostate cancer support groups have formed across Canada for men who are considering their options or undergoing treatment. These groups provide a forum where men can share their experiences, fears, and concerns.

PROSTATITIS   Many infectious agents can inflame the prostate, causing **prostatitis**. The chief symptoms are painful ejaculation and an ache or pain between the scrotum and the anal opening. In a study of men from Canada and several other countries, 19% of those with urinary tract infections reported pain on ejaculation (Nickel et al., 2005). Men whose symptoms were more severe were more likely to experience pain at ejaculation. And 72% of those with painful ejaculation experienced problems with erectile dysfunction.

Prostatitis is usually treated with antibiotics. Although aspirin and ibuprofen may relieve the pain, a man with these symptoms should consult a physician. Painful ejaculation may discourage masturbation or coitus, which is ironic, because regular flushing of the prostate through ejaculation may be helpful in treating prostatitis.

Researchers at Queen's University (Smith et al., 2007) studied the effects of chronic prostatitis on male patients and their partners. These couples experienced more sexual difficulties and psychological depression than the control couples did. The sexual functioning of the males significantly affected the sexual functioning of their partners. Yet the prostatitis did not seem to affect the couples' overall intimate relationships.

Prostatitis   Inflammation of the prostate gland.

Male Sexual Functions

The male sexual functions of erection and ejaculation provide the means for sperm to travel from the male's reproductive tract to the female's. There a sperm cell and an ovum may unite to conceive a new human being. Of course, the natural endowment of reproduction with sensations of pleasure helps ensure that it will take place with or without knowledge of these biological facts.

Erection

Erection   The enlargement and stiffening of the penis as a consequence of its engorgement with blood.

Erection is caused by the engorgement of the penis with blood until the penis grows in size and stiffens. The erect penis is an efficient conduit, or funnel, for depositing sperm deep within the vagina.

In mechanical terms, erection is a hydraulic event. The spongy, cavernous masses of the penis are equipped to hold blood. Filling them with blood causes them to enlarge, much as a sponge swells when it absorbs water. This simple description belies the fact that erection is a remarkable feat of biological engineering that involves the cooperation of the vascular (blood) system and the nervous system.

In a few moments—as quickly as 10 or 15 seconds—the penis can double in length, become firm, and shift from a funnel for passing urine to one that expels semen. Moreover, the bladder is closed off when the male becomes sexually aroused, so semen and urine cannot mix.

The corpora cavernosa are surrounded by a tough, fibrous covering. Just as the rubber of a balloon resists the pressure of pumped-in air, this covering resists expansion, stiffening the penis. The corpus spongiosum, which contains the urethra, also engorges with blood during erection. It doesn't become hard, however, because it lacks the fibrous casing. The penile glans, which is formed by the crowning of the spongiosum at the tip of the penis, turns a dark purplish hue as it becomes engorged, but it doesn't stiffen, either.

Erection is reversed when more blood flows out of the erectile tissue than into it, restoring the pre-arousal circulatory balance and shrinking the spongy masses. Loss of erection occurs when sexual stimulation ceases, or when the body returns to a (sexual) resting state after orgasm. Loss of erection can also occur in response to anxiety or perceived threats (Janssen, 2006; Janssen et al., 2006). Such loss can be abrupt, as when a man in the throes of passion suddenly hears a noise that sounds like an intruder. A man who's afraid he'll be unable to perform successfully may experience **performance anxiety**, which can prevent him from obtaining or maintaining an erection.

Performance anxiety   Feelings of dread and foreboding in connection with sexual activity (or any other activity that might be judged by another person).

Men have nocturnal erections every 90 minutes or so as they sleep. These generally occur during rapid eye movement (REM) sleep. REM sleep is associated with dreaming. It's so named because the sleeper's eyes dart about rapidly under their closed eyelids during this stage.

Spinal Reflexes and Sexual Response

Men may become sexually aroused by a range of stimuli, including tactile stimulation by their partners, visual stimulation (e.g., viewing photos of nudes on the internet), and sexual fantasies. Regardless of the source of stimulation, men's sexual responses—erection and ejaculation—occur by reflex.

Sexual reflexes are automatic, unlearned responses to sexual stimulation. Examples in women include vaginal lubrication and orgasm. We needn't *try* to become aroused—we need only expose ourselves to sexual stimulation, and allow our reflexes to do the job.

Men cannot will themselves to have erections. People do not control their sexual reflexes voluntarily, the way they might lift their arms, but they can set the stage for these reflexes to occur by seeking sexual stimulation. Efforts to control sexual responses consciously, by force of will, can backfire, making it more difficult to become aroused (e.g., to attain erection or vaginal lubrication).

The reflexes governing erection and ejaculation are controlled within the spinal cord. They're therefore called spinal reflexes. Erectile responses to direct stimulation, such as touching or licking, involve a simple spinal reflex that requires no

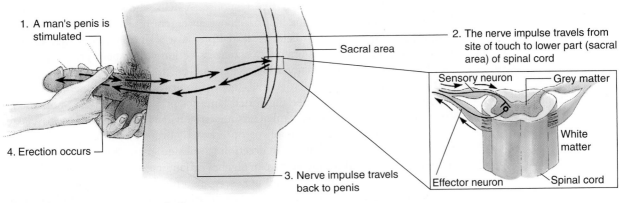

1. A man's penis is stimulated

4. Erection occurs

Sacral area

3. Nerve impulse travels back to penis

2. The nerve impulse travels from site of touch to lower part (sacral area) of spinal cord

Sensory neuron — Grey matter

White matter

Effector neuron — Spinal cord

Figure 3.16 The independent nature of reflexes.
Reflexes need not involve the brain, although messages to the brain may make us aware that reflexes are occurring.
Reflexes are the products of "local government" in the spine.

direct participation by the brain. (See Figure 3.16.) Erections can be initiated by the brain, such as when a man has sexual fantasies or catches a glimpse of an attractive person; in this case, stimulation from the brain travels to the spinal cord, where the erectile reflex is triggered.

Tactile stimulation (touching) of the penis and nearby areas (lower abdomen, scrotum, inner thighs) causes sensory neurons to transmit nerve messages (signals) to an erection centre in the lower back, in an area of the spinal cord called the **sacrum**. The sacral erection centre controls reflexive erections—that is, erections that occur in response to direct stimulation of the penis and nearby areas. When direct penile stimulation occurs, messages in the form of nerve impulses are received by this erection centre, which in turn sends impulses to the genitalia via nerves that serve the penis. These impulses cause arteries carrying blood to the corpora cavernosa and corpus spongiosum to dilate, so more blood flows into them, causing erection.

The sacral erection centre makes it possible for men whose spinal cords have been injured or severed above the centre to achieve erections (and ejaculate) in response to direct tactile stimulation of the penis. Erection occurs even though their injuries prevent nerve signals from reaching their brains. Because of the lack of communication between the genital organs and the brain, there are no sensations, but many spinal-cord-injured men report that sex remains psychologically pleasurable because they can observe their partners' responses.

THE ROLE OF THE BRAIN   If direct penile stimulation triggers erection at the spinal level, what's the brain's role? It may seem that the penis has a mind of its own sometimes, but the brain does play an important role in regulating sexual response.

Tactile (touch) stimulation of the penis may trigger erection through the spinal cord, but sexual sensations are then normally relayed to the brain, which generally results in pleasure and perhaps a decision to focus on erotic stimulation. The sight of one's partner, erotic fantasies, memories, and so forth can result in messages being sent by the brain through the spinal cord to the arteries servicing the penis, maintaining or strengthening the erection.

When the brain originates messages that trigger the erectile reflex, it transmits nerve impulses to a second erection centre, located higher than the first, in the lumbar region of the spinal cord in the upper back. This higher spinal erection centre serves as a switchboard between the brain and the penis, allowing perceptual, cognitive, and emotional responses to make contributions. When the nerve pathways between the brain and the upper spinal cord are blocked or severed, men cannot achieve erections solely in response to mental stimulation.

Sacrum   The thick, triangular bone located near the bottom of the spinal column.

The brain can also stifle sexual response. A man who's highly anxious about his sexual abilities may be unable to achieve an erection, even with intense penile stimulation. Or a man who believes sexual pleasure is sinful or dirty may be filled with anxiety and guilt, and unable to achieve erection with a partner.

In some males, especially adolescents, the erectile reflex is so easily tripped that incidental rubbing of the genitals against their own undergarments, the sight of attractive passersby, or fleeting sexual fantasies produce erections. Spontaneous erections may occur under embarrassing circumstances, such as before classes change in middle or high school, or on a beach. In an effort to distract himself from erotic fantasies and allow an erection to subside, many a male adolescent has desperately renewed his interest in an algebra or language textbook before the class bell has rung. (A well-placed towel may serve in a pinch on the beach.)

As men mature, they need more penile stimulation to achieve full erection. Partners of men in their thirties and forties shouldn't feel that their attractiveness has waned if their lovers no longer have instant "no-hands" erections when they disrobe. It takes men longer to obtain erection as they age, and direct stimulation becomes more important.

THE ROLE OF THE AUTONOMIC NERVOUS SYSTEM   Although stimulation that brings about an erection can originate in the brain, this doesn't mean erection is a voluntary response, like raising your arm. Whatever the original or dominant source of stimulation—direct penile stimulation or sexual fantasy—erection remains an unlearned, automatic reflex.

Automatic responses such as erections involve the division of the nervous system called the **autonomic nervous system (ANS)**. "Autonomic" means "automatic." The ANS controls automatic bodily processes such as heartbeat, pupil dilation, respiration, and digestion. In contrast, voluntary movement (such as raising an arm) is under the control of the **somatic** division of the nervous system.

The ANS has two branches, the sympathetic and the parasympathetic. These branches have largely opposing effects; when they're activated at the same time, their effects balance out to some degree. In general, the **sympathetic** branch is in command during processes that involve a release of bodily energy from stored reserves, such as running, performing some other athletic task, or being gripped by fear or anxiety. The sympathetic branch also governs general mobilization of the body, by increasing the heart rate and respiration rate in response to threat, for example.

The **parasympathetic** branch is most active during processes that restore reserves of energy, such as digestion. When we experience fear or anxiety, the sympathetic branch of the ANS quickens the heart rate. When we relax, the parasympathetic branch curbs the heart rate. The parasympathetic branch activates digestive processes, but the sympathetic branch inhibits digestive activity. Because the sympathetic branch is in command when we feel fear or anxiety, such emotions can inhibit the activity of the parasympathetic system, thereby slowing down the digestive process and possibly causing indigestion.

The divisions of the autonomic nervous system play different roles in sexual arousal and response. The nerves that cause penile arteries to dilate during erection belong to the parasympathetic branch of the autonomic nervous system. The parasympathetic system therefore largely governs erection. The nerves governing ejaculation, however, belong to the sympathetic branch. One implication of this division of neural responsibility is that intense fear or anxiety, which involves sympathetic nervous system activity, may inhibit erection by counteracting the activity of the parasympathetic nervous system. Because sympathetic arousal is involved in triggering the ejaculatory reflex, anxiety or fear may also accelerate ejaculation, causing **premature ejaculation**. Intense emotions such as fear and anxiety can thus lead to problems in achieving or maintaining erection, as well as causing hasty ejaculation.

Autonomic nervous system (ANS)   The division of the nervous system that regulates automatic bodily processes, such as heartbeat, pupil dilation, respiration, and digestion.

Somatic nervous system   The division of the nervous system that regulates voluntary movements, such as wiggling a toe or waving an arm.

Sympathetic nervous system   The branch of the ANS most active during emotional responses that draw on the body's reserves of energy, such as fear and anxiety. The sympathetic ANS largely controls ejaculation.

Parasympathetic nervous system   The branch of the ANS most active during processes that restore the body's reserves of energy, such as digestion. The parasympathetic ANS largely controls erection.

Premature ejaculation   A sexual dysfunction in which the male persistently ejaculates too early to afford the couple adequate sexual gratification. (Yes, what is on time in one relationship may be considered premature—or late—in another.)

Because erection seems spontaneous at times, and because it often occurs when the man would rather it didn't, the penis may seem to have a mind of its own. Despite this common folk belief, however, the penis possesses no guiding intelligence.

ERECTILE ABNORMALITIES   Some men find that their erect penises are slightly curved or bent. Some degree of curvature is perfectly normal, but men with **Peyronie's disease** have excessive curvature that can make erection painful and enjoyment of coitus difficult. The condition is caused by a buildup of fibrous tissue in the penile shaft. Although some cases of Peyronie's disease appear to clear up on their own, most require medical attention.

Some men experience erections that persist for hours or days. This condition is called **priapism**, after Priapus of Greek myth, the son of Dionysus and Aphrodite who personified male procreative power. Priapism is often caused by leukemia, sickle-cell anemia, or diseases of the spinal cord, although in some cases the cause remains unknown. Priapism occurs when the mechanisms that drain the blood that makes the penis erect are damaged, and cannot return the blood to the circulatory system. Priapism may become a medical emergency, because erection prolonged beyond six hours can starve penile tissues of oxygen, leading to tissue deterioration. Medical intervention in the form of drugs or surgery may be required to reverse the condition and allow blood to drain from the penis.

Ejaculation

Ejaculation, like erection, is a spinal reflex. It's triggered when sexual stimulation reaches a critical point or threshold. Ejaculation generally occurs together with **orgasm**, the sudden muscle contractions that occur at the peak of sexual excitement and result in abrupt release of the sexual tension that has built up during arousal. Orgasm is accompanied by subjective sensations that are generally intensely pleasurable. Ejaculation, however, is simply the expulsion of semen from the tip of the penis. Orgasm and ejaculation are not synonymous, nor do they always occur simultaneously. For example, a **paraplegic** can ejaculate if the area of the lower spinal cord that controls ejaculation is intact. He doesn't experience the subjective aspects of orgasm, however, because the sensations of orgasm don't reach his brain.

Conversely, a prepubescent boy may experience orgasms even though he emits no ejaculate. Orgasms without ejaculate are termed "dry orgasms." Boys do not begin to produce seminal fluid (and sperm) until puberty. A mature man, too, can experience dry orgasms. These can take the form of "little orgasms" preceding a larger orgasm, or they can follow "wet orgasms" when sexual stimulation is continued but seminal fluids have not been replenished.

Ejaculation occurs in two stages. The first stage, often called the **emission stage**, involves contractions of the prostate, the seminal vesicles, and the upper part of the vas deferens (the **ampulla**). The force of these contractions propels seminal fluid into the prostatic part of the urethral tract, a small tube called the **urethral bulb**, which balloons out as muscles close at either end, trapping the semen. At this point, the man perceives that orgasm is inevitable. Masters and Johnson (1966) called this feeling a sense of ejaculatory inevitability. Men might colloquially describe the feeling as being about to "come." The man feels that a point of no return has been passed and nothing can prevent ejaculation.

The second stage, often referred to as the **expulsion stage**, involves the propulsion of the seminal fluid through the urethra and out of the urethral opening at the tip of the penis. In this stage, muscles at the base of the penis and elsewhere contract rhythmically, forcefully expelling semen. The second stage is generally accompanied by the highly pleasurable sensations of orgasm.

In ejaculation, the seminal fluid is released from the urethral bulb and expelled by forceful contractions of the pelvic muscles that surround the urethral channel and the crura of the penis. During ejaculation, the bladder is closed off so urine

Peyronie's disease   An abnormal condition characterized by an excessive curvature of the penis, which can make erection painful.

Priapism   Persistent and painful erection of the penis.

Orgasm   The climax of sexual excitement.

Paraplegic   A person with sensory and motor paralysis of the lower half of the body.

Emission stage   The first phase of ejaculation, which involves contractions of the prostate gland, the seminal vesicles, and the upper part of the vas deferens.

Ampulla   A sac or dilated part of a tube or canal.

Urethral bulb   The small tube that makes up the prostatic part of the urethral tract. It balloons out as muscles close at either end, trapping semen prior to ejaculation.

Expulsion stage   The second stage of ejaculation, during which muscles at the base of the penis and elsewhere contract rhythmically, forcefully expelling semen and generally providing pleasurable sensations.

cannot escape. The first few contractions are most intense, and occur at 0.8-second intervals. Subsequent contractions lessen in intensity, and the intervals between them gradually increase. Seminal fluid is expelled in spurts during the first few contractions. The contractions are so powerful that seminal fluid may be propelled as far as 30 to 60 centimetres, according to observations made by Masters and Johnson. Some men, however, report that semen travels but a few centimetres, or just oozes from the penile opening. The force of the expulsion varies with the condition of the man's prostate, his general health, and his age. There's some correspondence between the force of the expulsion and the pleasure of orgasm. That is, more intense orgasms, psychologically speaking, often accompany more forceful ejaculations.

How long the male is sexually aroused prior to ejaculation influences how much ejaculate he produces. A longer period of arousal usually results in a greater volume of ejaculate and greater sperm concentration (Pound et al., 2002).

Although ejaculation occurs by reflex, a man can delay ejaculation by maintaining the level of sexual stimulation below the critical threshold, or "point of no return." Men who suffer from premature ejaculation have been successfully treated in programs that train them to recognize their points of no return and learn how to maintain sexual stimulation below those points.

Retrograde ejaculation
Ejaculation in which the ejaculate empties into the bladder.

RETROGRADE EJACULATION   Some men experience **retrograde ejaculation**, in which the ejaculate empties into the bladder rather than being expelled from the body. During normal ejaculation, an external sphincter opens, allowing seminal fluid to pass out of the body, while an internal sphincter closes off the opening to the bladder, preventing seminal fluid from backing up into the bladder. In retrograde ejaculation, the actions of these two sphincters are reversed. The external sphincter remains closed, preventing expulsion of the seminal fluid, while the internal sphincter opens, allowing the ejaculate to empty into the bladder. The result is a dry orgasm. No ejaculate is apparent, because semen has backed up into the bladder.

Retrograde ejaculation may be caused by prostate surgery (though far less often these days), drugs such as tranquillizers, certain illnesses, and accidents.

Retrograde ejaculation is usually harmless in itself, because the seminal fluid is later discharged with urine. Infertility can result, however, and there may be some changes in the sensations associated with orgasm. Persistent dry orgasms should be medically evaluated, since their underlying causes may threaten a man's health.

Summing Up

The external female sexual structures are collectively known as the vulva. They consist of the mons veneris, the labia majora and minora, the clitoris, the vestibule, and the vaginal opening.

The structures that underlie the external female sex organs include the vestibular bulbs, Bartholin's glands, the sphincters, the clitoral crura, and the pubococcygeus (PC) muscle.

The internal female sex organs—or female reproductive system—include the innermost parts of the vagina, the cervix, the uterus, the ovaries, and the fallopian tubes.

The G spot—an allegedly distinct area of the vagina within the anterior wall—may have special erotic significance. Some researchers suggest that prolonged stimulation of this spot produces an orgasm characterized by intense pleasure and, in some women, a type of ejaculation. The nature of this ejaculate remains uncertain.

Regular pelvic examinations are essential for early detection of problems involving the reproductive tract.

In some cultures, the breasts are viewed merely as biological instruments for feeding infants. In our culture, however, they have taken on erotic significance.

Breast cancer is the second leading cancer killer in women, after lung cancer. Women with breast cancer will have lumps in their breasts, but most breast lumps are benign.

Menstruation is the cyclical bleeding that stems from the shedding of the endometrium when a reproductive cycle has not led to fertilization of an ovum. The menstrual cycle is regulated by estrogen and progesterone.

The menstrual cycle involves finely tuned relationships among the hypothalamus, pituitary gland, ovaries, and uterus.

The menstrual cycle has four stages, or phases: the proliferative, ovulatory, secretory, and menstrual phases.

Couples are less likely to initiate sexual activity during menstruation than during any other phase of the woman's cycle.

Menopause, the cessation of menstruation, most commonly occurs between the ages of 46 and 50. Estrogen deficiency in menopause may give rise to night sweats, hot flashes, hot flushes, cold sweats, dry skin, loss of breast tissue, and decreased vaginal lubrication. For most women, menopausal problems are mild.

Most women experience some discomfort prior to or during menstruation. Dysmenorrhea is the most common menstrual problem, and pelvic cramps are the most common symptom.

Women with persistent menstrual problems may benefit from a number of active coping strategies for handling menstrual distress.

The external male sex organs include the penis and the scrotum.

Semen and urine pass out of the penis through the urethral opening. The penis contains cylinders that fill with blood and stiffen during sexual arousal.

Circumcision—the surgical removal of the prepuce—has historically been carried out for religious and hygienic reasons.

The scrotum is the pouch of loose skin that contains the testes. Each testicle is held in place by a spermatic cord, which contains the vas deferens and the cremaster muscle.

The internal male sex organs consist of the testes, a system of tubes and ducts that conduct sperm, and organs that nourish and activate sperm.

The testes secrete male sex hormones (androgens) and produce germ cells (sperm).

The hypothalamus, pituitary gland, and testes keep blood testosterone at a more or less constant level through a hormonal negative feedback loop.

Sperm is produced by seminiferous tubules. It matures in the epididymis, where it's stored.

Each epididymis empties into a vas deferens that conducts sperm over the bladder.

The seminal vesicles are glands that open into the ejaculatory ducts, where the fluids they secrete combine with and nourish sperm.

The prostate gland secretes fluid that accounts for semen's characteristic texture and odour.

During sexual arousal, the Cowper's glands secrete a drop or so of clear, slippery fluid that appears at the urethral opening.

Sperm and the fluids contributed by the seminal vesicles, the prostate gland, and the Cowper's glands combine to form semen, the whitish fluid that is expelled through the tip of the penis during ejaculation.

Men, like women, are subject to bladder and urethral inflammation, which is generally referred to as urethritis.

Cancer of the testes is the most common form of solid-tumour cancer to strike young men between the ages of 20 and 34.

The prostate gland generally becomes enlarged in men past the age of 50. Prostate cancer involves the growth of malignant prostate tumours that can metastasize to bones and lymph nodes. The chief symptoms of prostatitis are painful ejaculation and an ache or pain between the scrotum and the anal opening.

Erection is the process by which the penis becomes engorged with blood, increases in size, and stiffens.

Erection and ejaculation occur by reflex. Although erection is a reflex, penile sensations are relayed to the brain, where they generally result in pleasure. Erection and ejaculation also involve the autonomic nervous system (ANS). The parasympathetic branch of the ANS largely governs erection, whereas the sympathetic branch largely controls ejaculation.

Ejaculation is triggered when sexual stimulation reaches a critical threshold. Ejaculation usually (though not always) occurs with orgasm, but the terms are not synonymous.

In retrograde ejaculation, the ejaculate empties into the bladder, rather than being expelled from the body.

Test Yourself

Multiple-Choice Questions

1. The female external sex organs are called the:
   (a) Uterus.
   (b) Ovaries.
   (c) Vulva.
   (d) Cervix.

2. The only organ whose sole function is to provide sexual pleasure is the:
   (a) Penis.
   (b) Clitoris.
   (c) Vagina.
   (d) Mons.

continued

3. **Which of the following is not a recommended way to prevent vaginitis?**
(a) Wearing pants that fit loosely in the crotch.
(b) Wearing nylon underwear.
(c) Washing the vulva with a mild soap.
(d) Avoiding foods high in sugar and refined carbohydrates.

4. **The two pituitary hormones involved in the regulation of the menstrual cycle are:**
(a) GnRH and estrogen.
(b) Oxytocin and prolactin.
(c) FSH and LH.
(d) LH and testosterone.

5. **During menopause, lower levels of _____ may cause hot flashes and other physical symptoms.**
(a) prolactin
(b) oxytocin
(c) androgen
(d) estrogen

6. **The penis contains:**
(a) Bone.
(b) Muscle.
(c) Spongy material.
(d) All of the above.

7. **Sperm cells are carried out of the testicles through the:**
(a) Seminiferous tubules.
(b) Dartos muscles.
(c) Vas deferentia.
(d) Cremasteric tubes.

8. **Surgical removal of the foreskin is known as:**
(a) Excision.
(b) Infibulation.
(c) Incision.
(d) Circumcision.

9. **The purpose of testicular self-examination is to detect _____ in its early stages.**
(a) AIDS
(b) infertility
(c) cancer
(d) erectile dysfunction

10. **_____ is the most common form of cancer among Canadian men.**
(a) Prostate cancer
(b) Testicular cancer
(c) Penile cancer
(d) Inguinal cancer

Answers to the "Test Yourself" questions in each chapter are found on page 495.

Critical Thinking

1. Many people grow up with negative perceptions of menstruation. What negative messages did you hear as a child or adolescent? Who did you hear these messages from? Were any of these messages specific to your culture or ethnic group?

2. Female genital cutting or mutilation is a common practice in some countries, but illegal in Canada. To what extent do you think Canadians should try to persuade these countries to ban this practice?

3. Some people seem to be fixated on breast and penis size as measures of sexual attractiveness. Are these people losing sight of more important things? For you, what are the most important things that make a person sexually appealing?

4. Would you have a male child circumcised? Why or why not?

MySearchLab

MySearchLab offers extensive help to students with their writing and research project and provides round-the-clock access to credible and reliable source material. Take a tour at **www.mysearchlab.com**.

CHAPTER FOUR

Sexual Arousal and Response

Sex as a Traffic Stopper.
A lingerie model at the Galeries Lafayette, a Paris department store, checks out passersby—and vice versa. Scantily clad models used to stop traffic outside the store, until the store received complaints that they were being insensitive to women. Clearly, visual cues can be sexual turn-ons!

Judging by media, advertising, and pop culture images of what makes a person sexy, you might assume that human beings are quite uniform in what turns them on sexually. In reality, people vary greatly in the cues that excite them sexually and in the frequency with which they experience sexual thoughts and feelings.

In this chapter we look at factors that contribute to sexual arousal and processes related to sexual response. Because we experience the world largely through our senses, we begin the chapter by focusing on the role of the senses in sexual arousal.

The Senses and Sexual Arousal

We experience the world around us through our senses—vision, hearing, smell, taste, and the skin senses, which include that all-important sense of touch. Each of the senses plays some role in sparking sexual arousal.

Sight: The Better to See You With

Visual cues can be sexual turn-ons. We may be turned on by the sight of a lover in the nude, disrobing, or dressed in evening wear. Lingerie enhances women's sex appeal by strategically concealing and revealing body parts. Men appear to be more responsive to visual stimuli than women, although women are also clearly attuned to appealing eyefuls (Rupp & Wallen, 2009).

One study found that women tend to dress and ornament themselves in more appealing ways when they're in the fertile phases of their ovulatory cycles (Haselton et al., 2007). Forty-two subjects were asked to determine which photos showed women "trying to look more attractive." Most of the photos they identified were of women in their fertile (59.5%) phases, rather than their luteal (40.5%) phases. Other research shows that men's "mate-retention efforts" increase as their partners approach ovulation; perhaps the men are signaled, at least in part, by their partners' appearance (Haselton et al., 2007).

Science has endorsed what lingerie companies have known for decades—that women seeking male interest might do well to clothe themselves in red. Research shows that men are more likely to consider women dressed in red as more sexually desirable and attractive, although men seem to be unaware of this colourful effect (Elliot & Niesta, 2008). It's interesting to note that the males in the study did not rate red-robed women as kinder, more intelligent, or more likeable.

Some couples find it arousing to observe themselves making love in a mirror or on videotape. Some people find sexually explicit movies arousing. Others are bored or offended by them. Although both males and females can be sexually aroused by visually mediated erotica (a technical term for "porn flicks"), and some women enjoy it, men tend to be more interested in it than women are (Hamann et al., 2004; Schaller & Træen, 2008).

Subconscious Attraction.
How much sexual communication occurs below the level of conscious awareness? Research suggests that underarm secretions may make people more sexually attractive, even when others are unaware of sensing them. Are they drawn to each other's personal traits or to their pheromones?

Smell: Does the Nose Know Best?

Although the sense of smell plays a lesser role in governing sexual arousal in humans than in lower mammals, our body's natural odours can play a role in sexual attraction and arousal. Western society has become preoccupied (some would say obsessed) with personal cleanliness. Television commercials continually encourage us to mask bodily scents by using soaps, deodorants, and perfumes or colognes. Indeed, we are told that the artificial scents in a spray or soap can make us more sexually appealing. Unilever has been very successful in selling its Axe body spray to young men. Its advertisements unabashedly imply that young men who use the product attract women who are aroused by the scent. Or consider the popular television commercial in which the handsome, towel-clad Isaiah Mustafa says, "Hello, ladies. Look at your man. Now back to me . . . . Sadly, he isn't me. But if he stopped using ladies' scented body wash and switched to Old Spice, he could smell like he's me."

The propensity to find even a whiff of underarm odour or naturally occurring genital smells offensive likely reflects cultural conditioning, rather than biological predisposition. In some societies, genital secretions are considered **aphrodisiacs**.

PHEROMONES For centuries, people have searched for a love potion—a magical formula that could make others fall in love with or be strongly attracted to them. Some scientists suggest that such potions may already exist in the form of chemical secretions known as **pheromones**. Pheromones are odourless chemicals that many animals detect through a sixth sense—the vomeronasal organ (VNO). People possess VNOs in the mucous lining of the nose (Rodriguez et al., 2000). Infants apparently use pheromones to recognize their mothers, and adults might respond to them in seeking a mate (Martins et al., 2005). Male rodents, such as mice, are extremely sensitive to several kinds of pheromones (Leinders-Zufall et al., 2000).

Only a few years ago, most researchers didn't believe pheromones played a role in human behaviour, but today the issue has attracted new interest. In a typical study, Winnifred Cutler and her colleagues (1998) asked heterosexual men to wear a suspected male pheromone, and a control group to wear a placebo. The men wearing the pheromone increased the frequency of sexual intercourse with their female partners, but did not increase the frequency of masturbation. The researchers concluded that the substance increased the sexual attractiveness of the men to their partners, although they did not claim that it directly stimulated sexual behaviour.

In a double-blind experiment, 36 university women were randomly assigned to wear either a placebo or a perfume laced with a suspected pheromone extracted from their underarm secretions (McCoy & Pitino, 2002). The women recorded their sexual behaviours over three menstrual cycles (12 weeks). Three-quarters (74%) of the

CRITICAL THINKING QUESTIONS

Do you think there are differences between women and men in terms of the roles vision, smell, touch, taste, and hearing play in sexual arousal?

Aphrodisiac Any drug or other agent that's sexually arousing or that increases sexual desire.

Pheromones Chemical substances that are secreted externally by certain animals and that convey information to, or produce specific responses in, other members of the same species.

CRITICAL THINKING QUESTIONS

If pheromones were definitively shown to increase sexual attractiveness, would it be ethical to wear them on a date? Is wearing perfume or cologne the same as wearing a pheromone?

The Nose and Sexual Orientation.
Research by Yolanda Martins, George Preti, Charles J. Wysocki, and their colleagues (2005) suggests that gay men prefer the body odours of other gay men to those of heterosexuals and lesbians. Heterosexual males seem least likely to prefer the body odours of gay males.

women who wore the suspected pheromone showed significant increases in frequency of sexual intercourse, sleeping next to a partner, formal dates, and kissing, petting, and other displays of affection; only one-quarter (23%) of the women who wore the placebo showed such increases. Perhaps the suspected pheromone increased the women's attractiveness to men.

MENSTRUAL SYNCHRONY Research by several investigators suggests that exposure to other women's sweat can modify a woman's menstrual cycle. In one study, women exposed to other women's underarm secretions, which contained steroids that may function as pheromones, showed converging shifts in their menstrual cycles (Bartoshuk & Beauchamp, 1994; Preti et al., 1986). Similar synchronization of menstrual cycles has been observed among women who share dormitory rooms. In another study, 80% of the women who dabbed their upper lips with an extract of perspiration from other women began to menstruate in sync with the cycles of the donors after about three menstrual cycles (Cutler, 1999). A control group, whose members dabbed their lips with alcohol, showed no changes in their menstrual cycles.

BODY ODOURS AND SEXUAL ORIENTATION There's reason to believe body odours play a role in the selection of sex partners (Preti et al., 2003; Wyatt, 2003). Martins, Preti, Wysocki, et al., (2005) hypothesized that preferences for axillary (underarm) odours would be related to sexual orientation. They collected samples of axillary odours from 24 volunteers—six exclusively male heterosexual and six exclusively female heterosexual, and six exclusively gay male and six exclusively lesbian, according to the Kinsey heterosexuality–homosexuality scale. The study produced a number of interesting findings:

- Heterosexual males, heterosexual females, and lesbians preferred axillary odours taken from heterosexual males over those taken from gay males.
- Gay males preferred axillary odours taken from other gay males.
- Heterosexual males, heterosexual females, and lesbians preferred axillary odours taken from lesbians over those taken from gay males.
- Heterosexual males preferred axillary odours taken from lesbians over those taken from gay males.

The researchers suggest that gay males and lesbians may produce axillary odours that can be distinguished from those of heterosexuals. It also appears that gay males may perceive these typical odorants differently than heterosexual males do. The few studies that have investigated the relationships between body odours and sexual orientation indicate that gay males are most likely to be attracted to the body odours of other gay males, and heterosexual males are least likely to be attracted to the body odours of gay males.

Touch: Sex as a Touching Experience

The sense of touch has the most direct effects on sexual arousal and response. Any region of that sensitive layer we refer to as skin can become eroticized. The touch of your lover's hand upon your cheek or your lover's gentle massage of your shoulders or back can be sexually stimulating.

EROGENOUS ZONES **Erogenous zones** are parts of the body that are especially sensitive to tactile sexual stimulation—to strokes and other caresses. **Primary erogenous zones** are erotically sensitive because they are richly endowed with nerve endings. **Secondary erogenous zones** are parts of the body that become erotically sensitized through experience.

Erogenous zones Parts of the body that are especially sensitive to tactile sexual stimulation. "Erogenous" is derived from roots that mean "giving birth to erotic sensations."

Primary erogenous zones Erogenous zones that are particularly sensitive because they are richly endowed with nerve endings.

Secondary erogenous zones Parts of the body that become erotically sensitized through experience.

Primary erogenous zones include the genitals; the inner thighs, perineum, buttocks, and anus; the breasts (especially the nipples); the ears (particularly the earlobes); the mouth, lips, and tongue; the neck; the navel; and, yes, the armpits. Preferences vary somewhat from person to person, reflecting possible biological, attitudinal, and experiential differences.

Areas that are exquisitely sensitive for some people may produce virtually no reaction, or even discomfort, in others. Some women, for example, report little sensation when their breasts are stroked or kissed, while others find it very pleasurable. Many men are uncomfortable when their nipples are caressed. On the other hand (or foot), some people find the areas between their toes sensitive to erotic stimulation, and enjoy keeping toeholds on their partners during sexual activity.

Secondary erogenous zones become eroticized through association with sexual stimulation. For example, a woman might become sexually aroused when her lover gently caresses her shoulders, because such caresses have been incorporated as a regular feature of the couple's lovemaking. A man might become sexually aroused when his partner strokes his chest, because he has come to associate this caress as a prelude to more direct sexual interaction.

A Touching Experience.
The sense of touch is intimately connected with sexual experience. The touch of a lover's hand on the cheek, or gentle massage, can be sexually stimulating. Certain parts of the body—called erogenous zones—have special sexual significance because of their response to erotic stimulation.

Taste: On Savoury Sex

Some people are sexually aroused by the taste of genital secretions, such as vaginal secretions or seminal fluid. We don't know, however, whether these secretions are laced with chemicals that have biologically arousing effects, or whether arousal reflects the meaning these secretions may have for the individuals. That is, we may learn to become aroused by, or to seek out, flavours or odours we have associated with sexual pleasure.

Others are turned off by the taste or odour of these secretions.

Hearing: The Better to Hear You With

The sense of hearing also provides an important medium for sexual arousal and response. Like visual and olfactory cues, sounds can be turn-ons or turn-offs. The sounds of your lover—whether whispers, moans of pleasure, or animated sounds that may attend orgasm—can be arousing during the heat of passion.

For some people, key words or vocal intonations may become as arousing as direct stimulation of an erogenous zone. Many people are aroused when their lovers "talk dirty"—sexually explicit talk spurs their sexual arousal. Others find it vulgar.

Music itself can contribute to sexual arousal. Music can relax us and put us in the mood or evoke powerful associations—"They're playing our song!" Many couples find background music atmospheric, a vital accoutrement of lovemaking.

Aphrodisiacs, Anaphrodisiacs, and Psychoactive Drugs

An aphrodisiac is a substance that arouses or increases one's capacity for sexual desire or response. However, the belief that a substance has sexually stimulating effects may itself inspire sexual excitement. In other words, the effects of aphrodisiacs are subject to the **placebo effect** (Downs & Nazario, 2003). That is, a person who consumes a supposed aphrodisiac and feels sexually aroused may attribute the turn-on to the effects of the substance, when in reality it has no direct physiological effect on sexual desire or arousal. In other words, the person anticipates becoming sexually aroused, and it's the expectation of arousal, rather than the substance itself, that results in the perception of increased sexual desire or response.

Foods that in some way resemble genitals have now and then been considered aphrodisiacs. These include oysters, clams, bulls' testicles ("prairie oysters"), tomatoes, and phallic items such as celery stalks, bananas, and even ground-up reindeer antlers, elephant tusks, and rhinoceros horns (which is one derivation of the slang term "horny"). Sadly, myths about the sexually arousing properties of substances extracted from rhinoceroses and elephants are contributing to the rapidly diminishing numbers of these animals.

Drugs and psychoactive substances may have certain effects on sexual arousal and response. The drug arginine, an amino acid extracted from the African yohimbe tree, does stimulate blood flow to the genitals. However, its effects are limited and unreliable (Downs & Nazario, 2003).

Amyl nitrate (in the form of "snappers" or "poppers") is sometimes used, mostly by gay men, but also by some heterosexuals, in the belief that it heightens sensations of arousal and orgasm. Poppers dilate blood vessels in the brain and genitals, producing sensations of warmth in the pelvis and possibly facilitating erection and prolonging orgasm. Amyl nitrate does have some legitimate medical uses, such as helping reduce heart pain (angina) among cardiac patients. It's inhaled from ampoules that pop open for rapid use when heart pain occurs. However, poppers can cause dizziness, fainting, and migraine-type headaches. They should be taken only under a doctor's care for a legitimate medical need, not to intensify sexual sensations.

The drug Viagra was originally developed as a treatment for angina (heart pain), because it was thought to increase blood flow to the heart. It does so, modestly. However, it's more effective at dilating blood vessels in the genital organs, thereby facilitating vasocongestion and erection in the male. Viagra and the similar drug Cialis are treatments for male erectile dysfunction. Can Viagra and Cialis be considered aphrodisiacs? If we use a strict definition of "aphrodisiac," the answer is no. Although these drugs facilitate erection, they do not by themselves trigger sexual arousal. If the man is not sexually aroused, Viagra or Cialis will not produce an erection.

But certain drugs do appear to have aphrodisiac effects, apparently because they act on the brain mechanisms controlling the sex drive. Drugs that affect brain receptors for the neurotransmitter dopamine, for example, such as the antidepressant bupropion (sold under the trade name Wellbutrin) and the drug L-dopa, used in the treatment of Parkinson's disease, can increase the sex drive (Saks, 2008).

Placebo effect: Perception that consumption of a substance (e.g., a medication) results in an effect (e.g., relief of a headache) even though the substance does not contain properties (e.g., active ingredients that reduce pain) that cause the effect to occur.

The scientific literature examining the effects of substances popularly believed to be natural aphrodisiacs suggests that they have little actual effect. Rany Shamloul (2010) at the Department of Pharmacology and Toxicology at Queen's University extensively reviewed the scientific evidence concerning the sexual enhancement effects of such substances as ginseng, Spanish fly, yohimbine, chocolate, saw palmetto, and alcohol, and concluded that "there is little evidence from literature to recommend the usage of natural aphrodisiacs for the enhancement of sexual desire and/or performance" (p. 44).

The most potent chemical aphrodisiac may be a naturally occurring substance in the body—the hormone testosterone. It's the basic fuel of sexual desire in both males and females (Basson, Davis, & Rodenberg, 2009).

Anaphrodisiacs

Some people believe aphrodisiacs stimulate sexual response. **Anaphrodisiacs** have the opposite effect. Substances such as saltpetre (potassium nitrate) are considered inhibitors of sexual response. Saltpetre only indirectly dampens sexual arousal, however. As a diuretic that can increase the need for urination, it may make the thought of sex unappealing, but it doesn't directly dampen sexual response.

Other chemicals do dampen sexual arousal and response. Tranquilizers and central nervous system depressants such as barbiturates can lessen sexual desire and impair sexual performance. These drugs may, paradoxically, enhance sexual arousal in some people, by lessening sexual inhibitions and fear of possible repercussions of sexual activity. Antihypertensive drugs, which are used in the treatment of high blood pressure, may produce erectile and ejaculatory difficulties in men and reduction of sexual desire in both men and women. Certain antidepressant drugs, such as fluoxetine (brand name Prozac), amitriptyline (brand name Elavil), and imipramine (brand name Tofranil), appear to dampen the sex drive (Kennedy & Rizvi, 2009). Antidepressants may also impair erectile response and delay ejaculation in men and orgasmic responsiveness in women (Kennedy & Rizvy, 2009). Because they delay ejaculation, some of these drugs are used to treat premature ejaculation.

Nicotine, the stimulant in tobacco smoke, constricts the blood vessels. It can therefore impede sexual arousal, by reducing the capacity of the genitals to become engorged with blood. Several studies have shown that smoking can reduce men's ability to have erections (McKay, 2005). Chronic smoking can also reduce men's blood levels of testosterone, which can in turn lessen sex drive.

Antiandrogen drugs may have anaphrodisiac effects. They have been used in the treatment of deviant behaviour patterns, such as sexual violence and adult sexual interest in children, with some promising results (Roesler & Witztum, 2000).

Psychoactive Drugs

Psychoactive drugs, including alcohol and cocaine, are widely believed to have aphrodisiac effects. Yet their effects may reflect our expectations of them, or their effects on sexual inhibitions, rather than direct stimulation of sexual response.

ALCOHOL Small amounts of alcohol can induce feelings of well-being, but large amounts curb sexual response. This fact shouldn't be surprising, because alcohol is a depressant. Alcohol reduces central nervous system activity. Large amounts of alcohol can severely impair sexual function in both men and women.

People who drink moderate amounts of alcohol may feel more sexually aroused because of their expectations about alcohol, not because of its chemical properties (George et al., 2000). That is, people who expect alcohol to enhance sexual responsiveness may act the part. Moreover, men with problems achieving erection may turn to alcohol in hopes of finding a cure. The fact is that alcohol is a nervous system depressant, and therefore makes getting and keeping an erection more difficult.

Anaphrodisiac A drug or other agent whose effects are antagonistic to sexual arousal or sexual desire.

Antiandrogen A drug that reduces the levels of androgen in the blood system.

CRITICAL THINKING QUESTIONS

There's evidence that crack cocaine users have more sex partners than nonusers. It this relationship causal? Does using crack cause multiple partnering? Or could there be other explanations for the association between crack cocaine use and more partners?

Alcohol and Sexual Behaviour.
Alcohol can induce feelings of well-being and lower inhibitions, which could be connected with sexual interest and facilitate social and sexual behaviour. However, alcohol reduces fear of the consequences of engaging in risky behaviour—sexual and otherwise. Alcohol is expected to be sexually liberating, and people often live up to social and cultural expectations. Yet as a depressant drug, alcohol in large amounts will biochemically dampen sexual response, and may make sexual response impossible.

Alcohol may also lower sexual inhibitions, because it allows us to ascribe our behaviour to the effects of the alcohol, rather than to ourselves. Alcohol is connected with a liberated social role, and thus provides an excuse for dubious behaviour. "It was the alcohol," people can say, "not me." When drinking, people may express sexual desires and do things they wouldn't do when sober. For example, those who feel guilty about sex may become sexually active when drinking, because they can later blame the alcohol.

Alcohol can also induce feelings of euphoria, which may lead people to believe they're experiencing enhanced sexual arousal and sweep away their qualms about expressing sexual desires. Alcohol appears to impair the ability to weigh information (i.e., information processing) that might otherwise inhibit sexual impulses (MacDonald et al., 2000). When people drink, they may be less able to foresee the consequences of inappropriate or illegal behaviour, and less likely to stop and think about their own standards of acceptable conduct.

Consuming a small amount of alcohol (e.g., one beer or a glass of wine) is unlikely to have an impact on a person's sexual response. From a physiological perspective, the more alcohol a person consumes, the less able he or she is to respond sexually. A number of studies have shown that consuming large amounts of alcohol reduces the ability of both men and women to become sexually aroused and have orgasms (McKay, 2005).

HALLUCINOGENS There's no evidence that marijuana or other hallucinogenic drugs directly stimulate sexual response. In a review of the scientific evidence on the effects of drugs on sexual response and behaviour, researchers at the University of Western Ontario note that while a small number of studies have found that some participants report enhanced sexual pleasure with marijuana use, there's also evidence that chronic marijuana use may lower testosterone, which can inhibit sexual response (Frohmader, Pitchers, Balfour, & Coolen, 2010). Some marijuana users report that the drug reduces their ability to respond sexually (McCabe et al., 2005). The drug's effects on sexual response may depend on the individual's prior experience with and attitude toward the drug, as well as the amount he or she uses.

Other hallucinogens, such as LSD and mescaline, have also been reported by some users to enhance sexual response. Again, these effects may reflect dosage levels and user expectations, experiences, and attitudes toward the drugs, as well as altered perceptions.

STIMULANTS Stimulants such as amphetamines ("speed," "uppers," "bennies," "dexies") are reputed to heighten arousal and sensations of orgasm. High doses can give rise to irritability, restlessness, hallucinations, paranoid delusions, insomnia, and loss of appetite. These drugs generally activate the central nervous system, but are not known to have specific sexual effects. Nevertheless, arousing the nervous system can contribute to sexual arousal (Palace, 1995). The drugs can also elevate mood, and perhaps sexual pleasure is heightened by general elation.

Cocaine is a natural stimulant extracted from the leaves of the coca plant. It can be ingested in various forms, snorted as a powder, smoked in hardened rock form ("crack" cocaine) or in a freebase form, or injected directly into the bloodstream in liquid form. Cocaine produces a euphoric rush, which tends to ebb quickly. Physically, cocaine constricts blood vessels (reducing the oxygen supply to the heart), elevates blood pressure, and accelerates heart rate.

There's evidence that cocaine enhances sexual arousal in both males and females, in part by increasing levels of the neurotransmitter dopamine (Andersen et al., 2003; Andersen & Tufik, 2005; Festa et al., 2004). The use of crack cocaine is connected with a higher number of sex partners (Maranda et al., 2004).

Crystal methamphetamine ("crystal meth" or "ice") is used as an aphrodisiac, boosting sexual arousal and lowering sexual inhibitions. It's one of the most addictive street drugs, and its addiction is difficult to treat. Withdrawal typically results in severe pain and depression. It has several negative side effects, including irritability, insomnia, paranoia, and increased aggression. There's concern that it can also damage brain cells, causing memory loss, and can lead to heart attacks and strokes (Ah Shene, 2003). The Canadian AIDS Society has warned that using crystal meth may increase HIV infection, because lowered inhibitions may result in high-risk sexual behaviours.

In a detailed review of the research on recreational drugs and sexuality, Alex McKay (2005) of the Sex Information and Education Council of Canada (SIECCAN) has found that many new users of recreational drugs such as cocaine and methamphetamine report enhanced sexual experiences, but that continued use of these drugs often results in diminished sexual functioning over time, as well as numerous negative general health effects.

Sexual Response and the Brain

The brain may not be an erogenous zone, but it plays a central role in sexual functioning (Fisher, 2000). While genital stimulation without the brain's direct involvement triggers spinal reflexes that produce erection in the male and vaginal lubrication in the female, the same reflexes can be triggered by sexual stimulation that originates in the brain—that is, by erotic memories, fantasies, visual images, and thoughts. The brain may also inhibit sexual responsiveness, as when we experience guilt or anxiety in a sexual situation, or when we suddenly realize, well into a sexual encounter, that we've left the car lights turned on.

Parts of the brain—particularly the **cerebral cortex** and the **limbic system**—play key roles in sexual functioning. Cells in the cerebral cortex fire (transmit messages) when we experience sexual thoughts, images, wishes, and fantasies. These cells interpret sensory information as sexual turn-ons or turn-offs. Seeing your lover disrobe, anticipating a romantic kiss, thinking about a passing sexual fantasy, or viewing an erotic movie can trigger the cortical cells to fire. These cells, in turn,

Cerebral cortex   The wrinkled surface area (gray matter) of the cerebrum (main part of the brain).

Limbic system   A group of structures active in memory, motivation, and emotion. These structures form a fringe along the inner edge of the cerebrum.

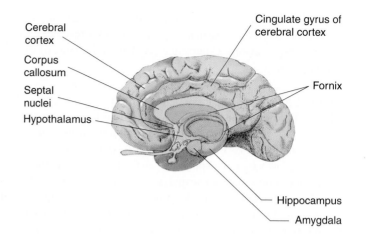

Figure 4.1 Parts of the brain involved in sexual functioning.
This is a cross-section of the human brain. When we experience sexual thoughts and mental images, cells in the cerebral cortex interpret this information as sexual turn-ons or turn-offs. The cerebral cortex may then transmit messages through the spinal cord that send blood coursing to the sex organs, leading to erection or vaginal lubrication. The limbic system lies along the inner edge of the cerebrum and is thought to play a role in regulating sexual behaviour.

transmit messages through the spinal cord that send blood rushing to the genitals, causing erection or vaginal lubrication. The cortex also provides the conscious sense of self. The cortex judges sexual behaviour as proper or improper, moral or immoral, relaxing or anxiety- or guilt-provoking.

Areas of the brain below the cortex, especially the limbic system (see Figure 4.1), also play roles in sexual processes (Kimble, 1992). For example, when the rear part of a male rat's hypothalamus is stimulated by an electrical probe, the animal mechanically runs through its courting and mounting routine. It nibbles at the ears and back of the neck of a female rat, and mounts her when she responds. Electrical stimulation of the hippocampus and septal nuclei in monkeys produces erections. Klüver and Bucy (1939) found that destruction of areas of the limbic system triggered continuous sexual behaviour in monkeys.

Sex Hormones and Sexual Behaviour

In a television situation comedy, a male adolescent is described as "a hormone with feet." Ask parents why teenagers act the way they do, and you're likely to hear a one-word answer: "Hormones!"

Hormones are chemical substances secreted by the ductless glands of the endocrine system and discharged directly into the bloodstream. Sex hormones released at puberty cause the flowering of **secondary sex characteristics**. In males, these include lengthening of the vocal cords (and consequent lowering of the voice) and growth of facial and pubic hair. In females, they include rounding of the breasts and hips with fatty tissue, and growth of pubic hair.

Organizing and Activating Influences

Sex hormones have organizing and activating effects on behaviour. That is, they influence the type of behaviour that's expressed (an organizing effect), and they influence the frequency or intensity of the drive that motivates the behaviour and the ability to perform the behaviour (activating effects). For example, sex hormones predispose lower animals and possibly people toward stereotypical masculine or feminine mating behaviours (an organizing effect). They also facilitate sexual response and influence sexual desire (activating effects).

James Pfaus at Concordia University is an international leader in research on the sexual behaviour of rodents and other animals. He and his associates have discovered that there are many similarities between animals and humans in terms of sexual arousal and response. Both are influenced not only by sex hormones, but also by social and situational variables. Pfaus has concluded that research findings on

Hormone A substance, secreted by an endocrine gland, that regulates various body functions.

Secondary sex characteristics Physical traits that differentiate males from females, but are not directly involved in reproduction.

animal sexual response can be highly predictive regarding many aspects of human sexual response (Pfaus et al., 2003).

Prenatal sex hormones are known to play a role in sexual differentiation of both the genitalia and brain structures such as the hypothalamus. Their role in patterning sexual behaviour in adulthood remains unknown. Researchers have speculated that the brains of **transsexual** individuals may have been prenatally sexually differentiated in one direction, while their genitals were differentiated in the other (Money, 1994). It's been speculated that prenatal sexual differentiation of the brain may also be connected with sexual orientation.

What of the activating effects of sex hormones on human sex drive and behaviour? Although countless attempts to extract or synthesize aphrodisiacs have failed to produce the real thing, men and women normally produce a genuine aphrodisiac—testosterone. Whatever the early organizing effects of sex hormones in humans, testosterone activates the sex drives of both men and women (Guzick & Hoeger, 2000).

Transsexual A person with a gender-identity disorder, who feels that he or she is really a member of the other gender, and trapped in a body of the wrong gender.

Male Sexual Behaviour

Evidence of the role of hormones in sex drive is found among men whose testosterone levels have declined as a result of chemical or surgical castration. Surgical castration (removal of the testes) is sometimes performed as a medical treatment for cancer of the prostate or other diseases of the male reproductive tract, such as genital tuberculosis. And some convicted sex offenders have voluntarily undergone castration as a condition of release.

In reviewing the scientific research, Canadian researchers Barbaree and Blanchard (2008) have shown that regardless of the reason for castration, men who are surgically or chemically castrated usually exhibit a gradual decrease in incidence of sexual fantasies and sexual desire. They also tend to gradually lose the capacity to attain erection and to ejaculate—an indication that testosterone is important in maintaining sexual functioning as well as drive, at least in males.

Hypogonadism A condition marked by abnormally low levels of testosterone production.

Castrated men show great variation in sexual interest and functioning, however. Some continue to experience sexual desire and are able to function sexually for years, even decades. Learning appears to play a large role in determining continued sexual response after castration. Men who are sexually experienced before castration show a more gradual decline in sexual activity afterwards. Those who are sexually inexperienced before castration show relatively little or no interest in sex later. Male sexual motivation and functioning thus involve an interplay of hormonal influence and experience.

Further evidence of the relationship between hormonal levels and male sexuality is found in studies of men with **hypogonadism**, a condition marked by abnormally low levels of testosterone production. Hypogonadal men generally experience loss of sexual desire and a decline in sexual activity (McElduff & Beange, 2003). Again, hormones don't tell the whole story. Hypogonadal men are capable of erection, at least for a while, even though their sex drives may wane (McElduff & Beange, 2003). The role of testosterone as an activator of sex drive in men is further supported by evidence of the effects of testosterone replacement in hypogonadal men. When such men have testosterone injections, their sex drives, fantasies, and activities often return to their former levels (Seidman, 2003).

Though minimal androgen levels are critical to male sexuality, there's no one-to-one correspondence between hormone levels and sex drive or sexual performance in adults.

"Hormones with Feet."
Research shows that androgen levels are connected with sexual interest in both male and female adolescents. Hormone levels are more likely to predict sexual behaviour in adolescent males, however, perhaps because society places greater restraints on female sexuality.

In men who have ample supplies of testosterone, sexual interest and functioning depend more on learning, fantasies, attitudes, memories, and other psychosocial factors than on hormone levels.

At puberty, however, hormonal variation may play a more direct role in stimulating sexual interest and activity in males. Udry (2001) found, for example, that testosterone levels among teenaged boys predicted sexual interest, masturbation rates, and likelihood of engaging in sexual intercourse. A positive relationship has also been found between testosterone levels in adult men and frequency of sexual intercourse (Dabbs & Morris, 1990). Moreover, antiandrogens, drugs that reduce androgen levels in the blood system, lead to reductions in sex drive and sexual fantasies (Bradford, 1998).

Female Sexual Behaviour

The female sex hormones estrogen and progesterone play prominent roles in promoting the changes that occur during puberty and in regulating the menstrual cycle. Female sex hormones do not, however, appear to play a direct role in determining sexual motivation or response in human females.

In most mammals, females are sexually receptive only during estrus (when they're "in heat"), a brief period of fertility corresponding to ovulation. Estrus occurs once a year in some species; in others, it occurs periodically during the year, in so-called sexual or mating seasons. Estrogen peaks at the time of ovulation, so there's a close relationship between fertility and sexual receptivity in most female mammals. Women's sexuality, however, is not clearly linked to hormonal fluctuations. Unlike most mammalian females, the human female is sexually responsive during all phases of the reproductive (menstrual) cycle—even during menstruation, when ovarian hormone levels are low—and after menopause.

There is some evidence, however, that sexual responsiveness in women is influenced by the presence of circulating androgens, or male sex hormones, in their bodies. Women's adrenal glands, like men's, produce small amounts of androgen (Guzick & Hoeger, 2000). The fact that women normally produce smaller amounts of androgen than men doesn't necessarily mean they have weaker sex drives. Rather, women appear to be more sensitive to smaller amounts of androgen. For women, it seems that less is more.

Ovariectomy Surgical removal of the ovaries.

Women who receive **ovariectomies**, which are sometimes carried out when hysterectomies are performed, no longer produce female sex hormones. Nevertheless, they continue to experience the same sex drives and interest as before. Loss of the ovarian hormone estradiol may cause vaginal dryness and make intercourse painful, but it doesn't reduce sexual desire. (The dryness can be alleviated by a lubricating jelly or an estrogen cream.) However, women whose adrenal glands *and* ovaries are removed—so they no longer produce androgens—gradually lose sexual desire (Nappi et al., 2006; Traish et al., 2006). Women who have previously experienced higher levels of sexual activity and enjoyment in their lives may experience less of a decline in sexual desire after surgery, suggesting that previous experience may condition sexual response.

Research provides further evidence of the links between testosterone levels and women's sex drives. In studies by Udry (2001), androgen levels have been found to predict sexual interest among teenaged girls. In contrast to boys' androgen levels, girls' levels are unrelated to likelihood of coital experience. Androgens apparently affect sexual desire in both genders, but sexual interest may be more likely to translate into sexual activity in men than in women (Peplau, 2003). This gender difference may be explained by society's imposing greater restraints on adolescent female than male sexuality.

Other researchers report that women's sexual activity increases at points in the menstrual cycle when androgen levels are high (Morley & Perry, 2003). Researchers at McGill studied women whose ovaries were surgically removed (resulting in "surgical menopause") to treat disease. The ovaries supply major quantities of estrogen. Following surgery, the women in this study were treated with estrogen replacement therapy (ERT), with ERT *plus* androgens, or with a placebo (an inert substance made to resemble an active drug). This was a double-blind study—neither the women nor their physicians knew which substances they received. The results showed that the combination of androgens and ERT heightened sexual desire and sexual fantasies more than ERT alone or the placebo (Sherwin et al., 1985). The combination of androgens and ERT also helps women maintain a sense of psychological well-being (Guzick & Hoeger, 2000).

Androgens thus play a more prominent role than ovarian hormones in activating and maintaining women's sex drives. Like men's, however, women's sexuality is too complex to be fully explained by hormone levels.

Factors Influencing Sexual Arousal

Robin Milhausen (2004) at the University of Guelph has analyzed factors that inhibit or enhance sexual arousal among female and male university students. She's found a number that are common to both sexes.

Both women and men in her study reported that sexual arousal could be enhanced by their partners' positive characteristics (e.g., sense of humour, self-confidence, and ability to make them feel desirable), sex that was varied (e.g., different activities and different settings), and anticipation of sexual encounters. Both sexes also agreed that sexual arousal could be inhibited by a partner's self-consciousness about his or her body, a feeling of giving more than receiving (e.g., always being the one to initiate sex), and worries about various issues (e.g., reputation, STIs, and having to use condoms).

Milhausen also found gender differences in the importance of certain factors. Women were more inhibited than men about possible sexual violence and exploitation, fear that they weren't good lovers, and fear that they were taking too long to become aroused and/or not having orgasms. They were more aroused than men by their partners' positive characteristics (e.g., relating well to others and doing helpful chores), feeling able to trust their partners, feeling emotionally connected, feeling their partners were sensitive to their needs, and the effects of hormones. Men were more aroused than women by specific sexual stimuli (e.g., seeing their partners' naked bodies, "talking dirty," seeing their partners in sexy outfits, watching erotic films, and quickly advancing to the genitals when starting to have sex).

Models of Sexual Response

Although we may be culturally attuned to focus on gender differences rather than similarities, Masters and Johnson (1966) found that the physiological responses of men and women to sexual stimulation (via intercourse, masturbation, or other sources) are quite alike. The sequence of changes in the body that take place as men and women become progressively more aroused is referred to as the **sexual response cycle**.

Masters and Johnson's Four-Phase Sexual Response Cycle

Masters and Johnson (1966) divided the cycle into four phases: excitement, plateau, orgasm, and resolution. Figure 4.2 suggests the levels of sexual arousal associated with each phase.

Both males and females experience **vasocongestion** and **myotonia** early in the response cycle. Vasocongestion is swelling of the genital tissues with blood, which causes erection of the penis and engorgement of the area surrounding the vaginal

Sexual response cycle Masters and Johnson's model of sexual response, which consists of four phases.

Vasocongestion Swelling of the genital tissues with blood, which causes erection of the penis and engorgement of the area surrounding the vaginal opening.

Myotonia Muscle tension.

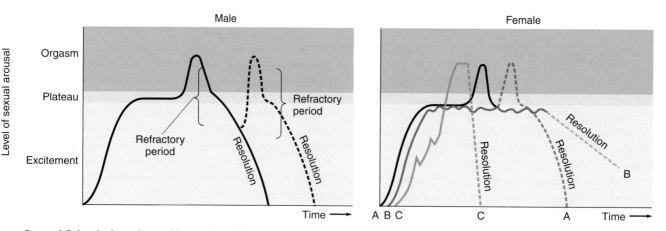

Figure 4.2 Levels of sexual arousal during phases of the sexual response cycle.
Masters and Johnson divide the sexual response cycle into four phases: excitement, plateau, orgasm, and resolution. During the resolution phase, the level of sexual arousal returns to the pre-aroused state. For a man, a refractory period follows orgasm. As shown by the broken line, however, a man can become re-aroused to orgasm once the refractory period is past and his level of sexual arousal has returned to the pre-plateau level. Pattern A for a woman shows a typical response cycle; the broken line indicates multiple orgasms, should they occur. Pattern B shows the cycle for a woman who reaches the plateau phase but for whom arousal is "resolved" without her experiencing orgasm. Pattern C shows the possibility of orgasm in a highly aroused woman who passes quickly through the plateau phase.

Innovative Canadian Research

GENDER, SEXUAL ORIENTATION, AND AROUSAL

Meredith Chivers, a researcher at Queen's University, has conducted groundbreaking research on sexual arousal. In particular, she and her colleagues have studied how sexual arousal patterns vary by gender and sexual orientation (Chivers et al., 2007). The study participants included both heterosexual and homosexual men and women. The four groups were shown videos depicting men and women engaging in nude exercise, solitary masturbation, same-sex intercourse, and male-female intercourse, as well as copulating chimpanzees. Genital and subjective sexual arousal were recorded.

Arousal was strongest in response to watching the sexual intercourse video, and weakest for the nude exercise one. The gender of the actor was far more important for men than for women, whereas level of sexual activity was more important for women than for men. Thus, heterosexual men were almost exclusively aroused by videos of women, homosexual men were almost exclusively aroused by videos of men, and heterosexual women responded to videos of both men and women.

Women were more strongly aroused than men by the video of the chimpanzees copulating. Homosexual women were more aroused by the video of nude women exercising and masturbating than by the one of nude men engaging in those activities. Yet homosexual women were also aroused when watching heterosexual couples engaging in intercourse.

The findings clearly indicate that women are more flexible than men in terms of which gender arouses them. The results challenge the commonly held belief that women are far less responsive than men to sexually explicit materials. Not only were the women as strongly aroused as the men by the erotic videos, they also became aroused as quickly as the men did.

In another study, Chivers and her colleagues (Rieger, Chivers, & Bailey, 2005) compared the sexual responses of bisexual men with those of homosexual and heterosexual men who were asked to watch either men or women engaging in sexual activity. As expected, the heterosexual men were more aroused by the female actors, and the homosexual men were more aroused by the male actors. Most of the bisexual men experienced greater genital arousal when watching the male actors, thus responding in a fashion similar to the homosexual males. However, the bisexual men were divided in their subjective feelings of arousal, and were just as likely to say they were aroused by the female as by the male actors.

Chivers and her colleagues (Lawrence, Latty, Chivers, & Bailey, 2005) also studied male-to-female transsexuals both before and after sex reassignment surgery. The transsexuals who were homosexual before reassignment were more aroused by sexual images of men, while the transsexuals who were heterosexual before reassignment were more aroused by images of women. The arousal responses after surgery were similar to the arousal responses before surgery.

opening. The testes, nipples, and even earlobes become engorged as blood vessels in these areas dilate. Myotonia is muscle tension. It causes voluntary and involuntary muscle contractions, which produce facial grimaces, spasms in the hands and feet, and eventually, the spasms of orgasm.

THE EXCITEMENT PHASE In younger men, vasocongestion during the **excitement phase** produces penile erection as early as three to eight seconds after stimulation begins. Erection may occur more slowly in older men, but the responses are essentially the same. Erection may subside and return as stimulation varies. The scrotal skin thickens, losing its baggy appearance. The testes increase in size. The testes and scrotum become elevated.

In a woman, vaginal lubrication may start 10 to 30 seconds after stimulation begins. Vasocongestion swells the clitoris, flattens and spreads the labia majora apart, and increases the size of the labia minora. The inner two-thirds of the vagina expands. The vaginal walls thicken and, because of the inflow of blood, turn from their normal pink to a deeper hue. The uterus becomes engorged and elevated. The breasts enlarge, and blood vessels near the surface become more prominent.

Late in this phase, the skin may take on a rosy **sex flush**, which varies with intensity of arousal and is more pronounced in women than in men. The nipples may become erect in both genders, especially in response to direct stimulation. Both men and women show some increase in myotonia, heart rate, and blood pressure.

THE PLATEAU PHASE The level of arousal remains somewhat constant during the **plateau phase** of sexual response. Nevertheless, it's an advanced state of arousal that precedes orgasm. A man in this phase shows a slight increase in the circumference of the coronal ridge of the penis. The penile glans turns a purplish hue, a sign of vasocongestion. The testes are elevated further into position for ejaculation, and may reach one and a half times their unaroused size. The Cowper's glands secrete a few droplets of fluid that are found at the tip of the penis. (See Figure 4.3.)

In a woman, vasocongestion swells the tissues of the outer one-third of the vagina, contracting the vaginal opening (thus preparing it to "grasp" the penis) and building the **orgasmic platform**. (See Figure 4.4.) The inner part of the vagina

Excitement phase The first phase of the sexual response cycle, characterized by erection in the male, vaginal lubrication in the female, and muscle tension and increased heart rate in both the male and the female.

Sex flush A reddish rash that appears on the chest or breasts late in the excitement phase of the sexual response cycle.

Plateau phase The second phase of the sexual response cycle, characterized by increased vasocongestion, muscle tension, heart rate, and blood pressure, in preparation for orgasm.

Orgasmic platform Thickening of the walls of the outer one-third of the vagina (due to vasocongestion) during the plateau phase of the sexual response cycle.

Innovative Canadian Research

PHYSICAL VERSUS PSYCHOLOGICAL AROUSAL

Although males and females are similar in terms of physiological response, they differ significantly in their subjective perceptions of arousal. When males are physically aroused, they're almost always subjectively aware of the fact. Women, however, vary in their degree of awareness.

Researchers in British Columbia have discovered that older women are more subjectively aware of physical arousal than are younger women (Brotto & Gorzalka, 2002). For many women, distinguishing the physical signs of sexual arousal seems to require time and learning.

Rosemary Basson (2002) at Vancouver General Hospital discusses how sexual arousal is a more complex process for women than

for men. According to Basson, when a woman experiences genital vasocongestion, she can experience a range of subjective responses:

- She may not be aware of the physical arousal.
- She may be only vaguely aware of the physical arousal.
- She may be aware of the physical sensations, yet not define them as sexual.
- She may interpret the arousal as sexual, but not experience the sensation as enjoyable.

Basson analyzes a number of factors that may account for these responses, such as negative sexual experiences in the past, feelings of inadequacy or guilt, and distractions such as concern over personal appearance, the safety of the situation, and feelings toward her partner.

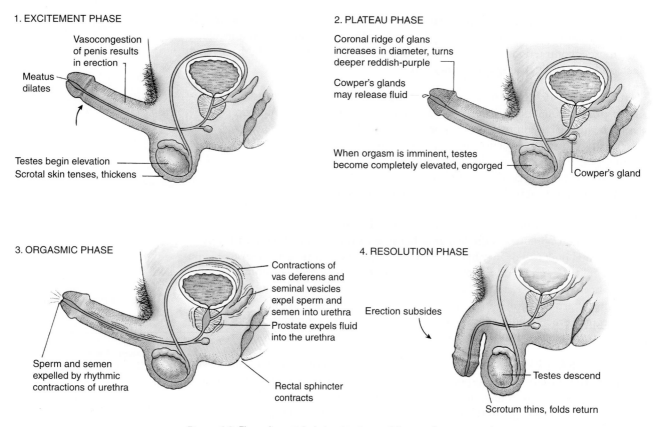

1. EXCITEMENT PHASE

Vasocongestion of penis results in erection

Meatus dilates

Testes begin elevation
Scrotal skin tenses, thickens

2. PLATEAU PHASE

Coronal ridge of glans increases in diameter, turns deeper reddish-purple

Cowper's glands may release fluid

When orgasm is imminent, testes become completely elevated, engorged

Cowper's gland

3. ORGASMIC PHASE

Contractions of vas deferens and seminal vesicles expel sperm and semen into urethra

Prostate expels fluid into the urethra

Sperm and semen expelled by rhythmic contractions of urethra

Rectal sphincter contracts

4. RESOLUTION PHASE

Erection subsides

Testes descend

Scrotum thins, folds return

Figure 4.3 The male genitals during the phases of the sexual response cycle.

expands fully. The uterus becomes fully elevated. The clitoris shortens and withdraws beneath the clitoral hood. The woman (or her partner) may feel that the clitoris has become lost, and mistake this as a sign that her sexual arousal is waning, when it's actually increasing.

The labia minora turn red, becoming a deep wine colour in women who have borne children, and bright red in women who have not. This reddened skin is known as **sex skin**. Further engorgement of the areolas of the breasts may make it seem that the nipples have lost part of their erection. (See Figure 4.5.) The Bartholin's glands secrete a fluid that resembles mucus.

About one man in four—and about three women in four—shows a sex flush, which often appears in the plateau phase. Myotonia may cause facial grimaces and spasmodic contractions in the hands and feet. Breathing becomes rapid, similar to panting, and the heart rate may increase to 100 to 160 beats per minute. Blood pressure continues to rise. The increase in heart rate is usually less dramatic with masturbation than during intercourse.

THE ORGASMIC PHASE The orgasmic phase in the male consists of two stages of muscular contraction. In the first stage, contractions of the vas deferens, seminal vesicles, ejaculatory duct, and prostate gland cause seminal fluid to collect in the urethral bulb at the base of the penis. (See Figure 4.3.) The bulb expands to accommodate the fluid. The internal sphincter of the bladder contracts, preventing seminal fluid from entering the bladder in a backward, retrograde ejaculation and preventing urine from mixing with semen. Collection of semen in the urethral bulb produces feelings of ejaculatory inevitability—the sensation that nothing will stop the ejaculate from "coming." This sensation lasts for about two to three seconds.

In the second stage, the external sphincter of the bladder relaxes, allowing the passage of semen. Contractions of muscles surrounding the urethra, the urethral

Sex skin The reddened skin of the labia minora during the plateau phase.

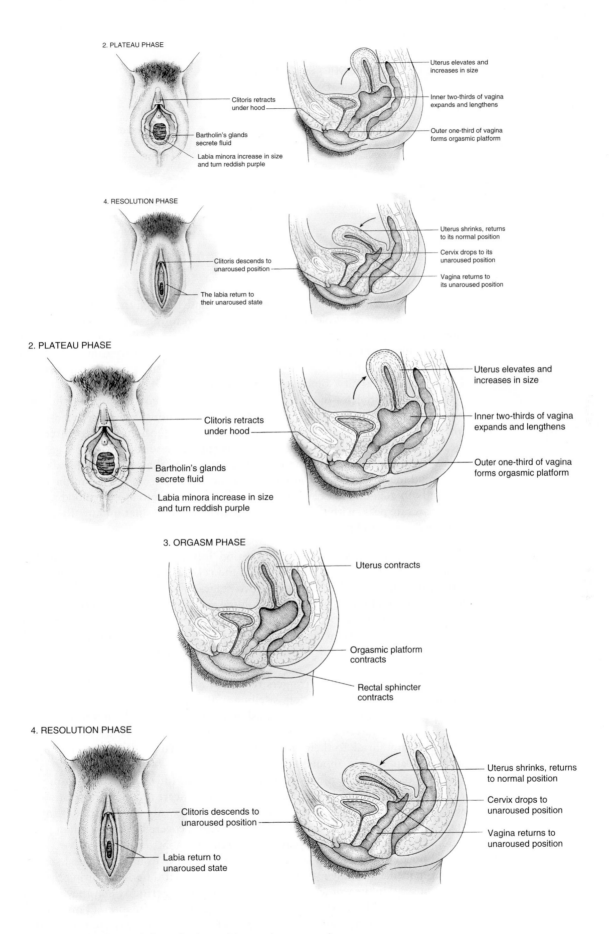

Figure 4.4 The female genitals during the phases of the sexual response cycle.

2. PLATEAU PHASE

Clitoris retracts under hood

Bartholin's glands secrete fluid

Labia minora increase in size and turn reddish purple

Uterus elevates and increases in size

Inner two-thirds of vagina expands and lengthens

Outer one-third of vagina forms orgasmic platform

3. ORGASM PHASE

Uterus contracts

Orgasmic platform contracts

Rectal sphincter contracts

4. RESOLUTION PHASE

Clitoris descends to unaroused position

Labia return to unaroused state

Uterus shrinks, returns to normal position

Cervix drops to unaroused position

Vagina returns to unaroused position

1. EXCITEMENT PHASE

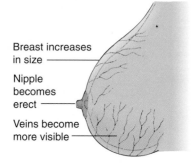

Breast increases in size

Nipple becomes erect

Veins become more visible

2. PLATEAU AND ORGASMIC PHASES

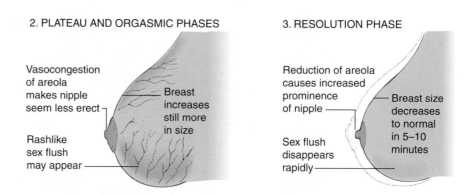

Vasocongestion of areola makes nipple seem less erect

Breast increases still more in size

Rashlike sex flush may appear

3. RESOLUTION PHASE

Reduction of areola causes increased prominence of nipple

Breast size decreases to normal in 5–10 minutes

Sex flush disappears rapidly

Figure 4.5 The female breasts during the phases of the sexual response cycle.

bulb, and the base of the penis propel the ejaculate through the urethra and out of the body. Sensations of pleasure tend to be related to the strength of the contractions and the amount of seminal fluid produced. The first three to four contractions are generally most intense, occurring at 0.8-second intervals (five contractions every four seconds). Another two to four contractions occur at a somewhat slower pace. Rates and patterns vary somewhat from man to man.

Orgasm in the female is manifested by 3 to 15 contractions of the pelvic muscles that surround the vaginal barrel. The contractions first occur at 0.8-second intervals, producing, as in the male, a release of sexual tension. Another three to six weaker, slower contractions follow. The spacing of these contractions is generally more variable in women than in men. The uterus and the anal sphincter also contract rhythmically. Uterine contractions occur in waves from the top to the cervix.

In both genders, muscles throughout the body go into spasm. Blood pressure and heart rate peak, with the heart beating up to 180 times per minute. Respiration may increase to 40 breaths per minute.

THE RESOLUTION PHASE The period following orgasm, when the body returns to its pre-aroused state, is called the **resolution phase.** Following ejaculation, the man loses his erection in two stages. The first occurs within about a minute: the erection loses half of its volume as blood from the corpora cavernosa empties into other parts of the body. The second stage occurs over several minutes: the remaining tumescence subsides as the corpus spongiosum empties, the testes and scrotum return to normal size, and the scrotum regains its wrinkled appearance.

In women, orgasm also triggers release of blood from engorged areas. In the absence of continued stimulation, swelling of the areolas decreases and the nipples return to their normal size. The sex flush lightens rapidly. In about 5 to 10 seconds, the clitoris descends to its normal position. The clitoris, vaginal barrel, uterus, and labia gradually shrink to their pre-aroused sizes. The labia minora turn lighter (the sex skin disappears) in about 10 to 15 seconds.

In both men and women, most muscle tension (myotonia) tends to dissipate within five minutes after orgasm. Blood pressure, heart rate, and respiration may also return to pre-arousal levels within a few minutes. About 30% to 40% of men and women find their palms, soles, or entire bodies covered with a sheen of perspiration. Both men and women may feel relaxed and satiated.

Although the processes by which the body returns to its pre-arousal state are similar in men and women, there's an important gender difference during the resolution phase. Unlike women, men enter a **refractory period,** when they're physiologically incapable of experiencing another orgasm or ejaculation. (This is similar to the way a flash on a camera can't be set off again immediately after it's used—it

Resolution phase The fourth phase of the sexual response cycle, during which the body gradually returns to its pre-aroused state.

Refractory period The time following a response (e.g., orgasm) when an individual no longer responds to stimulation (e.g., sexual stimulation).

Innovative Canadian Research

THE SUBJECTIVE EXPERIENCE OF ORGASM

The sensations of orgasm have challenged the descriptive powers of poets. Words like "rush," "warmth," "explosion," and "release" don't adequately capture them. We may assume (rightly or wrongly) that others of our gender experience pretty much what we do, but can we understand the sensations experienced by the other gender?

Studies suggest that the orgasms of both genders may feel quite similar. In one study, Kenneth Mah of Princess Margaret Hospital in Toronto and Yitzchak Binik at McGill University (2002) developed a scale to measure the subjective experiences of orgasm among men and women. They wanted to determine what characteristics were common to the human experience of orgasm. They asked university students to rate adjectives describing orgasms they experienced both during masturbation and during sex with partners.

The findings supported a two-dimensional model of the psychological experience of orgasm. The first dimension is sensory, with the following components:

■ A building sensation.
■ A flooding sensation.
■ A flushing sensation.
■ A spurting sensation.
■ A throbbing sensation.
■ General spasms.

The second dimension of the orgasm experience is emotional, with the following components:

■ Pleasurable satisfaction.
■ Relaxation.
■ Emotional intimacy.
■ Ecstasy.

In a subsequent analysis of the data, King, Belsky, Mah, and Binik (2010) found that the women in the study experienced differences in orgasm types, depending on whether they occurred during solitary masturbation or partnered sexual activity. On average, orgasms that occurred as a result of partnered activity included significantly more flushing sensations, general spasms, pleasurable satisfaction, emotional intimacy, and ecstasy. The women reported no differences between orgasms resulting from partnered activity and solitary masturbation with respect to sensations of building, flooding, spurting, and throbbing. Orgasms during solitary masturbation, however, resulted in greater feelings of relaxation than did orgasms from partnered sexual activity.

In another study, Mah and Binik (2005) found that emotional intimacy affected the rating of the orgasmic experience. Orgasm was rated as more satisfying when the individuals felt emotionally connected to their partners. Orgasms that were seen as more psychologically intense (e.g., involving feelings of relaxation and ecstasy) were related to higher levels of orgasmic pleasure and satisfaction. Higher degrees of sexual pleasure were also reported when the individuals experienced sensations of throbbing and, to a lesser degree, flushing.

has to be recharged.) The refractory period in adolescent males may last only minutes, whereas that in men aged 50 and over may last from several minutes to a day. Because women don't undergo a refractory period, they can become quickly rearoused to the point of repeated (multiple) orgasms, if they desire, and can receive continued sexual stimulation. (See Figure 4.2.)

Myotonia and vasocongestion may take an hour or more to dissipate in people who are aroused but don't reach orgasm. Persistent pelvic vasocongestion in a man may cause "blue balls"—the slang term for a throbbing ache. Some men plead with their partners to have intercourse, on the theory that it's unfair to decline after stimulating them to this point. The ache can be relieved through masturbation or intercourse, or allowed to dissipate naturally. Although it may be uncomfortable, it's not dangerous, and it's no excuse to pressure or coerce someone into sexual activity.

"Blue" sensations are not limited to men. Women, too, may experience unpleasant pelvic throbbing if they become highly aroused and don't find release. And women, too, can relieve pelvic throbbing through masturbation.

CRITICAL THINKING QUESTIONS

Masters and Johnson describe biological processes (i.e., excitement, plateau, orgasm, and resolution) in sexual response. Kaplan and Basson introduce psychological components (e.g., desire, intimacy). Is it important that models of sexual response include both biological and psychological components? Why or why not?

Kaplan's Three Stages of Sexual Response

Helen Singer Kaplan was a prominent sex therapist and author of several professional books (1974, 1987) on sex therapy. Whereas Masters and Johnson proposed a four-stage model of sexual response, Kaplan developed a three-stage model consisting of desire, excitement, and orgasm.

Kaplan's model was an outgrowth of her clinical experience with people with sexual dysfunctions. She believed their problems could best be classified according to the three stages of sexual response. Her model makes it convenient for clinicians to classify sexual dysfunctions involving desire (e.g., low or absent desire), excitement (e.g., problems with erection in the male or lubrication in the female), and orgasm (e.g., premature ejaculation in the male or orgasmic dysfunction in the female).

Kaplan's model is noteworthy for designating desire as a separate phase of sexual response. Lack of sexual interest or desire is one of the problems most commonly brought to sex therapists.

Basson's Intimacy Model of Female Sexual Response

Rosemary Basson (2008) at the BC Centre for Sexual Medicine at Vancouver General Hospital has developed an intimacy-based model of female sexual response that she argues is especially relevant for women in long-term relationships. While Kaplan's model assumes that the process of female sexual response begins with desire, Basson's model suggests that, for many women, the process does not necessarily begin with feelings of desire, but rather with feelings of intimacy with their partners. Basson argues that many women in longer-term relationships are motivated to respond to sexual stimuli if they feel that becoming sexually involved will enhance that intimacy.

According to the Basson model, a woman will often begin her sexual encounters with a nonsexual or neutral state of mind. Once she begins to feel sexually aroused for intimacy reasons, she'll continue the experience for sexual reasons. At this point, she's responsive to sexual stimulation, such as breast or genital touching, which increases her arousal and then sexual desire. If she finds the outcome both physically and emotionally satisfying, it increases her feelings of intimacy with her partner, and motivates her to become sexually involved again in the future.

This model allows for the possibility that arousal may precede sexual desire, and that arousal may not lead to orgasm. Basson acknowledges the possibility that spontaneous sexual desire may occur among women outside of the intimacy model, and that this may lead to self-stimulation or partnered sexual activity.

Comparing Models of Female Sexual Response

William Fisher at the University of Western Ontario and his colleague Michael Sand (Sand & Fisher, 2007) conducted a study to see how closely women felt their own sexual experiences corresponded to the Masters and Johnson, Kaplan, and Basson models of sexual response. The research sample consisted of 133 nurses living in the United States.

Interestingly, almost equal proportions of women endorsed each of the three models as best reflecting their own patterns of sexual response. This suggests that none of the models uniformly captures the sexual response patterns of all women. Perhaps there's considerable variability between women in terms of sexual response patterns, and more than one model is required for sexuality research and therapy.

The Enigmatic Orgasm

Orgasm is often thought of as the pinnacle of sexual experience. Some people think a sexual experience is incomplete unless both partners have an orgasm. "Did you come?" the hopeful lover asks his or her partner. With experience, however, many come to realize that achieving orgasm is not the be all and end all of a good sexual experience. Indeed, many sex therapists encourage their clients to refrain from making orgasm the goal of sex, emphasizing that it's just one component of the total experience.

Yet there can be no doubt that orgasm provides intensely pleasurable sensations, and biologically speaking, it does represent the peak of sexual excitement. One of the most fascinating things about orgasm is that, while we can easily describe it as a biological process (i.e., a series of involuntary contractions in the pelvic area), we find it much more difficult to describe exactly how it feels. How can we accurately put the sensations of orgasm into words? Do one person's orgasms feel the same as another person's? Do female orgasms feel similar to male orgasms? The answers to these questions are elusive. Although most of us are familiar with it through personal experience, orgasm remains somewhat of an enigma.

Orgasm is also often the subject of myth and misunderstanding. For example, there's long been a social expectation that women should have orgasms through vaginal penetration. In the past, some women have felt inadequate if they couldn't reach orgasm during intercourse. As public awareness of human sexuality has grown in recent years, however, more and more women—and their partners—have learned that many (if not most) women require some form of stimulation of the clitoris before they can have orgasms.

Multiple Orgasms

Kinsey and his colleagues (1953) reported that 14% of his female respondents regularly had **multiple orgasms**. This surprised both his fellow scientists and the community at large. Many people were aghast that women could have more than one orgasm at a time. There were comments that the women in the Kinsey surveys must be "nymphomaniacs" who were incapable of being satisfied with the "normal" complement of one orgasm per occasion. Just 13 years later, Masters and Johnson (1966) reported that most—if not all—women were capable of multiple orgasms.

Although all women may have a biological capability for multiple orgasms, not all women report them. In a survey of 720 nurses, 43% reported experiencing multiple orgasms (Darling et al., 1991)—and nearly half of those occurred when they used vibrators, which they generally applied to their clitorises. The women reported that the orgasms they experienced with vibrators were more intense than other kinds. Two-thirds of those who used vibrators did so in conjunction with sexual activity with their partners.

By Masters and Johnson's definition, men are not capable of achieving multiple orgasms, because they enter a refractory period following ejaculation. Men who want more than one orgasm during one session may have to pause for a while. Women, however, can maintain a high level of arousal between multiple orgasms, and can have them in rapid succession, because they don't have a refractory period. Women can continue to have orgasms if they continue to receive effective stimulation (and, of course, are interested in continuing). Some men thus refrain from reaching orgasm until their partners have had the desired number. The differential capacity for multiple orgasms is one of the major gender differences in sexual response.

Some men have two or more orgasms without ejaculation ("dry orgasms") before a final ejaculatory orgasm. These men may not enter a refractory period following their initial dry orgasms, and may therefore be able to maintain stimulation at near-peak levels.

Multiple orgasms One or more additional orgasms following the first, occurring within a short period of time and before the body has returned to its pre-plateau level of arousal.

Masters and Johnson (1966) found that some women experienced 20 or more consecutive orgasms by masturbating. Still, few women have multiple orgasms during most sexual encounters, and many are satisfied with just one per occasion. Some women who have read or heard about female orgasmic capacity wonder what's wrong with them if they're content with just one. Nothing is wrong with them, of course. A biological capacity does not create a behavioural requirement.

How Many Kinds of Orgasms Do Women Have?

Until Masters and Johnson published their laboratory findings, many people believed there were two types of female orgasm, as proposed by psychoanalyst Sigmund Freud: the clitoral orgasm and the vaginal orgasm. Clitoral orgasm was achieved through direct clitoral stimulation such as masturbation. It was seen by psychoanalysts (mostly male psychoanalysts, naturally) as emblematic of a childhood fixation—a throwback to an erogenous pattern acquired during childhood masturbation.

The term "vaginal orgasm" referred to an orgasm achieved through deep penile thrusting during intercourse. It was thought to be a sign of mature sexuality. Freud argued that women achieved sexual maturity when they gave up clitoral stimulation for vaginal stimulation.

This view would be little more than an academic footnote if it weren't for the fact that the many (if not most) adult women who require direct clitoral stimulation to reach orgasm, even during vaginal penetration, have been led to believe they're sexually inadequate. There's also an element of heterosexism in the Freudian view of mature female sexuality, since lesbians obviously don't rely on penile thrusting for sexual pleasure or orgasm.

Masters and Johnson (1966) were able to find only one kind of orgasm, physiologically speaking, regardless of whether stimulation was clitoral or vaginal. By monitoring physiological responses to sexual stimulation, they found that the female orgasm involves the same biological events whether it's reached through masturbation, petting, intercourse, or just breast stimulation. All orgasms involve spasmodic contractions of the pelvic muscles surrounding the vaginal barrel, leading to a release of sexual tension.

In men, it also doesn't matter how orgasm is achieved—whether through masturbation, petting, oral sex, intercourse, or fantasizing about another student in chem lab—because orgasm still involves the same physiological processes—involuntary contractions of the pelvic muscles at the base of the penis expel semen and release sexual tension. A woman or a man might prefer one source of orgasm to another (e.g., with a lover or by masturbation, or with one person rather than another), but the biological events that define orgasm remain the same.

Although orgasms attained through vaginal penetration or masturbation may be physiologically alike, they contain key psychological or subjective differences. (Were it not so, there would be fewer sexual relationships.) Partnered sexual activity can be accompanied by feelings of attachment, love, and connectedness to your partner. Solo masturbation, by contrast, is more likely to be experienced solely as a sexual pleasure and release.

The purported distinction between clitoral and vaginal orgasm also rests on the assumption that the clitoris isn't stimulated during intercourse. Masters and Johnson showed this to be false. Penile coital thrusting draws the clitoral hood back and forth against the clitoris. Vaginal pressure also heightens blood flow in the clitoris, further setting the stage for orgasm (Cai et al., 2008).

One might think Masters and Johnson's research settled the question of whether there are different types of female orgasm. Other investigators, however, have proposed that there are distinct forms of female orgasm, but not those suggested by psychoanalytic theory.

Singer and Singer (1972) have suggested that there are three types of female orgasm—vulval, uterine, and blended. According to the Singers, the vulval orgasm represents the type of orgasm described by Masters and Johnson (1966), which involves vulval contractions (contractions of the vaginal barrel). Consistent with the findings of Masters and Johnson (1966), the Singers note that the vulval orgasm remains the same regardless of the source of stimulation, whether clitoral or vaginal.

According to the Singers, the uterine orgasm does not involve vulval contractions; it occurs only in response to deep thrusting against the cervix. This thrusting slightly displaces the uterus and stimulates the tissues that cover the abdominal organs. The uterine orgasm is accompanied by a certain pattern of breathing. Gasping or gulping of air is followed by an involuntary holding of the breath as orgasm approaches. When orgasm is reached, the breath is explosively exhaled. The uterine orgasm is accompanied by deep feelings of relaxation and sexual satisfaction.

The third type, or blended orgasm, combines features of the vulval and uterine orgasms. It involves both an involuntary breath-holding response and contractions of the pelvic muscles. The Singers note that the type of orgasm a woman experiences depends on such factors as which parts of her body are stimulated and for how long. Each type of orgasm produces its own kind of satisfaction, and no one type is necessarily preferable to any other.

The Singers' hypothesis of three distinct forms of female orgasm remains controversial. Researchers initially scoffed at the idea that orgasms could arise from vaginal stimulation alone. The vagina, after all—especially the inner two-thirds of the vaginal cavity—is relatively insensitive to stimulation, erotic or otherwise. Proponents of the Singers' model counter that the type of uterine orgasm they describe is induced more by pressure resulting from deep pelvic thrusting than by touch.

Sexuality and Disability

Millions of Canadians live with physical or intellectual disabilities. Researchers at Trent University who study people with disabilities have found that the disabled are often seen as sexless and childlike (Scott & Humphreys, 2007). Such views are based on misconceptions. Some of these myths and stereotypes may be eroding, in part because of the success of civil and social rights movements for the disabled.

A person may be born with or acquire a bodily impairment, or suffer a loss of function or a disfiguring change in appearance. Although the disability may require adjustments before the person can engage in sexual activity, most people with disabilities have the same sexual needs, feelings, and desires as those without disabilities. Their ability to express these needs and feelings depends on the physical limitations imposed by their disabilities, how they adjust to their disabilities, and the availability of partners.

People with intellectual or developmental disabilities also face challenges with respect to sexuality. For example, youth with developmental disabilities may require sex education materials specifically designed to accommodate their levels of comprehension and pace of learning. People with profound intellectual or developmental disabilities may require guidance and education around issues of consent to sexual activity, as they may be sexually exploited by others, and some benefit from learning clear guidelines for appropriate sexual behaviours and relationships.

Perhaps the greatest challenge to the sexuality of disabled people, however, is that they must live in a society where myths, misconceptions, and negative stereotypes about sexuality and disability abound. For example, people with visible physical disabilities are confronted by narrow cultural representations of the "body beautiful" and standards of attractiveness. People with intellectual or developmental disabilities suffer immensely from the belief that they're incapable of healthy sexual and romantic relationships.

Researchers at the University of Alberta (Esmail, Darby, Walter, & Knupp, 2010) have conducted focus groups with service providers, people with disabilities, and the general public to identify societal perceptions and attitudes toward sexuality and disability. To stimulate discussion, they showed participants the documentary film *SexAbility*. Based on their research, the authors concluded that there's a significant stigma attached to the sexuality of disabled people. "Stigma can lead individuals to internalize concepts of asexuality," they wrote, "and may impact confidence, desire, and ability to find a partner, while distorting one's overall sexual self-concept, due to these sociocultural barriers" (p. 1154).

For young people, establishing mature sexual relationships generally demands some distance from parents. People with disabilities who are physically dependent on their parents may find it especially difficult to develop sexual relationships. Parents who acknowledge their children's sexual development can help facilitate dating. Far too often, however, as Cole (1988) reports, parents become overprotective:

> Adolescent disabled girls have the same ideas, hopes, and dreams about sexuality as able-bodied girls. They will have learned the gender role expectations set for them by the media and others, and may experience difficulty if they lack more substantive educational information about sexuality and sex function. In addition, their expectations may come in conflict with the family, which may have consistently protected or overindulged the child and not permitted her to "grow up." . . . In many cases, the families are intensely concerned about the sexual and emotional vulnerability of the daughter and hope that "nothing bad" will happen to her. They may, therefore, encourage her to wear youthful clothing and to stay a safe little girl. The families can mistakenly assume there may be no sexual life ahead of her, and protect her from this perceived bitter reality with youthful clothing and little-girlish ways. The result can be, of course, that the young, emerging woman may become societally handicapped in learning how to conduct herself as a sexual woman. She will be infantilized (pp. 282–283).

In such families, young people with disabilities get the message that sex is not for them. As they mature, they may need education to help them accept the normality of their sexual feelings.

Most health-care professionals are unequipped to provide sexuality counselling to the physically disabled. In a study of 226 health-care professionals in Ontario, 95% said they hadn't been adequately trained in sexuality and the physically disabled (Molloy & Herold, 1985). Sex education in schools and other sources of information about sexuality have typically neither included nor acknowledged the information needs of people with disabilities (Di Giulio, 2003; Esmail et al., 2010).

Fortunately, there are signs of progress. Sexuality education programs for people with disabilities are more common today. For example, the Anne Johnston Health Station (www.ajhs.ca) in Toronto offers a program called *SexAbility* that provides sexual health information to physically disabled youth through peer-to-peer workshops and resources. While information on sexuality and disability was once hard to locate, the internet now offers a wealth of information on disability and sexuality.

Physical Disabilities

According to Margaret Nosek and her colleagues (2004), sexual wellness for people with disabilities, as for all people, involves five factors:

- A positive sexual self-concept (i.e., seeing oneself as valuable, both sexually and as a person).
- Knowledge about sexuality.
- Positive, productive relationships.

- An ability to cope with social, environmental, physical, and emotional barriers to sexuality.
- Maintenance of good general and sexual health, within personal limitations.

This model applies to all of us, of course. Let's now consider aspects of specific physical disabilities and human sexuality.

MULTIPLE SCLEROSIS Multiple sclerosis (MS) is a chronic, unpredictable disease that affects the nervous system. The tissue called myelin, which surrounds and protects nerve cells, disintegrates, leaving scar tissue in its place. MS impairs sexual functioning, and people with MS report more sexual problems than people without the disorder (Forbes et al., 2006; McCabe, 2004). There's a good deal of individual variation, however. The disorder's progression and effects don't follow a straight line. Many people with MS in good relationships enjoy fine sex lives for many years.

Researchers at the University of Alberta (Esmail et al., 2007) interviewed couples in which the wives had MS, to find out how it affects sexual relationships. The wives reported that MS negatively affected their sexual functioning and enjoyment, as well as their feelings of sexual desirability. They kept these feelings hidden from their husbands, and focused instead on sexually pleasing them, worrying that otherwise their husbands might decide to leave them and find new partners. Because the wives didn't reveal their true sexual status, their husbands thought their wives' sexuality was unaffected by MS.

CEREBRAL PALSY **Cerebral palsy** doesn't generally impair sexual interest, capacity for orgasm, or fertility. Depending on the nature and degree of muscle spasticity and the lack of voluntary muscle control, however, afflicted people may be limited to certain types of sexual activity and positions (Cho et al., 2004).

People with disabilities such as cerebral palsy often suffer social rejection during adolescence, and perceive themselves as unfit for or unworthy of intimate sexual relationships, especially with people who aren't disabled. They're often socialized into an asexual role. Sensitive counselling can help them understand and accept their sexuality, promote a more positive body image, and provide the social skills to establish intimate relationships.

SPINAL-CORD INJURIES People who suffer physical disability as a result of traumatic injury or physical illness must not only learn to cope with their physical limitations, but also adjust to a world designed for able-bodied people. Most of those who suffer disabling spinal-cord injuries are young, active males. Automobile or pedestrian accidents account for about half of these cases. Other common causes include bullet or stab wounds, sports injuries, and falls.

Depending on the location of the injury relative to the spinal cord, a loss of voluntary control (paralysis) can occur in either the legs (paraplegia) or all four limbs (quadriplegia). A loss of sensation may also occur in parts of the body that lie below the site of injury.

The effect of spinal-cord injury on sexual response depends on the injury's site and severity. Men have two erection centres in the spinal cord—a higher centre in the lumbar region, which controls psychogenic erections, and a lower one in the sacral region, which controls reflexive erections. When damage occurs at or above the lumbar centre, the man loses the capacity for psychogenic erections, which occur in response to mental stimulation alone (e.g., viewing erotic films or fantasizing). He may still be able to achieve reflexive erections via direct stimulation of the penis, because this type of erection is controlled by the sacral erection centre, which is located in a lower portion of the spinal cord. He can't feel any genital sensations, however, because the nerve connections to the brain are severed. A man with damage to the sacral erection centre loses the capacity for reflexive erections, but can still achieve psychogenic erections as long as his upper spinal cord remains intact.

Cerebral palsy   A muscular disorder caused by damage to the central nervous system, usually before or during birth, and characterized by spastic paralysis.

Innovative Canadian Research

IMPROVING SEXUAL FUNCTION IN MEN WITH SPINAL-CORD INJURIES

In an experimental study, researchers in Quebec (Courtois et al., 2007) found that some vibrators are far more successful than others in helping men with spinal-cord injuries ejaculate. Some who cannot ejaculate with a vibrator alone can ejaculate when taking the prescription oral drug Midodrine about 30 minutes before using the vibrator. The researchers believe proper instruction and assistance, preferably in a hospital setting, will allow the majority of men with spinal injuries to ejaculate.

Ejaculation, however, is not the only source of the physical sensations associated with sexual pleasure. Researchers in Vancouver have conducted innovative experiments with spinal-cord-injured men who lack penile sensation, exploring the use of a sensory substitution devise that captures the motion of sexual activity and maps it to an electrotactile stimulation array on the man's tongue (Borisoff, Elliot, Hocaloski, & Birch, 2010). Using this system, they theorized, the men should have been able to perceive rhythmic up-and-down hand stroking of their penises as a flowing motion back and forth on their tongues. Although the men using the system did not report orgasm-like sensations, they did report increased levels of sexual pleasure.

Overall, researchers have found that about three out of four men with spinal-cord injuries are able to achieve erections, but only about one in ten continues to ejaculate naturally (Spark, 1991). Others can be helped to ejaculate with the aid of vibrators.

Although the frequency of sexual activity among men with spinal-cord injuries tends to decline after they're injured, about one in three continues to engage in sexual intercourse (Komisaruk & Whipple, 2005). These men typically report increased interest in alternative sexual activities, especially involving areas above the level of injury, such as the mouth, lips, neck, and ears.

Retention of sexual response in women also depends on the site and severity of the injury. Women may lose the ability to experience genital sensations or to lubricate normally during sexual stimulation. Breast sensations may remain intact, however, making this area even more erotogenic. Most women with spinal-cord injuries can engage in intercourse, become impregnated, and deliver vaginally. A survey of 68 spinal-cord-injured women showed that about half were able to achieve orgasm as a result of erotic audiovisual material combined with manual genital stimulation (Sipski et al., 2001).

Couples facing the challenge of spinal-cord injury may expand their sexual repertoires to focus less on genital stimulation (except to attain the reflexes of erection and lubrication) and more on parts of the body that retain sensation. Stimulation of some areas, such as the ears, neck, and breasts (in both men and women), can yield pleasurable erotic sensations.

SENSORY DISABILITIES Sensory disabilities, such as blindness and deafness, do not directly affect genital responsiveness. Still, sexuality may be affected in many ways. A person who has been blind since birth or early childhood may have difficulty understanding a partner's anatomy. Sex education curricula have been designed to enable visually impaired people to learn about sexual anatomy via models. Anatomically correct dolls may be used to simulate positions of intercourse.

Deaf people, too, often lack knowledge about sex. Their ability to comprehend the social cues involved in forming and maintaining intimate relationships may also be impaired. Sex education programs based on sign language help many hearing-impaired people become more socially perceptive and knowledgeable about the physical aspects of sex.

People with visual and hearing impairments often lack self-esteem and self-confidence, problems that make it difficult for them to establish intimate relationships. Counselling may help them become more aware of their sexuality and to develop social skills.

OTHER PHYSICAL DISABILITIES AND IMPAIRMENTS Specific disabilities pose particular challenges and limitations when it comes to sexual functioning. **Arthritis** may make it difficult or painful to bend your arms, knees, and hips. Sexual activities that minimize discomfort may be helpful, and so might applying moist heat to the joints before sexual relations.

Arthritis A progressive disease characterized by inflammation and pain in the joints.

For a heterosexual couple, a male amputee may find that he's better balanced in the lateral-entry or female-superior position than in the male-superior position. Gay and lesbian couples can experiment with different positions and techniques for sexual pleasuring that accommodate for limited mobility or function. A woman with limited hand function may find it difficult or impossible to insert a diaphragm, and may need to ask for her partner's help or switch to another method of contraception. Sensitivity to one another's needs is vital for couples in which one member has a disability, just as it is for able-bodied couples.

Intellectual and Developmental Disabilities

People with intellectual disabilities (e.g., impaired cognitive functioning), such as developmental disabilities (e.g., mental or physical impairments that begin to occur before age 18), are often stereotyped as incapable of understanding their sexual impulses. People with developmental disabilities are sometimes assumed to lack sexuality and to maintain childlike innocence throughout their lives. At the same time, it's widely acknowledged that individuals with limited mental capacity are vulnerable to sexual abuse, and may not be able to consent to sexual activity with others (Plaut, 2006; Servais, 2006).

Some people stereotype those with developmental disabilities in the opposite direction, as having stronger-than-normal sex drives that they're incapable of controlling. These stereotypes are exaggerated. In cases where people with developmental disabilities have acted inappropriately, it's often because they've never received adequate sexuality education, or they've been forbidden by their families or caregivers to express themselves sexually in any way. Not surprisingly, developmentally disabled people deprived of the opportunity to learn about sexuality and appropriate social conventions—like anyone under these conditions—may behave inappropriately. Appropriate sexual health and relationship education is crucial to the health and well-being of developmentally disabled people.

Although the physical changes of puberty may be delayed in people with developmental disabilities, most develop the same sexual feelings as other youth. Most are capable of learning about their sexuality and can enter into rewarding, responsible intimate relationships (Gross, 2006a).

Expanding Sexual Horizons

One of the greatest impediments to sexual fulfillment among people with disabilities is finding a loving and supportive partner. Hopefully, this barrier will decrease as stereotypes that portray disabled people as undesirable erode. Depending on the nature of the disability, a non-disabled partner may need to be open to assuming a more active sexual role, to compensate for the limitations of the partner with the disability. Two partners with disabilities need to be sensitive to one another's needs and physical limitations.

Living with disabilities can prompt individuals and couples to explore avenues for creative sexual expression. They might expand their sexual repertoires to incorporate ways of pleasuring one another that are not fixated on genital stimulation

CRITICAL THINKING QUESTIONS

Should group homes for intellectually or developmentally challenged people have policies about sexual activity between residents? If so, can you think of factors that should be considered in setting such a policy?

Applied Knowledge

A COMPREHENSIVE GUIDE TO SEX AND DISABILITY

Toronto educators Miriam Kaufman, Cory Silverberg, and Fran Odette (2007) conducted a survey of people with disabilities, asking about their beliefs, feelings, and unmet needs around sexuality. The survey responses provided the basis for their book *The Ultimate Guide to Sex and Disability: For All of Us Who Live with Disabilities, Chronic Pain, and Illness.*

This sex guide is aimed at people of all ages and all sexual identities. It's intended to improve readers' sexual self-esteem and sex lives, and to help them become sexually independent. Topics include:

- Where to find partners.
- How to talk to partners about sex and disability.
- How to discuss sex with health-care providers.

- Instruction on masturbation, oral sex, vaginal penetration, and anal sex.
- Sexual positions that minimize stress and maximize pleasure.
- How to deal with fatigue, pain, and spasms during sex.
- Adapting sex toys to make them work for you.

The book provides an extensive list of resources.

or conventional standards of sexual activity. Indeed, freeing themselves from conventional standards for what a satisfying sexual experience must include (e.g., vaginal or anal penetration, genital orgasm) can enable disabled people to use their imaginations to expand their sexual horizons in ways that non-disabled people might feel inhibited about. As Penny, a disabled woman, puts it, "If you're a sexually active disabled person, and comfortable with the sexual side of your life, it's remarkable how dull and unimaginative non-disabled people's sex lives can appear" (Shakespeare, 2000, p. 163).

Summing Up

Every sense plays a role in sexual experience, but some are more important than others.

Visual information plays a major role in human sexual attraction. Visual cues can be sexual turn-ons or turn-offs.

Although the sense of smell plays a lesser role in governing sexual arousal in humans than in lower mammals, particular odours can be sexual turn-ons or turn-offs for people. Many organisms are sexually aroused by naturally produced chemicals called pheromones, but their role in human sexual behaviour remains unclear.

The sense of touch has the most direct effects on sexual arousal and response. Erogenous zones are especially sensitive to tactile sexual stimulation.

Taste appears to play only a minor role in sexual arousal and response.

Sounds can be turn-ons or turn-offs.

Alleged aphrodisiacs, such as foods that in some way resemble the genitals, have not been shown to contribute to sexual arousal or response.

Some drugs, such as antidepressants, dampen sexual arousal and response.

The alleged aphrodisiac effects of psychoactive drugs such as alcohol and cocaine may reflect our expectations of them or their effects on sexual inhibitions, rather than their direct stimulation of sexual response. Alcohol is also connected with a liberated social role, and thereby provides an external excuse for dubious behaviour. Some people report increased sexual pleasure upon initial use of certain drugs, but frequent use can lead to sexual dysfunction.

The brain plays a central role in sexual functioning. The cerebral cortex interprets sensory information as sexual turn-ons or turn-offs.

Sex hormones have organizing and activating effects on behaviour. Both men and women produce one genuine aphrodisiac: testosterone.

Many factors affect the sexual arousal of men and women.

Women show greater flexibility than men in sexual arousal patterns.

Masters and Johnson found that the physiological responses of men and women to sexual stimulation are quite alike.

The excitement phase of sexual response is characterized by erection in the male and vaginal lubrication in the female.

The plateau phase is an advanced state of arousal that precedes orgasm.

The third phase of the sexual response cycle is characterized by orgasmic contractions of the pelvic musculature. Orgasm in the male occurs in two stages of muscular contractions. Orgasm in the female is manifested by contractions of the pelvic muscles that surround the vaginal barrel.

During the resolution phase, the body returns to its pre-aroused state.

Kaplan developed a three-stage model of sexual response: desire, excitement, and orgasm. Kaplan's model makes it more convenient for clinicians to classify and treat sexual dysfunctions.

Basson argues that for women, intimacy plays a key role in sexual response.

Multiple orgasm is the occurrence of one or more additional orgasms following the first, within a short period and before the body has returned to its pre-plateau level of arousal.

Freud theorized the existence of two types of orgasms in women: clitoral and vaginal. Masters and Johnson found only one kind of orgasm among women. Singer and Singer suggested that there are three types of female orgasm: vulval, uterine, and blended.

People with disabilities may suffer from prejudice that depicts them as sexless or as lacking the means to express their sexual needs or feelings.

Cerebral palsy does not usually impair sexual interest, capacity for orgasm, or fertility, but afflicted people may be limited to certain types of sexual activity and positions. People with spinal-cord injuries may be paralyzed and lose sensation below the waist, but they often respond reflexively to direct genital stimulation.

Most people with developmental disabilities can learn the basics of their own sexuality and develop responsible intimate relationships.

Test Yourself

Multiple-Choice Questions

1. **Which of the following statements about the impact of alcohol consumption on sexuality is false?**
   (a) For healthy young adults, drinking large amounts of alcohol is unlikely to interfere with the orgasmic phase of sexual response.
   (b) Drinking alcohol can impair judgment and information-processing ability, leading people to engage in sexual behaviours they wouldn't engage in when sober.
   (c) Drinking alcohol can induce feelings of well-being and lower sexual inhibitions.
   (d) Drinking one beer or a glass of wine is unlikely to negatively affect a person's ability to respond sexually.

2. **As aphrodisiacs, the effects of chocolate and oysters:**
   (a) Are similar to fluoxetine.
   (b) Have been proven in the laboratory.
   (c) Are subject to the placebo effect.
   (d) Are similar to testosterone.

3. **Parts of the brain involved in sexual function include:**
   (a) The cerebellum and the corpus callosum.
   (b) The cerebral cortex and the limbic system.
   (c) The thalamus and the auditory bulb.
   (d) The medulla and the central sulcus.

4. **Prolonged and frequent use of recreational drugs such as cocaine and methamphetamine are likely to:**
   (a) Lead to hypersexuality.
   (b) Have little or no impact on sexual function.
   (c) Increase the probability of sexual dysfunction.
   (d) Improve sexual function.

5. **According to Masters and Johnson, erection and lubrication occur during the _____ phase of the sexual response cycle.**
   (a) excitement
   (b) orgasmic
   (c) plateau
   (d) resolution

6. **According to research by King, Belsky, Mah, and Binik, women's orgasms during solitary masturbation are more likely to result in _____ than orgasms during partnered sexual activity.**
   (a) feelings of relaxation
   (b) pleasurable satisfaction
   (c) flushing sensations
   (d) throbbing sensations

7. **The hormone _____ activates the sex drives of both women and men.**
   (a) prolactin
   (b) oxytocin
   (c) progesterone
   (d) testosterone

8. **The three stages of Kaplan's model of sexual response are:**
   (a) Desire, excitement, and orgasm.
   (b) Plateau, desire, and arousal.
   (c) Desire, resolution, and orgasm.
   (d) Desire, plateau, and orgasm.

Continued

9. Basson's female sexual response model puts more emphasis on _____ than Masters and Johnson's or Kaplan's models do.
   (a) desire
   (b) affection
   (c) intimacy
   (d) orgasm

10. Which statement most accurately describes the sexuality of people with disabilities?
    (a) They generally have the same levels of sexual feelings and desires as non-disabled people.
    (b) They generally have lower levels of sexual feelings and desires than non-disabled people.
    (c) They're more likely to be over-sexed than non-disabled people.
    (d) They can easily shrug off the prejudice and ignorance they're subjected to regarding their sexuality.

You'll find answers to the "Test Yourself" questions on page 495.

Questions for Critical Thinking

1. You're a hearing-impaired student who uses a sign-language interpreter in your human sexuality class. The interpreter seemed comfortable earlier in the semester, but now that the topics are getting more personal and the lectures more graphic, he says he's no longer willing to attend the lectures, and that furthermore, he really doesn't think anyone with a disability should even be thinking about sex. How might you deal with this?

2. You're a woman who's read magazine articles telling you how great it is to have multiple orgasms, but you have difficulty having one, let alone several. How does this make you feel? Do you think that just because some women can have multiple orgasms, women who can't or who don't care should feel inadequate?

3. You're a man, who's read in magazines that some women can have multiple orgasms, but your partner sometimes has difficulty having just one. How does this make you feel? Is one (or both) of you sexually inadequate? Or is this just another example of the media setting goals for sexual performance that are unrealistic and counterproductive to a couple's sexual enjoyment?

MySearchLab

MySearchLab offers extensive help to students with their writing and research project and provides round-the-clock access to credible and reliable source material. Take a tour at www.mysearchlab.com.

Gender Identity and Gender Roles

Gender The psychological state of being female or male, as influenced by cultural concepts of gender-appropriate behaviour. Gender is distinct from anatomic sex, which is based on the physical differences between females and males.

Gender typing The process by which children acquire behaviours deemed appropriate for their sex.

Sexual differentiation The process by which males and females develop distinct reproductive anatomy.

Chromosome A rodlike structure found in the nucleus of every living cell. It carries the genetic code, in the form of genes.

Zygote A fertilized ovum (egg cell).

In this chapter, we'll address the biological, psychological, and sociological aspects of **gender**. First, we'll define gender as the psychological sense of being female or male, which is influenced by socially ascribed roles. While anatomic sex is based on anatomy, gender is a complex concept, based partly on anatomy, partly on the psychology of the individual, and partly on culture and tradition.

Next, we'll focus on sexual differentiation, or the process by which males and females develop distinct reproductive anatomy. We'll then turn to gender roles, the clusters of behaviour that are deemed masculine or feminine in particular cultures, and examine research findings on sex differences. We'll consider **gender typing**, the processes by which boys and girls come to behave in line with what's expected of men and women (most of the time). We'll also explore the concept of psychological androgyny, which applies to people in our culture who display characteristics associated with both gender roles.

Prenatal Sexual Differentiation

Over the years, many ideas have been proposed to account for **sexual differentiation**. Aristotle mistakenly believed that the anatomical difference between males and females was due to the heat of semen at the time of sexual relations. Hot semen generated males, whereas cold semen made females (National Center for Biotechnology Information, 2006).

When a sperm cell fertilizes an ovum, 23 **chromosomes** from the male parent normally combine with 23 chromosomes from the female parent. The **zygote**, the beginning of a new human being, is only 0.04 centimetres long. Yet, on this tiny stage, the stamp of a unique individual has already been ensured—whether the person will have black or blond hair, grow bald or develop a widow's peak, and become male or female.

The chromosomes from each parent combine to form 23 pairs. The twenty-third pair is the sex chromosomes. An ovum carries an X sex chromosome, but a sperm carries either an X or a Y sex chromosome. If a sperm with an X chromosome fertilizes the ovum, the newly conceived embryo will normally develop as a female, with an XX sex chromosomal structure. If the sperm carries a Y chromosome, the child will normally develop as a male, with an XY structure.

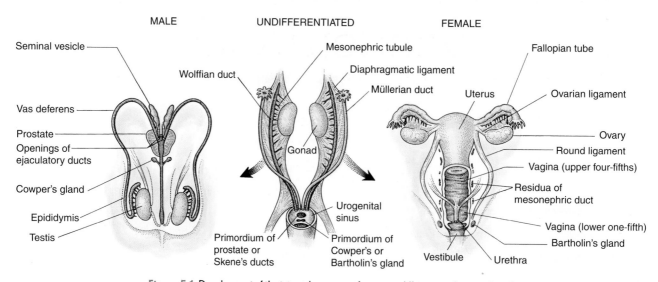

Figure 5.1 Development of the internal sex organs from an undifferentiated stage, about five or six weeks after conception.

After fertilization, the zygote divides repeatedly. Within a few short weeks, one cell becomes billions of cells. At about three weeks, a primitive heart begins to drive blood through the embryonic bloodstream. By about five or six weeks, when the **embryo** is only 0.5 centimetres to 1 centimetre long, it has a pair of sexually undifferentiated gonads, two sets of primitive duct structures called the Müllerian (female) ducts and the Wolffian (male) ducts, and primitive external genitals whose sex cannot be visually distinguished. (See Figures 5.1 and 5.2.)

During the first six weeks or so of prenatal development, embryonic structures of both genders develop along similar lines, resembling primitive female structures. At about the seventh week after conception, the genetic code (XX or XY) begins to assert itself, causing changes in the gonads, genital ducts, and external genitals. Genetic activity on the Y sex chromosome causes the testes to begin to differentiate (National Center for Biotechnology Information, 2006). If the Y chromosome is absent, ovaries begin to differentiate. Those rare embryos that have only one X sex

Embryo The stage of prenatal development that begins with implantation of a fertilized ovum in the uterus and concludes with development of the major organ systems at about two months after conception.

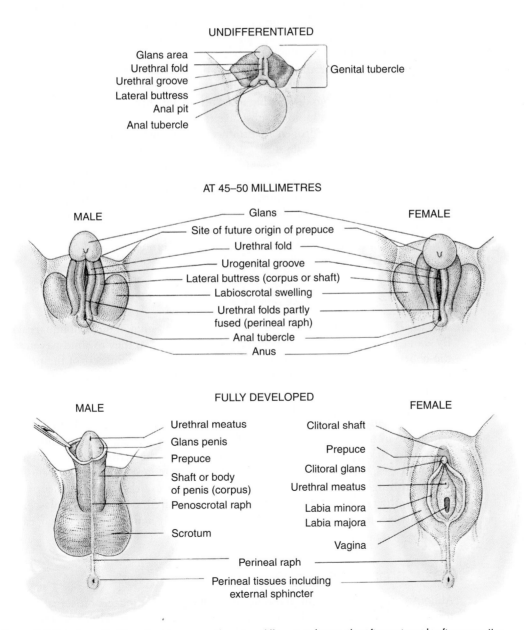

Figure 5.2 Development of the external sex organs from an undifferentiated stage, about five or six weeks after conception.

chromosome instead of the typical XY or XX arrangement become female, because they lack the Y chromosome. One could say the basic blueprint of the human embryo is female (De Vries et al., 2002; Steinemann & Steineman, 2005), and the genetic instructions in the Y chromosome cause the embryo to deviate from the female developmental course.

By about the seventh week of prenatal development, strands of tissue begin to organize into seminiferous tubules. Female gonads begin to develop somewhat later than male gonads. The forerunners of follicles that will bear ova are not found until the fetal stage of development, about 10 weeks after conception. Ovaries begin to form at 11 or 12 weeks.

Sex Hormones and Sexual Differentiation

Once genes have done their work and testes develop in the embryo, they begin to produce male sex hormones, or **androgens**. Without androgens, we'd all develop female external reproductive organs. The most important androgen, **testosterone**, spurs differentiation of the male (Wolffian) duct system. (See Figure 5.1.) Each Wolffian duct develops into an epididymis, vas deferens, and seminal vesicle. The external genitals, including the penis, begin to take shape at about the eighth week of development, under the influence of another androgen, dihydrotestosterone (DHT). Yet another testicular hormone, secreted during the fetal stage, prevents the Müllerian ducts from developing into the female duct system; it's appropriately termed the Müllerian-inhibiting substance (MIS).

Small amounts of androgen are produced in female fetuses, but they're not normally sufficient to cause male sexual differentiation. In female fetuses, the relative absence of androgens causes degeneration of the Wolffian ducts and prompts development of female sexual organs. The Müllerian ducts evolve into fallopian tubes, the uterus, and the upper two-thirds of the vagina. These developments occur even in the absence of female sex hormones. Although female sex hormones are crucial in puberty, they're not involved in fetal sexual differentiation. If a fetus with an XY sex chromosomal structure failed to produce testosterone, it would develop female sexual organs.

Descent of the Testes and Ovaries

The testes and ovaries develop from slender structures high in the abdominal cavity. By about 10 weeks after conception, they've descended so they're almost even with the upper edge of the pelvis. The ovaries remain there for the rest of the prenatal period, later rotating and further descending to their adult positions in the pelvis. About four months after conception, the testes normally descend into the scrotal sac through the **inguinal canal**, which then closes.

In a small percentage of males, at least one of the testes fails to descend, remaining in the abdomen at birth. The condition is termed **cryptorchidism**. In most cases of cryptorchidism, the testes migrate to the scrotum during infancy. In some cases, they descend by puberty. Men with undescended testes are usually treated through surgery or hormonal therapy, because they're at higher risk for cancer of the testes. Sperm production is also impaired, because the undescended testes are subjected to a higher-than-optimal body temperature, which causes sterility.

Sex Chromosome Abnormalities

Abnormalities of the sex chromosomes can have profound effects on sexual characteristics, physical health, and psychological development. **Klinefelter's syndrome**, a condition that affects about one in 500 males, is caused by an extra X sex chromosome,

---

Androgens Male sex hormones.

Testosterone The male sex hormone that fosters development of male sex characteristics and is connected with the sex drive.

Inguinal canal A fetal canal that connects the scrotum and the testes, allowing the latter to descend.

Cryptorchidism A condition in which at least one of the testes fails to descend.

Klinefelter's syndrome A disorder in which a male has an extra X sex chromosome (an XXY pattern, rather than an XY pattern).

giving the man an XXY rather than an XY pattern. Men with this pattern fail to develop appropriate secondary sex characteristics. They have enlarged breasts and poor muscular development, and because they fail to produce sperm, they're infertile. They also tend to have mild mental retardation.

Turner's syndrome, which affects about one in 2500 females, is caused by having one rather than two X sex chromosomes. Females with the syndrome may not naturally undergo puberty, so they usually begin hormone treatments when normal pubertal changes would otherwise start to spur the growth of secondary sex characteristics.

The brain, like the genital organs, undergoes prenatal sexual differentiation. Testosterone causes cells in the hypothalamus of a male fetus to become insensitive to the female sex hormone estrogen. In the absence of testosterone, the hypothalamus of a female fetus becomes sensitive to estrogen.

Sensitivity to estrogen is important in regulation of the menstrual cycle after puberty. The hypothalamus detects low levels of estrogen in the blood at the end of each cycle, and initiates a new cycle by stimulating the pituitary gland to secrete follicle-stimulating hormone (FSH). FSH, in turn, stimulates the ovaries to produce estrogen, and stimulates an immature follicle in an ovary to ripen.

Gender Identity

Gender identity is the psychological awareness of being male or female. It's one of the most obvious and most important aspects of self-concept. **Sex assignment** (also called gender assignment) reflects the child's anatomic sex, and usually occurs at birth. A child's sex is so important to parents that they may ask whether it's a boy or a girl before they count fingers and toes.

Most children become aware of their anatomic sex by about 18 months of age. By 36 months, most children have acquired a firm sense of gender identity (Rathus, 2006).

Nature and Nurture

What determines gender identity? Are our brains biologically programmed along masculine or feminine lines by prenatal sex hormones? Does the environment, in the form of postnatal learning experiences, shape our self-concepts as males or females? Or does gender identity reflect an intermingling of biological and environmental influences?

Gender identity is nearly always consistent with chromosomal gender. Such consistency does not, however, prove that gender identity is biologically determined. We also tend to be reared as males or females, in accordance with our anatomic sex. How, then, can we sort out the roles of nature and nurture, of biology and the environment?

Researchers have found clues in the experiences of rare individuals called **intersexuals**, who possess the gonads of one gender and external genitalia that are ambiguous or typical of the other gender (Zucker, 2005b). Intersexuals are sometimes reared as members of the gender opposite to their chromosomal genders. Researchers wonder whether the gender identity of these children reflects their chromosomal and gonadal genders or the genders they've been reared with. Before going further with this, let's distinguish between hermaphrodites and intersexuals.

Hormonal factors during prenatal development produce various congenital outcomes. Some individuals are born with both ovarian and testicular tissue. They're called **hermaphrodites**, after the Greek myth of the son of Hermes and Aphrodite, whose body became united with that of a nymph while he was bathing. True hermaphrodites may have one gonad of each gender (a testicle and an ovary) or gonads that combine testicular and ovarian tissue.

Turner's syndrome A disorder is which a female has just one X sex chromosome (an X pattern, rather than an XX pattern).

Gender identity One's view of oneself as being male or female.

Sex assignment The labelling of a newborn as a male or a female. It's also referred to as gender assignment.

Intersexual A person who possesses the gonads of one gender and external genitalia that are ambiguous or typical of the other gender. An intersexual is also referred to as a pseudohermaphrodite.

Hermaphrodite An individual who possesses both ovarian and testicular tissue.

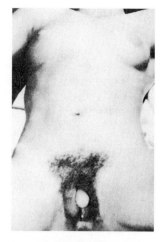

Figure 5.3 A hermaphrodite.
This genetic (XX) female has one testicle and one ovary, and the gender identity of a male.

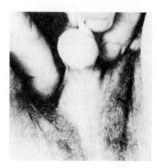

Figure 5.4 An intersexual.
This genetic (XX) female has female internal sexual structures (ovaries) and masculinized external genitals. This condition has been caused by congenital adrenal hyperplasia.

Congenital adrenal hyperplasia A form of intersexualism in which a genetic female has internal female sexual structures and masculinized external genitals.

Androgen insensitivity syndrome A form of intersexualism in which a genetic male is prenatally insensitive to androgens. As a result, his genitals do not become normally masculinized.

Dominican Republic syndrome A form of intersexualism in which a genetic enzyme disorder prevents testosterone from masculinizing the external genitalia.

Regardless of their genetic sex, hermaphrodites usually assume the identities and roles of the genders they're assigned at birth. The photo in Figure 5.3 shows a genetic female (XX) with a right testicle and a left ovary. This person married and became a stepfather with a firm male identity. The roles of biology and environment remain tangled, however, because true hermaphrodites have gonadal tissue of both genders.

True hermaphroditism is quite rare (Kuhnle et al., 2003). Less rare is intersexualism, which occurs in perhaps one infant in 5000 (Intersex Society of North America, 2006; Sax, 2002). Intersexuals have testes or ovaries, but not both. Unlike hermaphrodites, intersexuals' gonads (testes or ovaries) match their chromosomal sex. Because of prenatal hormonal errors, however, their external genitals and sometimes their internal reproductive anatomy are ambiguous or resemble those of the opposite sex. Intersexualism has given researchers an opportunity to examine the roles of nature (biology) and nurture (environmental influences) in shaping gender identity.

The most common form of female intersexualism is **congenital adrenal hyperplasia** (CAH), in which a genetic (XX) female has female internal sexual structures (ovaries) and masculinized external genitals. (See the right-hand photo in Figure 5.4.) The clitoris is so enlarged that it may resemble a small penis. CAH is caused by high levels of androgens.

Swedish investigator Anna Servin and her colleagues (2003) studied gender-typed behaviours and interests in 26 girls with CAH and 26 girls without CAH. All of the girls were 2 to 10 years of age. Those with CAH showed more interest in masculine-typed toys such as transportation toys, and less interest in feminine-typed toys such as dolls. The girls with CAH were more likely to have boys as playmates and to want masculine-typed careers. Parents rated the behaviour of daughters with CAH as more "boylike" in toy choice and aggressiveness.

Another type of intersexualism, **androgen insensitivity syndrome**, affects genetic (XY) males who, as a result of a mutated gene, have experienced lower-than-normal prenatal sensitivity to androgens (National Library of Medicine, 2006). Consequently, their genitals have not masculinized normally. At birth, their testes are undescended and their external genitals are feminized, including small vaginas. Because of androgen insensitivity, their male duct systems (epididymis, vas deferentia, seminal vesicles, and ejaculatory ducts) have failed to develop. Nevertheless, their fetal testes have produced Müllerian-inhibiting substance, preventing the development of uteruses and fallopian tubes. Genetic males with androgen-insensitivity syndrome usually have little or no pubic and axillary (underarm) hair, because development of hair in these locations is dependent on androgens.

Another type of intersexualism is called **Dominican Republic syndrome**, because it was first documented there, in a group of 18 affected boys in two rural villages (Imperato-McGinley et al., 1974). Dominican Republic syndrome is a genetic enzyme disorder that prevents testosterone from masculinizing the external genitalia. The boys were born with normal testes and internal male reproductive organs, but their external genitals were malformed. Their penises were stunted and resembled clitorises. Their scrotums were incompletely formed and resembled female labia. They also had partially formed vaginas.

The boys with Dominican Republic syndrome resembled girls at birth and were reared as females. At puberty, however, their testes swung into normal testosterone production, causing startling changes: The testes descended, their voices deepened, their musculature filled out, and their "clitorises" expanded into penises. Of the 18 boys who were reared as girls, 17 shifted to male gender identities. Sixteen assumed stereotypical masculine gender roles. Of the remaining two, one adopted a male gender identity but continued to maintain a feminine gender role, including the wearing of dresses, while the other maintained a female gender

Innovative Canadian Research

GENDER IDENTITY DISORDER: A CONTROVERSIAL DIAGNOSIS

Gender-identity disorder (GID) is one of the most controversial diagnoses in the *Diagnostic and Statistical Manual of Mental Disorders* (DSM). Canadian researchers have taken differing perspectives toward variations in gender identity among children.

One of Canada's leading researchers on gender identity is Ken Zucker, head of the Child and Adolescent Gender Identity Clinic at the Centre for Addiction and Mental Health in Toronto. This clinic maintains the world's largest database of children diagnosed with GID. According to Zucker (2002), "**intersexuality**" is now the preferred term to encompass "syndromes characterized by some abnormality or anomaly in physical sex differentiation" (p. 4). This term is broader than the traditional "hermaphroditism."

Zucker's research demonstrates both biological and psychological factors in GID. Biological influences were indicated in a study that found more left-handers among boys with GID than within a control group (Zucker et al., 2001). Social influences were indicated in a study that found boys more than six times as likely as girls to be referred to a special clinic for GID (Zucker et al., 1997). The first cross-cultural study in the field, conducted by Zucker and his colleagues (Cohen-Kettenis et al., 2003), also found that far more boys than girls were referred to gender identity clinics, in both Canada and the Netherlands.

Zucker and his colleagues believe society is less accepting of cross-gendering in boys than in girls, so parents of cross-gendered boys are more likely to see the situation as a problem in need of professional remedy. In both countries, boys with GID were more likely than girls with GID to have problems with peers. This further supports the idea that cross-gender behaviour is better tolerated among girls than among boys.

Some researchers have questioned the validity of GID. Some lesbian, gay, bisexual, and transgender activists argue that the GID diagnosis pathologizes transgendered people. Canadian researchers Paul Vasey and Nancy Bartlett (2007) have conducted a study in Samoa, where, compared to North America, there's a high level of tolerance for males with feminine characteristics. Most Samoans consider cross-gender behaviour in children an unproblematic variation, not a mental disorder.

Vasey and Bartlett (2007) interviewed men referred to in Samoan culture as *fa'afafine* (males who are sexually attracted to men, and typically effeminate) who had frequently engaged in cross-gender behaviours during childhood. The authors noted that, although some Western clinicians would likely diagnose *fa'afafine* children with GID, the *fa'afafine* they interviewed did not recall feeling distressed as a direct result of their cross-gendered behaviours and identities.

Vasey and Bartlett (2007) conclude that the distress felt by North American children with cross-gender behaviours and identities is not a disorder. Rather, the distress is caused by the discriminatory and hostile attitudes such children are subjected to by society. The researchers argue that the diagnostic category of GID in children should not be included in future editions of the DSM, " . . . as there is no compelling evidence that cross-gender behaviors or identities, in and of themselves, cause distress in the individual" (p. 482).

identity, and later sought gender-reassignment surgery to "correct" the pubertal masculinization.

Many scientists conclude that gender identity is influenced by complex interactions among biological and psychosocial factors. Some place relatively greater emphasis on psychosocial factors (Bradley et al., 1998; Money, 1994). Others emphasize the roles of biological factors (Diamond, 1996; Servin, 2003), even though they allow that nurture plays a role in gender identity. The debate over the relative contributions of nature and nurture is likely to continue.

Transsexualism/Transgenderism

In 1953, a former American soldier named George Jorgenson journeyed to Denmark for a sex-change operation, changed her name to Christine Jorgensen, and made headlines (Michel & Pédinielli, 2005). Since then, thousands of transsexuals (also referred to as transgendered people) have undergone sex-reassignment surgery.

Intersexuality All of the different syndromes characterized by some abnormality or anomaly in physical sex differentiation.

CRITICAL THINKING QUESTIONS

In your opinion, should boys and girls who show persistent cross-gender behaviours be considered disordered?

Transsexualism A condition in which an individual strongly desires to be and to live as a member of the other sex. The American Psychiatric Association calls this "gender-identity disorder."

Transgenderism A synonym for "transsexualism." Also an activist movement seeking rights and pride for transgendered individuals. For many in the transgender—or "trans"—movement, the label "transgendered" encompasses not only transsexual and transgendered people, but also cross-dressers or transvestites, drag queens, drag kings, intersexed individuals, and anyone who's unconventionally gendered (i.e., who identifies or behaves in a manner that runs counter to expected societal norms for the gender assigned at birth).

Gender dysphoria A sense of incongruity between your anatomic sex and your gender identity.

Homosexual transsexuals Extremely feminine gay men who seek sex reassignment.

Autogynephilic Sexually stimulated by fantasies that his own body is female. The word comes from roots meaning "self," "woman," and "love" or "desire."

This surgery is also referred to as gender-reassignment surgery. In this textbook, however, we use "sex" to refer to anatomic sex and "gender" to refer to the psychological state of feeling male or female. To be consistent with this usage, we therefore refer to the surgery as reassigning a person's sex, not gender.

In **transsexualism**, an individual wishes to possess the anatomic features of the other sex, and to live as a person of the other sex. The term "**transgenderism**" is sometimes used as a synonym for "transsexualism." However, "transgenderism" also refers to an activist movement that seeks rights and pride for various transgendered individuals, including not just transsexuals, but also intersexuals, transvestites, and anyone who is unconventionally gendered—that is, anyone who identifies with or behaves in a manner that runs counter to the gender roles traditional for his or her assigned sex.

Many transsexuals undergo hormone treatments and surgery to create the appearance of the external genitals typical of the other sex. This can be done more precisely with male-to-female than with female-to-male transsexuals. After surgery, people can participate in sexual activity and even attain orgasm. One survey found that 85% of transsexual women attained orgasm during sexual activity (Lawrence, 2005). However, they cannot conceive or bear children.

What motivates transsexuals to live as people of the other sex? According to John Money (1994), transsexuals experience **gender dysphoria**. That is, they experience incongruity between their genital anatomy and their gender identities or roles. Although they have the anatomic genitalia of one sex, they feel that they're members of the other. The discrepancy motivates them to wish to be rid of their own primary sex characteristics (their external genitals and internal sex organs) and to live as members of the other sex. A male-to-female transsexual perceives himself to be a female who, through some quirk of fate, was born with the wrong genital equipment. A female-to-male transsexual perceives herself as a man trapped in a woman's body.

Some researchers contend that many men who seek to become women tend to fall into other categories—men who are extremely feminine, or men who are sexually aroused by the idea of becoming women. The first category includes **homosexual transsexuals**, extremely feminine gay men who aren't fully satisfied by sexual activity with other men (Blanchard, 1988, 1989). The second category refers to men who are **autogynephilic**, or sexually stimulated by fantasies that their own bodies are female (Bailey, 2003a, 2003b; Lawrence, 2004).

Transsexuals vary in their sexual orientations. In a review of several studies, Lawrence (2007) concluded that there are two distinct types of male-to-female transsexuals—homosexuals and non-homosexuals. In a laboratory experiment, 11 male-to-female transsexuals were shown video clips depicting sexual activity between two males, two females, and one male and one female. Five homosexual transsexual participants (attracted exclusively to males before sex reassignment) showed greater genital and subjective responses to male stimuli than to female stimuli, while six non-homosexual transsexual participants showed the opposite pattern (Lawrence et al., 2005).

The conceptualizations of male-to-female (MTF) transsexuals presented by Blanchard, Bailey, and Lawrence have been highly controversial. In particular, transgender activists have been upset by their assumption that MTF transsexuals are motivated to seek sex change by erotic interests, rather than by distress over having the gender identity of one sex and body of the other (Dredger, 2008).

Homosexual transsexuals usually show cross-gender preferences in play and dress during early childhood. Some report feeling that they've belonged to the other sex for as long as they can remember (Zucker, 2005a, 2005b). Some male-to-female transsexuals recall that, as children, they preferred playing with dolls, enjoyed wearing frilly dresses, and disliked rough-and-tumble play. They were often perceived by their peers as "sissy boys." Some female-to-male transsexuals report that as children they disliked dresses, and acted like "tomboys." They preferred playing with boys and "boys' games." Female-to-male transsexuals appear to have an easier time adjusting than male-to-female transsexuals do. Even during adulthood, it may be easier for a female transsexual to don men's clothes and pass for a slightly built man than it is for a brawny man to pass for a tall woman.

SEX REASSIGNMENT   Surgery is one element of sex reassignment. Because the surgery is irreversible, health professionals conduct careful evaluations to determine that people seeking reassignment are competent to make such decisions and have thought through the consequences (Bockting & Fung, 2006). They usually require that transsexuals live openly as members of the other sex for extended trial periods before surgery.

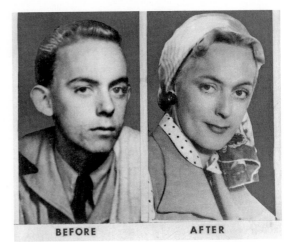

BEFORE   **AFTER**

George/Christine Jorgensen.
The concept of sex reassignment entered public consciousness in 1953, when Jorgensen had a sex-change operation.

After the decision is reached, a lifetime of hormone treatments is begun. A male-to-female transsexual receives estrogen, which fosters the development of female secondary sex characteristics. It causes fatty deposits to develop in the breasts and hips, softens the skin, and inhibits growth of the beard. A female-to-male transsexual receives androgens, which promote male secondary sex characteristics. The voice deepens, hair becomes distributed according to the male pattern, muscles enlarge, and the fatty deposits in the breasts and hips are lost. The clitoris may also grow more prominent. For a male-to-female transsexual, phonosurgery can raise the pitch of the voice (Bockting & Fung, 2006).

Despite its complexity and intimacy, sex reassignment surgery is largely cosmetic. Medical science cannot construct internal genital organs or gonads. Male-to-female surgery is generally more successful. The penis and testicles are first removed. Tissue from the penis is placed in an artificial vagina, where sensitive nerve endings will later provide sexual sensations. A penis-shaped plastic or balsa-wood form keeps the vagina distended during healing.

In a female-to-male transsexual, the internal sex organs (ovaries, fallopian tubes, uterus) are removed, along with fatty tissue from the breasts. Some female-to-male transsexuals engage in a series of operations, termed **phalloplasty**, to construct artificial penises, but the penises don't work very well, and the procedures are costly. Most female-to-male transsexuals are therefore content with hysterectomies, mastectomies, and testosterone treatments (Bailey, 2003b).

Phalloplasty Surgical creation of an artificial penis.

Some transsexuals hesitate to undertake surgery, because they're afraid of the prospect of extreme medical intervention. Others forgo surgery so as not to jeopardize high-status careers or family relationships. Such people continue to think of themselves as members of the other sex, even without surgery.

SURGICAL OUTCOMES   Most reports of transsexuals' postoperative adjustments are positive (Smith et al., 2005). A follow-up study of 116 transsexuals at least one year after surgery found that most were content with the results and were reasonably well adjusted (Blanchard et al., 1985). Positive results for surgery were also reported in a study of 141 Dutch transsexuals (Kuiper & Cohen-Kettenis, 1988).

A study of 326 Dutch candidates for sex reassignment surgery found that about two-thirds (222 individuals) began hormone treatment, whereas 103 did not (Smith et al., 2005). Of the 222, about 15% dropped out before surgery. Generally speaking, after surgery the group was no longer gender-dysphoric, and most individuals functioned well sexually, psychologically, and socially. Only two male-to-female transsexuals regretted their decisions. Although male-to-female transsexuals outnumbered female-to-males, postoperative adjustments were more

A World of Diversity

THIRD GENDER/THIRD SEX

The terms "third gender" and "third sex" describe people who are considered neither women nor men, as well as a social category in societies that recognize three or more sexes.

Being neither male nor female has ramifications not only in terms of the person's sex, but also in terms of the person's gender role, gender identity, and sexual orientation. In some cultures, or for some individuals, a third sex or gender may represent an intermediate state between man and woman, or it may represent a state of being both, as in the case of someone who has "the spirit of a man in the body of a woman."

It may also represent the state of being neither male nor female (neuter), the ability to cross or swap sexes and gender roles, or another category that's independent of maleness and femaleness. This last definition is favoured by those who argue for a strict interpretation of the third-gender concept.

The Ladyboys of Thailand

The kathoeys (or "ladyboys") of Thailand are an example of a third gender. Although a significant number of Thais—including many kathoeys themselves—perceive kathoeys as belonging to a third gender, some see them as either a kind of man or a kind of woman.

The Two-Spirits of North America

First Nations cultures are also associated with multiple genders. They often contain social gender categories that are collectively known as *berdache*, or "two-spirits." Examples include the *wi˜kte* of the Lakota culture, the *ninauposkitzipxpe* (manly-hearted woman) of the North Peigan community, and the *muxe* of the Zapotec people.

Various scholars have debated the nature of such categories, as well as the definition of "third gender." Various researchers characterize the *berdaches* as gender crossers, mixed genders, intermediate genders,

favourable for female-to-male transsexuals. One reason may be that society is more accepting of women who wish to become men (Smith et al., 2005). Female-to-male transsexuals tend to be better adjusted socially before surgery, as well, so their superior postoperative adjustment may be nothing more than a selection factor.

Aaron Devor, formerly Holly Devor, is dean of graduate studies at the University of Victoria. Prior to 2002, he was a self-described "masculine lesbian" (Macqueen, 2003). Devor, who is one of the world's experts on transsexualism, provides a comprehensive analysis of transsexual adjustment phases in the book *FTM: Female-to-Male Transsexuals in Society* (1997). Based on interviews with 45 participants living in the United States, Canada, and New Zealand, Devor concludes that female-to-male transsexuals progress through many stages. Table 5.1 summarizes these stages.

Researchers have conducted relatively few studies of societal attitudes toward transsexuals. B. J. Rye (2001) at the University of Waterloo found that university students were about evenly divided in liking or disliking transsexuals. The students reported more negative attitudes toward transsexuals than toward gays and lesbians, however.

More recently, B. J. Rye et al. (2007) studied how having a transsexual person speak to a university class could change perceptions about transsexuals. The researchers found that only 5% of the students in human sexuality classes had knowingly met transsexual individuals before. They then invited a male-to-female transsexual to speak to the students in a personal way about her own experience, and about transgender issues in general. The students reported that hearing directly from a transsexual person was the best way to learn about transgender issues. They also reported that they had better understandings of the issues and greater empathy toward transsexual people after hearing the person speak.

There are programs that help transsexuals come to terms with themselves and adjust to living in a society in which they often feel unwelcome. Central Toronto Youth Services, for example, provides services and resources related to work, and distinct third and fourth genders that are not dependent on male and female as primary categories. Those who argue for the last interpretation also point out that mixed-, intermediate-, cross- and non-gender social roles should not be understood as truly representing a third gender.

The Hijras of South-Central Asia

The *hijras* of India, Pakistan, and Bangladesh are probably the most well-known and populous third sex type in the modern world. The Mumbai-based community health organization known as the Humsafar Trust estimates there are five to six million hijras in India. In various areas they're known as aravani, aruvani, and jogappa.

Indian photographer Dayanita Singh writes about her friendship with a hijra named Mona Ahmed, and their two societies' beliefs about gender: "When I once asked her if she would like to go to Singapore for a sex change operation, she told me, 'You really do not understand. I am the third sex, not a man trying to be a woman. It is your society's problem that you only recognize two sexes'" (Singh et al., 1999). Hijra social movements have campaigned for recognition as a third sex, and in 2005, Indian passport application forms were updated with three gender options: M for male, F for female, and E for eunuch.

Thai Ladyboys.
The kathoeys (ladyboys) of Thailand are one example of a third gender.

Source: Adapted from Wikipedia ("Third Gender," http://en.wikipedia.org/wiki/Third_gender), with information from Agrawal (1997), Fausto-Sterling (1993), Goulet (2006), Hester (2005), Murray and Roscoe (1997), Roscoe (2000), Roughgarden (2004), Stockett (2005), Totman (2004), and Winter (2003).

TABLE 5.1
Identity Development Stages in Female-to-Male Transsexualism

Development Stage	Some Characteristics	Some Actions Taken
Abiding Anxiety	Unfocussed gender and sex discomfort.	Preference for masculine activities and companionship.
Identity Confusion	First doubts about suitability of assigned gender and sex.	Reactive gender and sex conforming activities or preference for masculineactivities and companionship.
Identity Comparison	Seeking and weighing alternative female identities.	Adoption of mannish lesbian identity. Secret identity as a man and a male.
Discovery	Learning that female-to-male transsexualism exists.	Accidental contact with information about transsexualism.
Identity Confusion	First doubts about the authenticity of own transsexualism.	Seeking more information about transsexualism.
Identity Comparison	Testing transsexual identity using transsexual reference group.	Start to disidentify as women and females. Start to identify as transsexual.
Identity Tolerance	Identify as probably transsexual.	Increasingly disidentify as women and females.
Delay	Waiting for changed circumstances. Looking for confirmation of transsexual identity.	Seeking more information about transsexualism. Reality testing in intimate relationships and against further information about transsexualism.
Identity Acceptance	Transsexual identity established.	Tell others about transsexual identity.
Delay	Transsexual identity deepens. Final disidentity as women and females. Anticipatory socialization as men.	Learning how to do gender and sex reassignments. Saving money. Organizing support system.
Transition	Changing genders, between sexes.	Gender and sex reassignments.
Identity Acceptance	Identities established as transsexual men.	Successful "passing" as men and as males.
Integration	Transsexuality mostly invisible.	Stigma management.
Identity Pride	Publicly transsexual.	Transsexual advocacy and activism.

Source: Devor, H. (1997). FTM: Female-to-Male Transsexuals in Society. Bloomington, IN: Indiana University Press, p. 600

A Closer Look

AN EXPERIMENT GONE WRONG

In 1966, Bruce Reimer, one of a pair of identical twins who lived in Winnipeg, lost much of his penis as a result of a circumcision accident. As Colapinto (2000) relates the case, Bruce's parents wondered what to do.

At that time, Johns Hopkins sexologist John Money believed gender identity was sufficiently malleable that the boy could undergo sex reassignment surgery (have his testes removed and an artificial vagina constructed) and female hormone treatments, and be successfully reared as a girl.

For a number of years, the case seemed to supply evidence for the view that children may be psychosexually neutral at birth. The sex-reassigned twin, renamed Brenda, seemed to develop like a "real girl," albeit with a number of tomboyish traits.

But at the age of 14, when she was told about the circumcision accident and the process of sex reassignment, Brenda

immediately decided to pursue life as a male, and chose to go by the name David.

As an adult, David recalled that he'd never felt quite comfortable as a girl—a view confirmed by his mother's recollections. At 25, he married a woman and adopted her children. He reported being sexually attracted only to women. According to researchers such as Milton Diamond (1996), this outcome would appear to support the view that gender identity may be determined to a considerable extent in the uterus, when the fetal brain is exposed to androgens.

Reimer committed suicide with a sawed-off shotgun in 2004, at the age of 38. When Colapinto received the news from David's father, he wrote, "I was shocked, but I cannot say I was surprised. Anyone

David Reimer.
After losing his penis during a botched circumcision as a baby, he was given female hormones and raised as a girl. When told the truth at fourteen, he resumed his male identity.

familiar with David's life—as a baby, after a botched circumcision, [after] an operation to change him from boy to girl—would have understood that the real mystery was how he managed to stay alive for 38 years, given the physical and mental torments he suffered in childhood and that haunted him the rest of his life" (Colapinto, 2004).

CRITICAL THINKING QUESTIONS

In the Rye et al. (2007) study, university students were more likely to report negative attitudes toward transsexuals than toward gays and lesbians. Can you think of reasons that might explain this difference?

school, and other areas for transsexual youth. Gay and lesbian organizations have expanded their services to include formerly excluded groups, such as transsexual and transgendered individuals. One such program is Supporting Our Youth in Toronto. This program provides cultural, recreational, and employment training opportunities, as well as a mentoring and housing program (Lepischak, 2004). Such programs help create a sense of community for people who feel alienated from the larger society.

BOYS WHO ARE REARED AS GIRLS   Are children psychosexually neutral at birth? Can you surgically reassign a boy as a female, rear him as a girl, and have him feel that he truly is a girl as the years go on? Will cosmetic surgery, female sex hormone treatments, and laces and ribbons do it? Or will he be maladjusted, and will his male gender identity sort of break through?

No one has sought to answer these questions by randomly selecting male babies and reassigning their genders. Evidence on the matter derives from studies of children whose penises have been lost or failed to develop, through accidents or unusual medical conditions. One such case is discussed in "A Closer Look: An Experiment Gone Wrong."

Gender Bending.
These two photos show the same woman. Some women enjoy the sensation of dressing as highly masculine males.
According to Hamilton photographer Melanie Gillis, women who do this report feeling more powerful as a result of
assuming masculine personas.

Gender Roles and Stereotypes

"Why can't a woman be more like a man?" You may recall this lyric from the song Professor Henry Higgins sings in the musical *My Fair Lady*. The song laments that women are emotional and fickle, whereas men are logical and dependable. The emotional woman is a **stereotype**—a fixed, oversimplified, sometimes distorted idea about a group of people. The logical man is also a stereotype, albeit a more generous one. Even emotions are stereotyped. People assume women are more likely to experience feelings of fear, sadness, and sympathy, whereas men are more likely to experience anger and pride (Plant et al., 2000). Gender roles are stereotypes in that they evoke fixed, conventional expectations of men and women.

Our gender identities—our identification of ourselves according to our concepts of masculinity and femininity—do not determine the roles or behaviours deemed masculine or feminine in our culture. Cultures have broad expectations of men and women that are termed **gender roles**.

Sexism

We've all encountered **sexism**—the prejudgment that a person will possess certain traits because of gender. These traits are assumed to disqualify the person for certain vocations, or to prevent him or her from performing adequately in these jobs or in some social situations.

Sexism may even lead us to interpret the same behaviour in different ways, depending on whether it's exhibited by a man or a woman. We may see a man as self-assertive, but a woman as pushy. We may look upon him as flexible, but brand her as fickle and indecisive. He may be rational, whereas she's cold. He's tough when necessary, but she's bitchy.

Children develop stereotypes about the differences between "men's work" and "women's work" (Rathus, 2011). Women have been historically excluded

Stereotype A fixed, conventional idea about a group of people.

Gender roles Complex clusters of ways males and females are expected to behave.

Sexism The prejudgment that a person will possess certain traits because of gender.

from male-dominated occupations, and stereotypical expectations about men's and women's work filter down to the primary grades. According to traditional stereotypes, for example, girls aren't expected to excel in math. Exposure to such negative expectations may discourage them from pursuing careers in science and technology. Even when they do choose careers in these fields, women are often subject to discrimination when it comes to hiring, promotions, and allocation of research facilities and funds (Loder, 2000). And only recently have men begun to enter occupational domains previously restricted largely to women, such as secretarial work, nursing, and teaching primary grades.

Sexism is psychologically damaging. In one study, women who were led to believe sexism was pervasive reported lower self-esteem than women who were led to believe sexism was rare (Schmitt et al., 2003). In another experiment, men and women were led to believe they'd been prevented from taking a course because of either sexism or personal reasons (Major et al., 2003). Attributing the rejection to prejudice rather than to personal worth ("It's not me; it's society") had the effect of protecting their self-esteem.

The feminist movement in Canada has played a major role in reducing discrimination and helping women achieve greater equality with men. Marlene Mackie (1991) has traced the evolution of Canadian feminism in her book *Gender Relations in Canada: Further Explorations*. She argues that feminism is not one homogeneous movement, but has three major dimensions—liberal, socialist, and radical. According to Mackie, liberal feminists have worked to achieve gender equality through education and legislation. Socialist feminists have focused on structural inequalities resulting not only from gender, but also from social class, sexual orientation, and ethnicity. Radical feminists have focused on issues such as sexual assault, harassment, and pornography, and have been instrumental in establishing sexual-assault support services and battered women's shelters, as well as changing Canada's pornography laws.

How far have we progressed with respect to gender equality in Canadian society? On some basic measures, we've made progress. For example, in 1976, a full-time female worker in Canada earned 59% of what a male full-time worker earned. By 2008, the corresponding figure was 71% (Williams, 2010). It seems likely that this trend toward gender equality in income will continue. Income potential depends to a large degree on educational achievement. In 2008–2009, 57% of students enrolled in Canadian universities were women (Statistics Canada, 2010). This suggests that women will increasingly occupy higher-paying jobs, which should further close the wage gap between men and women in Canada.

Gender Roles and Aggression

In most psychological studies on aggression, males have been found to behave more aggressively than females (Felson, 2002; Hines & Saudino, 2003; Zeichner et al., 2003). Nonetheless, females are likely to act aggressively under certain conditions. The rate of aggression among girls seems to have increased in recent years.

University of Western Ontario researchers Anne Cummings and Alan Leschied (2002) conducted extensive research on aggression among girls, and published their findings in *Research and Treatment for Aggression with Adolescent Girls*. They found that aggressive adolescent girls were more likely than aggressive adolescent boys to experience isolation, powerlessness, and depression. Most of the girls came from broken homes, and most had seen violence between their parents.

Among both genders, bullying in elementary school is highly predictive of aggression in later dating relationships. An Ontario study found that bullies started dating earlier than non-bullies, and were more likely to engage in physical and social aggression with their dating partners (Connolly, Pepler, Craig, & Taradash, 2000).

Gender Typing

We've chronicled the biological process of sexual differentiation and explored some gender differences in cognitive abilities and behaviour. In this section, we'll consider various explanations for **gender typing**, the process by which an individual becomes a man or a woman.

Gender typing The process by which a child acquires behaviours deemed appropriate for his or her gender.

Biological Perspectives

Biological views on gender typing tend to focus on the roles of genetics and prenatal influences in predisposing men and women to gender-linked behaviour patterns. Biological perspectives also focus on the possible roles of hormones in sculpting the brain during prenatal development.

THE EVOLUTIONARY PERSPECTIVE   From an evolutionary perspective, the story of our ancient ancestors' survival is etched in our genes. Those genes that bestow attributes that increase an organism's chances of surviving to produce viable offspring are most likely to be transmitted to future generations. We thus possess the genetic remnants of traits that helped our ancestors survive and reproduce (Buss, 2009). This heritage influences our social and sexual behaviours, as well as our anatomic features.

According to the evolutionary perspective, men's traditional roles as hunters and warriors, and women's roles as caregivers and gatherers of fruits and vegetables, are bequeathed to us in our genes. Men are better suited to war and the hunt because of physical attributes passed along since ancestral times. Upper-body strength, for example, enabled them to throw spears and overpower adversaries. According to this view, men also possess perceptual-cognitive advantages, such as superior visual-motor skills, which enabled them to aim spears or bows and arrows. Personality traits such as aggressiveness also make for effective hunting.

Women, it's argued, are genetically predisposed to be empathic and nurturant, because these traits enabled ancestral women to respond to children's needs and enhanced the likelihood that their children would flourish and eventually reproduce, thereby transmitting their own genetic legacy to future generations. Prehistoric women thus tended to stay close to home, care for the children, and gather edible plants, whereas men ventured from home to hunt and raid their neighbours' storehouses.

The evolutionary perspective is steeped in controversy. Although scientists do not dispute the importance of evolution in determining physical attributes, many are reluctant to attribute complex social behaviours, such as aggression and gender roles, to heredity. The evolutionary perspective implies that stereotypical gender roles—men as breadwinners and women as homemakers, for example—reflect the natural order of things. Critics contend that biology is not destiny, that our behaviour is not dictated by our genes.

PRENATAL BRAIN ORGANIZATION   Researchers have sought the origins of gender-typed behaviours in the organization of the brain. Is it possible that the cornerstone of gender-typed behaviour is laid in the brain before the first breath is taken?

The hemispheres of the brain are specialized to carry out certain functions. In most people, the right hemisphere (right brain) appears to be specialized to perform visual and spatial tasks. The left hemisphere (left brain) appears to be more critical for verbal functions.

We know sex hormones are responsible for prenatal sexual differentiation of the genitals and the gender-related structural differences in the hypothalamus of the prenatal brain. Sexual differentiation of the brain may also partly explain men's (slight!) superiority at spatial-relations tasks, such as interpreting road maps and visualizing objects in space. Testosterone in the brains of male fetuses spurs greater growth of the right hemisphere, and slows the rate of growth of the left hemisphere. This difference may be connected with the ability to accomplish spatial-relations tasks.

Might boys' inclinations toward aggression and rough-and-tumble play also be prenatally imprinted in the brain? Some theorists argue that prenatal sex hormones may masculinize or feminize the brain by creating predispositions that are consistent with gender-role stereotypes, such as rough-and-tumble play and aggressive behaviour in males (Cohen-Bendahen et al., 2005).

A study investigated the gender-typed visual preferences of human infants at the early ages of three to eight months (Alexander et al., 2009). The researchers hypothesized that preferences for gender-typed toys might be at least in part inborn, and should therefore emerge in children before they're self-aware of their gender identities. The researchers assessed interest in a toy truck and a doll among 30 infants, using eye-tracking technology to indicate the direction of visual attention. They did find the hypothesized sex differences in visual interest: girls showed a visual preference for the doll over the truck, and boys showed a higher number of visual fixations on the truck than on the doll. As noted, these sex differences emerge much earlier than self-awareness of one's sex, when there has been relatively little time for social influences to take effect.

Psychological Perspectives

Children become aware of gender-role stereotypes by the tender age of two to three (Rathus, 2011). When asked to describe the differences between the genders, both boys and girls in North America generally agree that boys build things, play with transportation toys such as cars and fire trucks, enjoy helping their fathers, and hit other children. Both boys and girls also agree that girls enjoy playing with dolls and helping their mothers cook and clean, and that they're talkative, dependent on others for help, and nonviolent.

Psychologists have used psychoanalytic, social-cognitive, and cognitive-developmental theories to explain how children acquire such knowledge and adopt stereotypical behaviour patterns.

PSYCHOANALYTIC THEORY   Sigmund Freud explained gender typing in terms of identification. Appropriate gender typing, in Freud's view, requires that boys come to identify with their fathers and girls with their mothers. Identification is completed, in Freud's view, as children resolve the **Oedipus complex** (which is sometimes called the Electra complex in girls).

According to Freud, the Oedipus complex occurs during the phallic period of psychosexual development, between the ages of three and five. During this period, the child develops incestuous wishes for the parent of the other gender, and comes to perceive the parent of the same gender as a rival. The complex is resolved by the child's forsaking incestuous wishes for the parent of the other gender and identifying with the parent of the same gender. Through identification with the same-gender parent, the child comes to develop behaviours that are typically associated with that gender.

Oedipus complex In psychoanalytic theory, a conflict of the phallic stage in which the boy wishes to possess his mother sexually, and perceives his father as a rival for her love.

SOCIAL-COGNITIVE THEORY   Social-cognitive theorists explain the development of gender-typed behaviour in terms of processes such as observational learning, identification, and socialization (Golombok et al., 2008; Zosuls et al., 2009). In social-cognitive theory, identification is viewed as a continuing and broadly based learning process in which rewards and punishments influence children to imitate adult models of the same gender—especially parents of the same sex. Identification is more than imitation, however. In identification, the child not only imitates the behaviour of the model, but also tries to become like the model in broad terms.

Socialization also plays a role in gender typing (Golombok et al., 2008; Zosuls et al., 2009). Almost from the moment a baby comes into the world, it's treated according to its gender. Parents tend to talk more to baby girls, and fathers especially engage in more roughhousing with boys. When children are old enough to speak, parents and other adults—even other children—begin to instruct them in how they're expected to behave. Parents may reward children for behaviour they consider gender-appropriate, and punish (or fail to reinforce) them for behaviour they consider gender-inappropriate. Girls are encouraged to practise caretaking behaviours, which are intended to prepare them for traditional feminine adult roles. Boys are handed Lego or doctor sets, to help prepare them for traditional masculine adult roles.

Parental roles in gender typing are apparently changing. With more mothers working outside the home, girls today are exposed to more career-minded female role models than girls of earlier generations were. More parents today encourage their daughters to focus on careers and engage in strenuous physical activities, such as organized sports. Many boys today have fathers who take larger roles in child care and household responsibilities than men used to.

Schools are also important socialization influences. Teachers often expect girls to perform better than boys in reading and language arts, and have higher expectations for boys in math and science. Special programs in math and science held for girls after school and in the summer have helped bolster the girls' confidence and

Socialization The process by which an individual is guiding into socially acceptable behaviour patterns through information, rewards, and punishment.

Gender Typing Through Observational Learning.
According to social-cognitive theory, children learn about the gender roles available to them—and expected of them—at an early age. Gender schema theory adds that once children learn the expected gender roles (i.e., the gender schema of their cultures), they blend these roles with self-concept. Self-esteem thereby comes to depend on adherence to these gender roles.

interest in these subjects. Educators are becoming increasingly concerned about the fact that boys are failing in school at a much higher rate than girls. In Ontario, the high school drop-out rate for boys is four times that for girls (Halley, 2004).

COGNITIVE-DEVELOPMENTAL THEORY   Psychologist Lawrence Kohlberg (1966) proposed a cognitive-developmental view of gender typing. From this perspective, gender typing is not the product of environmental influences that mechanically stamp in gender-appropriate behaviour; rather, children themselves play an active role. They form concepts, or **schemas**, about gender, then exhibit behaviours that conform to their gender concepts. These developments occur in stages and are entwined with general cognitive development.

According to Kohlberg, gender typing entails the emergence of three concepts: gender identity, gender stability, and gender constancy. Gender identity is usually acquired by the age of three. By the age of four or five, most children develop a concept of **gender stability**—the recognition that people retain their genders for a lifetime. Prior to this age, boys may think they'll become mommies when they grow up, and girls may think they'll be daddies.

The more sophisticated concept of **gender constancy** develops in most children by age seven or eight. They recognize that gender doesn't change even when people alter their dress or behaviour; gender remains constant even when appearances change. A woman who wears her hair short (or shaves it off) remains a woman. A man who dons an apron and cooks dinner remains a man.

According to cognitive-developmental theory, children are motivated to behave in gender-appropriate ways once they've established the concepts of gender stability and gender constancy. They then make active efforts to learn which behaviour patterns are considered masculine and which are considered feminine. Once they obtain this information, they imitate the gender-appropriate patterns.

GENDER-SCHEMA THEORY   Gender-schema theory proposes that children develop **gender schemas** as a means of organizing their perceptions of the world (Bem, 1993). A gender schema is a cluster of mental representations about male and female physical qualities, behaviours, and personality traits. Gender gains prominence as a schema for organizing experience because of society's emphasis on it. Even young children start to mentally group people of the same gender in accordance with the traits that represent that gender.

Once children acquire gender schemas, they begin to judge themselves in accordance with traits considered appropriate to their genders. In doing so, they blend their developing self-concepts with the prominent gender schemas of their culture. The gender schemas furnish standards for comparison. Children with self-concepts that are consistent with the prominent gender schemas of their culture are likely to develop higher self-esteem than children whose self-concepts are inconsistent.

Gender Roles and Sexual Behaviour

Gender roles affect sexual behaviour. Children learn at an early age that men usually approach women and initiate sexual interactions, whereas women usually serve as the gatekeepers in romantic relationships (Bailey et al., 2000). In their traditional role as gatekeepers, women are expected to wait to be asked out and to screen suitors. Men are expected to make the first (sexual) move, and women to determine how far advances will proceed.

The cultural expectation that men are initiators and women are gatekeepers is embedded within the larger stereotype that men are sexually aggressive and women are sexually passive. Men are expected to have a higher number of sex partners than women (Mikach & Bailey, 1999). Men consistently report having more sexual partners than women. In comparing data on number of partners in Canada, the United

Schema A concept, or a way of interpreting experience or processing information.

Gender stability The concept that people retain their genders for a lifetime.

Gender constancy The concept that people's genders do not change, even if they alter their dress or behaviour.

Gender schema A cluster of mental representations about male and female physical qualities, behaviours, and personality traits.

CRITICAL THINKING QUESTIONS

It's a common stereotype that heterosexual men usually make the first move sexually, and it's up to women to determine how far they'll go. In your experience and observations, has this stereotype become increasingly less accurate in recent years?

States, Great Britain, and Norway, Tom Smith (1992) at the University of Chicago argues that gender differences in reporting (with men over-reporting and women under-reporting) seem to be the most likely explanation for the discrepancy.

Men not only initiate sexual encounters, they're also expected to dictate all the moves thereafter, just as they're expected to take the lead on the dance floor. According to the stereotype, women are supposed to let men determine the choice, timing, and sequence of sexual positions and techniques. Unfortunately, the stereotype favours men's sexual preferences, denying women the opportunity to give and receive their preferred kinds of stimulation.

The stereotypical masculine role also imposes constraints on men. Men are expected to take the lead in bringing their partners to orgasm, but they shouldn't ask their partners what they like, because men are expected to be natural experts. ("Real men" not only don't eat quiche; they also don't have to ask women how to make love.) Fortunately, more flexible attitudes are emerging. Women are becoming more sexually assertive, and men are becoming more receptive to expressing tenderness and gentleness. Still, the roots of traditional gender roles run deep.

According to another stereotype, men become sexually aroused at puberty and remain at the ready throughout adulthood. A study conducted at an Ontario university found that 85% of the women believed "it's easy for a woman to sexually arouse a man if she really wants to" (Clements-Schreiber & Rempel, 1995). Women, the stereotype continues, don't share men's natural interest in sex, and a woman discovers her own sexuality only when a man ignites her sexual flame. This stereotype denies that "normal" women have spontaneous sexual desires or are readily aroused.

It was widely believed in the Victorian period (even by so-called sex experts!) that women were naturally asexual and "unbothered" by sexual desires. The contemporary residues of this stereotype hold that women don't enjoy sex as much as men, and that women who openly express their sexual desires are "whores" or "sluts." In the Ontario study, however, only 25% of the women agreed that "in general, women do not really enjoy sex as much as men" (Clements-Schreiber & Rempel, 1995).

So far, we've looked at gender roles related to sexuality according to traditional stereotypes. It's clear, however, that gender roles in many aspects of Western life have evolved considerably in recent decades. For example, more and more women are focused on establishing careers, and expect male partners to share in domestic chores. Although there are ethnocultural variations in gender roles, it's evident that women increasingly expect and enjoy equality in their relationships with men.

To what extent have changing gender roles in general translated into corresponding changes in gender roles related to sexuality? While the traditional stereotypes are in many respects still in place, there's growing evidence that traditional gender role differences related to sexuality may become smaller as we progress toward full gender equality.

Attitude and Behaviour Differences

A common assumption is that gender differences in sexual attitudes and behaviours are quite large. But are men and women that different when to comes to sex?

Jennifer Petersen and Janet Shibley Hyde (2011) examined meta-analytic reviews of previous studies and large sample data sets on heterosexual behaviours, masturbation, use of sexually explicit material, attitudes toward premarital sex, and other variables related to gender differences in sexuality. They found that although men are more likely to have engaged in heterosexual intercourse than women, the gender difference is small and decreasing. Differences in the percentages of men and women who have engaged in oral sex are also small.

The authors cited a large-sample study in the United States in which 77% of men and 68% of women said they'd performed oral on their partners, while 79%

A World of Diversity

ARE THERE UNIVERSAL DIFFERENCES IN SEXUAL STRATEGIES?

One of the more controversial theories is the suggestion that males are naturally polygamous and females are naturally monogamous. If this is so, it places a greater burden on societies in which men are expected to remain loyal to their mates. If a man strays, after all, he can take the attitude, "Don't blame me; it's in my genes." Women might wonder how realistic it is to expect their partners to remain faithful.

Evolutionary psychologists have developed a theory of sexual strategies, which holds that men and women differ in their long-term and short-term mating strategies, with men more interested in sexual variety in the short term (Klusmann, 2002). In the long term, according to this theory, both males and females may seek heavy investment in relationships, love, companionship, and resource sharing. Even so, men place more value on signals of fertility and reproductive value, as demonstrated by women's youthfulness and physical appearances. Women place relatively more value on men's social status, maturity, and resources—cues that indicate their ability to provide over the long term. The qualities men and women seek are believed to help solve adaptive problems humans have faced throughout their evolutionary history.

In the short term, according to this theory, men are more interested in one-night stands and relatively brief affairs. By impregnating as many women as possible, they have a greater chance of contributing their genes to future generations. Women, evolutionarily speaking, have little to gain from such encounters. Impregnation requires a long-term commitment to child-rearing, and evolutionary forces favour the survival of children whose mothers create long-term, nurturing environments for them.

Roving Males.
In a study of 10 areas of the world, men in every culture surveyed were more likely than women to desire multiple sex partners. According to the sexual-strategies theory, this sex difference reflects human adaptation to environmental forces. Does this research finding mean it's unnatural to expect men to remain faithful to their partners?

Because a universal form of behaviour would likely be embedded in our genes, the evolutionary theory of different sexual strategies would find support if males and females in various cultures showed similar sex differences in their short-term mating strategies.

In seeking such evidence, David Schmitt (2003) supervised a survey of 16 288 people across 10 major regions of the world, including North America, South America, western Europe, eastern Europe, southern Europe, the Middle East, Africa, Oceania, south and southeast Asia, and east Asia. He indeed found universal sex differences in the desire for sexual variety.

Table 5.2 and Figure 5.5 reveal some of Schmitt's key findings about the desire for variety in short- and long-term relationships. Men from all 10 areas of the world were significantly more likely than women to say they'd like to have more than one sex partner within the next month. For example, 23.1% of North American men said they'd like more than one partner, compared with just 2.9% of North American women. (See Table 5.2.) And when asked about the mean (average) number of sex partners they'd like over the next 30 years, men from every area wanted significantly more partners than women did. (See Figure 5.5.)

The probability that any sex differences Schmitt found within a given region were due to chance was less than 1 in 1000 ($p < 0.001$).

Intriguing as they are, we cannot conclude that these research findings prove the validity of the evolutionary approach to understanding differences between men's and women's "sexual strategies." For example, Oceanic women reported that they wanted more sex partners in the long term than African men did. (See Figure 5.5.) We can accept the universality of the findings, but consider rival explanations for the data. In a world with common global communication, for instance, it might not be surprising to find worldwide overlap in gender roles. This overlap might affect the ways parents

TABLE 5.2

Percentage of Men and Women Who Desire More than One Sex Partner "In the Next Month" Across 10 World Regions

World Region	Percentage of Men Wanting More Than One Sexual Partner	Percentage of Women Wanting More Than One Sexual Partner
North America	23.1%	2.9%
South America	35.0	6.1
Western Europe	22.6	5.5
Eastern Europe	31.7	7.1
Southern Europe	31.0	6.0
Middle East	33.1	5.9
Africa	18.2	4.2
Oceania	25.3	5.8
South/Southeast Asia	32.4	6.4
East Asia	17.9	2.6

Source: Schmitt, D. P. (2003). Universal sex differences in the desire for sexual variety: Tests from 52 nations, 6 continents, and 13 islands. Journal of Personality and Social Psychology, 85(1), 85-104.

and cultural institutions influence children around the world.

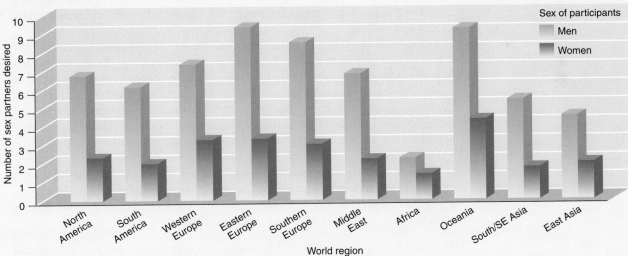

Figure 5.5 Mean number of sex partners desired by men and women "in the next 30 years" across 10 world regions.

Source: Schmitt, D. P. (2003). Universal sex differences in the desire for sexual variety: Tests from 52 nations, 6 continents, and 13 islands. Journal of Personality and Social Psychology, 85(1), 85-104.

CRITICAL THINKING QUESTIONS

Why do you think some feminists and queer theorists argue that evolutionary theory is little more than a sophisticated excuse for maintaining social power imbalances?

of men and 73% of women said they'd received oral sex (Laumann et al., 1994). It's been generally assumed that men are far more sexually permissive in their attitudes than women, but Petersen and Hyde (2011) found that differences in general sexual permissiveness were relatively small, and decreasing over time. Both men's and women's attitudes toward premarital sex have also become more accepting, and gender difference in these attitudes smaller. According to Petersen and Hyde, in large studies of adolescents and adults, while men were more likely to report more lifetime sexual partners than women, the difference was actually quite small.

It appears that common perceptions may overemphasize gender differences. There's usually greater variation within each gender than between the genders (Muehlenhard, 2000), and the differences that do exist seem to be getting smaller. Among older Canadians, for example, men consistently report having had intercourse at much earlier ages than women, but among Canadians in their twenties, there's hardly any difference between men and women (Fischtein & Herold, 2002).

According to Petersen and Hyde's (2011) review, some significant gender differences in sexual attitudes and behaviours have been maintained. Although men's and women's attitudes toward masturbation are similar, and gender differences in the percentages who report that they've masturbated is somewhat smaller in recent studies, men are still more likely to masturbate than women. In the Laumann et al. (1994) study of 18- to 59-year-old Americans, for example, 63% of the men said they'd masturbated during the previous year, compared to 42% of the women. The largest gender difference Peterson and Hyde found concerned the use of sexually explicit material: men were more likely than women to access magazines, videos, and the internet for sexual content.

Gender and Sex-Advice Literature

Carleton University researchers Erin Connell and Alan Hunt (2006) have analyzed literature containing marital and sexual advice for heterosexuals from the early part of the twentieth century to the present. They've found that throughout the years, gender stereotypes have heavily influenced the type of relational and sexual advice provided to couples.

Throughout the first part of the twentieth century, this literature presented the husband as the wife's tutor and the initiator of sex, and the wife as the passive student. It was the husband's responsibility to arouse his wife and to control the speed of his own orgasm. The assumption was that wives entered marriage as inexperienced virgins who lacked any knowledge of sexual pleasure. In the period between the First and Second World Wars, marriage manuals (as they were called) increasingly emphasized the necessity for the husband to provide his wife with sexual pleasure.

During the sexual revolution of the 1960s, sex was no longer tied to marriage, and marriage manuals were renamed sex manuals. They focused on the need for a couple to master new sexual techniques, to maximize sexual pleasure. In the following years, although research shows that many women did have strong sexual desires, the sex manuals continued to focus on gender differences.

THE DOUBLE STANDARD   The stereotype that women are undersexed also supports the traditional double standard: it's natural for men to sow their wild oats, but women who are sexually active outside of committed relationships are "sluts" or "nymphomaniacs."

In a University of Guelph study of university students and singles-bar patrons (Milhausen & Herold, 2001), 79% of the men and 89% of the women reported that women with many sexual partners were more harshly judged than men with many partners. In another study, the majority of women reported that women were more severe than men in judging women's sexual behaviour (Milhausen & Herold, 1999).

Of the respondents in Milhausen and Herold's (2001) study, twice as many women (67%) as men (35%) felt that men had greater sexual freedom than women.

The women thought it was easier for men to have many partners and to engage in casual sex; the men, on the other hand, felt that women had greater freedom, because they were the ones who decided whether sex would occur. The men typically felt at a disadvantage, because they wanted sex more than women did.

Although most respondents believed a double standard exists in Canada, the majority personally endorsed a single standard for both women and men. This was determined by measuring attitudes toward such behaviours as watching sexually explicit videos and having multiple sex partners. While only a minority of men held a sexual double standard, some women held a reverse double standard, judging men's behaviour more negatively than women's.

In another possible indication of a reverse double standard, both genders were more likely to discourage a female friend from dating a man who'd had many sexual partners than to discourage a male friend from dating a highly experienced woman. It appears that they saw the experienced man as more likely to be exploitative. Indeed, a common term the study participants used to describe such a man was "player," meaning someone who deceived women into having sex. Although the majority of both genders used negative words to describe both men and women who'd many partners, none of the respondents used the word "player" for a woman. Table 5.3 presents a summary of the word categories used in the study.

In a study of 18- to 24-year-olds in Nova Scotia and British Columbia, all 40 participants reported that the sexual double standard was evident when they were adolescents (Shovellor, Johnson, Langille, & Mitchell, 2004). Both males and females indicated that girls were judged by stricter rules than boys for sexual behaviour, and that girls were more likely to be negatively labelled by their peers for the same behaviours boys would be admired for.

The 2001 study illustrates the complexity of the double standard, and the need to use diverse measures when studying the topic. The divergence between the belief that the double standard existed and the fact that most respondents didn't support it calls for more research. More diverse samples are also needed. It may be, for example, that the double standard is still practised among certain ethnic groups and within lower income groups (Milhausen & Herold, 2001).

Highly Sexual Women

Despite the stereotype that women are undersexed, they're no less arousable than men. Nor do they wait for men to discover their sexuality. Long before they have intimate relationships, children of both genders routinely discover that touching their genitals produces pleasurable sensations.

TABLE 5.3

Word Categories Used to Describe Men and Women With Many Sexual Partners

	Descriptions of Men		Descriptions of Women	
	Men	**Women**	**Men**	**Women**
Sexual predator	38%	37%	0%	0%
Promiscuous	40	30	75	66
Psychologically damaged	10	3	7	9
Stud	25	8	0	0
Sexually liberated	11	5	8	16

Source: Milhausen, R. R., & Herold, E. H. (2001). Reconceptualizing the sexual double standard. Journal of Psychology and Human Sexuality, 13, 63–83.

Jocelyn Wentland and her colleagues (2006; 2009) at the University of Guelph conducted an online survey to compare women who considered themselves highly sexual with women who did not. The sample of 1 549 included university students, as well as women from various communities.

More than 80% of the highly sexual women agreed with the following statements:

- I think about sex a lot.
- I enjoy fantasizing about sex.
- When it comes to sex, I'm willing to try almost anything.
- I'm confident about my sexual ability.
- Fantasizing about sex can quickly get me sexually aroused.
- I really enjoy masturbating to orgasm.

Several of the study participants said it was important for society to recognize that many women are highly interested in sex and in obtaining sexual pleasure.

Many women are attempting to change the perception that women are disinterested in sex. In her book *Fearless Sex: A Babe's Guide to Overpowering Your Romantic Obsessions and Getting the Sex Life You Deserve*, sex therapist Joy Davidson (2004) encourages women to:

- Let go of sexual inhibitions and "bad girl" attitudes.
- Electrify their libidos.
- Liberate their most daring fantasies.
- Feel good about their "kinkier" sexual desires, and explore them safely.

In interviews with women in Canada and the United States, Canadian author Wendy Dennis (1992) found that some specifically wanted men to be informed that women's sex drives can be just as strong as men's. This perspective is reinforced by female singers such as Nelly Furtado, whose bestselling album *Loose* contains the singles "Promiscuous" and "Maneater." Furtado says her album reflects a late-blooming sexuality: "I'm admitting to all my fans that I'm a woman and I love sex" (Wheeler, 2006). There are also many sex blogs written by women who openly discuss their strong sex drives. (See Chapter 15.)

Age is an important factor in determining the strength of the female sex drive. Researchers have surveyed women from different parts of Canada and the United States to determine whether there's any truth to the stereotype that women reach their sexual peak in their early thirties (Schmitt et al., 2002). While women in their early thirties do in fact report higher levels of sexual desire than women in any of the other age groups, they do not report having more partners. The findings are similar for both Canadian and American women. The researchers have concluded that women in the 30-to-34 age group are more lustful than the average of all other women, thus supporting the idea of a sexual peak for this age range. Yet the researchers have also cautioned that their findings are exploratory, and that more research is needed to confirm their conclusions.

In recent years, the media have turned the spotlight on women who have sex with younger men. "Cougars" are women in their thirties and older who seek out younger men solely for sex. In her book *Cougar: A Guide for Older Women Dating Younger Men*, *Toronto Sun* columnist Valerie Gibson (2002) describes dating younger men as liberating, empowering, and fun. A self-proclaimed pioneer cougar, Gibson says cougars want lots of great sex with hot young men.

A trend toward casual sex is also seen among certain groups of lesbians. In 1999, a group of lesbians in Toronto began renting a gay men's bathhouse on a monthly basis, to provide a supportive environment for women who wanted to have casual sex with other women. They named it the Pussy Palace. In her book *Good Girls Do: Sex Chronicles of a Shameless Generation*, Simona Chiose (2001) describes her visit to the Pussy Palace. She quotes one of the organizers: "We are socialized to not own our desires. The bathhouse challenges that. We're all here because we're horny" (p. 55). Chiose details the various activities that transpired at the Palace, including striptease dancing, masturbation, group sex, and watching lesbian sex videos. She

A World of Diversity

WHAT DO MEN VALUE MOST?

A study of more than 27 000 men in eight countries (Germany, the United States, the United Kingdom, Spain, Brazil, Mexico, Italy, and France) analyzed characteristics of masculinity and sexual functioning (Sand et al., 2008).

Contrary to the stereotype that men consider sexual performance the most important determinant of masculinity, the men in the study placed the highest value on being honourable, self-reliant, and respected. Being seen as attractive, sexually active, and successful with women were less central to their vision of masculinity.

When it came to quality of life, the men cited good health, harmonious family lives, and good relationships with their partners as more important than sexual concerns. Most important, across all of the societies and age ranges, the men said they valued coupled relationships more highly than pure sexual pleasure (Sand et al., 2008).

argues that the women were able to engage in behaviours they might not have otherwise, because they were in an environment where they weren't afraid of being judged: "I think of that night as a walk on the wild side of female sexuality," Chiose writes, "of what women are capable of, and of how open they can be about their desires" (p. 56).

Yet, despite her acceptance of casual sex for others, Chiose notes (p. 53) that she has difficulty accepting casual sex for herself:

> I have always been envious of friends I've had who have said in passing that they were going to meet a new man for an evening, and in response to my question as to whether they thought it might become something, shrugged and said they didn't want it to be. They just wanted to get laid, to have a moment of physical and emotional union with someone they didn't know very well, nor did they wish to know them. I can't do it, and I'm sorry for that sometimes—for not being able to leave my thinking self behind and simply immerse myself in experience—but I am a product of the world I grew up in, and it's pointless for me to try.

On the Prowl.
"Cougars" are women in their thirties and older who seek out younger men solely for sex.

Psychological Androgyny

Most of us think of masculinity and femininity as opposite ends of one continuum. We tend to assume that the more masculine a person is, the less feminine he or she must be, and vice versa. Thus, a man who exhibits the stereotypical feminine traits of nurturance, tenderness, and emotionality is often considered less masculine than other men. Women who compete with men in business are perceived not only as more masculine than other women, but also as less feminine.

Some behavioural scientists, including Sandra Bem (1993), argue that masculinity and femininity instead constitute separate personality dimensions. Whether male or female, someone who is highly masculine may also possess feminine traits, and vice versa. An individual in Western society who exhibits "masculine" assertiveness and instrumental skills (e.g., abilities in science or business) along with "feminine" nurturance and cooperation fits both masculine and feminine gender-role stereotypes. This person shows **psychological androgyny**. Someone who's high only in assertiveness and instrumental skills fits the masculine stereotype. A person who's high only in traits such as nurturance and cooperation fits the feminine stereotype. Someone who's low in both the stereotypical masculine and the stereotypical feminine patterns is considered undifferentiated in terms of gender-role stereotyping.

People who are psychologically androgynous may be capable of summoning up a wider range of masculine and feminine traits to meet the demands of various situations, and to better express their desires and talents. Researchers have found psychologically androgynous individuals of both genders who show "masculine" independence under group pressures to conform, and "feminine" nurturance during interactions with kittens or babies (Bem, 1975; Bem et al., 1976). Psychologically androgynous adolescents are less likely to stereotype occupations as masculine or feminine (Kulik, 2000).

People who oppose the constraints of traditional gender roles may perceive psychological androgyny as a desirable goal. Some feminist writers, however, criticize the model of psychological androgyny because it's defined in terms of—and thereby perpetuates—masculine and feminine gender roles (Denmark et al., 2008).

There's some evidence that psychologically androgynous men and women are more comfortable with their sexuality than masculine men and feminine women are (Walfish & Mayerson, 1980). Perhaps psychologically androgynous people can draw upon broader repertoires of sexual behaviour. They may be comfortable with cuddling and tender holding *and* with initiating and directing sexual interactions. Researchers also find that androgynous women experience orgasm more frequently than feminine women do (Radlove, 1983), and express greater sexual satisfaction (Kymlicka et al., 1983).

Psychological androgyny A state characterized by possession of both stereotypical masculine traits and stereotypical feminine traits.

Summing Up

During the first six weeks or so of prenatal development, embryonic structures in both genders develop along similar lines, and resemble primitive female structures.

At about the seventh week after conception, the genetic code (XX or XY) begins to assert itself, causing changes in the gonads, genital ducts, and external genitals.

Testosterone spurs differentiation of the male (Wolffian) duct system. In the absence of testosterone, the Wolffian ducts degenerate, and female sex organs develop.

Abnormalities of the sex chromosomes can have profound effects on sexual characteristics, physical health, and psychological development. Examples include Klinefelter's syndrome and Turner's syndrome.

Gender-specific changes occur in the hypothalamus during prenatal development. Testosterone causes cells in the hypothalamus of a male fetus to become insensitive to estrogen.

One's gender identity is one's sense of being male or of being female.

Gender identity is nearly always consistent with anatomic gender.

Some individuals—hermaphrodites—are born with both ovarian and testicular tissue.

Transsexuals harbour a deep sense of discomfort about their anatomic genders. Hormone treatments and sex-reassignment surgery provide transsexuals with many of the characteristics of the other gender.

Cultures have broad expectations of men and women, which are termed gender roles. In our culture, the stereotypical female is seen as gentle, dependent, kind, helpful, patient, and submissive. The stereotypical male is tough, competitive, gentlemanly, and protective.

Sexism is the prejudgment that simply because of gender, a person will possess certain traits.

Stereotypical gender preferences for toys and play activities are in evidence at an early age. Males are more aggressive than females. The question is why?

Biological views about gender typing focus on the roles of genetics and prenatal influences in predisposing males and females to gender-linked behaviour patterns. Psychologists have attempted to explain gender typing in terms of psychoanalytic, social-cognitive, and cognitive-developmental theories.

Gender-schema theory proposes that children develop gender schemas to organize their perceptions of the world. They then begin to judge themselves in terms of traits considered appropriate for their genders.

Stereotypical gender-role expectations affect dating practices and sexual behaviours.

According to this stereotype, men are sexual initiators and women are sexual gatekeepers. Men not only initiate sexual encounters; they're also expected to initiate all the moves.

According to another stereotype, women don't share men's interest in sex. Current research, however, suggests that many women do have a strong interest in sexual pleasure.

Gender differences related to sexuality do exist, but many of them appear to be less pronounced than common wisdom suggests. Some gender differences in sexuality appear to be getting smaller.

Masculinity and femininity may be two independent personality dimensions. People who combine stereotypically masculine and feminine behaviour patterns are psychologically androgynous.

Test Yourself

Multiple-Choice Questions

1. The process by which males and females develop distinct sexual anatomies is known as:
(a) Sexualization.
(b) Homologous development.
(c) Sexual differentiation.
(d) The Müllerian stage.

2. The basic blueprint for the human embryo is:
(a) Male.
(b) Female.
(c) Both male and female.
(d) Neither male nor female.

3. Which chromosome pattern is found in males with Klinefelter's syndrome?
(a) YYY.
(b) XXX.
(c) XYY.
(d) XXY.

4. A transsexual is most likely to have:
(a) Gender dysphoria.
(b) An extra X chromosome.
(c) Aggressive tendencies.
(d) Passive-aggressive tendencies.

5. Research suggests that a part of the brain known as the _____ may be involved in the development of gender identity.
(a) amygdala
(b) hippocampus
(c) frontal cortex
(d) hypothalamus

6. A Dutch study found that after sex reassignment, most transsexuals:
(a) Regret their decision.
(b) Function well sexually, psychologically, and socially.
(c) Develop psychological disorders they showed no evidence of before.
(d) Discontinue hormone treatments.

7. According to Kohlberg, gender _____ develops last.
(a) stability
(b) identity
(c) exclusivity
(d) constancy

(continued)

8. **Children learn behaviours appropriate for their genders by the process of:**
(a) Gender typing.
(b) Gender expectation.
(c) Gender reinforcement.
(d) Gender fixation.

9. **Teasing or belittling a woman because she studies engineering is an example of:**
(a) Gender typing.
(b) Sexism.
(c) Gender reassignment.
(d) Homophobia.

10. **Research suggests that gender differences in sexual attitudes and behaviours:**
(a) Are uniformly large.
(b) Do not exist.
(c) Appear, in many cases, to be getting larger.
(d) Appear, in many cases, to be getting smaller.

You'll find answers to the "Test Yourself" questions on page 495.

Critical Thinking

1. What's your ultimate definition of "gender"? Is it biological? Psychological? A bit of each?

2. When transsexuals undergo sex-reassignment surgery to bring their physical appearances more into line with their gender identities, has anything really changed?

3. When you were growing up, what messages about traditional gender roles did you receive from your parents? Did you receive different messages from your friends? How did you reconcile any conflicts?

4. Have you ever experienced sexism? What were the circumstances? What effect, if any, did it have on you?

5. Do you think men have stronger sex drives than women? Why or why not?

MySearchLab

MySearchLab offers extensive help to students with their writing and research project and provides round-the-clock access to credible and reliable source material. Take a tour at **www.mysearchlab.com.**

Attraction and Love

From ancient philosophers to medieval poets to modern-day advice columnists, many have attempted to unlock the mysteries of attraction and love—with varying degrees of success. Whether William Shakespeare or *Cosmopolitan* magazine better captures the essence of attraction and love we leave to you to decide.

In this chapter, we'll broach these topics from a scientific point of view, using theoretical and research-based approaches to help understand what draws one person to another . . . and the perhaps indefinable concept of romantic love. We don't claim to have one up on Shakespeare, but we do think it's important for students of human sexuality to grasp the essential elements of a scientific approach to matters of the heart.

Attraction

What attracts one person to another? Can you think personal attributes that have attracted you to particular individuals? To what extent do you think factors such as looks, personality, age, race or ethnicity, education, and social status have contributed to your personal attractions?

Keep your answers in mind as we explore some of the factors that research suggests govern interpersonal attraction.

The Attraction-Similarity Hypothesis: Who's Right for You?

Attraction-similarity hypothesis The concept that people tend to develop romantic relationships with those whose levels of attractiveness are similar to their own.

Propinquity Proximity.

The **attraction-similarity hypothesis** holds that people tend to develop romantic relationships with those whose levels of physical attractiveness and other traits are similar to their own (Montoya et al., 2008; Morry & Gaines, 2005; van Stratten et al., 2009). Researchers have found that people in committed relationships are likely to be similar to their partners in terms of attitudes and cultural attributes (Amodio & Showers, 2005).

Our partners tend to resemble us in race and ethnicity, age, level of education, and religion. For example, 95% of Canadians choose partners (whether married or common-law) from their own racial backgrounds (Riedmann, Lamanna, & Nelson, 2003).

Do Opposites Attract, or Do Birds of a Feather Flock Together?

Contrary to common wisdom, opposites do not attract. We're actually less apt to be attracted to people who disagree with our views and tastes than we are to people who share them.

Why do the great majority of us have partners from our own backgrounds? One reason is **propinquity**. That is, relationships are made in the neighbourhood, and not in heaven. Although mobility has increased in Western society, we tend to live among—and come into contact with—people whose backgrounds are reasonably similar to ours. Another reason is that we're drawn to people whose attitudes are similar to our own. People from similar backgrounds are more likely to hold similar attitudes than people from different backgrounds. Similarity in attitudes and tastes is a key contributor to attraction, friendships, and love relationships (Brown et al., 2003; Morry & Gaines, 2005).

Let's note a sex difference: evidence shows that women are more likely than men to place greater weight on similar attitudes as a determinant of attraction, whereas men are likely to place more value on physical attractiveness (Furnham, 2008).

Ancient Alchemy
What's the secret of attraction and love?

We tend to assume that people we find attractive share our attitudes (Montoya et al., 2009). When sexual attraction is strong, perhaps we want to think we can iron out all the kinks in the relationship. Although similarity may be important in determining initial attraction, however, compatibility appears to be a stronger predictor of maintaining an intimate relationship (Amodio & Showers, 2005).

Reciprocity: If You Like Me, You Must Have Excellent Judgment

When we feel admired and complimented, we tend to return these feelings and behaviours. This is called **reciprocity**. Reciprocity is a potent determinant of attraction (Levine, 2000). We tend to be much more warm, helpful, and candid when we're with strangers who seem to like us. We even tend to welcome positive comments that we know are inaccurate (Levine, 2000).

Reciprocity Mutual exchange.

The power of reciprocity may enable many couples to become happy with one another and reasonably well adjusted. By reciprocating positive words and actions, a person can sometimes stoke neutral or mild feelings into robust, affirmative feelings of attraction.

Physical Attractiveness: How Important Is It to Look Good?

We might like to think of ourselves as so sophisticated that physical attractiveness doesn't move us. We might like to claim that sensitivity, warmth, and intelligence are more important. However, we may never learn about other people's personalities if we don't find ourselves physically attracted to them in some way.

Research shows that physical attractiveness is a major determinant of interpersonal and sexual attraction (Langlois et al., 2000; Sangrador & Yela, 2000; Strassberg & Holty, 2003). Some researchers, in fact, contend that physical appearance is the key factor in consideration of partners for dates, sex, and long-term relationships (Wilson et al., 2005). The importance of physical attractiveness is perhaps accentuated by the "what's beautiful is good" effect (Dion, Berscheid, & Walster, 1972). This is the tendency for people to assume attractive people have more socially desirable personalities and are likely to be happier and more successful than less attractive people.

IS BEAUTY IN THE EYE OF THE BEHOLDER?   What determines physical attractiveness? Among certain African peoples, long necks and round, disc-like lips are signs of feminine beauty. Women therefore stretch their necks and lips to make themselves more appealing. Women of the Nama culture persistently tug at their labia majora to make them beautiful—that is, prominent and elongated (Ford & Beach, 1951).

In general, women around the world consider taller men to be more attractive (Furnham, 2009; Kurzban & Weeden, 2005). Height can play a role in mate choice because it suggests social dominance, status, access to resources, and a positive heritable trait (Salska, 2008). Undergraduate North American women prefer to date men who are about 15 centimetres taller than they are themselves. Undergraduate men, on the average, prefer women who are about 11 centimetres shorter (Gillis & Avis, 1980).

"Thin is in" reflects the dominant perspective of North American culture. Some young women are so affected by the cultural ideal that they suffer from the eating disorder anorexia nervosa, in which they literally starve themselves. Both females and males tend to find slenderness (though not anorexic thinness) attractive, especially in females (Furnham, 2009; Glasser et al., 2009; Wilson et al., 2005).

An examination of internet dating profiles in 5810 personal ads on Yahoo showed that males from various cultures and European-American males and females prefer thin partners (Glasser et al., 2009). European-American males are more likely than African-American and Latino males to want to date slender, physically fit women. African-American and Latino-American men are significantly more likely to be interested in women with large or thick bodies. The study also found that African-American and Latina women are significantly more likely than European-American women to be satisfied with their bodies.

The hourglass figure is popular in Canada and in most other cultures. In a study at Dalhousie University (Lalonde et al., 2004), female students rated women of average weight with waist-to-hip ratios of 0.7 as most attractive. Small and medium waists were generally preferred, regardless of body weight. Moderate and heavy figures with large hips received the lower attractiveness ratings; larger figures with more tubular body shapes were considered more attractive. The results indicated that in evaluating physical attractiveness, body weight, waist size, and hip size all interact to influence ratings of women's attractiveness.

Walking style or gait is also a physical feature that influences attractiveness ratings. Researchers at Queen's University (Provost, Quinsey, & Troje, 2008) discovered that the gaits of women who were not using hormonal birth-control pills varied with their menstrual cycles. The researchers hypothesized, on the basis of evolutionary theory, that women would be more attractive to men during the fertile periods of their menstrual cycles. A sample of university men were shown images of women walking and asked to rate their attractiveness. Contrary to the researchers' prediction, women who were shown walking during their luteal—or least fertile—phases were judged most attractive.

Cohen and Tannenbaum (2001) conducted an internet study in which they posted various women's body shapes and asked lesbian and bisexual women to indicate which they found most sexually attractive. The respondents, like heterosexual men and women, found women with 0.7 waist-to-hip body ratios most attractive. However, they differed from heterosexual women and men in naming *heavy* women with 0.7 waist-to-hip body ratios and large breasts as their first choice. Their second choice was heavy women with the same waist-to-hip body ratio but with small breasts. The authors suggested that the study participants were rejecting what they might have viewed as societal emphasis on excessive slenderness.

It's no secret that most men in Western society are more attracted to women with ample bustlines (Hill et al., 2005). In one study, men rated a continuum of female figures that differed only in the size of the bust (Thompson & Tantleff, 1992). Men, as predicted, preferred women with larger busts—but not with huge busts.

People who are attractive know it. In one study, men and women rated both themselves and one another for attractiveness (Marcus & Miller, 2003). By and large, the self-ratings meshed with the ratings of others, both female and male. Women's judgments were most closely related to how men perceived them, suggesting that they were reflecting men's opinions of them, more than women's.

An experiment manipulated men's voices and asked women to rate them for attractiveness. Heterosexual women in the fertile (late follicular) phases of their menstrual cycles found men with deeper (more "masculine") voices more attractive than men with higher voices (Feinberg et al., 2006). The study didn't assess possible differences between heterosexual and lesbian women.

At the beginning of this section, we asked how important it is to look good. The research we've reviewed shows that, on average, men and women are attracted to partners with particular physical attributes. But it's important to remember that, just as there's almost endless variation in how people look, there's also a great deal of variation in what people find attractive. Although most women prefer their male partners to be taller than they are themselves, some fall for men who are shorter

Innovative Canadian Research

WHAT DO WOMEN WANT?

Do women who are more open to casual sex differ in their preferences for potential male partners than women who are less open to casual sex? Researchers at Queen's University and the University of Victoria (Provost et al., 2006) conducted two studies to find out. They predicted that women who were more sociosexual—that is, who were more open to short-term sexual relationships—would be more likely to prefer highly masculine male faces and bodies than women who were less sociosexual.

In the first study, they asked women to rate the attractiveness of male faces and various masculine body types. In general, all of the women preferred more masculine faces and more muscular bodies. However, the women who were more sociosexual showed much greater preferences for men with muscular bodies.

In the second study (Provost et al., 2006), a different sample of women met with two equally attractive men (one highly masculinized and one less masculinized) in a "speed dating" setting. After meeting with each man, the women completed a questionnaire that asked about their interest in each man for a short-term or a long-term relationship. A key finding was that the more sociosexual women were more strongly attracted to the highly masculinized man for a short-term relationship than the less sociosexual women were, and the less sociosexual women preferred the less masculinized man for a long-term relationship. Assuming that a higher level of masculinity is associated with "healthier" genes, the researchers theorized that evolutionary theory was supported by the finding that women who were more open to casual sex were more likely to choose more masculine-looking men for casual sex.

In a similar study, researchers at the University of Western Ontario (Wilbur & Campbell, 2010) found that both women who scored high and women who scored low in sociosexuality preferred physically attractive men as short-term sexual partners, though physical attractiveness was far more important to the highly sociosexual women. Interestingly, when it came to long-term romantic partners, both groups of women preferred physical attractiveness to the same extent. They also both preferred long-term romantic partners who were ambitious.

---

than they are. Some men are attracted to heavier-set women. Look at it this way: if all heterosexual men were attracted only to relatively thin women with large breasts, and all heterosexual women were attracted only to tall men with deep voices, most of us would be out of the picture.

NON-PHYSICAL TRAITS AND ATTRACTIVENESS   Although our culture judges beauty by physical standards, our perceptions of beauty are also affected by non-physical traits. For example, how beautiful we find a partner is likely to be enhanced by non-physical traits such as familiarity, liking, respect, and shared values and goals (Kniffin & Wilson, 2004). Both females and males rate faces as more attractive when they're smiling than when they're not (O'Doherty et al., 2003).

Gender-role expectations may affect perceptions of attractiveness. Women are more likely to be attracted to socially dominant men than men are to be attracted to socially dominant women (Graziano & Bruce, 2008). In one study, men and women were shown videos of prospective dates. The women found men who acted outgoing and self-expressive more appealing than men who were passive, while the men were put off by outgoing, self-expressive women (Riggio & Woll, 1984). In another study, highly feminine women were more likely than less feminine women to be attracted to dominant, "macho" men (Maybach & Gold, 1994). In yet another study, women rated videos of dominant college men (defined as exhibiting social control over troublesome interactions with instructors) as more appealing than submissive men. Again, male viewers were put off by similarly dominant women (Sadalla et al., 1987). Men are more likely to be jealous of socially dominant men, whereas women are more likely to be jealous of physically attractive women (Dijkstra & Buunk, 2002).

A World of Diversity

CROSS-CULTURAL BEAUTY

Some aspects of beauty seem to be largely cross-cultural. Research suggests that European Americans, African Americans, Asian Americans, and Latino and Latina Americans tend to agree on the facial features they find attractive (Cunningham et al., 1995). They all prefer female faces with large eyes, greater distance between the eyes, small noses, narrower faces with smaller chins, high, expressive eyebrows, larger lower lips, and well-groomed, full heads of hair.

Consider the methodology of a study that compared the facial preferences of people in Japan and England. Perrett (1994) created computer composites of the faces of 60 women. The picture on the left-hand side of Figure 6.1 (a) is a composite of the 15 women who were rated as most attractive. Since both Japanese and British men had identified women with large eyes, high cheekbones, and narrow jaws as the most attractive, Perrett then used computer enhancement to exaggerate the differences between the composite of the 60—that is, the average face—and the composite of the 15 most attractive women. The result is the picture on the right-hand side of Figure 6.1 (b). This composite has larger eyes, higher cheekbones, and a narrower jaw than the image on the left. Perrett found that men rated this second composite as the more attractive of the two images. He obtained similar results with an image that resembled a Japanese woman.

Susan Sprecher and her colleagues (1994) surveyed a national sample of 13 017 English- or Spanish-speaking people, aged 19 or above, living in households in the United States. In one section of their questionnaire, they asked how willing respondents would be to marry someone who was older, younger, of a different religion, unlikely to hold a steady job, not good-looking, and so forth. Each item was followed by a seven-point scale in which 1 meant not at all willing and 7 meant very willing. As shown in Table 6.1, women were more willing than men to marry someone who wasn't good-looking. On the other hand, women were less willing than men to marry someone unlikely to hold a steady job.

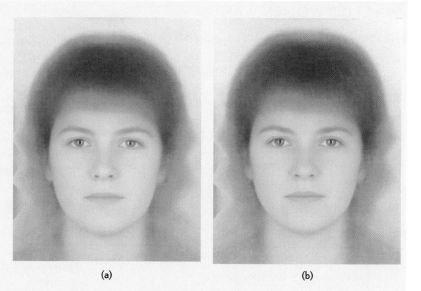

(a)   (b)

Figure 6.1 Wide-eyed beauty.
In both England and Japan, such features as large eyes, high cheekbones, and narrow jaws contribute to perceptions of women's attractiveness. The left-hand picture (a) is a computer composite of the faces of 15 women who were rated as most attractive out of a group of 60. The right-hand picture (b) is a computer composite that exaggerates the features of these 15 women. That is, it develops them further in the direction that separates them from the average features of the full group.

TABLE 6.1

Gender Differences in Mate Preference

How willing would you be to marry someone who . . .	Men	Women
was not "good-looking"?	3.41	4.42**
was older than you by five or more years?	4.15	5.29**
was younger than you by five or more years?	4.54	2.80**
was not likely to hold a steady job?	2.73	1.62**
would earn much less than you?	4.60	3.76**
would earn much more than you?	5.19	5.93**
had more education than you?	5.22	5.82**
had less education than you?	4.67	4.08**
had been married before?	3.35	3.44
already had children?	2.84	3.11*
was of a different religion?	4.24	4.31
was of a different race?	3.08	2.84**

*Difference statistically significant at the 0.01 level of confidence.

**Difference statistically significant at the 0.001 level of confidence.

Source: Based on information in Sprecher, S., Sullivan, Q., & Hatfield, E. (1994). Mate selection preferences: Gender differences examined in a national sample. Journal of Personality and Social Psychology, 66(6), 1074–1080. © 1994 American Psychological Association. Reprinted with permission.

WHAT DO YOU LOOK FOR IN A RELATIONSHIP?   When it comes to selecting a long-term partner, women place relatively greater emphasis than men on such traits as vocational status, earning potential, expressiveness, kindness, consideration, dependability, and fondness for children. Men give relatively more consideration to youth, physical attractiveness, cooking ability, and frugality (Kniffen & Wilson, 2004).

In a study at the University of Guelph (Milhausen et al., 2007), women rated responsibility as more important in a future spouse than men did, whereas men rated physical attractiveness as more important than women did. In contrast, when choosing a casual sex partner, women thought physical attractiveness was more important than men did. Both men and women rated responsibility as most important when choosing a future spouse, followed by physical attractiveness, sexual skill, and status or popularity. This was one of the first studies to consider the importance of sexual skill in selecting a partner.

In 2005, a Compas survey asked a national sample of Canadians what they felt were the attributes of the ideal spouse. The men valued only one characteristic more than the women did: "good-looking." Women valued such traits as "manages money well," "is financially successful," "is well educated and intelligent," and "shares your religion" more highly than the men did.

There have been relatively few studies of mate preference attributes among ethnic groups in Canada. Researchers at York University (Lalonde et al., 2004) found that for second-generation Southeast-Asian Canadians, the strength of connectedness to their own families was the strongest predictor of traditional mate attribute preferences. Despite extensive exposure to Canadian values, most respondents preferred their future spouses to have traditional attributes. Men had more traditional sex-role expectations than women did.

AN EVOLUTIONARY PERSPECTIVE ON MATE PREFERENCE   Many people view contemporary gender differences in perception of attractiveness in the opposite sex as highly sexist. On one level, most of us would agree that the emphasis on physical beauty for women and economic power and professional status for men as primary indicators of attractiveness is a strong reflection of a patriarchal (male-dominated) society. Some evolutionary psychologists believe evolutionary forces favour the continuation of gender differences in mate preference, because certain preferred traits offer reproductive advantages (Buss, 2005, 2009).

According to this theory, human beings, like all organisms, are genetically motivated to reproduce. (Without this motivation, a species would soon become extinct.) As a result, some physical features—such as cleanliness, good complexion, clear eyes, good teeth, good hair, firm muscle tone, and a steady gait—are universally appealing to both genders, because they're markers of reproductive potential (Buss, 2005). Youth and health may be relatively more important to a woman's appeal because these characteristics tend to be associated with her reproductive capacity—the "biological clock" limits her reproductive potential. Physical characteristics associated with a woman's youthfulness, such as smooth skin, firm muscle tone, and lustrous hair, may have thereby become more closely linked to a woman's appeal (Buss, 1994). A man's reproductive value, however, may depend more on how well he can provide for his family than on his age or physical appeal. From a female perspective, a man's value as a reproducer, therefore, is more intertwined with factors that contribute to a stable environment for child-rearing, such as economic status and reliability. Evolutionary psychologists argue that these gender differences in mate preference may have been passed down through the generations as part of our genetic heritage (Buss, 2009).

Mate preferences that have evolved over millions of years of human evolution are not expressed consciously; they're more like gut-level attractions (Buss & Schmitt, 1993). In other words, from the perspective of evolutionary psychology,

A World of Diversity

SEX DIFFERENCES IN MATE PREFERENCE ACROSS 37 CULTURES

What do men in Nigeria, Japan, Brazil, Canada, and the United States have in common? For one thing, they all like to be older than their mates.

Buss (1994) reviewed survey evidence for preferred age differences between individuals and their mates in 37 cultures (representing 33 countries) in Europe, Africa, Asia, Australia, New Zealand, and North and South America.

In every culture, men wanted their mates to be 0.38 to 6.45 years younger than they were. Women, however, preferred mates who were 1.82 to 5.1 years older. These preferred age differences paralleled the actual age differences between men and women at time of marriage.

Buss found that in all 37 cultures, men placed greater value than women did on prospective partners' "good looks." Women in 36 of the 37 cultures placed greater value on prospective mates' "good earning capacity."

The consistency of Buss's findings lends credence to the notion that there are widespread differences between men's and women's preferences when it comes to a prospective mate's age, physical characteristics, and financial status. Generally speaking, men place greater value on physical attractiveness and relative youth, while women place greater value on earning capacity.

Buss interprets women's preferences for relatively older mates as additional evidence that women appraise future mates on the basis of their ability to provide for wives and families, because age and income tend to be linked in men.

Who is Mr. or Ms. Right?
Are your judgments of attractiveness based on universal standards, or on your cultural experiences? Evolutionary psychologist David Buss found some nearly universal standards for beauty in his study of 37 cultures.

CRITICAL THINKING QUESTIONS

Do your own preferences in a romantic partner appear to support or contradict the theory of evolutionary psychology?

having a preference for particular qualities in a mate is similar to having a preference for certain types of food. Over many generations when food was scarce, for example, human beings developed a taste for food that was rich in sugars and fats, because it gave them a greater chance of survival. We don't have a sweet tooth because we choose to, but because it's been bred into us by the forces of evolution. According to evolutionary psychology, these same dynamics influence sexual attraction.

The theory of evolutionary psychology is subject to caveats and criticisms when it comes to mate preference. (See Chapter 9 for an evolutionary explanation for homosexuality.) Among the most prominent caveats is the argument that male-dominated social structures are the main reason so many cultures emphasize female physical beauty and male economic status in their standards of attractiveness. In this view, as cultures develop higher levels of gender equality, male and female standards of attractiveness will gradually change. Some would argue that we're already beginning to see these changes. Are women placing more emphasis

Innovative Canadian Research

PARTNER PREFERENCES AND AGE, GENDER, AND ORIENTATION

Researchers at Queen's University compared the age-based partner preferences of heterosexual men, heterosexual women, gay men, and lesbians (Silverthorne & Quinsey, 2000).

They asked adults to rate pictures of 15 male and 15 female faces that were sorted into five age-based categories, ranging from 18 to 60.

The lesbians rated 42- to 60-year-old female faces as most attractive, and 19-year-olds as least attractive. Gay and heterosexual men found younger partners more sexually appealing than lesbian and heterosexual women did. Gay men found younger partners more sexually appealing than did heterosexual men, while lesbians found older partners more sexually appealing than heterosexual women did.

In another study of gay and bisexual men in three Ontario cities, Barry Adam (2000a) of the University of Windsor found widespread acknowledgment of the ideal of youthfulness in the gay community. In particular, men who preferred their partners to be older than they were noted that they often faced ridicule as a result. Nevertheless, the study showed considerable diversity in the age preferences of gay and bisexual men.

Your Ideal Match.
Research shows that people tend to pair off with others who are similar in physical characteristics and personality traits.

on men's physical appearance as they begin to equal men in economic power? Are men increasingly enticed by high-powered professional women? As Western society continues to progress toward gender equality, it will be fascinating to see the extent to which standards of attractiveness for men and women also change. Many evolutionary psychologists would contend that while changes in social structure may indeed affect our opinions and choices, we are, at a very basic level, still unavoidably influenced by forces of human evolution.

Love

Our culture idealizes the concept of romantic love. We readily identify with the plight of the star-crossed lovers in *Romeo and Juliet* and *West Side Story*, who sacrificed themselves for love. We learn that "love makes the world go round" and "love is everything."

A Canadian study found that people who felt they were loved had better health than people who didn't (Nakhaie & Arnold, 2010). In Reginald Bibby's (2001) survey of Canadian teenagers, three-quarters viewed being loved as a very important

A World of Diversity

ONLINE ATTRACTION

Physical closeness, or proximity, has always been a factor in interpersonal attraction. People have always been drawn to the boy or girl next door. We tend to form romantic relationships with people we meet in our neighbourhoods, schools, religious communities, and jobs.

In the age of electronics, proximity is paradoxical. We can find ourselves corresponding with—and perhaps feeling attracted to—people who are as close as the monitors in front of our noses, yet thousands of miles away in the flesh.

When we meet people in person, we immediately see what they look like, hear their voices, and—according to some researchers—perhaps get something like a whiff of their pheromones. But when we meet people in chat rooms or computer-mediated multi-user dungeons, the cues that might spark interest are different.

Mantovani (2001) notes that in online relationships, written (keyboarded) language is important, timing and speed in writing and responding are crucial, and punctuation and smiley-faced emoticons make a difference. Frequency of contact in the virtual world also plays a role, just as it does in the real world (Levine, 2000; Mantovani, 2001). Repeatedly visiting the same chat room allows mutual awareness to develop and suggests similarity of interests.

Deb Levine (2000) notes that people are more likely to disclose intimate information about themselves on the internet, perhaps because the actual—or unknown—distance between the parties provides a sense of security. Some people are also quicker to reciprocate expressions of interest online than they would be face to face.

Levine notes that flirting and erotic activity on the internet can be extremely exciting, but can also build unrealistic expectations and disqualify participants for relationships in the physical world. (Would you want to have a real-world relationship with someone who quickly enters sexual discussions online?)

Levine and Mantovani both warn that expressions of similarity are easy to feign on the net. Levine (2000) warns against becoming overly wrapped up in people who are reluctant to exchange sound files or pictures. And she adds that it makes sense to meet in the real world within a month or so, to check out the accuracy of computer-mediated impressions—preferably in a safe, public place.

We'll further discuss how the new communication technologies have affected dating in Chapter 7.

CRITICAL THINKING QUESTIONS

Is it possible to be genuinely attracted to someone only on the basis of online communication?

Storge (STORE-gay) Loving attachment and nonsexual affection. This is the type of emotion that binds parents to children.

Agape (AH-gah-pay) Selfless love. This kind of love is similar to generosity and charity.

Philia (FEEL-yuh) Love between friends. This kind of love is based on liking and respect, rather than sexual desire.

Eros The kind of love that's closest to our modern-day concept of passion.

goal. About one-half of adult Canadians report that they're very satisfied with the amount of love in their lives (*Maclean's*, 1998).

Like other aspects of human sexual and social behaviour, the concept of love must be understood within a cultural context.

A Greek Heritage

The concept of love can be traced back at least as far as the classical age of Greece. The Greeks distinguished four concepts related to the modern meanings of love: **storge, agape, philia,** and **eros.**

Eros is closest in meaning to our concept of passion. Eros was a character in Greek mythology (transformed in Roman mythology into Cupido, now called Cupid) who would shoot unsuspecting people with his love arrows, causing them to fall madly in love with whoever was nearest to them at the time. Erotic love embraces sudden passionate desire—"love at first sight" and "falling head over heels in love." Younger university students are more likely to believe in love at first sight and that "love conquers all" than older (and wiser?) students (Knox et al., 1999). Passion can be so gripping that you're convinced your life has been changed forever (Aron et al., 2008). Romantic love can also be earthy and sexy. In fact, sexual arousal and desire may be the strongest component of passionate or romantic love. Romantic love begins with a powerful physical attraction or feelings of passion, and is associated with strong physiological arousal.

Unlike the Greeks, we tend to use the word "love" to describe everything from feelings of affection toward another to romantic ardour to sexual intercourse ("making love"). Still, different types or styles of love are recognized in our own culture, as we shall see.

Romantic Love

The experience of romantic love, as opposed to loving attachment or sexual arousal per se, occurs within a cultural context that idealizes the concept. Western culture has a long tradition of idealizing romantic love, as represented, for instance, by romantic fairy tales that have been passed down through the generations. Our exposure to the concept of romantic love may begin with the fairy tales of Sleeping Beauty, Cinderella, and Snow White and their respective Princes Charming. Later, perhaps, the concept of romantic love blossoms with exposure to romantic novels, television and film scripts, and the heady tales of friends and relatives.

During adolescence, strong sexual arousal together with idealized images of the objects of our desires leads us to label our feelings "love." We speak of love, rather than lust, because sexual desire in the absence of committed relationships might be viewed as primitive or animalistic. Being "in love" ennobles attraction and sexual arousal—in our own minds, as well as in society's view. Unlike lust, love can be discussed at the dinner table. If others think we're too young to experience "the real thing"—which presumably includes knowledge of and respect for our partners' personality traits—our feelings may be called "puppy love" or "crushes."

Western society retains much of its old double standard for sexuality. Women, more often than men, are expected to justify their sexual experiences as involving people they love. Young men usually needn't attribute their sexual urges to love, and are therefore more likely to deem love a "mushy" concept. Nonetheless, the vast majority of people in Canada believe romantic love is a prerequisite for marriage. Romantic love is rated by young Canadians as the most important reason for marriage (Compas, 1998).

A national survey in 2008 found that around half of Canadians (59% of the men and 51% of the women surveyed) believed in love at first sight. Thirty-eight percent said they'd actually experienced it (La Rose, 2008). Overall, 98% said they'd been in love at least once.

When reciprocated, romantic love is usually a source of deep fulfillment and ecstasy. When love is unrequited, however, it can lead to emptiness, anxiety, and despair. Romantic love can thus shift between ecstasy and misery (Hatfield, 1988). Perhaps no other feature of our lives can lift us as high or plunge us as low as romantic love.

INFATUATION VERSUS TRUE LOVE   Perhaps you first noticed one another when your eyes met across a crowded room. Or perhaps you met when you were both assigned to the same Bunsen burner in chemistry lab—less romantic, but closer to the flame. However it happened, the meeting triggered such electric charges through your bodies that you couldn't get one another out of your minds. Were you truly in love, however, or was it merely a passing fancy? Was it infatuation or the real thing—a true, lasting, mutual love? How do you tell them apart?

Perhaps you don't, at least not at first. **Infatuation** is a state of intense absorption in or focus on another person. It's usually accompanied by sexual desire, elation, and general physiological arousal or excitement. Some refer to infatuation as "passion." Others dub it a "crush." Both monikers suggest that it's a passing fancy. In infatuation, your heart may pound whenever the other person draws near or enters your fantasies.

For the first month or two, infatuation and the more enduring forms of romantic love are hard to differentiate. At first, both may be characterized by intense focusing or absorption. Infatuated people may become so absorbed that they can't sleep, work, or carry out routine chores. Logic and reason are swept aside. Infatuated people hold idealized images of their love objects, overlooking their

Infatuation A state of intense absorption in or focus on another person, usually accompanied by sexual desire, elation, and general physiological arousal or excitement. Infatuation is also referred to as passion.

faults. They may cast caution to the winds. In some cases, couples in the throes of infatuation rush to get married, only to find, a few weeks or months later, that they're not well suited for each other.

As time goes on, signs that distinguish infatuation from a lasting romantic love begin to emerge. The partners begin to view one another more realistically, and are better able to determine whether the relationship should continue. Although the tendency to idealize one's lover is strongest at the outset of a relationship, a so-called "positive illusion" does tend to persist in relationships (Aron et al., 2008). That is, we maintain some tendency to differentiate our partners from the average and to differentiate the value of our relationships from the average.

Infatuation is based on intense feelings of passion, but not on the deeper attachment and caring that typify a more lasting mutual love (Hatfield & Rapson, 2002). Infatuation can lead to a more lasting love relationship, but it's not a necessary first step on the path. Some couples develop deep feelings of love without ever experiencing the fireworks of infatuation (Barnes & Sternberg, 1997). And sometimes one partner is infatuated, while the other manages to keep his or her head below the clouds.

Contemporary Models of Love

Despite the importance of love, scientists have historically paid little attention to it. Some people believe love can't be analyzed scientifically. Love, they maintain, should be left to the poets, philosophers, and theologians. Yet researchers are now applying the scientific method to the study of love. They recognize that love is a complex concept, involving many areas of experience—behavioural, emotional, cognitive, and motivational (Berscheid, 2003). Let's consider some of the views of love that have emerged from modern theory and research.

BIOLOGICAL MECHANISMS   Some researchers focus on the bodily changes that occur when we experience feelings of romantic love. There are many. Some focus on the search for distinct neural pathways (road maps in the brain) that define feelings of love (Marazziti, 2005). Others involve chemistry, with a special focus on the monoamines and neuropeptides involved in the brain's pleasure system (including dopamine and the naturally produced opium look-alikes we call endorphins), as well as the hormones oxytocin and vasopressin.

As we noted in "A Closer Look: Watching Love as it Sears the Brain," functional MRI research shows heightened activity in the caudate nucleus, part of the brain's limbic system, which is intimately connected with emotional arousal.

Let's consider several psychologically oriented views of love. They may touch indirectly on things that happen in the body, but as we'll see, they do so almost apologetically.

Romantic love Love character-ized by feelings of passion and intimacy.

LOVE AS APPRAISAL OF AROUSAL   Social psychologists Elaine C. Hatfield and Richard L. Rapson (2002) define **romantic love** in terms of a state of intense physiological arousal and the cognitive appraisal of that arousal as love. You may experience a pounding heart, sweaty palms, and butterflies in your stomach when you're in the presence of—or thinking about—your love interest. Cognitive appraisal of the physiological arousal means you attribute it to some cause, such as fear or love.

The perception that you've fallen in love is thus derived from several simultaneous events: a state of intense physiological arousal in connection with an appropriate love object (i.e., a person, not an event such as a rock concert), a cultural setting that idealizes romantic love, and your attribution of the physiological arousal to feelings of love for the person.

STYLES OF LOVE   Some psychologists talk about styles of love. Susan Hendrick and Clyde Hendrick (2002) speak of love as a positive emotion that contributes to happiness, psychological well-being, and optimism about the future.

A Closer Look

WATCHING NEW LOVE SEAR THE BRAIN

New love can look for all the world like mental illness—a blend of mania, dementia, and obsession that cuts people off from their friends and families and prompts out-of-character behaviours such as compulsive phone calling, serenading, and yelling from rooftops. It could almost be mistaken for psychosis.

Now neuroscientists have produced brain-scan images of this fevered activity before it has settled into the wine-and-roses phase of romance or the joint-holiday-cards routine of long-term commitment. In an analysis of the images in *The Journal of Neurophysiology,* researchers argue that romantic love is a biological urge that's distinct from sexual arousal.

Helen Fisher at Rutgers, Lucy Brown at the Albert Einstein College of Medicine, and Arthur Aron at the State University of New York, Stony Brook, led a team that analyzed about 2500 brain images from 17 college students who were in the first weeks or months of new love. The students looked at pictures of their beloveds while an MRI machine imaged their brains. The researchers then compared these brain scans with others taken while the students looked at pictures of acquaintances.

Functional MRI technology detects increases and decreases of blood flow in the brain, which reflect changes in neural activity. A computer-generated map of particularly active areas showed hot spots deep in the brains of the study participants, below conscious awareness, in areas called the caudate nucleus and the ventral tegmental area, which communicate with one another as part of a circuit. These areas are dense with cells that produce or receive dopamine, a brain chemical that actively circulates when people desire or anticipate rewards. As shown in studies of gamblers, cocaine users, and even people playing computer games for small amounts of money, these dopamine sites become extremely active as people score or win.

Yet falling in love is among the most irrational of human behaviours, not merely a matter of securing a simple pleasure or reward.

The researchers found that one particular spot in the MRI images, in the caudate nucleus, was especially active in people who scored high on a questionnaire measuring passionate love. Located on the opposite side of the brain from the area that registers physical attractiveness, this passion-related region appears to be involved in longing, desire, and the inexplicable tug people feel toward sole individuals even in the presence of many attractive alternate partners.

This distinction between liking and wanting someone—that is, between finding a person attractive and desiring him or her—"is all happening in an area of the mammalian brain that takes care of most basic functions, like eating, drinking, eye movements, all at an unconscious level," Brown

Anthropologist Helen Fisher. Fisher and her colleagues have investigated the biochemical aspects of attraction and love in human sexuality.

wrote. "And I don't think anyone expected this part of the brain to be so specialized."

The intoxication of new love mellows with time, of course, and the brain-imaging findings show some evidence of this change. The researchers saw individual differences in the group of smitten lovers, correlated with how long the participants had been in their relationships. Compared with the students who were in the first weeks of a new love, those who had been paired off for a year or more showed significantly more activity in an area of the brain linked to long-term commitment.

Source: Carey, B. (2005, May 31). Watching new love as it sears the brain. The New York Times. *Reprinted with permission.*

They've developed a Love Attitudes Scale that suggests the existence of six styles of love (Hendrick & Hendrick, 2003):

- Romantic love (eros)—"My lover fits my ideal"; "My lover and I were attracted to one another immediately."
- Game-playing love (ludus)—"I keep my lover up in the air about my commitment"; "I get over love affairs pretty easily."
- Friendship (storge, philia)—"The best love grows out of an enduring friendship."
- Logical love (pragma)—"I consider a lover's potential in life before committing myself"; "I consider whether my lover will be a good parent."

CRITICAL THINKING QUESTIONS

If someone asked you what it means to fall in love, how would you respond?

- Possessive, excited love (mania)—"I get so excited about my love that I can't sleep"; "When my lover ignores me, I get sick all over."
- Selfless love (agape)—"I'd do anything I could to help my lover"; "My lover's needs and wishes are more important than my own."

As you can see, these styles of love owe a debt to the Greeks.

Most people who are in love experience a number of these styles, but Hendrick and Hendrick (1986) have found some interesting gender differences. University men are significantly more likely to develop game-playing and romantic love styles. University women are more apt to develop friendly, logical, and possessive love styles. Hendrick and Hendrick (2003) have also found that romantically involved couples tend to experience the same love styles.

STERNBERG'S TRIANGULAR THEORY OF LOVE   Psychologist Robert Sternberg (1988) has offered a triangular theory that organizes the relationships between the different kinds of love discussed by many theorists, including passionate love, romantic love, and companionate love (Gouveia et al., 2009; Hendrick & Hendrick, 2003).

Sternberg's three components of love are:

- Intimacy—the experience of warmth toward another person that arises from feelings of closeness, bondedness, and connectedness, including the desire to give and receive emotional support and to share one's innermost thoughts.
- Passion—an intense romantic or sexual desire for another person, accompanied by physiological arousal.
- Commitment—dedication to maintaining the relationship through good times and bad.

According to Sternberg's model, love can be conceptualized in terms of a triangle, with each vertex representing one of these basic elements of love. (See Figure 6.2.)

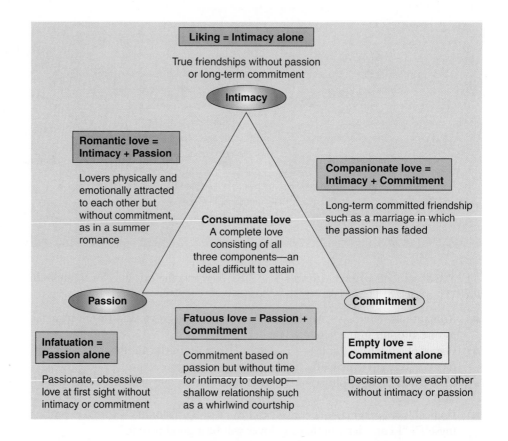

Figure 6.2 The triangular model of love.
According to psychologist Robert Sternberg, love consists of three components, represented by the vertices of this triangle. The various kinds of love consist of different combinations of these components. Romantic love, for example, consists of passion and intimacy. Consummate love—the cultural ideal—consists of all three components.

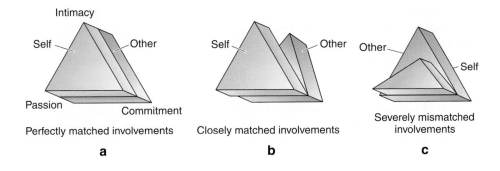

Figure 6.3 Compatibility and incompatibility, according to the triangular model of love.
Compatibility in terms of Sternberg's components of love can be represented as triangles. The first image (a) shows a perfect match, in which the triangles are congruent. The second image (b) shows a good match, since the partners are similar on the three dimensions. The third image (c) is a mismatch—there are major differences between the partners on all three components.

The way the components are balanced can be represented by the shape of the triangle. For example, a love in which all three components are equally balanced—as in a consummate love—is represented by an equilateral triangle, as illustrated in Figure 6.2.

Couples are well matched if they possess corresponding levels of passion, intimacy, and commitment (Drigotas et al., 1999; Sternberg, 1988). Compatibility can be represented visually in terms of the congruence of the love triangles. Figure 6.3(a) shows a perfect match, with the two triangles congruent. Figure 6.3(b) depicts a good match, since the partners are similar in the three dimensions. Figure 6.3(c) shows a mismatch, with major differences between the partners on all three components.

Relationships may run aground when partners are mismatched. A relationship may fizzle, rather than sizzle, if one partner experiences more passion than the other, or if one wants a long-term relationship when the other's idea of commitment is to stay the whole night.

According to Sternberg's model, various combinations of the three components of love characterize six different types of love relationship (Sternberg, 1986, 1988) (see Figure 6.3): infatuation, liking, romantic love, consummate love, empty love, and fatuous love.

Infatuation (passionate love) is typified by strong sexual desire, but not by intimacy and commitment. Each partner may feel passionate love for the other, or such feelings may go unrequited.

Liking is a basis for friendship. It consists of feelings of closeness and emotional warmth, but without passion or commitment. Liking isn't felt toward passing acquaintances; it's reserved for people to whom we feel close enough to share our innermost feelings and thoughts. We sometimes develop these intimate relationships without committing ourselves to maintaining the long-term relationships that typify other types of love. Liking may develop into passionate love, or into a more committed form of friendship called companionate love according to many writers, including Sternberg (1988), Hendrick and Hendrick (2003), and Hatfield (Hatfield et al., 2008).

Can lovers also be friends, or shall the twain never meet? There's no reason people in love shouldn't become good friends—perhaps even the best of friends. Sternberg's model recognizes that the intimacy we find in true friendships and the passion we find in love are blended in two forms of love—romantic love and consummate love. These types of love differ along the dimension of commitment.

Romantic love has both passion and intimacy, but lacks commitment. It may burn brightly and then flicker out. Or it may develop into the more complete love called consummate love, in which all three components flower—that is, desire is accompanied by a deeper intimacy and commitment. The flames of passion can be stoked across the years, even if they don't burn quite as brightly as they once did. Consummate love is the ideal many Westerners strive for.

In empty love, by contrast, there's nothing *but* commitment. It contains neither the warm, emotional embrace of intimacy nor the flame of passion. With empty love, your partner is someone you tolerate and remain with because of a sense of duty. People often remain in empty-love relationships because of either personal or social prescription (Cox et al., 1997). Personal prescription is based on the belief that you should persist in a relationship. Social prescription is based on the belief that your friends and family members believe it's right to persist in a relationship.

Sometimes a love relationship contains both passion and commitment, but lacks intimacy. Sternberg calls this fatuous (foolish) love. It's associated with whirlwind courtships that burn brightly but briefly, as the partners come to realize they're not well matched. Intimacy can develop in such relationships, but couples experiencing fatuous love who rush into marriage often find that the reality doesn't match their expectations.

In companionate love, intimacy and commitment are strong, but passion is lacking. This form of love typifies long-term (so-called platonic) friendships, and marriages in which passion has ebbed, but deep, abiding friendship remains (Hatfield & Rapson, 2002; Hendrick & Hendrick, 2003).

For many of us, a strong dose of all three components—as found in consummate love—typifies the ideal relationship. The balance among Sternberg's three aspects of love, however, is likely to shift through the course of a relationship (Hatfield et al., 2008). At the outset, passion may be strong, but intimacy weak, as a couple is just getting to know one another's innermost thoughts and feelings. Time alone doesn't cause intimacy and commitment to grow. Some couples are able to peer into one another's deeper selves and form meaningful commitments at relatively early stages, while others who've been together for many years may remain distant, or waver in their commitment. Some couples experience only a faint flickering of passion early in their relationships, then it's quickly extinguished. For others, the flames of passion burn ever brightly. Many couples, though, find that passion tends to fade, while intimacy and commitment grow stronger.

Knowing the components of love can help you avoid pitfalls. Couples who recognize that passion exerts a strong pull early in a relationship may be less likely to let passion rush them into premature long-term legal commitments. Couples who recognize that it's normal for passion to fade needn't assume their love is at an end just when it may, in fact, be changing into a deeper, more intimate, committed form of love.

Summing Up

A number of factors determine interpersonal attraction.

Physical attractiveness is a major determinant of sexual attraction. In our culture, slenderness is in style. Both genders find smiling faces more attractive than unsmiling faces. Socially dominant men, but not dominant women, are usually found attractive. Women place greater emphasis on such traits as vocational status and earning potential in potential mates, whereas men give more consideration to physical attractiveness. Evolutionary psychologists believe that evolutionary forces favour such gender differences in preferred traits because these traits offer reproductive advantages.

According to the attraction-similarity hypothesis, we tend to develop romantic relationships with people who are similar to us.

Through reciprocation of positive words and actions, neutral or mild feelings may be stoked into feelings of attraction.

The Greeks had four concepts that relate to our modern definitions of love: storge, agape, philia, and eros.

Western culture has a long tradition of idealizing romantic love. Most people in Canada see romantic love as a prerequisite to marriage. Early in a relationship, infatuation may be indistinguishable from a more enduring form of romantic love.

Researchers are now applying the scientific method to the study of love.

Berscheid and Hatfield define romantic love in terms of intense physiological arousal, and cognitive appraisal of that arousal as love.

Hendrick and Hendrick suggest that there are six styles of love among college students: romantic love, game-playing love, friendship, logical love, possessive love, and selfless love.

Sternberg suggests that there are three distinct components of love: intimacy, passion, and commitment. Various combinations of these components typify different kinds of love. Romantic love is characterized by the combination of passion and intimacy.

Test Yourself

Multiple-Choice Questions

1. Susan Sprecher and her colleagues found that women are more willing than men to marry people who are:
   (a) Six or more years younger than they are.
   (b) Not good-looking.
   (c) Less well educated than they are.
   (d) Unlikely to hold steady jobs.

2. In his study of sex differences in mate preference across 37 cultures, Buss found that:
   (a) Men preferred women who earned more money than they did.
   (b) Women preferred men who were older than they were.
   (c) Only European men expressed an interest in marriage.
   (d) Evolutionary forces contributed to preferences in some cultures, but not in others.

3. Helen Fisher and her colleagues found that the _____ is highly active when we experience a new romantic love.
   (a) reticular activating system
   (b) prefrontal cortex
   (c) metatarsophalangeal joint
   (d) caudate nucleus

4. A number of studies have shown that:
   (a) Men are more attracted to socially dominant women.
   (b) Women are more attracted to socially dominant men.
   (c) There are no gender differences in attraction.
   (d) Social dominance is not important in attraction.

5. Loving attachment, deep friendship, and nonsexual affection describe the ancient Greek concept of:
   (a) Agape.
   (b) Storge.
   (c) Eros.
   (d) Philia.

6. People who say, "I keep my lover up in the air about my commitment" or "I get over love affairs pretty easily" appear to be in the _____ style of love.
   (a) logical
   (b) romantic
   (c) game-playing
   (d) possessive

7. The idea that people are more likely to look for romantic relationships with those who are similar to themselves is known as the:
   (a) Reciprocity theory.
   (b) Attraction-similarity hypothesis.
   (c) Love profile.
   (d) Intimacy theory.

8. Hendrick and Hendrick found that college men were significantly more likely than college women to develop a _____ love style.
   (a) friendly
   (b) logical
   (c) romantic
   (d) possessive

9. Sternberg's triangular theory of love includes intimacy, passion, and:
   (a) Reciprocity.
   (b) Sexuality.
   (c) Commitment.
   (d) Delight.

10. In the early stages of a relationship, love and _____ may be difficult to distinguish.
    (a) infatuation
    (b) friendship
    (c) empty love
    (d) fatuous love

You'll find answers to the "Test Yourself" questions on page 495.

Critical Thinking

1. Have you ever been in love? How would you distinguish between love and infatuation?

2. What traits or characteristics are most important to you when you think about a potential date? A marriage partner? Are they the same or different? Why?

3. Would you have a relationship with someone of another religion or ethnic group? Why or why not? How do you think your friends and family would react?

MySearchLab

MySearchLab offers extensive help to students with their writing and research project and provides round-the-clock access to credible and reliable source material. Take a tour at www.mysearchlab.com.

CHAPTER SEVEN

Relationships, Intimacy, and Communication

Social-exchange theory The view that a relationship's development reflects the unfolding of social exchanges—that is, the rewards and costs of maintaining the relationship, as opposed to those of ending it.

ABCDE model Levinger's view, which approaches romantic relationships in terms of five stages: attraction, building, continuation, deterioration, and ending.

In this chapter we'll first define the stages that lead to intimacy in relationships. We'll see that not all relationships achieve this level of interrelatedness, even some supposedly deep and permanent relationships, such as marriage. Moreover, we don't all have partners to develop intimate relationships with; some of us remain alone and, perhaps, lonely. Finally, we'll discuss the ways communication contributes to relationships and sexual satisfaction, and enumerate ways to enhance communication skills.

The ABC(DE)s of Romantic Relationships

Romantic relationships, like people, undergo stages of development. According to **social-exchange theory**, this development reflects the unfolding of social exchanges, which involve the rewards and costs of maintaining a relationship, compared with the rewards and costs of dissolving it. During each stage, positive factors sway the partners toward maintaining and enhancing their relationship. Negative factors incline them toward letting it deteriorate and end.

Numerous investigators have viewed the development of romantic relationships in terms of phases or stages (Berscheid & Reis, 1998; Dindia & Timmerman, 2003; Hendrick & Hendrick, 2000; Honeycutt & Cantrill, 2001). From their work, we can build a five-stage **ABCDE model** of romantic relationships, consisting of (A) attraction, (B) building, (C) continuation, (D) deterioration, and (E) ending, or termination. Before proceeding with a more in-depth discussion of relationships, intimacy, and communication, let's briefly define each of these five stages.

ATTRACTION   Attraction occurs when two people become aware of and find one another appealing or enticing. We may find ourselves attracted to an enchanting person across a crowded room, in a nearby office, or in a new class. We may meet others through blind dates, introductions by mutual friends, computer match-ups, or by accident.

BUILDING   Building a relationship follows initial attraction. Factors that motivate us to build a relationship include similarity in level of physical attraction, similarity in attitudes and interests, and a generally positive evaluation of the partner. Factors that may deter us from trying to build a relationship include lack of physical appeal, dissimilarity in attitudes, and a mutually negative evaluation.

CONTINUATION   Once a basic level of attachment and intimacy has been established, a relationship typically enters a stage of continuation, during which established patterns of interaction remain relatively stable. While these patterns often continue, they don't remain entirely static. Within this stage, a relationship will mature and evolve as time passes and circumstances change. A relationship in the continuation stage that doesn't balance the stability of established patterns of intimacy and communication with the need for ongoing adaptation and development may enter a stage of deterioration.

DETERIORATION   A relationship begins to deteriorate when it becomes less rewarding than it was. A couple can respond to deterioration actively or passively. Active means of response include doing something that may enhance the relationship (e.g., working on improving communication skills, negotiating differences, or seeking professional help) or deciding to end the relationship. Passive methods of response include merely waiting for something to happen, doing little or nothing. The couple can sit back and wait for the relationship to improve on its own (occasionally, it does) or to deteriorate to the point where it ends. ("Hey, these things happen.")

It's irrational (and damaging to a relationship) to assume good relationships require no investment of time and effort. No two people are matched perfectly. When problems arise, it's better to work to resolve them than to act as though they don't exist and hope they'll just disappear.

ENDING   According to social-exchange theory, relationships draw to a close when the partners find little satisfaction in the affiliation, when the barriers to leaving the relationship are low (that is, the social, religious, and financial constraints are manageable), and especially when alternative partners are available. Problems with jealousy and communication are common reasons for ending a relationship.

Various factors can save a deteriorating relationship. For example, people who continue to find some source of satisfaction, are committed to maintaining the relationship, or believe they'll eventually be able to overcome their problems are more likely to invest what they must to prevent the collapse.

CRITICAL THINKING QUESTIONS

Would you be less likely to accept a date with someone who asked you out via a text message than over the phone? Why or why not?

A Closer Look

REELING IN A DATE

If Markus Frind's example is anything to go by, the best way to earn a cool few million is to do not much at all, and certainly much less than your competitors. Frind, 30, runs one of the world's busiest dating sites out of his home in Vancouver. Operating in New Zealand, Australia, the United States, the United Kingdom, and Canada, he has single-handedly managed to become a major player in the world of online matchmaking.

Frind started PlentyofFish.com in March 2003. He wanted to create a free dating site in a market that usually charges members $20 to $60 per month.

Dating sites are usually very niche. If you're a member of a particular group, or have a sexual fetish, or an obscure hobby or interest, there's likely a dating site for you. There's TrekPassions.com (for Trekkies), BikerKiss.com, LoveMeLoveMyPets.com, BlackPlanet.com, Prescription4Love.com (for people with everything from Tourette's syndrome to herpes), SeniorFinder.com, and AshleyMadison.com (strictly for adulterers).

The clients mostly self-select, but some sites build in barriers to weed out those who don't fit their target demographics. For example, Match.com requires a lengthy and involved 400-item questionnaire that can take several hours to complete, says Evan Marc Katz, a dating coach and author of *I Can't Believe I'm Buying This Book: A Commonsense Guide to Successful Internet Dating.* The quiz is designed to discourage those who aren't serious about relationships.

Then, there's ItsJustLunch.com, exclusively for busy professionals. The $1 600 fee for arranging 14 lunch dates, excluding meal costs, is supposed to turn off anyone who can't afford to pick up the tab.

PlentyofFish.com has taken the opposite approach. The registration process is deliberately short, and open to everyone. It aims to attract large numbers of people from a broad cross-section of society. The downside, critics say, is that the site inevitably draws people who prefer not to spend any money in their search for companionship. In Canada, the average user age is 38, and in the United States it's 39, but people in their twenties and seniors are also well represented in both countries. "It's brilliant, because it's really easy to use," explains Bonny Albo, who writes About.com's *Dating* pages. "People really like it, especially because it's free."

While other dating websites offer a range of video and messaging functions, PlentyofFish.com offers the bare basics. Rather than taking compatibility tests and receiving referrals, visitors to PlentyofFish.com search for their own dates. Instead of video clips, they see profiles accompanied by simple head shots. If they run into problems, there's no customer service number to call. They can send emails, although the site warns that only a couple of people read the incoming emails, so responses often take days. There's no banner advertising, because PlentyofFish.com relies on word of mouth for traffic and Google ads for revenue.

"They let people do their own thing," Katz explains. "There is no real quality control or filter on who is joining the site. If you want to find what you are looking for, you probably have to sift through a lot of people. It's a big, sloppy, under-managed site that's very laissez-faire."

The site posts thousands of photos, testimonials and thank you letters from couples who have met their partner or spouse through the service. And in sheer volume and traffic, it remains No. 1. With 18 million hits per month in Canada, and 58 million worldwide, it is the nation's most popular dating site. Roughly 1.2 million people visit the site every month in Canada. Lavalife is a distant second with 752 000 people for the same duration, according to Comscore. Revenues total about $10 million per year, says Frind, compared to annual operating costs of about $1 million, covering advertising, site maintenance and the cost of employing two customer service staffers. The rest of the profits go to Frind, who works about 10 hours per week, and is planning to expand into Brazil and Germany next. In the dating site world, growth can feed off itself, explains Katz. "If you throw two billion people in a barrel, you don't have to do much for some of them to meet and hit it off. PlentyofFish.com does well mainly because of the law of averages."

Source: Shimo, A. (2008, July 16) "Reeling in a date: Plenty of Fish has become the dating site for the masses." The Toronto Star.

Applied Knowledge

SEXTING AND CANADIAN YOUTH

Until a few years ago, the word "sexting" didn't exist. A combination of "sex" and "texting," the word refers to the sending of sexually explicit images from one mobile phone to another. In most instances, sexting includes nude or semi-nude photos of the senders.

The media in Canada have recently begun to pay attention to the topic of teen sexting. Headlines in Canadian newspapers and magazines include "Sexting Nude Photos a Teen Concern" (Baute, *The Toronto Star*, January 7, 2010) and "The Sexting Scare" (Kingston, *Maclean's*, March 12, 2009).

To date, no published studies have examined how many Canadian youth have used their cell phones to send or receive nude photos. An Associated Press and MTV (2009) survey of 1247 14- to 24-year-old respondents in the United States found that 13% of females and 9% of males had sent naked photos or videos of themselves.

A Pew Research Center (2009) study held focus groups asking young people to describe the situations in which teens are likely to sext. They found that most cases of sexting fall into three categories:

- Exchange of photos solely between romantic partners in a relationship.
- Exchange of photos between two people who aren't in a relationship, but one of the individuals sends a sext in the hope that it will help start a romantic relationship between the two.
- Exchange of photos between romantic partners, or from an individual who

hopes to start a relationship with the recipient and then sends the photos to additional people (Pew Research Centre, 2009).

For adults, exchanging nude photos electronically is legal under most circumstances. However, creating and sending nude photos of people who are under 18 does, technically, break Canada's child-pornography laws. Specifically, creating and distributing images depicting sexual activity or depicting the sexual organ of a person under the age of 18 is an criminal offense under Canada's Criminal Code.

In general, the intended purpose of the child pornography law does not include the prosecution of teens for taking and sharing nude photos, as long as the photos are kept private (Slane, 2009). Nevertheless, sending nude photos of teens under age 18 is, technically, a criminal offense.

In 2007, an 18-year-old male in Alberta was charged with distribution and possession of child pornography after he showed other people nude pictures of a 15-year-old female that she'd emailed him. He was allowed to plead guilty to the less severe charge of corrupting morals (Baute, 2010). In similar scenarios in the United States, the teens involved have been charged and convicted of distributing child pornography.

In the Associated Press and MTV (2009) survey, 17% of those who'd received sexts reported that they'd passed them along to others. In most cases, when people send nude photos of themselves to others, we can safely assume they want

those photos kept private. As this study shows, that doesn't always happen.

What's the take-home message?

You may feel comfortable that your privacy will be protected, because you're sending a picture of yourself to a relationship partner you trust. But most relationships don't last forever. Will you feel the same level of trust and comfort with an ex-partner who still has the nude photos you sent months or years ago? In many cases where nude photos have been sent to large numbers of people, they've been sent by ex-partners of the individuals in the photos.

As the authors of a study conducted for the National Campaign to Prevent Teen and Unplanned Pregnancy and CosmoGirl.com (2008) note, "There is no changing your mind in cyberspace—anything you send or post will never truly go away" (p. 2).

Whether it's the result of a current or ex-partner's breaking your trust or simply the result of an accident (e.g., a lost or stolen cell phone with your image in it, an intercepted email), sexting images that are eventually seen by family members, friends, people who don't like you, and even future employers can have lasting consequences.

And remember, if it involves nude images of people under the age of 18, sexting may violate Canadian child pornography laws.

Source: Adapted from SIECCAN. (2011). Check the research: Sexting considerations for Canadian youth. SexualityAndU.ca. Ottawa: The Society of Obstetricians and Gynaecologists of Canada. http://sexualityandu.ca/uploads/files/CTRsextingEnglishApril2011.pdf

On the other hand, the swan song of a relationship—moving on—can be a sign of healthful decision-making, not a sign of failure. When people are highly incompatible and genuine attempts to preserve the relationship have failed, ending it can offer each partner a chance for happiness with someone else.

Small talk A superficial kind of conversation that allows exchange of information but stresses breadth of topic coverage rather than in-depth discussion.

NOT-SO-SMALL TALK: AN AUDITION FOR A RELATIONSHIP In the early stages of building a relationship, we typically look for common ground in the form of overlapping attitudes and interests, and we check out our feelings of attraction. At this point, we often use **small talk** to help determine whether to develop the relationship. Small talk allows an exchange of information, stressing breadth of topic coverage rather than in-depth discussion. Engaging in small talk may seem "phony," but premature self-disclosure of intimate information may repel the other person, as we'll see.

Small talk is a trial balloon for friendship. Successful small talk encourages a couple to venture beneath the surface. At a cocktail party, people may flit about from person to person, exchanging small talk, but now and then a couple finds common ground and pairs off.

THE OPENING LINE   One kind of small talk is the greeting, or opening line. We usually precede verbal greetings with eye contact and decide to begin talking if this eye contact is reciprocated. Avoidance of eye contact may mean the person is shy, but it could also signify lack of interest. If you'd like to progress from initial attraction to surface contact, try a smile and direct eye contact. If the eye contact is reciprocated, choose a greeting. Because your opening line can be important, you may prefer to say something more meaningful than "one, two, one, two."

Here are some types of opening lines:

- Verbal salutes, such as "Good morning."
- Personal inquiries, such as "How are you doing?"
- Compliments, such as "I like your outfit."
- References to your mutual surroundings, such as "What do you think of that painting?" or "This is a nice apartment house, isn't it?"
- References to people or events outside the immediate setting, such as "How do you like this weather we've been having?" (An opening gambit about the weather may work best when accompanied by a self-deprecating grin, to acknowledge how corny the remark might seem.)
- References to the other person's behaviour, such as "I couldn't help noticing you were sitting alone," or "I see you out on this track every Saturday morning."
- References to your own behaviour, or to yourself, such as "Hi, my name is Allan Felix." (Feel free to use your own name, if you prefer.)

Opening Lines.
What do you say when you meet someone new? Do you make small talk? About what? Do you use an opening line? Which one? Are you genuine? Are you phony? Are you tense? At ease? Small talk actually isn't so small at all. People use it to search for common ground and test possible feelings of attraction.

The simple "hi" or "hello" is very useful. A friendly glance followed by a cheerful hello ought to give you some idea of whether the attraction is reciprocated. If the hello is returned with a friendly smile and inviting eye contact, follow it up with another greeting, such as a reference to your surroundings, the other person's behaviour, or your name.

EXCHANGING NAME, RANK, AND SERIAL NUMBER   Early exchanges are likely to include name, occupation, marital status, and hometown. This has been likened to exchanging "name, rank, and serial number" with the other person. Each person seeks a sociological profile of the other, to discover common ground that may provide a basis for pursuing the conversation (Cunningham & Barbee, 2008). An unspoken rule seems to be at work: "If I provide you with some information about myself, you will reciprocate by giving me an equal amount of information about yourself. Or . . . I'll tell you my hometown if you'll tell me yours" (Knapp & Vangelista, 2000). If the other person is unresponsive, she or he may not be attracted to you. But you may also be awkward in your approach or perhaps turn the other person off if you disclose too much about yourself at the outset.

A generation or two ago, women rarely approached men to signal romantic interest or initiate relationships. Today, however, many women in developed nations do precisely that (Wade et al., 2009). Moreover, both women and men rate direct opening lines—lines that signal interest—as most effective in launching relationships (Wade et al, 2009).

DATING IN THE ERA OF NEW COMMUNICATION TECHNOLOGIES

Has the increasing utilization of communication technologies such as email, texting, and Facebook transformed dating practices? Jocelyn Wentland at the University of Ottawa and her colleagues Amy Muise and Serge Desmarais (2010) at the University of Guelph surveyed 296 undergraduate university students to investigate the extent to which young people endorse the use of newer communication technologies as part of the contemporary dating script. As you can see in Table 7.1, while most men and women found it acceptable to communicate with a potential date online or via texting, the preferred way of asking someone out was over the phone or in person. This suggests that the newer communication technologies are accepted ways for potential dating partners to get to know one another in advance of a date, but that they're less accepted for actually asking a person for a date.

Wentland, Muise, and Desmarais (2010) were also interested in whether the newer communication technologies have affected traditional gender roles related to dating. The researchers found that in many respects, traditional gender roles were still in place. For example, 71% of the students in the survey agreed that it was part of the dating script for men to pay the bill, but only 4.1% said it was part of the script for women; 71.3% agreed that wearing sexy underwear was part of the dating script for women, but only 1.4% said it was part of the script for men.

Newer communication technologies, however, were viewed as part of the dating scripts for both men and women. For example, most students (89.2%) indicated that getting to know a potential dating partner via email or texting was part of the dating script for both men and women, rather than for one gender in particular. The endorsement of newer communication technologies as part of the dating script for both men and women was also evident in the responses about getting to know a potential dating partner via Facebook (83.1%) and planning a date via email or texting (70.3%). The authors conclude that " . . . the use of technology for dating appeared to allow women more freedom in terms of initiation and planning dates with a new

TABLE 7.1
Acceptability of Different Technologies for Dating

It's acceptable to . . .	Men's Responses	Women's Responses
Communicate with a potential date via the phone.	87.7%	88.0%
Communicate with a potential date online.	78.6%	88.0%
Communicate with a potential date via a text message.	78.8%	90.0%
Ask someone on date via a text message.	26.7%	35.5%
Ask someone on a date via MSN.	28.3%	30.9%
Ask someone on a date via Facebook.	21.2%	28.2%
Ask someone on a date via the phone.	73.8%	78.8%
Ask someone on a date in person.	95.9%	98.6%

Source: Wentland, J., Muise, A., & Desmarais, S. (2010). Out with the old, in with the new: The new technologized dating script. Poster presented at the 53rd Annual Meeting of the Society for the Scientific Study of Sexuality, Las Vegas NV.

partner, which have traditionally been primarily male dating activities."

SELF-DISCLOSURE: YOU TELL ME AND I'LL TELL YOU . . . CAREFULLY Opening up, or **self-disclosure**, is central to building an intimate relationship (Derlega et al., 2008). But just what sort of information is it safe to disclose upon first meeting someone? If you refuse to go beyond name, rank, and serial number, you may look uninterested or like you're trying to keep things under wraps. If, on the other hand, you blurt out the fact that you have a terrible rash on your thigh, it's likely that you've disclosed too much too soon.

Research suggests that we should refrain from disclosing certain types of information too rapidly if we want to make a good impression (Punyanunt-Carter, 2006). We may say we value openness and honesty in our relationships, but it may be a social mistake to open up too soon.

Not Interested.
How will she get rid of him? Perhaps she'll give him a phony email address. Some women now use email as a method of avoiding seeing people they don't want to go out with. They may give out their actual email addresses but never respond, or they may give out seldom-used or erroneous email addresses. It's like giving out the wrong phone number. (Bye bye.)

SELF-DISCLOSURE ON DATING WEBSITES On the other hand, rapid self-disclosure seems to be something of a new norm when people meet in cyberspace (Brunet & Schmidt, 2008). Cyberspace allows for relative anonymity and enables people to control what they want to reveal—to safeguard their privacy even as they increase their emotional closeness and openness. The very nature of privacy changes in cyberspace.

If the surface contact provided by small talk and initial self-disclosure has been mutually rewarding, partners in a relationship tend to develop deeper feelings of liking for each other (Abell et al., 2006). Self-disclosure may continue to build gradually through the course of a relationship as the partners come to trust each other enough to share confidences and more intimate feelings.

Self-disclosure The revelation of personal—perhaps intimate—information.

Innovative Canadian Research

SEXUALLY DIRECT APPROACHES IN SINGLES BARS

While most people follow traditional strategies for meeting potential partners, in some situations initial approaches are more explicitly sexual.

In a survey of female students at the University of Guelph who went to singles bars, more than 80% reported that men had used sexually overt approach behaviours to approach them (Huber & Herold, 2006). About half of the women had initiated such behaviours themselves with people they didn't know. The specific behaviours were buttock touching over clothes, breast or chest touching over clothes, genital touching over clothes, grinding pelvis to pelvis, and grinding from behind. The grinding behaviours were the most common, while breast and genital touching were

the least common. About 90% said they would be bothered by breast and/or genital approaches, and about half said they would be bothered by buttock touching or grinding.

Sexually overt approaches are far less common in other contexts. Indeed, in most other contexts, these behaviours would be almost universally defined as sexual harassment or sexual assault. In the bar context, however, only about one-quarter of the women defined buttock touching or grinding approaches as harassment, while about three-quarters saw breast or genital touching as harassment.

Although there's a broader acceptability of certain types of behaviour in a singles bar than in other contexts, there are still limitations. At a Guelph bar, a University of Windsor student pleaded guilty to assault after having ground against a woman from behind. The woman complained to police after the man ejaculated on her (Mercury Staff, 2007).

Sex, Toys & Chocolate.
Robin Milhausen and Michael Cho were hosts of the Canadian television series Sex, Toys & Chocolate. Unlike most Canadians, the guests on this show were extremely open in disclosing their sexual preferences and behaviours.

In Canada, real people have openly discussed their sex lives on programs such as *Sex with Sue*, *Kink*, and *Sex, Toys & Chocolate*. Even the more conservative CBC television network *Newsworld* has shown the documentary *Sex, Truth and Videotape*, which involved 30 women of various ages speaking openly and explicitly about their own sexuality. The openness of participants on these programs is in direct contrast to the reticence of most Canadians.

The internet, because of its anonymity, facilitates self-disclosure. Frank sexual self-disclosure is seen on many sex blog sites. Amy Muise (2006), a University of Guelph researcher, has conducted a qualitative analysis of female sex blog sites. She gives examples of how the women describe their sexual fantasies and sexual behaviours in lustful detail. Most of the women also provide insight into their feelings and reactions regarding the development of their sexuality. Some refer to this process as "releasing their inner slut." In general, the women state that they're much more revealing about their sex lives on the web than in real life. We'll discuss this more in Chapter 15.

The belief that women are open and men tight-lipped appears to be something of a myth. Overall, researchers find that women are only slightly more revealing about themselves than men are. When Canadians were asked in the Compas (1998) survey how much detail they shared with close friends about their sexual lives, close to as many females (43%) as males (50%) said they didn't share any information. Hardly any of the females (6%) or males (4%) said they shared a lot of details. Age was a much stronger predictor of disclosure than gender. Among those who were 18 and 19, 86% disclosed to their friends, compared with only 16% of those who were 60 and older.

SEX DIFFERENCES IN SELF-DISCLOSURE   A woman complains to a friend, "He never opens up to me. It's like living with a stone wall." Women commonly say men are loath to express their feelings. Researchers find that masculine-typed (i.e., aggressive, assertive) individuals, whether male or female, tend to be less willing to disclose their feelings, perhaps in adherence to the traditional "strong and silent" masculine stereotype. A study by Susan Basow and Kimberly Rubenfeld (2003) found that feminine-typed (i.e., expressive, nurturing) individuals are more likely to be empathetic and to listen to other people's troubles than masculine-typed individuals, regardless of their anatomic sex.

A New Brunswick study of students in dating relationships found that women disclosed slightly more information about both sexual and nonsexual issues than men did (Byers & Demmons, 1999). However, in a more recent study at Trent University (Humphreys & Newby, 2007), there were no gender differences in sexual self-disclosure.

In the New Brunswick study, the students disclosed to their dating partners more about nonsexual than sexual issues, and more about their sexual likes than their sexual dislikes. Those who disclosed more about nonsexual issues also

CRITICAL THINKING QUESTIONS

Can you think of why couples—even those in long-term relationships—might not disclose their sexual likes and dislikes to each other?

disclosed more about sexual issues (although most didn't fully reveal all of their true sexual feelings). A key factor in the amount of disclosure was whether the partner also disclosed. Those who were more open were more satisfied with their level of sexual communication, and ultimately with their sexual relationships.

SEXUAL SELF-DISCLOSURE   University of New Brunswick psychology professor E. Sandra Byers (2011) has been conducting research on the sexual communication of Canadians for three decades. In collaboration with Sheila MacNeil at Dalhousie University, she's focused much of her work on sexual self-disclosure within couple relationships. They've found that individuals who disclose more about their sexual likes and dislikes report higher sexual satisfaction (MacNeil & Byers, 2005, 2009). In a study of 104 couples in long-term relationships, averaging 14 years in duration, men and women indicated how much they disclosed to their partners about their sexual likes and dislikes, using a 7-point scale that ranged from telling their partners nothing at all to telling their partners everything. On average, both men (mean = 4.1) and women (mean = 4.6) scored in the middle of the scale. Thus, even after being in relationships for an average of 14 years, many of the people in this study kept information about their sexual likes and dislikes from their partners (MacNeil & Byers, 2009).

In another New Brunswick study, the process by which sexual self-disclosure related to sexual satisfaction seemed to differ for men and women (MacNeil, 2004). For men, there was a direct relationship between sexual disclosure and sexual satisfaction. For women, disclosing about nonsexual issues seemed to be more important—women who could freely disclose about other aspects of their relationships were more satisfied with their relationships in general, and this accounted for their greater sexual satisfaction. In other words, it seems that for women, relationship satisfaction is a key factor in sexual satisfaction.

In an earlier study, female students at the University of Guelph were asked how much they disclosed about eight sexual topics (Herold & Way, 1988). The least disclosed topics were masturbation and sexual thoughts. The women were divided about revealing their sexual pasts, with less than half believing "a woman who truly loves her partner should be willing to tell him about all her previous sexual experience."

It's likely that a person's cultural background affects his or her patterns of sexual self-disclosure in a relationship. In a culture where explicit discussion of sexual topics is less socially acceptable, verbal sexual disclosure to a partner may also be less accepted or less common. This doesn't necessarily mean couples with cultural backgrounds that are less accepting of "sex talk" are less satisfied with their relationships. Rather, it may be that they place less emphasis on the importance of sexual satisfaction as it's defined in Western culture, and/or they typically use different or less direct methods of communication about sexuality.

SEXUAL INITIATION   Initiating sex is stereotypically considered the man's role. In a study of cohabiting and married individuals in New Brunswick (Byers & Heinlein, 1989), men initiated sex twice as often as women did. The men also considered initiating sex without actually doing so more often than the women. Contrary to the stereotype that men are always available for sex, however, men refused invitations to have sex proportionally as often as women, and women accepted sexual initiations as often as men.

Sarah Vannier and Lucia O'Sullivan (2010) at the University of New Brunswick asked 63 18- to 24-year-old men and women in heterosexual relationships to keep diaries for 3 weeks, recording which partner initiated sex in each instance, whether the initiation was indirect or direct, and whether it was verbal or nonverbal. Examples of indirect verbal initiation were saying something like "I love you" or "I missed you," and examples of direct verbal initiation were "You make me so hot" or "I want you right now." Examples of indirect nonverbal initiation were smiling at the partner or lying on a bed, and examples of direct nonverbal initiation were fondling a partner's breasts or removing clothing.

Vannier and O'Sullivan (2010) found that almost half (49%) of the instances of sexual activity recorded in the diaries were initiated by the male partners, 32% were initiated by the female partners, and 19% were initiated equally by the male and female partners. Almost two-thirds (65%) of the instances involved some form of verbal initiation, with indirect verbal initiation more common than direct verbal initiation. Almost all (91%) of the instances of sexual activity involved some form of nonverbal initiation, with indirect nonverbal strategies more common than direct nonverbal strategies. When it came to initiating sex with their partners, the young adult Canadians in this study were more likely to rely on indirect verbal and non-verbal initiation strategies than on direct strategies.

What about situations where the woman wants to have sex, but her partner is reluctant? How does she influence her partner to have sex? To answer this question, researchers at the University of Waterloo (Clements-Schreiber & Rempel, 1995) surveyed a community sample of married and single women. About half of the women said they would directly ask their partners to have sex. The most common strategies, which more than 90% said they would use, included arranging opportunities to be alone with their partners, paying a lot of attention to them, and touching them affectionately. The next most common strategies, as indicated by 70% or more of the women, involved passionately kissing their partners, setting a romantic mood with candlelight and music, dressing in a seductive way, rubbing their partners' backs and shoulders, and letting their hands wander around their partners' bodies.

CRITICAL THINKING QUESTIONS

To what extent do you agree with the idea that one major reason cohabitation is more common today than in the past is that it provides access to regular sex without commitment?

Commitment

Numerous studies find that men tend to be more reluctant than women to make commitments. David Popenoe, co-director of the National Marriage Project at Rutgers University in New Jersey, conducted a study with 60 unmarried hetero-sexual men, and found that the commonness of cohabitation was one reason they were reluctant to make commitments. In cohabitation, sex—traditionally a key reason for men to marry—is readily available. Popenoe (cited in Hussain, 2002) notes that "In a sense, with cohabitation, he gets a quasi-wife without having to commit."

In a committed relationship, a delicate balance exists between individuality and mutuality. In a healthy union, a strong sense of togetherness does not eradicate indi-viduality. Partners in such a relationship remain free to be themselves. Neither seeks to dominate the other or to submerge him or herself into the personality of the other. Each partner maintains individual interests, likes and dislikes, needs, and goals.

Factors that can throw continuing relationships into a downward spiral include boredom, such as the feeling of falling into a rut in leisure activities or sexual prac-tices. Yet boredom doesn't always end relationships. Consider a study of 12 men who admitted to experiencing sexual boredom in long-term heterosexual relation-ships (Tunariu & Reavey, 2003). The men weren't happy with sexual boredom, particularly in a culture in which men are viewed as highly sexual and romantic love is supposed to remain passionate. On the other hand, they viewed their boredom as a normal trade-off for so-called true love and long-term companionship.

Other factors that contribute to discontinuation of a relationship include evi-dence of negative evaluation (e.g., bickering, forgetting anniversaries and other important dates, or pretending they don't exist), lack of fairness in the relationship (e.g., one partner always deciding how the couple will spend their free time), jeal-ousy, and general dissatisfaction.

Jealousy

Anthropologists find evidence of jealousy in all cultures, although it may vary in amount and intensity across and within cultures. It appears to be more common

Innovative Canadian Research

OBTAINING SEXUAL CONSENT

A great deal has been written about the necessity of obtaining sexual consent before initiating sexual relations with a partner. There's been limited research on this topic, however (Beres, 2007).

University of Guelph students were asked how they asked for and gave sexual consent (Humphreys, 2004). Only about one-third said they explicitly asked for sex. The three most common nonverbal behaviours used by both genders were kissing their partners, moving closer, and touching their partners sexually. The most common ways two-thirds of both males and females indicated consent for sex were by not stopping their partners from kissing and sexual touching them, kissing their partners, moving closer, and touching their partners sexually. About half said they gave consent by *not* saying no. About half of the men and one-third of the women indicated consent by saying yes. The study clearly indicated that young people find directly asking for sex to be problematic. Two-thirds agreed that verbally asking for sexual consent was awkward.

When asked how consent should be obtained, more than half (65% of the females and 53% of the males) preferred that someone ask first, before engaging in any sexual activity. But a large minority (35% of the females, 47% of the males) preferred to assume consent and continue with the sexual behaviour until their partners indicated otherwise. Interestingly, although sexual consent has been stressed in many campus educational programs, only about half of the students had discussed the topic with their friends.

This research made a major contribution to the development of scales that measure sexual consent attitudes and sexual consent behaviours. These scales have solid reliability and validity (Humphreys & Herold, 2007).

In a follow-up study, Humphreys (2007a) found that students believed it was not as necessary to obtain sexual consent in a longer-term relationship as it was at the beginning of a relationship. This was true for sexual behaviours ranging from hugging to sexual intercourse. The one exception was anal intercourse, where students felt that explicit consent was required regardless of the status of the relationship. Humphreys speculates that students felt this way because most had not engaged in anal intercourse.

A controversial policy developed by Antioch College in Ohio requires that verbal consent be obtained at every step of a sexual encounter. For example, if a woman wants to kiss her partner, according to the policy, she needs to directly ask whether she can. Later, if he wishes to touch her breasts, he needs to ask directly whether he can do so, and she has to say yes, verbally, before he can proceed. When asked their opinions of this policy, students at the University of Guelph felt this type of consent procedure wasn't practical and wouldn't be followed by the great majority of young people (Humphreys & Herold, 2003).

In Banff, Alberta, Melanie Beres (2006) interviewed young men and women about how they communicated sexual consent with casual sex partners. When Beres analyzed the interviews, three main themes emerged.

First, the respondents said they simply knew whether their partners were interested in having casual sex, and therefore felt it was unnecessary to make formal requests to initiate sexual activity.

Second, there were variations on the idea that "no means no" when communicating about casual sex. Rather than directly saying no, women used a diversity of tactics, such as saying they had boyfriends. Women also showed their discomfort with proceeding by pulling away or letting their bodies become tense and stiff. In the absence of these kinds of signals, men assumed women were interested in having sex.

And third, "yes means yes" was communicated via subtle cues. For example, it was assumed that if someone was willing to leave a bar setting and go to a more private location, such as the other person's home, this indicated an interest in engaging in casual sex. Other indications included pulling the partner closer and listening to physical signs such as sighing, heavy breathing, and moaning. However, the respondents agreed that despite these signals, it was possible at any stage that the other person (usually the woman) might change his or her mind and decide not to have sex (Beres, 2006).

These studies demonstrate the complexity of the process of obtaining and granting sexual consent. For most people, the process is more subtle than blatant.

and intense among cultures with stronger machismo traditions, in which men are expected to display their virility. It's also powerful in cultures where men view women's infidelities as threats to their honour. Jealousy is found among gay males and lesbians as well as among heterosexuals (Peluso, 2008).

Sexual jealousy is aroused when we suspect that our intimate relationships are threatened by rivals (Buss, 2009). We can become jealous when others show sexual interest in our partners, or when our partners show interest (even casual or

Jealousy.
How do we explain feelings of jealousy? What does jealousy do to an intimate relationship?

nonsexual interest) in others. Jealousy can lead to loss of affection, feelings of insecurity and rejection, anxiety, loss of self-esteem, and mistrust of our partners and potential rivals. Jealousy is a common reason for relationship failure.

Feelings of possessiveness, which is related to jealousy, can also subject relationships to stress. In extreme cases, jealousy can cause depression or give rise to spousal abuse, suicide, or murder (Harmon-Jones et al., 2009). But milder forms of jealousy are not necessarily destructive to relationships. They may even serve the positive function of revealing how much we care for our partners. For this reason, we can distinguish between normal jealousy, which reflects occasional self-doubts and the belief that our partners are attractive to others, and obsessive jealousy, in which we're consumed by our fears of interference in our relationships.

What causes jealousy? Experience and personality variables play roles. People may become mistrustful of their partners because former partners have cheated. People with low self-esteem may experience sexual jealousy because they've become overly dependent on their partners. They may fear that they won't be able to find new partners if their present partners leave.

JEALOUSY AND FACEBOOK   Facebook is a popular social networking site. It allows you access to information about your partner that you might not otherwise know. Three-quarters of the students in a University of Guelph study reported that they and their partners had former romantic or sexual partners as Facebook friends (Muise et al., 2008), and 92% said their partners had Facebook friends they didn't know. Correspondence with or seeing photos of these individuals triggered feelings of jealousy, especially among partners who already felt jealous. Those who spent the most time on Facebook were likely to be the most jealous (Muise et al., 2008).

JEALOUSY AND EVOLUTIONARY THEORY   Sex differences in jealousy appear to support evolutionary theory. Males seem to be more upset by sexual infidelity, females by emotional infidelity (Buss, 2009; Shackelford et al., 2002). That is, males become more insecure and angry when their partners have sexual relations with others. Females become more insecure and angry when their partners become emotionally attached to others. Why?

Evolutionary theory hypothesizes that sexual jealousy has been shaped by natural selection as a method of assuring males that their female partners' offspring are their own, and of assuring females that their male partners will continue to provide resources to facilitate child-rearing (Buss, 2009).

SAME-SEX AFFAIRS   Interestingly, the hypothesized gender difference in reactions to infidelity disappears when our partners have affairs with others of their own sex (Sagarin et al., 2003). Is it because the affairs carry no threat of impregnation, a view that would be consistent with evolutionary theory?

Or is it because we console ourselves by thinking we really aren't competing in the same arenas with the intruders? Are both explanations and other explanations possible?

CRITICAL THINKING QUESTIONS

Evolutionary theory suggests that males are more upset by sexual infidelity and females are more upset by emotional infidelity. To what extent do you think this statement is accurate?

A COGNITIVE PERSPECTIVE   In recent years, cognitive theory has gained importance in many areas of the behavioural sciences, and sexual jealousy is no exception.

In two studies, Stacie Bauerle and her colleagues (2002) presented 156 college undergraduates and 128 members of the general population with various scenarios in which their partners were unfaithful. By and large, jealousy increased when the individuals attributed their partners' infidelity to internal causes, such as clear personal choice. When they attributed the infidelity to external causes, such as alcohol or social pressure, they reported feeling significantly less jealous. ("Don't blame me; it was the alcohol.")

Stalking a Former Partner.
People who've been rejected sometime stalk their former partners. Stalking includes such behaviours as breaking into their former partners' email. (Hint: change your passwords from time to time.)

Breaking Up

Breaking up, as the song goes, can be hard to do—both for the person terminating the relationship and for the person being let go. Some people obviously take breaking up better than others. A study of more than 5000 people who responded to an internet survey found that anxious people were more likely to be highly preoccupied with their lost partners, suffer more physical and emotional distress, attempt to re-establish the relationships, and be angry and vengeful (Davis et al., 2003). Emotionally secure individuals were most likely to seek social support among their friends and families. Insecure individuals were most likely to turn to alcohol and drugs.

Breaking up is sometimes followed by **stalking**, or other unwanted pursuit behaviours, such as unwelcome phone calls or emails, asking third parties about the person who dissolved the relationship, and following, threatening, or attacking the person and/or his or her new partner (Davis et al., 2002; Langhinrichsen-Rohling et al., 2002). Jealousy, abusiveness, and physical violence in relationships are key predictors of unwanted pursuit (Puente & Cohen, 2003). Stalkers and violent individuals also tend to have strong needs to control others (Dye & Davis, 2003).

Stalking Following or observing a person persistently, especially because of obsession with the person. This can occur online as well as in person, such as when a person breaks into someone else's email.

Intimacy

Intimacy is a feeling of emotional connectedness and the desire to share your innermost thoughts and feelings with another person (Yela, 2006). Partners in the throes of romantic love usually want to disclose everything and know everything about one another (Kito, 2005; Vaculík & Hudecek, 2005).

Along with sex, intimacy is one of the key ingredients in passionate relationships (Firestone et al., 2006; Korobov & Thorne, 2006). Feelings of intimacy and affection tend to grow as romantic relationships develop (Aron et al., 2008; Derlega et al., 2008). Relationships also develop from casual and superficial to relatively committed. As couples age, intimacy becomes one of the most valued—if not *the* most valued—components of their relationships (Villar et al., 2005). Intimate relationships are also characterized by trust, caring, and acceptance.

Sternberg's (2007) triangular theory of love regards intimacy as a basic component of romantic love, but people can be intimate and not in love—at least, not in romantic love. Close friends and family members become emotionally intimate when they care deeply for one another and share their feelings and experiences.

Intimacy Feelings of closeness and connectedness, marked by sharing of one's innermost thoughts and feelings.

Working on the Relationship.
When one partner works on the relationship, the other partner is more motivated to reciprocate.
Why did one partner give this gift? "Just because."

Mutual cyclical growth The view that your need for your partner promotes commitment, which promotes acts that enhance the relationship, and that these acts build trust, increasing your partner's commitment to the relationship.

People need not be sexually intimate to be emotionally intimate. Nor does sexual intimacy automatically create emotional intimacy. People who are sexually involved may not achieve emotional closeness. People can be more emotionally intimate with friends than with lovers.

Because intimacy involves sharing your innermost thoughts and feelings, honesty is a core feature of intimacy. You needn't be an open book to develop and maintain intimacy, however. Some aspects of experience are better kept even from your most intimate partner, especially when they're embarrassing or threatening (Finkenauer & Hazam, 2000; Korobov & Thorne, 2006). For example, you wouldn't expect your partner to disclose every passing sexual fantasy. Nor would you expect your intimate partner to divulge details of past sexual experiences.

Intimacy is important not only to your interpersonal relationships but also to your health. Researchers have found that intimacy fosters well-being, and its absence can be psychologically and physically harmful (Driver et al., 2003). Research also shows that people come to trust their partners when they see them making sincere investments in the relationships, such as incurring their families' disapproval by remaining in the relationships (Rusbult & Van Lange, 2003; Wieselquist et al., 1999).

Commitment and trust within a relationship can be seen as developing according to a model of **mutual cyclical growth,** which includes five stages:

- The feeling that you need your partner promotes your commitment to and dependence on the relationship.
- Your commitment to the relationship encourages you to do things that are good for the relationship.
- Your partner sees your pro-relationship acts.
- Your partner's perception of your pro-relationship acts enhances his or her trust in you and in the relationship.
- Your partner's feelings of trust increase his or her willingness to depend on the relationship.

Caring is an emotional bond that allows intimacy to develop. Caring means both partners try to satisfy each other's needs, gratify each other's interests, and make sacrifices, if necessary.

Heterosexual and LGB Relationships

Numerous researchers have studied the factors that predict satisfaction in a relationship or the deterioration and ending of a relationship (Holmberg et al., 2009). Much of this research has sought to determine whether there are differences in the factors that satisfy heterosexual and non-heterosexual (lesbian, gay, and bisexual) couples. The interesting finding is that we're hard pressed to find differences (Holmstrom, 2009).

One difference that does stand out favours gay and lesbian couples: they tend to distribute household chores evenly, and not in terms of gender-role stereotypes (Kurdek, 2005, 2006).

Now for the similarities. Sexual satisfaction is tied to satisfaction with the relationship among both heterosexual and lesbian women (Matthews et al., 2006;

Schwartz & Young, 2009). Gay, lesbian, and heterosexual couples are all more satisfied when they receive social support from their partners, they share power within their relationships, they fight fairly, and they perceive that their partners are committed to the relationships. But a couple of differences favour stability in the heterosexual relationships: they're more likely to have the support of their families, and they're less likely to be stigmatized by society at large.

Couples therapists who work with lesbian, gay, and bisexual individuals and couples find problems akin to those experienced by heterosexual couples, such as infidelity. They also find issues that require special sensitivity toward these commonly stigmatized subpopulations (Schwartz & Young, 2009):

- Lesbian/gay/bisexual (LGB) identity development, and its effect on the couple's functioning.
- Parenting, and its impact on the couple.
- LGB individuals as members of families.
- The kinds of stressors that affect individuals who are underrepresented in the LGB literature, including older LGB people, LGB members of ethnic minority groups, and LGB members of religious groups.
- Legal issues and their impact on the couple.
- Workplace issues, and their impact on the couple.

Communication Skills

Relationship counsellors and sex therapists might be less busy if more couples communicated with one another about their sexual feelings. Unfortunately, when it comes to sex, the most overlooked four-letter word may be "talk."

Many couples suffer for years because at least one partner is unwilling to speak up. Or problems arise when one partner misinterprets the other. One partner might interpret the other's groans or grimaces of pleasure as signs of pain, and pull back during sex, leaving the other frustrated. Improved communication may not be a panacea, but it helps. Clear communication can take the guesswork out of a relationship, averting misunderstanding, relieving resentment and frustration, and increasing both sexual and general satisfaction with the relationship.

In a University of Guelph study of communication about sexual health issues such as HIV and pregnancy prevention (Cleary et al., 2002), female students typically reported that they didn't discuss these issues prior to engaging in sexual intercourse for the first time with new partners. Generally, the women reported feeling uncomfortable about initiating discussions about sexual health topics, and sensed that their partners were uncomfortable, as well. They feared offending their partners and risking negative reactions from them.

There's considerable variation in how comfortable people are with talking to their partners about sexual matters. Carleton University researchers Melanie Kristel Oates and Alia Offman (2007) found that individuals with higher sexual self-esteem were better able to communicate their sexual desires to their partners. Sexual self-esteem was measured by such statements as "I feel self-assured about my sexual abilities." Sexual self-esteem was a stronger predictor of sexual communication than general self-esteem was. Researchers at Trent University (Humphreys & Newby, 2007) found that students who felt more positive about their sexuality were more likely to use diverse verbal and nonverbal tactics to ask their partners to try something new sexually. Those who'd had more previous partners were more willing to make verbal requests to try new sexual activities.

Obstacles to Sexual Communication

Why is it so difficult for couples to communicate about sex? Following are some possibilities.

Communication.
Would it have been easier for him if he'd just listened to her? Listening can take skill, especially when a couple is in conflict.

SEX TALK Is sex talk vulgar? Vulgarity, like beauty, is to some degree in the eye of the beholder. One couple's vulgarity may be another couple's pillow talk. Some people may maintain a Victorian belief that no talk about sex is fit for mixed company, even between intimate partners. Sex is something you may do, but not something you talk about. Other couples may be willing in principle to talk about sex, but find the reality difficult because they lack an agreeable, common language.

How, for example, are they to refer to their genitals and to sexual activities? One partner may prefer to use coarse words to refer to them. (As forbidden fruit is often sweetest, some people feel sexually aroused when they or their partners "talk dirty.") The other might prefer more clinical terms. A partner who likes to use slang for the sex organs might be regarded by the other as vulgar or demeaning. One who uses clinical terms, such as "fellatio" and "intercourse," might be regarded as, well, clinical.

Some couples compromise, and try to use terms that are neither vulgar nor clinical. They might speak, for example, of "doing it" rather than "screwing" (and the like) at one extreme, or "engaging in sexual intercourse" at the other. Or they might speak of "going down on me" rather than "eating me" or "practising fellatio or cunnilingus."

IRRATIONAL BELIEFS Many couples also harbour irrational beliefs about relationships and sex, such as the notion that people should somehow *know* what their partners want, without having to ask. Men, in particular, seem burdened with the stereotype that they should have a natural expertise at sex. Women may feel it's unladylike to talk openly about their sexual needs and feelings. Both partners may hold the idealized romantic notion that all you need to achieve sexual happiness is love. But such knowledge doesn't arise from instinct or from love. It's learned—or it remains unknown.

A related irrational belief is that our partners will read our minds. We may erroneously assume that if our partners truly loved us, they'd somehow know what types of sexual stimulation we desire. Unfortunately—or fortunately—others can't read our minds. We must assume the responsibility for communicating our preferences.

Some people communicate more effectively than others, perhaps because they're more sensitive to others' needs, or because their parents served as good models as communicators. But communication skills can be acquired at any time. Learning takes time and work, but the following guidelines should prove helpful if you want to enhance your communication skills. The skills can also improve communication in areas of intimacy other than the sexual.

Getting Started

How do you broach sexual topics? Here are some ideas.

You can admit that it's difficult to talk about sex. You can say your sexual relationship is important to you, and that you want to do everything you can to enhance it. Gently probe your partner's willingness to set aside time to talk about sex, preferably when you can dim the lights and avoid interruptions.

The right time may be when you're both relaxed, rested, and not pressed for time. The right place can be anywhere you can enjoy privacy and talk undisturbed.

Applied Knowledge

ARE YOU SEXUALLY COMPATIBLE?

Because many couples find it difficult to discuss sexual issues openly, they may not learn whether they're sexually compatible until late in their relationships. Guy Grenier (2007), a sex therapist in London, Ontario, believes it's essential that you determine whether you're sexually compatible before you commit to a long-term relationship. He notes that sexual incompatibility can lead to serious conflict and can end a relationship. Carleton University researchers Alia Offman and Kimberly Matheson (2005) found that couples who were sexually compatible had higher levels of sexual satisfaction.

In his book *The 10 Conversations You Must Have Before You Get Married (And How to Have Them)*, Grenier outlines how you and your partner can determine whether you sexually suit each other. Indicators of sexual compatibility include your feelings about monogamy, how often you'd like to have sex, what you want to know about your partner's past sexual history, how to signal that you're are in the mood for sex, when you prefer to have sex, what type of foreplay you pre-fer, and whether it's always necessary to have intercourse when you start a sexual encounter.

Grenier believes both partners should indicate what they like and don't like when it comes to specific sexual activities. He suggests that you describe for your partner your thoughts and feelings about engaging in each of the following activities:

- Manually stimulating your partner's genitals.
- Sexual intercourse.
- Giving oral sex.
- Receiving oral sex.
- Anal sex (again, talk about giving and receiving).
- Mutual masturbation.
- Intercourse during menstruation.
- Using enticing clothing (or costumes) to enhance arousal.
- Using sexually explicit material to enhance arousal.
- Recording your own sexual behaviour (i.e., using still or video cameras) to enhance arousal.
- Having three-person (or more) sex.
- Having sex in public or risky places (i.e., where you might be discovered by others).
- Using food for sex play.
- Using sex toys.
- Wearing each other's clothing or the clothing of the other gender (i.e., cross-dressing).
- Having phone sex.
- Sharing personal sexual fantasies.
- Being tied up or restrained during sex.
- Using various types of pain to enhance sensual and sexual feelings.
- Viewing sexual performances (e.g., strip or sex shows).
- Attending sex shows or clubs.

Grenier emphasizes that it's not essential that you and your partner be in complete agreement about these behaviours. Nevertheless, strong disagreements about the desirability of some of the behaviours could indicate sexual incompatibility, and could lead to conflict and dissatisfaction in the relationship.

Source: Grenier, G. (2007). The 10 conversations you must have before you get married (and how to have them). *Toronto: Key Porter.*

Sex talk needn't be limited to the bedroom. You may feel more comfortable talking about sex over dinner, when cuddling on the sofa, or when just relaxing together.

Another possibility is asking permission to raise an issue. You can say something like this: "There's something on my mind. Do you have a few minutes? Is now a good time to tell you about it?" Or you can say, "There's something we need to talk about, but I'm not sure how to bring it up. Can you help me with it?"

You can tell your partner that it's okay to point out ways you can become a more effective lover. For example, you can say, "I know you don't want to hurt my feelings, but I wonder if I'm doing anything you'd rather I didn't do?"

Criticism Can Be Hard to Take.
How can you criticize a partner in a way that enhances the relationship? How can you receive criticism in a helpful way?

Applied Knowledge

COMMUNICATING SEXUAL NEEDS

Listening is basic to learning about another person's needs, but sometimes it helps to go a few steps further.

Asking Questions to Draw the Other Person Out

You can ask open-ended questions that allow for a broader exploration of issues, such as these:

- "What do you like best about the way we make love?"
- "Do you think I do things to bug you?"
- "Does it bother you that I go to bed later than you do?"
- "Does anything disappoint you about our relationship?"
- "Do you think I do things that are inconsiderate when you're studying for a test?"

Closed-ended questions that call for a limited range of responses tend to be most useful when you're looking for a simple yes-or-no type of response. ("Would you rather make love with the stereo off?")

Using Self-Disclosure

Self-disclosure is essential to developing intimacy. You can also use self-disclosure to learn more about your partner's needs, because communicating your own feelings and ideas invites reciprocation. For example, you might say, "There are times when I feel that I disappoint you when we make love. Should I be doing something differently?"

Granting Permission for the Other Person to Say Something That Might Upset You

You can ask your partner to level with you about an irksome issue. You can say you recognize that it may be awkward to discuss it, but you'll try your best to listen conscientiously and not get too disturbed. You can also limit communication to one difficult issue per conversation. If the entire emotional dam were to burst, the job of mopping up could be overwhelming.

Providing Information

There are many skillful ways of communicating information, including accentuating the positive and using verbal and nonverbal cues. When you want to get something across, remember that it's irrational to expect your partner to read your mind. He or she can tell when you're wearing a grumpy face, but your expression doesn't provide much information about your specific feelings. When your partner asks, "What would you like me to do?" responding with "Well, I think you can figure out what I want" or "Just do whatever you think is best" isn't very helpful. Only you know what pleases you. Your partner is not a mind reader.

Accentuating the Positive

Let your partner know when he or she does something right! Speak up or find another way to express your appreciation. Accentuating the positive is rewarding, and informs your partner about what pleases you. In other words, don't just wait around until your partner does something wrong, then seize the opportunity to complain!

Using Verbal Cues

Sexual activity provides an excellent opportunity for direct communication. You can say something like "Oh, that's great" or "Don't stop." Or you can ask for feedback, as in "How does this feel?" Feedback provides direct guidance about what's pleasing. Partners can also make specific requests and suggestions.

Using Nonverbal Cues

Sexual communication also occurs without words. Couples learn to interpret one another's facial expressions as signs of pleasure, anxiety, boredom, even disgust. Body language also communicates likes and dislikes. If your partner leans toward or away from you when you touch him or her, or relaxes or tenses up, he or she speaks volumes in silence.

The following exercises may help you use nonverbal cues to communicate your sexual likes and dislikes. Similar exercises are used by sex therapists to help couples with sexual dysfunctions.

1. **Take turns petting.** This can help you and your partner learn what turns you both on. You take turns caressing each other, stopping frequently enough to receive feedback by asking questions like "How does that feel?" When you're receiving caresses, you're responsible for giving feedback, which can be expressed verbally (e.g., "Yes, that's it—yes, just like that" or "No, a little lighter than that") or nonverbally (e.g., making certain appreciative or disapproving sounds). Verbal feedback is usually more direct and less prone to misinterpretation. The knowledge you and your partner gain through this exercise can be incorporated into your regular pattern of lovemaking.

2. **Direct your partner's hand.** Gently guiding your partner's hand—to show your partner where and how you like to be touched—is a direct way of communicating your sexual preferences. While taking turns petting, and during other acts of lovemaking, one partner can gently guide the other's fingers and hands through the most satisfying strokes and caresses. You might show your partner how to caress your breasts or clitoral shaft in this manner, or you might cup your partner's hands to show how to stroke your penile shaft or caress your testes.

3. **Signal.** You can use agreed-upon nonverbal cues to signal sexual pleasure. For example, you might rub or tap your partner in a certain way to signal that he or she is doing something right. Your partner then makes a mental note and incorporates the pleasurable stimulation into your lovemaking. This is a sort of hit-or-miss technique, but even near misses can be rewarding.

TABLE 7.2

How Comfortable Canadians Are with Asking Their Partners to Try Something New in Their Sexual Relationships

	Males	**Females**	**Total**
Very	45.2%	46.5%	45.8%
Somewhat	39.8	34.5	37.2
Not really	10.2	11.5	10.8
Not at all	4.8	7.5	6.1

Source: Compas. (1998). Modern life survey of the Canadian adult population. Toronto: Compas Inc.

Making Sexual Requests

A basic part of improving your relationship or lovemaking involves asking your partner to change his or her behaviour—to do something differently, or to stop doing something that hurts or is no longer gratifying. As shown in Table 7.2, almost half of Canadians (46%) report that they're very comfortable with asking their sexual partners to try something new or different in their sexual relationships. Only 17% say they're not comfortable (Compas, 1998). Those who are 50 or older are least comfortable about this.

Listening Effectively

Listening involves such skills as active listening, paraphrasing, using reinforcement, and valuing your partner even when the two of you disagree.

To listen actively rather than passively, first adopt the attitude that you may actually learn something—or perceive things from another vantage point—by listening. Second, recognize that even though the other person is doing the talking, you shouldn't just sit there. It's not helpful to stare off into space while your partner is talking. Instead, you can listen actively by maintaining eye contact and modifying your facial expression to show that you understand his or her feelings and ideas. For example, nod your head when appropriate.

Listening actively also involves asking helpful questions, such as "Would you please give me an example?"

Good listeners do not interrupt, change the topic, or walk away when their partners are speaking.

Paraphrasing shows that you understand what your partner is trying to say. In paraphrasing, you recast or restate the speaker's words to confirm that you've understood correctly. For example, suppose your partner says, "You hardly ever say anything when we're making love. I don't want you to scream or make obligatory grunts or do something silly, but sometimes I wonder if I'm trying to make love to a brick wall." You can paraphrase this comment by saying something like "So, it's sort of hard to know if I'm really enjoying it."

Even when you disagree with what your partner says, you can maintain good relations and keep channels of communication open by saying something like "I really appreciate your taking the time to try to work this out with me," or "I hope you'll think it's okay if I don't see things entirely the same way, but I'm glad we had a chance to talk about it."

When you disagree with your partner, do so in a way that shows you still value him or her as a person. In other words, say something like "I love you very much, but it annoys me when you . . . " rather than "You're really contemptible for . . . ." By so doing, you encourage your partner to disclose sensitive material without any risk of attack or of losing your love or support.

Summing Up

Many Canadians use the internet to meet possible dating partners. However, one needs to be cautious of internet-romance scams.

Levinger proposes an ABCDE model of romantic relationships. The letters refer to five stages: attraction, building, continuation, deterioration, and ending.

The major promoter of attraction is propinquity.

We're motivated to build relationships by similarity in physical attractiveness, similarity in attitudes, and liking.

Factors that encourage us to continue in relationships include variety, caring, positive evaluations, lack of jealousy, perceived fairness, and mutual satisfaction.

Factors that foster deterioration include failure to invest time and energy in the relationships, deciding to end the relationships, and simply permitting deterioration to proceed unchecked.

Relationships tend to end when the partners find little satisfaction in the affiliation, alternative partners are available, the partners aren't committed to preserving the relationships, and they expect the relationships to falter.

Intimacy involves feelings of emotional closeness with one another, and the desire to share your innermost thoughts and feelings.

Intimate relationships require trust, caring, and tenderness.

Honesty is a core feature of intimacy.

Communication is a two-way street. It embraces sending *and* receiving messages. We often express feelings through nonverbal channels, such as tone of voice, gestures, body posture, and facial expressions.

Couples may find it difficult to talk about sex because they lack an agreeable common language. Many couples also harbour irrational beliefs about relationships and sex.

Ways of getting started with communication include talking about talking, asking permission to raise an issue, and granting your partner permission to say things that might be upsetting.

Skilled listening involves such elements as active listening, paraphrasing, using of reinforcement, and valuing your partner even when you disagree.

A basic part of improving your relationship or lovemaking is asking your partner to change his or her behaviour.

Test Yourself

Multiple-Choice Questions

1. According to research by Wentland and Muise, which one of the following is an acceptable way to ask a person for a date?
   (a) A text message.
   (b) MSM.
   (c) A phone call.
   (d) Facebook.

2. Small talk:
   (a) Is a phony way to begin a relationship.
   (b) Stresses breadth of topic coverage.
   (c) Promotes premature self-disclosure.
   (d) Is an in-depth discussion of topics of mutual interest.

3. All of the following encourage the continuation of relationships except:
   (a) Maintaining interest.
   (b) Evidence of caring.
   (c) Mutual satisfaction.
   (d) Jealousy.

4. All of the following can cause jealousy except:
   (a) Having a former partner cheat on you.
   (b) A lack of self-confidence.
   (c) A fear of not being able to find another partner.
   (d) A high level of independence.

5. Recent research shows that men are more upset by _____ infidelity and women are more upset by _____ infidelity.
   (a) sexual/emotional
   (b) emotional/sexual
   (c) sexual/sexual
   (d) emotional/emotional

6. A study of 5000 people who responded to an internet survey found that after a relationship breakup, emotionally secure people were more likely to:
   (a) Seek support from friends and family.
   (b) Be preoccupied with their lost partners.
   (c) Attempt to re-establish the relationships.
   (d) Console themselves by drinking alcohol.

7. According to MacNeil and Byers, couples who disclose more about their sexual likes and dislikes report:
   (a) Lower levels of sexual satisfaction.
   (b) Higher levels of sexual satisfaction.
   (c) The same levels of sexual satisfaction as couples who disclose less.
   (d) Disclosing more about their sex lives to their friends.

8. Which of the following is NOT an irrational belief about communication?
   (a) Men should have a natural expertise at sex.
   (b) People should know what their partners want sexually without having to ask.
   (c) Good communication can enhance all aspects of a relationship.
   (d) It's unladylike for women to talk about their sexual needs and feelings.

9. All of the following are suggestions that enhance communication of sexual needs except:
   (a) Accentuating the positive.
   (b) Asking open-ended questions.
   (c) Giving permission for the other person to say something that might upset you.
   (d) Honestly rating each other's sexual performance on a scale of one to ten.

10. The most successful intimate relationships are characterized by:
   (a) Total honesty about past sexual experiences.
   (b) Secrecy about past sexual experiences.
   (c) Totally honest criticism.
   (d) Discretion in revealing details of past relationships..

You'll find answers to the "Test Yourself" questions on page 495.

Critical Thinking

1. Have you ever signed up with an online dating service? How did the experience turn out? Would you do it again? If you haven't, would you? Why or why not?

2. Have you ever had a partner who was extremely jealous? What was the most difficult part of the relationship? How did you deal with the jealousy?

3. Have you ever met someone online and then met face to face? Was this a successful experience? Did your impressions of this person change after you met face to face?

4. Have you ever sat next to someone on a bus or a plane and disclosed details of your life that you wouldn't share with a friend? How did you feel about this afterwards? Why do many people find it easy to talk openly with total strangers?

5. Have you ever had communication problems in a relationship? How did they affect the relationship?

MySearchLab

MySearchLab offers extensive help to students with their writing and research project and provides round-the-clock access to credible and reliable source material. Take a tour at www.mysearchlab.com.

CHAPTER EIGHT

Sexual Techniques and Behaviour Patterns

This is the chapter that describes sexual techniques and statistical breakdowns of who does what with whom. There's significant variation in human sexual expression. Some of us practise few, if any, of the techniques described in this chapter. Some of us practise most or all of them. Some of us practise some of them, some of the time.

Readers are as varied as society in general when it comes to sexual values, preferences, and attitudes. Some of the techniques we discuss may strike you as indecent. Our aim is to provide information about the diversity of sexual expression. We're not seeking consensus on what's acceptable, and we're not passing judgment or encouraging you to expand your sexual repertoire.

The human body is sensitive to many forms of sexual stimulation. Yet we reiterate the theme that biology is not destiny—a biological capacity does not impose a behavioural requirement. Cultural expectations, personal values, and individual experience—not just our biological capacities—determine our sexual behaviour. What's right for you is right for you, but not necessarily for your neighbour.

We'll begin by reviewing the techniques people practise by themselves to derive sexual pleasure—masturbation and sexual fantasy. We'll then consider techniques that involve a partner.

Solitary Sexual Behaviour

Various forms of sexual expression do not require a partner. Masturbation, which involves direct stimulation of the genitals, is one of the principal forms of one-person sexual expression. Other forms of individual sexual experience, such as thinking about sex and sexual fantasy, may or may not be accompanied by genital stimulation.

Sexual Fantasy

A **sexual fantasy** can be defined as "almost any mental imagery that is sexually arousing or erotic to the individual" (Leitenberg & Henning, 1995, p. 470). Sexual fantasies can occur because an individual wants them to (e.g., during masturbation), or they can happen spontaneously, without conscious effort. A sexual fantasy can range from a brief, erotic mental picture lasting a few seconds to a lengthy, highly explicit scenario. Nearly all of us have sexual fantasies of one kind or another. Sexual fantasies can be experienced as positive, negative, or both. A study at the University of New Brunswick revealed that students experienced positive feelings more often than negative ones as a result of sexual fantasies (Renaud & Byers, 1999).

Studies suggest that most of us consider sexual fantasies normal. One study of 178 university students and staff found that most people believe sexual fantasies are common, moral, socially acceptable, and more beneficial than harmful. Still, about one-quarter of the sample reported feeling guilty about having sexual fantasies (Cado & Leitenberg, 1990).

How common are sexual fantasies? Several surveys have simply asked people how often they think about sex. In a national survey conducted by Compas, Canadian men reported thinking about sex much more often than women did. This gender difference crossed all ages and educational levels (Fischtein & Herold, 2002). About half of the men (46%) but only 11% of the women reported that they thought about sex several times a day. A survey of adults in the United States produced similar results—43% of the men and 13% of the women reported that they thought about sex "a few times a day" (ABC News, 2004).

MySearchLab

- Self-grading practice tests
- Media links
- Flashcards
- Access to thousands of full-text articles from academic journals and help on the research and writing process

Sexual fantasy Mental imagery that's sexually arousing or erotic.

In the Compas poll, those who were younger and university-educated thought about sex more often than those who were older and hadn't completed high school. Among women, 49% of those in their twenties thought about sex at least once a day, compared to 10% in their sixties. Among men, 90% of those in their twenties had sexual thoughts at least once a day, compared to 35% in their sixties.

SEXUAL FANTASY CONTENT   A number of studies have examined sexual fantasies among university students. Renaud and Byers (1999) at the University of New Brunswick have found that the content of male and female heterosexual undergraduate students' sexual fantasies is similar. More than 90% in their study reported fantasies about having intercourse with loved partners, kissing passionately, having sex in places other than the bedroom, having sex outdoors in romantic settings, and giving and receiving oral sex. According to Renaud and Byers, the men were more likely to enjoy fantasies reflecting themes of anonymous or impersonal sex (e.g., participating in orgies, having sex with strangers), whereas women enjoyed fantasies that could be described as romantic (e.g., kissing passionately, being undressed).

At an Ontario university, 97% of the female students reported that they'd experienced sexual fantasies (Pelletier & Herold, 1988). Of those who'd masturbated, 87% had fantasized during masturbation, and 57% said they always fantasizing during masturbation. Of those with intercourse experience, 73% had fantasized during intercourse, but only 10% said they usually or always fantasized during intercourse. Most (84%) had also fantasized in nonsexual situations. Interestingly, the women experienced more types of fantasies in nonsexual than in sexual situations. This suggests that in sexual situations, women focus on fantasies they find most arousing. Table 8.1 presents a complete breakdown of these data.

The most common fantasies in the Pelletier and Herold (1988) study were about the respondents' boyfriends. This is inconsistent with studies of married women. Davidson and Hoffman (1986) found that married women commonly fantasize about other men. It appears that when women become involved in long-term relationships, the objects of their fantasies switch to other men. In the Pelletier and Herold (1988) study, about a quarter of the women had sexual fantasies at least once a day, and about half fantasized a few times a week. When asked why they fantasized, three-quarters said it was a pleasant way to pass the time. About half said they fantasized to become aroused, and 30% said they fantasized to help achieve orgasm. Interestingly, 30% used fantasy to help them fall asleep.

In keeping with gender-role stereotypes, studies also find that males are more likely to fantasize about forcing women into sexual activity, while women are more likely to fantasize about being victimized (Critelli & Bivona, 2008; Yost & Zurbriggen, 2006). Such fantasizing doesn't mean the fantasizers want these events to occur (Leitenberg & Henning, 1995). Women who imagine themselves being sexually coerced remain in control of their fantasies. Real assault victims are not in control. Needless to say, sexual fantasies that in any way involve sexual activity that's not consensual and legal should remain in the realm of fantasy, and not become reality.

There are also deviant sexual fantasies, such as sadistic rape fantasies. Research evidence obtained with the Minnesota Multiphasic Personality Inventory (MMPI), a commonly used personality test, suggests that men who experience frequent deviant sexual fantasies are more likely to be socially isolated and emotionally unstable than men who don't (Curnoe & Langevin, 2002). The extent to which deviant sexual fantasies contribute to crimes involving sex and aggression is unclear. Nevertheless, many helping professionals hope that changing men's deviant sexual fantasies will reduce the likelihood that these men will commit crimes of violence (Leitenberg & Henning, 1995).

TABLE 8.1

Sexual Fantasies of University Females

	Situation During Which Fantasy Occurred			
Fantasy	Masturbation	Intercourse	Nonsexual	Total
Sex with boyfriend	54%	49%	69%	90%
Undressed by male	46	39	54	79
Previous sexual experience	44	31	58	78
Intercourse in exotic place	33	43	55	72
Undressing a male	26	28	54	71
Cunnilingus	48	46	41	66
Intercourse with male friend	31	14	47	60
Forced sex with male	30	26	31	51
Fellatio	21	28	34	49
Intercourse with male stranger	24	9	34	46
Intercourse with famous person	19	6	34	38
Doing striptease	15	10	26	37
Male masturbating	32	12	19	33
Sex with many men	26	11	17	29
Sex with objects	25	9	13	23
Sex with other watching	20	11	6	21
Female masturbating	18	4	7	18
Sex with female	15	4	9	18
Forced sex with more than one male	15	9	9	18
Anal sex	9	12	9	17
Group sex with males and females	10	3	9	16
Sex with relative	3	0	12	14
Sex with animal	8	3	4	9
Sadomasochistic sex	1	4	4	7

Note: The percentages in the "Masturbation" and "Intercourse" columns represent respondents who experienced the fantasies while engaging in the behaviours listed on the left. The percentages in the "Total" column represent respondents who experienced the fantasies in one or more of the situations (i.e., during masturbation, intercourse, and/or nonsexual activities).

Source: Pelletier, L. A., & Herold, E. S. (1988). The relationship of age, sex guilt, and sexual experience with female sexual fantasies. The Journal of Sex Research, 24, 250-256.

LGB Fantasy

A survey of 129 women (85 lesbian, 44 bisexual) who'd been in same-sex relationships for 5 to 10 years found connections between satisfaction in their relationships and the nature of their sexual fantasies (Robinson & Parks, 2003). By and large, the happier the women were with their relationships, the more likely they were to fantasize about common activities with their partners. If their relationships weren't going so well, they were more likely to fantasize about things they used to do with their partners, or things they'd done with former partners.

A study in India compared the sexual fantasies of 30 heterosexual males with those of 30 gay males (Bhugra et al., 2006). The heterosexual men's fantasy spheres appeared to be more limited, restricting these men to more standard sexual activities with females. The gay men were more open to fantasizing about a wider range of sexual behaviour.

Theoretical Perspectives on Sexual Fantasy

Evolutionary theorists conjecture that women are more likely than men to fantasize about familiar lovers, because female reproductive success in ancestral times was more likely to depend on emotionally close, protective relationships with reliable partners (Buss, 2009; Symons, 1995). Women can bear and rear relatively few offspring. They therefore have relatively greater genetic investments than men in each reproductive opportunity. Men, on the other hand, can enhance their reproductive success (i.e., improve their chances on passing on their genes to future generations) by having intercourse with high numbers of sexual partners. Men are therefore, according to evolutionary theory, more likely to have fantasies about casual sex with different partners.

Other researchers have noted that the tendency for women's sexual fantasies to be more romantic than men's, and the greater tendency for men's fantasies to involve new sexual partners, is a reflection of society's traditional sexual scripts—the double standard for male and female sexual behaviour (Renaud & Byers, 1999). That is, females in most cultures are raised to be more romance-oriented and more sexually passive than men, while males are raised to be sexually assertive and to desire a high number of sexual partners. According to this perspective, the content of our sexual fantasies is influenced primarily by the gender roles we learn as we grow up. As gender roles become more egalitarian in Western culture, it will be interesting to see whether men's and women's sexual fantasies become less reflective of society's traditional double standard. (See Chapter 5 for further discussion of gender roles related to sexuality.)

Sexual Dreams

There's been limited research on sexual dreams. Nevertheless, researchers at Trent University and University of British Columbia (Humphreys et al., 2007; King, DeCicco, & Humphreys, 2009) have found that sexual dreams are common among university students, and that most have sexual dreams at least once a week.

Almost all of the students in these studies rated their sexual dreams as pleasurable; many reported that their dreams were as pleasurable as having sexual intercourse. The most common activities in their dreams were kissing and sexual intercourse. Rarely did anyone dream about masturbation.

Students generally dreamed about behaviours they'd engaged in with partners, rather than untried behaviours. The females were more likely to dream about their current partners, whereas the males were more likely to dream about other people.

Masturbation in History

In solitude he pollutes himself, and with his own hand blights all his prospects for both this world and the next. Even after being solemnly warned, he will often continue this worse than beastly practice, deliberately forfeiting his right to health and happiness for a moment's mad sensuality.
—Kellogg, J. H. (1881). Plain facts for old and young. Burlington, IA: Segner and Condit.

Don't knock masturbation. It's sex with someone I love.
—Woody Allen as Alvy Singer. In Allen, W., & Brickman, M. *Annie Hall*. Hollywood: Metro-Goldwyn-Mayer, 1977.

Within the Judeo-Christian tradition, sexual self-stimulation, commonly known as masturbation, has been strongly condemned as sinful (Soble, 2009; Thomas & Murray, 2009). Early Judeo-Christian attitudes toward masturbation reflected the censure that was applied to non-procreative sexual acts. The Biblical story of Onan is often interpreted as a condemnation of masturbation. The influential philosopher and theologian St. Augustine (354–430 CE) associated sexual desire with original sin, and argued that all non-procreative sex, including masturbation, was sinful (Bullough, 2002; Guttmann, 2006).

St. Augustine's views were carried into medicine in the eighteenth century, and the medical profession translated sin into disease (Polansky, 2006). One of the more influential writers was the superintendent of the Battle Creek Sanitarium in Michigan, Dr. J. H. Kellogg (1852–1943). Kellogg believed sexual desires could be controlled by sticking to a diet of simple foods, especially grains, including the Corn Flakes he and his brother invented.

Many nineteenth-century physicians also advised parents to take measures to prevent their children from masturbating. Kellogg suggested that parents bandage or cage their children's genitals or tie their hands. Some of the contraptions devised to prevent masturbation were barbarous. (See Figure 8.1.)

Despite this history, there's no scientific evidence that masturbation is harmful, except for rare injuries to the genitals from rough stimulation. Sex therapists have even found that masturbation has therapeutic benefits. Indeed, most people, including doctors, view masturbation as a harmless pleasure. A more contemporary view is that masturbation can be an important part of healthy sexual development and a way for people to learn about their own sexual responses (Coleman, 2002).

Of course, people who consider masturbation wrong, harmful, or sinful may experience anxiety or guilt if they masturbate or wish to masturbate (Ortega et al., 2005). But these negative emotions are linked to their attitudes toward masturbation, not to masturbation itself.

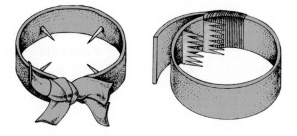

Figure 8.1 Devices to curb masturbation.
Because of the widespread belief that masturbation was harmful, various contraptions were introduced in the nineteenth century to prevent the practice in children. Some of the devices were barbarous.

Masturbation Today

Surveys indicate that most people—including many married people—masturbate at some time. The incidence of masturbation is generally greater among men than women. There are women who masturbate frequently, however, and men who rarely if ever do so (Michael et al., 1994).

Table 8.2 presents data on masturbation from a population-based sexual health survey of 5865 14- to 94-year-old men and women in the United States

CRITICAL THINKING QUESTIONS

If a younger brother or sister who was starting to go through puberty asked why people masturbate and whether it's an okay thing to do, how would you respond?

Innovative Canadian Research

ONLINE MASTURBATION

In a survey of 217 students with an average age of 19.5 years, University of New Brunswick and University of Windsor researchers Krystelle Shaughnessy, E. Sandra Byers, & Lindsay Walsh (2011) found that 83.3% of the men and 30.8% of the women had looked at sexually explicit online videos or photos during the previous month.

Almost three-quarters of the men (73.6%) and 17.8% of the women reported that they'd masturbated while watching sexually explicit online videos during the previous month. In addition, 11.1% of the men and 1.7% of the women reported that they'd masturbated while looking at strangers on webcams during that time.

CRITICAL THINKING
QUESTIONS

According to the data in
Table 8.2, women in their
forties and fifties are more
likely than women in their
teens to report that they've
masturbated during the
previous month. Can you
think of reasons for this?

TABLE 8.2

Percentages of Males and Females, Aged 14 to 70+, Who Reported Masturbating During the Past Month and the Past Year

Age	Past Month		Past Year	
	Male	Female	Male	Female
14–15	42.9	24.1	62.1	40.4
16–17	58.0	25.5	74.8	44.8
18–19	61.6	26.0	80.6	60.0
20–24	62.8	43.7	82.7	64.3
25–29	68.6	51.7	83.6	71.5
30–39	66.4	38.6	80.1	62.9
40–49	60.1	38.5	76.0	64.9
50–59	55.7	28.3	72.1	54.1
60–69	42.3	21.5	61.2	46.5
70+	27.9	11.5	46.4	32.8

Source: Herbenick, D., et al. (2010). Sexual behavior in the United States: Results from a national probability sample of men and women ages 14–94. The Journal of Sexual Medicine, 7(Supplement s5), 255-265.

(Herbenick et al., 2010). A majority of respondents reported masturbating at least occasionally from ages 18 to 59. Among those aged 70 and up, almost one-third of the women and just under half of the men reported masturbating during the previous year. Men were more likely to masturbate than women, but just over half of the women in the 25-to-29 age group reported masturbating at least once during the previous month. Women in the 40-to-49 and 50-to-59 age groups were more likely than teenaged women to report masturbating during the previous month.

A World of Diversity

MASTURBATION IN BRITAIN

In a large national survey conducted in Britain (Gerressu et al., 2008), twice as many men (73%) as women (37%) reported that they'd masturbated during the previous weeks.

Men who reported more frequent vaginal sex had lower masturbation rates. In contrast, women who had more sexual activity (more vaginal sex, more oral sex, and more sexual partners) had higher rates of masturbation. It seems that for men, masturbation is compensation for less vaginal sex, whereas for women, more partnered sex increases the desire to masturbate. Both men and women with same-sex partners were more likely to masturbate than men and women with opposite-sex partners.

Despite the sexual revolution, women may still find masturbation less pleasurable or acceptable than men do. Women may still be subject to traditional socialization pressures that teach that sexual activity for pleasure's sake is more taboo for women than for men. In the British study (Gerressu et al., 2008), women who were more religious were less likely to masturbate than women who were less religious.

Education would appear to be a liberating influence on masturbation. For both genders, people with more education reported more frequent masturbation (Gerressu et al., 2008). Perhaps better-educated people are less likely to believe the old horror stories about masturbation, or are less susceptible to traditional social restrictions. Conservative religious beliefs appear to constrain masturbation.

Research suggests that the more education a person has, the more likely he or she is to masturbate. An American study found that 33.6% of men and 13.7% of women with advanced degrees masturbated at least once a week, compared to 20.0% of men and 5.6% of women with no college or university education (Laumann et al. 1994). At an Ontario university, more men (84%) than women (62%) had first masturbated before the age of 16 (Rye, 2001). More than 90% of the students had fantasized during masturbation, with 27% of the women and 7% of the men using mechanical aids such as vibrators. While 75% of the women and 92% of the men reported having had orgasms in more than half of their masturbation experiences, more women (17%) than men (6%) said they'd had more than one orgasm in more than half of these experiences (Rye, 2001).

In our efforts to correct misinformation about masturbation, we don't wish to leave the impression that there's anything wrong with people who choose *not* to masturbate. Rather, we believe it's up to individuals to decide for themselves.

MALE MASTURBATION TECHNIQUES

> Sex is like bridge—if you don't have a good partner, you'd better have a good hand.
> —Bathroom graffiti

Although masturbation techniques vary widely, most men report that they masturbate by manual manipulation of the penis. (See Figure 8.2.) Men tend to grip the penile shaft with one hand, jerking it up and down in a milking motion. Some men move the whole hand up and down the penis, while others use just two fingers, generally the thumb and index finger. Men usually shift from a gentler rubbing action during the flaccid or semi-erect state of arousal to a more vigorous milking motion once full erection takes place. Men are also likely to stroke the glans and frenulum lightly at the outset, tightening their grip and speeding up their motions as orgasm nears. At orgasm, they may grip the penile shaft tightly, but usually avoid touching the glans, which has become sensitive. (Likewise, because of increased sensitivity, women usually avoid directly stimulating the clitoris during orgasm.)

Some men use soapsuds (which can become irritating) as a lubricant for masturbation during baths or showers. They may use other lubricants, such as petroleum jelly or K-Y jelly, to reduce friction and simulate the moist conditions of intercourse.

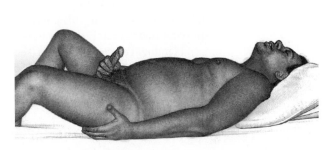

Figure 8.2 Male masturbation.
Masturbation techniques vary widely, but most men report that they masturbate by manual manipulation of the penis. They tend to grip the penile shaft with one hand and jerk it up and down in a milking motion.

Figure 8.3 Female masturbation.
Female masturbation techniques vary so widely that Masters and Johnson never observed two women masturbating in precisely the same way. Most women, however, masturbate by massaging the mons, labia minora, and clitoral region, either with circular or back-and-forth motions.

A few men prefer to masturbate by rubbing the penis and testicles against clothing or bedding. A few men rub their genitals against inflatable dolls sold in sex shops. These dolls may come with artificial mouths or vaginas that can be filled with warm water, to mimic the sensations of intercourse. Artificial vaginas are also for sale.

FEMALE MASTURBATION TECHNIQUES   Masturbation techniques for women also vary widely. Masters and Johnson reported never seeing two women masturbate precisely the same way. Even when the general technique was similar, women varied in the tempo and style of their self-caresses. Some general trends have been noted, though. Most women masturbate by massaging the mons, labia minora, and clitoral region with circular or back-and-forth motions (Hite, 1976). They may also straddle the clitoris with their fingers, stroking the shaft rather than the glans. (See Figure 8.3.) In a study of university women, half (53%) preferred stimulation of the external part of the genitals when masturbating to orgasm, while 36% preferred using both external and internal stimulation (Maisel & Meggars, 2007). Only 11% preferred internal stimulation of the vagina.

Women may lightly touch the glans during early arousal, but because of its exquisite sensitivity, they rarely stroke it for any length of time. Women typically achieve clitoral stimulation by rubbing or stroking the clitoral shaft or pulling or tugging on the vaginal lips. Some women also massage other sensitive areas, such as their breasts or nipples, with their free hand. Many women, like men, fantasize during masturbation.

Sex shops sell dildos and penis-shaped vibrators, which women can insert vaginally or use to rub the vulva. Many women masturbate during baths, sometimes by spraying their genitals with water-massage showerheads.

Handheld electric vibrators (see Figure 8.4) provide a constant massaging action against the genitals that can be erotic. Women who use vibrators often experiment with different models, to find one with a suitable shape and intensity of vibration.

Sexual Behaviour with Others

Partners' feelings for one another, and the quality of their relationships, may be stronger determinants of sexual arousal and response than the techniques they employ. Partners are most likely to experience mutually enjoyable sexual interactions when they're sensitive to each other's sexual needs and incorporate techniques they're both comfortable with. As with other aspects of sharing relationships, communication is the most important sexual technique.

Foreplay

Foreplay consists of various forms of sexual activity that occur prior to penetrative sex, such as cuddling, kissing, petting, and oral–genital contact. The pattern and duration of foreplay vary widely within and across cultures. Foreplay is important because most couples aren't ready for penetrative sex without first building arousal and sexual response.

Figure 8.4 Electric vibrators and other sex toys.
There are many different types of sex toys used by women—a few of which are shown in this photo.

The sexual activities we commonly think of as foreplay are pleasurable in and of themselves—perhaps even more so than penetration, in some cases. Some sex therapists advise their clients to make sexual activity less goal-oriented, and to enjoy activities such as mutual masturbation and oral sex for their own sake, rather than as activities that must inevitably lead to penetration.

Foreplay Physical interactions that are sexually stimulating and set the stage for intercourse.

TANTRIC SEX   Tantric sex is a type of lovemaking that emphasizes prolonged foreplay. It's based on Eastern spiritual philosophies that promote the integration of the mind and the body.

Tantric sex focuses on sexual union as a spiritual connection that leads to heightened sexual pleasure and ecstasy. The techniques include deep breathing, slowed sexual interactions, and delayed ejaculation. Some tantric sex instructors teach men how to have orgasms without ejaculating. There are numerous variations of tantric sex.

Kissing

Kissing is almost universal in our culture, but it's unknown in some societies, such as those of the Thonga in Africa and the Siriono in Bolivia. Kissing is now practiced in Japan, because of the influence of Western culture, but it was previously unknown there.

There are cross-cultural variations in kissing style (Ford & Beach, 1951). Instead of kissing, the Balinese of Indonesia used to bring their faces close enough to smell each other's perfume and feel the warmth of each other's skin. This practice has been dubbed "rubbing noses" by Europeans. Among some preliterate societies, kissing consists of sucking the partner's lips and tongue, and allowing saliva to pass from one mouth to the other.

In simple kissing, the partners keep their mouths closed. Simple kissing may develop into caresses of the lips with the tongue, or nibbling of the lower lip. In what Kinsey called deep kissing, which we also call French kissing or soul kissing, the partners part their lips and insert their tongues into each other's mouths. Some prefer parting their lips slightly, while others open their mouths widely.

Kissing.
It's almost universal in our culture, but kissing is practised less often in some societies, and not at all in others.

Innovative Canadian Research

DESIRED DURATION OF FOREPLAY

In a study of heterosexual couples, Andrea Miller and E. Sandra Byers (2004) at the University of New Brunswick found that men and women were similar in terms of how long they wanted foreplay to last.

The women, however, underestimated how long their partners—and the average male—wanted foreplay to continue. Perhaps women are influenced by the stereotype that men are mainly interested in intercourse.

The men were accurate in estimating how much time their partners—and the average woman—wanted to spend on foreplay. Like the women, though, the men underestimated how much time the average man likes to spend on foreplay.

Kissing may be an affectionate gesture without erotic significance, as when you kiss someone good night. Some people kiss relatives and close friends affectionately on the lips. Others kiss relatives only on the cheeks. Sustained kissing on the lips and deep kissing are almost always erotic gestures.

Touching

Touching or caressing the erogenous zones with the hands or other parts of the body can be highly arousing. Even simple hand-holding can be sexually stimulating for couples who are sexually attracted to one another. The hands are rich in nerve endings.

Touching is a common form of foreplay. Both men and women generally prefer manual or oral stimulation of the genitals as a prelude to intercourse. Women generally prefer that direct caressing of the genitals be focused around the clitoris, but not directly on the extremely sensitive clitoral glans. Men sometimes assume (often mistakenly) that their partners want them to insert their finger or fingers into the vagina as a form of foreplay, but not all women enjoy this form of stimulation.

Some women go along with it because it's what their partners want, or something they *think* their partners want. Ironically, men may do it because they assume

How Touching.
Touching is a common form of foreplay. Most people like manual or oral stimulation of the genital organs as a prelude to sexual intercourse.

their partners want it. When in doubt, it doesn't hurt to ask. If you're not sure what to say, you can always blame us: "Listen, I read this thing in my human sexuality textbook, and I was wondering . . . ." In a survey of students at an Ontario university, more than 90% reported that they'd experienced manual stimulation of their genitals by their partners (Rye, 2001).

Men typically like their partners to directly stroke their genitals early in sexual interaction. Women, however, tend to prefer that their partners caress their genitals after a period of general body contact that includes holding, hugging, and non-genital massage. This isn't a hard and fast (or slow) rule, but it concurs with other observations that men tend to be more genitally oriented than women.

Breast Stimulation

Men are more likely to stimulate women's breasts than to enjoy having their own breasts fondled, even though the breasts (and especially the nipples) are erotically sensitive in both sexes. Most (but not all) women enjoy having their breasts stimulated, and some women are capable of achieving orgasm from breast stimulation alone.

The hands and the mouth can be used to stimulate the breasts and nipples. The desired type and intensity of breast stimulation varies from person to person, so partners need to communicate their preferences.

In general, women usually prefer several minutes of body contact and gentle caresses before they want their partners to kiss their breasts or suck or lick their nipples. Many women also usually don't prefer a hard sucking action unless they're highly aroused. Often, women are reluctant to tell their partners when sucking hurts, because they don't want to interfere with their partners' pleasure.

BREAST STIMULATION IN GAY MALES   Gay men apparently stimulate their partner's nipples more than heterosexual women do. Gay male couples tend to engage in sexual activities such as kissing, hugging, petting, mutual masturbation, fellatio, and anal intercourse. Masters and Johnson's (1979) laboratory observations of sexual relations between gay males showed that they spent a good deal of time caressing their partners' bodies before approaching the genitals. After hugging and kissing, 31 of the 42 gay male couples observed by Masters and Johnson used oral or manual nipple stimulation.

Although some heterosexual men enjoy having their breasts and nipples stimulated, many do not. Many men are unaware that their breasts are erotically sensitive.

Oral-Genital Sex

Oral stimulation of the male genitals is called **fellatio**. It's often referred to by slang terms such as "blow job," "sucking," "sucking off," and "giving head." Oral stimulation of the female genitals is called **cunnilingus**, which is referred to by slang expressions such as "eating" or "going down on" her.

> **Fellatio** Oral stimulation of the male genitals.
>
> **Cunnilingus** Oral stimulation of the female genitals.

The popularity of oral–genital sex has increased dramatically since Kinsey's research in the 1940s and '50s. In analyzing marriage and sex-advice manuals published over the course of the twentieth century, Carleton University researchers Alan Hunt and Bruce Curtis (2006) found a number of changes in advice about oral sex. Beginning as a taboo subject, oral sex became viewed as a normal activity over time, as first cunnilingus and then fellatio were accepted. Initially, oral sex was seen as a way of arousing the couple, especially the woman, in preparation for intercourse, and later it became accepted as a means of sexual pleasure in its own right. Of course, gays and lesbians have always used oral sex as a source of pleasure for its own sake. Recently, however, considerable anxiety has been raised among parents because of sensationalized media reports of group oral sex parties among youth.

If orgasm is reached through oral–genital sex, a partner may be concerned about tasting or swallowing the ejaculate. There's no scientific evidence that swallowing semen is harmful to your health, unless the man has an infection that can be transmitted via semen. Be aware, though, that oral–genital contact with the genitals of an infected partner—even if you don't contact any semen—may transmit the infection. Oral sex, in other words, isn't risk-free.

SURVEY DATA   Large-sample surveys of the Canadian and American populations reveal that oral sex is common. A recent large-sample survey of people in the United States who were 14 and older asked whether they'd given or received oral sex within the previous month or year. Several findings from this survey are noteworthy.

First, there's a common assumption that women in general, and young women in particular, are more likely to give their male partners oral sex than to receive it. Yet the survey indicates that, for most age groups, women are only slightly less likely to report receiving than giving oral sex.

Second, it's also commonly assumed that oral sex is predominantly practised by younger people, who are presumably more sexually adventurous than their elders.

CRITICAL THINKING QUESTIONS

Some people don't consider oral-genital contact to be "having sex." For them, only penile-vaginal intercourse counts as sex. What's your opinion?

TABLE 8.3

Percentages of Males and Females, Aged 14 to 70+, Who Reported Giving and Receiving Heterosexual Oral Sex During the Past Year

	14-15	16-17	18-19	20-24	25-29	30-39	40-49	50-59	60-69	70+
Male received	11.9	30.9	53.6	62.8	77.2	77.6	62.1	48.5	37.5	19.2
Male gave	7.8	18.3	50.7	54.9	73.5	68.7	57.4	44.1	34.3	24.3
Female received	10.0	23.5	58.0	70.4	71.8	58.7	52.3	34.2	24.8	7.8
Female gave	11.8	22.4	58.5	74.3	75.9	59.2	52.7	36.2	23.4	6.8

Source: Herbenick, D., et al. (2010). Sexual behavior in the United States: Results from a national probability sample of men and women ages 14-94. The Journal of Sexual Medicine, 7(Supplement s5), 255-265.

While previous research has shown that people who grew up before the sexual revolution of the 1960s and '70s were less likely to engage in oral sex, a sizable percentage of people in their forties, fifties, and sixties report that they also engage in oral sex. (See Table 8.3.)

The 1998 Compas poll is the only national survey to have asked Canadians about oral sex. Although almost all of the participants answered them, the questions about oral sex had the highest refusal rates, with three times as many women (15%) as men (5%) refusing to answer them (Fischtein & Herold, 2002). The majority of both men (89%) and women (78%) reported giving and/or receiving oral sex, a gender difference that may be at least partially accounted for by the women's higher rate of refusal to answer the questions.

Canadians who hadn't completed high school were least likely to report experiencing oral sex. This was especially true for women—half of those who hadn't completed high school said they hadn't experienced oral sex (Fischtein & Herold, 2002). The data on oral sex and other sexual practices suggests that those with less education are less experimental, and perhaps more concerned about whether these practices are "normal."

In a more recent study at the University of Guelph, Tanya Hill (2005) found that 89% of female students had engaged in oral sex with their most recent partners. About half reported that they engaged in oral sex most of the time when having sexual relations with their partners.

A study of gay and bisexual men in Ontario found that almost all of the men surveyed had engaged in oral sex during the previous three months (Myers et al., 2004).

NOT EVERYONE LIKES ORAL SEX   Despite oral sex's popularity today, some people choose to abstain from it. Some simply don't enjoy giving or receiving oral sex. Others object on grounds of cleanliness. They view the genitals as dirty, because of their proximity to the urinary and anal openings. Some abstain because they're concerned or embarrassed about providing (or receiving) direct views of parts of the body we've been reared to keep private. Some prefer not to taste or swallow semen, because they consider it dirty, sinful, or repulsive. Others are put off by the taste or texture; semen has a salty taste and a texture similar to egg white. Some people worry whether oral sex is morally accepted by their religion or culture.

If a couple wishes to engage in oral sex, open discussion of their feelings can enhance their pleasure and diminish anxiety. The man can be encouraged to tell his partner or remove his penis from her or his mouth as he nears ejaculation. And they can alleviate any concerns about offensive odours and cleanliness by thoroughly washing their genitals beforehand.

Oral Sex Techniques

FELLATIO   Although the word "fellatio" is derived from a Latin root that means "to suck," a sucking action is generally not highly arousing. The up-and-down movements of the penis in the partner's mouth and the licking of the penis are generally the most stimulating. (See Figure 8.5.) Gentle licking of the scrotum may also be highly arousing.

The mouth is stimulating to the penis because, like the vagina, it contains warm, moist mucous membranes. Muscles of the mouth and jaw can create varied pressure and movements. Erection may be stimulated by gently pulling the penis with the mouth (being careful never to touch the penis with the teeth) and simultaneously providing manual stimulation, as described earlier.

Higher levels of sexual arousal or orgasm can be promoted by moving the penis in and out of the mouth. The motions can be varied in speed and combined with manual stimulation.

Some people may gag during fellatio, a reflex triggered by pressure of the penis against the back of the tongue or against the throat. Gagging may be avoided by grasping the shaft of the penis with one hand and controlling the depth of penetration.

Gagging is less likely to occur if the partner giving fellatio is on top, rather than below, and if there's verbal communication about how deep the man should penetrate. Gagging may also be overcome by allowing gradually deeper penetration over successive occasions, while keeping the throat muscles relaxed.

CUNNILINGUS   A woman can be highly aroused by her partner's tongue, because it's soft, warm, and well lubricated. (See Figure 8.6.) In giving cunnilingus, the partner may begin by kissing and licking the woman's abdomen and inner thighs, gradually nearing the vulva. Gentle tugging or sucking of the labia minora can be stimulating, but the partner should take care not to bite. Many women enjoy licking of the clitoral region, and others desire sucking of the clitoris itself. The tongue may also be inserted into the vagina. A woman may be most receptive to direct clitoral contact by the tongue or circling of the clitoris with the tongue.

Cunnilingus provides such intense stimulation that many women find it the best means for achieving orgasm.

Figure 8.5 Fellatio
Fellatio involves stimulation of the penis and surrounding genital area with the mouth, lips, and tongue.

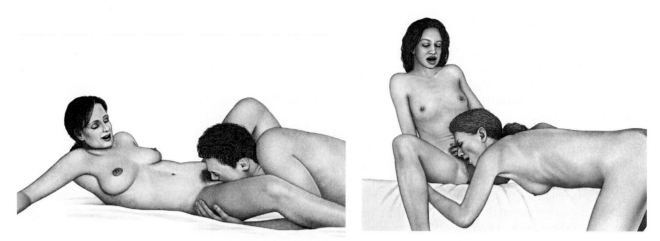

Figure 8.6 Cunnilingus.
Cunnilingus involves stimulation of the vulva with the mouth, lips, and tongue.

"69"   The term "69" describes mutual, simultaneous oral–genital stimulation. The numerals "6" and "9" are used because they resemble two partners who are upside down and facing each other. The "69" technique may be practised side by side or with one partner on top of the other. Again, there are no strict rules, and couples often alternate positions.

The "69" position has the psychologically positive feature of allowing two people to experience simultaneous stimulation, but it can be awkward if the two are dissimilar in size. Some couples avoid "69" because it deprives each partner of the opportunity to fully focus on receiving or providing sexual pleasure.

Intercourse Techniques

In sexual intercourse, or coitus, the penis is inserted into the vagina. Intercourse can take place in many different positions, as long as the genitals are aligned so the vagina contains the penis. In addition to varying positions, couples vary the depth and rate of thrusting (in-and-out motions) and the sources of additional sexual stimulation.

Though the number of intercourse positions is virtually endless, we'll focus on four of the most common: male superior (man on top), female superior (woman on top), lateral entry (side entry), and rear entry. We'll also discuss anal intercourse, a sexual technique used by both male–female and male–male couples.

THE MALE-SUPERIOR (MAN-ON-TOP) POSITION   The male-superior position (this "superiority" simply reflects the couple's body positions, but it has sometimes been taken as a symbol of male domination) has also been called the **missionary position**. In this position, the partners face each other. The man lies above the woman, perhaps supporting himself on his hands and knees rather than resting his full weight on her. (See Figure 8.7.) Even so, moving is easier for the man than for the woman, which suggests that he's responsible for directing their activity.

Many sex therapists suggest that it's preferable for the woman to guide the penis into the vagina, rather than having the man do so. The woman can feel the location of the vaginal opening and determine the proper angle of entry. To accomplish this, the woman must feel comfortable taking charge of the couple's lovemaking. With the breaking down of the traditional passive-female stereotype, women are feeling more comfortable taking this role.

The male-superior position has the advantage of permitting the couple to face one another, so kissing is easier. The woman may run her hands along her partner's

Missionary position The intercourse position in which the man is on top. It's also called the male-superior position.

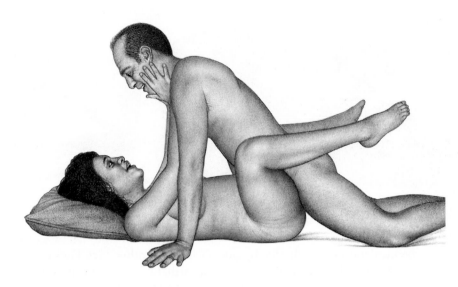

Figure 8.7 The male–superior (man-on-top) intercourse position.
The man-on-top position requires somewhat more physical effort on the part of the male. This is the most common sexual intercourse position in Western cultures.

body, stroking his buttocks and perhaps cupping a hand beneath his scrotum to increase stimulation as he reaches orgasm.

But the male-superior position makes it difficult for the man to caress his partner while simultaneously supporting himself with his hands. The position may not be favoured by women who enjoy having their partners provide manual clitoral stimulation during intercourse.

THE FEMALE-SUPERIOR (WOMAN-ON-TOP) POSITION   In the female-superior position, the partners face each other, with the woman on top. The woman straddles the man from above, controlling the angle of penile entry and the depth of thrusting. (See Figure 8.8.) Some women maintain a sitting position; others lie on top of their partners. Many women vary their positions.

In the female-superior position, the woman may feel psychologically and physically in charge. She can move as rapidly or as slowly as she wishes, with little effort, adjusting her body to vary the angle and depth of penetration. She can, in effect, guarantee that she receives adequate clitoral stimulation, either from the penis or from his or her own hand. This position thus facilitates orgasm in the woman.

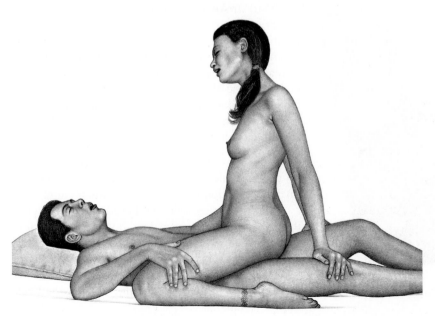

Figure 8.8 The female-superior (woman-on-top) intercourse position.
The female-superior position allows the woman more control over the angle and depth of penetration, and greater control over the orgasm.

Figure 8.9 The lateral-entry (side-by-side) intercourse position. The side-by-side position requires less physical effort for both partners, and allows more freedom of movement for mutual caressing during intercourse.

THE LATERAL-ENTRY (SIDE-ENTRY) POSITION   In the lateral-entry position, the man and woman lie side by side, facing each other. (See Figure 8.9.) This position has the advantages of allowing each partner relatively free movement and easy access to the other. The man and woman can kiss freely and stroke each other's bodies with a free arm.

The position isn't physically taxing, because both partners rest easily on the bedding. It's therefore an excellent position for prolonged coitus, older couples, and couples who are somewhat fatigued. The lateral position is also useful during pregnancy, at least until the final stages, when distension of the woman's abdomen may make lateral entry difficult.

THE REAR-ENTRY POSITION   In the rear-entry position, the man faces the woman's back. In one variation (see Figure 8.10), she supports herself on her hands and knees while he supports himself on his knees, entering her from behind. In another, the two lie alongside each other and the woman lifts one leg, draping it backward over her partner's thigh. The second position is particularly useful during the later stages of pregnancy.

The rear-entry position may be highly stimulating for both partners. The man may enjoy viewing and pressing his abdomen against his partner's buttocks. He can reach around or underneath to provide additional stimulation of the clitoris and breasts, and she can reach behind (if she's on her hands and knees) to stroke or grasp his testicles.

Some couples feel uncomfortable about the position, however, because of its association with animal mating patterns. The position is also impersonal, in that the partners don't face each other, which may create a sense of emotional distance. Moreover, some couples dislike the feeling that the man is psychologically in charge, since he can see his partner, but she can't readily see him.

ANAL SEX   Anal intercourse can be practised by male–female couples and male–male couples. It involves insertion of the penis into the rectum.

The rectum is richly endowed with nerve endings, and thus highly sensitive to sexual stimulation. Anal intercourse is also referred to as "Greek culture," or lovemaking in the "Greek style," because of male bisexuality in ancient Greece. Both women and men may reach orgasm through receiving the penis in the rectum.

Figure 8.10 The rear-entry intercourse position. The rear-entry position can be highly stimulating for both partners. It's particularly useful during the later stages of pregnancy.

In anal intercourse, the penetrating male usually situates himself behind his partner. (He can also lie above or below his partner, in a face-to-face position.) The receiving partner can supplement anal stimulation with manual stimulation of the clitoral region or penis to reach orgasm. Because the rectum produces no natural lubrication, people engaging in anal intercourse are advised to use an artificial lubricant, such as K-Y jelly.

Some people want their partner's fingers in the anus at the height of passion or at the moment of orgasm. A finger in the rectum during orgasm can heighten sexual sensation because the anal sphincters contract during orgasm.

Many couples are repulsed by the idea of anal intercourse. They view it as unnatural, immoral, or risky. Yet others find anal sex to be an enjoyable sexual variation, though perhaps not a regular feature of their sexual diet.

The National Health and Social Life Survey (NHSLS) of Americans found that one man in four (26%) and one woman in five (20%) had engaged in anal sex at some time during their lives (Laumann et al., 1994). Yet only about one person in 10 (10% of the men and 9% of the women) had engaged in anal sex during the previous year. Like oral sex, anal sex was more common among more highly educated respondents. Among men, about 30% of the college graduates had engaged in anal sex, compared to 23% of the high school graduates. Among women, about 29% of those with college degrees had engaged in anal sex, compared to about 17% of those who had graduated only from high school (Laumann et al., 1994). In a more recent national study of 18- to 26-year-old Americans in long-term relationships, 22% reported engaging in anal sex (Kaestle, 2007).

In a study of university students in British Columbia, 19% of the non-Asian females reported that they engaged in anal intercourse, compared with 3% of the Asian females; 5% of the non-Asian men and 6% of the Asian men reported that they engaged in anal intercourse (Meston et al., 1996). More of the respondents had engaged in caressing of the anal area. About half (45%) of the non-Asian women and 28% of the non-Asian men reported having their anal areas caressed. About one-fifth of the Asian men and women had experienced caressing of the anal area.

In a University of Waterloo study (Rye, 2001), more students reported that they'd engaged in anal intercourse without a condom (15%) than with a condom (9%). In a University of Guelph study, 13% of the female respondents reported that they'd engaged in anal intercourse with their most recent partners, though most of those who'd engaged in anal sex said they rarely did so (Hill, 2005).

Anal intercourse is more common among gay males than heterosexual couples. In a study of almost 5000 gay males across Canada, 62% reported engaging in anal intercourse during the previous three months (Myers et al., 1996). In a more recent survey of 1139 men visiting gay venues in Vancouver, about 70% reported having anal sex during the previous six months (Trussler et al., 2010).

Not all gay males enjoy or practise anal intercourse. Of those who do, most alternate between being the inserter and being the recipient of the penis. Interviews with 51 gay men suggest that playing the inserter role in anal intercourse is sometimes associated with fantasies of domination, and the recipient role with fantasies of submission (Kippax & Smith, 2001). But some gays who practise anal intercourse deny that sex has anything to do with power or activity versus passivity; they feel that sex is about sharing.

Some individuals engage in the sexual practice called "fisting." Fisting is the insertion of the fist or hand into the vagina or the rectum. Fisting is more common among male–male than male–female couples. It carries the risk of infection or injury to the rectum or anus. A survey of 75 gay men in Australia found that fisting was usually done with gloves, although fingering was not (Richters et al., 2003).

Some couples kiss or lick the anus during foreplay. This practice is called **anilingus**. Oral–anal sex carries a serious health risk, however, because micro-organisms that cause intestinal diseases and various sexually transmitted diseases can be spread through oral–anal contact.

Anilingus Oral stimulation of the anus.

Many couples today hesitate to engage in anal intercourse, for fear of HIV (the virus that causes AIDS) and other sexually transmitted infections (STIs). HIV and other micro-organisms that cause STIs, such as gonorrhea, syphilis, and hepatitis, can be spread by anal intercourse, because small tears in the rectal tissues allow the microbes to enter the recipient's blood system. Women run a greater risk of contracting HIV from anal intercourse than from vaginal intercourse, just as gay men carry a high risk of infection from receptive anal intercourse (Voeller, 1991). It's important for couples engaging in anal intercourse to use condoms.

A Woman's Perspective.
Like heterosexual women, lesbians are less genitally oriented and less fixated on orgasm than men are.

Gay and Lesbian Sexual Behaviour

In an Ontario survey of Canadian gay and bisexual men, more than half reported that they'd had sex with at least one regular partner (i.e., someone they'd had sex with more than once) in the three months prior to the survey. More than half had engaged in sex with at least one casual partner (i.e., someone they'd had sex with only once) during this time (Myers et al., 2004). The most common sexual activities they reported were deep-tongue kissing, oral sex without condoms, and mutual masturbation. (See Table 8.5.) The types of sexual behaviour they experienced were fairly similar for both regular and casual partners, with the exception of anal sex without condoms, which was experienced twice as often with regular as with casual partners. Forty-four percent said they'd never engaged in receptive anal intercourse without condoms.

Most research on the sexual behaviour of gay men, including that cited here, has been conducted with the express purpose of determining the risk of contracting HIV and other STIs. In other words, research on gay male sexuality has overwhelmingly focused on reducing risk, as opposed to increasing pleasure. While research on STI-related risk behaviours among heterosexuals, gay men, and lesbians are all important, perhaps the tendency to focus gay male research specifically on infection risk, rather than on capacity to give and receive pleasure, has caused many of us to view gay sex as inherently more dangerous than lesbian or heterosexual sex.

A World of Diversity

SEXUAL BEHAVIOUR IN AUSTRALIA

In a national Australian survey involving 19 307 respondents between the ages of 16 and 59, researchers (Richters et al., 2006) asked heterosexuals which sexual behaviours they'd engaged in the last time they'd had sex with partners. The study made an important contribution by analyzing combinations of behaviours, rather than behaviours in isolation.

The researchers found than almost all of the encounters (95%) included vaginal intercourse, but only 12% of the encounters consisted of vaginal intercourse alone.

The most common combinations were intercourse and manual stimulation of the genitals (49%) and intercourse and manual and oral stimulation of the genitals (32%). Only 1% had anal intercourse, and 17% of the men and 14% of the women reported digital anal stimulation.

Men had orgasms in 95% of the encounters, while women had orgasms in 69%. Women were more likely to reach orgasm when the encounters included more sexual practices, especially cunnilingus.

TABLE 8.5

Sexual Behaviours of Gay and Bisexual Men in Ontario over a Period of Three Months

	With Regular Male Partner	With Casual Male Partner
Mutual masturbation	81%	78%
Oral sex—no condom (I)	86	80
Deep tongue kissing	86	78
Oral sex—no condom (R)	80	73
Anal sex with condom (I)	44	47
Oral–anal sex	53	40
Anal sex—no condom (I)	41	21
Anal sex with condom (R)	36	35
Anal sex—no condom (R)	34	6

Note: I = Insertive, R = Receptive

Source: Myers, T., Allman, D., Calzavara, L., et al. (2004). Ontario men's survey. Toronto: HIV Social, Behavioural, and Epidemiological Studies Unit, Faculty of Medicine, University of Toronto.

Sexual techniques practised by lesbians vary. Lesbian couples report kissing, manual and oral stimulation of the breasts, and manual and oral stimulation of the genitals. Manual genital stimulation is a common and frequent sexual activity among lesbian couples. Many lesbian couples also engage in genital apposition. That is, they position themselves so as to rub their genitals together rhythmically. Like gay males, lesbians spend a good deal of time holding, kissing, and caressing each other's bodies before they approach the breasts and genitals

Innovative Canadian Research

HOW TO HAVE GREAT SEX: ADVICE IN POPULAR MAGAZINES

University of Ottawa researchers Dana Menard and Peggy Kleinplatz (2008) analyzed the advice for achieving "great sex" given by popular men's and women's magazines. The advice fell into five categories:

■ Technical, mechanical, and physical factors— Recommendations included improving or learning new sexual techniques and positions, having sex for appropriate lengths of time, and improving physical health through diet and exercise.

■ Variety—Readers were encouraged to experiment sexually, try "mild kink," watch steamy movies or porn, and engage in "rough" female-initiated sex.

■ Relationship factors—Suggestions included improving communication about sexual desires and becoming more emotionally intimate.

■ Personal and psychological improvements—Readers were encouraged to relax during sex, focus on sexuality both during and outside of sex, improve their body image (for females), and increase their self-knowledge (usually through masturbation).

■ Preparation for sex—Readers were encouraged to make themselves more physically attractive and to make the sexual settings more seductive.

Most of the advice centred on the first two categories—improving sexual techniques and increasing the variety of sexual experiences.

The magazines relied on a number of gender stereotypes, such as the belief that men preferred "quickies" and women preferred long, drawn-out sex. The magazines also relied on traditional scripts—that is, recommending regular partners, but not casual partners. Sometimes messages were contradictory; one magazine might suggest that couples view pornography, while another magazine discouraged this activity.

With the exception of *Men's Health*, sexual advice was more common in women's magazines than in men's magazines.

In your experience, does the advice on how to have "great sex" provided in popular magazines sometimes reflect stereotypes about male and female sexuality?

There's been far less research into lesbian sexual behaviour than into gay male and heterosexual sexual behaviour. One recent detailed survey was conducted in Australia (Richters, 2007). It found that almost all of the women had engaged in manual and oral sex. (See Table 8.6.) The survey also asked about the use of dental dams as a means of preventing STD infection during oral sex. Only 7% of the

TABLE 8.6

Sexual Behaviours with Another Woman Reported by Women in Contact with the Gay and Lesbian Community in Sydney, Australia

Behaviours Experienced	Percent
Fingers on external genitals	96%
Fingers inside vagina	94
Oral sex giving	85
Oral sex receiving	81
Sex toy used on external genitals	56
Sex toy used in vagina	57
Fingers inside anus	31
Rimming (her mouth, your anus)	15
Rimming (your mouth, her anus)	16
Sex toy inside anus	14

Source: Richters, J. (2007). Researching sex between women. Paper presented at the 1st World Congress for Sexual Health, Sydney, Australia.

women reported that they'd used a dental dam during oral sex with other women. Of those who had used dental dams, three-quarters had used them only once (Richters, 2007).

Feelings About Sexual Behaviour

The fact that people engage in certain behaviours doesn't necessarily mean they have positive feelings about those behaviours.

McGill University researchers Eric Ochs and Yitzchak Binik (1999) surveyed 70 couples about their experiences and comfort levels with 68 sexual behaviours. Women rated themselves as more comfortable than men on the least sexually explicit behaviours (cuddling, hugging, and dancing). Men were more comfortable than women with fellatio, anal intercourse, woman-on-top intercourse, and rear-entry vaginal intercourse.

In this chapter, we've observed many of the variations in human sexual expression. No other species shows such diversity in sexual behaviour.

Summing Up

Sexual fantasies are often incorporated into masturbation or into sex with another person, to heighten sexual response.

Masturbation can be practised by means of manual stimulation of the genitals, perhaps with the aid of an electric vibrator or an object that provides tactile stimulation. Surveys indicate that most people have masturbated at some point in their lives.

The pattern and duration of foreplay varies widely within and across cultures. Couples in many cultures kiss for its own enjoyment or as a prelude to intercourse.

Touching or caressing erogenous zones with the hands or other parts of the body can be highly arousing.

Men typically prefer direct stroking of their genitals by their partners early in lovemaking.

Women, however, tend to prefer that their partners caress their genitals after a period of general body contact.

Most, but not all, women enjoy stimulation of the breasts.

Oral–genital sex is a common sexual practice.

Four of the most commonly used sexual intercourse positions are the male-superior position, the female-superior position, the lateral-entry position, and the rear-entry position.

Most gay males and a significant minority of heterosexuals engage in anal sex. There's been limited research on the sexual behaviours of lesbians.

Test Yourself

Multiple-Choice Questions

1. Which of the following statements about sexual fantasies is false?
 (a) A fantasy is a mental image that's sexually arousing or erotic.
 (b) Sexual fantasies can be experienced as either positive or negative.
 (c) Fantasizing about being forced to have sex means you want to experience this in real life.
 (d) Research suggests that gay males are open to fantasizing about a wider range of sexual behaviours than heterosexual males.

2. In Pelletier and Herold's survey of female university students, the most common sexual fantasy was having sex with a:
 (a) Stranger.
 (b) Famous person.
 (c) Boyfriend.
 (d) Woman.

3. In a survey of 14- to 94-year-old males and females, the group most likely to report masturbating during the previous month was aged:
 (a) 16 to 17.
 (b) 18 to 19.
 (c) 20 to 24.
 (d) 25 to 29.

4. What connection does the research show between masturbation and education?
 (a) Less educated men and women are more likely to masturbate.
 (b) Less educated women, but not men, are more likely to masturbate.
 (c) Less educated men, but not women, are more likely to masturbate.
 (d) More educated men and women are more likely to masturbate.

5. According to a survey of 14- to 94-year-old males and females, at what age is a male most likely to report that he's given oral sex to a female partner during the past year?
 (a) 20 to 24.
 (b) 25 to 29.
 (c) 30 to 39.
 (d) 40 to 49.

6. In a survey of 14- to 94-year-old males and females, what percentage of the 60- to 69-year-old women reported that they'd received oral sex from male partners during the previous year?
 (a) 24.8.
 (b) 15.8.
 (c) 5.8.
 (d) 0.8.

7. The varieties of physical contact that occur before sexual intercourse are collectively called:
 (a) Prologue.
 (b) Foreplay.
 (c) Othercourse.
 (d) Afterplay.

(continued)

8. **Tantric sex includes:**
(a) A slowing of the sexual interaction process.
(b) A speeding-up of the sexual interaction process.
(c) Techniques that enable both partners to have as many orgasms as possible.
(d) Techniques for attracting new sex partners.

9. **Which of the following statements about the woman-on-top position is least accurate?**
(a) It allows either partner access to the woman's clitoris.
(b) It allows a woman to move as rapidly or as slowly as she wishes.

(c) It allows a woman to bring her partner to orgasm quickly.
(d) It allows a woman to feel psychologically in charge.

10. **According to the textbook, the tendency for research on the sexual behaviour of gay men to focus on HIV and STI risk may:**
(a) Increase compassion for men with HIV/AIDS.
(b) Raise awareness of the risk of HIV infection from anal intercourse.
(c) Call attention to the need for more research on HIV risk for heterosexuals.
(d) Have biased us to view gay sex as inherently dangerous.

You'll find answers to the "Test Yourself" questions on page 495.

Critical Thinking

1. Have you ever wondered whether your sexual fantasies are normal?

2. Have your ideas about sexual fantasies, masturbation, oral sex, and anal sex changed as a result of reading this chapter? If so, how? If not, why not?

3. How do you feel about masturbating to online sexual images? If you did so, would you tell your best friend? Your girlfriend or boyfriend? Why or why not?

4. Were you ever discouraged from masturbating as a child? Do you think this has affected your behaviour as an adult? Explain.

MySearchLab

MySearchLab offers extensive help to students with their writing and research project and provides round-the-clock access to credible and reliable source material. Take a tour at **www.mysearchlab.com**.

Sexual Orientation

Sexual orientation The directionality of one's erotic attraction—that is, to members of the same sex, the other sex, or both.

Heterosexual orientation Erotic attraction to—and preference for romantic relationships with—members of the other sex.

Homosexual orientation Erotic attraction to—and preference for romantic relationships with—members of your own sex.

Bisexual orientation Erotic attraction to—and interest in romantic relationship with—members of both sexes.

Getting Oriented to Sexual Orientation

Sexual orientation refers to a person's erotic attraction to—and interest in developing romantic relationships with—members of one sex or the other.

A **heterosexual orientation** is an erotic attraction to members of the other sex. Many people refer to heterosexuals as "straight."

A **homosexual orientation** is an erotic attraction to members of your own anatomic sex. Homosexual men are often referred to as gay males, or gays, while homosexual women are often called lesbians. Gay males and lesbians may also be collectively referred to as gays, gay people, or homosexuals.

A person with a **bisexual orientation** is sexually attracted to—and interested in forming romantic relationships with—both males and females.

Coming to Terms with Terms

The term "homosexuality" is somewhat controversial. Some gay and lesbian people object to it because they feel it draws attention to sexual behaviour. The term bears a social stigma, having historically been associated with deviance and mental illness. Moreover, the term is often used only in reference to men, rendering lesbians invisible. Many people therefore prefer such terms such "gay male" and "lesbian sexual orientation." We use the word "homosexuality" in this book because it provides a broad but useful way to differentiate same-sex attraction from opposite-sex attraction. We intend our use of the word to be respectful and nonjudgmental.

The word "homosexual" is ambiguous (Savin-Williams, 2006). Does it refer to sexual behaviour or sexual orientation? When we speak of gay, lesbian, and bisexual orientations, we're referring to sexual attraction to the same sex. In other words, sexual orientation is defined not by sexual activity, but by the direction of romantic interest and erotic attraction (Mosher et al., 2005). This distinction is useful because many heterosexual people have same-sex experiences, and many gay and lesbian people have opposite-sex experiences.

Sexual Orientation and Gender Identity

Since gay and lesbian people are attracted to members of their own sex, some people assume they'd prefer to be members of the other sex. Like most heterosexuals, however, most gays and lesbians have gender identities consistent with their anatomic sex. A small percentage of gays and lesbians become transexual—that is, adopt gender identities that are different from their anatomic sex. But feeling trapped in the body of the other sex is not part of the definition of homosexuality.

When heterosexuals think about homosexuals, they tend to focus almost exclusively on the sexual aspects of male–male and female–female relationships. But the relationships of homosexuals, like those of heterosexuals, involve more than sex. In a study of Ontario men, Barry Adam (2000b) at the University of Windsor found that for gay men, the concept of being gay centred on the possibility for emotional involvement and

Brokeback Mountain.
In the film Brokeback Mountain, *Jake Gyllenhaal and Heath Ledger portray two cowboys who begin a love affair in 1963 Wyoming. Neither understands what it means to have a gay orientation.*

relationships with other people who felt the same way, rather than on sexual behaviour. Homosexuals, like heterosexuals, spend only a small amount of time in sexual activity. More basic to a gay male or a lesbian sexual orientation is the formation of romantic attachments with members of one's own sex. These attachments, like male–female attachments, provide a framework for love and intimacy.

Kevin Alderson at the University of Calgary has been researching the concept of sexual orientation for several years. His findings have resulted in a new scale called the sexuality questionnaire. Alderson (2007) has concluded that sexual orientation should be conceptualized and measured as a combination of several factors: sexual attraction, sexual fantasies, sexual preference, sexual partners, tendency to fall in love romantically, and experience of falling in love romantically. The scale also measures a person's self-identified sexual identity.

Classifying Sexual Orientation

Determining a person's sexual orientation might seem clear-cut. Some people are exclusively gay and limit their sexual activities to partners of their own sex. Others are exclusively heterosexual and limit their sexual activities to partners of the other sex. However, a significant percentage of people are neither exclusively heterosexual nor exclusively homosexual, falling somewhere in between.

It's not unusual for heterosexuals to have sexual experiences with people of their own sex (Mosher et al., 2005; Savin-Williams, 2006). In the absence of heterosexual outlets, adolescents and people in isolated populations (e.g., prison inmates) may have sexual experiences with members of their own sex while maintaining heterosexual identities. A number of studies have found that Asians, Blacks, and Latinos may be less likely than whites to identify themselves as gay, lesbian, or bisexual even when they engage in sexual activity with people of their own sex (Chae & Ayala, 2010; Reback & Larkins, 2010).

Gay males and lesbians, too, may engage in male–female sexual activity while maintaining gay sexual orientations. In the Ontario Men's Survey of gay and bisexual men, 83% of respondents identified themselves as gay, yet 61% reported having had sex with women (Myers et al., 2004). In the past, when homosexuality was more stigmatized in Western society than it is now, it wasn't uncommon for some gay and lesbian people to marry in order to fulfill social expectations, yet still have unfulfilled desire for members of their own sex. And some people are bisexual, but may not act on their attraction to members of their own sex (Edser & Shea, 2002).

Sexual orientation isn't necessarily expressed in sexual behaviour. Many people see themselves as gay or heterosexual long before they ever have sex with members of their own sex (Thompson & Morgan, 2008; Savin-Williams & Diamond, 2000). And some people, gay or heterosexual, adopt celibate lifestyles for religious or ascetic reasons.

People's erotic interests and fantasies may also shift over time. Gay males and lesbians may experience sporadic **heteroerotic** interests. Heterosexual people may have occasional **homoerotic** interests. Women's sexual orientations are apparently somewhat more flexible, or plastic, than men's, and women are somewhat more dependent on social experience (Diamond, 2003a; Thompson & Morgan, 2008). Lisa M. Diamond (2003b) conducted a survey of lesbian and bisexual women that involved three interviews over a five-year period. She found that more than 25% of the women relinquished their lesbian or bisexual orientations as time went on. Half of these relabelled themselves as heterosexual, and the other half renounced any effort at self-labelling.

Chivers and Bailey (2005) exposed men and women to visual male and female sexual stimuli and measured both their genital responses and their self-reports of sexual arousal. Male heterosexuals responded genitally only to the female stimuli, and gay males showed the reverse pattern. Their genital

Heteroerotic Of an erotic nature and involving members of the other sex.

Homoerotic Of an erotic nature and involving members of one's own sex.

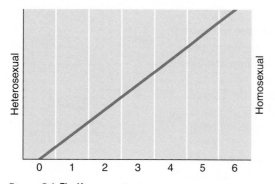

Figure 9.1 The Kinsey continuum.
Kinsey and his colleagues conceived of a seven-point heterosexual-homosexual continuum that classifies people according to their sexual behaviour and the magnitude of their attraction to members of their own gender.

responses bore out their verbal reports. The women, both heterosexual and lesbian, were more likely to be aroused by both male and female sexual stimuli. Chivers and Bailey's findings are consistent with research showing that women's sexual orientations are more flexible than men's, and apparently more intertwined with their social experience (Bailey, 2003a; Diamond, 2003b).

Attraction to people of the other sex and attraction to people of the same sex may thus not always be mutually exclusive. People may have various degrees of sexual interest in, and sexual experience with, people of either sex. Kinsey and his colleagues recognized that the boundaries between homosexual and heterosexual orientations are sometimes blurry.

THE KINSEY CONTINUUM Kinsey and his colleagues (1948, 1953) found evidence of a continuum of sexual orientation among the people they surveyed, with bisexuality representing a midpoint between exclusively heterosexual and exclusively homosexual orientations. (See Figure 9.1.) People are located on the continuum according to their patterns of sexual attraction and behaviour. People in category 0 are considered exclusively heterosexual, while those in category 6 are considered exclusively gay.

Kinsey and his colleagues reported that about 4% of the men and 1% to 3% of the women in their samples were exclusively gay (scoring six points on their scale). A larger percentage were considered predominantly gay (scoring four or five points) or predominantly heterosexual (scoring one or two points). All in all, Kinsey's data suggested that close to 10% of the United States population was gay or predominantly gay—a number that dramatically exceeded today's estimates. Some people were classified as equally gay and heterosexual in orientation, and could be labelled bisexual (scoring three points). Most people were classified as exclusively heterosexual (scoring zero points).

Statistics concerning past sexual activity with a member of one's own sex can be misleading. They may represent a single episode or a brief period of adolescent experimentation. Half of the men who reported male–male sexual activity in Kinsey's sample limited it to the ages of 12 to 14. Another third had male–male sexual experiences by age 18, but not again.

Kinsey's research also showed that sexual behaviour patterns can change, sometimes dramatically. Sexual experiences or feelings involving people of the same sex are common, especially in adolescence, and don't necessarily mean these individuals will engage in sexual activity exclusively with people of their own sex in adulthood (Diamond, 2003a).

CHALLENGES TO THE KINSEY CONTINUUM Alfred Kinsey believed that exclusive heterosexual and homosexual orientations lay at opposite poles on a single continuum. The more heterosexual a person was, the less gay s/he was, and vice versa.

Using self-reported content of erotic fantasies as an indication of sexual orientation, Storms (1980) found evidence that there are separate dimensions of responsiveness to male–female sexual stimulation (heteroeroticism) and same-sex sexual stimulation (homoeroticism). (See Figure 9.2.) According to Storms's model, bisexuals are high in both dimensions, whereas people who are low in both are essentially asexual.

Kinsey would see bisexuals as less responsive than heterosexuals to stimulation by the other sex, and more responsive to stimulation by the same sex. But Storms's two-dimensional model allows someone to be as responsive as a heterosexual to stimulation by the other sex, and as responsive as a gay person to stimulation by the same sex.

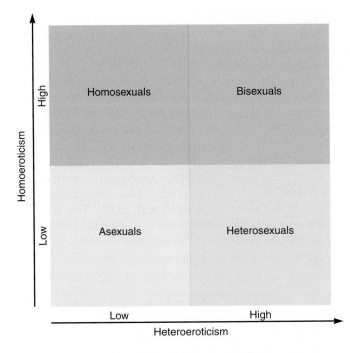

Figure 9.2 **Heterosexuality and homosexuality as separate dimensions.**
According to this model, homosexuality and heterosexuality are independent dimensions. A person can therefore be high or low on both dimensions at the same time. Most people are high on one dimension. Bisexuals are high on both dimensions. People who are low on both are considered asexual.

ESTIMATES OF SEXUAL ORIENTATION The controversy about how many people aren't heterosexual continues. About 3% of the men surveyed in the United States, Britain, France, and Denmark have identified themselves as gay (Mosher et al., 2005; Savin-Williams, 2006). About 1% to 2% of the American women surveyed have identified themselves as lesbian (Mosher et al., 2005; Savin-Williams, 2006). Similar results have been found in a sample of 8000 university and college students in Canada and the United States, with 3% of the males identifying themselves as gay or bisexual and 2% of the females identifying themselves as lesbian or bisexual (Ellis et al., 2005).

The 1998 Compas survey asked Canadians, "In general, whom are you most attracted to?" As shown in Table 9.1, about 8% of males and 10% of females were not exclusively heterosexual in their reported attractions. However, less than 2% of the men said they were attracted only to men, and less than 1% of the women said they were attracted only to women.

In the Canada Youth and AIDS Survey (Boyce, 2003), students were asked their sexual orientations, as indicated by their physical attraction to members of the same sex, the other sex, or both sexes. Girls were more likely to report same-sex attractions. In grade 11, more males (1.5%) and females (3%) indicated that they were physically attracted to both sexes than exclusively to their own sex (0.9% of males and 1.7% of females).

TABLE 9.1
Sexual-Attraction Preferences of Canadian Men and Women

	Males	**Females**
Only men	1.6%	90.1%
Mostly men	0.5	6.7
Both men and women	1.9	2.2
Mostly women	4.5	0.1
Only women	91.4	0.8

Source: Based on Compas Polling. (1998). Modern life survey of the Canadian adult population. Unpublished raw data.

Kris Wells at the University of Alberta conducted a survey of 13- to 29-year-old Canadians, in which 3.5% of the respondents identified themselves as gay, lesbian, bisexual, or transgendered (Youthography Ping Survey, 2004). Slightly more males than females identified themselves as GLBT (Wells, 2008).

In 2003, for the first time, Statistics Canada included a question on sexual orientation as part of its Canadian Community Health Survey. Of the 135 000 respondents who were 18 to 59 years old, 1.0% reported that they were gay or lesbian, and 0.7% said they were bisexual. Twice as many men (1.3%) as women (0.7%) said they were homosexual. However, more women (0.9%) than men (0.6%) said they were bisexual (Statistics Canada, 2004b).

Another approach to determining sexual orientation involves measuring physiological responses to sexual stimuli. Researchers in Quebec have devised a method of measuring sexual preference in virtual reality (Renaud et al., 2002). This involves analyzing a respondent's computer interaction with an image of a naked woman as a measure of his or her sexual preference.

Bisexuality

Bisexual people are sexually attracted to both males and females. Many have somewhat stronger attractions to one sex than the other. Weinrich and Klein (2002) speak of bisexuals as being bi-gay, bi-straight, or bi-bi, meaning some have stronger leanings toward people of their own sex (bi-gays), some toward people of the other sex (bi-straights), and some to people of both sexes equally (bi-bis).

About 1% of the people (0.8% of the men and 0.9% of the women) surveyed in the American NHSLS study (Laumann et al., 1994) reported having a bisexual identity. These percentages are very similar to the percentages of people who reported that they were bisexual in Statistics Canada's 2003 Canadian Community Health Survey (discussed above in "Estimates of Sexual Orientation").

Some homosexuals (and some heterosexuals) believe claims to bisexuality are a cop-out used by some people to deny that they're gay or lesbian. Perhaps they fear leaving their spouses or coming out (i.e., publicly declaring their gay or lesbian orientations). Others view bisexuality as a form of sexual experimentation by people who are mostly heterosexual. Surveys of more than 600 college undergraduates confirm that **biphobia**, or hatred of bisexuals, can be found in both heterosexual and homosexual populations (Mulick & Wright, 2002). To help bisexuals deal with these issues, groups such as Bisexual Women of Toronto (BiWoT) provide counselling and support. One of BiWoT's objectives is to educate community service groups about the effects of prejudice and discrimination against bisexuals.

Many avowed bisexuals and researchers assert that bisexuals can maintain erotic interests in—and romantic relationships with—members of both sexes. They insist that bisexuality is an authentic sexual orientation with its own developmental patterns, and not just a cover for a gay or lesbian orientation (Brown, 2002; Weinrich & Klein, 2002).

Some bisexual people follow lifestyles that permit them to satisfy their dual inclinations. Others feel pressured by heterosexual and gay people alike to commit themselves one way or the other (Edser & Shea, 2002). Some gays and lesbians also mask their sexual orientations by adopting bisexual lifestyles; that is, they get married and also have sexual liaisons with members of their own sex.

Asexuality

Anthony Bogaert (2006a) at Brock University in Ontario argues that asexuality should be considered a sexual orientation. He defines asexuals as people who have a low sexual attraction for both sexes—that is, they're low on both heteroeroticism and homoeroticism. However, they might be romantically attracted to others. Most have low interest in any kind of sexual stimulation, including masturbation.

Biphobia Negative attitudes and feelings toward bisexual people, including intolerance, hatred, and fear.

In a population-based survey in the United Kingdom, 1% of respondents agreed with the statement "I have never felt sexually attracted to anyone at all" (Bogaert, 2004). One-third of these people said they were in long-term marital or cohabiting relationships, and another 11% had been in such relationships in the past. Some of the asexual people still engaged in sexual activity with partners, but the frequency was very low.

Researchers at the University of British Columbia studied 54 men and 133 women recruited from the Asexuality Visibility and Education Network (Brotto et al., 2010). According to their questionnaire responses, their sexual response levels were low, but the respondents didn't experience this lack of response as distressing. Participants who were in romantic relationships reported that they had to "negotiate" sexual activity with their partners.

Bogaert (2006a) notes that his definition of asexuality is narrow in scope, since it doesn't take into account whether someone is romantically attracted to another person or is engaging in sexual activity. C. J. DeLuzio Chasin (2011) at the University of Windsor notes that there is considerable diversity within the asexual community, and that future research needs to account for varying levels of romantic and sexual attraction and sexual desire among people who identify themselves as asexual.

Researchers have only recently begun to explore asexuality. So far, research suggests that asexuality isn't pathological and shouldn't be seen as a sexual dysfunction, and that asexual people can live happy lives (Bogaert, 2006a; Brotto et al., 2010; Brotto & Yule, 2011).

QUEER, QUESTIONING, TRANSGENDERED, AND TWO-SPIRITED Most surveys about sexual orientation ask whether people are heterosexual, homosexual, or bisexual. This classification system doesn't necessarily correspond to the way people see or identify themselves. Some people self-identify as queer, questioning, transgendered, or two-spirited.

Most organizations that represent gays and lesbians today also include transgendered people, although this wasn't true in the past. As a sign of inclusivity, many organizations have adopted the label *LGBTQ* (lesbian, gay, bisexual, transgendered, and queer). Some people who previously classified themselves as gay, lesbian, or bisexual now prefer to identify themselves as "queer." In general, queer people reject the labels "gay," "straight," and "bisexual" as too limiting, viewing them as designations that reflect the oppression so often faced by non-heterosexual people. "Queer," from their perspective, is a positive, self-affirming term for people who don't see themselves as fitting into standard classifications of sexual orientation.

Some lesbians are uncomfortable with the term "queer," and worry that general use of the term may hide some of the issues they face. For example, Alberta therapists Bonita Decaire and Deborah Foster (2010) believe lesbians, because of sexism, have more in common with other women than with gay men when it comes to power inequity and discrimination.

Other people, especially youth, may describe themselves as "questioning." They're unsure which of the currently available labels best describe their sexual orientations. They may consider themselves to be in the process of discovering their sexual identities, or in some cases, coming to terms with the possibility that they're not heterosexual. In a survey of high school students in California, 28.8% of those who identified themselves as non-heterosexual said they were questioning or queer or used terms other than gay, lesbian, and bisexual to describe themselves (Russell, Clarke, & Clary, 2009).

Holly Devor (2002)—now Aaron Devor—argues that transgendered people (discussed in Chapter 5) should be included in discussions of sexual orientation. Devor reasons that, since transgendered people are the most visible minority among people engaged in same-sex practices, they face many of the same issues and concerns as gays, lesbians, and bisexual people. Yet transgendered people lack

A World of Diversity

THE NEW GAY TEENAGER

In his controversial book *The New Gay Teenager*, Ritch C. Savin-Williams of Cornell University argues that today's urban teenagers no longer accept traditional gender and sexual orientations. In the preface, he states:

> Gay people have historically too readily accepted the inevitability and desirability of divisions based on sexual categories. It's not that same-sex attractions are disappearing—indeed, they appear to be on the upswing as young people more freely share with each other their same-sex feelings. They're not embarrassed by gayness, don't consider it deviant, and see it all around them—on television, in movies, in songs, in cultural icons, among their friends.

In his interviews with urban American teenagers, Savin-Williams discovered that many no longer consider gender categories important. Rather, they view themselves as "pansexuals," or bisexuals who reject gender labels.

Savin-Williams believes the media have played a key role in changing the gender perspectives of young people by normalizing same-sex attraction in television and films. And school boards in large urban centres such as New York and Los Angeles have introduced programs to increase students' acceptance of a range of sexual orientations.

Savin-Williams is highly critical of social scientists who force their research participants to label themselves as either gay or straight. Bisexuals are typically ignored or forced into one of these categories. The researchers don't allow for broader choices, such as polysexual, or for multiple identities, such as bi-lesbian.

Savin-Williams argues that the standard image of gay youth as depressed, isolated, drug-dependent, and suicidal is exaggerated. He believes many of the studies have been flawed, purposely oversampling troubled teens. From his own research, he concludes that most gay males and lesbians are psychologically healthy, and in this regard no different from heterosexual youth.

We need to consider whether the trends and conclusions reported by Savin-Williams are applicable only to a small minority of sophisticated urban youth, or accurately represent what's occurring.

Kristopher Wells (2008) of the University of Alberta reports on a Canadian study that found similar trends among gay youth. According to Wells, Canadian youth are challenging the traditional stereotypes of sexuality and gender, and are reluctant to have their sexual identities forced into narrow categories.

Source: Savin-Williams, R. C. (2005). The New Gay Teenager. Cambridge, MA: Harvard University Press.

the legal protections granted to gays and lesbians. Unlike Devor, some within the transgendered community identify themselves as "trans" and view their issues as related to gender, not to sexual orientation.

Within aboriginal North American communities, there are people who identify themselves as "two-spirited." Aboriginal communities are less likely to incorporate simple divisions of gay/lesbian and straight (Tafoya, 1997). "Two-spirited" refers to gender or social identity, and in many cases also includes same-sex behaviour. Many two-spirited people would not easily identify as gay, lesbian, or bisexual.

The queer, questioning, transgendered, and two-spirited examples show that while the gay, lesbian, and bisexual classifications have been useful basic categories, they need to be expanded to more accurately reflect the diversity of ways people conceptualize and identify their sexual orientations. Increasingly, researchers are incorporating identities such queer, questioning, transgendered, and two-spirited into research that asks people to identify their sexual orientations.

Perspectives on Gay and Lesbian Sexual Orientations

Gay and lesbian sexual orientations have existed throughout history. Attitudes toward them have varied widely. They've been tolerated in some societies, openly encouraged in others, and condemned in most.

Historical and Religious Perspectives

Some ancient societies, such as that of the Greeks, as we discussed in Chapter 1, openly accepted male–male sexual behaviour. Many famous people throughout history have been gay; Alexander the Great is just one example. Yet most cultures have held negative attitudes toward homosexuality.

Jews and Christians have traditionally referred to male–male sexual activity as the sin of Sodom. This has given us the term "sodomy," which generally denotes anal intercourse (and sometimes oral–genital contact). According to the Book of Genesis, the city of Sodom was destroyed by God, though it's unclear what behaviour incurred God's wrath. Pope Gregory III wasn't ambiguous in his eighth-century account of the city's obliteration, however, calling it a punishment for sexual activity between members of the same sex.

Despite the history of opposition to gay and lesbian orientations, some churches today perform marriages for gay couples—or at least "bless" their relationships. The Universal Fellowship of Metropolitan Community Churches has many gay male and lesbian parishioners in Canada. The first Canadian church to perform formal marriage ceremonies for same-sex couples was the Metropolitan Community Church of Toronto. Since then an increasing number of churches have performed same-sex marriages.

Many Canadian churches allow ordination of gay and lesbian clergy, as long as they remain celibate. Some, however, such as the Unitarian Church and the United Church of Canada, do accept clergy who are involved in same-sex relationships. The more conservative churches continue to oppose equal rights, including same-sex marriage, for anyone whose sexual orientation is not heterosexual.

A major international legal and political struggle over gay rights is taking place today, based on the opposing values of gay equality and religious freedom. At the United Nations (UN), a coalition of mainly Islamic countries has been leading a campaign to develop international laws to prohibit "defamation of religions" (Savage, 2008). One intent of this movement is to deter the United Nations and other international organizations from discussing issues such as gay rights, which are viewed by Islamic countries as an affront to their religious beliefs and therefore an act of religious discrimination (Savage, 2008). Nevertheless, in 2011 the UN Human Rights Council passed a non-legally-binding resolution by a vote of 23 to 19 asserting that people should not be subject to discrimination or violence based on their sexual orientation or gender identity (*The Globe and Mail*, 2011). Notable in their opposition to the resolution were Russia, Pakistan, Saudi Arabia, and a number of African countries, while China abstained from voting.

Some countries still harshly punish people convicted of engaging in homosexual acts. In 2008, five men in Egypt were sentenced to three years in prison for "debauchery," the term used in Egypt for homosexual acts (Associated Press, 2008).

Cross-Cultural Perspectives

Male–male sexual behaviour has been practised in many preliterate societies. In their review of the literature, Ford and Beach (1951) found that male–male sexual interactions were viewed as normal and deemed socially acceptable for some members in 49 (64%) of 76 preliterate societies. Although the other 27 societies (36%) had sanctions against male–male sexual behaviour, male–male sexual activity persisted there.

Sexual activity between males is sometimes limited to rites that mark boys' initiation into manhood. In some preliterate societies, semen is believed to boost strength and virility. Older males thus transmit semen to younger males through oral or anal sexual activities. Among the Sambia of New Guinea, a society of war-like headhunters, 9- to 12-year-old males leave their parents' households and live

A World of Diversity

ETHNICITY AND SEXUAL ORIENTATION

Because of social prejudice, it's difficult for many young people to come to terms with their emerging lesbian and gay orientations.

You might assume that members of ethnic minorities, having also been subjected to prejudice and discrimination, would be more tolerant of lesbian and gay sexual orientations than mainstream Canadians. Such an assumption, however, might not be warranted. Lesbian and gay orientations are rejected by many ethnic minority groups in Canada.

About 80% of First Nations people in Ontario believe homosexuality is wrong (Myers et al., 1993).

The Canadian Ethnocultural Communities Facing AIDS study sponsored by Health Canada in 1996 found that both the Chinese and the South Asian communities strongly disapprove of same-sex relationships, which they view as abnormal. Because they fear bringing shame to their families, lesbians and gay males in these communities feel pressured to keep their sexual orientations secret, or to move to communities where they can live openly without sanction.

In a study of gay male Vietnamese immigrants in Toronto, Cynthia Vo (2001), a graduate student at the University of Guelph, found that only a small minority chose to come out to their parents. Many felt their parents would no longer be proud of them. They were worried about bringing shame to their families and causing their parents to lose face in their communities.

If any generalization is possible, it may be that lesbians and gay men find more of a sense of belonging in the gay community than in their ethnic communities.

Yet members of some minority groups may feel that their issues aren't addressed by mainstream gay and lesbian organizations. Some gay Vietnamese men in Toronto, for example, said they felt more discrimination from the white gay community than from Canadian society at large (Vo, 2001). As a result, gay Asians have formed their own groups, including Gay Asians of the Vancouver Area and the Bubble Tea Lounge community in Toronto.

in "clubhouses" with other prepubertal and adolescent males. There they undergo sexual rites of passage. To acquire the fierce manhood of the headhunter, they perform fellatio on older males and drink "men's milk" (semen) (Bailey, 2003b). By age 19, however, young men are expected to take brides and enter exclusively male–female sexual relationships.

These Sambian practices might seem to suggest that male sexual orientation is fluid and malleable. The practices involve behaviour, however, not sexual orientation. Male–male sexual behaviour among Sambians takes place within a cultural context that bears little resemblance to consensual male–male sexual activity in Western society. The prepubertal Sambian male doesn't seek sexual liaisons with other males; he's removed from his home and thrust into male–male sexual encounters by older males (Baldwin & Baldwin, 1989).

Sambian culture has a different perspective on gay identity than we find in Western societies. So does Turkish culture—according to Tarik Bereket of the University of Toronto and Barry D. Adam of the University of Windsor (2006), Turkish men also have same-sex relations without sharing the Western concept of gay identity. For example, Turkish men who assume the inserter role in anal intercourse don't consider themselves gay.

Little is known about female–female sexual activity in non-Western cultures. Evidence of female–female sexual behaviour was found by Ford and Beach in only 17 of the 76 societies they studied. Perhaps female sexual behaviour in general, not just sexual activity with other females, was more likely to be repressed.

Cross-Species Perspectives

Biologists have observed male–male and female–female sexual behaviour in at least 450 animal species, in every part of the world (Hird, 2006).

A male baboon may present his rear and allow himself to be mounted by another male. But is the behaviour sexually motivated? Mounting behaviour among male baboons may represent a type of dominance ritual, in which lower-ranking males adopt a submissive (feminine) posture to ward off attack by dominant males.

Paul Vasey of the University of Lethbridge has done considerable research on sexual preference and orientation in female Japanese macaques. Vasey (2002) has found that the females routinely engage in sexual behaviour with both males and females. Female Japanese macaques often have sex with other females even when willing male partners are available. Vasey and his colleagues (2006) have also found that female macaques mount other females differently than the males do. The female mounting styles are more varied, and done in a way that provides greater genital pleasure. This physical drive for sexual pleasure with other females supports the assumption that this behaviour is sexual, and indicates a bisexual orientation (Vasey et al., 2006).

Biological Perspectives

Biological perspectives focus on the possible roles of evolution, genetics, and hormonal influences in shaping sexual orientation.

THE EVOLUTIONARY PERSPECTIVE It might seem odd that evolutionary theorists have endeavoured to explain gay and lesbian sexual orientations. After all, gays and lesbians aren't motivated to engage in sexual activity with the other sex, so how can their sexual orientations confer any evolutionary advantage?

To answer this question, we must look to the group or the species, rather than the individual. Kirkpatrick (2000) suggests that male–male and female–female sexual behaviours derive from individual selection for reciprocal altruism. That is, strong male–male and female–female alliances have advantages for group survival, in that they bind group members together emotionally. This hypothesis remains speculative.

Researchers have also compared the family trees of homosexuals with those of heterosexuals, and found a significant increase in fecundity among women related to homosexuals in the maternal line, but not among women related to homosexuals in the paternal line (Iemmola & Ciani, 2009). These findings suggest that genetic factors linked to the X sex chromosome that might influence homosexual orientation in males aren't eliminated by natural selection, because they also increase fecundity in female carriers. That is, women related to gay males apparently bear more children, compensating for the lesser likelihood that homosexuals will reproduce.

GENETICS AND SEXUAL ORIENTATION There's considerable evidence that gay and lesbian sexual orientations run in families (Dawood et al., 2009). In one study, 22% of the brothers of 51 predominantly gay men were either gay or bisexual—nearly four times as many as you'd expect in the general population (Pillard & Weinrich, 1986). Although such evidence is consistent with a genetic explanation, families also share common environments.

Twin studies also shed light on the possible role of heredity (Bailey, 2003b; Kendler et al., 2000). **Monozygotic (MZ) twins,** or identical twins, develop from a single fertilized ovum and share 100% of their heredity. **Dizygotic (DZ) twins,** or fraternal twins, develop from two fertilized ova. Like other brothers and sisters, DZ twins share only 50% of their heredity. Thus, if a gay or lesbian sexual orientation were transmitted genetically, it would be found about twice as often among identical twins as among fraternal twins born to gay and lesbian people. Because MZ and DZ twins who are reared together share similar environmental influences, differences in the degree of concordance for a given trait between MZ and DZ twin pairs are further indicative of genetic origins.

CRITICAL THINKING QUESTIONS

To what extent has your own cultural or religious background influenced your attitude toward homosexuality?

Monozygotic (MZ) twins
Siblings who develop from the same fertilized ovum. They're also called identical twins.

Dizygotic (DZ) twins
Siblings who develop from different fertilized ova. They're also called fraternal twins.

Several studies have looked at gay men with twin brothers (Kendler et al., 2000). In one of the most carefully conducted twin studies, about 52% of identical (MZ) twin pairs were found to be concordant (in agreement) for a gay male sexual orientation, compared with 22% of fraternal (DZ) twins and only 11% of adoptive brothers (Bailey, 2003a). Bear in mind that MZ twins are more likely than DZ twins to be dressed alike and treated alike. Their greater concordance for a gay sexual orientation may therefore reflect environmental factors, at least in part (Kendler et al., 2000).

Researchers have found evidence linking a region on the X sex chromosome to a gay male sexual orientation (Bailey et al., 1999). Dean Hamer and his colleagues (1993) found that gay males were more likely than the general population to have gay male relatives on their mothers' sides of their families, yet they didn't have a greater than expected number of gay male relatives on their fathers' sides. This pattern of inheritance is consistent with genetic traits, such as hemophilia, that are linked to the X chromosome, which men receive from their mothers.

The researchers then examined the X chromosomes of 40 pairs of gay brothers who were not twins. In 33 of the pairs, the brothers had identical DNA markers on the ends of their X chromosomes. For pairs of brothers in the general population, about half would be expected to have inherited this chromosomal structure. This chromosomal region may therefore hold a gene that predisposes men to a gay sexual orientation.

HORMONAL INFLUENCES AND SEXUAL ORIENTATION Sex hormones strongly influence the mating behaviours of other species (Crews, 1994). Researchers have therefore looked into the role hormonal factors may play in determining sexual orientation in humans.

Testosterone is essential to male sexual differentiation. Levels of testosterone and its by-products in the blood and urine have therefore been studied as possible influences on sexual orientation. Research has failed to connect sexual orientation in either sex with differences in male or female sex hormone levels in adulthood (Friedman & Downey, 2001, 2008). Testosterone appears to have **activating effects** in adulthood. That is, it affects the intensity of sexual desire, but not the preference for partners of one sex or the other (Aarts & van Honk, 2009; Yeh et al., 2009).

Sari van Anders and Elizabeth Hampson (2005) at the University of Western Ontario have found that women who aren't strictly heterosexual have better spatial abilities than heterosexual women. Anders and Hampson suggest that the relationship between increased spatial ability and heteroflexible sexual orientation may be affected by high androgen levels before birth.

BRAIN STRUCTURE AND SEXUAL ORIENTATION Researchers at the Stockholm Brain Institute (Savic & Lindstrom, 2008) have found structural differences between the brains of heterosexuals and the brains of homosexuals. In a study of 40 heterosexuals and 50 homosexuals, they used MRIs and PET scans to examine the functioning of the amygdala, a part of the brain that's less likely than other parts to be affected by social conditioning. They also considered brain size, because both sides of a woman's brain are usually similar, while the right side of a man's brain is usually larger than the left side.

The researchers found similarities between the brains of gay men and heterosexual women, and similarities between the brains of lesbians and heterosexual men. In the lesbians and heterosexual men, the right hemisphere of the brain was larger than the left. In the gay men and heterosexual women, both sides of the brain were about the same size. The amygdala's functioning was similar for lesbians and heterosexual men, and it was similar for gay men and heterosexual women. These findings suggest that brain organization differs by sexual orientation as well as by gender, which further suggests that biology predisposes a person to be homosexual or heterosexual. Additional research is needed to confirm these findings.

Activating effects Those effects of sex hormones that influence sex drive levels, but not sexual orientation.

Innovative Canadian Research

BIRTH ORDER AND SEXUAL ORIENTATION

Ray Blanchard and his colleagues at the Centre for Addiction and Mental Health in Toronto have conducted several studies analyzing the relationship of birth order to sexual orientation. Blanchard et al. (2002) have built upon their previous findings that the odds of a man's being gay increase in proportion to the number of his older brothers. They concluded that a gay male with three or more older brothers can attribute most of the origin of his sexual orientation to this effect.

They also concluded that femininity in male children tends to be predictive of homosexuality (although not all gay men were feminine as boys). In their 2002 study, they analyzed a sample of feminine boys whom they assumed (on the basis of previous research) were likely to be gay. They confirmed that those with two or more older brothers weighed less at birth than heterosexual males with older brothers, and concluded that prenatal factors increase the odds of homosexuality in later-born males.

In explaining this finding, the researchers hypothesized that the process is immunological—that anti-male antibodies are produced by the mothers in response to immunization by male fetuses—and that this could decrease the birth weights of later male fetuses, as well as increase the odds of their becoming gay. In effect, this process influences aspects of sexual differentiation in the fetal brain.

In 2004, Blanchard analyzed data from 10 143 respondents, and again found that homosexuality in males was predicted by a higher number of older brothers, but not by numbers of older or younger sisters or younger brothers. This relationship between older brothers and sexual orientation has not been found among females.

Anthony Bogaert (2005b) at Brock University has reported that fraternal birth order is more influential than sibling sex ratio in affecting men's sexual orientation. Blanchard and Bogaert (2004) estimate that about one in four gay men can attribute his sexual orientation to this fraternal birth order effect. In a more recent study, Bogaert (2006b) has found that the effect of having older brothers only applies to genetically related brothers, and not to those with stepbrothers or adopted brothers. These findings strongly support a prenatal biological basis for sexual orientation.

Further evidence for prenatal influences is seen in a literature review by Lalumière et al. (2000) regarding handedness and sexual orientation. The reviewers concluded that "non-right-handedness" is related to homosexual orientation. More recently, Blanchard and Lippa (2007) have extended this line of research by analyzing the relationships among fraternal birth order, hand preference, and sexual orientation in a large British internet sample. They've found that having older brothers increases the odds of being homosexual for right-handed males, but not for non-right-handed males. These findings have been replicated in another study (Blanchard et al., 2006), which also found that, among men with no older brothers, homosexuals are more likely than heterosexuals to be non-right-handed, and among men with one or more older brothers, homosexuals are less likely than heterosexuals to be non-right-handed.

Simon LeVay (1991), a neurobiologist at the Salk Institute in La Jolla, California, carried out autopsies on the brains of 35 AIDS victims—19 gay men and 16 (presumably) heterosexual men. He found that a segment of the hypothalamus (specifically, the third interstitial nucleus of the anterior hypothalamus) in the gay men was less than half the size of the same segment in the heterosexual men. This brain segment was larger in the heterosexual men than in a comparison group of 6 presumably heterosexual women. LeVay found no significant size differences between the gay men and the women.

LeVay's findings are intriguing, but preliminary. We don't know, for example, whether the structural differences are innate or the result of something in the study subjects' environments.

BIOLOGY AND SEXUAL ORIENTATION Researchers in the United States and Canada (Mustanski, Chivers, & Bailey, 2003) have conducted a comprehensive review of the research relating to the role of biology in determining sexual orientation. They've concluded that, to some degree, sexual orientation is influenced by biological factors. These factors seem to play a stronger role for men than for women.

CRITICAL THINKING QUESTIONS

There's considerable evidence that sexual orientation is at least partly determined by biological factors. In your view, is it relevant to consider such evidence when discussing gay and lesbian rights?

Biological factors likely play a key role prior to birth, as indicated by the handedness research and the older brothers research we've discussed. Genetic factors may be another important influence. Brain differences between gay and heterosexual men, and between lesbian and heterosexual women, suggest that biological influences are at play.

Psychological Perspectives

Psychoanalytic theory and learning theory are two major social-psychological approaches to understanding the origins of sexual orientation.

PSYCHOANALYTIC VIEWS Sigmund Freud, the originator of psychoanalytic theory, believed children enter the world open to all forms of sexual stimulation. Through proper resolution of the Oedipus complex, a boy will forsake his incestuous desires for his mother and come to identify with his father. As a result, he'll eventually transfer his erotic attraction from his mother to more appropriate female partners. A girl, through proper resolution of her Electra complex, will identify with her mother and seek erotic stimulation from men when she becomes sexually mature.

In Freud's view, a gay or lesbian sexual orientation results from failure to successfully resolve the Oedipus complex by identifying with the parent of the same sex. In a man, faulty resolution of the Oedipus complex is most likely to result from the so-called classic pattern of an emotionally "close-binding" mother and a "detached-hostile" father. A boy reared in such a family may come to identify with his mother, and even to "transform himself into her" (Freud, 1922/1959, p. 40). He may thus become effeminate and develop a sexual interest in men.

Freud believed the mechanism of unresolved **castration anxiety** plays a role in a gay male orientation. During the throes of the Oedipus complex, the boy unconsciously comes to fear that his father, his rival for his mother's love, will retaliate by removing the organ the boy has come to associate with sexual pleasure. His fear causes him to repress his sexual desire for his mother and to identify with the potential aggressor—his father. The boy thus overcomes his castration anxiety and is headed along the path of adult heterosexuality. If he doesn't successfully resolve his Oedipus complex, his castration anxiety may persist. When he's sexually mature, he won't be able to tolerate sex with women—their lack of penises will arouse unconscious castration anxiety within him.

The supposed Electra complex in little girls follows a somewhat different course. Freud believed little girls become envious of boys' penises because they lack their own. This concept of **penis envy** was one of Freud's most controversial beliefs. In Freud's view, jealousy leads the little girl to resent her mother, whom she blame for her anatomic "deficiency," and to turn from her mother to her father as a sexual object. She now desires to possess her father, because his penis provides what she lacks. But incestuous desires bring the girl into competition with her mother. Motivated by fear that her mother will withdraw her love if these desires persist, the girl normally represses them and comes to identify with her mother. She develops traditional feminine interests and eventually seeks erotic stimulation from men. She supplants her childhood desire for a penis with a desire to marry a man and bear children. The baby, emitted from between her legs, serves as the ultimate penis substitute.

A nagging problem in assessing the validity of Freudian theory is that many of its concepts, such as castration anxiety and penis envy, are believed to operate at an unconscious level. As such, they lie beyond the scope of scientific observation and measurement.

LEARNING THEORY Learning theorists agree with Freud that early experiences play important roles in the development of sexual orientation. They focus, however, on the role of reinforcement of early patterns of sexual behaviour, rather than on

Castration anxiety In psychoanalytic theory, a man's fear that his genitals will be removed. An element of the Oedipus complex, castration anxiety is implicated in the directionality of erotic interest.

Penis envy In psychoanalytic theory, a girl's wish to have a penis.

the resolution of unconscious conflicts. We generally repeat pleasurable activities and discontinue painful ones. By connecting sexual pleasure with childhood sexual experimentation with same-sex friends, we may learn to engage in sexual activity with members of our own sex.

Although learning may play a role in the development of a gay or lesbian orientation, learning theorists have not identified specific learning experiences that would lead to these orientations. Moreover, most adolescent encounters with members of the same sex, even if they're pleasurable, don't lead to adult gay or lesbian sexual orientations. Many heterosexual people have had adolescent encounters with members of their own sex, without affecting their adult orientations. This is true even of people whose early sexual interactions with the other sex were fumbling and frustrating. The overwhelming majority of gay males and lesbians were aware of sexual interest in people of their own sex before they had sexual encounters with them, pleasurable or otherwise (Savin-Williams & Diamond, 2000).

GENDER NONCONFORMITY Gender nonconformity means not behaving in a way that's consistent with the gender-role stereotype associated with one's anatomic sex in a given culture. On average, gay males tend to be somewhat feminine, and lesbians to be somewhat masculine, but there's a good deal of variation within each group (Dawood et al., 2009; Rieger et al., 2008). It seems that stereotypes of the effeminate gay male and the masculine lesbian are exaggerated.

Gender nonconformity begins in childhood. Gay men and lesbians are more likely than heterosexuals to report childhood behaviours stereotypical of the other sex (Green, 2008; Lippa, 2008). Many gays and lesbians recall acting and feeling different from their childhood peers. Gay males are more likely to recall feeling more sensitive than their peers during childhood (Green, 2008; Lippa, 2008). They had more artistic interests, and were more likely than their heterosexual counterparts to prefer "girls' toys" (Dawood et al., 2000).

According to researchers at the University of British Columbia, this childhood gender nonconformity found in many gay males often leads to social rejection by parents and peers (Landolt et al., 2004). This rejection is a major factor in the difficulty many gay males have in accepting their sexual orientation.

There's also evidence of masculine-typed behaviour among lesbians in childhood (Lippa, 2008). Lesbians are more likely than heterosexual women to say they were tomboys. They were more likely to prefer rough-and-tumble games to playing with dolls, and enjoyed wearing boys' clothing, rather than dresses.

An important study by Devendra Singh and his colleagues (1999) relates gender nonconformity in lesbians to the butch–femme dimension and biological factors. The investigators compared self-identified **butch** (traditionally masculine) and **femme** (traditionally feminine) lesbians on various personality, behavioural, and biological measures. They found that butch lesbians were significantly more likely than femme lesbians to recall gender-atypical behavioural preferences in childhood. Butch lesbians also had higher waist-to-hip ratios and higher testosterone levels in their saliva, both of which are more typical of males. The Singh group suggests that their findings support the validity of the butch–femme distinction, and that the distinction may be caused by differences in exposure to prenatal androgens.

Butch A lesbian who assumes a traditional masculine gender role.

Femme A lesbian who assumes a traditional feminine gender role.

How might extreme childhood effeminacy lead to a gay male sexual orientation? Those who support an environmental perspective speculate that the social detachment of these boys from male peers and role models (especially fathers) creates strong, unfulfilled cravings for male affection. This craving then leads them to seek males as partners in sex and love relationships in adolescence and adulthood (Green, 2008).

Of course, there's another possibility (Green, 2008; Dawood et al., 2009): gender nonconformity appears to be somewhat heritable. If a tendency toward homosexuality is inherited, gender nonconformity could also be an expression of that tendency.

Current Attitudes

Historically, negative attitudes toward gay people have pervaded our society. Today, however, there's far greater acceptance of equal rights for gay people in Canadian society. According to University of Manitoba professor Bob Altemeyer (2001), a major factor in this acceptance has been increased contact with individuals known to be gay, brought about by the fact that gays and lesbians have been increasingly open about revealing their sexual orientations. According to a survey of civic leaders in Hamilton conducted by McMaster University's Rhoda Howard-Hassmann (2001), learning that a relative, neighbour, co-worker, or client is gay not only makes people more accepting of gays, but humanizes gays in their minds. A more recent survey of Canadians found that people with gay or lesbian friends or relatives are more likely to approve of same-sex marriage (Angus Reid, 2010).

Approximately three-quarters of teenagers and adults feel that homosexuals should be entitled to the same rights as other Canadians. Older adults, however, are less accepting of equal rights than younger Canadians (Bibby, 2001). Slightly more than half of all Canadians (54% of teenagers and 60% of adults) approve of homosexual relationships. More than half of Canadian adults report that they've become more approving of homosexuality than they were in their teens, and fewer than 10% have become less approving. Women tend to be somewhat more approving than men (Bibby, 2001).

Despite opposition by a vociferous minority, most Canadians accept same-sex marriage. In a 2010 public opinion survey conducted by Angus Reid, 61% of Canadian adults approved of same-sex couples' continuing to have the right to marry, and another 23% approved of same-sex couples' forming civil unions. Younger Canadians are more likely to approve of same-sex marriage than older Canadians. In the Angus Reid (2010) survey, 81% of people born between 1980 and 1995 said same-sex couples should continue to be allowed to marry, compared to only 43% of people born before 1946 and 53% of people born between 1946 and 1964.

Homophobia A cluster of negative attitudes and feelings toward gay, lesbian, and bisexual people, including intolerance, hatred, and fear.

Gay bashing Violence against homosexuals.

HOMOPHOBIA   **Homophobia** takes many forms, including the following:

- Using derogatory names (e.g., queer, faggot, dyke).
- Telling disparaging "queer jokes."
- Barring gay people from housing, employment, and social opportunities.
- Taunting (e.g., verbal abuse).
- **Gay bashing** (e.g., physical abuse, which is sometimes lethal).

Innovative Canadian Research

MEASURES OF HOMONEGATIVITY

Waterloo, Ontario, researchers (Rye et al., 2008) analyzed three measures of homonegativity to determine which instrument best measured negative attitudes toward homosexuals:

- Herek's attitudes toward lesbians and gay men scale (ATLGS).
- Morrison and Morrison's modern homonegativity scale (MHS).
- Hudson and Ricketts's index of homophobia (IH).

All three scales were found to be good measures of homonegativity.

For a sample of university students, each scale determined that attitudes toward homosexuals were more positive than negative. The ATLGS and the MHS did the best job of assessing both cognitive and emotional reactions, whereas the IH focused mainly on emotional reactions.

The MHS had a slight edge over the two other scales, with stronger psychometrics.

High school students in Ottawa protest the bullying of Jamie Hubley, who committed suicide after being relentlessly bullied because he was gay.

Homophobia derives from root words that mean "fear of homosexuals." Although some psychologists link homophobia to fear of a gay or lesbian orientation within oneself, homophobic attitudes may also be embedded within a cluster of stereotypical gender-role attitudes (Lewis & White, 2009; Rosky, 2009). People who have strong stakes in maintaining stereotypical gender roles may feel more threatened by homosexuals, since gay people appear to confuse and reverse these roles. Men have more at stake in maintaining the tradition of male dominance, so perhaps it's not surprising that college men are more intolerant of gay males than college women are (Lewis & White, 2009; Rosky, 2009).

Homophobic attitudes are more common among males who identify with traditional male gender roles and conservative political orientations (Cotten-Huston & Waite, 2000), and among people who hold fundamentalist religious views (Davies, 2004). But those who actually engage in violence against gay people, especially those who kill, tend to be criminal psychopaths (Parrot et al., 2006). That is, they're in frequent conflict with the law, and they don't feel guilt or shame when they inflict pain.

Some homophobic men may have homoerotic impulses they're unaware of. Denial of these impulses may be connected with their fear and disapproval of gay men. Henry Adams and his colleagues (1996) showed men sexually explicit videotapes of male–female, female–female, and male–male sexual activity, and measured their sexual responses by means of a penile plethysmograph (which measures the size of an erection.) Subjects were also asked to report how sexually aroused they felt in response to the videos. The men were also evaluated for their attitudes toward gay males.

Heterosexual men who were not homophobic were sexually aroused (according to penile circumference) only by videos of male–female and female–female sexual activity. The homophobic viewers were also physiologically aroused (again according to penile circumference) by the video of male–male sexual activity, but reported that they didn't feel aroused by it. Were they out of touch with their biological responses, or were their biological responses misleading?

HARASSMENT OF LGBTQ YOUTH IN CANADA Although Canadian society has made significant strides toward sexual-orientation equality, in many respects Canada remains a hostile and damaging environment for LGBTQ youth.

In a national survey of Canadian youth conducted by the marketing organization Ping, 28% of those between the ages of 15 and 19 reported witnessing acts of violence or verbal abuse directed toward LGBTQ youth (Wells, 2008).

EGALE Canada's national survey of more than 3700 students on homophobia, biphobia, and trans-phobia in Canadian schools revealed that 64% of LGBTQ students felt unsafe at school, and 21% reported that they'd been physically harassed or assaulted due to their sexual orientations (Taylor et al., 2011). LGBTQ students attending schools with anti-homophobia policies were less likely than students attending schools without anti-homophobia policies (20% versus 33%) to report that they'd been physically harassed at school.

Canadian and American studies have also found that LGBTQ youth are more likely than heterosexual youth to have been physically and sexually abused, both by family members and by people from outside their families (Saewyc et al., 2006b).

CRITICAL THINKING QUESTIONS

Generally, would you describe your high school as homophobic, positive toward gays and lesbians, or something in between?

HETEROSEXISM Heterosexism, also known as heterosexual bias, is the tendency of society to view the world in heterosexual terms—that is, to assume that heterosexual relationships are "normal." This perspective devalues other kinds of relationships, such as same-sex relationships, and tends to make them invisible.

Lesbians and gay males are often just as concerned about heterosexism as they are about homophobia, because it's so pervasive in society.

SEXUAL ORIENTATION AND CANADIAN LAW The fight for legal equality for gays and lesbians has progressed considerably. The first major breakthrough came in 1969, when Parliament passed an amendment to Canada's Criminal Code that decriminalized same-sex behaviour between consenting adults. Since then, other major pieces of legislation have benefited gay men and lesbians:

- In 1996, Parliament added the words "sexual orientation" as a prohibited ground of discrimination in the Canadian Human Rights Act.
- In 1996, Parliament amended the Criminal Code to increase sentences when criminal offenses are motivated by bias, prejudice, or hate based on sexual orientation (and other characteristics such as race and religion).
- In 2003, the House of Commons extended hate-propaganda protection to gay males and lesbians.
- In 2005, the House of Commons and the Senate passed legislation to extend civil marriage rights to same-sex couples. In 2006, Stephen Harper's Conservatives reopened the issue of same-sex marriage, but the majority of the members in the House of Commons voted against changing the 2005 law.

The national lobby group Equality for Gays and Lesbians Everywhere (EGALE) is at the forefront in fighting for equality through the legal system. Other significant advances for gay rights have come from court rulings under the Canadian Charter of Rights and Freedoms and the Canadian Human Rights Act:

- In 1992, the Supreme Court of Canada ruled that the Canadian Forces cannot discriminate against gays and lesbians, and must allow them the right to join the military.
- In 1998, the Supreme Court of Canada ordered the Alberta government to include protection for gays and lesbians under Alberta human rights legislation.

- In 1999, the Supreme Court of Canada ruled that the province of Ontario's definition of spouse violated the Charter of Rights and Freedoms because it applied only to heterosexuals and not to gay males and lesbians.
- In 2002, when the Durham Catholic District School Board in Oshawa refused to allow Marc Hall to take his same-sex partner to his high school prom, Hall went to court to appeal the board's decision. The Ontario Supreme Court judge ruled that Hall and his date could go to the prom because the school board had violated his constitutional right to equality. (We'll discuss this case in Chapter 12.)
- In 2002, the Ontario Superior Court ruled that because the legal definition of marriage is discriminatory, it should be changed to include same-sex couples. (We'll discuss this in Chapter 12.)
- In 2004, the Supreme Court of Canada ruled that Parliament has the authority to redefine marriage to include same-sex couples.
- Many provinces have allowed only a mother and a father to be registered on a birth certificate. In 2007, an Ontario court ruled that two women can be registered, and in another case, the Ontario Court of Appeal held that two women and a man can be registered.
- In 2010, the Saskatchewan Court of Appeal ruled that a proposed provincial law allowing marriage commissioners to refuse on religious grounds to marry same-sex couples would be unconstitutional.

GAY ACTIVISM During the past generation, gay people have organized effective political action to fight discrimination. In a comprehensive analysis of the history of same-sex relationships and the gay rights movement in Canada, Gary Kinsman (1996) of Laurentian University argues that, by challenging heterosexuality as the societal norm and affirming their right to sexual self-determination, gays and lesbians are also helping other groups achieve greater sexual freedom.

The AIDS epidemic has had a profound effect on the political agendas of gay rights organizations. Most Canadian cities have AIDS organizations, the largest being the AIDS Committee of Toronto. These organizations combat the AIDS epidemic on several fronts:

- They lobby for increased funding for AIDS research and treatment.
- They educate the gay and wider communities about the dangers of high-risk sexual behaviour.
- They encourage gay men and others to adopt safer sex practices, including the use of condoms.
- They protect the civil rights of people with HIV and AIDS with respect to employment, housing, and medical and dental treatment.
- They provide counselling and support services for people with HIV and AIDS.

STEREOTYPES AND SEXUAL BEHAVIOUR Among heterosexual people, sexual aggressiveness is linked to the stereotypically masculine gender role, and sexual passivity to the feminine role. Some heterosexual people assume that in a gay or lesbian relationship, one partner consistently assumes the masculine role and the other partner assumes the feminine role in sexual relations.

This assumption is often mistaken. Many gay couples vary the active and passive roles. Gay male couples, for example, often alternate their roles in anal intercourse (i.e., insertive versus receptive) and fellatio. And contrary to popular assumptions, sexual behaviour between lesbians seldom reflects distinct butch–femme gender roles. Most lesbians report both providing and receiving oral–genital stimulation. Typically, partners alternate roles or simultaneously perform and receive oral stimulation.

Many gay people claim that the labels "masculine" and "feminine" represent nothing more than the straight community's efforts to pigeonhole them in terms straights can understand.

CRITICAL THINKING QUESTIONS

What myths and stereotypes about sexual orientation have you encountered within your family, at school, or among your friends?

The Coming-Out Process

Because of the backdrop of social condemnation and discrimination, gays and lesbians in our culture often struggle to come to terms with their sexual orientations (Hammack & Cohler, 2009). Homosexuals usually speak of the process of accepting and then disclosing their sexual orientations to others as "coming out" or "coming out of the closet." This is a two-pronged process: coming out to themselves (recognizing and accepting their sexual orientations) and then coming out to others (declaring their orientations to the world).

Coming out can create a sense of pride in their sexual orientations and foster their ability to form emotionally and sexually satisfying relationships with same-sex partners (Grov et al., 2006).

Self-Acceptance and Coming Out

Given the stigma historically associated with homosexuality, it's not surprising that some gay, lesbian, and bisexual people have a difficult time recognizing—let alone accepting—their sexual orientations.

Youths with emerging gay, lesbian, and bisexual identities who live in generally hostile climates face particular dilemmas. They're well aware that in many high schools, the words "fag" and "dyke" are terms of denigration, and that anyone who's openly gay, lesbian, or bisexual is open to social exclusion and psychological and physical persecution. Some of their families also express negative feelings about people who are gay, lesbian, or bisexual. Young people in such families may be victimized if they disclose the fact that they're not heterosexual (Bagley & D'Augelli, 2000).

Self-acceptance of being gay, lesbian, or bisexual becomes part of a person's self-definition. The terms "gay identity" and "homosexual identity" refer to the subjective sense of being gay. According to Ritch Savin-Williams and Lisa Diamond (2000), the development of sexual identity in gay males and lesbians involves four steps or features:

- Attraction to members of the same sex.
- Self-labelling as gay or lesbian.
- Sexual contact with members of the same sex.
- Disclosure of their sexual orientation to other people.

The researchers have found, by and large, a 10-year gap between initial attraction to members of one's own sex, which tends to occur at about the age of 8 or 9, and disclosure of one's orientation to other people, which usually occurs around age 18. In keeping with the sex differences we discussed in Chapter 5, females are more likely to focus on the emotional or romantic aspects of their budding feelings, and males are more likely to focus on the sexual aspects. Males—who are generally more open than females to sexual experimentation—are likely to become involved in sexual activity with other males before they label themselves as gay. Females, on the other hand, are more likely to label themselves as lesbians before pursuing relationships with other females. Males also tend to form sexual identities and come out about two years earlier than females (Grov et al., 2006).

Younger cohorts (people who are 18 to 24 years old) tend to come out earlier than older cohorts (Grov et al., 2006). Factors such as the growing acceptance of homosexuality and more common portrayals of gays and lesbians in the media have contributed to more younger people feeling comfortable enough to come out.

For some people, coming to recognize and accept their gay or lesbian orientations involves gradually stripping away layers of denial. Others may experience sudden awakenings. Alberta professors Kevin Alderson and Ronna Jevne (2003) have explored the psychic conflict in the coming-out process for gay men. They conceptualize the conflict as a struggle between catalysts that push

CRITICAL THINKING QUESTIONS

How do you account for differences between males and females in the coming-out process?

Applied Knowledge

COUNSELLING GAYS AND LESBIANS

Karine Blais and her colleagues (2004) at the Université de Montréal have outlined some key issues pertaining to sexual orientation that therapists need to be knowledgeable about.

They include homophobia, HIV, the lack of conjugal role models, and the coming-out process.

It's also important for therapists to recognize that gay and lesbian couples face many of the same issues as heterosexual couples.

Toronto's Centre for Addiction and Mental Health has prepared a handbook to guide therapists who counsel gay and lesbian clients. It's called *Asking the Right Questions 2: Talking with Clients About Sexual Orientation and Gender Identity in Mental Health, Counselling and Addiction Settings.*

acknowledgment of sexual orientation and hindrances that block acceptance of that identity. Alderson and Jevne believe the major catalyst is increased awareness of being gay and of gay culture, and the major hindrance is fear and condemnation of homosexuals. They reason that a person will self-identify as gay only when the catalysts overpower the hindrances.

Alderson (2003) criticizes fixed-stage models of gay identity development, such as those proposed by Savin-Williams and Diamond (2000), which assume that everyone who comes out goes through a series of well-defined stages. Alderson believes identity development is an individualized process, affected by environmental influences. In other words, not everyone goes through the same stages in the same order.

Alderson (2003) has developed an ecological model of gay male identity that incorporates the external (social and environmental) and the internal (psychological) influences that lead to a gay self-definition. In his model, cognitive dissonance about being gay plays a key role in the movement toward identity development. Alderson believes his ecological model provides clinicians with a useful framework for counselling gay males, and in particular for helping those who are questioning their sexual identities.

In a survey of 14 Canadian universities, Alderson (2003) found that graduate students in clinical psychology and counselling receive little training on issues facing lesbians, gays, and bisexuals. Graduates of these programs feel unprepared to work with sexual-minority clients.

Coming Out to Others

There are different patterns of coming out to others. Coming out occasionally means making an open declaration to the world. Some individuals inform only one or a few select people. Others may tell friends, but not family members.

In Ontario, Brock University researchers Anthony Bogaert and Luanne Jamieson (2008) have analyzed several factors to determine which ones might predict the age of coming out among gay and bisexual men. They've found that men who are attractive and men who believe in a just world are more likely to come out at a younger age. Those with more feminine behavioural traits in childhood tend to delay coming out.

Many gays and lesbians remain reluctant to declare their sexual orientations, even to friends and family. Disclosure is fraught with the risk of losing jobs, friendships, and social standing (Bagley & D'Augelli, 2000; Rosario et al., 2009). On the other hand, if a person's place of work is generally supportive, coming out can be related to greater job satisfaction and less anxiety (Griffith & Hebl, 2002).

Coming Out to Parents.
Coming out to their parents can be scary, and many lesbians and gays avoid it for years—even lifetimes.

Gays and lesbians often anticipate negative reactions from family members, including denial, anger, and rejection (Bagley & D'Augelli, 2000). Barrett (1990) has found that parents, children, neighbours, and friends of lesbians may deny, compartmentalize, or struggle with their knowledge the same way the women do themselves.

> My parents know I've lived with my partner for six years. She goes home with me. We sleep in the same bed there. The word "lesbian" has never been mentioned. I told my mother, and she said, "Well, now that's over with. We don't need to mention it again." She never has, and that was 10 years ago. I don't know if she ever told my father. (Barrett, 1990, p. 52)

Some families are more accepting. They may have wondered whether their children were gay or lesbian, and prepared themselves for such news. Many families are initially rejecting, but eventually come to at least grudging acceptance that family members are gay or lesbian.

Dave Vervoort (1999), a University of Guelph graduate student, conducted an online survey of gay fathers, almost all of whom lived in Canada or the United States. Most had full or joint custody of their children. In coming out to their children, the fathers reported that their children's responses were generally more positive than they'd anticipated. Only about 10% of the children were clearly upset about the disclosure. Older children were more negative. Over time, however, many of these children became more positive about accepting their fathers' gay status.

Another University of Guelph graduate student, Daniel Mahoney (1994), interviewed parents who belonged to the support group Parents, Families, and Friends of Lesbians and Gays (PFLAG), to find out how they'd reacted on discovering that their children were gay or lesbian. All of the parents reported that their initial reactions were highly emotional, involving shock, denial, guilt, and shame. Each felt he or she had to deal with a new identity as the parent of a lesbian or gay child. They all felt it was essential to accept their children's sexual orientations, however, or risk losing their children. Acceptance was a way of expressing their unconditional love. Of course, some parents aren't as accepting as those in Mahoney's study.

As Canadian society becomes more accepting of diverse sexual orientations, and as positive gay and lesbian role models such as politicians, Olympic athletes, and media celebrities become more visible, it's likely that more and more parents will be better able to adjust to the reality that their children are gay or lesbian.

Gay and Lesbian Adjustment

King and his colleagues (2008) identified 13 706 research articles about the mental health of gay men, lesbians, and bisexuals. They selected 476 of these for analysis, ultimately comparing the mental health of 214 344 heterosexuals and 11 971 non-heterosexuals. A sophisticated statistical averaging technique revealed that lesbian, gay, and bisexual people were more than twice as likely as heterosexuals to attempt suicide. They were also one and a half times as likely to be diagnosed with depression, anxiety, and dependence on alcohol and other substances.

To many health professionals, it's clear that societal oppression contributes to the greater incidence of such mental disorders among gays, lesbians, and bisexuals. "Surely," writes psychologist J. Michael Bailey (1999), "it must be difficult for young people to come to grips with their homosexuality in a world where homosexual people are often scorned, mocked, mourned, and feared" (p. 884).

In a large-scale British Columbia study of students in grades 7 to 12, gays, lesbians, and bisexuals had much higher rates of psychological and social difficulties than heterosexual females and males did (McCreary Centre Society, 2007). For example, compared to heterosexual youth, LGB youth:

- Were more likely to have experienced physical and sexual abuse, harassment in school, and discrimination in the community.
- Were more likely to have run away from home at least once during the previous year.
- Were more likely to be sexually experienced.
- Were more likely to have been pregnant or gotten someone pregnant.
- Were more likely to have reported emotional stress, suicidal thoughts, and suicide attempts.
- Were less likely to participate in sports and physical activities.
- Were more likely to spend time on the computer.
- Felt less cared about by parents and less connected to their families.
- Felt less connected to school (lesbian and bisexual females).

The study also found that LGB youth who felt highly connected to their families and schools were far less likely to attempt suicide than bisexual teens who felt less connected. This was true even for LGB youth who were strongly at risk for suicide because of histories of sexual abuse and symptoms of emotional distress, for example.

Lesbian, gay, and bisexual youth are less likely than heterosexual youth to have supportive family and school environments (Saewyc, 2006a). For some, adjustment is related to conflict over their sexual orientations (Simonsen et al., 2000). Yet most gay males and lesbians are well adjusted. Those who accept their sexual orientations and, in particular, those who are openly gay or lesbian are more likely to be well adjusted.

An international study of lesbian, gay, and bisexual youth in Canada, New Zealand, and the United States found that those who had experienced stigma because of sexual orientation were more likely to engage in HIV-risky sexual behaviours (Meininger et al., 2007). These findings suggest that helping sexual-minority youth deal with stigmatization could help reduce their sexual risk-taking.

The British Columbia study found that gay, lesbian, and bisexual youth were also more likely than heterosexuals to engage in HIV-risky behaviour (Saewyc et al., 2006b). In each sexual-orientation group, those who had experienced sexual abuse had higher risk scores. The findings indicate that because sexual-minority youth experience greater sexual abuse than heterosexual youth, they're more likely to engage in risky sexual behaviours.

In their classic research, Bell and Weinberg (1978) found variations in adjustment in the gay community that seem to mirror the variations in the heterosexual community. Gay people who lived with partners in stable, intimate relationships—so-called close couples—were about as well adjusted as married heterosexual

Applied Knowledge

INCREASING RESILIENCE AMONG LGBTQ YOUTH

In reviewing studies of the social adjustment of LGBTQ youth, Kristopher Wells (2008) concluded that the following protective factors are crucial in providing a social environment that results in greater resiliency and fewer adjustment problems:

- Positive representations of LGBTQ people in classrooms and the media.
- Family acceptance and support.
- School support programs, including gay-straight alliances.

- School policies that explicitly prohibit discrimination on the grounds of sexual orientation.
- Support networks that include other LGBTQ youth.
- Inclusive, nonjudgmental sexual health education that challenges negative stereotypes about specific sexual identities.

couples. Older gay people who lived alone and had few sexual contacts were less well adjusted. So are many heterosexual people with solitary lifestyles. All in all, Bell and Weinberg found that differences in adjustment were more likely to reflect individuals' lifestyles than their sexual orientations.

Most gays and lesbians who share close relationships with their partners are satisfied with the overall quality of their relationships. Researchers find that heterosexual and gay couples report similar levels of relationship satisfaction (Henderson et al., 2009; Kurdek, 2005). Gay men and lesbians in enduring relationships generally report high levels of love, attachment, closeness, caring, and intimacy.

Like those of heterosexuals, not all gay people's relationships are satisfying. Among both groups, satisfaction is higher when both partners feel that the benefits outweigh the costs of the relationship (Henderson et al., 2009). Like heterosexual people, gay men and lesbians are happier in relationships where they share power and make joint decisions.

Gay and Lesbian Relationship Differences

Researchers have consistently found that gay males are more likely than lesbians to engage in casual sex with multiple partners. Lesbians more often confine their sexual activity to committed, affectionate relationships. These differences parallel those found for heterosexuals. As we discussed in Chapter 5, heterosexual men are more likely than heterosexual women to engage in casual sex and have sex with more partners.

University of Guelph graduate student Melanie Beres conducted an internet study of men who have sex with men (MSM) and women who have sex with women (WSW). She located the study participants, most of whom lived in Canada and the United States, mainly through university websites. Beres and her colleagues (2004) found that the number of partners was much higher for the men—32% of the MSM had had 22 or more partners, compared with only 2% of the WSW. And 80% of the WSW reported having had six or fewer partners, compared with just 31% of the MSM. The Ontario survey of gay and bisexual men (Myers et al., 2004) found that only 24% had had sex with just one partner during the previous year, while 10% had had sex with 30 or more partners.

In the Ontario survey, respondents were asked where they'd looked for sex with men during the previous year (Myers et al., 2004). By far the most common place was gay bars (60%), and the next most common places were the internet (35%) and bathhouses (31%). An earlier Canadian survey had found that 57% of gay men attended gay bars at least once a week, while only 7% went to bathhouses at least once a week (Myers et al., 1993). In a 2004 Ontario study of bathhouse culture (Haubrich et al., 2004), gay

Innovative Canadian Research

INNOVATION IN GAY MALE RELATIONSHIPS

Barry Adam (2006) of the University of Windsor interviewed 70 gay men in couple relationships in Toronto about how they managed sexual inclusivity.

He found that monogamy was most common among younger men and among men involved in new relationships. Monogamy was more accepted among men from cultural settings where they weren't exposed to—or had limited exposure to—autonomous gay scenes such as gay bars.

Most of the couples, however, were involved in sexually open relationships that allowed sexual experiences with other men. They wanted both the emotional security of committed love relationships and the experience of sexual pleasure with other men.

To achieve this, they agreed that their couple relationships were their primary or most important ones, and they negotiated rules for having sex with others. They typically practiced sexual exclusivity during the first two years of their relationships. This allowed mutual trust to develop. Some couples were monogamous for longer periods, but for most, monogamy was a passing phase.

Adam notes that his sample consisted of men who were in successful relationships, but that many other gay men who engage in casual sex wish they could develop deeply emotional relationships with someone.

men were asked their reasons for going to bathhouses. Most stated that the predominant reason was for sexual release in an environment they considered personally safe. They didn't expect to develop relationships with people they met there.

Bathhouses typically provide free condoms and advertisements providing information about—and encouraging—safer sex practices. Members of AIDS organizations regularly visit bathhouses to provide counselling about safer sex. Accordingly, Dave Holmes, Patrick O'Byrne, and Denise Gastaldo (2007) argue that bathhouses are safer venues for casual sex than other locations such as parks and washrooms.

Bathhouses for casual sex have traditionally not been a part of lesbian culture. For some lesbians, however, this appears to be changing. A few times a year, a group of lesbian and bisexual women in Toronto rent a gay men's bathhouse to engage in casual sex with other women. (We discussed this in Chapter 5.)

The Beres (2002) study found that three-quarters of both MSM and WSW in Canada and the United States had met their partners through friends. The MSM (65%) were more likely than the WSW (29%) to use the internet to find partners.

Gay and Lesbian Lifestyles

One of the mistakes lay people (and some researchers) make is treating gay people as though they're all the same. Variations in sexual expression exist within and across sexual orientations. Descriptions of gay and heterosexual lifestyles must consider individual differences.

University of Lethbridge researchers Doug VanderLaan and Paul Vasey (2008) compared homosexual and heterosexual couples with respect to the strategies they used to "retain their mates." They found that, in a number of aspects, gay and heterosexual males were typical of their sex, whereas homosexual females were less so. For example, homosexual women and both homosexual and heterosexual men were less concerned than heterosexual women about their partners' economic status. Heterosexual women were more concerned than the other groups about their physical appearance. Heterosexual women were also more likely to be concerned about their partners' spending time away, and more likely to threaten to end their relationships if their partners were to have sex with others. Heterosexual men were more likely than gays and lesbians to threaten to end their relationships over infidelity. Gay men, however, were more likely than straight women to denigrate potential competitors.

A Lesbian Family.
Many lesbian couples have children. Sometimes the children derive from earlier marriages, and sometimes they're adopted. Some lesbians are artificially inseminated or engage in sexual intercourse with men for the purpose of becoming pregnant.

Gays and lesbians in larger urban centres can usually look for services and supports from gay communal structures. These include gay rights organizations and gay-oriented newspapers, magazines, bookstores, housing cooperatives, and medical services. The gay community provides a sense of acceptance and belonging that gays and lesbians don't typically find in society at large.

Not all gays and lesbians feel a part of the gay community, however, or participate in gay rights organizations. For many, their sexual orientations are part of their identities, but not dominant themes governing their social and political activities. Homosexuals, like heterosexuals, have many different styles of life. Things are no simpler in the gay world than in the straight world.

In closing this chapter, we wish to acknowledge a study of human sexuality textbooks, including this one, that contained a chapter devoted to sexual orientation. Researchers Glenn Meaney of Wilfrid Laurier University and B. J. Rye of the University of Waterloo (2008) concluded that each of the textbooks they examined provided adequate, accurate information about homosexuality, and promoted more positive attitudes toward homosexuals.

GAY AND LESBIAN PARENTING Questions have been raised about the effects—if any—of being reared by gay parents. There's been relatively little research on lesbian and gay couples and parenting.

Deborah Foster (2005a), a therapist in Alberta, has provided a comprehensive analysis of the research on lesbian families. She notes that most lesbian families have formed as a result of the birth mothers' having children in heterosexual relationships, leaving those relationships, and then living in lesbian relationships.

Foster has summarized her key findings from comparisons of children raised in lesbian families with those raised in heterosexual families. She's found that children raised in lesbian families:

- Develop typical gender identities and gender roles.
- Develop typical peer relationships.
- Exhibit normal emotional and behavioural development.
- Have fewer issues regarding their sexual identity than children raised in heterosexual families.
- Are no more likely to grow up gay or lesbian than children raised in heterosexual families. (Foster, 2005a, pp. 291–292)

According to Foster, a key factor in the tendency for children in lesbian families to develop normally is the fact that that lesbian families tend to be equalitarian, nurturing, and empathic (Foster, 2005b). Foster concludes that children raised in lesbian families are at least as well adjusted as those raised in heterosexual families. Similar findings have been reported for children raised by gay male parents (Vervoort, 1999).

Summing Up

Sexual orientation describes the directionality of your sexual and romantic interests—toward members of your sex, members of the other sex, or both. A gay male or a lesbian orientation involves sexual and romantic interest in members of one's own sex.

Gay males and lesbians have gender identities that are consistent with their chromosomal and anatomic sex.

Kinsey and his colleagues found evidence of degrees of homosexuality and heterosexuality, with bisexuality representing a midpoint between the two.

Bisexual people are attracted to both males and females.

Throughout much of Western history, gay people have been deemed sinful and criminal.

Male–male sexual behaviour is practised by at least some members of many preliterate societies.

Many animals engage in behaviours that resemble male–male and female–female contacts among humans, but we must be cautious in ascribing motives to animals.

Attitudes toward gay people have shifted, though homophobia persists. The majority of Canadians now approve of same-sex relationships.

Evidence of a genetic contribution to sexual orientation is accumulating. Prenatal sex hormones may also play a role in determining sexual orientation in humans.

Psychoanalytic theory connects sexual orientation with unconscious castration anxiety and improper resolution of the Oedipus complex.

Learning theorists focus on the role of reinforcement of early patterns of sexual behaviour.

Coming out is a two-pronged process: coming out to yourself and coming out to others.

Many gay males and lesbians fear rejection if they disclose their sexual orientations. Some families struggle with the knowledge, while others are more accepting.

Gay males are more likely than lesbians to engage in casual sex with many partners. Lesbians more often confine sexual activity to committed, affectionate relationships.

Gay people do not adopt a single, stereotypical lifestyle.

Test Yourself

Multiple-Choice Questions

1. **Sexual orientation is:**
(a) The gender identity of a person who feels trapped in the body of the other sex.
(b) The constellation of biological and environmental factors that contribute to the development of a homosexual identity.
(c) Sexual behavior with people of the same sex.
(d) Erotic attraction toward members of the same sex, the other sex, or both.

2. **Most gay and lesbian people:**
(a) Wish they were the other sex.
(b) Have gender identities consistent with their anatomical sex.
(c) Seek to change their sexual orientations at some point.
(d) Always behaved like the other sex in childhood.

3. **According to Statistics Canada, more men than women report that they're _____ and more women than men report that they're _____.**
(a) bisexual; homosexual
(b) homosexual; bisexual
(c) homosexual; asexual
(d) asexual; homosexual

4. **Psychologist Michael Storms suggests that:**
(a) Heterosexuality and homosexuality are at opposite ends of a continuum of sexual orientation.
(b) Asexuality is a completely separate dimension.
(c) Homosexuality and heterosexuality are separate and independent dimensions.
(d) Bisexual individuals are at the midpoint of a continuum between heterosexuality and homosexuality.

(Continued)

5. Bell and Weinberg found that gay couples' adjustment was related to:

(a) The level of stability and intimacy in their relationships.
(b) The ability of one partner to take on decision-making authority.
(c) Their frequency of sexual activity.
(d) Their acceptance of multiple sexual partnerships.

6. A 2010 poll of Canadians found that _____ approved of same-sex couples retaining the right to marry.

(a) 21%
(b) 41%
(c) 61%
(d) 81%

7. According to Savin-Williams and Diamond, the first step in the development of sexual identity among gay and lesbian people is:

(a) Sexual contact with members of the same sex.
(b) Attraction to members of the same sex.
(c) Self-labelling as gay or lesbian.
(d) Disclosure to other people.

8. The cluster of negative attitudes toward gay, lesbian, and bisexual people that includes intolerance, hatred, and fear is referred to as:

(a) Heterophobia.
(b) Homophobia.
(c) Heteroeroticism.
(d) Homoeroticism.

9. _____ are most likely to share a gay sexual orientation.

(a) Monozygotic twins
(b) Dizygotic twins
(c) Parents and their biological children
(d) Adoptive parents and their adopted children

10. In comparing homosexual and heterosexual couples, Doug VanderLaan and Paul Vasey found that _____ were most likely to be concerned about their partners' economic status.

(a) heterosexual women
(b) gay men
(c) lesbians
(d) heterosexual men

You'll find answers to the "Test Yourself" questions on page 495.

Critical Thinking

1. What messages about homosexuality did you receive from your parents? Were they positive or negative? Did you receive different messages from your friends?

2. Why do you think men tend to be more homophobic than women?

3. People who believe sexual orientation is biological tend to be more tolerant of homosexuality than people who don't. How would you explain this?

MySearchLab

MySearchLab offers extensive help to students with their writing and research project and provides round-the-clock access to credible and reliable source material. Take a tour at www.mysearchlab.com.

CHAPTER TEN

Conception, Pregnancy, and Childbirth

Conception

Conception is the union of a sperm cell and an ovum. On one hand, conception is the beginning of a new human life. On the other hand, conception is the end of a fantastic voyage, in which a viable ovum—one of only several hundred that will mature and ripen during a woman's lifetime—unites with one of several hundred million sperm produced by a man in the average ejaculate.

Ova carry X sex chromosomes. Sperm carry either X or Y sex chromosomes. Girls are conceived from the union of an ovum and an X-bearing sperm, boys from the union of an ovum and a Y-bearing sperm. Sperm that bear Y chromosomes appear to be faster swimmers than those bearing X chromosomes. This is one of the reasons 120 to 150 boys are conceived for every 100 girls. What seem to be natural balancing factors favour the survival of female fetuses, however. Male fetuses are more likely to be lost in spontaneous abortions, which often occur during the first month of pregnancy. In many cases of early spontaneous abortion, the women never realize they've been pregnant. Despite spontaneous abortions, however, boys still outnumber girls at birth, but boys suffer a higher incidence of infant mortality.

The 200 to 400 million sperm in an average ejaculation may seem excessive, given that only one can fertilize an egg. Only 1 in 1000 will ever arrive in the vicinity of an ovum, however. Millions deposited in the vagina simply flow out of the woman's body because of gravity, unless she remains prone for quite some time. Normal vaginal acidity kills many more. Many surviving sperm swim (against the current of fluid coming from the cervix) through the os and into the uterus. Surviving sperm may reach the fallopian tubes 60 to 90 minutes after ejaculation. About half of the sperm end up in the wrong tube—that is, the one that doesn't contain the egg. Perhaps some 2000 sperm find their way into the right tube. Fewer still manage to swim the final 5 centimetres against the currents generated by the cilia that line the tube.

The journey of sperm may be blind, but it's not random. Ova secrete a chemical that attracts sperm. Because sperm cells have odour receptors, it's conceivable (pardon the pun) that sperm are attracted to ova through a variation of the sense of smell.

Fertilization normally occurs in a fallopian tube. (Figure 10.1 shows sperm swarming around an egg in a fallopian tube.) Ova contain chromosomes, proteins, fats, and nutritious fluid, and are surrounded by a gelatinous layer called the **zona pellucida**. This layer must be penetrated if fertilization is to occur. Sperm that have completed their journey secrete the enzyme **hyaluronidase**, which briefly thins the zona pellucida, enabling one sperm to penetrate. Once a sperm has entered, the zona pellucida thickens, locking other sperm out. The corresponding chromosomes in the sperm and the ovum line up opposite one another. Conception occurs as the chromosomes from the sperm and the ovum combine to form 23 new pairs of chromosomes, which carry a unique set of genetic instructions.

Figure 10.1 Human sperm swarming around an ovum in a fallopian tube.
Fertilization normally occurs in a fallopian tube, not in the uterus.

Zona pellucida A gelatinous layer that surrounds an ovum.

Hyaluronidase An enzyme that briefly thins the zona pellucida, enabling one sperm to penetrate.

Infertility Inability to conceive a child.

Infertility and Assisted Reproductive Technologies

For couples who want children, few problems are more frustrating than the inability to conceive. Physicians often recommend that couples try to conceive on their own for six months before seeking medical assistance. The term "**infertility**" isn't usually applied until a couple has failed to conceive for more than a year.

Applied Knowledge

OPTIMIZING THE CHANCES OF CONCEPTION

Some couples wish to optimize their chances of conceiving during a particular month so birth occurs at a desired time. Others may have difficulty conceiving, and wish to maximize their chances for a few months, before consulting a fertility specialist. Some fairly simple procedures can dramatically increase the chances of conceiving for couples without serious fertility problems.

The ovum can be fertilized for about 4 to 20 hours after ovulation (Wilcox et al., 2000). Sperm are most active within 48 hours after ejaculation. One way of optimizing the chances of conception is to engage in coitus within a few hours of ovulation. There are a number of ways to predict ovulation.

Using the Basal Body Temperature Chart

Few women have perfectly regular cycles, so they can only guess when they're ovulating (Wilcox et al., 2000). A basal body temperature (BBT) chart (see Figure 10.2) may help provide a more reliable estimate.

As Figure 10.2 shows, body temperature is fairly even before ovulation. Early-morning body temperature is generally below 37°C. Just before ovulation, basal temperature dips slightly. On the day after ovulation, temperature tends to rise by about 0.2°C to 0.4°C, and it remains higher until menstruation. Thermometers that provide finely graded readings, such as electronic digital thermometers, are best suited for determining these minor changes.

In using the BBT method, a woman attempts to detect these temperature changes by tracking her temperature just after she awakens each morning, before she rises from her bed. She records her temperature, the day of her cycle, and the day of the month, and indicates whether she and her partner have engaged in sexual intercourse. With regular charting for six months—assuming her cycles are fairly regular—she may learn to more accurately predict the day of ovulation.

Opinion is divided about whether it's better to have intercourse every 24 hours or every 36 to 48 hours for the several days when ovulation is expected. More frequent intercourse around the time of ovulation gives more chances for conception. Less frequent intercourse—that is, every 36 to 48 hours—results in a higher sperm count during each ejaculation. Most fertility specialists recommend that a couple seeking to conceive have intercourse once every day or two during the week in which the woman expects to ovulate. They may advise a man with a lower-than-normal sperm count to wait for 48 hours between ejaculations.

Analyzing Urine or Saliva for Luteinizing Hormone

Over-the-counter kits are more accurate than the BBT method for predicting ovulation. These kits analyze a woman's urine or saliva for the surge in luteinizing hormone (LH) that occurs about 12 to 24 hours before ovulation (Peris, 2006).

Tracking Vaginal Mucus

A woman can track the thickness of her vaginal mucus during the phases of the menstrual cycle by rolling it between her fingers and noting changes in texture. The mucus is thick, white, and cloudy during most phases of the cycle. It becomes thin, slippery, and clear for a few days before ovulation. A day or so after ovulation, the mucus again thickens and becomes opaque.

Additional Considerations

A woman may improve her chances of conceiving by lying on her back and drawing her knees close to her breasts after ejaculation. This position, perhaps aided by the use of a pillow beneath the buttocks, may elevate the pool of semen in relation to the cervix and prevent sperm from dripping out quickly. It thus makes gravity work for rather than against conception. She may also lie as still as possible for about 30 to 60 minutes after ejaculation, to help sperm move toward the cervical opening.

A woman with a severely retroverted (tipped) uterus may profit by supporting herself on her elbows and knees and having her partner enter her from behind. This position helps prevent semen from dripping out of the vagina.

The man should penetrate the woman as deeply as possible just before ejaculation, hold still during ejaculation, and then withdraw slowly, in a straight line, to avoid dispersing the pool of semen.

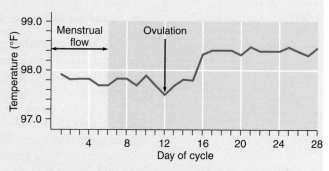

Figure 10.2 A basal body temperature (BBT) chart.
Because most women have somewhat irregular menstrual cycles, they may not be able to predict ovulation perfectly. The basal body temperature (BBT) chart helps them to do so.

Body temperature is fairly even before ovulation but dips slightly just before ovulation. On the day after ovulation, a woman's body temperature increases about 0.4 to 0.8°F above the level before ovulation.
Source: Adapted from Kolodny, R. C., Masters, W. H., & Johnson, V. E. (1979). Textbook of Sexual Medicine. New York: Little, Brown and Company.

Infertility can have significant psychological and emotional effects on individuals and couples. Some psychologists have found that dealing with infertility can be likened to dealing with the death of a child. Couples often go through a grief process that involves acceptance of the diagnosis of infertility before proceeding to treatment to help them conceive.

Because the likelihood of infertility increases with age, the current somewhat elevated incidence of infertility is partly the result of a rise in the number of couples who've postponed childbearing until their thirties and forties (Shevell et al., 2006). All in all, about 15% of couples in North America have fertilitre problems (American Fertility Association, 2006). It's estimated that more than a quarter of a million couples in Canada are infertile (Norris, 2001). About half of them eventually succeed in conceiving, however. Many treatment options are available, ranging from drugs that stimulate ovulation to newer reproductive technologies such as in vitro fertilization (IVF).

Infertility treatments can be costly. In vitro fertilization can cost up to $15,000. There's debate in Canada about whether government medical insurance should cover the cost of IVF (Alcoba, 2009). Much of this debate centres around the question of whether infertility should be considered a medical condition requiring publicly funded medical treatment. Quebec is the only province or territory that currently covers the cost of IVF. A 2009 expert panel in Ontario recommended that that province also cover the cost of the procedure, but it has yet to do so.

Male Fertility Issues

Although most concerns about fertility have traditionally centred on women, in about 30% of cases, the difficulty lies with men. In about 20% of cases, problems are found in both partners (Hatcher et al., 2008; Hatcher et al., 2006).

Fertility problems in the male reflect a variety of abnormalities:

- Low sperm counts.
- Irregularly shaped sperm (e.g., malformed heads or tails).
- Low sperm **motility**.
- Chronic diseases such as diabetes.
- Infections such as sexually transmitted infections.
- Injuries to the testes.
- **Autoimmune responses**, in which the man produces antibodies that deactivate his sperm.
- A pituitary imbalance and/or thyroid disease.

Problems in producing normal, abundant sperm may be caused by genetic factors, advanced age, hormonal problems, diabetes, injuries to the testes, varicose veins in the scrotum, drugs (alcohol, narcotics, marijuana, and/or tobacco), antihypertensive medications, environmental toxins, excess heat, and emotional stress.

Low sperm count (or the absence of sperm) is the most common problem. Sperm counts of 40 million to 150 million sperm per millilitre of semen are considered normal. A count of less than 20 million is generally regarded as low. Sperm production may be low among men with undescended testes that weren't surgically corrected before puberty. Frequent ejaculation can reduce sperm counts. Sperm production may also be impaired in men whose testicles are consistently one or two degrees above the typical scrotal temperature of 34°C to 35°C. Frequent hot baths and tightly fitting underwear may also be responsible for low sperm production, at least temporarily. Some men may encounter fertility problems from prolonged athletic activity, electric blankets, or even long, hot baths. In such cases, the problems can be easily corrected. Male runners with fertility problems are often advised to take time off to increase their sperm counts.

Motility Self-propulsion. Motility is a measure of the viability of sperm cells.

Autoimmune response The production of antibodies that attack naturally occurring substances that are (incorrectly) recognized as foreign or harmful.

Sometimes the sperm count is adequate, but prostate, hormonal, or other factors reduce motility or deform the sperm. Motility can also be hampered by scar tissue from infections, which may prevent sperm from passing through the vas deferens or other parts of the male reproductive system. To be considered normal, sperm must be able to swim for at least two hours after intercourse, and most (60% or more) must be normal in shape.

Sperm counts have been increased by surgical repair of varicose veins in the scrotum. Microsurgery can also open blocked passageways that prevent the outflow of sperm. Researchers are investigating the effects of special cooling undergarments. Most men whose infertility is the result of higher-than-normal scrotal temperatures show increased sperm counts and sperm quality when they wear such undergarments.

ARTIFICIAL INSEMINATION The sperm of men with low sperm counts can be collected and quick-frozen. The sperm from multiple ejaculations can then be injected into a woman's uterus at the time of ovulation. This is one kind of **artificial insemination**. The sperm of a man with low sperm motility can also be injected into his partner's uterus, so the sperm begin their journey closer to the fallopian tubes. Sperm from a donor can be used to artificially inseminate a woman whose partner is completely infertile or has an extremely low sperm count. The child then bears the genes of just one of the natural parents—the mother. A donor can be chosen who resembles the father in physical traits and ethnic background.

A variation of artificial insemination has been used with some men with very low (or zero) sperm counts, immature sperm, or immotile sperm. Immature sperm is removed from a testicle via a thin needle, and directly injected into an egg in a laboratory dish.

Artificial insemination The introduction of sperm into the reproductive tract through means other than sexual intercourse.

Female Fertility Issues

Infertility in women, like in men, has a variety of causes:

- Irregular ovulation, including failure to ovulate.
- Obstructions or malfunctions of the reproductive tract, often caused by infections or diseases involving the reproductive tract.
- Endometriosis.

Between 10% and 15% of female infertility problems stem from failure to ovulate. Many factors can play roles, including hormonal irregularities, malnutrition, genetic factors, stress, and chronic disease. Failure to ovulate may occur in response to low levels of body fat, as we see in athletes and women with eating disorders (Frisch, 2002).

Ovulation can often be induced by fertility drugs such as clomiphene (sold as Clomid), which stimulates the pituitary gland to secrete FSH and LH, which in turn stimulate the maturation of ova. Clomiphene leads to conception in most cases of infertility that are due solely to irregular or absent ovulation. But because infertility can have multiple causes, only about half of the women who use clomiphene become pregnant.

Another infertility drug, Pergonal, contains a high concentration of FSH, which directly stimulates maturation of ovarian follicles. Like clomiphene, Pergonal has a high success rate with women whose infertility is due to lack of ovulation.

Clomiphene and Pergonal have been linked to multiple births, including quadruplets and even quintuplets (Shevell et al., 2005). McGill University researchers found that 41% of patients at an infertility clinic actually preferred to have multiple births, so they could have instant families (Child, Henderson, & Tan, 2004). This desire was especially strong in couples who had no children and had been infertile for a long time.

Local infections that scar the fallopian tubes and other organs impede the passage of sperm or ova. Such infections include chlamydia, gonorrhea, and pelvic inflammatory disease. (We'll discuss STIs in Chapter 14.) Sexually transmitted diseases are therefore a major cause of infertility.

In **endometriosis**, endometrial tissues, which are normally found in the lining of the uterus, implant and grow elsewhere. When they develop on the surface of the ovaries or fallopian tubes, they may block the passage of ova or impair conception. About one in six cases of female sterility is believed to be due to endometriosis. Hormone treatments and surgery sometimes reduce the blockage to the point where the woman can conceive. A physician may suspect endometriosis during a pelvic exam, but it's diagnosed with certainty by **laparoscopy**. A long, narrow tube is inserted through an incision in the navel, permitting the physician to visually inspect the organs in the pelvic cavity. The incision is practically undetectable.

Several methods help many women with problems such as blocked fallopian tubes bear children, as we'll see next.

IN VITRO FERTILIZATION When Louise Brown was born in England in 1978, after being conceived by **in vitro fertilization (IVF)**, she made headlines around the world. Louise was dubbed the world's first "test-tube baby." Conception actually took place in a laboratory dish (not a test tube), and the embryo was implanted in her mother's uterus, where it developed to term.

Before a woman undergoes in vitro fertilization, she's given fertility drugs to stimulate her ova to ripen. The ripe ova are then surgically removed from one of her ovaries, and placed in a laboratory dish with the man's sperm. Fertilized ova are then injected into the woman's uterus, where they become implanted in the uterine wall.

A variation of IVF is vitrification, which involves rapid freezing of a woman's ova. Rapid freezing prevents ice crystals from forming, which ensures that a high proportion of the ova will survive. This procedure appeals to women who want to delay becoming mothers until they're older, but want to preserve their young ova, to improve their fertility chances. The McGill Reproductive Centre in Montreal has pioneered research on this procedure (Ogilvie, 2008).

GIFT In **gamete intrafallopian transfer (GIFT)**, sperm and ova are inserted together into a fallopian tube for fertilization. Conception occurs in a fallopian tube, rather than in a laboratory dish.

ZIFT **Zygote intrafallopian transfer (ZIFT)** involves a combination of IVF and GIFT. Sperm and ova are combined in a laboratory dish. After fertilization, the zygote is placed in the mother's fallopian tube, to begin its journey to the uterus for implantation.

ZIFT's advantage over GIFT is that the fertility specialists can ascertain that fertilization has occurred before insertion is performed.

DONOR IV **Donor IVF** is a variation of the IVF procedure. The ovum is taken from another woman, fertilized, and then injected into the uterus or fallopian tube of the intended mother. The procedure is used when the intended mother doesn't produce ova.

EMBRYONIC TRANSFER **Embryonic transfer** can be used with women who don't produce ova of their own. A female volunteer is artificially inseminated by the male partner of the infertile woman. Five days later, the embryo is removed from the volunteer and inserted into the uterus of the mother-to-be, where it becomes implanted.

INTRACYTOPLASMIC SPERM INJECTION **Intracytoplasmic sperm injection (ICSI)** can be used when a man has too few sperm for IVF, or when IVF fails. A sperm cell is injected directly into an ovum.

Endometriosis An abnormal condition in which endometrial tissue is sloughed off into the abdominal cavity, rather than out of the body during menstruation. The condition is characterized by abdominal pain, and may cause infertility.

Laparoscopy A medical procedure in which a long, narrow tube (a laparoscope) is inserted through an incision in the navel, permitting visual inspection of organs in the pelvic cavity.

In vitro fertilization A method of conception in which mature ova are surgically removed from an ovary, and placed in a laboratory dish with sperm.

Gamete intrafallopian transfer (GIFT) A method of conception in which sperm and ova are inserted into a fallopian tube, to encourage conception.

Zygote intrafallopian transfer (ZIFT) A method of conception in which an ovum is fertilized in a laboratory dish, then placed in a fallopian tube.

Donor IVF A variation of in vitro fertilization in which an ovum is taken from one woman, fertilized, and injected into the uterus or fallopian tube of another woman.

Embryonic transfer A method of conception in which a female volunteer is artificially inseminated by the male partner of the intended mother, then the embryo is removed from the volunteer and inserted into the uterus of the intended mother.

Intracytoplasmic sperm injection A method of conception in which a single sperm is injected directly into an ovum.

This method may be associated with an increase in birth defects, including heart, stomach, kidney, and bladder problems, cleft palates, hernias, and malformation of the penis (Shevell et al., 2005).

SURROGATE MOTHERHOOD A **surrogate mother** is artificially inseminated by the partner of an infertile woman. She carries the baby to term and then turns the baby over to the father and his partner.

ASSISTED PARENTHOOD FOR GAYS AND LESBIANS Many gays and lesbians use reproductive technologies to become parents. At some fertility clinics in Toronto, about one-third of the clients are gay men or lesbians (Epstein, 2008).

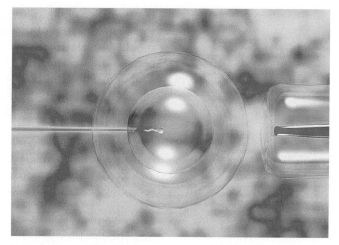

Intracytoplasmic Sperm Injection.
ICSI is sometimes used when the man has too few sperm for IVF, or when IVF fails. As you can see in the photograph, a very thin needle injects a single sperm directly into an ovum.

Of course, a key difference between same-sex couples and heterosexuals who visit fertility clinics is that most same-sex couples don't have infertility problems. Rather, they seek access to donor sperm and ova. Their counselling needs are therefore different from those of heterosexuals. The fact that many fertility clinics have a heterosexual focus and are unable to provide proper counselling for same-sex couples is a major concern for them (Epstein, 2008).

RISKS OF ASSISTED REPRODUCTIVE TECHNOLOGIES There's some evidence that assisted reproductive technologies may be linked to complications for both mothers and children.

The most common risk is multiple gestation (twins, triplets), which increases the risk of premature birth. In reviewing the available research, Metwally and Ledger (2011) also found links between the use of assisted reproductive technologies and abnormal placentation, miscarriage, gestational diabetes, and hypertensive disorders. It's unclear whether these complications were caused by the technologies or resulted from the characteristics of the patients undergoing infertility treatment.

There's evidence that assisted reproductive technologies may increase the risks of several fetal and neonatal complications. Metwally and Ledger (2011) are careful to point out that research into these increased risks is inconclusive, and more research needs to be done.

Surrogate mother A woman who is impregnated with the sperm of a prospective father via artificial insemination, carries the embryo and fetus to term, and then gives the child to the prospective parents.

ADOPTION Adoption is another way for people to have children. Despite the occasional conflicts between adoptive parents and biological parents who change their minds about giving up their children, most adoptions create loving new families.

Adopted children may, in some cases, feel less secure than biological children with their caregivers (Gilmore, 2008). Everything else being equal, however, the younger a child is at the time of adoption, the more smoothly the adoption seems to go (Brodzinsky & Palacios, 2005). Despite potential challenges, most adopted children and adoptive parents fare well.

Daly and Sobol (1994) found that the biggest restriction on adoption placement was sexual orientation. Only about 4% of the agencies they surveyed said they would place children with same-sex couples without reservation. In the 1990s, however, court rulings and provincial legislation providing greater equality for same-sex couples paved the road for increases in same-sex adoptions. In 1995, for example, an Ontario lesbian went to court seeking the right to adopt her partner's child. The judge ruled that the Ontario adoption law defining a spouse as a person of the opposite sex was unconstitutional, and that the woman should be able to adopt (Gower & Philp, 2002a). In 1996, British Columbia became the first province to pass legislation granting same-sex couples the same adoption rights as heterosexual couples. Since then, most provinces have passed similar legislation. Canada has become a world leader in facilitating adoptions for gays and lesbians. This doesn't mean same-sex couples don't still face prejudice by adoption agencies, however.

Rye and Meaney (2008) looked at university students' attitudes toward gay and lesbian adoption. While the students were generally positive about homosexual adoption, they were more positive about heterosexual adoption. Women were more accepting than men of adoption by homosexual parents.

Canadian Legislation and Reproductive Technologies

In 2004, Parliament passed legislation to regulate reproductive technologies. This legislation came 12 years after the first commission on reproductive technologies was established, a fact that highlights just how contentious the issues are.

The main provisions of the Assisted Human Reproduction Act include:

- A ban on human cloning.
- A ban on selection of a baby's sex for non-medical purposes.
- A ban on payment to a surrogate mother.
- A ban on payment to a sperm donor.

After the act was passed, there were fewer sperm donations in Canada, and fertility clinics had to import sperm from the United States. The United States allows payment to sperm donors and surrogate mothers.

One of the most controversial provisions was the permitting of research using stem cells from embryos left over from infertility treatments. Activists calling themselves "pro-life" are critical of the legislation, arguing that the use of embryos in this way diminishes the value of human life. Proponents of the research argue that stem cells can play vital roles in finding cures for such diseases as cancer, diabetes, and Parkinson's.

In December 2006, the Conservative government of Stephen Harper named eight people to a board that implements polices for the regulatory agency Assisted Human Reproduction Canada. The board members included people who had spoken out against abortion and stem-cell research. The board didn't appear to include any stem-cell scientists or fertility experts. Critics of the appointments were concerned that the government intended to use the board as a means of adopting policies that would appeal to religious conservatives, rather than focus on the scientific aspects of reproductive technologies (Abraham, 2006).

In December 2010, the Supreme Court of Canada ruled that those aspects of the 2004 legislation pertaining to fertility clinic licensing and monitoring should be provincial rather than federal responsibilities (Fitzpatrick, 2010).

Gay Adoption.
Robert Gibson and Thomas Jones of Brampton, Ontario, adopted two half-brothers with the help of the Children's Aid Society of Toronto. They're among a growing number of gay couples in Canada who are applying to adopt.

As a result, much of the work of Assisted Human Reproduction Canada is currently on hold.

Pregnancy

Women react to becoming pregnant in different ways. For those who are psychologically and economically prepared, pregnancy may be greeted with joyous celebration. On the other hand, an unwanted or unexpected pregnancy may evoke feelings of distress or uncertainty. Planned or not, a pregnancy, especially for women experiencing it for the first time, is likely to cause some level of anxiety.

In this section we examine biological and psychological aspects of pregnancy: signs of pregnancy, prenatal development, complications, influences on prenatal development, sexual activity during pregnancy, and the psychological experiences of pregnant women and fathers.

Early Signs of Pregnancy

For many women, the first sign of pregnancy is a missed period. But some women have irregular menstrual cycles, or miss periods because of stress. Missing a period is therefore not a fully reliable indicator.

Some women also experience cyclic bleeding or spotting during pregnancy, although the blood flow is usually lighter than normal. If a woman's basal body temperature remains high for about three weeks after ovulation, there's reason to suspect pregnancy, even if she spot-bleeds two weeks after ovulation.

Pregnancy Tests

You may have heard your grandparents say they learned your grandmother was pregnant by means of a "rabbit test." Once commonly used to confirm pregnancy, this procedure involved injection of a sample of a mother's urine into a laboratory animal. The procedure relied on the fact that women produce **human chorionic gonadotropin** (hCG) shortly after conception, and hCG causes rabbits, mice, and rats to ovulate.

Today, pregnancy can be confirmed within minutes—and without animals—by tests that directly detect hCG in the urine as early as the third week of pregnancy. A blood test (the radioimmunoassay [RIA] of beta subunit hCG) can detect hCG in the woman's blood as early as the eighth day of pregnancy, about five days before her expected period.

Over-the-counter home pregnancy tests are available. Intended to be used as early as one day after a missed period, they test the urine for hCG. Laboratory-based tests are considered 98% or 99% accurate; home-based tests performed by lay people are somewhat less accurate. Women are advised to consult their physicians if they suspect that they're pregnant or wish to confirm home pregnancy test results.

Early Effects of Pregnancy

Just a few days after conception, a woman may note tenderness in her breasts. Hormonal stimulation of the mammary glands may make her breasts more sensitive and cause sensations of tingling and fullness.

The term **"morning sickness"** refers to the nausea, food aversions, and vomiting a woman may experience during pregnancy. It's actually not a sickness at all, but a perfectly normal part of pregnancy (Flaxman & Sherman, 2000). Morning sickness can be so severe that a woman can't eat regularly, and must be hospitalized to ensure that she and her fetus receive adequate nutrition. In milder cases, it can be helpful to eat small amounts of food throughout the day. Many women find that eating a few crackers at bedtime and before getting up in the morning are effective. Other

Human chorionic gonadotropin (hCG) A hormone produced by a woman shortly after conception. HCG stimulates the corpus luteum to continue producing progesterone. The presence of HCG in a woman's urine indicates that she's pregnant.

Morning sickness Symptoms of pregnancy, including nausea, aversions to specific foods, and vomiting.

women benefit from medication. Morning sickness usually—but not always—subsides by about the twelfth week of pregnancy.

Pregnant women may experience greater-than-normal fatigue during the early weeks, sleeping longer and falling asleep more readily than usual. They may also experience frequent urination.

Miscarriage

Miscarriage A spontaneous abortion.

In most cases of **miscarriage**, a specific cause is not identified. Known causes include chromosomal defects in the fetus and abnormalities of the placenta and uterus. Miscarriage is more prevalent among older mothers (Stein & Susser, 2000). About three in four miscarriages occur in the first 16 weeks of pregnancy, and the great majority of these occur in the first 7 weeks. Some miscarriages occur so early that the women don't know they're pregnant.

After a miscarriage, a couple may feel a deep sense of loss and undergo a period of mourning. Emotional support from friends and family often helps the couple cope with the loss. Most women who miscarry are able to carry subsequent pregnancies to term.

Sexual Activity During Pregnancy

Most health professionals concur that intercourse is safe throughout the pregnancy, until the start of labour, as long as the pregnancy develops normally and the woman has no history of miscarriage. Women who experience bleeding or cramps during pregnancy may be advised by their obstetricians not to engage in intercourse.

Pregnant women often experience an initial decline in sexual interest during the first trimester, followed by increased interest during the second trimester, and another decline during the third (Fox et al., 2008). The declines in sexual interest and activity during the first trimester result from hormonal changes and, in many cases, fatigue and nausea. Vasocongestion may cause tenderness of the breasts at this time, discouraging the desire for fondling and sucking.

During the third trimester, some women want to continue with sexual activity, and some don't. In one study, three women in five (61%) reported having intercourse at least once a month during the third trimester, and 24% reported having intercourse at least once a week (Fox et al., 2008). During the 2 weeks prior to delivery, 40% reported having intercourse, and almost one woman in five (17%) reported having intercourse during the 2 days prior to delivery.

As a woman's abdominal region swells, the male-superior position becomes uncomfortable. For heterosexual couples, the female-superior, lateral-entry, and rear-entry positions are common alternatives. Masturbation and oral sex can continue.

Some women are concerned that the uterine contractions of orgasm may dislodge an embryo, but such concerns are usually unfounded. Still, women and their partners are advised to ask their obstetricians about sex during pregnancy.

Psychological Changes During Pregnancy

A woman's psychological response to pregnancy reflects her desire to be pregnant, her physical changes, and her attitudes toward these changes. Women with the financial, social, and psychological resources to meet the needs of pregnancy and child-rearing may welcome pregnancy. Other women may question their ability to handle pregnancy and childbirth. Or they may fear that pregnancy will interfere with their careers or their mates' feelings about them.

The first trimester may be difficult for women who are ambivalent about pregnancy. At that stage, symptoms like morning sickness are most pronounced, and women must come to terms with being pregnant. The second trimester is generally smoother. Morning sickness and other symptoms largely vanish. It's not yet difficult to move about, and the woman needn't face delivery just yet. Women first note fetal movement during the second trimester, and for many the experience is stirring:

> I was lying on my stomach and felt—something, like someone lightly touching my deep insides. Then I just sat very still and . . . felt the hugeness of having something living growing in me. Then I said, no, it's not possible, it's too early yet, and then I started to cry . . . . That one moment was my first body awareness of another living thing inside me. (Boston Women's Health Book Collective, 2005)

In general, men respond to pregnancy according to the degree to which they want to become fathers. Many men are proud, and look forward with great anticipation to having babies. In such cases, pregnancy may bring parents closer together. But male partners who are financially or emotionally unprepared or who don't want to become fathers may consider the pregnancies unwanted.

Prenatal Development

We can date pregnancy from the onset of the last menstrual cycle before conception, which makes the normal gestation period 280 days. We can also date pregnancy from the date at which fertilization is assumed to have taken place, which normally corresponds to two weeks after the beginning of the woman's last menstrual cycle. In this case, the normal gestation period is 266 days. A pregnancy can also be dated through an ultrasound scan during the first trimester.

Once pregnancy is confirmed, you can use Naegele's rule to calculate the delivery date:

1. Write down the date of the first day of the last menstrual period.
2. Add seven days.
3. Subtract three months.
4. Add one year.

Few babies are born exactly when they're due, but the great majority are delivered during 10-day periods that span their due dates.

The Germinal Stage

Within 36 hours of conception, the zygote divides into two cells. It then divides repeatedly, becoming 32 cells within another 36 hours as it continues its journey to the uterus. It takes the zygote three or four days to reach the uterus. This mass of dividing cells then wanders about the uterus for another three or four days before it begins to implant itself in the uterine wall. Implantation takes about another week. This period from conception to implantation is termed the **germinal stage** or the **period of the ovum**. (See Figure 10.3.)

Several days into the germinal stage, the cell mass takes the form of a fluid-filled ball of cells, which is called a **blastocyst**. Already some cell differentiation has begun. Cells begin to separate into groups that will eventually become different structures.

Implantation may be accompanied by some bleeding, which results from the usual rupturing of some small blood vessels that line the uterus. Bleeding can also be a sign of miscarriage—although most women who experience implantation bleeding don't miscarry, but go on to have normal pregnancies and deliver healthy babies.

The Embryonic Stage

The period from implantation to about the eighth week of development is called the **embryonic stage**. The major organ systems of the body begin to differentiate during this stage.

Germinal stage The period of prenatal development before implantation in the uterus.

Period of the ovum Germinal stage.

Blastocyst An embryo that consists of a sphere of cells surrounding a cavity of fluid. This occurs at the germinal stage of embryonic development.

Embryonic stage The stage of prenatal development that lasts from implantation through the eighth week. It's characterized by differentiation of the major organ systems.

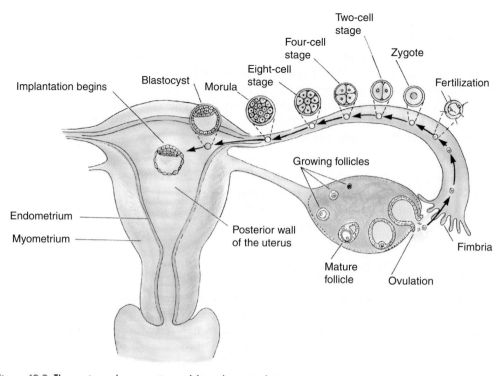

Figure 10.3 The ovarian cycle, conception, and the early germinal stage.
The zygote first divides about 36 hours after conception. Continuing division creates the hollow sphere of cells termed the blastocyst, which normally becomes implanted in the wall of the uterus.

Development of the embryo follows two trends: cephalocaudal growth and proximodistal growth. Growth of the head (the cephalic region) takes precedence over growth of the lower parts of the body. You can also think of the body as containing a central axis that coincides with the spinal cord. The growth of the organ systems that lie close to this axis (that is, proximal to the axis) takes precedence over the growth of those that lie farther away, toward the extremities (that is, distal to the axis). Relatively early maturation of the brain and organ systems that lie near the central axis allows these organs to facilitate further development of the embryo and fetus.

The embryo—and later the fetus—develops within a protective environment in the mother's uterus called the **amniotic sac**, which is surrounded by a clear membrane. The embryo or fetus is suspended within the sac in **amniotic fluid**. The amniotic fluid acts like a shock absorber, cushioning the embryo.

Nutrients and waste products are exchanged between mother and embryo (or between mother and fetus) through a mass of tissue called the **placenta**. Unique in origin, the placenta develops from material supplied by both the mother and the embryo. The fetus is connected to the placenta by the **umbilical cord**.

Ultimately, the placenta passes from the woman's body after delivery. For this reason, it's also called the afterbirth.

The Fetal Stage

The fetal stage begins by the ninth week and continues until birth. By about the ninth or tenth week, the fetus begins to respond to the outside world by turning in the direction of external stimulation. By the end of the first trimester, the major organ systems, fingers, toes, and external genitals are formed, the gender can be visually determined, and the eyes are clearly distinguishable.

Amniotic sac The sac containing the fetus.

Amniotic fluid Fluid within the amniotic sac. It suspends and protects the fetus.

Placenta An organ connected to the fetus by the umbilical cord. The placenta serves as a relay station between the mother and the fetus, allowing the exchange of nutrients and wastes.

Umbilical cord A tube that connects the fetus to the placenta.

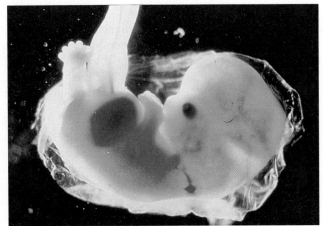

Prenatal Development.
Developmental changes are most rapid and dramatic during prenatal development. Within a few months, a human embryo becomes a fetus and advances from a gram to several kilograms in weight, and from one cell to billions of cells.

Near the end of the second trimester, the fetus approaches the **age of viability**. Still, only a minority of babies born at the end of the second trimester who weigh under a kilogram will survive—even with intense medical efforts.

During the final months of pregnancy, the mother may become concerned that the fetus seems less active. Most of the time, the change in activity level is normal. The fetus has merely grown so large that it's cramped, and its movements are restricted.

Environmental Influences

MATERNAL DIET Malnutrition in the mother can adversely affect fetal development and result in a low birth weight. Pregnant women who are adequately nourished are more likely to deliver babies of average or above-average size. Their infants are also less likely to develop colds and serious respiratory disorders. Maternal obesity, however, is linked with a higher risk of stillbirth (Cnattingius et al., 1998).

MATERNAL DISEASES AND DISORDERS Pre-existing conditions in the mother, such as diabetes, can have significant impacts on prenatal grow and development. Environmental influences and agents that cause permanent, harmful structural alterations of the embryo or fetus are called **teratogens**. They include alcohol, the metals lead and mercury, radiation, and disease-causing organisms such as viruses and bacteria. Although many disease-causing organisms cannot pass through the placenta to infect the embryo or fetus, some extremely small organisms, such as those that cause syphilis, measles, mumps, and chicken pox, can. Substances produced by the mother's body, including Rh-positive antibodies, can also affect the fetus.

Teratogens Environmental influences or agents that can damage an embryo or fetus.

Critical period of vulnerability A period when an embryo or fetus is vulnerable to the effects of a teratogen.

Rubella A viral infection that can cause mental retardation and heart disease in an embryo. It's also called German measles.

Syphilis A sexually transmitted disease caused by a bacterial infection.

Stillbirth Birth of a dead fetus.

Acquired immunodeficiency syndrome (AIDS) A sexually transmitted infection that destroys white blood cells in the immune system, leaving the body vulnerable to various opportunistic infections.

Pregnancy-induced hypertension A life-threatening condition characterized by high blood pressure.

Ectopic pregnancy A pregnancy in which the fertilized ovum becomes implanted somewhere other than the uterus.

Rh incompatibility A condition in which antibodies produced by a pregnant woman are transmitted to the fetus, where they may cause brain damage or death.

CRITICAL PERIODS OF VULNERABILITY The times at which exposure to particular teratogens can cause the greatest harm are termed **critical periods of vulnerability**. Critical periods correspond to the times when the structures most affected by the teratogens are developing. The heart, for example, develops rapidly from the third to the fifth week after conception. It may be most vulnerable to certain teratogens at this time.

RUBELLA (GERMAN MEASLES) **Rubella** is a viral infection. Women who contract rubella during the first month or two of pregnancy, when rapid differentiation of major organ systems take place, may bear children who are deaf or who develop mental retardation, heart disease, or cataracts.

Most Canadian women have either had rubella as children or been vaccinated against it. Women who don't know whether they're immune to rubella may be tested. If they're not immune, they can be vaccinated *before pregnancy*.

SYPHILIS Maternal **syphilis** can cause miscarriage or **stillbirth**, or it can be passed along to the child in the form of congenital syphilis. Congenital syphilis can impair the vision and hearing, damage the liver, and deform the bones and teeth.

Routine blood tests early in pregnancy can diagnose syphilis. The fetus will probably not contract syphilis if the infected mother is successfully treated with antibiotics before the fourth month of pregnancy.

HIV/AIDS **Acquired immunodeficiency syndrome (AIDS)** is caused by the human immunodeficiency virus (HIV). Because it's blood-borne, HIV is sometimes transmitted through the placenta to infect the fetus. Rupturing blood vessels in the mother and baby during childbirth provide more opportunities for HIV transmission.

The majority of babies born to mothers who are infected with HIV do not become infected themselves. Using antiviral medication can minimize the probability of transmission. (We'll discuss this in Chapter 14.)

HIV can also be transmitted to children by breastfeeding.

PREGNANCY-INDUCED HYPERTENSION **Pregnancy-induced hypertension**, also known as pre-eclampsia, is a life-threatening condition characterized by high blood pressure. It may afflict women late in the second or in the third trimester of pregnancy. If left untreated, it can lead to maternal and/or fetal death. Babies born to women with pregnancy-induced hypertension are often undersized or premature.

ECTOPIC PREGNANCY In an **ectopic pregnancy**, the fertilized ovum implants itself somewhere other than the uterus. Most ectopic pregnancies occur in fallopian tubes ("tubal pregnancies"). If ectopic pregnancies don't abort spontaneously, they must be removed by surgery or via medicines.

Rh INCOMPATIBILITY Rh is a blood protein found in some people's red blood cells. **Rh incompatibility** occurs when an Rh-negative woman (who doesn't have the Rh blood protein) carries an Rh-positive fetus (who does have the Rh factor). This can happen if the father is Rh-positive. In Rh incompatibility, antibodies produced by the mother are transmitted to a fetus or newborn infant, potentially causing brain damage or death. This becomes a problem, however, only in a minority of the resulting pregnancies.

MATERNAL DRUG USE Some widely used drugs, including nonprescription drugs, are linked with birth abnormalities. Several antibiotics can harm a fetus, especially if they're taken during certain periods of fetal development. Tetracycline may yellow the child's teeth and deform his or her bones (Koren et al., 1998). Other antibiotics have been implicated in deafness and jaundice. Acne drugs such as Accutane can cause physical and mental handicaps in the children of women who use them during pregnancy. Antihistamines, commonly used for allergies, may deform the fetus.

Women who are (or suspect they might be) pregnant should review the drugs they're taking with their obstetricians, and consult with them again before taking any new drugs, including non-prescription drugs.

VITAMINS Many pregnant women are prescribed daily doses of multivitamins, to maintain their own health and promote healthy pregnancies. Too much of a good thing, however, can be hazardous. While normal doses can be beneficial, high doses of vitamins such as A, B6, D, and K have been linked to birth defects.

NARCOTICS Narcotics such as heroin and methadone can readily pass from mother to fetus through the placental membrane. Narcotics are addictive. Fetuses of mothers who use them regularly during pregnancy can become addicted in utero. At birth, such babies may experience withdrawal.

Women who use narcotics should tell their obstetricians, so measures can be taken to aid their infants before and after delivery.

MARIJUANA The active ingredient in marijuana, THC, readily crosses the placenta. Research into the cognitive effects of maternal marijuana use suggests that there may be no impairment in the child's global intellectual functioning per se (Fried & Smith, 2001). Nevertheless, the child's problem-solving and decision-making abilities may be affected. One study of the behavioural problems of 635 10-year-olds found that prenatal marijuana use was significantly related to increased hyperactivity, impulsivity, and attention problems (Goldschmidt et al., 2000).

Fetal alcohol syndrome (FAS) A cluster of symptoms in the infant caused by maternal alcohol consumption during pregnancy. These symptoms are typified by developmental lags, characteristic facial features, and a smaller-than-average body and brain.

ALCOHOL A mother who drinks during pregnancy increases the risk of birth defects, infant mortality, sensory and motor problems, and mental retardation in her child (Conner et al., 2006). Nearly 40% of children whose mothers drink during pregnancy develop **fetal alcohol syndrome (FAS)**. FAS is a cluster of symptoms typified by developmental lags and characteristic facial features, such as underdeveloped upper jaws, flattened noses, and widely spaced eyes. Infants with FAS are often smaller than average, and have smaller-than-average brains. They're also more susceptible to developing conduct disorders in middle childhood (Disney et al., 2008).

Although research suggests that light drinking is unlikely to harm the fetus, FAS has been found among the children of mothers who drank only 60 millilitres of alcohol a day during the first trimester (Astley & Clarren, 2001).

A high proportion of children in Canadian foster homes waiting for adoption have FAS. It's estimated that about half of the permanent wards of Winnipeg Child and Family Services, for example, have FAS (Gower & Philp, 2002b). Yet not all adoptive parents are aware of FAS, or realize that their adopted children are likely to have been damaged by alcohol in the womb.

CIGARETTE SMOKING Cigarette smoke contains chemicals such as carbon monoxide and the stimulant nicotine, which are transmitted to the fetus. It also lessens the amount of oxygen received by the fetus.

Don't Do It!
Cigarettes and pregnancy don't mix.

Maternal smoking increases the risks of spontaneous abortion, premature ruptur-ing of the amniotic sac, stillbirth, premature birth, low birth weight, and early infant mortality (Cnattingius, 2004; Secker-Walker & Vacek, 2003). These risks increase with the amount smoked (Bernstein et al., 2005). Low birth weight is a common risk factor for infant disease, mortality, and learning problems (O'Keeffe et al., 2003).

The combination of smoking and drinking alcohol places the child at greater risk for low birth weight than either practice alone (Spencer, 2006). Maternal smok-ing affects fetal heart rate, and increases the risk of sudden infant death syndrome (SIDS) (Gordon et al., 2002; Pollack, 2001). Maternal smoking has been linked to reduced lung function in newborns (Sasaki et al., 2008) and asthma in children (Goodwin et al., 2009). Evidence also points to reduced attention spans, hyperac-tivity, and lower IQs and achievement test scores in children exposed to maternal smoking during and after pregnancy.

Smoking by the father (or another household member) may be dangerous to a fetus, because secondary smoke (exhaled by the smoker or emitted from the tip of a lit cigarette) may be absorbed by the mother and passed to the fetus. Passive exposure to second-hand smoke during infancy is linked to increased risk of SIDS (Gordon et al., 2002).

Many women don't stop using alcohol or cigarettes until they learn that they're pregnant, which may not occur until weeks into their pregnancies (Cnattingius, 2004). It may be easier for a woman to quit if she thinks of it as quitting for the duration of her pregnancy, rather than forever. If she remains abstinent after deliv-ery, perhaps she won't be disappointed.

Chromosomal and Genetic Abnormalities

Not all of us have the normal complement of chromosomes. Some of us have genes that threaten our health.

On the basis of a couple's medical background and family histories, a genetic counsellor can help assess the risks of passing genetic defects to a child. Some couples who face high risks decide to adopt. Others decide to abort fetuses that are determined to have certain abnormalities.

Various medical procedures are used to detect fetal disorders. Parental blood tests can suggest the presence of sickle-cell anemia, Tay-Sachs disease, and neural tube defects. Tests of fetal DNA can indicate the presence of Huntington's disease, cystic fibrosis, and other disorders.

The risk of giving birth to a child with Down's syndrome increases with the mother's age. Amniocentesis can detect Down's syndrome before birth.

Childbirth

Early in the ninth month of pregnancy, the fetus's head settles in the pelvis. This shift is called "dropping" or "lightening." The woman may actually feel lighter, because there's less pressure on her diaphragm.

About a day or so before labour begins, the woman may notice blood in her vaginal secretions, because fetal pressure on the pelvis has ruptured superficial blood vessels in the birth canal. Tissue that has plugged the cervix, possibly pre-venting the entry of infectious agents from the vagina, has become dislodged, with a resultant discharge of bloody mucus. At about this time, one woman in 10 also has a rush of warm "water" from the vagina. This is amniotic fluid, and its presence means the amniotic sac has burst.

Labour usually begins within a day of rupture of the amniotic sac. For most women, the amniotic sac doesn't burst until the end of the first stage of childbirth. Labour begins with the onset of regular uterine contractions.

The first uterine contractions are relatively painless and are called **Braxton Hicks contractions,** or false labour contractions. They're considered false because they don't widen the cervix or advance the baby through the birth canal. They tend to increase in frequency, but are less regular than labour contractions. Real labour contractions, by contrast, become more intense when the woman moves around or walks.

Stages of Childbirth

Childbirth begins with the onset of labour, and has three stages.

In the first stage, uterine contractions **efface** and **dilate** the cervix to about 10 centimetres in diameter, so the baby can pass. Stretching of the cervix causes most of the pain of childbirth. A woman may experience little or no pain if her cervix dilates easily and quickly. The first stage may last from a couple of hours to more than a day. Twelve to 24 hours of labour is considered about average for a first pregnancy. In later pregnancies, labour takes about half this time.

The initial contractions are usually mild and widely spaced, at intervals of 10 to 20 minutes. They may last 20 to 40 seconds. As time passes, contractions become more frequent and regular, longer, and stronger.

Transition is the process that occurs when the cervix becomes almost fully dilated and the baby's head begins to move into the vagina, or birth canal. Contractions usually come quickly now. Transition usually lasts for up to 30 minutes, and is often accompanied by nausea, chills, and intense pain.

The second stage of childbirth begins after transition, when the cervix is fully dilated and the baby begins to move into the birth canal (vagina). Each contraction propels the baby farther along the birth canal. When the baby's head becomes visible at the vaginal opening, it's said to have crowned. Typically, the baby fully emerges a few minutes after crowning. Full emergence ends the second stage of childbirth, which lasts from a few minutes to a few hours and is shorter than the first stage.

Sometimes an **episiotomy** is performed on the mother when the baby's head has crowned. This prevents random tearing of the **perineum,** which can occur if it becomes extremely effaced. Episiotomies are controversial. The incision can cause infection and pain, creating discomfort and itching as it heals. In some cases, the discomfort interferes with intercourse for months. Physicians generally agree that an episiotomy should be performed if the baby's shoulders are too wide to emerge without causing tearing, or if the baby's heartbeat drops for an extended period of time (Eason & Feldman, 2000).

In Canada, the number of episiotomies is decreasing. In 1991, episiotomies were performed in almost half of all vaginal births. By 2001, they occurred in only about one-quarter of vaginal births. Rates have also fallen in the United States and other countries (Canadian Institute for Health Information, 2004).

The third, or placental, stage of childbirth can last from a few minutes to an hour or more. During this stage, the placenta is expelled and the uterus begins the process of contracting. Detachment of the placenta from the uterine wall may cause some bleeding.

The attending physician now sews up the episiotomy or any tears in the perineum.

INTO THE WORLD As the baby's head emerges, the doctor may use suction aspiration to clear away mucus from its mouth and prevent obstruction of the breathing passageway. Once the baby is breathing adequately, the doctor clamps and severs the umbilical cord about 7.5 centimetres from the baby's body. The stump of the umbilical cord dries and falls off in its own time, usually within 7 to 10 days.

While the mother is in the third stage of labour, the caregiver may perform procedures on the baby, such as placing drops of silver nitrate or an antibiotic ointment into the eyes. This procedure prevents bacterial infections in the newborn's eyes.

Braxton Hicks contractions So-called false labour contractions, which are relatively painless.

Efface Cause to become thin.

Dilate Open or widen.

Transition The process during which the cervix becomes almost fully dilated and the infant's head begins to move into the birth canal.

Episiotomy A surgical incision in the perineum that widens the birth canal, preventing random tearing during childbirth.

Perineum The area between the vulva and the anus.

Methods of Childbirth

Until the twentieth century, childbirth usually happened at home and involved the mother, a midwife, family, and friends. Today, women in Canada typically give birth in hospitals, attended by physicians who use surgical instruments and anaesthetics to protect them and their babies from infection, complications, and pain.

Medical procedures save lives, but make childbearing more impersonal. Social critics argue that these procedures have medicalized a natural process, usurping control over women's bodies and, through the use of drugs, denying many women the experience of giving birth.

MEDICATED CHILDBIRTH During the past two centuries, science and medicine have led to the expectation that women should experience minimal discomfort during childbirth. Today, some anesthesia is used to minimize or eliminate pain in most Canadian deliveries.

Anesthetic drugs, as well as tranquillizers and narcotics, decrease the strength of uterine contractions during delivery. They may thus delay the process of cervical dilation and prolong labour. They also reduce a woman's ability to push the baby through the birth canal. Because they cross the placental membrane, they also lower the newborn's overall responsiveness. There's little evidence, however, that medicated childbirth has serious, long-term consequences for children.

PREPARED CHILDBIRTH (THE LAMAZE METHOD) When the French obstetrician Fernand Lamaze visited the Soviet Union in 1951, he found that many Russian women bore babies without anaesthetic and without reporting a great deal of pain. Lamaze returned to Western Europe with some of the techniques the women used. These are now termed the **Lamaze method**, or prepared childbirth.

Lamaze (1981) argued that women could learn to conserve energy during childbirth and reduce the pain of uterine contractions by associating the contractions with other responses, such as thinking of pleasant mental images (e.g., beach scenes) and engaging in breathing and relaxation exercises.

A pregnant woman typically attends Lamaze classes with a coach—usually the father or a partner—who will aid her in the delivery room by timing contractions, offering emotional support, and coaching her in the breathing and relaxation exercises. The partner is integrated into the process. Many couples report that their relationships are strengthened as a result.

The Lamaze method is flexible about the use of anaesthetics. Many women report some pain during delivery, and are given anaesthetics. However, the Lamaze method appears to help women to gain a greater sense of control over the delivery process.

CAESAREAN SECTION In a **Caesarean section**, the baby is delivered via surgery, rather than naturally, through the vagina. In a Caesarean section (or C-section, for short) the woman is anaesthetized, and incisions are made in the abdomen and uterus, so the surgeon can remove the baby. The incisions are then sewn up and the mother can begin walking, often on the same day, although generally with some discomfort for a while.

C-section is most likely to be advised when normal delivery is difficult or threatens the health of the mother or the child. Vaginal delivery can be difficult if the baby is large, the mother's pelvis is small or misshapen, or the mother is tired, weak, or aging. C-section is used to bypass herpes and HIV infections in the birth canal. C-section is also likely to be performed if the baby presents for delivery in the breech position (feet downward) or in the **transverse position** (lying crosswise), or if the baby is in distress.

Lamaze method A childbirth method during which a woman learns how to relax and breathe in patterns that conserve energy and lessen pain, with the help of a coach (usually the father) who's present during the birth. The Lamaze method is also called prepared childbirth.

Caesarean section A method of childbirth in which the fetus is delivered through a surgical incision in the abdomen.

Transverse position A crosswise birth position.

Use of the C-section has mushroomed. In 2006, C-section rates in Canada reached an all-time high of 26.3% of all in-hospital deliveries, compared with 17% in 1993 (Canadian Institute for Health Information, 2007). In 2009, the C-section rate was slightly higher, at 26.9% (Canadian Institute for Health Information, 2010). More Canadian women are having C-sections the first time they give birth, and fewer are delivering vaginally after having previous C-sections (Canadian Institute for Health Information, 2004).

The Society of Obstetricians and Gynaecologists of Canada (SOGC) is concerned by the rising use of C-sections. The Society urges women to opt for C-sections only when medically necessary (Society of Obstetricians and Gynaecologists of Canada, 2008). According to the SOGC, women considering C-sections should be informed that a C-section is potentially more dangerous than a vaginal delivery for a healthy mother. Women who have C-sections take substantially longer to recover. C-sections present greater risks for complications such as infection, bleeding, scarring, chronic pelvic pain, and damage to the intestines or the bladder. C-sections also increase the risks during subsequent pregnancies, making repeat C-sections more likely (Society of Obstetricians and Gynaecologists of Canada, 2008).

Sometimes, however, there are excellent reasons for having a C-section. It makes no sense to avoid a C-section if vaginal delivery might put the mother or the baby at risk.

Birth Difficulties

Most deliveries are uncomplicated, or "unremarkable" in the medical sense—although childbirth is the most remarkable experience of many parents' lives. Difficulties with birth can and do occur, however.

Preterm Born before 37 weeks of gestation.

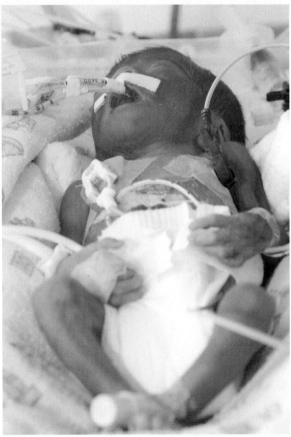

PRETERM AND LOW-BIRTH-WEIGHT CHILDREN

A neonate is considered premature, or **preterm**, if it's born before 37 weeks of gestation. The normal period of gestation is 40 weeks. Prematurity is generally linked with low birth weight, because the fetus normally makes dramatic gains in weight during the last weeks of pregnancy.

Regardless of the length of its gestation, a newborn baby is considered to have a low birth weight if it weighs less than about 2500 grams. Preterm and low-birth-weight babies face heightened risks of infant mortality from causes that range from asphyxia and infections to sudden infant death syndrome (SIDS) (Berger, 2000; Kramer et al., 2000). Neurological and developmental problems are also common among preterm infants, especially those born at or before 25 weeks of gestation (Wood et al., 2000).

Preterm infants usually remain in the hospital for a time. They're monitored and placed in incubators that provide temperature-controlled environments and offer some protection from infection. If necessary, they may also receive oxygen. Although remarkable advances are being made in our ability to help preterm babies survive, the likelihood of developmental disabilities continues to dramatically increase for babies who are born at 25 weeks of gestation or earlier (Cole, 2000).

STILLBIRTH Stillbirth, in which the baby is born dead, is the gravest of birth problems. Stillbirth is connected

Too Early.
A baby is considered premature if it's born before 37 weeks of gestation. Premature babies are vulnerable to various developmental problems.

A World of Diversity

MATERNAL AND INFANT MORTALITY AROUND THE WORLD

Contemporary medicine has made great contributions to the safety of childbirth and infancy, but they're not distributed equally throughout the world.

Save the Children, a nonprofit relief and development organization, tracks the likelihood that women will die during pregnancy and childbirth (maternal mortality) and that infants will die within five years of birth (infant mortality).

The likelihood of both maternal and infant mortality is connected with the empowerment of women within a society, as measured by such factors as availability of modern methods of contraception, number of years of formal schooling for girls, and female participation in national government.

The safest place for a woman to deliver and for her baby to survive is Ireland, where the chances of maternal death are about 1 in 47 000. Perhaps it's no coincidence that the typical Irish girl receives 18 years of formal education.

Afghanistan may have the world's most frightening statistics. One woman in eight will die as a result of pregnancy, and one-quarter of the children will die by age five. In Afghan society, girls receive an average of four years of education.

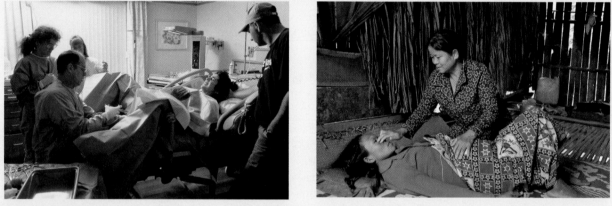

Special Delivery?
A mother's safety depends on where she gives birth. It's not just about the medical care—it's about the wider issue of whether the culture empowers women.

Source: Data from Save the Children (2008). State of the World's Mothers 2008: Closing the Survival Gap for Children Under 5. Westport, CT: Save the Children. Retrieved from http://www.savethechildren.org/publications/mothers/2008/SOWM-2008-full-report.pdf

with fetal abnormalities, infection, the mother's medical condition, and pregnancy complications such as pre-eclampsia and problems with the placenta (Pasupathy & Smith, 2005). Yet the majority of cases have no clear cause, and are considered unexplainable. In Canada there are about 2200 stillbirths each year, or 6.4 stillbirths for every 1000 total births (Statistics Canada, 2007b).

Stillbirth has a deep psychological impact on parents, leading in many cases to post-traumatic stress disorder (PTSD), which is characterized by ruminations about the loss, intrusive thoughts, and nightmares (Born et al., 2006). When a baby is declared dead while still within the mother, she may need a few hours to adjust to the fact before labour is induced (Trulsson & Rådestad, 2004).

The Postpartum Period

Postpartum Following birth.

The weeks after delivery are called the **postpartum** period. The first few postpartum days are frequently happy ones. The long wait is over, and so are the discomforts of childbirth. However, about 70% of new mothers have periods of tearfulness, sadness, and irritability that the American Psychiatric Association (2000) refers to as "baby blues." Baby blues and other postpartum mood problems are so common that they're statistically normal (Gavin et al., 2005).

Baby blues affect most women in the weeks after delivery. Researchers believe they're common because they're caused by the hormonal changes that accompany and follow delivery (Bloch et al., 2006; Morris, 2000). They last for about 10 days, and aren't severe enough to impair the mother's functioning.

One in five or 10 women encounters a more serious mood disorder called postpartum depression (PPD). PPD begins within four weeks after delivery, and may linger for weeks or months. PPD is symptomized by serious sadness, feelings of hopelessness and helplessness, feelings of worthlessness, difficulty concentrating, and major changes in appetite (usually loss of appetite) and sleep patterns (often insomnia). There can also be severe fluctuations in mood, from depression to elation and then back to depression. Some women show obsessive concern over the well-being of their babies at this time.

Some researchers suggest that PPD is caused by the interactions of biological (mainly hormonal) factors, including that precipitous drop-off in estrogen (Johnstone et al., 2001). Psychological factors may also be involved, such as concerns about the life changes wrought by motherhood, concerns about whether she'll be a good mother, marital problems, and a baby who is sick or unwanted.

The research focus, however, is on biological factors, because the body undergoes major chemical changes during and after pregnancy, and because women around the world seem to experience similar disturbances in mood, even when their life experiences and support systems are very different from those we find in Canada and the United States (Cohen et al., 2006).

Women who experience PPD may benefit from psychotherapy or drugs. Medications that increase estrogen levels or antidepressants may help. Most women recover from PPD on their own. At the very least, women need to know the problem isn't unusual, and doesn't necessarily mean something is seriously wrong with them, or that they're not living up to their obligations.

LESBIAN MOTHERS Lesbian mothers are also at risk for maternal depression. In reviewing the research literature, University of Toronto researcher Lori Ross has concluded that lesbian mothers may experience more stress than heterosexual mothers, because they receive less support from their own parents, and because of societal prejudices.

On the other hand, there are factors that reduce stress and the likelihood of postpartum depression in lesbians. Their pregnancies are more likely to be planned, and the division of child-care labour is more equal for lesbian couples than for heterosexual couples (Ross, 2005).

Breastfeeding

Health Canada and the Canadian Paediatric Society recommend breastfeeding as the preferred method for feeding infants because it provides optimal nutritional, immunological, and emotional benefits for the child's growth and development. The percentage of Canadian women who breastfed their last babies increased from 81.5% in 2001 to 87.0% in 2005, and has held steady since then (Statistics Canada, 2010).

The most common reasons mothers give for not breastfeeding are medical factors, such as premature or multiple births or the medical condition of the mother or the infant. Many also find breastfeeding unappealing or bottle-feeding easier.

One drawback of breastfeeding is that HIV can be transmitted to infants via breast milk. According to United Nations estimates, one-third of the infants around the world with HIV have been infected via breast milk (United Nations Special

CRITICAL THINKING QUESTIONS

Some women are ashamed to tell friends, family, and their doctors that they're experiencing the "baby blues." Why might they feel ashamed?

Prolactin A pituitary hormone that stimulates milk production. It comes from root words that mean "for milk."

Lactation Production of milk by the mammary glands.

Lochia A reddish vaginal discharge that may persist for a month after childbirth.

Session on AIDS, 2001). Another drawback is that when undernourished mothers in developing countries breastfeed, their babies can also become malnourished.

The hormones prolactin and oxytocin are involved in breastfeeding. **Prolactin** stimulates milk production, or **lactation**, two to three days after childbirth. Oxytocin, which is secreted in response to suckling, causes the breasts to eject milk. When an infant is weaned, prolactin and oxytocin secretion are discontinued, and lactation comes to an end.

Uterine contractions that occur during breastfeeding help return the uterus to its typical size, flattening the belly. Because of the expenditure of energy, breast-feeding may also help women lose the extra weight of pregnancy.

Although breastfeeding delays resumption of normal menstrual cycles, it's not a reliable birth-control method.

DOES BREASTFEEDING AFFECT SEXUAL BEHAVIOUR? In analyzing the literature, researchers at the University of British Columbia found that women who breastfeed are more likely than those who bottle-feed to experience decreased sexual desire, decreased frequency of sexual intercourse, and painful intercourse due to lack of vaginal lubrication (LaMarre et al., 2003).

LaMarre and her colleagues (2003) concluded that breastfeeding decreases both androgen levels, leading to decreased sexual desire, and estrogen levels, leading to vaginal dryness. Breastfeeding mothers are also more fatigued, from having to get up at night to feed their infants. Sexuality differences between breastfeeders and bottle-feeders diminish considerably after 12 months.

Should a woman breastfeed her baby? The issue has become highly politicized (Knaak, 2005). Much of the vast literature on breastfeeding has little to do with the relative advantages of breast milk or formula, but with occupational and domestic arrangements, daycare, maternal bonding, and the politics of domestic decision-making. Although breast-feeding has benefits for both mother and infant, each woman must weigh these benefits against the difficulties breastfeeding may pose for her.

Resumption of Ovulation and Menstruation

For close to a month after childbirth, women experience a reddish vaginal discharge called **lochia**. A non-nursing mother doesn't resume actual menstrual periods until two to three months postpartum. The first few cycles are likely to be irregular.

Many women incorrectly assume that they'll resume menstruating after childbirth by having a menstrual period and then ovulating two weeks later. In most cases, the opposite is true. Ovulation precedes the first menstrual period after childbirth. A woman can therefore become pregnant before the menstrual phase of her first postpartum cycle.

Some (but not all) women who suffer premenstrual syndrome before pregnancy find that their periods give them less discomfort after they give birth.

Resumption of Sexual Activity

The resumption of intercourse depends on a couple's level of sexual interest, the healing of episiotomies or other injuries, fatigue, the recommendations of physicians, and, of course, tradition. Obstetricians usually advise a six-week waiting period, for safety and comfort. One study of 570 women found that

Breast Is Best?
Breastfeeding seems to be the gold standard for mothers in Canada today. Why? Is it always possible? Under what circumstances should women not breastfeed their children?

they actually resumed sexual intercourse an average of seven weeks after childbirth (Byrd et al., 1998).

Women typically prefer to delay intercourse until it becomes physically comfortable—generally, when episiotomies and other lacerations have healed and the lochia has ended. This may take several weeks. Women who breastfeed may find that they have less vaginal lubrication, resulting in discomfort during intercourse. K-Y Jelly and other lubricants can help. Couples may enjoy other forms of sexual activity earlier, as soon as both partners are comfortable and interested.

The return of sexual interest and the resumption of sexual activity may take longer for some couples than for others. Sexual interest depends more on psychological than on physical factors. Many couples encounter declining sexual interest and activity in the first year after childbirth, generally because child care can sap energy and limit free time. Generally, couples whose sexual relationships were satisfying before parenthood tend to show greater sexual interest and to resume sexual activity earlier than those who had less satisfying relationships beforehand.

Canadian Birth Rates and Teen Pregnancy

Birth Rates

Birth rates in Canada have varied considerably over time. Immediately after the Second World War, the Canadian birth rate dramatically rose to its highest level since 1921, the previous high. In 1947, Canada's fertility rate was 3.6 children per woman. In the mid-1960s, with the introduction of the birth control pill, the number of births dropped sharply, reaching an all-time low in 2000.

Since then, the number of births has increased, mainly because of the increase in the birth rate among women who are 30 and older. The average age at which women have their first babies has climbed from 25.9 in 1980 to 29.2 in 2005. Thirty- to 34-year-old women have the highest proportion of births (Statistics Canada, 2007b).

Canadian women today have an average of 1.54 children each. This is below the level needed to replace the population, which is 2.1 children per Canadian woman. As Figure 10.4 shows, the lowest birth rates are in Newfoundland and Labrador, and the highest are in Nunavut and the Northwest Territories (Statistics Canada, 2007c.)

The provinces and territories with the highest birth rates also have the largest proportions of aboriginal people. Birth rates among aboriginal populations are much higher than among the general population.

Why is the birth rate among Canadian women lower now than in past generations? Why are women giving birth later in life? There are a number of reasons:

- Improved access to safe, effective contraception allows women to choose whether and when they'll have children, how many they'll have, and how far apart they'll space them.
- More women are completing post-secondary education during their child-bearing years, and are therefore delaying motherhood.
- Increasing numbers of women choose to limit the number of children they have, so they can continue working full time.
- Financial constraints lead some women to limit the number of children they decide to have.
- It's becoming more and more socially acceptable in Western society to choose not to have children.

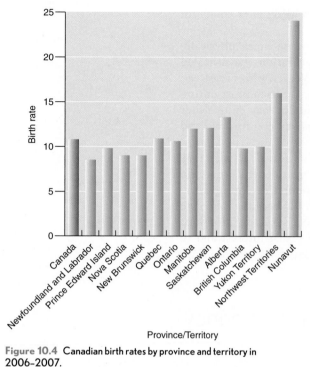

Figure 10.4 Canadian birth rates by province and territory in 2006–2007.

Note: From July 1 of 2006 to June 30 of 2007.

Source: Statistics Canada. CANSIM Tables 051-0001 and 051-0004 and Catalogue no. 91-213-X.

TEEN PREGNANCY The percentage of Canadian teens who become pregnant each year has declined sharply since the mid-1970s (McKay, 2006; McKay & Barrett, 2010). Looking at the most recent period for which Canadian statistics are available, the combined birth/abortion rate fell from 44.2 per 1000 15- to 19-year-old women in 1996 to 27.9 in 2006 (McKay & Barrett, 2010). When looked at separately, the birth rate among teens fell from 22.1 per 1000 in 1996 to 13.7 in 2006, and the abortion rate fell from 22.1 to 14.2 during the same period.

As Figure 10.5 shows, teen pregnancy rates have also been falling in other Western countries, such as the United States, England, and Wales (McKay & Barrett, 2010). The decline has been greater in Canada than in the United States, England, and Wales. Sweden has typically had a low teen pregnancy rate, but it has increased in recent years, until Canada's teen pregnancy rate is now lower than Sweden's.

A number of factors influence teen pregnancy rates. Anderson Moore (2008) categorizes these factors as compositional (e.g., demographic aspects of the population), distal (e.g., economic inequality), and proximal (e.g., contraceptive use).

COMPOSITIONAL FACTORS One compositional factor affecting teen pregnancy rates in Canada is the province or territory in which the young women live. In 2005, the teen birth/abortion rates were higher than the national average of 28.6 per 1000 in Saskatchewan (42.4), Manitoba (40.5), Alberta (33.0),

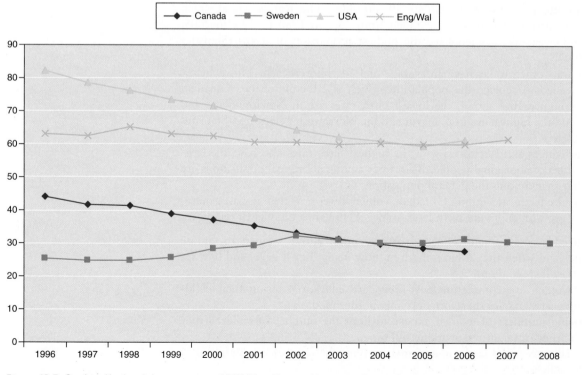

Figure 10.5 Combined birth and abortion rates per 1000 15- to 19-year-old women in Canada, Sweden, the United States, England, and Wales, 1996 to 2006.

Source: McKay, A., & Barrett, M. (2010). Trends in teen pregnancy rates from 1996–2006: A comparison of Canada, Sweden, USA, and England/Wales. The Canadian Journal of Human Sexuality, 19(1-2), 43–52.

Innovative Canadian Research

LIFE AFTER TEENAGE MOTHERHOOD

Teen motherhood has generally been associated with long-term, negative socioeconomic consequences, but it doesn't necessarily condemn women to low incomes for a lifetime, according to a Statistics Canada study.

The study, "Life After Teenage Motherhood," published in *Perspectives on Labour and Income*, used the Survey of Labour and Income Dynamics to examine the personal and long-term socioeconomic characteristics of 30- to 39-year-old women who'd given birth as teenagers. Specifically, it compared women who'd been teen mothers with those who'd been adult mothers on the basis of educational outcome, long-term labour force participation, and income status.

Overall, teen mothers in Canada had a lower probability than their adult counterparts of completing high school and post-secondary education, even after controlling for family background and other characteristics.

But the study found that education may help counter the negative impact of teen motherhood on labour-force participation and income status. Overall, women with similar education levels, regardless of when they'd first had children, had a similar likelihood of full-year, full-time employment. Teen and adult mothers with less than high school education were both less likely to be working in full-time jobs for the full year. On the other hand, teen mothers who completed post-secondary studies were actually more likely than their adult counterparts to work full time.

The study found similar results for the probability of living with low incomes. One-fifth (21%) of families of women who'd been teen mothers had incomes below Statistics Canada's low-income measure (LIM), compared with just 12% of families of women who'd been adults when they'd first given birth.

But education made a big difference. Both teen and adult mothers who both had less than high school were more likely to be living below the LIM than adult mothers with high school diplomas. Likewise, teen mothers and adult mothers who had completed postsecondary studies were less likely to fall below the LIM.

The study suggested that other unobserved characteristics—such as family support, social networks, and a variety of other resources, psychological traits, and other factors—may also influence socioeconomic outcomes. Family background remains influential even in the long run. Women whose mothers finished high school or post-secondary studies were five percentage points more likely to work full time through the full year than women whose mothers had less than high school.

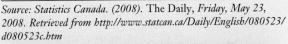
Source: Statistics Canada. (2008). The Daily, *Friday, May 23, 2008. Retrieved from http://www.statcan.ca/Daily/English/080523/d080523c.htm*

Teen Motherhoo.
Giving birth to a child during the teenage years can present significant challenges to a young woman. Teen mothers who receive adequate support from their families and communities and who are able to continue with their education are more likely to do well in the future.

Quebec (32.4), Yukon (31.4), and British Columbia (29.3), and lower than the national average in Nova Scotia (23.7), Ontario (23.0), New Brunswick (22.6), Newfoundland (22.5), and Prince Edward Island (18.9) (Statistics Canada, 2007).

DISTAL FACTORS It's been shown that teen pregnancy rates are higher among economically disadvantaged populations (Best Start, 2007).

The rates for under-18 children in households whose incomes are lower than the national medians are higher in the United States and England than in Canada and Sweden (UNICEF, 2007). And as we have seen, the United States and England have higher teen pregnancy rates than Canada and Sweden.

It's likely that teenaged women who feel optimistic about their futures with respect to education and employment opportunities are more likely to delay childbearing until they're older (Best Start, 2008).

CRITICAL THINKING QUESTIONS

Can you think of reasons the teen pregnancy rate is higher in some parts of Canada than in others?

TABLE 10.1

Sexual Orientation and Pregnancy Rates Among Sexually Active Teenagers in British Columbia

Sexual Orientation	Males*	Females
Gay	17%	
Lesbian		13%
Bisexual	17%	9%
Heterosexual	5%	5%

*Note: Male percentages refer to teenage males who had a heterosexual partner who became pregnant.

Source: Saewyc, E. M., Poon, C., Wang, N., Homma, Y., Smith, A., & McCreary Centre Society. (2007). Not yet equal: The health of lesbian, gay & bisexual youth in BC. Vancouver: McCreary Centre Society.

PROXIMAL FACTORS It's obviously no coincidence that as the teen pregnancy rate in Canada has fallen, the percentage of sexually active teenagers who use contraception has increased.

A study of British Columbia youth found that the percentage who'd used an effective birth control method (e.g., the pill, condom) at last intercourse increased from 77.4% in 1998 to 86.9% in 2003 (Saewyc, Taylor, Homma, & Ogilvie, 2008).

Why are more sexually active teens using contraception now than in the past? It's likely that a range of factors are involved. Perhaps it's because today's teens have an easier time finding information about contraception and sexual health, using sources such as the internet, and this has made them more knowledgeable about the issues. Perhaps it's because teens feel more comfortable buying condoms or asking their doctors for prescriptions for birth-control pills. Perhaps it's because more teens are getting high-quality sexual-health education in schools. (We'll discuss sexual-health education in Chapter 12.)

SEXUAL ORIENTATION AND TEEN PREGNANCY A study of 74 000 teenagers in British Columbia led by the University of British Columbia's Elizabeth Saewyc (2007) found that pregnancy rates are higher among sexually active gay, lesbian, and bisexual teenagers than among heterosexual teenagers. (See Table 10.1.)

According to Saewyc, many gay and lesbian youth, fearing stigmatization because of their sexual orientations, engage in heterosexual sex to mask their sexual preferences. Some want to experiment to see whether they can "cure" themselves of their same-sex orientations. Others may use pregnancy as a means of proving to their peers that they're heterosexual. Sexual assault can also lead to pregnancy among lesbian youth (Saewyc et al., 2007).

Summing Up

Conception is the union of a sperm cell and an ovum. Fertilization normally occurs in a fallopian tube.

Optimizing the chances of conception means engaging in intercourse at the time of ovulation. Ovulation can be predicted by calculating the woman's basal body temperature, analyzing the woman's urine for luteinizing hormone, or tracking the thickness of vaginal mucus.

Fertility problems in the male include low sperm counts, irregularly shaped sperm, low sperm motility, certain chronic or infectious diseases, trauma to the testes, autoimmune responses to sperm, and pituitary imbalances and/or thyroid disease.

The major causes of infertility in women include irregular ovulation, obstructions or malfunctions of the reproductive tract, endometriosis, and the decline of hormone levels with age. Failure to ovulate can often be overcome by fertility drugs. Methods for overcoming other female fertility problems include in vitro fertilization, GIFT, ZIFT, donor IVF, embryonic transfer, and surrogate motherhood.

In Canada, the federal government act respecting assisted human reproduction and related research, whose short title is the Assisted Human Reproduction Act, includes a controversial provision that allows researchers to use stem cells from embryos left over from infertility treatments.

Early signs of pregnancy include a missed period and the presence of human chorionic gonadotropin (hCG) in the blood or urine.

Pregnancy tests detect hCG in the woman's urine or blood.

Miscarriages have many causes, including chromosomal defects in the fetus and abnormalities of the placenta and uterus.

Most health professionals concur that, in most cases, intercourse is safe until the start of labour.

A woman's psychological response to pregnancy reflects her desire to be pregnant, her physical changes, and her attitudes toward these changes.

The germinal stage is the period from conception to implantation.

The embryonic stage begins with implantation, extends to about the eighth week of development, and is characterized by differentiation of the major organ systems.

The fetal stage begins by the ninth week, continues until the birth of the baby, and is characterized by continuing maturation of the fetus's organ systems and dramatic increases in size.

Environmental factors that affect prenatal development include maternal diet, maternal diseases and disorders, and maternal drug use. Maternal malnutrition has been linked to low birth weight and infant mortality. Exposure to particular teratogens causes the greatest harm during critical periods of vulnerability.

Chromosomal and genetic abnormalities can lead to birth defects.

In the first stage of childbirth, uterine contractions efface and dilate the cervix, so the baby can pass through. The second stage begins when the cervix is fully dilated, and ends with the birth of the baby. During the third stage, the placenta is expelled.

Contemporary methods for facilitating childbirth include anaesthetized childbirth, natural childbirth, the Lamaze method, and Caesarean section.

Prenatal anoxia can cause brain damage and mental retardation in the child. Preterm and low-birth-weight babies have heightened risks of infant mortality.

Many new mothers experience transient mood changes after childbirth. Women with postpartum depression experience lingering depression after childbirth.

Breastfeeding is associated with fewer infections and allergic reactions in the baby than bottle-feeding.

Obstetricians usually advise waiting about six weeks after childbirth before resuming intercourse. Couples needn't wait this long to enjoy other forms of sexual activity.

In recent years, the teen pregnancy rate has fallen substantially in Canada. Teen mothers are more likely to fare well if they have the support of their families and are able to continue with their education.

Test Yourself

Multiple-Choice Questions

1. **According to Statistics Canada, in 2005, the average age of Canadian women having their first babies was:**
   (a) 25.2
   (b) 27.2
   (c) 29.2
   (d) 31.2

2. _____ **may carry either X or Y chromosomes.**
   (a) Sperm
   (b) Ova
   (c) Gametes
   (d) Blastocysts

3. **The most common cause of fertility problems in males is:**
   (a) Sexually transmitted infections.
   (b) Injury to the testes.
   (c) Low sperm counts.
   (d) Older age.

4. **All of the following can lead to infertility in women except:**
   (a) Failure to ovulate.
   (b) Sexually transmitted infections.
   (c) Declining levels of estrogen.
   (d) Use of illicit drugs.

(continued)

5. As of 2010, the only province or territory to cover the cost of in vitro fertilization was:
   (a) British Columbia.
   (b) Quebec.
   (c) New Brunswick.
   (d) Alberta.

6. The first stage of prenatal development is the _____ stage.
   (a) embryonic
   (b) placental
   (c) fetal
   (d) germinal

7. Most ectopic pregnancies occur in the:
   (a) Ovaries.
   (b) Cervix.
   (c) Fallopian tubes.
   (d) Uterus.

8. Which of the following had the lowest teen pregnancy rate in 2005?
   (a) Sweden.
   (b) Canada.
   (c) United States.
   (d) England and Wales.

9. Approximately _____ of women experience some sadness, irritability, or low mood following the birth of a baby.
   (a) 25%
   (b) 40%
   (c) 50%
   (d) 70%

10. Which statement about postpartum depression (PPD) is false?
   (a) Women who lack social support are more likely to suffer from PPD.
   (b) PPD can involve feelings of extreme sadness and apathy.
   (c) PPD may be caused by a combination of physiological and psychological factors.
   (d) Women with PPD are always a danger to their babies.

You'll find answers to the "Test Yourself" questions on page 495.

Critical Thinking

1. A couple you're friends with tells you they're pregnant with a fetus that has a chromosomal or genetic abnormality. They're considering an abortion, and want your opinion. How do you respond?

2. A good friend of yours is pregnant. You notice that she's still drinking alcohol and smoking cigarettes. Do you talk to her about how these behaviours could harm her fetus? Why or why not?

3. In your opinion, what are the most important factors that explain the decline in teen pregnancy rates in Canada?

4. Sex selection raises many moral and ethical issues. Some people wonder whether people have the right to select the sex of their children. Where do you stand on this issue?

MySearchLab

MySearchLab offers extensive help to students with their writing and research project and provides round-the-clock access to credible and reliable source material. Take a tour at **www.mysearchlab.com**.

CHAPTER ELEVEN

Contraception and Abortion

Condom A sheath made of animal membrane or latex that covers the penis during coitus and serves as a barrier to sperm following ejaculation.

People have been devising means of contraception since they became aware of the relationship between penile–vaginal intercourse and conception. Greek and Roman women placed absorbent materials within their vaginas to absorb semen.

The use of sheaths or coverings for the penis has a long history. Sheaths worn over the penis as decorative covers can be traced to ancient Egypt (1350 BCE). Sheaths of linen were first described in European writings in 1564 by the Italian anatomist Fallopius (after whom the fallopian tube is named). The term **"condom"** wasn't used to describe the penile sheath until the eighteenth century. At that time, sheaths made of animal intestines became popular as a means of preventing sexually transmitted infections and unwanted pregnancies.

Condoms made of rubber (hence the slang term "rubbers") were introduced shortly after Charles Goodyear invented vulcanization of rubber in 1843. Many other forms of contraception were also widely used in the nineteenth century, including withdrawal, vaginal sponges, and douching.

Contraception in Canada

Contraceptive Use Among Canadian Women

Amanda Black and her colleagues (2009) conducted a national survey of the contraceptive practises of 2751 Canadian women of reproductive age who'd had penile–vaginal intercourse within the previous six months. Although none of the women were trying to get pregnant, 410 (14.9%) used no contraception. The methods used by the women who did use contraception are shown in Table 11.1.

TABLE 11.1

Contraceptive Methods Used by Canadian Women for Penile-Vaginal Intercourse Within the Previous Six Months (%)

Contraceptive Method	Ages 15–19	Ages 20–29	Ages 30–39	Ages 40+
Male condom	74.6	55.5	48.8	42.5
Oral contraceptive	66.6	58.3	31.5	17.1
Withdrawal	17.3	12.0	10.3	8.1
Male sterilization	0.2	1.4	9.6	19.6
Female sterilization	0.0	0.7	8.1	16.4
Rhythm method	1.5	2.8	3.0	6.6
Natural family planning	1.5	1.3	5.2	2.4
Injection	1.8	3.4	2.6	1.0
IUD	0.5	1.8	5.8	0.8
Morning-after pill	4.4	1.7	1.5	0.0
Contraceptive patch	1.6	2.3	0.7	0.0
Contraceptive sponge	0.2	1.0	0.7	1.0
Female condom	0.4	0.2	0.0	0.8
Diaphragm	0.3	0.5	0.0	0.0
Cervical cap	0.2	0.0	0.0	0.0

Note: Column totals may exceed 100%, as women were allowed to choose more than one method.

Source: Adapted from Black, A., Yang, Q., Wen, S. W., Lalonde, A. B., Guilbert, E., & Fisher, W. (2009). Contraceptive use among Canadian women of reproductive age: Results of a national survey. Journal of Obstetrics and Gynaecology Canada, *31(7), 627-640.*

A World of Diversity

A HISTORY OF BIRTH CONTROL IN CANADA

Birth control was legal in Canada until the nineteenth century, when laws were introduced forbidding both birth control and abortion. It was even illegal to provide information about birth control. Because contraceptives were associated with loose morals and prostitution, it was considered unacceptable for doctors to discuss birth control with their patients.

The movement to legalize contraception in Canada began in the 1920s, when female activists in Vancouver formed the Canadian Birth Control League. In the following years, several women's groups across Canada began to lobby politicians to change the law that prohibited the use of birth control. A few men also joined the cause.

Despite protests by some physicians, Mary Hawkins established the first Canadian birth control clinic in Hamilton, Ontario, in the early 1930s. In 1937, clinics were also set up in Windsor and Kitchener. A prominent supporter of birth control education at that time was A. R. Kaufman, a

wealthy Kitchener businessman who hired women to deliver birth-control information door to door.

The first major legal challenge to the law forbidding the dissemination of birth control information came with the arrest of Dorothea Palmer (an employee of Kaufman) for promoting birth control in the poorer districts of the Ottawa region. Her arrest sparked protests and support by birth-control activists, including Kaufman, who helped win her acquittal in court. This victory helped legitimize birth-control education and spurred the birth-control movement to make greater efforts in the struggle to legalize all birth-control activities.

By the 1960s, the use of contraceptives (particularly the birth-control pill) had become so widespread that most Canadians didn't realize contraceptives were still illegal. The 1960 arrest of Toronto pharmacist Harold Fine for selling condoms enraged many Canadians. As a result, Barbara Cadbury and her husband George Cadbury established the Planned Parenthood Association of Toronto in 1961, with the objective of amending the Criminal Code.

In 1965, another leader in the birth control movement, Dr. Marion Powell, opened the first city-funded public health clinic (focused on family planning) in Scarborough, Ontario. It wasn't until 1969, under the leadership of Prime Minister Pierre Trudeau, that contraception became legal and abortion was allowed under restricted conditions.

Today, contraceptives are widely advertised in popular magazines and openly displayed on pharmacy shelves.

The use of **artificial contraception** continues to be opposed by many groups, including the Roman Catholic Church. Yet many individual Catholics, including many priests, hold liberal attitudes toward contraception.

Sources: Planned Parenthood Federation of Canada. (1999). A history of birth control in Canada. Brochure. Ottawa: Planned Parenthood Federation of Canada. Liu, K. E., & Fisher, W. A. (2002). Canadian physicians' role in contraception from the 19th century to now. Journal of Obstetrics and Gynaecology Canada, 24(3), 239–44.

It's immediately apparent from these finding that the vast majority of Canadian women rely on male condoms and oral contraceptives for birth control. When all age groups were combined, 54.3% used condoms and 43.7% used oral contraceptives. Withdrawal was the third most popular method, used by 11.6% of the women.

Artificial contraception
A method of contraception that applies a human-made device.

Contraceptive Use Among Canadian Teens

A 2005–2006 Canadian study called "Health Behaviour in School-Aged Children" found that about one-quarter of students in grade 10 had experienced sexual intercourse (Boyce et al., 2008). The contraceptive methods used most often by these sexually experienced youth at last intercourse were condoms (males, 47%; females, 40%) and birth-control pills (males, 25%; females, 33%). Withdrawal was the third most common method (males, 8%; females, 14%).

A large-scale study of teenagers in British Columbia (Saewyc et al., 2007) found that condom use during last intercourse increased between 1992 and 2003 (from 64% to 75% among males, and from 53% to 64% among females). As teenagers get older and form longer-term relationships, they switch from condoms to the pill.

CRITICAL THINKING QUESTIONS

What are some of the obstacles teens and young adults might encounter in discussing birth control with their sexual partners?

Methods of Contraception

Oral Contraceptives (The Pill)

Oral contraceptive A contraceptive that consists of sex hormones and is swallowed.

Combination pill A birth-control pill that contains synthetic estrogen and progesterone.

Minipill A birth-control pill that contains synthetic progesterone, but no estrogen.

An **oral contraceptive** is commonly referred to as a birth-control pill, or simply "the pill." There are many kinds of birth-control pills, varying in hormone types and dosages. Birth-control pills fall into two major categories: combination pills and minipills.

    Combination pills contain a combination of synthetic forms of the hormones estrogen and progesterone. (The synthetic form of progesterone is called progestin.) Most combination pills provide a steady dose of synthetic estrogen and progesterone. Other combination pills, called multiphasic pills, vary the dosages of these hormones across the menstrual cycle, reducing the overall dosages and possible side effects women are exposed to. The **minipill** contains only synthetic progesterone (progestin).

HOW IT WORKS Women can't conceive when they're already pregnant, because their bodies suppress maturation of egg follicles and ovulation. The combination pill fools the brain into thinking the woman is already pregnant, so no additional ova mature or are released. If ovulation doesn't take place, a woman can't become pregnant.

    In a normal menstrual cycle, low estrogen levels during and just after the menstrual phase stimulate the pituitary gland to secrete follicle-stimulating hormone (FSH), which in turn stimulates maturation of the ovarian follicles. The estrogen in the combination pill inhibits FSH production, so follicles don't mature. The progestin inhibits the pituitary's secretion of luteinizing hormone (LH), which would otherwise lead to ovulation. The woman continues to have menstrual periods, but there are no unfertilized ova to be sloughed off in the menstrual flow.

    The combination pill is taken for 21 days of the typical 28-day cycle. Then, for seven days, the woman takes no pill, or she takes an inert placebo pill, to maintain the habit of taking a pill a day. The sudden drop in hormone levels causes the endometrium to disintegrate and menstruation to follow three or four days after the last pill is taken. The cycle is then repeated.

    The progestin in the combination pill also increases the thickness and acidity of the cervical mucus. The mucus thus becomes a more resistant barrier to sperm, and inhibits development of the endometrium. Therefore, even if an egg were somehow to mature and be released, sperm wouldn't be likely to survive the passage through the cervix. Even if sperm were somehow to succeed in fertilizing an egg, the failure of the endometrium to develop would mean the fertilized ovum couldn't become implanted in the uterus. Progestin may also impede the progress of ova through the fallopian tubes and make it more difficult for sperm to penetrate the ova.

    The minipill contains progestin, but no estrogen. Minipills are taken daily through the menstrual cycle, even during menstruation. They act in two ways: they thicken the cervical mucus, to impede the passage of sperm through the cervix, and they render the inner lining of the uterus less receptive to a fertilized egg. Thus, even if the woman does conceive, the fertilized egg will pass from her body, rather than becoming implanted in her uterine wall.

EFFECTIVENESS When it's used consistently and correctly, the failure rate of the birth-control pill is very low—0.5% or less, depending on the type of pill. (See Table 11.2.) Under typical use, the failure rate increases to 3%. Failures can occur when women forget to take the pill for two days or more, don't use backup methods when they first go on the pill, or switch from one brand to another.

    In 2004, the World Health Organization (WHO) issued new guidelines for missed pills. A woman who misses a pill should take one as soon as possible,

CRITICAL THINKING QUESTIONS

Most methods of birth control, such as the pill, are used by women. Does this mean birth control is primarily a woman's responsibility? To what extent do men share the responsibility for protection from unwanted pregnancy?

TABLE 11.2

Failure Rates, Reversibility, and Protection Against Sexually Transmitted Infections by Various Methods of Birth Control (in Percentage of Women Who Become Pregnant Within the First Year of Use)

Method	Percent (%) of Women Who Have an Unplanned Pregnancy Within the First Year of Use		Is It Reversibie?	Does It Protect Against Sexually Transmitted Infections (STIs)?
	Typical Use[1]	Consistent, Correct Use		
None	85	85	yes	no
Spermicides	26	6	yes	no
Rhythm Methods	20		yes	no
Calendar		9		
Ovulation Method		3		
Basal Body Temperature		2		
Post-Ovulation		1		
Withdrawal	19	4	yes	no
Cervical Cap[2]	20–40	10–30	yes	some
Diaphragm[2]	20	6	yes	some
Condom alone				
Female condom	21	5	yes	(scarce information)
Male condom	14	3	yes	yes
The Pill	3		yes	no, but may *reduce* the risk of pelvic inflammatory disease.
Progestin Only		0.5		
Combined		0.1		
IUD				
Progestasert	2.0	1.5	yes, except if fertility is impaired	no, and may *increase* the risk of pelvic inflammatory disease.
ParaGard Copper T 380A	0.8	0.6	yes, except if fertility is impaired	no, and may *increase* the risk of pelvic inflammatory disease.
Depo-Provera	0.3	0.3	yes	no
Injectable Contraceptives	0.3	0.3	yes	no
Female Sterilization	0.5	0.5	questionable	no
Male Sterilization	0.15	0.10	questionable	no

[1]Accidental pregnancies among typical couples. [2]With spermicide.

Sources: American Academy of Family Physicians. (2006). Depo-Provera: An injectable contraceptive. Retrieved from http://familydoctor.org/043.xml?printxml
Hatcher, R. A., Trussell, J., Nelson, A. L., Cates, W., Stewart, F., & Kowal, D. (Eds.) (2007). Contraceptive technology, 19th rev. ed. New York: Ardent Media.
Planned Parenthood Federation of America Inc. (2006). Planned parenthood. Retrieved from http://www.plannedparenthood.org/pp2/portal

and then continue taking one each day. If she misses three or more combination pills in a row, however, she should use condoms or abstain from sexual intercourse until she has taken pills for seven days in a row. With the lowest-dose pills, a woman should take extra precautions after missing just two pills (Info Reports, 2005).

REVERSIBILITY A woman may temporarily experience reduced fertility after discontinuing oral contraceptives, but their use is not associated with permanent infertility. Nearly all women begin ovulating regularly within three months of suspending use (Hatcher et al., 2008). When a woman appears not to be ovulating after going off the pill, a drug like clomiphene is often used to induce ovulation.

ADVANTAGES AND DISADVANTAGES The great advantage of oral contraception is that it's nearly 100% effective when it's used properly. Unlike many other forms of contraception, such as the condom and the diaphragm, its use doesn't interfere with sexual spontaneity or diminish sexual sensation.

The birth-control pill may also have some healthful side effects. It appears to reduce the risk of pelvic inflammatory disease (PID), benign ovarian cysts, and fibrocystic (benign) breast growths. The pill regularizes menstrual cycles and reduces menstrual cramping and premenstrual discomfort.

Most oral contraceptives in Canada are approved for 28-day cycles, meaning a woman takes a hormone-containing pill each day for 21 days in a row, then takes no pill or a sugar (placebo) pill for the next seven days. Some physicians prescribe oral contraceptives (mainly multiphasics) for extended cycles for women who have menstrual difficulties such as heavy bleeding, crampy periods, and endometriosis. The recently introduced Seasonale is the only oral contraceptive that's been specifically approved by Health Canada for an extended cycle of 91 days. For 84 days, a woman takes an active pill that contains ethinyl estradiol and levonorgestrel, then for seven days she takes no pill or a sugar (placebo) pill. Taking the pill in this way means fewer menstrual cycles—typically, four periods per year.

The pill may be helpful in treating iron-deficiency anemia and facial acne. The combination pill reduces the risks of ovarian and endometrial cancer, even for a number of years after the woman stops taking it (Hatcher et al., 2008).

The pill does have some disadvantages. It confers no protection against STIs. Moreover, it may reduce the effectiveness of antibiotics used to treat STIs. Going on the pill requires medical consultation, so a woman must plan to begin using the pill at least several weeks before becoming sexually active or before discontinuing the use of other contraceptives.

There has been concern about a potential link between oral contraceptive use and breast cancer. However, results from several large-scale studies show no overall increase in the rates of breast cancer among pill users (Hatcher et al., 2008). Marchbanks and her colleagues (2002) compared 4575 women who had breast cancer with 4682 controls, for example, and found no increased risk for breast cancer among women who were using or had used oral contraceptives. The pill didn't increase the risk of breast cancer in women with family histories of the disease, either.

Among the main drawbacks of birth-control pills are potential side effects and health risks. Although a good deal of research suggests that the pill is safe for healthy women, in 2006 the American College of Obstetricians and Gynecologists released a bulletin suggesting caution for women with various pre-existing medical conditions. These include hypertension, diabetes, migraine headaches, fibrocystic breast tissue, uterine fibroids, and elevated cholesterol levels.

The estrogen in combination pills may produce side effects such as nausea and vomiting, fluid retention (which leaves a woman feeling bloated), weight gain, increased vaginal discharge, headaches, tenderness in the breasts, and dizziness. Many of these are temporary. When they persist, women may be switched from one pill to another, perhaps to one with lower doses of hormones. Pregnant women produce high estrogen levels in the corpus luteum and placenta. The combination pill artificially raises levels of estrogen, so it's not surprising that some women who use it have side effects that mimic the early signs of pregnancy, such as weight gain and nausea ("morning sickness"). Weight gain can result from estrogen (through fluid retention) or progestin (through increased appetite and muscle development) (Hatcher et al., 2008). Women who experience high blood pressure from taking the pill are usually advised to switch to another form of contraception.

Many women experience hormone withdrawal symptoms during the week they don't take the active pill (Sulak et al., 2000). These include headaches, pelvic pain, bloating, and breast tenderness.

Many women have avoided the pill because of the risk of blood clots. Most birth-control pills today have lower dosages of estrogen than pills in the 1960s and 1970s, and therefore much lower risks for blood clotting (Hatcher et al., 2008). Still, women who are at increased risk for blood clotting, such as those with histories of circulatory problems or stroke, are typically advised not to use the pill.

Women who are considering the pill need to discuss the benefits and risks with their physicians. For the great majority of young, healthy women in their twenties and early thirties, the pill is unlikely to cause blood clots or other cardiovascular problems (Hatcher et al., 2008). Although research has found the pill safe for most women under age 35 who don't smoke, pill users may have a slightly higher chance than nonusers of experiencing blood clots in the veins and lungs, strokes, and heart attacks (Rako, 2003).

Some women shouldn't be on the pill at all. Woman should avoid the pill if they've had circulatory problems, blood clots, coronary disease, heart attacks, strokes, breast or uterine cancers, undiagnosed genital bleeding, liver tumours, or sickle-cell anemia (because of associated blood-clotting problems). Because of the increased risk for cardiovascular problems, women over 35 who smoke should exercise caution with the combination pill (Hatcher et al., 2008). Nursing mothers should also avoid the pill, to prevent passing the hormones to their babies through their milk.

The pill may also have psychological effects. Some users report depression and irritability. Switching brands or altering the dosage may help. There's insufficient evidence about the effects of lower-estrogen pills on sexual desire.

Because they can produce vaginal dryness, minipills can hinder vaginal lubrication during intercourse, decreasing sexual sensation and making sex painful. Irregular bleeding between menstrual periods, or so-called breakthrough bleeding, is another common side effect of the minipill. Irregular bleeding should be brought to a doctor's attention.

Evidence linking the pill to increased risk of cervical cancer is mixed. Some studies show a link, and others don't (Hatcher et al., 2008).

Women considering the pill are advised to have thorough medical evaluations, to rule out pre-existing conditions that might make its use unsafe. Women who begin to use the pill, regardless of their age or risk status, should pay attention to changes in their physical condition, have regular checkups, and promptly report any physical complaints or unusual symptoms to their physicians.

EMERGENCY CONTRACEPTION (EC) Emergency contraception—the so-called morning-after pill—is taken after unprotected sexual intercourse or when contraception fails, such as when a condom breaks.

Two forms of EC are available in Canada (Katzman & Taddeo, 2010). The most popular is two 0.75-milligram tablets of levonorgestrel (known as Plan B), taken together. The other, known as the Yuzpe regimen, is a hormonal method that combines multiple birth-control pills.

According to Katzman and Taddeo (2010), Plan B has fewer side effects and is more effective than the Yuzpe regimen. Plan B isn't generally considered an abortion pill, because it can't end an established pregnancy. It prevents pregnancy by preventing the joining of sperm and egg and preventing a fertilized egg from attaching to the uterine wall. About half of Canadian women report that they're familiar with the morning-after pill (Fisher et al., 2003).

Innovative Canadian Research

EMERGENCY CONTRACEPTION USE

In British Columbia, Soon and her colleagues (2005) studied EC use both before and after the treatment became available without a prescription. They made several key findings:

- EC use was highest among women who were 20 to 24 years old, and second highest among women who were 15 to 19 years old.
- More than half of the users (56%) obtained EC within 24 hours of having unprotected intercourse, and almost all (98%) within 72 hours.

- Very few women used EC on a regular basis. Only 2.5% received EC three or more times a year, and just 1.1% obtained EC for future use.
- More than half of the women receiving EC (56%) reported that they'd used birth control methods that had failed.
- The availability of EC without a prescription significantly increased its use.

The researchers concluded that availability of EC without a prescription will be an important factor in reducing unwanted pregnancies and abortions in Canada.

EC should be taken as soon as possible after unprotected intercourse. It's most effective when taken within 72 hours, though recent research suggests it may be effective even when taken within 120 hours. Overall, EC is relatively effective in reducing the probability of pregnancy after unprotected intercourse. Studies have shown pregnancy rates of 1% to 3% among women using Plan B (Katzman & Taddeo, 2010).

In 2005, Health Canada allowed pharmacists to provide Plan B without a prescription. Pharmacies were required to keep supplies of Plan B behind the counter, which meant women who wanted Plan B had to first consult with the pharmacists. In British Columbia, more than half of the women who obtained the morning-after pill from pharmacists did so during evenings and weekends (Planned Parenthood Federation of Canada, 2002). In 2008, Health Canada permitted Plan B to be available on customer-accessible pharmacy shelves, rather than behind the counter. Along with this change, it was expected that women would no longer need to consult pharmacists about its use. Some pharmacists have resisted this change, however, and kept Plan B behind the counter, believing their customers should be counselled on the proper use of this medication.

EC pills have a higher hormone content than most birth-control pills. For this reason, nausea is a common side effect. Nausea is usually mild and passes within a day or two after treatment, but it can be treated with antinausea medications.

The Contraceptive Patch

The contraceptive patch is another method of delivering estrogen and progestin, to prevent ovulation and implantation. A patch named Ortho Evra has been available in Canada since 2004. The patch is thin and measures about five centimetres. It's worn on the abdomen, buttocks, upper arm, or upper torso, but not on the breasts. The patch contains a week's worth of hormones, which it gradually releases into the bloodstream. The patch is worn weekly for three weeks, then the fourth week is patch-free, to allow menstrual bleeding. It can be worn in water.

Like the birth-control pill, when used correctly, the patch is more than 99% effective. Women who use the patch needn't think about contraception daily. Also like the pill, the patch doesn't interrupt sex. Its side effects and potential hazards are similar to those of the pill.

The Vaginal Ring

A relatively new contraceptive in Canada is a vaginal ring, called the NuvaRing. The vaginal ring delivers hormones through the skin. Shaped like a diaphragm, the ring contains a combination of estrogen and progestin. A doctor's prescription is needed to obtain the ring from a pharmacy.

The ring is inserted into the vagina and worn for three consecutive weeks, followed by a ring-free week, to allow menstruation. At the end of the ring-free week, the woman inserts another ring, beginning a new cycle.

The ring is left in place during sex. If it slips out of the vagina, it can be reinserted. Most men and women don't notice it during intercourse, although some women may experience vaginal discomfort. The ring is as effective as the birth control pill, and may be more effective if a woman has trouble remembering to take her pill every day.

More research is needed on both the ring and the patch, to determine whether they have long-term side effects.

Plan B.
The morning-after pill is now available in Canada without a prescription.

Injectable Contraception

Depo-Provera is an injectable hormone solution that's available by prescription. Containing just progestin, it prevents ovulation, and is 99.7% effective in preventing pregnancy. It's administered by a needle in the muscle of the arm or buttocks every 12 weeks, preventing pregnancy for three months.

Injectable contraception has the advantage of being highly effective, permitting spontaneous sex, and remaining effective without having to be taken every day. It has side effects similar to those of other types of hormonal contraceptives, including oral contraceptives. These include vaginal bleeding, headaches, tenderness in the breasts, irregular menstrual cycles, weight gain, bloating, nausea, and vomiting. Prolonged use—two years or more—has been associated with bone loss. Depo-Provera's effects on fertility are reversible, but ovulation may take a few months to return.

Injectable contraceptives are usually not recommended for women who smoke or have elevated blood pressure, breast or uterine cancers, histories of blood clotting, histories of heart attack or stroke, diabetes, liver disease, or hormone allergies.

Intrauterine Devices (IUDs)

Intrauterine devices (IUDs) are used by more than 100 million women around the world (Hatcher, 2008). Most of them live in China, where nearly one in three married women uses an IUD during her child-bearing years. By contrast, IUDs are used by less than 5% of sexually active women of reproductive age in Canada (Black et al., 2009).

An IUD is a small object that comes in a variety of shapes and is inserted into the uterus by a physician or a nurse practitioner. A fine plastic thread or string hangs down from the IUD into the vagina, so the woman can check to be sure it's still in place.

Two main intrauterine devices and systems are currently available in Canada: copper IUDs (Flexi-T and Nova-T) and a levonorgestrel-releasing IUD system (Mirena). These devices are about 99% effective for up to five years. The IUD prevents sperm from fertilizing an egg. If sperm does fertilize the egg, the IUD prevents the fertilized egg from implanting in the uterus. Women who

Intrauterine device (IUD)
A small object that is inserted into the uterus and left in place to prevent conception.

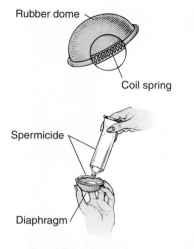

Rubber dome

Coil spring

Spermicide

Diaphragm

Figure 11.1 A diaphragm.
The diaphragm is a shallow cup or dome made of latex. It must be fitted to the contours of the vagina by a health professional. The diaphragm forms a barrier to sperm, but should be used in conjunction with a spermicidal cream or jelly.

Diaphragm A shallow rubber cup or dome that's fitted to the contours of a woman's vagina. It's coated with a spermicide and inserted before intercourse, to prevent conception.

use IUDs are advised to check the strings several times a month, to ensure that the IUDs are in place.

IUDs can be readily removed by professionals. About nine out of 10 former IUD users who wish become pregnant do so within a year. A major advantage of the Mirena IUD system is that it reduces menstrual bleeding and cramping (Hatcher et al., 2006).

IUDs are highly effective and relatively maintenance-free. So, why aren't they more popular? One reason is side effects. The most common are excessive menstrual cramping, irregular bleeding (spotting) between periods, and heavier-than-usual menstrual bleeding (Hatcher et al., 2008). A more serious concern is the risk of pelvic inflammatory disease, which is serious and can become life-threatening if left untreated. PID can produce scar tissue that blocks the fallopian tubes, causing infertility.

Women with pelvic infections shouldn't use IUDs. Women with risk factors for PID—including recent episodes of gonorrhea or chlamydia—may also wish to consider the advisability of using IUDs. IUD users are also at greater risk for ectopic pregnancies.

The Diaphragm

The **diaphragm** is a shallow cup or dome made of thin latex rubber. (See Figure 11.1.) The rim is a flexible metal ring covered with rubber. Diaphragms come in different sizes, to allow a precise fit.

A diaphragm is available by prescription, and must be fitted to the contours of the vagina by a health-care professional. Several sizes and types may be tried during a fitting.

HOW IT WORKS The diaphragm is inserted and removed by the woman, much like a tampon. It's akin to a condom in that it forms a barrier against sperm when placed snugly over the cervical opening. Yet it's unreliable when used alone. It should be used in conjunction with a spermicidal cream or jelly.

HOW IT'S USED The woman (or her partner) places a tablespoon of spermicidal cream or jelly on the inside of the cup and spreads it inside the rim. The woman opens the inner lips of her vagina with one hand, and squeezes the ring to fold the diaphragm with the other. She inserts the diaphragm against the cervix, with the inner side facing upward (see Figure 11.2).

The diaphragm should be left in place *at least six hours* after intercourse, to allow the spermicide to kill all remaining sperm in the vagina (Hatcher et al., 2008).

EFFECTIVENESS As Table 11.2 indicates, if the diaphragm is used consistently and correctly, is failure rate is estimated to be 6% during the first year of use. In typical use, however, the failure rate is believed to be three times as high—18%. Some women become pregnant because they don't use their diaphragms during every intercourse experience. Effectiveness is also seriously compromised when the diaphragm is used without a spermicide.

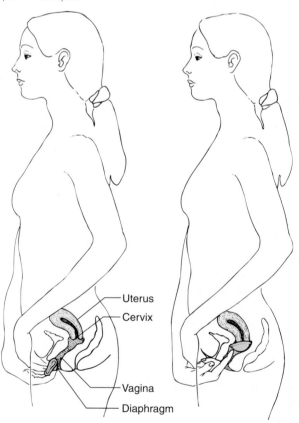

Uterus

Cervix

Vagina

Diaphragm

Insertion of diaphragm

Figure 11.2 Inserting and checking the diaphragm.
Women are instructed in how to insert of the diaphragm by health-care professionals.

ADVANTAGES AND DISADVANTAGES The major advantage of the diaphragm is that it's a fairly

The Condom.
Condoms were once considered a man's domain. Today, many Canadian women insist on their use, and it's often the woman who buys and carries them.

effective means of birth control when it's used correctly. It can be used as needed, whereas the pill must be used every day.

The major disadvantage of the diaphragm is the high pregnancy rate associated with typical use. Nearly one in five typical users (18%) of the diaphragm combined with spermicidal cream or jelly become pregnant during the first year of use (Hatcher et al., 2008). Another disadvantage is the need to insert the diaphragm before intercourse, which the couple may find disruptive.

The Cervical Cap

The cervical cap is a dome-shaped rubber cup. It comes in different sizes, and must be fitted by a health-care professional. It's smaller than the diaphragm—about the size of a thimble—and is meant to fit snugly over the cervical opening.

Like the diaphragm, the cap is intended to be used with a spermicide applied inside it. When inserting it, the woman (or her partner) fills the cap about a third full of spermicide. Then, squeezing the edges together, the woman inserts the cap high into her vagina, so it presses firmly against her cervix. It should be left in place for at least eight hours after intercourse. The cap provides continuous protection for upwards of 48 hours without the need for additional spermicide.

The failure rate in typical use is estimated to be high, ranging from 18% in women who haven't borne children to 36% in women who have (Hatcher et al., 2008).

Some women find the cap uncomfortable. Side effects include urinary tract infections and allergic reactions or sensitivities to the rubber or spermicide.

Spermicides

Spermicides coat the cervical opening, blocking the passage of sperm and killing sperm by chemical action. They come in different forms, including jellies, creams, suppositories, and aerosol foams.

Spermicides should be left in place in the vagina (no douching) for several hours after intercourse (Hatcher et al., 2008). Unlike spermicidal jellies, creams, and foams, which become effective as soon as they're applied, suppositories must be inserted at least 10 to 15 minutes before intercourse, so they have sufficient time to dissolve (Hatcher et al., 2008).

In typical use, the first-year failure rate for spermicides used alone is 21% (Hatcher et al., 2008). When used correctly and consistently, the failure rate is estimated to drop to about 6%. All forms of spermicide are more effective when combined with other forms of contraception, such as the condom.

Spermicides occasionally cause vaginal or penile irritation, and some partners find the taste unpleasant. Couples can engage in oral sex before applying spermicides.

It was once thought that spermicides containing nonoxynol-9 might provide protection against STIs such as chlamydia and HIV. Research has found that it doesn't provide protection against STIs, and that it actually increases susceptibility to HIV infection (Hatcher et al., 2008).

The Contraceptive Sponge

The contraceptive sponge is a soft, disposable device. Like the diaphragm, it provides a barrier that holds a spermicide, but the spermicide is built in. Unlike the diaphragm, the sponge doesn't need to be fitted.

The sponge can be inserted into the vagina several hours before intercourse, and has the advantage of absorbing sperm. On the negative side, about one user in 20 (male and female) is mildly irritated by the spermicide.

The sponge is currently unavailable in Canadian pharmacies.

The Male Condom

The vast majority of condoms used in Canada are made from latex rubber. Latex condoms are effective in preventing pregnancy and reducing the risk of STIs, especially HIV.

Condoms made from polyurethane are also now available in Canada. Although they can be effective in preventing pregnancy and STIs, they have higher rates of breakage and slippage than latex condoms (Gallo, Grimes, Lopez, & Schulz, 2006). Polyurethane condoms provide an alternative for people who are allergic to latex.

There are also condoms made from the intestinal membranes of lambs. These are often referred to as lambskin or natural condoms. Although they can reduce the risk of pregnancy, condoms made of animal intestines have pores large enough to permit HIV and other viruses, such as the one that causes hepatitis B, to slip through (Hatcher et al., 2008).

Many condoms have nipples or reservoirs to catch semen. (See Figure 11.3.) These reservoirs may help prevent the condoms from bursting during ejaculation.

Condoms come in different sizes. Men with larger penises should use larger condoms, to lessen the chances of condom breakage. Tight, uncomfortable condoms may discourage men from using them.

HOW IT WORKS A condom is a cylindrical sheath that serves as a barrier, preventing the passage of sperm and disease-carrying micro-organisms from the man to his partner. It also helps prevent infected vaginal fluids (and micro-organisms) from entering the man's urethral opening or penetrating through small cracks in the skin of the penis.

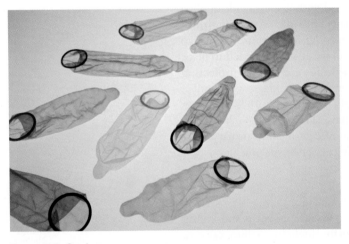

Figure 11.3 Condoms.
Some condoms are plain-tipped, whereas others have nipples or reservoirs that catch semen and may help prevent the condoms from bursting during ejaculation. Latex condoms form effective barriers to the tiny virus that causes AIDS.

HOW IT'S USED The condom is rolled onto the penis once erection is achieved, but before contact between the penis and the vagina (see Figure 11.4). If the condom isn't used until moments before the point of ejaculation, sperm-carrying fluid from pre-orgasmic spasms may already have passed into the vagina. Nor does the condom afford protection against STIs if it's fitted after penetration.

In a study of condom users at Indiana University, 43% of the men reported that sometimes they didn't put the condoms on until after they'd started intercourse, and 15% sometimes removed the condoms before they'd finished intercourse (Crosby et al., 2002). In such circumstances, the effectiveness of condoms against pregnancy and STIs is sharply reduced.

EFFECTIVENESS In typical use, the male condom's failure rate is estimated at 12%. This rate drops dramatically if the condom is used correctly and in combination with a spermicide (Hatcher et al., 2008).

ADVANTAGES AND DISADVANTAGES Condoms offer a protection against STIs that's unparalleled among contraceptive devices. Research has definitively demonstrated that condoms provide impermeable barriers to STI/HIV pathogens, and that the proper, consistent use of latex condoms substantially reduces the risk of such infections (McKay, 2007).

Both partners can share in putting on the condom, making it an erotic part of lovemaking, rather than an intrusion. The use of textured or ultra-thin condoms may increase sensitivity, especially for the male. It's tempting to claim that the condom has a perfect safety record and no side effects, but let's settle for calling it close to perfect.

Some people have allergic reactions to the spermicides some lubricated condoms are coated with, or that women may apply. In such cases, a couple may need to use a condom without a spermicidal lubricant, or stop using supplemental spermicides. Some people are allergic to latex. Condoms also sometimes slip off, break, or tear, allowing sperm to leak through.

One disadvantage of the condom is that it may make sex less spontaneous. The couple must interrupt lovemaking to put the condom on. Condoms may also lessen sensation.

Some men experience erectile difficulties when using condoms. In a study of heterosexual university males, one-fifth lost their erections before the condoms were put on, and one-fifth lost their erections after the condoms were on and intercourse had begun (Crosby et al., 2002). Men who reported erection loss were less likely to use condoms. An Australian study found that HIV-positive gay men who had difficulty achieving or maintaining erections sometimes decided not to use condoms (Richters et al., 2003). Some men take Viagra to overcome this problem. Unfortunately, the problem of erection loss with condoms isn't given serious consideration by some sex educators. The issue should be discussed in educational and counselling situations.

Although health educators emphasize the importance of using condoms to prevent transmission of STI/HIV, many people use them to prevent pregnancy. In a sample of men and women from Ottawa, more than two-thirds said the most important reason they used condoms was to prevent pregnancy (Edgley, 2002). And only 7% of the women in the 2002 Canadian Contraception Study said they chose to use condoms primarily to protect against STIs or HIV (Fisher & Black, 2007).

The Canadian Contraception Study also found that many women used condoms when first beginning sexual relationships with new partners, then switched to oral contraceptives (Fisher et al., 2003). The most common reasons they gave for discontinuing condom use were having only one partner (47%) and knowing and trusting their partners (46%). Other reasons were decreased sexual sensation for themselves (14%) and for their partners (19%). Only 4% of women say they'd

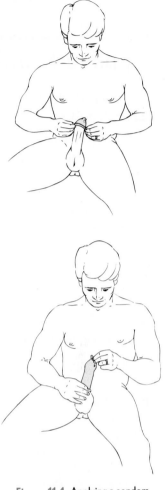

Figure 11.4 Applying a condom. The rolled-up condom is placed on the head of the penis, then rolled down the shaft of the penis. If a condom without a reservoir tip is used, a one-centimetre space should be left at the tip, where the ejaculate can accumulate.

Applied Knowledge

USING A CONDOM EFFECTIVELY

To use a condom effectively and to prevent it from breaking or falling off, a couple should observe the following guidelines.

- Use a condom each and every time you have intercourse. If you're an inexperienced user, practise putting a condom on before you have occasion to use one with a partner.
- Handle the condom carefully, making sure you don't damage it with fingernails, teeth, or sharp objects.
- Place the condom on the erect penis before it touches the vulva.
- If you're uncircumcised, pull the foreskin back before putting the condom on.
- If you use a spermicide, put some inside the tip of the condom before placing the condom on your penis. You may also wish to use an applicator to place additional spermicide inside the vagina for extra protection, especially in the event that the condom breaks.

- Some condoms come equipped with reservoir (nipple) tips that hold semen. If you're using a condom without a reservoir tip, leave a small empty space—about one centimeter—at the end of the condom, to hold semen, but don't allow any air to be trapped at the tip.
- Unroll the condom all the way to the base of the penis.
- Ensure that adequate vaginal lubrication is present during intercourse, using a lubricant, if necessary. Use only water-based lubricants, such as contraceptive jellies or K-Y Jelly. Because they can weaken the latex material, never use oil-based lubricants such as petroleum jelly (Vaseline), cold cream, baby oil, baby lotion, mineral oil, massage oil, vegetable oil, shortening, hand lotion, body lotion, or most skin creams.
- If the condom breaks during intercourse, withdraw your penis immediately, put on a new condom, and use more spermicide.
- After ejaculation, carefully withdraw your penis while it's still erect.

- Hold the rim of the condom firmly against the base of your penis as you withdraw from the vagina, to prevent the condom from slipping off.

Because condoms can be eroded by exposure to body heat or other sources of heat, they shouldn't be kept for any length of time in a pocket or the glove compartment of a car. Nor should a condom be used more than once. Here are some other things you should *never* do with a condom:

- Never use a condom after its expiration date.
- Never use a condom that's sticky, gummy, discoloured, brittle, or showing other signs of deterioration. The condom may be damaged.
- Never use a condom if the sealed packet containing it is damaged, cracked, or brittle. The condom itself may be damaged or defective.
- Don't open the sealed packet until you're ready to use the condom.
- Never use the same condom twice.

Innovative Canadian Research

ATTITUDES ABOUT SUGGESTING CONDOM USE

One of the stereotypes about condom use is that people are reluctant to suggest using them, for fear of offending their partners.

In a study of Ontario university students, Davidson-Harden, Fisher, and Davidson (2000) surveyed attitudes toward people who initiate condom use within the context of exclusive dating relationships. Both men and women rated individuals of either gender who initiated condom use more favourably than unfavourably. The

researchers concluded that it has become less socially acceptable to engage in sexual intercourse without using a condom.

A study among male and female aboriginal youth in Saskatchewan found that assertively communicating with a partner about using a condom was associated with condom use self-efficacy. That is, youth who felt comfortable being assertive in bringing up and discussing condom use with their partners were more likely to feel confident that they would actually use condoms during sex (Shercliffe et al., 2007).

stopped using condoms because their partners refused to use them. Fourteen percent, however, said it would be difficult to get their partners to use condoms. Fisher and his colleagues noted that, in switching from condoms to oral contraceptives, many women are putting themselves at increased risk for STIs.

The Female Condom

The female condom consists of a polyurethane (plastic) sheath that's used to line the vagina during intercourse. It's held in place at each end by a flexible plastic ring. The female condom provides a secure but flexible shield that barricades against sperm, but allows the penis to move freely within the vagina during intercourse. It can be inserted as much as eight hours before intercourse, but should be removed immediately afterwards (Hatcher et al., 2008). A new one must be used for each act of intercourse.

The female condom (sold under the brand name Reality) carries a warning label that it appears to be less effective than the male latex condom in preventing pregnancies and transmission of STIs. During test trials, the pregnancy rate was estimated to range between 21% and 26%, though it's estimated to be as low as 5% among cautious users (Hatcher et al., 2008).

Many women complain that the female condom is bulky and difficult to insert. It costs several times as much as the male condom. Fisher and his colleagues (2004) found that only 34% of Canadian women had heard of the female condom, and only 6% had a very favourable opinion of it.

Douching

Many couples believe that if a woman douches shortly after intercourse, she won't become pregnant. Women who **douche** for contraceptive purposes often use syringes to flush their vaginas with water or spermicidal agents. Douching is ineffective, however, because large numbers of sperm move beyond the range of the douche seconds after ejaculation. Regular douching can also alter the natural chemistry of the vagina, increasing the risk of vaginal infection. Douching, in short, is a "non-method" of contraception.

Douche Rinse or wash the vaginal canal by inserting a liquid and allowing it to drain out.

Withdrawal

In using withdrawal, the man removes his penis from the vagina before ejaculating.

Withdrawal has a first-year failure rate among typical users of about 20% (Hatcher et al., 2008). There are several reasons for failure. The man may not withdraw in time. Even if he withdraws his penis just before ejaculation, some ejaculate may still fall onto the vaginal lips, and sperm may find its way to the fallopian tubes. A man may not be aware that he has begun to ejaculate seminal fluid, especially if he's trying to delay his orgasm. It's also possible that active sperm is present in the pre-ejaculatory secretions of fluid from the Cowper's glands, a discharge the man is usually unaware of and cannot control. Despite the risks of using withdrawal as a method of birth control, 11.2% of Canadian women report using this method (Black et al., 2009).

Fertility-Awareness Methods

Fertility-awareness methods, or rhythm methods, rely on awareness of the fertile segments of a woman's menstrual cycle. Terms such as "natural birth control" and "natural family planning" also refer to these methods. The essence of such methods is that intercourse is avoided on days when conception is most likely.

Because the rhythm method doesn't employ artificial devices, it's acceptable to the Roman Catholic Church. However, as Table 11.1 shows, few Canadian women rely on this method of birth control.

HOW THEY WORK A number of rhythm methods are used to predict the likelihood of conception. They're mirror images of the methods couples use to increase their chances of conceiving. (See Chapter 10.) Methods for enhancing the chances of conception seek to predict the time of ovulation, so the couple can arrange to have sperm present in the woman's reproductive tract at about that time. As methods of birth control, however, rhythm methods seek to predict ovulation so the couple can abstain from intercourse when the woman is fertile.

THE CALENDAR METHOD The **calendar method** assumes that ovulation occurs 14 days before menstruation. The couple abstains from intercourse during the period that begins three days before day 13 (because sperm are unlikely to survive for more than 72 hours in the female reproductive tract) and ends two days after day 15 (because an unfertilized ovum is unlikely to remain receptive to fertilization for longer than 48 hours). The period of abstention thus covers days 10 to 17 of the woman's cycle.

When a woman has regular 28-day cycles, predicting the period of abstinence is relatively straightforward. Women with irregular cycles are generally advised to chart their cycles for 10 to 12 months, to determine their shortest and longest cycles. The first day of menstruation counts as day one of the cycle. The last day of the cycle is the day preceding the onset of menstruation.

Most women who follow the calendar method need to abstain from intercourse for at least 10 days during the middle of each cycle. The calendar method cannot ensure that the woman's longest or shortest menstrual cycles will occur during the 10- to 12-month period of baseline tracking. Some women have such irregular cycles that the range of unsafe days cannot be predicted reliably, even if baseline tracking is extended.

THE BASAL-BODY-TEMPERATURE (BBT) METHOD In the **basal-body-temperature (BBT) method**, the woman tracks her body temperature upon awakening each morning, to detect the small changes that occur directly before and after ovulation. A woman's basal body temperature sometimes dips slightly just before ovulation, then tends to rise between 0.2°C and 0.4°C just before, during, and after ovulation. It remains elevated until the onset of menstruation. Thermometers that provide finely graded readings, such as electronic thermometers, are best suited for determining minor changes.

A major problem with the BBT method is that it doesn't indicate the several unsafe pre-ovulatory days when sperm deposited in the vagina may remain viable. Rather, the BBT method indicates when a woman *has* ovulated. Many women therefore use the calendar method to predict the number of safe days prior to ovulation, and the BBT method to determine the number of unsafe days after. They avoid intercourse during the unsafe pre-ovulatory period (as determined by the calendar method), and continue to avoid it for three days when their temperatures rise and remain elevated.

Another drawback of the BBT method is that changes in body temperature may result from factors unrelated to ovulation, such as infections, sleeplessness, and stress. This is why some women triple-check by also tracking their cervical mucus.

THE CERVICAL-MUCUS (OVULATION) METHOD The **ovulation method** tracks changes in the **viscosity** of the cervical mucus.

Following menstruation, the vagina feels rather dry. There's also little or no discharge from the cervix. These dry days are relatively safe. Then a mucus discharge appears in the vagina that's thick, sticky, and white or cloudy in colour. Unprotected intercourse should be avoided at the first sign of any mucus.

As the cycle progresses, the mucus discharge thins and clears, becoming slippery or stringy, like raw egg white. These are the **peak days**. This mucus discharge, called the ovulatory mucus, may be accompanied by a feeling of vaginal lubrication

Calendar method A fertility-awareness (rhythm) method of contraception that relies on predicting ovulation by tracking menstrual cycles, typically for 10 to 12 months, and assuming that ovulation occurs 14 days before menstruation.

Basal-body-temperature (BBT) method A fertility-awareness method of contraception that relies on predicting ovulation by tracking the woman's temperature during the course of the menstrual cycle.

Ovulation method A fertility-awareness method of contraception that relies on predicting ovulation by tracking the viscosity of cervical mucus.

Viscosity Stickiness, consistency.

Peak days The days during the menstrual cycle when a woman is most likely to be fertile.

or wetness. Ovulation takes place about a day after the last peak day (about four days after this ovulatory mucus first appears). Then the mucus becomes cloudy and tacky once more. Intercourse may resume four days following the last peak day.

One problem with the mucus method is that some women have difficulty detecting changes in the mucus discharge. Such changes may also result from infections, certain medications, and contraceptive creams, jellies, and foams. Sexual arousal may also induce changes in viscosity.

OVULATION-PREDICTION KITS Predicting ovulation is more accurate with ovulation-prediction kits. These kits enable women to test their urine every day for the presence of luteinizing hormone. LH levels surge about 12 to 24 hours before ovulation.

Some couples use the kits to enhance their chances of conceiving, by engaging in intercourse when ovulation appears imminent. Others use them as a means of birth control, to find out when to avoid intercourse.

EFFECTIVENESS The estimated first-year failure rate for typical use of fertility-awareness methods is 20%. Fewer failures occur when these methods are applied conscientiously, a combination of rhythm methods are used, and women's cycles are quite regular.

ADVANTAGES AND DISADVANTAGES Because they're natural forms of birth control, rhythm methods appeal to many people who, for religious or other reasons, prefer not to use artificial means. No devices or chemicals are used, so there are no side effects. Rhythm methods are inexpensive, except for ovulation-prediction kits.

One disadvantage of the rhythm methods is low reliability. They may be unsuitable for women with irregular cycles. Those who ovulate as early as a week after their menstrual flows can become pregnant even if they engage in unprotected intercourse only when they're menstruating, because some sperm can survive in the female reproductive tract for up to eight days, fertilizing ova that are released then. Moreover, the rhythm methods require abstaining from intercourse for several days, or perhaps weeks, each month.

Sterilization

Many people decide to be sterilized when they plan to have no children or no more children. As Table 11.1 shows, male and female sterilization are most popular among people who are forty and older.

Sterilization is the most effective form of contraception. Yet the prospect of **sterilization** arouses strong feelings, because a person is transformed all at once, and presumably permanently, from someone who might be capable of bearing children to someone who isn't. This transformation often involves a profound change in self-concept. These feelings are especially strong in men and women who link fertility to their senses of masculinity and femininity.

Sterilization Surgical procedures that render people incapable of reproduction, without affecting sexual activity.

MALE STERILIZATION The male sterilization procedure used today is the **vasectomy**. It's usually carried out in a doctor's office, under local anaesthesia, in 15 to 20 minutes.

Small incisions are made in the scrotum. Each vas is cut, a small segment is removed, and the ends are tied off or cauterized (to prevent them from growing back together). (See Figure 11.5.) Now sperm can no longer reach the urethra. Instead, they're harmlessly reabsorbed by the body.

According to guidelines established by the World Health Organization in 2004, men are advised to wait for three months after a vasectomy before relying on

Vasectomy The surgical method of male sterilization in which each vas deferens is cut and tied back or cauterized, to prevent sperm from reaching the urethra.

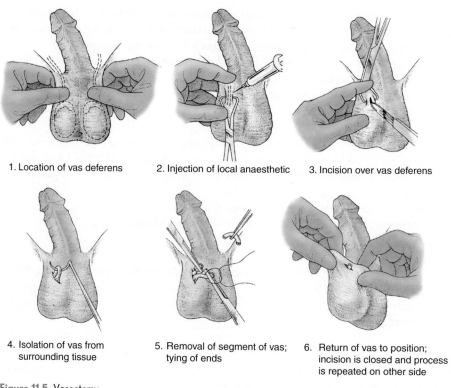

1. Location of vas deferens

2. Injection of local anaesthetic

3. Incision over vas deferens

4. Isolation of vas from surrounding tissue

5. Removal of segment of vas; tying of ends

6. Return of vas to position; incision is closed and process is repeated on other side

Figure 11.5 Vasectomy.
Small incisions are made in the scrotum. Each vas deferens is cut, and the ends are tied off or cauterized, to prevent sperm from reaching the urethra. The vasectomy is nearly 100% effective. The few failures occur when sperm remains in the male's genital tract shortly after the operation, or when the segments of a vas deferens grow back together.

it for contraception. This advice is based on an analysis of several studies that have found vasectomies completely effective after three months for the great majority of men (Info Reports, 2005).

Vasectomy does not diminish the sex drive or result in any change in sexual arousal, erectile or ejaculatory ability, or sensations of ejaculation. Male sex hormones and sperm are still produced by the testes. Without a passageway to the urethra, however, sperm are no longer expelled with the ejaculate. Sperm account for only about 1% of the ejaculate, so the volume of the ejaculate is not noticeably different.

Few serious complications from vasectomies have been reported, but minor complications are not uncommon. They typically involve temporary local inflammation or swelling after the operation. Ice packs and anti-inflammatory drugs such as Aspirin can help reduce swelling and discomfort. More serious but rarer medical complications include infection of the epididymis.

Reversibility is simple in concept, but not in practise. Vasectomies should therefore be considered permanent. In an operation to reverse a vasectomy, called a **vasovasotomy**, the ends of the vas deferens are sewn together, and in a few days they grow together. Estimates of success at reversal, as measured by subsequent pregnancies, range from 16% to 79% (Hatcher et al., 2008).

FEMALE STERILIZATION **Tubal sterilization**, also called tubal ligation, is the most common method of female sterilization. Tubal sterilization prevents ova and sperm from passing through the fallopian tubes.

The two main surgical procedures for tubal sterilization are minilaparotomy and laparoscopy. In a **minilaparotomy**, a small incision is made in the abdomen, just above the pubic hairline, to provide access to the fallopian tubes. Each tube is

Vasovasotomy The surgical method of reversing a vasectomy. The cut or cauterized ends of the vas deferentia are sewn back together.

Tubal sterilization The most common method of female sterilization, in which the fallopian tubes are surgically blocked, to prevent the meeting of sperm and ova. It's also called tubal ligation.

Minilaparotomy A kind of tubal sterilization in which a small incision is made in the abdomen to provide access to the fallopian tubes.

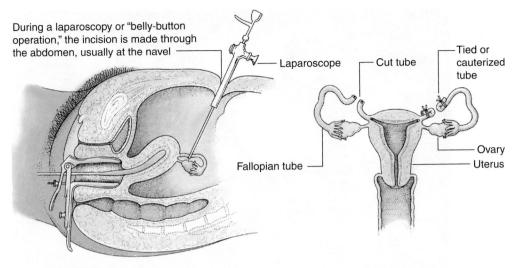

During a laparoscopy or "belly-button operation," the incision is made through the abdomen, usually at the navel

Laparoscope

Fallopian tube

Cut tube

Tied or cauterized tube

Ovary

Uterus

Figure 11.6 Tubal ligation via laparoscopy.
In this method of female sterilization, the surgeon approaches the fallopian tubes through a small incision in the abdomen, just below the navel. S/he inserts a narrow instrument called a laparoscope through the incision, and cauterizes, cuts, or clamps a small section of each fallopian tube, to prevent ova from joining with sperm.

cut and either tied back or clamped with a clip. In a **laparoscopy** (see Figure 11.6), sometimes called belly-button surgery, the fallopian tubes are approached through a small incision in the abdomen, just below the navel. The surgeon uses a narrow, lighted viewing instrument called a laparoscope to locate the tubes, then cauterizes, cuts, or clamps a small section of each tube. The woman usually returns to her daily routine in a few days, and can resume intercourse when it becomes comfortable. In an alternative sterilization procedure, a **culpotomy**, the fallopian tubes are approached through an incision in the back wall of the vagina.

None of these methods disrupts sex drive or sexual response. The menstrual cycle is undisturbed. The unfertilized egg is simply reabsorbed by the body, rather than sloughed off in the menstrual flow.

A **hysterectomy** also results in sterility. A hysterectomy is a major operation that's commonly performed because of cancer and other diseases of the reproductive tract. It's inappropriate as a method of sterilization. Hysterectomy carries the risks of major surgery, and when the ovaries are removed along with the uterus, it induces a "surgical menopause," because the woman no longer produces female sex hormones.

Female sterilization is highly effective in preventing pregnancy, although slightly less effective than male sterilization. Overall, about one woman in 200 (0.4%) is likely to become pregnant in the first year after a tubal sterilization (Hatcher et al., 2008). This is most likely to result from a failed surgical procedure, or the pregnancy may have been undetected at the time of the procedure.

Like vasectomy, tubal ligation should be considered irreversible. Although reversals are successful, as measured by subsequent pregnancies, in 43% to 88% of cases (Hatcher et al., 2008), reversal is difficult and costly.

ADVANTAGES AND DISADVANTAGES The major advantages of sterilization are effectiveness and permanence. Sterilization is nearly 100% effective. Following surgery, the couple needn't do anything more to prevent conception. The permanence is also its major drawback, however. People sometimes change their minds about wanting to have children.

Sterilization procedures create varying risks for complications following surgery, and women generally incur greater risks than men.

Sterilization gives no protection against STIs.

Laparoscopy A procedure used for tubal sterilization. A laparoscope is inserted through a small incision just below the navel, and used to cauterize, cut, or clamp the fallopian tubes. This is sometimes called belly-button surgery.

Culpotomy A kind of tubal sterilization in which the fallopian tubes are approached through an incision in the back wall of the vagina.

Hysterectomy Surgical removal of the uterus. This procedure is not appropriate as a method of sterilization.

*Selecting a Contraceptive.
Should you and your partner use
contraception? If so, how can you determine
which method is right for you?*

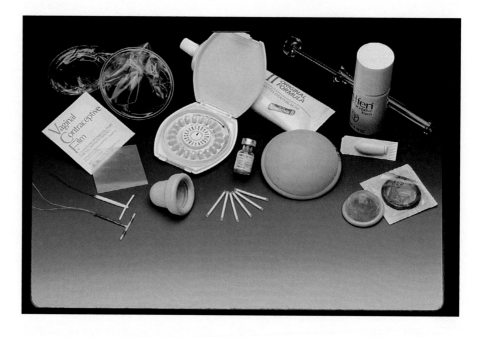

Applied Knowledge

SELECTING A METHOD OF CONTRACEPTION

If you don't want to risk pregnancy, you're well advised to practise contraception when engaging in penile-vaginal intercourse—whether you're male or female. How can you determine which method is right for you?

There's no simple answer. What's right for your friends may be wrong for you. You and your partner must make your own selections. You may want to consider the following issues when deciding:

- *Convenience*—A method's convenience depends on a number of factors. Does it require a device that must be purchased in advance? If so, can it be purchased over the counter as needed, or are a consultation with a doctor and a prescription required? Will the method work at a moment's notice, or, like the birth-control pill, will it require time to reach maximum effectiveness?
- *Moral acceptability*—A method that's morally acceptable to one person

may be objectionable to another. For example, those who strictly follow the teachings of the Roman Catholic Church may find any artificial means of contraception objectionable.

- *Cost*—Methods vary in cost.
- *Sharing responsibility*—Most forms of birth control place the burden of responsibility largely (if not entirely) on the woman. Some couples prefer methods that allow for greater sharing of responsibility, such as alternating the use of condoms and diaphragms. A man can also share the responsibility for the birth-control pill by accompanying his partner on her medical visits, sharing the expense, and helping her remember to take her pill.
- *Safety*—How safe is the method? What are its side effects?
- *Reversibility*—In most cases, the effects of birth control methods can be fully reversed by discontinuing their use. Sterilization should be considered irreversible, although many attempts at reversal have been successful.
- *Protection against STIs*—Birth-control

methods vary in the degree of protection they afford against sexually transmitted infections. Condoms provide greater protection against STIs than any other form of birth control.

- *Effectiveness*—Techniques and devices vary widely in their effectiveness in actual use. The failure rate for a particular method refers to the percentage of women who become pregnant when using the method for a given period, such as during the first year of use. Most contraceptive methods are not used correctly all or even much of the time. It's instructive to compare the failure rate among people who use a particular method or device consistently and correctly with the failure rate among typical users of that method of device. Failure rates among typical users are often considerably higher, because of incorrect, unreliable, or inconsistent use.

Table 11.2 shows the failure rates, reversibility, and degrees of STI protection associated with various contraceptive methods.

The Search Goes On

Even now, in the third millennium, the ideal contraceptive doesn't seem to be within our grasp. However, it does appear that we'll make new advances in mechanical and chemical barrier methods, systems for delivering hormones, intrauterine devices, and systemic methods for men (such as a male pill).

It seems that many women are uncomfortable with the idea of a male pill. In a 2004 Ipsos-Reid poll; 63% of 18- to 24-year-old Canadian women said they wouldn't trust a man to take a pill every day.

A major contraceptive breakthrough was announced in 2008 when Canadian and European researchers discovered a gene (liver receptor homolog-1, or LRH-1) that controls ovulation (Duggavathi et al., 2008). When this gene was removed in mice, the mice stopped ovulating. The gene works mainly through the follicle cells surrounding the ova. The discovery of the gene may be useful in treating infertility, as well as for contraception.

Abortion

An **induced abortion** (in contrast to a spontaneous abortion, or miscarriage) is the purposeful termination of a pregnancy. Perhaps more than any other contemporary social issue, induced abortion—hereafter referred to simply as abortion—has divided neighbours and family members into opposing camps.

Abortion is rarely used as a primary means of birth control. It usually comes into play when other methods have failed. The many reasons women have abortions include psychological factors, as well as external circumstances. Abortion is often motivated by a desire to reduce the risk of physical, economic, psychological, and social disadvantages the woman perceives for herself and her family, should she take the pregnancy to term.

Moral concerns about abortion often turn on the question of when human life begins. The question of when *human* life begins is a matter of definition that's apparently unanswerable by science.

Induced abortion The purposeful termination of a pregnancy before the embryo or fetus is capable of sustaining independent life.

Historical and Legal Perspectives

Attitudes toward abortion have varied across cultures and eras. Abortion was permitted in ancient Greece and Rome. The Bible doesn't specifically prohibit abortion (Sagan & Dryan, 1990). For much of its history, the Roman Catholic Church held to Thomas Aquinas's belief that ensoulment of the fetus didn't occur for at least 40 days after conception. In 1869, Pope Pius IX declared that human life began at conception, and abortion at any stage of pregnancy became murder in the eyes of the Church, and grounds for excommunication.

The right-to-life or pro-life movement asserts that human life begins at conception, and views abortion as the murder of an unborn child. Some in the pro-life movement brook no exception to their opposition to abortion. Others would permit abortion to save the mother's life, or when a pregnancy results from rape or incest. The pro-choice movement contends that abortion is a matter of personal choice, and that the government has no right to interfere with a woman's right to terminate a pregnancy. Pro-choice advocates argue that women are free to control what happens within their bodies, including pregnancies.

Many people in the pro-choice movement argue that if abortions were to be made illegal again, thousands of women, especially poor women, would suffer serious physical consequences or die from unsterile or botched abortions. People in the pro-life movement counter that alternatives to abortion, such as adoption, are available to pregnant women. Pro-choice advocates argue that the

CRITICAL THINKING
QUESTIONS

What factors have
influenced your opinion
about abortion?

debate about abortion should be framed not only by notions of the mother's right
to privacy, but also by the issue of quality of life for an unwanted child. They
argue that minority and physically or mentally disabled children are often hard
to place for adoption. These children often spend their childhoods being shuffled
from one foster home to another. Pro-life advocates counter that killing a fetus
eliminates any potential that it might have, despite hardships, of living a fruitful,
meaningful life.

At Canadian universities, there have been clashes between student unions and
anti-abortion groups over whether the latter should be allowed to operate on campus as official student organizations. The anti-abortion groups have argued that the
student unions violate their constitutional human rights to free speech and discriminate against religious beliefs. The student unions have countered that these groups
threaten women's right to abortions (Brean, 2008).

Although Canadians are divided in their opinions, most accept abortion under
certain circumstances. Reginald Bibby (2001) of the University of Lethbridge
found that most Canadian adults (90%) and teenagers (84%) believe abortion
should be legal when rape is involved, but fewer (43% of adults and 55% of teenagers) believe it should be legal for any reason. In a 2010 poll (EKOS Research
Associates, 2010), 52% of Canadians described themselves as pro-choice, 27%
said they were pro-life, 10% were neither pro-choice nor pro-life, and 11% didn't
know or didn't respond.

Abortion in Canada

Abortion was illegal in Canada until 1969, when Parliament amended the Criminal
Code to allow abortion under limited circumstances. Abortions could be performed only in accredited hospitals, with the approval of Therapeutic Abortion
Committees. It had to be shown that the abortions were justified, in that continuation of the pregnancies would endanger the women's health or lives.

The struggle has continued between pro-life groups, which seek greater
restrictions on abortion, and the pro-choice movement, which seeks to make abortion available to any Canadian woman who wants
one. Both sides have heavily lobbied politicians to
support their causes.

Some pro-life groups use such tactics as picketing
hospitals and clinics where abortions are performed,
as well as the homes of physicians who perform abortions. Three Canadian physicians have been shot in
their homes by anti-abortion extremists. The harassing tactics used by some of these groups have led
provinces such as Ontario and British Columbia to
restrict picketing outside abortion clinics.

Dr. Henry Morgentaler, the leader of the pro-
choice movement in Canada, has been challenging
the law by establishing private abortion clinics since
1969. He has won several legal challenges against
provincial governments that have wanted to close
his clinics, although in 1974 he was imprisoned
for 10 months after the Quebec Court of Appeal
overturned a jury's acquittal. Juries have refused to
convict Morgentaler because they have believed he
provides an important medical service for women.
Morgentaler was awarded the Order of Canada in
2008 for his commitment to increased health-care
opportunities for women and his efforts to influence

*Pro-life groups marched in Ottawa in support of Prime Minister Harper's decision not
to fund international aid organizations that provide abortions.*

public policy. This award was strongly opposed by pro-life groups, and caused considerable controversy. Nevertheless, according to a national Ipsos-Reid poll taken in July of 2008, 65% of Canadians supported the awarding of Canada's highest civilian honour to Dr. Morgentaler.

The Supreme Court of Canada overturned the abortion law in 1988, stating that it violated the Charter of Rights and Freedoms, and there has been no federal law restricting abortion since. In 1989, after a Quebec man went to court in an attempt to prevent his former girlfriend from having an abortion, an important precedent was set when the Supreme Court of Canada ruled that he couldn't stop the abortion because the law doesn't recognize a father's right to do so.

Dr. Henry Morgentaler.
Dr. Henry Morgentaler fought numerous court battles to secure Canadian women greater access to abortion.

Despite these legal decisions, only a minority of hospitals perform abortions today, and these are only in urban areas. In 2007, just 16% of the general hospitals in Canada provided abortion services (Shaw, 2007). Prince Edward Island offers no abortion services, while some provinces, such as New Brunswick, restrict women's access to abortions at public hospitals and refuse to pay for abortions performed at private abortion clinics. In 2008, Morgentaler launched a court challenge against New Brunswick's refusal to fund private abortion clinics in that province.

Women who live in rural or northern areas of Canada often have to travel long distances to obtain abortion services (Shaw, 2007). When Ottawa researcher Jessica Shaw telephoned hospitals that did offer abortions and asked to talk to someone about abortion, she was often given misinformation and/or connected to someone at the hospital who was opposed to abortion.

Some members of Stephen Harper's governing federal Conservative party have been vocally opposed to abortion. In 2007, Conservative Member of Parliament Ken Epp introduced a private member's bill (C-484, known as the Unborn Victims of Crime Act) "to protect fetuses from violence," which would award the fetus legal rights from the time of conception. Critics of the bill stated that if it were passed, the bill would lead to restriction of abortion in Canada. The Quebec government was so concerned about this bill that all members of the National Assembly of Quebec voted to ask the federal government not to pass it.

In 2010, the Conservative government announced Canada's participation in a maternal health initiative to benefit women in developing countries. Considerable controversy occurred when it was revealed that no Canadian funds for the program would be made available for abortion services. Polls taken at the time showed that almost 60% of Canadians opposed the exclusion of funding for abortion services (Canadian Press, May 17, 2010).

In the federal election campaign of 2011, Prime Minister Stephen Harper pledged that his government would not seek to pass new legislation restricting access to abortion in Canada.

Canadian Abortion Statistics

Current, reliable abortion statistics for Canada as a whole are not available. The majority of abortions conducted in Canada are performed in clinics, which are not legally required to report the number of abortions they perform, and in many provinces don't do so. The most recent national statistics are from 2005. They're shown in Table 11.3.

TABLE 11.3
Induced Abortions in Canadian Provinces in 2005

	Number of Abortions	Rate per 1000 Women
Total	96 815	14.1
Newfoundland and Labrador	883	8.1
Prince Edward Island	126	4.4
Nova Scotia	1897	9.7
New Brunswick	941	6.1
Quebec	29 259	18.8
Ontario	33 546	12.3
Manitoba	2 236	9.2
Saskatchewan	1824	9.1
Alberta	10 859	14.8
British Columbia	14 444	15.9
Yukon, Northwest Territories, and Nunavut	615	24.9
Residence unknown	185	...

Note: Users should be aware of certain limitations with the Therapeutic Abortion Survey. Data for 2005 cover induced abortions performed in hospitals and clinics in provinces and territories, except those performed in Manitoba clinics, which have been unavailable since 2004. As of 2004, induced abortions obtained by Canadian women in some American states are no longer collected. The survey also doesn't include abortions performed in doctors' offices.

Source: Statistics Canada. (2008d). Inducted abortions. The Daily. Retrieved from http://www.statcan.ca/Daily/English/080521/d080521c.htm

If we look at the available national abortion statistics we can see that in the years leading up to 2005, the number of abortions among Canadian women had been declining, and the decline occurred mostly among women under 20 years of age. A total of 96 815 induced abortions were performed on Canadian women in 2005, down from 105 154 in 2002. Induced abortion rates fell in all age groups, except among women aged 35 to 39, for whom the rate remained the same. Teenage women, under the age of 20, experienced the largest decline in rates.

The induced abortion rate for these women had declined gradually since 1996, when it peaked at 18.9 induced abortions per 1000 women in the age group, to 13.0 induced abortions per 1000 women in 2005. Induced abortions continued to be the most common among women in their early twenties. This age group accounted for 31% of all women who obtained an induced abortion in 2005. On average, 28 women out of every 1000 aged 20 to 24 obtained an induced abortion.

The Canadian Institute for Health Information (CIHI) currently collects abortion data from hospitals and the clinic data from the provinces from which it is available. Three provinces for which more recent CIHI data are available for both hospital and clinic abortions are Quebec, Ontario, and Alberta. When we compare the combined number of abortions in these provinces for 2007 and 2008, we find that the number of abortions performed remained stable. That is, in these three provinces, 72 735 abortions were performed in 2007 compared to 72 725 in 2008 (Canadian Institute for Health Information, 2007, 2008).

Methods of Abortion

The two methods of abortion most often used in Canada are vacuum aspiration and dilation and evacuation.

VACUUM ASPIRATION **Vacuum aspiration**, or suction curettage, is the safest, most common method of abortion used in Canada. Relatively painless and inexpensive, it can be done with little or no anaesthesia in a medical office or clinic.

The cervix is dilated either via insertion of progressively larger curved metal rods, or dilators, or by insertion hours earlier of a stick of seaweed called Laminaria digitata, which expands as it absorbs moisture, providing a gentler means of opening the os. An angled tube connected to an aspirator (suction machine) is then inserted through the cervix into the uterus, and used to evacuate (empty) the uterine contents by suction.

Vacuum aspiration is used only during the first trimester. Later, thinning of the uterine walls increases the risks of perforation and bleeding.

DILATION AND EVACUATION (D&E) The **dilation and evacuation (D&E)** method is used most often during the second trimester, when vacuum aspiration alone is too risky. The D&E is usually performed under general anesthesia in a hospital.

The cervix must be dilated more fully than with vacuum aspiration, to allow for passage of the larger fetus. A suction tube is then inserted and used to remove some of the uterine contents. Suction alone cannot safely remove everything from the uterus, so forceps are used to remove whatever remains. A blunt scraper may also be used to scrape the uterine walls, to be sure the lining has been fully removed.

ABORTION DRUGS RU-486, or mifepristone, was developed and approved in France in the late 1980s. It hasn't yet been approved for use in Canada, although it is available in several European countries and the United States. Mifepristone induces early abortion by blocking the effects of progesterone, the hormone that stimulates proliferation of the endometrium and allows implantation of the fertilized ovum.

Nearly half of the French women who seek abortion prefer RU-486 to surgical methods (Christin-Maitre et al., 2000). Supporters of RU-486 argue that it offers a safe, non-invasive substitute for the more costly and unpleasant abortion procedures (Christin-Maitre et al., 2000).

RU-486's introduction in Canada is being delayed largely because of opposition by pro-life groups. Opponents argue that RU-486 makes abortions more accessible and difficult to regulate. Pro-life groups consider abortion to be murder, whether it's induced by surgery or by a pill.

Psychological Consequences of Abortion

The woman who faces an unwanted pregnancy may experience a range of negative emotions, including fear, anger that she directs inward ("How could I let this happen?"), guilt ("What would my parents think, if they knew I was having an abortion?"), and ambivalence ("Will I regret it, if I have an abortion? Will I regret it more if I don't?").

Women's reactions depend on various factors, including the support they receive (or don't receive) from others and the strength of their relationships with their partners. Women with greater support from their male partners or parents tend to show more positive emotional reactions following abortion (Williams, 2001).

Generally speaking, the sooner the abortion occurs, the less stressful it is. Women who have a difficult time reaching a decision, blame the pregnancy on their own character, have lower coping ability, and have less social support experience more distress following abortion.

Consider one survey of 882 women who showed up at three sites for first-trimester abortions, as reported in *Archives of General Psychiatry* (Major et al., 2000). The researchers followed 442 of these women for two years. As Figure 11.7 shows,

Vacuum aspiration Removal of the uterine contents via an aspirator (suction machine).

Dilation and evacuation (D&E) Removal of the uterine contents via a suction tube and forceps. The uterine wall may be scraped, to ensure that the lining has been fully removed.

Figure 11.7 Women's psychological adjustment two years after abortion.
Of several hundred respondents in an *Archives of General Psychiatry* survey, 72% of those who'd had abortions reported satisfaction with their decisions two years later. How do you interpret this finding? Do you focus on the fact that the great majority of women are satisfied with their choices, or on the fact that significant numbers of women (28%) are not satisfied with their choices?

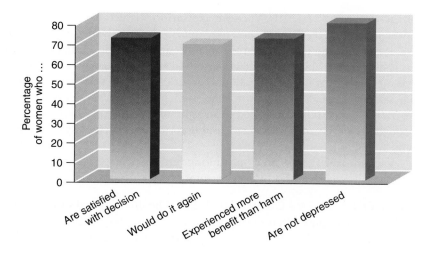

the majority (72%) said they were satisfied with their decisions to have the abortions. A majority said they'd make the same decision if they had to do it over (69%), and that they'd experienced more benefit than harm from having the abortions (72%). Moreover, 80% were *not* depressed.

Innovative Canadian Research

WOMEN WHO HAVE REPEAT ABORTIONS

In Canada, about one-third of induced abortions are for women who've had previous abortions.

A group of University of Western Ontario researchers led by William Fisher (2005) conducted a study to determine the characteristics of women who have repeat abortions. Contrary to the stereotype, most of these women were not using abortion as a method of birth control. About one-half of those undergoing repeat abortions reported that they or their partners had been using some method of birth control at the time of conception.

They were, in fact, more likely to be using birth control than a comparison group of women who were having their first abortions.

The key finding of the study was that women who had repeat abortions were significantly more likely to have experienced physical abuse by their male partners, sexual abuse, or coercion. Women seeking abortions should therefore be screened for their experience with physical or sexual abuse. This could result in counselling that might help avert subsequent abuse, and possibly help prevent future abortions (Fisher et al., 2005).

Summing Up

The provision of contraceptive information and services was illegal in Canada until 1969.

Birth-control pills include combination pills and minipills. Combination pills contain estrogen and progestin, and fool the brain into thinking the woman is already pregnant, so no additional ova mature or are released. Minipills contain progestin, thicken the cervical mucus to impede the passage of sperm through the cervix, and render the inner lining of the uterus less receptive to a fertilized egg. Morning-after pills prevent implantation of a fertilized ovum in the uterus.

The intrauterine device (IUD) is highly effective, but there are possible troublesome side effects, and the potential for serious health complications.

The diaphragm covers the cervix, and should be used with a spermicidal cream or jelly.

Spermicides block the passage of sperm and kill sperm. Their failure rate is high.

Latex condoms afford protection against STIs, as well as against pregnancy.

Withdrawal requires no special equipment, but has a high failure rate.

Rhythm methods rely on awareness of the fertile segments of the woman's menstrual cycle. Rhythm methods include the calendar method, the basal-body-temperature method, and the cervical-mucus method. Their failure rates are high in typical use.

Sterilization methods should be considered permanent, although they can be reversed in many cases.

Less commonly used methods of contraception include hormone-delivery systems (e.g., Depo-Provera injections, the skin patch, and the vaginal ring) and barrier/spermicide methods (e.g., the cervical cap, the female condom, and the contraceptive sponge).

Moral concerns about abortion often turn on the question of when human life begins. It's a question of definition.

Societal attitudes toward abortion have varied across cultures and history. In 1988, the Supreme Court of Canada ruled that the abortion law restricting the rights of women was unconstitutional, and that women should therefore have an unrestricted right to abortion. In reality, however, abortion services are limited in many parts of Canada.

The two most common methods of abortion used in Canada are vacuum aspiration and dilation and evacuation.

Women may experience distress after an abortion, but most are satisfied with their decision to have one.

Test Yourself

Multiple-Choice Questions

1. Canadian women of reproductive age most often use the _____ method of contraception.
(a) IUD
(b) rhythm
(c) oral contraceptive
(d) male condom

2. Which of the following is the most effective method of birth control?
(a) Withdrawal.
(b) Oral contraceptives.
(c) The rhythm method.
(d) The cervical cap.

3. Which of the following methods of birth control has the most side effects?
(a) The IUD.
(b) The male condom.
(c) The diaphragm.
(d) The minilaparotomy.

4. All of the following are potential side effects of birth-control pills except:
(a) Nausea and vomiting.
(b) Low blood pressure.
(c) Fluid retention.
(d) Weight gain.

5. In Canada, emergency contraception (the morning-after pill):
(a) Is illegal.
(b) Is available without a prescription.
(c) Contains higher levels of testosterone than the pills available in Europe.
(d) Is available only to victims of sexual assault.

6. Research has found that nonoxynol-9 _____ a woman's susceptibility to HIV infection.
(a) has no measurable effect on
(b) has mixed effects on
(c) increases
(d) decreases

7. Rhythm methods rely on:
(a) Fertility awareness.
(b) Hormonal preparations.
(c) Barriers.
(d) Spermicides.

8. According to a 2010 EKOS survey, what percentage of Canadians described themselves as pro-choice?
(a) 12
(b) 22
(c) 52
(d) 72

9. There has been no federal law restricting abortion in Canada since the Supreme Court ruling of:
(a) 1965.
(b) 1977.
(c) 1988.
(d) 2004.

10. The safest, most common method of abortion is:
(a) Dilation and evacuation (D&E).
(b) Intra-amniotic infusion.
(c) Dilation and curettage (D&C).
(d) Vacuum aspiration.

You'll find answers to the "Test Yourself" questions on page 495.

Critical Thinking

1. Have you ever discussed the use of birth control with a partner or potential partner? If not, why not? If you have, did you find it difficult to talk about? Why or why not?

2. If you're female, have you ever been faced with an unintended pregnancy? If so, what did you do about it? What factors influenced your decision? Were your friends supportive of your choice? Your partner? Your family?

3. If you're male, has a sexual partner of yours ever been faced with an unintended pregnancy? If so, what was done about it? Were you part of the decision-making process? Why or why not?

4. A friend of yours, whom you know doesn't want a child, tells you she's sexually active but not using birth control. Do you discuss this behaviour with her? Why or why not?

MySearchLab

MySearchLab offers extensive help to students with their writing and research project and provides round-the-clock access to credible and reliable source material. Take a tour at www.mysearchlab.com.

CHAPTER TWELVE

Sexuality Across the Life Span and Sexual-Health Education

We don't often think of children as sexual beings. Many people assume the development of sexuality begins at puberty, when we become biologically capable of reproduction. Although young children typically don't have conscious sexual desires the same way teens and adults do, in many respects, sexuality begins to develop in the womb and continues throughout childhood. The seeds of adult sexuality are planted during childhood, and this early development partially shapes the extent to which adult sexuality is characterized by self-confidence and satisfaction or by doubt and shame.

This chapter is divided into two parts. In the first part, we discuss sexuality across the life span, examining the developmental tasks related to sexuality at each phase of life. In the second part, we look at sexual-health education, placing particular emphasis on sexuality education for teens and young adults.

Childhood Sexuality

We know far less about the development of sexuality in childhood than we do about sexuality in adolescence and adulthood. Few empirical studies on the sexual behaviour of children are available (Thigpen, 2009). One reason is the cultural belief that children are sexually innocent, and that this innocence should be protected. Researchers have been reluctant to ask children about their sexual behaviour or their understanding of sexuality. We tend to rely either on adults' often unreliable retrospective reports of their experiences during childhood or on the observations of caregivers (Thigpen, 2009). In Canada, as in other countries, far more attention has been paid to the impact of child sexual abuse than to the course of normal child sexual development.

Table 12.1 provides an overview of the how sexuality develops in childhood. In addition to common characteristics and behaviours that may be evident in each age category, the table lists the appropriate learning domains and corresponding developmental outcomes for children at these ages. You'll notice that the age categories overlap somewhat (e.g., 0–2 and 2–4). This is because not all children develop at the same pace. There's considerable variability in the precise ages at which children exhibit different sexuality-related behaviours and the rates at which their bodies develop.

The table reflects a primarily Western and secular conceptualization of both child development and sexuality. In other words, it reflects the assumption that, beginning in early childhood, the sequential acquisition of increasingly sophisticated knowledge and skills related to sexuality is beneficial. This assumption may conflict with religious and cultural traditions. Within some traditions, for example, sexuality-related exploratory play and masturbatory behaviour may be viewed as unhealthy or inappropriate for children.

Infancy (Birth to Two Years)

Infants (and fetuses!) engage in a variety of "sexual" behaviours, although the meanings of these behaviours—if there are any—are a matter for speculation. Imaging techniques such as ultrasound have shown, for example, that male fetuses have erections. Most boys have erections during the first few weeks of life. Signs of sexual arousal in infant girls, such as vaginal lubrication, are less readily detected, though evidence of lubrication and genital swelling has been reported (Mazur, 2006). Table 12.1 shows the initial aspects of child sexual development.

Stimulation of the genitals in infancy can produce pleasure. Parents who touch their infants' genitals while changing or washing them may find the infants smiling or becoming excited. Infants discover the pleasure of self-stimulation (masturbation) for themselves when they gain the ability to manipulate their genitals with their hands.

TABLE 12.1

Development of Childhood Sexuality, 0 to 12 Years of Age

Age (Years)	Common Characteristics and Behaviours	Learning Domains	Developmental Outcomes
0–2	• Explores own body, including genitals • Displays spontaneous, reflexive sexual response (erection, lubrication) • Enjoys touch from caregivers • Enjoys nudity	• Learns correct names for body parts, including genitals • Learns to differentiate between male and female • Learns to experience pleasure from touch (cuddling, nonsexual touching)	• Develops capacity to trust caregivers • Develops capacity to experience sensory (touch) pleasure • Begins to distinguish between males and females • Begins to develop sense of autonomy • Begins first social/play interactions with peers
2–5	• Engages in occasional masturbation (focused on soothing, not arousal) • Engages in consensual exploration of same-aged playmates' bodies in curiosity-focused manner • Enjoys nudity • Uses slang terms for bodily functions	• Learns basics of reproduction • Learns basic rules of privacy • Learns "your body belongs to you" • Learns difference between appropriate and inappropriate touching (good touch versus bad touch)	• Develops ability to identify self as male or female • Begins to understand basics of human reproduction • Understands concept of privacy related to nudity and sexuality
5–8	• Engages in curiosity-based body exploration with same-sex and opposite-sex playmates • Engages in occasional masturbation (may begin to focus on pleasure) • Uses slang words to describe body parts and sexual behaviours • May have crushes	• Acquires basic understanding of human reproduction • Acquires preparatory understanding of basic physical changes associated with puberty • Acquires understanding of basic distinction between heterosexuality and homosexuality	• Has well established sense of gender identity (male or female) • May show early signs of puberty (breast development) • Understands terminology for body parts (penis, vagina) • Develops basic understanding of sexual orientation (heterosexuality, homosexuality, bisexuality)
9–12	• May masturbate more regularly, with a sexual focus • Experiences more frequent crushes, which can develop into relationships • May begin partnered sexual activity (though it's rare in this age group) • Becomes more curious about sexuality • Becomes interested in sexually oriented media	• Acquires reasonably complete knowledge of physical and psychological aspects of puberty • Acquires basic knowledge of concepts of delaying first intercourse and contraception/safer sex • Learns social skills related to rights and responsibilities in relationships • Learns media literacy skills, to understand and evaluate sexual imagery and messages	• Exhibits physical and psychological changes associated with puberty • Understands basic rights and responsibilities related to sexuality and relationships

Source: Adapted from Society of Obstetricians and Gynaecologists of Canada. (2006). Sexuality and child development. SexualityAndU.ca. Ottawa: Society of Obstetricians and Gynaecologists of Canada. Retrieved from http://www.sexualityandu.ca/health-care-professionals/sexuality-and-child-development

Be careful not to interpret children's reflexes according to adult concepts of sexuality. The reflexes of lubrication and erection don't necessarily signify interest in sex. We can't say what, if anything, infants' sexual reflexes mean to them. Masturbation is typical for infants and young children, and may start as early as five months of age (Health24.com, 2006; Narchi, 2003), but masturbation to orgasm is rare until the second year (Reinisch, 1990). Some children begin masturbating to orgasm later. Most people do not purposely masturbate to orgasm as a means of sexual gratification until adolescence.

It's important for young children to begin to learn about their bodies, including their genitals. Parents can teach them the proper names for their genitals, just as they do for their other body parts.

Early Childhood (Two to Five Years)

As Table 12.1 shows, the major developmental tasks related to sexuality during early childhood include the ability to identify oneself as a boy or a girl. (This is a more complex process for the small number of children whose genitalia are neither clearly male nor clearly female.) Children at this age may play doctor, and show their curiosity about sexual anatomy in other ways, such as wanting to watch parents take showers and baths (Health24.com, 2006; Pike, 2005).

Children in Canada typically don't engage in genital play with others until about they're about two or older. To satisfy curiosity about their surroundings and other people, they may investigate other children's genitals, or hug, cuddle, kiss, or climb on top of them. None of this need cause concern. There's no reason to infer that children are seeking sexual gratification. Rough-and-tumble play, including touching the genitals, is common among children. Three- and four-year-olds commonly express affection through kissing.

At this phase in their development, children should begin to learn the basic rules of privacy, that they have basic autonomy over their own bodies, and that there's a distinction between good touch (e.g., nonsexual touch by a trusted adult) and bad touch (e.g., non-consensual touch by a peer or sexual touch by an older person).

Dawning Curiosity.
Children are naturally inquisitive about sexual anatomy and sexual behaviour. Much curiosity is triggered when they become aware that males and females differ in anatomy.

Middle Childhood (Five to Eight Years)

Many adults still recall their first crushes, which often involved classmates. Childhood crushes, while typically not overtly sexual in nature, represent our first conscious romantic attachments. Some children at this age have relationships with special friends that resemble an early form of dating. Two children may hold hands and share a strong attachment, but this relationship doesn't usually involve explicitly sexual feelings.

Curiosity about the genitals increases at this stage. Sex games like show and playing doctor may begin earlier, but they become common between the ages of six and 10 (Pike, 2005). Much of this sexual activity takes place in same-sex groups, although mixed-sex games are not uncommon. Children may show their genitals to one another, touch one another's genitals, and, in rare cases, masturbate together.

Exploratory same-sex play may be more common at this age than play with the other gender. It typically involves handling the other child's genitals, although it may include oral or anal contact. It may also include an outdoor variation of

CRITICAL THINKING
QUESTIONS

How should a parent who sees a seven-year-old son or daughter playing doctor with a friend of the same age handle the situation? How should a babysitter who sees this situation react?

Barbie and Ken.
Some children sexualize their Barbie and Ken dolls.

the game of show, in which boys urinate together and see who can reach farthest or highest. Same-sex sexual play in childhood does not foreshadow adult sexual orientation (Reinisch, 1990). In the mind of the child, these experiences aren't interpreted as overtly sexual in terms of desire or sexual gratification. Rather, they function as opportunities to satisfy their curiosity.

It's common for children in middle childhood to be very curious about human reproduction, asking the quintessential question "Where do babies come from?" Very basic factual explanations usually satisfy children, although they may outwardly express revulsion ("Yuck! Gross!") when first learning that reproduction involves the insertion of a penis into a vagina.

Children at this age may also have some degree of awareness that not all people are heterosexual. They may ask what slang terms for homosexuality mean, or they may hear about a family that has two mommies or two daddies. Again, basic, factual explanations will likely satisfy them. In same-sex families, parents are likely to proactively discuss these differences in family structures.

Preadolescence (Nine to Twelve Years)

Some preadolescent behaviours are sexually related, rather than sexual per se. Preadolescents typically form relationships with best friends of the same sex, enabling them to share secrets and confidences. Preadolescents also tend to socialize with larger networks of friends in sex-segregated groups. At this stage, boys are likely to think girls are dorks. To girls at this stage, "dork" is too nice an epithet to apply to most boys.

Preadolescents grow increasingly preoccupied with—and self-conscious about—their bodies. They feel pressure from their peers to conform to dress codes, the proper slang, and group norms concerning sex and drugs. Peer disapproval can be an intense punishment. Sexual urges are experienced by many preadolescents, but may not emerge until adolescence (O'Sullivan, 2003).

As Table 12.1 indicates, one of most important developmental tasks of the preadolescent period is preparation for puberty. Some girls and a few boys begin the physical changes associated with puberty before age thirteen. Most of their peers follow soon afterwards. It's therefore critical for children in this age group to be properly educated about the physical and emotional changes they'll experience. The onset of puberty can be a source of stress and anxiety. The better informed a child is about the changes s/he can expect, the more likely s/he is to accept these changes in a positive way when they begin.

Kinsey and his colleagues (1948, 1953) reported that masturbation is the primary means of achieving orgasm for both boys and girls during preadolescence. They found that 45% of males and 15% of females had masturbated by age 13. Although these frequencies are suspect, other studies agree that adolescent males are more likely to masturbate than adolescent females (Pinkerton et al., 2002). As Steven Pinkerton and his colleagues (2002) have noted, frequency of masturbation is connected with social norms that appear to hold masturbation as more acceptable or normal for males than for females.

Preadolescent sex play often involves mutual display of the genitals, with or without touching. Such sexual experiences are quite common, and don't appear to affect future sexual adjustment (Guttmacher.org, 2009; Health24.com, 2006).

Although preadolescents tend to socialize in same-sex groups, interest in the other sex among heterosexuals tends to increase gradually as they approach puberty. Sexual intercourse in this age group is uncommon. A study of British Columbia youth found that 6.2% of males and 4.5% of females had experienced intercourse before age 14 (Saewyc, Taylor, Homma, & Ogilvie, 2008).

Exploratory sexual behaviour with members of the same sex occurs among children of all sexual orientations. Just like younger children, preadolescents are more likely to have same-sex than opposite-sex exploratory experiences (Guttmacher. org, 2009; Health24.com, 2006). These activities are usually limited to touching each other's genitals or mutual masturbation. Most same-sex sexual experiences at this age involve single episodes or short-lived relationships, and don't necessarily indicate a child's sexual orientation.

Adolescent Sexuality

In reflecting on how contemporary Canadian society views adolescence, Maticka-Tyndale (2001) notes that although teens, fuelled by surging sex hormones, are biologically ready for sexual activity, parents and adults in general often see them as too cognitively, emotionally, and socially immature to be sexually active. Combine this with a culture saturated with sexual imagery—on television, on the internet, in music, and in advertising—and it's not surprising that adolescence can be a turbulent time.

There are four major developmental tasks of adolescent sexuality:

- Adapt to the physical and emotional changes of puberty.
- Accept yourself as a sexual being.
- Explore romantic and sexual relationships.
- Learn to protect your sexual health.

Each task can play an important role in determining the extent to which a young person successfully navigates this sensitive, important period of sexual development. What takes place now will impact what happens later in life. Just as child sexual development sets the stage for adolescent sexuality, adolescent sexual development influences adult sexuality.

Adapting to the physical and emotional changes of puberty is a task for early adolescence. Self-acceptance as a sexual being is an ongoing process that begins in and likely extends beyond the adolescent years. Exploring romantic and sexual relationships and learning to protect sexual health also begin in early adolescence, or soon after, and are continually addressed throughout life.

When adolescence begins and ends is open to interpretation. In many respects, adolescence formally begins with the onset of puberty, and ends at some point in the late teen years. The psychological and social tasks of adolescent sexual development unfold throughout the teen years.

Applied Knowledge

TALKING WITH YOUR CHILDREN ABOUT SEX

"Daddy, where do babies come from?"

"What are you asking me for? Go ask your mother."

Most children don't find it easy to talk to their parents about sex. Yet most young children are curious about where babies come from, how girls and boys differ, and so on (Pike, 2005). Parents who avoid discussing these matters convey their own uneasiness about sex, and may teach children that sex is something to be ashamed of.

Parents needn't be sex experts to talk to their children about the subject. They can read books or surf the internet to fill gaps in their knowledge, or consult books written for parents to read to children. They can admit they don't know all the answers. Children often respect such honesty.

In answering children's questions, parents need to think about what the children can understand (Pike, 2005). The four-year-old who wants to know where babies come from is probably not interested in sexual details. It may be enough to say, "From Mommy's uterus," and point to the abdominal region. Why say "tummy"? "Tummy" is wrong and confusing.

Sex educators offer the following pointers for discussing sex with children.

- Be approachable. Be willing to answer questions about sex.
- Use appropriate language. Children need to learn the correct names of their sex organs, and that the dirty words others use to refer to the sex organs are unacceptable in most social settings. Nor should parents use silly words like "pee-pee" or "privates" to describe sex organs.
- Give advice in the form of information the child can use to make sound decisions, not as an imperial edict. Parents who lay down the law may be less effective than parents who provide information and encourage discussion.

- Share information in small doses. Pick a time and a place that feels natural for these discussions, such as when the child is preparing for bed, or when you're in the car.
- Encourage the child to talk about sex. Children may feel embarrassed about talking about sex, especially with family members. You can leave a children's book about sex around, or give it to the child with a suggestion such as "I thought you might be interested in this

book about sex. If you want to read it, we can talk about it."
- Respect the child's privacy rights. Most of us—parents and children alike—value privacy at times. A parent who feels uncomfortable sharing a bathroom with a child can say so. The parent might explain, "I like privacy when my door is closed. If you knock, I'll tell you whether you may come in. I'll knock when your door is closed, too." Fair is fair.

Talking with a Child About Sex.
Answer the questions truthfully. Use language the child will understand, but don't make it silly child language. In other words, don't talk about "pee-pees" and "wee-wees" and "Mommy's tummy." Use words like "penis," "vagina," and "uterus." Get a book with drawings or pictures.

Puberty The stage of development when reproduction first becomes possible. Puberty begins with the appearance of secondary sex characteristics and ends when the long bones make no further gains in length.

Secondary sex characteristics Physical characteristics that differentiate males and females, usually appearing at puberty but not directly involved in reproduction. Examples include bodily distribution of hair and fat, development of muscle mass, and deepening of the voice.

Primary sex characteristics Physical characteristics that differentiate males and females and are directly involved in reproduction. These are the sex organs.

Critical fat hypothesis The view that a girl must reach a certain body weight to trigger pubertal changes such as menarche.

Menarche The onset of menstruation; first menstruation.

In Western culture, parents, educators, and society at large have disproportionately focused on two of these four tasks. Discussion of adolescent sexuality has typically centred on the physical changes of puberty and the need for teens to protect themselves from unwanted pregnancy and sexually transmitted infections (STIs). These tasks tell only part of the story. Equally important are the tasks of accepting oneself as a sexual being and exploring romantic and sexual relationships. We'll therefore devote considerable attention to these issues, in addition to discussing topics such as puberty and statistics on adolescent sexual health (e.g., age of first intercourse, pregnancy rates, and condom use).

Puberty

Puberty begins with the appearance of **secondary sex characteristics** and ends when the long bones make no further gains in length. The appearance of strands of pubic hair is often the first visible sign of puberty. Puberty also involves changes in **primary sex characteristics**. Once puberty begins, most major changes occur within three years in girls and within four years in boys.

Toward the end of puberty, reproduction becomes possible. The two principal markers of reproductive potential are menarche in girls and first ejaculations in boys, though these events may not signify immediate fertility.

Rose Frisch (2002) has presented evidence that a particular ratio of fat to lean mass is usually necessary for both menarche and regular ovulatory cycles. According to the **critical fat hypothesis**, a girl must reach a certain body weight (perhaps 46.8 to 59.5 kilograms) to trigger pubertal changes such as menarche (Frisch, 2002). Body fat plays a key role, because fat cells secrete a chemical called leptin, which signals the body to secrete hormones that increase estrogen levels in the body. Higher body weight is associated with earlier menarche (Anderson et al., 2003), and children today grow faster than they used to. Menarche also comes later to athletes, who have lower percentages of body fat (Frisch, 2002; Robert-McComb, 2008).

Girls experience menarche between the ages of 10 and 18. The average age of menarche has declined sharply in Western countries since the 1800s, most likely because of improved nutrition and health care. In the 1890s, Canadian girls typically reached menarche by about 14.8 years. Today the average age in Canada is between 12 and 13 (Wyshuk & Frisch, as cited by Maticka-Tyndale, 2001). In the United States, the average age is 12.1 years for African-American girls and 12.6 years for European-Americans (Anerson et al., 2003).

Brock University researcher Anthony Bogaert (2005a) has found that age of puberty is related to the absence of a father. In Bogaert's study, 14-year-old females and males with absent fathers showed earlier signs of puberty, such as menarche and voice change, than females and males whose fathers were present in their lives. Absent mothers had no effect on the age of puberty. The findings suggest that certain psychosocial factors, such as paternal absence, may affect the development of both girls and boys (Bogaert, 2005).

FEMALE CHANGES First menstruation, or **menarche**, is the most obvious sign of puberty in girls. Yet other less obvious changes have already set the stage for menstruation. Between eight and 14 years of age, FSH released by the pituitary gland causes the ovaries to begin to secrete estrogen. Estrogen has several major effects on pubertal development. For one thing, it stimulates the growth of breast tissue ("breast buds"), perhaps as early as age eight or nine. The breasts usually begin to enlarge during the tenth year.

Estrogen also promotes growth of the uterus, thickening of the vaginal lining, and growth of fatty and supporting tissue in the hips and buttocks. This tissue and the widening of the pelvis causes the hips to become rounded, to permit childbearing. But growth of fatty deposits and connective tissue varies considerably. Some women may have pronounced breasts; others may have relatively large hips.

Small amounts of androgens produced by the female's adrenal glands, along with estrogen, stimulate development of pubic and underarm hair, beginning at about age 11. Excessive androgen production can darken or thicken facial hair.

Estrogen stimulates growth of the vagina, uterus, and labia during puberty, while androgens cause the clitoris to develop. Estrogen also typically slows the female growth spurt (some years before the male's growth spurt begins to slow down). As it becomes cyclical, estrogen production regulates the menstrual cycle.

Following menarche, a girl's early menstrual cycles are typically **anovulatory**—without ovulation. Girls cannot become pregnant until ovulation occurs, and ovulation may lag behind menarche by as much as two years. Ovulation may be unreliable at first, so a girl may be relatively infertile. Some teenagers, however, are highly fertile soon after menarche.

Anovulatory Without ovulation.

MALE CHANGES At puberty, the hypothalamus signals the pituitary to increase production of FSH and LH. These hormones stimulate the testes to increase their output of testosterone, which in turn prompts growth of the testes, scrotum, and penis. Testosterone also fosters differentiation of secondary male characteristics—growth of facial, body, and pubic hair, and deepening of the voice. Testicle growth, in turn, accelerates testosterone production and pubertal changes. The testes continue to grow, and the scrotal sac becomes larger and hangs loosely from the body. The penis widens and lengthens, and pubic hair appears.

By age 13 or 14, erections become frequent. Many middle-school boys dread being caught with erections between classes, or being asked to stand before their classes.

Under the influence of testosterone, the prostate and seminal vesicles—the organs that produce semen—increase in size, and semen production begins. Boys typically experience their first ejaculations by age 13 or 14, most often through masturbation. About a year after their first ejaculations, boys may begin to experience **nocturnal emissions**, which are also called wet dreams because they usually accompany erotic dreams.

Nocturnal emission Involuntary ejaculation of seminal fluid while asleep.

Underarm hair appears at about age 15. Facial hair is at first a fuzz on the upper lip; a beard doesn't appear for another two or three years. Only half of all boys have to shave by age 17. Beard and chest hair continue to develop past age 20.

At age 14 or 15, the voice deepens as the **larynx** grows and the vocal cords lengthen.

Larynx A structure of muscle and cartilage that lies at the upper end of the trachea and contains the vocal cords. It's also called the voice box.

Boys and girls undergo general growth spurts during puberty. Although girls usually shoot up before boys, individuals differ, and some boys spurt sooner than some girls.

Increases in muscle mass produce increases in weight. The shoulders and the circumference of the chest widen. Males stop growing taller at age of 18 or so, because estrogen prevents their long bones from getting longer. Males normally produce some estrogen in the adrenal glands and testes. Estrogen also causes nearly one in two boys to experience temporary enlargement of the breasts during puberty.

With all of these dramatic physical changes occurring so quickly, it's no surprise that body image can be of great concern to both boys and girls. Adolescent girls are typically more concerned than adolescent boys about body-image issues. More Canadian teenaged girls (45%) than boys (21%) report that they're greatly troubled by their weight, while 51% of girls and 38% of boys say they're bothered by their looks "a great deal" or "quite a bit" (Bibby, 2001).

SEXUAL SELF-ACCEPTANCE As Moore and Rosenthal note, "It is especially important that the adolescent be able to integrate his or her sexual feelings, needs, and desires into a coherent and positive self-identity, which contains, as one aspect, a sexual self" (Moore & Rosenthal, 1993, p. x). In other words, young women and men are getting to know themselves as sexual beings. They're becoming more familiar with what their sexual desires are (their likes and dislikes), whether they're more assertive or more passive, and what types of people they're attracted to (in terms of personality, physical attributes, and gender).

Adolescence is a time of rapid physical change and intense pressure to meet physical and social expectations (such as being "cool"). Body image can be a huge concern, with a significant impact on sexual well-being. Western culture—indeed, every culture—places considerable pressure on young people to conform to stereotypes of sexual desire and attraction. For example, young men are supposed to be attracted to and aggressively pursue young women, who are supposed to take passive roles in relationship development and conform to cultural ideals of feminine attractiveness. Many (if not most) adolescents realize that they don't exactly fit these stereotypes, which can be a source of considerable anxiety.

Lesbian, gay, bisexual, transgendered, and queer (LGBTQ) youth are obvious examples of adolescents who don't fit the traditional, stereotypical molds of what it means to be sexual beings. Girls who are assertive about their sexual feelings and desires and boys who aren't aggressive about asserting traditional expressions of masculinity are more examples of adolescents who don't conform to cultural stereotypes of "normal." There's an endless array of less obvious examples, too. The point is that these stereotypes can make it difficult for adolescents to fully accept themselves for who they are. Being able to move beyond these stereotypes, not using them to judge ourselves, is an important factor in fully accepting ourselves as sexual beings.

Developing self-acceptance as sexual beings can be especially challenging for LGBTQ youth, who face the additional burden of integrating their sexual orientations into their self-concepts while growing up in a heterosexist society. The process of sexual identity integration among LGBTQ youth is linked to overall psychological development and well-being. Social context issues such as the degree of support LGBTQ youth receive from their friends and families can affect this integration process (Rosario, Schrimshaw, & Hunter, 2011).

Researchers at the University of Guelph (Muise, Preyde, Maitland, & Milhausen, 2010) explored the relationship between sexual well-being and sexual identity—the definition of oneself as a sexual being—among female university students. They found that young women who devoted more attention to exploring their sexual identities scored higher on measures of sexual well-being (e.g., satisfaction with their sex lives).

Developing a sense of self-acceptance as a sexual being isn't always easy, especially in a culture with rigid standards for behaviour and appearance. Although the process typically begins in early adolescence, many people are well into adulthood before they fully accept themselves as sexual beings.

ROMANTIC AND SEXUAL RELATIONSHIPS It's during the teenage years that most adolescents have their first romantic and sexual relationships. (See Table 12.3 for statistics on Canadian teen sexual behaviour.) Many young people fall in love for the first time, experiencing the emotional turmoil that comes along with that. Adolescents face the developmental task of learning to integrate romantic relationships, with or without sexual components, into their lives in the absence of any prior experience. Learning to develop satisfying, mutually beneficial relationships is often a process of trial and error, and few emerge from this learning process without at least one experience of heartbreak.

At any age, communication is a key component of a mutually satisfying romantic or sexual relationship. However, relatively little research has explored sexual communication among adolescents. In one of the few studies of its kind, Laura Widman and her colleagues (2006) found that open communication about sex was associated with greater relationship satisfaction for dating couples who were 14 to 21 years of age.

Lily Tsui and Elena Nicoladis (2004) surveyed students at the University of Alberta on their first intercourse experiences. On average, the students who were sexually active reported an average age of 17 for first intercourse. Most (84%) said they were in romantic relationships when they had their first intercourse experiences. Fewer—63% of females and 43% of males—said they were in love with their partners at the time. Of the males, 62% reported that their first sexual intercourses were physically satisfying, and 42% said they were emotionally satisfying. Among females, less than half (35%) said it was physically satisfying, and 54% found it emotionally satisfying. Far more males (76%) than females (12%) reported that they'd had orgasms.

Trent University researcher Terry Humphreys (2007b) found that twice as many university females (40%) as males (21%) viewed their first intercourse experiences as giving their partners the gift of their virginity. On the other hand, about three times as many men (22%) as women (6%) viewed their virginal status as a stigma or an embarrassment that they were glad to get rid of when they had intercourse for the first time. Students who perceived virginity as a stigma were more likely to lose their virginity with a stranger or a friend, rather than with a love partner. More than half of both genders viewed first intercourse as a naturally occurring process that was a desirable and inevitable transition to adulthood.

Lucia O'Sullivan and Joann Majerovich (2008) at the University of New Brunswick examined sexual satisfaction and sexual functioning among 17- to 21-year-old students. They found that, overall, this group of young people reported fairly high levels of sexual desire, pleasure, and satisfaction. Nevertheless, a sizable percentage reported sexuality-related problems. For example, 81.4% of the males and 75% of the females reported that they'd felt anxious about "performing sexually" at some point. And 60.5% of the males and 66.9% of the females reported that they hadn't found sex pleasurable on at least one occasion.

Perhaps not surprisingly, research has found that adolescents tend to overestimate how much sex their peers are having, especially in comparison with themselves. ("Everybody's doing it except me.") A study of university students with an average age of 18.5 found that about 90% of both males and females thought they'd had fewer sex partners than their classmates (Stephenson & Sullivan, 2009). Sexual behaviour data from the sample indicated that they'd significantly overestimated the number of sex partners their peers had had in their lifetimes. What's particularly interesting about this study is the finding that the more students overestimated their peers' sexual experience, the more likely they were to report that they were unsatisfied with their own sex lives. In other words, our often inaccurate assumptions about what our peers are doing sexually can negatively affect how we assess our own sex lives.

These findings suggest that, contrary to media portrayals and the boasting of peers about their sexual exploits, adolescent sexual experiences and relationships are not uniformly blissful. Learning from the trials and errors of early relationships and developing patterns of open communication with partners about all aspects of a relationship, including the sexual component, sets the stage for a satisfying sex life in adulthood.

Adolescent Sexual Behaviour

MASTURBATION Masturbation is a major sexual outlet during adolescence. Surveys consistently show that boys are more likely than girls to masturbate (Friedman & Downey, 2008; Larsson & Svedin, 2002). Boys who masturbate may do so frequently—several times a week. Girls who masturbate are likely to do it less frequently. It's unclear whether this sex difference reflects a stronger sex drive in boys (Peplau, 2003), greater social constraints on girls (Pinkerton et al., 2002), or both. Cultural and religious norms surrounding masturbation can affect the likelihood and frequency of masturbation among both male and female adolescents.

There's considerable variation in the prevalence and frequency of masturbation among adolescent and adult males and females. That is, some people masturbate regularly, and some masturbate infrequently or not at all. Researchers find no links between adolescent masturbation and sexual adjustment in adulthood (Leitenberg et al., 1993).

SEXUAL TOUCHING (PETTING) Most adolescents experiment with various forms of sexual touching (sometimes known as petting). A study of Canadian teens found that the percentage who'd experienced "touching below the waist" increased with age, until about three-quarters had done so by grade 11. For some adolescents who choose to be sexually active but don't feel ready for oral sex or intercourse, or who want to avoid sexually transmitted infections or pregnancy, mutual masturbation (i.e., partners masturbating one another) is the primary form of partnered sexual expression.

ORAL SEX Traditionally, research examining adolescent sexual behaviour has focused almost exclusively on penile–vaginal intercourse. In recent years, however, oral sex—teen oral sex, in particular—has captured public attention. In the popular media, anecdotal stories about young teenagers engaging in frequent and indiscriminate oral sex have led to an unsubstantiated assumption that oral sex is increasingly common among Canadian young people (e.g., Wente, 2004). As we'll see from the available research, although oral sex is practised by some adolescents, it's about as common as intercourse, and often occurs at about the same age.

The 2002 Canadian Youth, Sexual Health, and HIV/AIDS Study (Boyce et al., 2006) found that less than one-third of grade nine males (32%) and females (28%) reported that they'd ever had oral sex, compared to about one-half of grade 11 males (53%) and females (52%). Interestingly, when these figures are compared to a 1994 study (Warren & King, 1994), we find that the percentages of youth engaging in oral sex increased only slightly in the intervening 12 years. Perhaps the recent media suggestions that the frequency of adolescent oral sex has increased to the point of becoming "epidemic" is exaggerated. Research from the United States also indicates that oral sex and intercourse tend to occur at roughly the same age. (See Table 12.2.)

INTERCOURSE In 2006, researchers at Queen's and Carleton Universities (Boyce, Craig, & Elder, 2008) conducted a large-scale health survey of 11- to 15-year-old students from across Canada. One-quarter of the boys and girls in grade 10 reported having experienced sexual intercourse. This figure was unchanged from the 2002 survey.

Data on older adolescents from the Canadian Community Health Survey reveals a similar trend (Rotermann, 2008). (See Table 12.3.) The survey shows that

CRITICAL THINKING QUESTIONS

There are significant differences of opinion about the age and circumstances in which it's appropriate to become sexually active. In your opinion, what are the most important factors to consider?

TABLE 12.2

Oral Sex and Vaginal Intercourse Experience Among Male and Female Teens in the US, 2002

Age	Male Gave Oral Sex	Female Gave Oral Sex	Male Received Oral Sex	Female Received Oral Sex	Male Experienced Intercourse	Female Experienced Intercourse
15–17	28.3%	30.4%	39.1%	38.0%	36.2%	36.4%
18–19	52.4%	62.8%	66.0%	66.6%	64.8%	72.3%

Source: Lindberg, L. D., Jones, R. & Santelli, J. S. (2008). Noncoital sexual activities among adolescents. Journal of Adolescent Health, 43(3), 231–238.

TABLE 12.3

Percentage of 15- to 19-Year-Old Canadians Who Have Had
Sexual Intercourse, 1996–2005

	1996–1997	2003	2005
Male	43%	46%	43%
Female	51%	45%	43%
Aged 15 to 17	32%	30%	29%
Aged 18 to 19	70%	68%	65%

Source: Rotermann, M. (2008). Trends in teen sexual behaviour and condom use. Health Reports, 19(3), 53-57.

from 1996–97 to 2005, the percentage of females who'd experienced intercourse declined, while the percentage for males remained stable. Overall, the most recent data suggest that about two-thirds of Canadians have sexual intercourse by the time they're 19.

Canadian street youth have more sexual experience than those in high school. A British Columbia study has found that 82% of street youth have had sexual intercourse—two-thirds by age 14 or younger (Smith et al., 2007).

The 2005 Canadian Community Health Survey asked sexually active young people how many sexual partners they'd had in the previous 12 months (Rotermann, 2008). Twenty-nine percent of those aged 15 to 17 and 36% of those aged 18 to 19 reported more than one sexual partner in the previous 12 months. This suggests that most sexually active youth have only one intercourse partner at a time.

EARLY AGE AT FIRST INTERCOURSE Various social factors are predictive of intercourse at a young age. According to the 2001 National Longitudinal Survey of Children and Youth, Canadian adolescents who begin having sex at younger ages also tend to begin smoking by age 12 or 13, which indicates that they don't conform to societal norms in general. Drinking alcohol at age 12 or 13 is associated with early intercourse for girls, but not for boys.

There's a striking gender difference in the role of self-esteem. Girls with weak self-concepts are more likely to have early intercourse, whereas boys with strong self-concepts are more likely to engage in early intercourse. Physical characteristics also play a stronger role with girls. Those who reach puberty at a young age and are not overweight are more likely to have early intercourse than those who reach puberty later or are overweight (Statistics Canada, 2005d).

The 2002 Canadian Youth, Sexual Health, and HIV/AIDS Study indicated that poor school attachment and poor relationships with parents are also predictive of early sexual intercourse (Boyce et al., 2003). And among both male and female students in Regina, having male and female peers who are having sex is strongly predictive of intercourse experience (Hampton et al., 2005).

In Nova Scotia, Donald Langille (2002) of Dalhousie University found that the strongest predictors for sexual intercourse at a young age among high school girls were single-mother families, fathers' low educational levels, and infrequent church attendance. In British Columbia, sexual intercourse at a young age for both boys and girls was linked with low connectedness to family, low connectedness to school, and sexually permissive peers (Saewyc et al., 2008).

CASUAL SEX Most adolescent sexual behaviour, especially intercourse, takes place within ongoing dating relationships. Some sexual behaviour, however, is more casual.

A World of Diversity

DO SEXY TV SHOWS ENCOURAGE TEEN SEX AND PREGNANCY?

What happens when teenagers watch *Sex in the City* and other shows with sexual content? Does what they see roll off their backs or encourage them to go for a roll in the hay?

A study reported in *Pediatrics* (Collins et al., 2004) found an association between watching sexual content on television and initiation into sexual intercourse. The study included more than 1 700 12- to 17-year-olds.

The researchers followed up with the same cohort of adolescents after three years, to determine whether watching sex on television led to a higher incidence of pregnancy (Chandra et al., 2008).

The 718 adolescents (57% male, 43% female) who reported having engaged in sexual intercourse and who provided information about pregnancy were included in the analysis. The researchers controlled for other variables connected with teenage pregnancy, such as school grades and conduct problems.

They found that teenage pregnancy, like initiation into sexual intercourse, was significantly correlated with exposure to sexual content on television. Teenagers categorized as having high levels of exposure (that is, those in the ninetieth percentile on the variable) were two to three times more likely to have been pregnant or responsible

Generally, males are more in favour of casual sex than females. In the 2002 Canadian Youth, Sexual Health, and HIV/AIDS Study, twice as many grade 11 boys (66%) as girls (32%) approved of casual sex (Boyce et al., 2003). A study of high school students in Vancouver, British Columbia, and Amherst, Nova Scotia, found that girls were judged more negatively than boys for engaging in casual sex. Girls who displayed greater self-confidence and whose parents were from higher social classes were less likely to be judged negatively (Shoveller et al., 2004).

Four different measures of casual sex were used in a study of 230 female university students in Ontario (Weaver & Herold, 2000). The results showed how choosing a particular indicator has a strong impact on the percentage of people who report that they engage in casual sex. Only 13% of the female students said they'd engaged in sexual intercourse with someone they'd met the same day or night, but three times as many (36%) said they'd had sexual intercourse with someone they weren't in a committed relationship with. The rates of casual sex jumped substantially when the researchers measured non-intercourse sexual experiences. One-half of the respondents had engaged in hand–genital and/or oral sex with someone they'd met that day, and three-quarters had done so with someone they weren't in a committed relationship with. Most reported having only one or two casual sex partners.

Seventy-six percent of the women who'd experienced casual sex (as measured by any of the indicators in the study) thought casual sex was enjoyable, compared with 57% of the women who had not experienced casual sex. When asked what aspects of casual sex they found appealing, one-third said they found nothing about it appealing.

Sexual pleasure was by far the most common reason the women gave for having casual sex. Other reasons they gave were living it up, fulfilling their sexual fantasies, experiencing the novelty of new partners, improving their sexual technique, doing something forbidden, heightening their self-esteem, feeling good about their bodies, and experiencing the thrill of attracting new partners.

When asked which factors might prevent them from engaging in casual sex, more than 90% of the women surveyed said they were concerned about AIDS, STIs, and pregnancy. The next biggest concerns related to morality, guilt, loose reputation, and fear of physical harm. Those who hadn't experienced casual sex were far more concerned about the moral issue than those who had.

for a pregnancy than teenagers in the tenth percentile. Total hours of television watching was not significantly correlated with pregnancy.

Conclusions

It might seem that we can conclude that watching sexual content on television is a cause of sexual initiation and teenage pregnancy.

However, the study showed a correlation between what teenagers watched and sexual outcomes. As we noted in Chapter 2, correlational studies may show

relationships, but they don't show cause and effect. Because the researchers didn't run an experiment in which some teens watched shows with sexual content while others did not, there may be rival explanations for the correlation researchers found.

The research findings could be due to a selection factor. For example, it's possible that teenagers who had more interest in sex, who came from more permissive homes, or who had friends who touted sexy shows were more likely to watch sexy television shows, and also more likely to have sex and get pregnant. In this case, sexual

interest, home atmosphere, and peer relationships would be more likely to be causal than sexy television content.

Critical Thinking

Consider why researchers can't run experiments in which watching sexy shows is the treatment or independent variable. What ethical issues would be involved in showing racy TV to teens? Moreover, could the researchers prevent teens assigned to non-sexy shows from watching racy TV on their own?

A new set of terms for various forms of casual sex have appeared. These include "hooking up," "booty call," and "friends with benefits." Many of these terms are simply new names for pre-existing practices, while others may represent new types of sexual relationships. "Hooking up," for example, refers to a casual sexual encounter with a new partner without ongoing romantic involvement. In the past, this activity would have been called a "one-night stand." Whether hooking up is more common today than one-night stands were in the past remains an open question.

"Friends with benefits," as the name implies, refers to friends who have sex but aren't romantically committed to each other. One small study of students on an American college campus found that 60% of students had engaged in some form of friends-with-benefits relationship (Bisson & Levine, 2009). In 18.7% of the cases, the friends had sex just once, while 52.1% had sex occasionally, and 29.3% had sex frequently. When asked how their friends-with-benefits relationships had turned out, 28% reported that they were still friends with benefits, 35.8% said they'd stopped having sex but were still friends, 9.8% said they'd become romantic partners, and 25.9% said they'd ended their relationships. In other words, a friendship was more than twice as likely to end as to become a committed romantic relationship.

Among the potential problems of a friends-with-benefits relationships is that one partner may begin to want a more committed relationship, while the other doesn't. In some cases, the friendship ends over conflict about the sexual aspect of the relationship, or when one partner wants to stop having sex.

ATTITUDES ABOUT PREMARITAL SEX The most significant changes in sexual attitudes in Canada occurred in the late 1960s and early 1970s. Before then, societal attitudes were firmly opposed to premarital sex (Herold, 1984). Canadian youth are more accepting than older people of premarital sex today. A large majority of adolescents (82%) approve of premarital sex if the two people love each other, and more than half (58%) approve if the two people like each other. Fewer than half (49%) of youth who attend religious services on a weekly basis approve of premarital sex (Bibby, 2001).

In the 2002 Canadian Youth, Sexual Health, and HIV/AIDS Study, only 11% of the girls and 5% of the boys in grade nine said wanting to be a virgin at marriage was a reason for abstaining from intercourse. Just 3% of the boys and 4% of the girls gave religious beliefs as a reason for avoiding sex. The most common reasons they gave for abstaining were not being ready, not having the opportunity, and not meeting the right person (Boyce et al., 2003).

A study in Regina found that most high school students thought their parents would disapprove of their having sexual intercourse. Females were more likely than males to believe their fathers would disapprove (Hampton et al., 2005). There was no relationship between whether students' thought their parents would disapprove and whether the students were having sex. Only one-third of the students were comfortable talking to their parents about sex, and these students were more likely to tell their parents if they were having sex (Hampton et al., 2005).

Obstacles Faced by Sexual-Minority Youth

It's important to examine some of the obstacles faced by lesbian, gay, bisexual, transgendered, and queer (LGBTQ) youth in the developmental tasks of adolescent sexuality. Canadian society has become more accepting of diverse sexual orientations in recent years, but LGBTQ youth continue to face discrimination, prejudice, and violence because of their sexual orientations. Self-acceptance as sexual beings is therefore more challenging for sexual-minority youth, because they have to grow up in a society that doesn't fully accept their sexual orientations. The vast majority of research on the sexual behaviour of Canadian adolescents groups all teens together, or looks at behaviours such as heterosexual intercourse. We know comparatively little about the timing and context of sexual behaviour among sexual-minority youth.

The Adolescent Health Surveys conducted in 1992, 1998, and 2003 by the McCreary Centre Society in British Columbia included lesbian, gay, bisexual, and heterosexual youth in grades seven to 12. The proportion of LGB students in the surveys varied between 2% and 4%. The surveys asked about the genders of their sexual partners, and whether they'd experienced sexual intercourse with opposite-sex partners. Unfortunately, the survey was mainly focused on heterosexual behaviours, and didn't ask about same-sex behaviours (Saewyc et al., 2007).

As Table 12.4 shows, many of the LGB youth had opposite-sex as well as same-sex partners. A small minority (14% of bisexual males and 5% of bisexual females) reported having only same-sex partners in the previous year. In comparison, 55% of gay males and 29% of lesbians reported having only same-sex partners in the previous year. More LGB youth than heterosexual youth reported having sexual

---

TABLE 12.4

Sexual Orientations and Genders of Sexual Partners Within the Past Year

	Opposite Gender Only	Same Gender	Both Genders Only
MALE			
Bisexual	55%	32%	14%
Gay	26	19	55
FEMALE			
Bisexual	62	33	5
Lesbian	15	56	29

Source: Saewyc, E., Poon, C., Wang, N., Homma, Y., Smith, A., and the McCreary Centre Society. (2007). Not Yet Equal: The Health of Lesbian, Gay, & Bisexual Youth in BC. *Vancouver, BC: McCreary Centre Society. Courtesy of McCreary Centre Society.*

intercourse with opposite-sex partners. The highest rates of intercourse were among bisexual females and males (Saewyc et al., 2007).

In a national Canadian survey of students in grades nine and 11, Stephen Fergus (2006) of Queen's University compared the sexual experiences of those who felt attracted to the same sex with those who felt attracted to the opposite sex. Those with same-sex attractions were more likely to be sexually experienced and to have had sex at a younger age. They were also more likely to have been pressured to engage in sex, and to have had sexually transmitted infections.

Wells (2009) reviewed research on sexual-minority youth and found that, in addition to experiencing higher rates of sexual violence, lesbian, gay, and bisexual youth were more likely than their heterosexual counterparts to feel emotionally distressed and to report low self-esteem. A recent Canadian study found that school could be a very unwelcoming place for sexual-minority youth. Among the findings: 76% heard expressions like "that's so gay" on a daily basis, 60% had been verbally harassed, and 25% had been physically harassed because of their sexual orientations (EGALE Canada, 2009). A welcoming, nonthreatening school environment can reduce the negative health and social outcomes for sexual-minority youth (Saewyc et al., 2009).

School-based sexual-health education in Canada tends to be predominately—if not exclusively—heterosexual in focus. This can make it difficult for LGBTQ youth to acquire accurate sexual-health information that's specific to their needs. To fill this gap, many LGBTQ youth are able to find information from alternate sources, such as LGBTQ-friendly community organizations and the internet. As Canadian society becomes more accepting of sexual diversity, more and more LGBTQ youth will successfully complete the developmental tasks of adolescent sexuality.

Protecting Sexual Health in Adolescence

As we've seen, most Canadian young people become sexually active to some extent during their teen years. Protecting their sexual health is therefore an important developmental task. Preventing unintended pregnancy and STIs are priorities. STIs are common among Canadian youth, presenting significant threats to their health and well-being.

Canadian teen pregnancy rates have fallen significantly over the last several decades (McKay, 2006). The pregnancy rate among 15- to 19-year-old females declined from 47.6 per 1000 in 1995 to 29.2 per 1000 in 2005 (Statistics Canada, 2009).

Adolescents can use a number of strategies to protect their sexual health. Obviously, abstaining from partnered sexual activity protects them from pregnancy and STIs. Some adolescents choose to engage only in sexual activities with lower risks for these outcomes, such as petting and oral sex. (For a full discussion of lower-risk sexual behaviours, see Chapter 17.)

For Canadian youth, using condoms is by far the most popular choice for protecting sexual health. Condoms are relatively easy to get; unlike the birth-control pill, they don't require a prescription. Condoms also provide protection against both unwanted pregnancy and STIs. Most Canadian teens who have intercourse use condoms, and the rate of condom use has increased in recent years. The Canadian Community Health Survey found that among 15- to 19-year-olds, condom use increased from 72% in 2003 to 75% in 2005 (Rotermann, 2008). It appears that younger teens are more responsible than older teens when it comes to condom use. The same survey indicated that 81% of sexually active 15- to 17-year-olds used condoms, compared to just 70% of 18- and 19-year-olds. Some of these older teens may have switched to other forms of birth control, in the belief that they were at low risk for STIs. This belief is often mistaken, as rates of common STIs such as chlamydia are higher among older teens and young adults.

A World of Diversity

A GAY PROM DATE

They dance d the night away.

Marc Hall, the shy, blue-coiffed 17-year-old Oshawa student who wouldn't take no for an answer when told he couldn't take his boyfriend to his high-school prom, won a major court victory for Catholic students in 2002.

In a comprehensive and clear decision granting Hall's request for an injunction, Mr. Justice Robert MacKinnon of the Superior Court of Justice said a ban on same-sex dates at the prom was a clear violation of Hall's constitutional rights, and ordered the Durham Catholic School Board to allow Hall and Jean-Paul Dumond, 21, to attend the dance.

School board chair Mary Ann Martin said the board was extremely disappointed with the ruling, but that Hall and his date would be allowed to attend the prom.

Hall, in a white tuxedo and blue tie, said he "was very happy and so excited that we won." When he first heard the news from his lawyer at his home in Oshawa, he said, "I was jumping up and down, and everybody was shouting."

"I feel at ease now, knowing that we are free of discrimination," said the grade 12 student at Monsignor John Pereyma Catholic High School.

Source: Josey, S. (2002, May 11). "Gay Prom Battle Ends with a Waltz." The Toronto Star.

A Gay Prom Date.
Marc Hall, 17, heads to his Toronto school prom with Jean-Paul Dumond, 21. Coming to terms with adolescence is often a difficult struggle, but it's often more intense for gay people.

Taking decreasing teen pregnancy rates and higher levels of condom use into account, we can conclude that the sexual health of Canadian youth is improving in many respects. Challenges remain, however. STI rates remain high among Canadian young people, and sexual-health educational needs are less well addressed for lesbian, gay, bisexual, transgendered, and queer youth than for heterosexual youth.

Adult Sexuality

So far in this chapter we've looked at sexuality in childhood and adolescence from a developmental perspective. Does our development as sexual beings finish once we complete the transition from adolescence to adulthood? Do growth and development of sexuality stop as we begin to settle into adult roles?

We can answer these questions with a definitive "no." With respect to sexuality, each phase of life brings new challenges and new opportunities for growth. Adulthood has its own set of developmental tasks. We'll now discuss four of the most important ones.

Developmental Tasks

While adolescent romantic relationships tend to be inherently unstable, with little sense of permanence or longevity, adults (some of them, anyway) tend to seek more stable, more long-term, complete relationships, including permanent romantic relationships. Marriage has traditionally been the primary relationship form for adult Canadians, and it continues to be, though less so than in the past.

The successful integration of sexuality into longer-term relationships implies a number of developmental tasks.

PASSION In Western culture, romantic relationships usually begin with some element of physical and emotional attraction. The first episodes of sexual interaction tend to be fuelled by passion and spontaneous sexual arousal. Physical attraction ("chemistry") is often the spark that initially brings a couple together. At first, the degree to which a couple is compatible in other ways, such as mutual interests or perspectives, may take a back seat to sexual passion as the determinant of each partner's satisfaction with the relationship.

As the relationship progresses, the initial passionate infatuation inevitably wanes, and broader aspects of compatibility become more important. If, once the novelty of the new sexual partnership subsides, the partners discover that they're not so compatible in other important dimensions, it's not uncommon to hear them say, "I was blinded by passion."

Understanding that other factors beyond passion will determine the sustainability of sexual or romantic relationships is therefore a necessary developmental task of adult sexuality.

FRIENDSHIP By early adulthood, most individuals have some level of experience with sexual and romantic relationships. This experience usually teaches us that sexual passion alone is not enough to sustain a relationship, especially if the couple hopes to maintain the relationship over time.

There are many dimensions to a strong, mutually satisfying relationship, and a sense of friendship is one of the most important. The qualities that contribute to a mutually beneficial friendship—such as shared interests and goals—also contribute to the intimacy of a romantic relationship. Over time, sexual satisfaction becomes a function of the couple's sense of shared intimacy along a range of dimensions, including both physical pleasure and friendship.

Learning to approach sexual and romantic relationships in a broader way that includes a range of aspects of intimacy is an important developmental task for adults hoping to maintain relationships beyond the short term.

COMMUNICATION For many couples, openly discussing specific sexual likes and dislikes doesn't come naturally. Many people rely on nonverbal cues ("body language") to make assumptions about their partner's' sexual preferences. This isn't always the most effective form of communication. More direct communication about sexuality may be an important contributor to a mutually satisfying longer-term relationship. In a study of men and women in long-term relationships, University of New Brunswick researchers MacNeil and Byers (1997) found that better communication, particularly about specific sexual likes and dislikes, was associated with overall sexual satisfaction.

For many adults, learning to communicate directly and effectively with partners about sexuality is an important developmental task.

SEXUAL HEALTH As we have seen, protecting their sexual health is a major developmental task for adolescents. It's no less so for adults. Taking measures to prevent STI and HIV infection and unwanted pregnancy are still important, particularly since more and more adults are remaining single, or becoming single after separation or divorce.

A national study of sexually active Canadian women of reproductive age who were not trying to conceive found that, while most used some form of contraception, a sizable number were putting themselves at risk for unintended pregnancy (Black et al., 2009). Condoms and oral contraceptives were the most popular methods of contraception. Almost 15% of the women said that they "never" used birth control, and only 65.2% said they "always" did.

CRITICAL THINKING QUESTIONS

How would you explain the finding that condom use among sexually active, unmarried, non-cohabitating 20- to 34-year-old Canadians declines as they get older?

It appears that as adolescents make the transition to adulthood, their commitment to using condoms often decreases, even though their risks for STIs and HIV remain high. Rotermann and McKay (2009) looked at trends in condom use at last intercourse among unmarried, non-cohabiting 20- to 34-year-old Canadians, and found that condom use decreased as people got older. For example, 63.7% of males and 53.8% of females in the 20-to-24 age group used condoms at last intercourse, compared to 56.0% of males and 47.1% of females in the 25-to-29 age range, and 54.7% of males and 42.2% of females in the 30-to-34 age group. In the total sample, 35.8% of those with more than one partner during the previous year and 30% of males and nearly 40% of females with three or more partners didn't use condoms at last intercourse. These statistics clearly suggest that many young Canadian adults are placing themselves at high risk for STIs and HIV.

Being Single

Recent years have seen a sharp increase in the number of single young people in our society. "Singlehood," not marriage, is now the most common lifestyle among people in their twenties. (See Table 12.5.)

Several factors contribute to the increased proportion of singles. More people are postponing marriage to pursue educational and career goals. Many young people are deciding to "live together" (also referred to as cohabiting and living common-law), at least for a while, rather than get married.

Much has been written about a "shortage of men available for single heterosexual women." According to the 2006 census, there are 96 men for every 100 Canadian women, (Bonoguore, 2007). This gap is largest in major Canadian cities such as Toronto. There are more men than women in Canada's north, rural Alberta, and skiing towns such as Whistler.

As Figure 12.1 shows, people are getting married later than they used to. In 2004, the typical man in Canada got married for the first time at 30.5 years of age, compared with 25 in 1960. The typical woman got married at 28.5, compared with 22 in 1960 (Statistics Canada, 2007). The average age at marriage is highest in Quebec and lowest in Saskatchewan.

Many young adults in Canada, especially males, live in their parental homes. Two-thirds of 20- to 24-year-old men live with their parents, compared with about half of 20- to 24-year-old women (Statistics Canada, 2002). Many young adults live with their parents while they go to university or try to find jobs. Because of the high cost of rental housing, many cannot afford their own apartments.

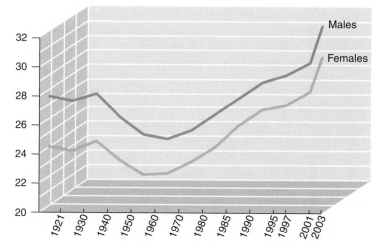

Figure 12.1 Average age at first marriage in Canada.
The age at first marriage has substantially increased in Canada, partly because many adults now live together before getting married.

Source: Statistics Canada. (2010). CANSIM Table 101-1002: Mean age of males and females, by type of marriage and marital status, Canada, provinces and territories, annual. Ottawa: Government of Canada.

Many single people don't choose to be single. Some remain single because they haven't found Mr. or Ms. Right. Many, however, see singlehood as an alternative, open-ended way of life, not just a temporary stage that precedes marriage. Now that career options for women have expanded, they're not as financially dependent on men as their mothers and grandmothers were. A number of career-oriented women, like young career-oriented men, choose to remain single (at least for a time) so they can focus on their careers.

Singlehood is not without its problems. Many single people are lonely. Some singles express concern about their lack of steady, meaningful social relationships. Some, usually women, worry about their physical safety. Some people who live alone find it difficult to satisfy their needs for intimacy, companionship, sex, and emotional support. Despite these concerns, however, most singles are well adjusted and content. Singles with more friends and supportive social networks tend to be more satisfied with their lifestyles.

There's no one "singles scene." Single people differ in their sexual interests and lifestyles. Many achieve emotional and psychological security through a network of intimate relationships with friends. Most are sexually active and practise **serial monogamy**.

Modern technology, especially the internet, has transformed the singles scene. While the proverbial "singles bar" was the predominant setting for singles to meet before the new millennium, online dating sites such as Lavalife and eHarmony have since gained widespread acceptance. Social networking sites such as MySpace and Facebook are another form of internet-based communication that allows singles to become familiar with potential sexual and romantic partners.

The Canadian-based online dating site Lavalife boasts 1.7 million members (Lavalife.com, 2011). On Lavalife, singles can choose from a variety of relationship types: dates, relationships, and intimate encounters. This allows potential partners to make clear what types of relationship they're interested in before meeting potential partners, removing a layer of ambiguity about their intentions. While some might feel that this level of up-front disclosure removes some of the mystery, intrigue, and romance of dating, others think the direct matching of compatible partners provided by internet dating sites increases the likelihood that mutually satisfactory relationships will form.

Serial monogamy A pattern of becoming involved in one exclusive relationship after another, as opposed to engaging in multiple sexual relationships at the same time.

Meeting Other Singles.
There's no one "singles scene." Although some people meet in singles bars, many meet in more casual settings, such as neighbourhood laundromats. Some singles advertise online and in newspapers and magazines.

Research indicates that an increasing number of marriages and long-term relationships begin through some form of internet communication (Sprecher, 2009). A 2002 survey of Canadian university students found that 18% of males and 10% of females had used online dating sites during the previous year (Boies, 2002). It's very likely that if the same survey were conducted today, these percentages would be considerably higher.

Some singles remain celibate, either by choice or for lack of opportunity. People choose **celibacy** for a number of reasons. Nuns and priests do so for religious reasons. Others believe celibacy allows them to focus their energies and attentions on work or important causes. They see celibacy as a temporary accommodation to other pursuits. Still others remain celibate because they view sex outside of marriage as immoral. And some remain celibate because they find the prospect of sexual activity repulsive or unalluring, or because they're afraid of STIs.

Cohabitation

Social scientists believe **cohabitation** has become acceptable within the social mainstream. Eighty-four percent of Canadians approve of cohabitation (Bibby, 2001). We seldom hear cohabitation referred to as "living in sin" or "shacking up" anymore. People today are more likely to refer to cohabitation with value-free expressions such as "living together."

Statistics Canada defines a relationship as a **common-law relationship** if it consists of two people of the opposite or the same sex who live together as a couple but are not legally married. Canadians of various ethnic backgrounds differ considerably in their acceptance of cohabitation. Acceptance is higher among those of British origin than among Southern Europeans. The Chinese are less accepting, and the Indo-Canadian community is the least accepting (Michell, 2001).

As Table 12.5 shows, common-law relationships are becoming increasingly prevalent in Canadian society. Clearly, more and more people in their twenties are opting for common-law relationships as an alternative to marriage.

COHABITATION BEFORE MARRIAGE Cohabiting couples may believe cohabitation will strengthen their eventual marriages by helping them iron out the kinks in their relationships. Yet cohabiters who later marry run a serious risk of divorce. Canadian couples who live together before marriage are twice as likely to separate as those who don't (Statistics Canada, 2002c). Sixty-three percent of those in their thirties who live together before marriage separate, compared with 30% of those who don't live together before marriage.

Celibacy Complete sexual abstinence. The term is sometimes used to describe the state of being unmarried, especially for people who take vows to remain single.

Cohabitation The state whereby two people live together as a couple but are not legally married.

Common-law relationship A relationship in which two people live together as a couple but are not legally married. The term can refer to both opposite- and same-sex couples. Some jurisdictions recognize a common-law relationship as marriage.

TABLE 12.5

Percentage of Canadians Who Were Single, Cohabiting, and Married in 1986, 1996, and 2006

Ages 20–24	Single (%)	Cohabiting (%)	Married (%)
1986	71.6	9.3	19.1
1996	79.2	12.0	8.8
2006	82.2	12.6	5.2
Ages 25–29			
1986	37.7	10.2	52.1
1996	47.6	12.5	34.9
2006	51.5	22.6	25.9

Source: Statistics Canada. (1986, 1996, 2006). Census Data Products. Ottawa: Government of Canada.

Why might couples who cohabit before marriage run a greater risk of divorce than couples who don't? Cohabiters tend to be more committed to personal independence than non-cohabiters (Bumpass, 1995). They also tend to be less traditional and less religious. All in all, people who cohabit before marriage tend to be less committed to the values and interests traditionally associated with the institution of marriage. Their attitudes, and not cohabitation itself, may thus account for their higher rates of marital dissolution (see Figure 12.2).

Marriage

Marriage is found in all human societies. Most people in every known society—sometimes nearly all—get married at least once. Marriage is our most common lifestyle. Statistics Canada (2005e) estimates that three-quarters of Canadians who are in their thirties will marry at some point in their lives. Most people see marriage as something they hope will be permanent.

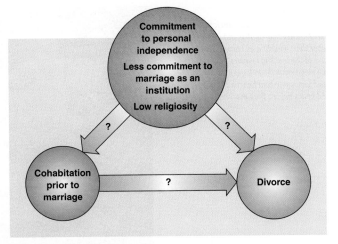

Figure 12.2 Does cohabitation prior to marriage increase the risk of divorce?
There's a correlation between premarital cohabitation and divorce. Does cohabitation increase the risk of divorce, or do other factors—such as a commitment to personal independence—contribute to the likelihood of both cohabitation and eventual divorce?

SAME-SEX MARRIAGE Traditionally, societies have defined marriage as applying only to heterosexual couples. This definition was challenged by same-sex couples in Canada, who argued that not allowing same-sex marriage restricted their freedom. In July 2002, ruling that the traditional definition of marriage was discriminatory to lesbians and gays, the Ontario Superior Court of Justice ordered governments to redefine the term "marriage" to include same-sex couples. In this landmark decision, the judges argued that prohibiting same-sex couples from marrying was a violation of the Canadian Charter of Rights and Freedoms. In 2005, Canadian Parliament passed legislation allowing same-sex couples to marry. (We also discussed same-sex marriage in Chapters 1 and 9.)

In recent years, there's been considerable analysis and debate about gay and lesbian marriage. The changes in Canadian law that allow gay marriage to take place have accelerated these discussions.

The Canadian census obtained data about same-sex couples for the first time in 2001. There were 34 200 same-sex common law couples in Canada, representing 0.5% of all couples (Statistics Canada, 2002f). Eighty-five percent of male couples and 75% of female couples live in Canada's larger urban areas. About 15% of female same-sex couples have children living with them, compared with just 3% of male couples. The Canadian census counted same-sex married couples for the first time in 2006. It found 37 885 same-sex common-law partnerships—an increase of 11% over the previous five years—and 7500 same-sex marriages (Statistics Canada, 2007).

Two Canadian studies have analyzed married lesbian and gay couples (Alderson, 2004; MacIntosh, Reissing, & Andruff, 2010), and found the following benefits of marriage:

- Greater acceptance of their relationships by friends and family members.
- Equality with heterosexuals in terms of making decisions for ill partners, caring for children, and receiving inheritance and insurance benefits.
- Greater relationship satisfaction, including feeling closer to their partners and more secure about their relationships.
- Decreased feelings of internalized homophobia.
- More openness to the idea of having children.

CRITICAL THINKING QUESTIONS

More and more Canadians in their twenties are living in common-law relationships, rather than getting married. In your opinion, what are the advantages and disadvantages of each lifestyle?

Married at Last.
Douglas Elliott, second from left, and Greg Lawrence, centre, are congratulated after their wedding in Toronto. Elliot was one of the leading lawyers in the fight to make gay marriage legal in Canada. He and Lawrence had been a couple for 32 years before they married.

Not everyone in the gay community supports same-sex marriage. Opponents tend to criticize marriage as a patriarchal, heterosexual institution. Married same-sex couples don't share this view; they argue that legalization of same-sex marriage offers freedom of choice.

WHY DO PEOPLE MARRY? In this era of serial monogamy and cohabitation, people still get married. Why?

Because marriage meets personal and cultural needs. It legitimizes sexual relations, and provides a legal sanction for deeply committed relationships. It permits maintenance of a home life, and provides an institution in which children can be supported and socialized into adopting the norms of the family and the culture at large. Marriage restricts sexual relations, so a man can be assured—or at least can assume—that his wife's children are his. Marriage also permits the orderly transmission of wealth from one family to another, and from one generation to another.

Notions such as romantic love, equality, and the radical concept that men as well as women would do well to aspire to the ideal of faithfulness are recent additions to the structure of marriage in Western society. Not until the nineteenth century did the notion of love as a basis for marriage become widespread in Western culture.

When Canadians were asked in 1998 why people should get married, almost all (95%) said for love (Compas, 1998). The next common reasons were for companionship (83%) and to have children (82%). Two-thirds cited having a regular and safe sex partner as a reason to get married.

In another national survey almost 10 years later, Canadians were asked about the importance of marriage (Canadian Press, 2007). There was a major discrepancy between the importance of marriage in the respondents' own lives and their perception of its importance in society. When asked about their personal attitudes, 42% said marriage had become more important in their own lives, 17% said it had become less important, and 39% said its importance hadn't changed. Only 13% believed marriage had become more important in society, while 53% felt it had become less important. Three-quarters said making a marriage work was harder today than in the past (Canadian Press, 2007).

TYPES OF MARRIAGE There are two major types of marriage—monogamy and polygamy. In **monogamy**, a husband and wife are wed only to each other. But let's not confuse monogamy, which is a form of matrimony, with sexual exclusivity. People may have extramarital affairs, but they're considered to be married to just one person at a time. In **polygamy**, a person has more than one spouse and is permitted sexual access to all of them.

In Bountiful, British Columbia, a breakaway sect of the Mormon Church has been openly practising polygamy since the 1950s. Teenaged girls are often forced to marry much older men who already have wives. The British Columbia government has been reluctant to charge community members with violating Canada's anti-polygamy law, because the Canadian Charter of Rights and Freedoms protects religious freedom (Canadian Press, 2005b). Yet in 2009, after 20 years of investigations, the British Columbia government brought charges of polygamy against two leaders of the community, Winston Blackmore and James Oler.

Some Muslims in Canada also have plural wives, although the great majority do not (Javed, 2008). Aly Hindy, imam at an Islamic centre in Scarborough, claims to have officiated at more than 30 polygamous marriages over a five-year period (Javed, 2008). Islam allows men to marry up to four wives, while the Mormon sect in British Columbia allows an unlimited number of wives. Whereas the Bountiful sect requires polygamous marriage in order to reach heaven, Islam accepts but does not require polygamy.

Polygyny is by far the most prevalent form of polygamy among the world's preliterate societies (Frayser, 1985). **Polyandry** is practised only rarely. In polygynous societies, men are permitted multiple wives if they can support them; less often, a man will have one wife and one or more concubines. Economic factors and the availability of prospective mates, however, usually limit the opportunities for men to wed more than one woman at a time. In many cases, only wealthy men can afford to support multiple wives and their children. Few societies have enough women to allow most men to have two or more wives (Harris & Johnson, 2000; Whitten, 2001). For these reasons, even in societies that prefer polygyny, fewer than half of the men at any given time actually have multiple mates (Ford & Beach, 1951).

ARRANGED MARRIAGE In Western cultures, mate selection is presumably unrestricted. Parents today seldom arrange marriages, although they may still encourage their children to date those wonderful sons and daughters of the solid churchgoing couples who live down the street. Among recent immigrants to Canada from the Middle East and East Asia, however, arranged marriage is relatively common.

WHO WE MARRY The universal incest taboo proscribes mating between close relatives. Other societal rules and customs also determine which people are desirable mates, and which are not.

Because we make choices, we tend to marry people who attract us. These people are usually similar to us in physical attractiveness and attitudes, and even in minute details. We're more often than not similar to our mates in characteristics such as height, weight, personality traits, and intelligence (Buss, 1994). The people we marry also seem likely to meet our material, sexual, and psychological needs. The concept

Monogamy Marriage to one person.

Polygamy Simultaneous marriage to more than one person.

Polygyny A form of marriage in which a man is married to more than one woman at the same time.

Polyandry A form of marriage in which a woman is married to more than one man at the same time.

Attracted to Similarity.
We tend to marry people who are similar to us in physical appeal and attitudes. We also tend to be similar in height and weight, intelligence, and use of alcohol and other drugs.

Homogamy The practise of marrying someone who's similar to yourself in social background and standing.

of "like marrying like" is termed **homogamy**. We usually marry people of the same racial or ethnic background, educational level, and religion. With Canada's increased cultural diversity, however, the number of people who choose partners outside of their racial or ethnic groups is increasing. In 2001, 452 000 individuals were in mixed unions—a 35% increase from 1991. Mixed unions represented 3.2% of all couples in Canada. In the 20-to-29 age group, 13% of couples in Vancouver, 11% of couples in Toronto, and 6% of couples in Montreal were mixed. Japanese Canadians are most likely to choose partners from outside of their ethnic group, and South Asian Canadians are least likely (Statistics Canada, 2004c). Marriages between individuals who are alike may stand a better chance of survival, because the partners are more likely to share values and attitudes.

We also tend to follow age homogamy, selecting partners who fall into our own age ranges. On average, bridegrooms tend to be two to five years older than their wives in European, North American, and South American countries (Buss, 1994). Individuals who marry late or who remarry tend not to select partners so close in age.

When it comes to picking mates, men tend to be the romantics and women the pragmatists. When Canadians were asked "whether men or women were more choosy in selecting marriage partners," both men and women (57%) were more likely to say women (Compas, 1998). Considerably fewer believed men were more choosy (28%), or that the genders are equally choosy (15%). In studying male–female relationships in Canada and the United States, Dennis (1992) has concluded that women have raised their expectations so high that many will never meet their ideal men, and will have to decide whether to lower their standards or remain single.

Marital Sexuality

Patterns of marital sexuality vary across cultures, yet anthropologists have noted some common threads (Harris & Johnson, 2000; Whitten, 2001). Privacy for sexual relations is valued in nearly all cultures. Most cultures also place restrictions on intercourse during menstruation, during at least some stages of pregnancy, and for a time after childbirth.

The sexual revolution, however, ushered in profound changes in marital sexuality. In particular, it helped dislodge the view that sexual pleasure is meant only for men and that it's women's duty to satisfy their husbands' sexual needs.

How frequently do married couples engage in intercourse? As Table 12.6 shows, Canadian adults most commonly report having sex once or twice a week. People who are married or in common-law relationships have sex more often than

TABLE 12.6

Frequency of Sexual Intercourse During the Previous Four Weeks, by Relationship Status

Frequency	Single	Married	Common-Law	Total
Did not have sex	47.5%	11.3%	8.1%	25.3%
Less than once a week	12.5	15.0	12.9	13.8
Once or twice a week	21.9	52.9	41.1	39.3
Three to four times a week	14.4	17.8	29.0	17.7
Five or more times a week	3.7	3.0	8.9	3.9

Note: Single includes never married, divorced, and widowed.

Source: Compas (1998). Modern life survey of the Canadian population.

singles, and those who are in common-law relationships have sex more often than those who are married. These data certainly call into the question the image of the "swinging single."

The frequency of sexual relations declines with age (Compas, 1998). Regardless of a couple's age, sexual frequency also appears to decline with years of marriage.

In intercourse, as in foreplay, the marital bed since Kinsey's day has become a stage on which the players act more varied roles. In one study of Montreal couples, the male-superior and female-superior were the two most popular positions (Ochs & Binik, 1999).

In a study of 77 cohabiting and married individuals in New Brunswick (Byers & Heinlein, 1989), sexual episodes were reported to last about half an hour on average, and ranged from five minutes to two hours. Intercourse itself lasted an average of a quarter of an hour, and ranged from two minutes to an hour and a quarter.

SEXUAL SATISFACTION Researchers at the University of New Brunswick have found that perception of rewards and costs is related to feelings of sexual satisfaction (Lawrence & Byers, 1995). Rewards include the amount of fun people experience during sex, pleasurable physical sensations from touching and caressing, and feeling comfortable with their partners. Costs include too-infrequent sexual activity and poor sexual communication with their partners.

People who believe they're getting many sexual rewards and low sexual costs are likely to have higher levels of sexual satisfaction. This is especially true when the rewards turn out to be greater and the costs lower than they expect.

Other researchers have found that wives who talk openly to their husbands about their sexual feelings and needs report higher levels of sexual satisfaction than wives who don't. Among both men and women in New Brunswick who are in long-term relationships, sexual satisfaction is higher for those who can tell their partners about their sexual likes and dislikes (MacNeil & Byers, 1997). Satisfaction is also higher for those who can openly communicate about nonsexual topics.

Couples who are in more-committed relationships report higher levels of sexual satisfaction than those who are in uncommitted relationships. When asked how satisfied they are with their sex lives, two-thirds of Canadians who are married or in common-law relationships say they're very satisfied, compared with 44% of those who are single (Compas, 1998) (see Figure 12.3).

SEXUAL CONFLICT Couples can experience conflict over any number of sexual issues. In a study of couples in New Brunswick, one-quarter of the men agreed with the comment "I like to do things my partner does not," and one-third of the women agreed with the comment "My partner chooses inconvenient times for sex"

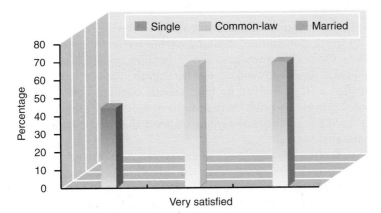

Figure 12.3 Relationship status and sexual satisfaction.
According to the 1998 Compas study, married Canadians report greater satisfaction than Canadians who are single (including those who are divorced and widowed) or live common-law. Those who are married also report the highest frequency of having sex. Do these results mean married people are more satisfied, or are they just more likely to say they're satisfied?

Source: Compas Inc. (1998). Modern life survey of the Canadian adult population. Unpublished raw data. Toronto: Compas Inc.

TABLE 12.7

Frequency of Conflicts Canadians Experience With Their Partners Over Sex

	Males		Females	
	Common-Law	Married	Common-Law	Married
Often	1.4%	1.4%	3.6%	2.5%
Several times a month	4.2	3.5	8.9	7.8
Once or twice a month	39.4	30.1	35.7	28.6
Never	54.9	65.1	51.8	61.2

Source: Compas. (1998). Modern life survey of the Canadian population.

(MacNeil & Byers, 1997). More than one-third of Canadians have conflicts over sex at least once a month. Those in common-law relationships having conflicts more often than married couples (Compas, 1998). (See Table 12.7.)

B. J. Rye (2001) at the University of Waterloo found that 21% of students often had serious disagreements about the occurrence of sex. Almost three times as many males (45%) as females (15%) were concerned that their partner's sexual desires were lower than what they would have liked.

Sexual Orientation and Relationship Satisfaction

Numerous researchers have studied the factors that predict relationship satisfaction and deterioration. Much of the research has asked whether there are differences in the factors that satisfy heterosexual versus homosexual couples, and few have emerged. One difference is that gay and lesbian couples tend to distribute household chores evenly, whereas in heterosexual couples, women tend to do more of the chores than their male partners (Kurdek, 2005, 2006).

For both heterosexual and lesbian women, sexual satisfaction is tied to relationship satisfaction (Mathews et al., 2006; Twist, 2005). Gay, lesbian, and male–female couples are all more satisfied when they receive social support from their partners, share power within their relationships, fight fairly, and perceive that their partners are committed to their relationships. But there are a couple of differences that favour stability in the relationships of male–female couples: they're more likely to have the support of their families, and less likely to be stigmatized by society at large.

Extramarital Sex

Why do people engage in extramarital sex? Some do it for variety (Peluso, 2008). Some have affairs to break the routine of confining marriages (Allen & Atkins, 2005; Markman, 2005). Others enter affairs to express hostility toward their spouses or to retaliate for injustice. Husbands and wives who engage in affairs often report that they're not satisfied with or fulfilled by their marital relationships. Curiosity and desire for personal growth are often more prominent motives than marital dissatisfaction. Middle-aged people may have affairs to boost their self-esteem, or to prove that they're still attractive.

The sexual motive is often less pressing than the desire for emotional closeness. Some women say they're seeking someone they can talk to or communicate with (Lamanna & Riedmann, 2005). There's a notable gender difference here (Peplau, 2003). According to Janis Abrahms Spring, author of *After the Affair: Healing the*

A World of Diversity

MATING IN CAPTIVITY

Do love and intimacy lead to hot sex?

In her best-selling book *Mating in Captivity: Reconciling the Erotic and the Domestic,* New York therapist Esther Perel offers a provocative analysis that challenges commonly held views of the relationship between intimacy and sex.

The book stems from Perel's counselling of heterosexual and gay couples who have secure, caring relationships but dull, unsatisfactory sex lives. Using case studies, she illustrates how the desire for intimacy and security can stifle marital lust.

Perel argues that the human desire for safety and closeness in a long-term relationship conflicts with the desire for novelty, excitement, and risk-taking. In particular, she believes that too much closeness can feel like imprisonment. Desire needs freedom to thrive. People are most sexually attracted to partners they see as separate individuals. This requires that they not totally rely on their partners to satisfy all of their emotional needs.

The women and men discussed in Perel's book long for more vibrant, exciting sex lives with their partners. Perel asserts that couples need to unlock their erotic intelligence, by removing the restraints they have placed on their lustful imaginations. This requires moving away from the security of dull but comfortable ways of having sex, and accepting the risk-taking involved in adventurous sex. Sexual desire, response, and pleasure are heightened by the erotic elements of anticipation, surprise, and mystery.

One of Perel's most controversial conclusions is that hot sex requires not only that we feel a sense of independence from our partners, but also that we're more sexually aroused and alive when we're free to objectify our partners.

She writes:

We are socialized to control ourselves, to restrain our impulses, to tame the animal within. So as dutiful citizens and spouses we edit ourselves and mask our ravenous appetites and conceal our fleeting need to objectify the one we love. To my thinking, cultivating a sense of ruthlessness in our intimate relationships is an intriguing solution to the problem of desire. While it may appear at first glance to be detached and even uncaring, it is in fact rooted in the love and security of our connection. It is a rare experience of trust to be able to let go completely, without guilt or fretfulness, knowing that our relationship is vast enough to withstand the whole of us. We reach a unique intimacy in the erotic encounter. It transcends the civility of the emotional connection and accommodates our unruly impulse and primal appetites. The flint of rubbing bodies gives off a heat not easily achieved through tamer expressions of love. (Perel, 2006, pp. 122-123)

Source: Perel, E. (2006). Mating in Captivity: Reconciling the Erotic and the Domestic. *New York: HarperCollins. Reprinted by permission.*

Pain and Rebuilding Trust When a Partner Has Been Unfaithful, women are usually seeking "soulmates," whereas men are seeking "playmates." Women tend to justify affairs when they're based on love, but men tend to do so when they're not based on love (Smart, 2006).

Men are more likely than women to "separate sex and love; women appear to believe that love and sex go together and that falling in love justifies sexual involvement" (Glass & Wright, 1992, p. 361). Men—whether single, married, or cohabiting—are generally more approving of extramarital affairs than women are (Glass & Wright, 1992). But note that these are all *group* differences. Many individual men are interested primarily in the extramarital relationships, rather than in the sex, while many women are out for the sex, and not for the relationships.

PATTERNS OF EXTRAMARITAL SEX Let's begin with a few definitions. **Extramarital sex** (an "affair") is usually conducted without the spouse's knowledge or approval. A secret affair is referred to as **conventional adultery**, infidelity, or "cheating." Conventional adultery runs the gamut from the one-night stand to the affair that persists for years. In **consensual adultery**, an extramarital relationship is conducted openly—that is, with the knowledge and consent of the partner. And in what's called **swinging, comarital sex,** or mate swapping, the partner participates.

In a 1994 poll by *Maclean's,* fewer Canadians (14% of men, 7% of women) admitted to extramarital affairs than surveys have reported for Americans. The

Extramarital sex Sexual relations between a married person and someone other than his or her spouse.

Conventional adultery Extramarital sex that's kept hidden from one's spouse.

Consensual adultery Extramarital sex that's engaged in openly, with the knowledge and consent of one's spouse.

Swinging A form of consensual adultery in which both spouses share extramarital sexual experiences. This is also referred to as mate swapping.

Comarital sex Swinging, or mate swapping.

rates for extramarital sex are higher in Quebec than for any other province. Similar rates were found in a 2005 Compas poll, in which 10% of married Canadians said extramarital affairs had occurred in their marriages.

In the 2005 Compas survey, about half of the respondents believed that being faithful isn't as important as it once was. One reflection of this belief might be the popularity of the Toronto-based website AshleyMadison.com, which targets attached people who want sexual flings. The Ashley Madison agency claims that more than half a million people have signed up as members since the site was launched in 2002. We don't know how many of these members actually had affairs as a result.

Some people who suspect that their spouses are having affairs collect DNA samples from bedsheets, underwear, cigarette butts, and other places, and send them for DNA testing. Paragon Genetics in Toronto receives such samples from across North America and Europe. Forty percent of the samples test positive, indicating that the DNA is from people other than the spouses (White, 2008).

Surveys about extramarital sex may result in under-reporting of affairs. People may be reluctant to reveal on a survey that they've had affairs, even when they're assured of anonymity (Parker-Pope, 2008; Peluso, 2008).

ATTITUDES TOWARD EXTRAMARITAL SEX Most married couples embrace the value of monogamy as the cornerstone of the marital relationship. As Table 12.8 shows, almost all Canadians in married or common-law relationships say they'd be bothered if their partners had sexual intercourse with others. About one-half of them would accept their partners having "very close but nonsexual relationships" with members of the opposite sex, however (Compas, 1998).

In a 2005 Compas survey, Canadians were asked whether acts of unfaithfulness by their partners would mean the ends of their relationships. Fewer than half (41%) said they definitely would, and 27% said they probably would.

EFFECTS OF EXTRAMARITAL SEX The discovery of infidelity can evoke a range of emotional responses. The spouse may be filled with anger, jealousy, or even shame. Feelings of inadequacy and doubts about one's attractiveness and desirability may surface. Infidelity may be seen by the betrayed spouse as a serious breach of trust and intimacy. A marriage that's not terminated in the wake of such a disclosure may survive in a damaged condition.

The harm an affair does to a marriage may reflect the meaning the affair has to both marriage partners. Deborah Lamberti, director of a counselling and psychotherapy centre in New York City, points again to women's traditional intertwining of sex with relationships, and argues that "Men don't view sex with another person as a reason to leave a primary relationship" (1997, pp. 131–132). Women may

TABLE 12.8

Percentage of Canadians Who'd Be Bothered if Their Partners Had Sexual Intercourse with Others

	Males		Females	
	Common-Law	Married	Common-Law	Married
Very	93.0%	89.6%	100.0%	92.4%
Somewhat	4.2	8.7	0.0	6.1
Not really	2.8	0.7	0.0	0.6
Not at all	0.0	0.0	0.0	0.9

Source: Compas. (1998). Modern life survey of the Canadian population.

recognize this, and be able to tell themselves their husbands are sleeping with others merely for physical reasons. But women are more concerned about remaining monogamous, so if a woman is sleeping with another man, she may already have a foot out the door, so to speak. A wife's affair may be an unforgivable blow to the husband's ego or pride (Rasmussen & Kilborne, 2008). A woman may be more likely to see the transgression as a threat to the structure of her life (Allen & Atkins, 2005; Peluso, 2008).

If a person has an affair because the marriage is deeply troubled, the affair may be one more factor that speeds its dissolution. The effects on the marriage may depend on the nature of the affair. It may be easier to understand that a spouse has fallen prey to an isolated, unplanned encounter than to accept an extended affair (Rasmussen & Kilborne, 2008). In some cases, the discovery of infidelity stimulates the couple to work to improve their relationship.

SWINGING Swinging—also called mate swapping, or comarital sex—is a form of consensual adultery in which both partners openly share sexual experiences with other people. Most swingers seek to avoid emotional entanglements with their swinging partners, but they may fail to separate their emotions from their sexual activities. Emotional intimacy between swinging partners can be even more threatening to the swingers' primary relationships than sexual intimacy.

Until recently, Canadians who engaged in swinging or ran swingers' clubs could be charged with various offences under the Criminal Code, usually with having sex in a public place (public indecency) or with running a common bawdy house (a place used for prostitution or for acts of indecency). In 2005, the Supreme Court of Canada ruled that swinging was not illegal. The case, which involved the owners of two Montreal swingers' clubs, turned on the concept of indecency. The Court declared that the sexual activity of consensual swingers wasn't harmful to Canadian society, and therefore wasn't indecent. The Supreme Court's verdict is highly significant, because it used the criteria of harm to society, rather than community standards of morality, as a test for indecent behaviour.

Polyamory Any form of open relationship that allows for consensual sexual and/or emotional interactions with more than one partner.

Polyamory

A term commonly used today to refer to extramarital relationships in various forms is **"polyamory."** Based on the view that people's needs for intimacy are unlikely to be gratified through one relationship, polyamory refers to open relationships that allow for consensual sexual and/or emotional interactions with more than one partner. Proponents argue that the core marriages can be enhanced if the partners have opportunities to develop emotionally intimate relationships with others.

Divorce

> My wife and I were considering a divorce, but after pricing lawyers we decided to buy a new car instead.
> —Henny Youngman

According to Statistics Canada projections, 37.9% of marriages that took place in 2004 will end in divorce, and the average age at divorce will be 44 years for men and 41.2 years for women

A Website for Flings.
Ashley Madison, the online site that helps people have affairs, deliberately targets young women with ads like this one.

(Vanier Institute of the Family, 2010). The divorce rate in 2003 was about three times as high as in 1968. The peak was reached in 1987, in response to 1985 changes in the Divorce Act in 1985 that made it easier to obtain a divorce.

There's also been a significant increase in the number of people experiencing second divorces. In 2003, 16.2% of divorces involved men who had been previously divorced, compared with just 5.4% in 1973 (Statistics Canada, 2005f). Divorces are most likely to occur after three to four years of marriage. Quebec has the highest rate of divorce, and Newfoundland and Labrador have the lowest (Statistics Canada, 2005).

With the increasing acceptance of cohabitation, more and more divorced people choose to live common-law instead of remarrying (Statistics Canada, 2005f). The rate of breakups in common-law relationships, however, is much greater than for married couples.

Canada's no-fault divorce laws allow divorces without findings of marital misconduct. Women's increased economic independence has also contributed to the rising divorce rate, enabling them to break away from troubled marriages. And more people today consider marriage an alterable condition than prior generations did.

Today Canadians have higher expectations for marriage than their parents and grandparents did. They expect marriage to be personally fulfilling, as well an institution for rearing children. Many demand the right to be happy. The most common reasons for divorce today are problems in communication and lack of understanding. When women seek to end their marriages, their reasons often include husband's criticism, defensiveness, contempt, and stonewalling, not lack of financial support (Carrère et al., 2000; Mahoney & Knudson-Martin, 2009).

THE COSTS OF DIVORCE Divorce often causes financial and emotional problems. When a household splits, the resources often can't maintain the earlier standard of living for both partners. Financially, divorce hits women harder than men. Divorced mothers often face the combined stresses of being solely responsible for rearing their children and needing to increase their incomes to make ends meet. Divorced fathers may find it difficult to pay alimony and child support while attempting to establish new lifestyles.

Divorce can prompt feelings of failure as a spouse and parent, loneliness, uncertainty about the future, and depression. Married people appear better able to cope

For the Sake of the Children?
Research suggests that children may fare better when parents who are in regular conflict separate than when they stay together.

with the stresses and strains of life, perhaps because they can rely on one another for emotional support. Divorced and separated people have the highest rates of physical and mental illness in the population, and divorced people have higher rates of suicide than married people (Carrère et al., 2000). On the other hand, divorce can be a catalyst for personal growth and renewal. It can provide an opportunity for people to take stock of themselves and establish new, more rewarding lives.

Senior Sexuality

According to Statistics Canada (2007), more than 4.3 million people in Canada are senior citizens, and their number is growing twice as fast as the general population (Statistics Canada, 2007). People are also living longer. According to the 2006 census, the average age at death is now 74 years for men and 77 years for women (Statistics Canada, 2008). This "greying" of the population may have a profound effect on our views of older people, especially concerning sexuality. Many people in our culture see sexual activity as appropriate only for the young. This belief falls within a constellation of unfounded cultural myths about older people, including the notions that older people are sexless, older people with sexual urges are abnormal, and older males with sexual interests are "dirty old men."

Research doesn't support the belief that people inevitably lose their sexuality as they age. Yes, the physical ability to function sexually diminishes somewhat. However, a number of studies have shown that psychological and social factors may be at least as important as physical factors in determining sexual behaviour and satisfaction among older people (Delamater & Karraker, 2009).

Using data from a study of 1384 people who were 45 and older, Delamater and Moorman (2007) explored associations between age, biological and social factors, and sexual behaviours. The average age of the participants was 60 for men and 61 for women. Although the researchers found that sexual behaviour decreased as people got older, they also found that positive attitudes toward sexuality and satisfaction with relationships were important factors in determining the frequency of sexual activity with partners. Not surprisingly, they also found that social-context factors such as whether participants had partners affected sexual frequency. The researchers concluded that "individuals who are healthy and satisfied with their relationships remain sexually active into their seventies and eighties. The nature of sexual expression in later life reflects the interplay of body, mind, and social context" (Delamater & Moorman, 2007, p. 944).

Since Viagra was introduced in Canada in 1999, millions of these pills have been sold, many to older men. Stephen Katz and Barbara Marshall (2003) at Trent University in Ontario have analyzed Viagra's role in changing our perceptions of sexual functioning in older men. They note that declining sexual function in older men used to be seen as a normal part of the aging process—a process that men are now encouraged not to accept as inevitable.

We've discussed the sexuality-related developmental tasks of children, adolescents, and adults. With the increasing recognition that sexuality can play a vital role in the lives of older people, it's appropriate to consider the sexuality-related developmental tasks of later life. These include:

- Maintaining self-perception as a sexual being while living in a culture that tends to equate sexuality with youth.
- Adapting to reduced frequency of sexual desire.
- Adapting to reduced intensity of genital sexual response.
- Adapting to the death of a partner.
- Adapting to entry into a long-term-care facility such as a nursing home.
- Using protection against STIs and HIV. (Ryerson University, 2011)

Physical Changes

Although many older people retain the capacity to respond sexually, physical changes do occur as the years pass. (See Table 12.9.) If we're aware of these changes, we won't view them as abnormal or find ourselves unprepared to cope with them. We can avert many potential problems by adjusting our expectations and making changes to accommodate the aging process. By fine-tuning our expectations, we may find ourselves leading some of the most sexually fulfilling years of our lives when we reach our senior years (Trudel et al., 2000). Indeed, a survey of Canadians over the age of 40 has found that 61% agree with the statement "Sex gets better with age" (Leger Marketing, 2010).

TABLE 12.9

Changes in Sexual Arousal Often Associated with Aging

Changes in the Female	Changes in the Male
Reduced myotonia (muscle tension)	Longer time to erection and orgasm
Reduced vaginal lubrication	Need for more direct stimulation for erection and orgasm
Reduced elasticity of the vaginal walls	Less semen emitted during ejaculation
Smaller increases in breast size during sexual arousal	Erections may be less firm
Reduced intensity of muscle spasms at orgasm	Testicles may not elevate as high into the scrotum
	Less intense orgasmic contractions
	Lessened feeling of a need to ejaculate during sex
	Longer refractory period

Source: Copyright © 1990 by The Kinsey Institute for Research in Sex, Gender, and Reproduction. From The Kinsey Institute New Report on Sex. Reprinted with permission from St. Martin's Press, New York.

CHANGES IN THE FEMALE Many of the physical changes in women stem from the decline in estrogen production around menopause.

The uterus decreases in size, no longer becoming so congested during sexual arousal. The vaginal walls lose a great deal of elasticity, as well as the thick, corrugated texture that's typical of the childbearing years. As the walls grow paler and thinner, intercourse may become irritating. Thinning walls may also lead to greater pressure on the bladder and urethra during intercourse, leading in some cases to urinary urgency and burning urination that can persist for days.

Women produce less vaginal lubrication after menopause, and the lubrication they do produce may take minutes, rather than seconds, to appear. Lack of adequate lubrication is another major reason for painful intercourse.

The vagina shrinks in size, while the labia majora lose a great deal of their fatty deposits and become thin. The introitus becomes relatively constricted, sometimes making penile entry difficult. This "problem," however, has a positive aspect: increased friction between the penis and the vaginal walls may heighten sexual sensations.

Many of these changes can be slowed or reversed through estrogen-replacement therapy (see Chapter 3) or topical application of estrogen cream. Natural lubrication may also be increased through more elaborate foreplay. The need for more foreplay may encourage men to become more considerate lovers. (Older men are also likely to need more time to become aroused.) An artificial lubricant can ease problems posed by difficult entry or painful thrusting.

Women's breasts show smaller increases in size with sexual arousal as they age, but the nipples still become erect. Because the muscle tone of the urethra and the anal sphincters decreases, the spasms of orgasm become less powerful and fewer in number, making orgasm feel less intense. The uterine contractions that occur during orgasm become discouragingly painful for some postmenopausal women. Despite these changes, women can retain their ability to achieve orgasm well into their advanced years.

CHANGES IN THE MALE Age-related changes tend to occur more gradually in men, and are not clearly connected with any single biological event. Male adolescents may achieve erection in a matter of seconds through sexual fantasy alone. After about age 50, men take progressively longer to achieve erections. Their erections become less firm, perhaps because of lowered testosterone production, and may require minutes of direct penile stimulation to achieve. Couples can adjust to these changes by extending the length and variety of foreplay.

Most men remain capable of erection throughout their lives. Erectile dysfunction is not inevitable with aging. Men generally require more time to reach orgasm as they age, however, which may also reflect lowered testosterone production. In the eyes of their sex partners, however, delayed ejaculation may make them better lovers.

Testosterone production gradually declines from about age 40 to age 60, then begins to level off. The decline is not inevitable, however, and may be related to the man's general health. Sperm production tends to decline as the seminiferous tubules degenerate, but viable sperm may be produced late in life. Men in their seventies, eighties, and even nineties have fathered children.

Nocturnal erections tend to diminish in intensity, duration, and frequency as men age, but they don't normally disappear in healthy men (Perry et al., 2001). The refractory period tends to lengthen with age. An adolescent may require only a few minutes to regain erection and ejaculate again after a first orgasm, whereas a man in his thirties may require half an hour. After age 50, the refractory period may increase to several hours.

Older men produce less ejaculate, and it may seep rather than shoot out. The contractions of orgasm become weaker and fewer. Still, older men may enjoy orgasm as thoroughly as they did when they were younger. Attitudes and expectations can be as important as the contractions themselves.

Most physical changes don't bring men's and women's sex lives to a grinding halt. People's attitudes, sexual histories, and partners are usually more important factors in sexual behaviour and enjoyment.

Patterns of Sexual Activity

Despite the decline in certain physical functions, older people can continue to lead vibrant, fulfilling sex lives. In fact, years of sexual experience may more than compensate for any diminution of physical responsiveness (Laumann et al., 2006).

Unfortunately, people who overreact to expected changes in sexual response may conclude that their sex lives are over, and give up on sexual activity, or even on expressing any physical affection (Dunn, 1998).

Despite general trends, sexuality is variable among older people. While some simply lose interest, other older people engage in intercourse, oral sex, and masturbation at least as often as they did when they were younger.

Many older Canadians continue to engage in sexual intercourse. In the 1998 Compas survey, 65% of Canadian men and 39% of Canadian women over the age of 60 reported that they were having intercourse. Of this group, 74% of the men and 39% of the women were having sex at least once a week. These gender differences can be partly explained by the fact that women generally outlive men, leaving more older women than men without available sexual partners and therefore with fewer sexual opportunities. Four-fifths of the survey respondents who were 50 years and older reported that general health problems negatively affected their sex lives (Compas, 1998).

One of the most recent comprehensive studies of sex and aging was conducted by researchers at the University of Chicago, who sampled more than 3000 American adults between the ages of 57 and 85 (Tessler Lindau et al., 2007). They found that:

- Sexual relations declined with age.
- Seventy-three percent of those aged 57 to 64, 53% of those aged 65 to 74, and 26% of those aged 75 to 85 reported having sex with partners during the previous year.
- The average frequency of sex for those who were sexually active was two to three times a month.
- Women were less likely than men to have sexual relations, because more women than men were widowed.
- People in good health were twice as likely as those in poor health to be sexually active.
- Half of those who were sexually active had one or more sexual problems, yet most hadn't discussed these problems with doctors after turning 50.
- Fourteen percent of the men used Viagra or other supplements to improve their sexual functioning.
- Only a minority (13% of men and 35% of women) felt that sex was "not all that important." (Tessler Lindau et al., 2007)

In a study of 35- to 55-year-old women, researchers found that body image is a more important influence than menopause on sexual functioning and satisfaction (Koch et al., 2005). One-fifth of the respondents were unable to name even one attractive feature about themselves and reported overall dissatisfaction with their bodies. The features women considered least attractive were their stomachs and abdomens, hips, and thighs and legs. The less attractive a woman thought she was, the less likely she was to experience sexual desire and activity during the previous 10 years. Two-thirds of the women reported one or more changes in their sexual response, such as desiring sex less and engaging in sex less often. Some women, however, had improved sexual response, and when these women did have sex, they experienced high levels of enjoyment (Koch et al., 2005).

Taking an innovative, more positive approach, University of Ottawa researcher Peggy Kleinplatz and her team focused on couples who experienced optimal sexuality, rather than sexual problems (Kleinplatz et al., 2010). They found that for some couples, "great sex" didn't occur until mid-life, and that great sex was possible well into the later years. The couples talked about such factors as erotic intimacy, interpersonal exploration, authenticity and the freedom to be themselves, and communication as the ingredients for great sex. For them, having young, toned bodies and quickly responding genitalia had little to do with satisfying sexual relationships.

Couples may accommodate the physical changes of aging by broadening their sexual repertoires to include more diverse forms of stimulation, including oral–genital sex, sexual fantasy, sexually explicit materials, anal stimulation, vibrators, and other techniques. They may derive sexual satisfaction from manual and oral stimulation, cuddling, caressing, and tenderness, as well as from intercourse to orgasm.

LOSING A PARTNER As people enter the later stages of life, the death of a partner becomes a reality for many. The surviving partner faces a loss of companionship and physical intimacy, including sexual expression. In many cases, reduced sexual activity among older people is due more to the loss of partners than to reduced physical capacity.

Since women tend to live longer than men, partner loss and its impact on sexuality affects them disproportionately. One study found that 42% of married 60- to 69-year-old women had been sexually active during the previous three months, compared to just 7% of unmarried 60- to 69-year-old women, and that 22% of married 70- to 79-year-old women were sexually active, compared to a mere 3% of unmarried 70- to 79-year-old women (Patel, Gillespie, & Foxman, 2003).

It's important to recognize that the need for and the benefits of physical intimacy don't decline with age.

Aging and Gay and Lesbian Sexuality

Limited research has been carried out on the effects of aging on gay men. James Murray of the AIDS Committee of Toronto and Barry Adam of the University of Windsor (2001) conducted interviews in Toronto with gay and bisexual men who were 40 and over, to determine some of their concerns about aging in the context of HIV. They found that, because the gay community values youth and attractiveness, many older men felt at a disadvantage in finding sexual partners, and saw themselves as "invisible" to younger men. Several of the men clearly believed they were no longer desirable, and felt unwelcome in gay social gatherings. Feelings of isolation and loneliness were common, especially among those who had lost partners and close friends to AIDS.

They also expressed positive feelings about aging. For some, attaining intimate relationships outweighed diminished sexual prowess. And because their sex drives were now less urgent, some men felt they could be in greater control of their sexuality. Those who were most involved in gay community organizations felt that the social connections they established there would be sources of support as they aged (Murray & Adam, 2001).

Montreal researchers have found that older gays and lesbians feel excluded by gay and lesbian organizations because of age discrimination (Brotman et al., 2003). The older groups feel doubly discriminated against in their interactions with health agencies in the broader society, because of both sexual orientation and age. Many among the older generation have not been open about their sexual orientations, and experience considerable fear when dealing with health and social agencies. Not surprisingly, most agencies don't know how to respond to the unique needs of older lesbians and gay men, especially in settings such as nursing homes, where workers may be homophobic (Brotman et al., 2003).

In the United States, the National Resource Center on LGBT Aging (www.lgbtagingcenter.org) seeks to improve the quality of services and supports offered to lesbian, gay, bisexual, and transgendered older adults. Established in 2010 through a grant from the United States Department of Health and Human Services, the organization provides training, technical assistance, and educational resources for aging-related service providers, LGBT organizations, and LGBT older adults.

PROTECTING SEXUAL HEALTH IN LATER LIFE A number of factors have led to increased risks for STIs among older Canadians. Changes in attitudes toward sexuality in later life have made it more socially acceptable for older people to pursue active sex lives. Medical advances have increased the likelihood that older people are healthy enough for sexual activity. As divorce rates have increased, more older Canadians have again become part of the singles scene. Together, these factors add up to higher percentages of older people with new or multiple sex partners. However, many older singles may not be getting the message about the need to practise safer sex. A study of 46- to 64-year-old Canadians commissioned by the Canadian Liver Foundation in 2010 found that while 82% said it was important to have an active sex life at any age, and 65% of those who were single had dated, some were at high risk for STIs and HIV. Almost one-quarter of the men (22%) and 12% of the women had engaged in unprotected sex with new partners after age 40. As we'll see in Chapter 14, rates of common STIs such as chlamydia are increasing among older Canadians (Fang, Oliver, Jayaraman, & Wong, 2010). Clearly, just as there are developmental tasks related to sexuality at all phases of the life cycle, there is also a need for sexual-health education at every stage of life.

CRITICAL THINKING QUESTIONS

On a scale of 1 to 10, how would you rate the sexual-health education you received in high school?

Sexual-Health Education

Sexual health is a key aspect of personal health and social welfare that influences individuals across their life spans. It is thus important that health-promotion programs focusing on enhancing positive sexual health outcomes are available to all Canadians, regardless of their age, race, ethnicity, gender identity, sexual orientation, socioeconomic background, physical/cognitive abilities, religious background, or other such characteristics. (Public Health Agency of Canada, 2008, p. 2)

This statement from *Canadian Guidelines for Sexual Health Education* represents the ideal that all Canadians have access to the high-quality sexual-health education and services they need. All age groups need sexual-health education. Although we have access to a wide variety of credible sources for sexual-health education, many of us turn to sources that may not be entirely reliable or accurate.

SOURCES OF INFORMATION When a representative sample of Canadian 14- to 17-year-olds were asked to identify their sources of information about sexuality, they identified school as their number-one choice (80%), followed by friends (76%), parents (63%), television (54%), books (52%), the internet (44%), magazines (39%), doctors, (37%), chat lines (20%), and nurses (19%) (Frappier, et al., 2008). When asked which of these sources were most useful and valuable, they ranked school and parents highest.

Some people believe parents should have the main responsibility for sex education. In the Canada Youth and AIDS Survey, about one-quarter of the boys said they could talk openly about sex with their fathers or mothers, while 37% of the girls said they could talk to their mothers and far fewer (12%) said they could talk to their fathers (Boyce et al., 2003). About two-thirds of high school students in a New Brunswick survey rated the sex education they'd received from their parents as good to excellent, but about one-half didn't want to talk more with their parents about sexuality (Byers et al., 2003).

In Regina, most high school students said they preferred learning about topics such as pregnancy and STI prevention at school. When the topics were dating and relationships, however, most preferred learning from personal experience, friends, and parents (Hampton et al., 2005).

The popular media are especially important sources of information about topics that aren't covered in school programs, such as sexual techniques and pleasure. A study of women at an Ontario university found that women's magazines were a common source of sexuality information (Bielay & Herold, 1995). The magazine most frequently read (by 79% of the respondents) was *Cosmopolitan*. The women reported that *Cosmopolitan* was their major magazine source of information for 25 of the 34 sexuality topics included in the survey. Students with more liberal sexual attitudes read the magazine more often than students with more conservative values.

Websites have been developed by health, educational, and social agencies to provide sex information. One of the most comprehensive is SexualityAndU.ca, sponsored by the Society of Obstetricians and Gynaecologists of Canada. The site is based on Fisher's information-motivation-behavioural skills (IMB) theoretical model, which emphasizes the motivation and the behavioural skills required for adopting behaviours that promote sexual health (Fisher & Fisher, 1998). In addition to providing information specifically for adolescents, the site has modules for adults, parents, and health-care providers.

Although its producers usually intend it to be a form of entertainment rather than a source of education, more and more people are acquiring their assumptions and beliefs about sexuality from online pornography. We don't yet have comprehensive research on how viewing online pornography may affect sexuality. We do know plenty of people, including youth, look at online porn. A study of Canadian university students found that 72% of the males and 24% of the females used the internet to access sexually explicit material (Boies, 2002).

Sex Education.
Despite the availability of sex education in most schools, many young people learn about sex from their peers. Survey data show that most parents want sex education to cover abstinence, pregnancy, sexually transmitted infections, abortion, and sexual orientation.

There's considerable concern about how online porn may affect young people (Bryant, 2010). As anyone who has surfed the net looking for sexual titillation knows, online pornography often presents distorted pictures of sexual behaviour and relationships. The question is, are people able to separate the fantasy life of porn from the reality of real-life sexuality and relationships, and use the internet as a safe way to explore their sexuality? Or is internet pornography an influential source of very inaccurate information and harmful attitudes about sexuality? We don't have the research to help us understand the role of online porn in sexual education.

Sexual-Health Education in the Schools

Because education in Canada is a provincial and territorial responsibility, the extent and quality of sexual health education in the schools can vary from province to province, from school board to school board, from school to school, and from classroom to classroom. And rather than being taught as a separate subject, sexual health education—which is only a small part of the overall school curriculum—is usually part of a broader health curriculum that covers a wide range of topics. Sexual-health education therefore often receives limited time and attention in the classroom.

During the 1970s, teenage pregnancy was a major concern in Canada, which encouraged many school boards to incorporate sex-education topics, particularly contraception, into their curricula. Until then, contraception hadn't been taught in schools, primarily because contraceptives were illegal until 1969. The spread of HIV in the 1980s further encouraged the teaching of sexual-health education, especially about condoms.

Currently, all provincial and territorial ministries of education mandate or recommend some level of instruction on sexual health. In the elementary grades, instruction tends to focus on biological development and, as students approach their teen years, the changes associated with puberty. At the secondary level, the most extensive coverage of sexual-health topics often occurs as part of a grade-nine health course. Information on STIs is typically a central focus, although discussion of methods of prevention, such as abstinence and condom use, can be highly variable, depending on the school. Because of this variability, it's nearly impossible to reach general conclusions about the quality of sexual-health education in Canadian schools.

A number of factors can influence the quality of sexual-health education. The importance school administrators place on sexual-health education, and the degree to which they sense community support for it, can dramatically influence the quality of the sexual-health education that's delivered in the classroom.

CANADIAN GUIDELINES To facilitate the development of broadly based sexual-health education programs, the Public Health Agency of Canada (2008) has produced *Canadian Guidelines for Sexual Health Education*. The first edition, developed by experts from across Canada, was published in 1994; the third and most recent edition appeared in 2008. The guidelines are designed to guide and unify professionals who provide sexual health education in Canada. They recommend an approach that focuses not only on prevention of sexual problems (e.g., STIs, HIV, and unwanted pregnancy), but also on enhancement of sexual health (e.g., development of a positive self-image and non-exploitative sexual satisfaction).

The fundamental elements of sexual-health education proposed by the *Guidelines* are based on the information-motivation-behavioural skills approach to sexual health (Fisher & Fisher, 1998). Research has shown that sexual-health programs containing all three of the IMB elements can be effective in reaching their behavioural objectives (Public Health Agency of Canada, 2008). The *Canadian*

Guidelines for Sexual Health Education can be downloaded from the Public Health Agency of Canada website (www.phac-aspc.gc.ca) and the Sex Information and Education Council of Canada website (www.sieccan.org).

YOUTH ATTITUDES Several surveys have indicated that Canadian youth want sexual-health education taught in school (Byers et al., 2003; McKay & Holowaty, 1997). In a survey of New Brunswick high school students, 92% agreed that "sexual-health education should be provided by the schools." The students rated topics such as puberty, reproduction, personal safety, sexual coercion and assault, sexual decision-making in dating relationships, birth control and safer-sex practises, and STIs as "very important" or "extremely important" (Byers et al., 2003).

Unfortunately, many students are disappointed with the quality of sex education they receive. In the New Brunswick survey, only 13% rated their sexual-health education as very good or excellent (Byers et al., 2003). In Newfoundland and Labrador, most adolescents felt they had only limited access to sex education and services (Johns & Lush, 2004).

A major criticism of school-based sex-education programs is that they focus on harm. In an interview study, young adults in British Columbia and Nova Scotia expressed dissatisfaction because their sex education neglected the emotional and potentially positive aspects of sex. They felt these programs were concerned only with providing information about pregnancy and STI prevention (Shoveller et al., 2004).

A more recent study of first-year university students in Ontario who were asked to assess the sexual-health education they'd received in school presents a somewhat more optimistic picture (Meaney, Rye, Wood, & Solovieva, 2009). Overall, the students reported that they were generally satisfied with their school-based sexual-health education and the teachers who had taught it.

PARENTAL ATTITUDES The provision of sexual-health education in the schools can be controversial. In the spring of 2010, the Ontario government was forced to withdraw its revised sexual-health curriculum for grades one to eight after a contentious debate played out in the media about whether it was appropriate to provide elementary school children with information about sexuality. Although the government retreated, it wasn't clear that the majority of parents actually disapproved of sexual-health education in the schools. Contrary to the impression given by media accounts, surveys have consistently shown that most Canadian parents want their children to receive sexual-health education at school. In reviewing studies from Ontario, New Brunswick, and Nova Scotia, the Sex Information and Education Council of Canada (2010) found that more than 85% of parents agreed with the statement "Sexual health education should be provided in the schools," and a majority of parents approved of the teaching of a wide variety of topics, including puberty, reproduction, healthy relationships, STI and AIDS prevention, birth control, abstinence, sexual orientation, and sexual abuse and coercion.

EDUCATION AND SEXUAL ACTIVITY Opponents of school-based sexual-health education have often argued that teaching young people about sexuality, including birth control and the use of condoms to prevent STIs and HIV, gives them the green light to become sexually active. This has become a central question in debates about whether sexual-health education belongs in school.

A large number of studies have examined this question. A review of studies measuring the behavioural impact of sexual health education programs has found that "the evidence is strong that programs do not hasten or increase sexual behaviour" (Kirby, Laris, & Rolleri, 2007, p. 206). In other words, sexual-health programs are unlikely to encourage young people to become sexually active at an earlier age.

REDUCING PREGNANCY AND STI/HIV INFECTION According to the Sex Information and Education Council of Canada (2010), a large number of studies indicate that sexual-health education can have a significant, positive impact on behaviour. The Kirby, Laris, and Rolleri (2007) review of 83 sex and HIV program evaluations found that two-thirds of the programs had positive behavioural effects on youth. In particular, the study showed that sexual-health education can effectively equip youth to delay first intercourse and to use condoms if they're sexually active.

Have sex-education programs in Canadian schools been effective in this regard? While many have provided youth with basic information, it's unlikely that most programs have been extensive enough to have sustained effects on behaviour. To be effective, sexual-health education must be carefully structured and do more than provide basic information.

ABSTINENCE-ONLY PROGRAMS Abstinence-only programs have been a popular form of sex education in the United States, where they've received millions of dollars in government funding. As the name implies, abstinence-only programs teach that having sex before marriage is both immoral and unhealthy. Information about birth control and safer sex is left out. The abstinence-only approach has been less popular in Canada, where most schools provide some level of information about birth control and safer sex.

Many studies have been conducted to see whether abstinence-only sex education works. Most have found that it does not. An evaluation of abstinence-only programs conducted for the United States Congress indicated that students who'd taken abstinence-only courses were no more likely to be sexually abstinent, to delay first intercourse, or to have fewer sexual partners than students who didn't receive such courses (Trenholm et al., 2007). Many other studies have replicated the finding that abstinence-only programs are usually ineffective (e.g., Bennett & Assefi, 2005; Kohler, Manhart, & Lafferty, 2008).

Abstinence-only programs have been criticized as unethical, because they don't provide the information young people need to make their own choices about sexual behaviour. In this respect, abstinence-only programs appear to be in conflict with *Canadian Guidelines for Sexual Health Education* (Public Health Agency of Canada, 2008), which stress that sexual-health education should support "informed decision-making" (p. 25). Others have argued that abstinence-only programs violate young people's human rights by withholding potentially life-saving information about the prevention of HIV and AIDS (Ott & Santelli, 2007).

EFFECTIVE SEXUAL-HEALTH EDUCATION Incorporation of a theoretical model such as IMB is just one of the key ingredients in effective education about sexual health. There's extensive research into what's required for such education to be effective (Albarracin et al., 2005; Kirby, Laris, & Rolleri, 2007; World Association of Sexology, 2008). The Sex Information and Education Council of Canada (2010) has summarized this research, outlining 10 key ingredients for effective sexual-health education, as shown in Table 12.10.

While most sexual-health education programs in Canadian schools don't contain most of these key ingredients, documents such as *Canadian Guidelines for Sexual Health Education* (Public Health Agency of Canada, 2008) point the way to a new generation of programs that will make more meaningful contributions to the sexual health of Canadians.

INNOVATIVE CANADIAN CURRICULA AND RESOURCES An Ontario group led by University of Waterloo researcher B. J. Rye (2008) developed and tested *Girl Time: Grade 7/8 Healthy Sexuality Program*, based on the information-motivation-behavioural skills model (Fisher & Fisher, 1998). The objectives were to encourage young girls to delay sexual intercourse until they were mature enough for

TABLE 12.10
Key Ingredients for Effective Sexual-Health Education

1. Provide sufficient classroom time to achieve the program's objectives.

2. Give teachers the training and administrative support required for delivering the program effectively.

3. Use a theoretical model such as IMB to develop and deliver the curriculum materials.

4. Tailor the program to the students' characteristics, needs, learning styles, ethnocultural backgrounds, sexual orientations, and developmental stages.

5. Target behaviours (e.g., unprotected sex) that lead to negative sexual-health outcomes (e.g., STIs and HIV infection).

6. Deliver and reinforce prevention messages that target the setting of sexual limits (e.g., delaying first intercourse) and the use of condoms.

7. Include program activities that focus on students' social environments and social contexts (e.g., peer pressure).

8. Incorporate the information, motivation, and behavioural skills necessary for students to refuse sexual activity and practise safer sex.

9. Give the students opportunities to practise (e.g., role playing) the setting of sexual limits, negotiation of condom use, and other communication skills, so they're active participants in the program, rather than passive recipients of information.

10. Evaluate the program's strengths and weaknesses, to improve future delivery.

Source: Sex Information and Education Council of Canada. (2010). Sexual health education in the schools: Questions and answers. *Toronto: SIECCAN.*

it, and to practise safer sex when they were ready. Girls who participated in the program were more likely than nonparticipants to discuss sexual topics with their parents, feel confident about their ability to have safer sex (e.g., by obtaining condoms), and plan to engage in safer-sex practises such as abstinence (Rye et al., 2008).

Community agencies such as public health units, sexual health centres, and Planned Parenthood groups provide valuable assistance and resources to schools. The Calgary Sexual Health Centre, for example, provides comprehensive sexuality education throughout Calgary, to students as well as to youth and adults who are no longer in school. Alberta teachers and health professionals have developed an innovative website at www.teachingsexualhealth.ca, where teachers can browse and download lesson plans by grade level and by topic.

Nova Scotia has made improving the sexual health of youth a key priority, launching an integrated approach that involves sexual health education, services, and support systems for youth. The program is based on a document called *Framework for Action: Youth Sexual Health in Nova Scotia.* A key aspect of this program is youth participation in every phase, including development of content for school sex-education programs. The Department of Health Promotion and Protection consulted with 500 youth in developing a book called *Sex? A Healthy Sexuality Resource.* Young people were asked what they "wanted and needed to know and wished they'd been told" to prepare them to make decisions about healthy sexuality. Consultations were also held with parents, teachers, and experts in sexual health. The book is colourful and presents practical information, such as how to avoid STIs and talk to parents about sex.

Alberta educators and researchers have developed and evaluated a theatrical play for 14- to 16-year-olds (Esmail et al., 2007). *Are We There Yet?* is a theatre-based sexual-education program based on learning theory. It uses a student-centred approach to present real-life situations students can relate to. This encourages greater student participation in the play. Student evaluations indicate that the play is an effective means of providing sex education to youth (Esmail et al., 2007).

The website SexualityAndU.ca, developed by the Society of Obstetricians and Gynaecologists of Canada, provides sexual-health information for all age groups. The site contains a section for teachers that includes curriculum materials, as well as guidance for parents and health professionals about teaching sexuality.

TRAINING FOR SEXUAL-HEALTH PROFESSIONALS A major limit to the effectiveness of sex-education programs is the lack of training for teachers. Many teachers and therapists receive inadequate training in sexuality. Two-thirds of New Brunswick elementary and middle school teachers, for example, report that they haven't received training to teach sex education (Cohen et al., 2004). Although many Canadian universities offer undergraduate courses in human sexuality, a surprising number have no sexuality courses.

The Université du Québec à Montréal offers both undergraduate and graduate degree programs in human sexuality (in French). St. Jerome's University at the University of Waterloo offers an undergraduate program in sexuality, marriage, and family studies, directed by Dr. B. J. Rye. Programs are also offered at York University and the University of Toronto. Other Canadian universities, such as the University of Guelph, provide undergraduate and graduate courses and/or research specialization opportunities in sexuality. Nearly every university in Canada now has one or more faculty members who have specialties in sexuality and/or sexual health. They can be found in a range of disciplines, including psychology, sociology, nursing, medicine, education, and social work.

The Guelph Sexuality Conference offered by the University of Guelph is the largest annual conference on human sexuality in Canada, providing a range of training opportunities for teaching and promoting sexual health. The Western Canadian Sexual Health Conference is another major conference, offered every two years.

MEETING THE NEEDS OF SEXUAL-MINORITY YOUTH Many sex-education programs don't address the needs of gay, lesbian, bisexual, and transgendered youth. University of Alberta researchers Andre Grace and Kristopher Wells (2007) have analyzed many of the difficulties these people face, including feelings of isolation, fear of humiliation, and lack of social support. Grace and Wells (2006) have developed a series of professional-development workshops for teachers, to help them address sexual-minority issues in schools.

The Public Health Agency of Canada (2010) has published a booklet called *Questions & Answers: Sexual Orientation in Schools*, which provides teachers and other school personnel with guidance on supporting sexual-minority youth. The Agency (2010) has also produced a parallel document, *Questions & Answers: Gender Identity in Schools*, to help support gender-variant youth.

Sexual-minority high school students play important activist roles in challenging heterosexism and homophobia in schools. They promote inclusivity through such strategies as creating gay–straight student alliances, initiating positive-space campaigns, and sharing LGBTQ resources (Grace & Wells, 2007).

Teachers' organizations across Canada have adopted policies that support LGBTQ youth. The Alberta Teachers' Association has been in the forefront in fighting discrimination based on sexual orientation. Kristopher Wells (2006) has written a *Gay-Straight Student Alliance Handbook*, published by the Canadian Teachers' Federation. Its primary objective is to help Canadian educators create safe, inclusive, welcoming spaces for LGBTQ youth. Gay–straight student alliances (both student-run and teacher-supported groups) are an important means of achieving this objective. The Canadian Teachers' Federation has also published *Challenging Silence, Challenging Censorship: Inclusive Resources and Policy Directives for Addressing Bisexual, Gay, Lesbian, Trans-Identified and Two-Spirited Realities in School and Public Libraries* (Schrader & Wells, 2007), which discusses practical resources to help educators and decision-makers challenge discrimination and promote positive change for sexual minorities.

The development of these resources indicates that many Canadian schools are recognizing the need to address the requirements of sexual-minority youth. Although most Canadian classrooms likely have at least one non-heterosexual or gender-variant student, the bottom line is that sexual-health education is often taught in a strictly heterosexual context. A British Columbia study has found that parents, students, educators, and public health personnel acknowledge that sexual-education curricula often fail to address the needs of sexually diverse students (Options for Sexual Health, 2004).

MEETING THE NEEDS OF DISABLED YOUTH As we discussed in Chapter 4, physical and developmental disabilities can affect sexuality. Although young people with disabilities are as fully sexual as their able-bodied peers, their specific sexual-health-education needs are often ignored. This may be the result of inaccurate negative stereotypes about the sexuality of disabled people. This lack of attention is especially problematic since studies indicate that young people with disabilities are more than twice as likely as young people without disabilities to be sexually abused (Murphy & Young, 2005).

In examining key issues related to sexuality and disability, Gina Di Giulio (2003) at the University of Ottawa has noted that the five principles of effective sexual-health education outlined in *Canadian Guidelines for Sexual Health Education* can be applied to the development and delivery of education specific to the needs of people with physical and developmental disabilities.

Fortunately, as physically and developmentally disabled youth's right to comprehensive sexual-health education designed to meet their needs is increasingly being recognized, appropriate curricular are becoming available. The teachers' section of SexualityAndU.ca, for example, provides guides for teaching sexual-health education to people with physical and developmental disabilities.

MEETING THE NEEDS OF ADULTS Sexual-health education is usually associated with the need to provide children and adolescents with school-based programs. This is where the vast majority of research attention has been focused. In many respects, however, adults need sexual-health education just as much. Many are at high risk for STIs and HIV. And as people grow older, they often have emerging concerns about sexual functioning, and need related education and health services.

The most accessible and credible sources of sexual-health education and services for many adults are their physicians. Research suggests that many patients are reluctant to ask their doctors about sexual concerns, and many doctors don't proactively bring up sexual-health issues (Wittenberg & Gerber, 2009). A survey of Canadian women found that while 58% had one or more sexual concerns, only 34% had discussed a sexual issue with a doctor (Fisher, Boroditsky, & Morris, 2004). A survey of North American medical schools also revealed that physicians in training often receive inadequate education in discussing sexuality with patients (Solursh et al., 2003).

Fortunately, this situation may be changing. Physicians are increasingly provided with guidance on screening patients for STI and HIV risk and on providing STI and HIV education (Public Health Agency of Canada, 2010). As public awareness of sexual dysfunction increases, patients may feel more comfortable asking their doctors about sexual-function concerns. Television advertisements for erectile dysfunction medications that encourage men to ask their doctors about sexual functioning may make people more comfortable about such discussions.

This greater awareness of sexual-function issues combined with a greater emphasis on sexual issues within the medical community has resulted in a substantial growth in the literature advising physicians about interviewing techniques for assessing sexual functioning in male and female patients. Since the 1970s, there's been an exponential growth in the sexual medicine field, to the point where it's now an established academic and clinical discipline (Schultheiss & Glina, 2010). Although there's controversy about the extent to which the medicalization of sexuality is appropriate (e.g., Tiefer, 1996), it's likely that people will increasingly view doctors as important sources of sexual-health information and services.

Accessing health care that's specifically relevant to their sexuality can still be a challenge for gay, lesbian, bisexual, and transgendered people. Some doctors don't ask their patients about sexual orientation (Dahan, Feldman, & Hermoni, 2008).

EDUCATION AND SERVICES IN A MULTICULTURAL SOCIETY Canada is a diverse country with respect to religion, ethnicity, and culture. This presents a challenge to sexual-health educators and health-care providers. It's clear that ethnic differences extend to the realm of sexuality, creating differences in attitudes (Ahrold & Meston, 2010). Canadian studies have found, for example, that East Asian men have more conservative sexual attitudes than men of European descent (Brotto, Woo, & Ryder, 2007), and that recent Iranian immigrants to Canada have more conservative sexual norms and values (Shirpak, Maticka-Tydale, & Chinichian, 2007). Iranian women often have difficulty communicating with health-care providers about issues pertaining to sexuality and reproductive health (Shirpak, Maticka-Tydale, & Chinichian, 2007). And a survey of Toronto teens has found that the extent to which they access and benefit from sexual health services varies with cultural heritage and length of residence in Canada (Flicker at al., 2009).

To meet the needs of all Canadians, educators and health-care providers must be aware of the increasingly multicultural fabric of Canadian society. This includes not just immigrant cultures, but also First Nations, Inuit, and Métis cultures, which have distinct values and norms pertaining to sexuality. This requires consulting and establishing partnerships with diverse communities to create and implement sexual-health education programs and to deliver sexual-health services.

Summing Up

Developmental tasks pertaining to sexuality can be identified for each phase of the life cycle.

The developmental tasks of childhood sexuality include learning the correct names for genitals, differentiating between males and females, developing a sense of gender identity, distinguishing between good touch and bad touch, understanding the basics of human reproduction, and acquiring a basic knowledge of the physiological and psychological aspects of puberty.

The developmental tasks of adolescent sexuality include adapting to the physical and emotional changes of puberty, learning self-acceptance as a sexual being, exploring romantic and sexual relationships, and learning to protect sexual health.

The developmental tasks of adult sexuality include understanding the role of passion in romantic and sexual relationships, understanding the role of friendship in romantic and sexual relationships, learning to communicate effectively with partners about sexuality, and protecting sexual health.

The developmental tasks of sexuality in later life include maintaining self-perception as a sexual being while living in a culture that equates sexuality with youth, adapting to a reduced frequency of desire for sex and to a reduced intensity of sexual response, and using protection against STIs and HIV. The extent and quality of sexual health education in schools varies across Canada.

Canadian Guidelines for Sexual Health Education are based on the information-motivation-behavioural skills (IMB) model.

Research has shown that sexual-health education programs don't lead to earlier sexual activity among youth, but can help protect their sexual health. Research has also shown that abstinence-only programs are usually ineffective. The sexual-health-education needs of sexual-minority youth and youth with disabilities are not being adequately met.

Among the challenges facing Canadian sexual-health educators is the need to provide high-quality education in the context of a multicultural society.

Test Yourself

Multiple-Choice Questions

1. **Masturbation in childhood:**
(a) Almost always indicates that the child has been sexually abused.
(b) Can be observed in children of all ages.
(c) Rarely occurs among girls.
(d) Reflects a premature interest in sex.

2. **Same-sex sexual play in childhood:**
(a) Is a sign that the children will grow up gay or lesbian.
(b) Is much more common among boys than girls.
(c) Is much more common among girls than boys.
(d) Does not predict adult sexual orientation.

3. **Between 1996–1997 and 2005, the percentage of Canadian 15- to 19-year-olds who'd had sexual inter-course:**
(a) Increased among both males and females.
(b) Decreased among both males and females.
(c) Decreased among males, but stayed about the same among females.
(d) Decreased among females, but stayed about the same among males.

4. **Over the last several decades, rates of teen pregnancy in Canada have:**
(a) Significantly increased.
(b) Significantly decreased.
(c) Remained stable.

5. **According to Statistics Canada, _____ of 25- to 29-year-old Canadians in 2006 were married.**
(a) 5.9%
(b) 25.9%
(c) 50.9%
(d) 60.9%

6. **In a study of about 3 000 American adults, _____ of 65- to 74-year-olds said they'd had sex with partners during the previous year.**
(a) 10%
(b) 25%
(c) 50%
(d) 70%

7. **When surveyed, Canadian teens indicated that their most valuable sources of information about sexuality were:**
(a) Schools and parents.
(b) Parents and the internet.
(c) The internet and friends.
(d) Friends and television.

8. **Canadian Guidelines for Sexual Health Education is based on a theoretical model called the:**
(a) Social-cognitive model.
(b) Trans-theoretical model.
(c) Information-motivation-behavioural skills model.
(d) Health-belief model.

9. **Canadian studies have found that:**
(a) Youth want sexual-health education taught in school, but parents don't.
(b) Parents want sexual-health education taught in school, but youth don't.
(c) Both parents and youth want sexual-health education taught in school.
(d) Neither parents nor youth want sexual-health education taught in school.

10. **According to the available research, which of the following statements about sexual-health education is false?**
(a) Most evaluated abstinence-only programs have resulted in delayed first intercourse.
(b) Most evaluated sexual-health education programs don't result in earlier or more frequent sexual activity.
(c) Sexual-health education can result in more frequent condom use among sexually active youth.
(d) None of the above.

You'll find answers to the "Test Yourself" questions on page 495.

Critical Thinking

1. There's a growing perception that sexual imagery in the media damages child and adolescent sexual development. To what extent do you think this is the case?

2. The average age of marriage has been increasing. What impact do you think this has had on our sex lives? Because of this change, are people today happier with their sex lives than previous generations were?

3. The idea that sexuality gets better with age is heard more and more these days. Is this just hype from an aging Baby Boomer generation, or is there something to it? In your opinion, at what point in life are we likely to have the highest levels of sexual satisfaction?

MySearchLab

MySearchLab offers extensive help to students with their writing and research project and provides round-the-clock access to credible and reliable source material. Take a tour at www.mysearchlab.com.

CHAPTER THIRTEEN

Sexual Dysfunction

Sexual dysfunction A persistent or recurrent difficulty with a lack of sexual desire or arousal, or difficulty reaching orgasm.

Sexual dysfunction is a persistent or recurring lack of sexual desire or difficulty becoming sexually aroused or reaching orgasm. Many (if not most) people experience some type of sexual problem from time to time. Many men occasionally have difficulty getting and keeping erections, or ejaculate more quickly than they or their partners would like. Some women notice that their desire for sexual activity is sometimes lower than they'd like it to be, or that they occasionally have difficulty becoming sexually aroused or reaching orgasm. Temporary or occasional problems with sexual response, such as those experienced by nearly everyone at some point, do not qualify as sexual dysfunctions. A person is not considered to have a sexual dysfunction unless the problem persists over time and causes distress.

People who do have sexual dysfunctions may avoid opportunities for sexual interaction with partners. They may anticipate that sex will result in frustration or physical pain, rather than pleasure and gratification. Because of the emphasis our culture places on sexual competence, people with sexual dysfunctions may feel inadequate or incompetent, which diminishes their self-esteem. They may experience guilt, shame, frustration, depression, and anxiety.

Many people with sexual problems or dysfunctions find them difficult to talk about with their partners and health professionals. A woman who can't have an orgasm may be reluctant to mention it to her doctor, and a man who can't get an erection may never bring up the topic during his annual physical. Patient embarrassment about bringing up sexual concerns is often compounded by physicians who may never ask about them.

Prevalence of Sexual Problems and Dysfunctions

Because many people are reluctant to reveal their problems with sexual functioning to researchers, we don't have precise figures on their prevalence. Furthermore, studies measuring their prevalence have yielded different results.

One of the best sources of information we have about sexual problems among women in Canada is the Canadian Contraception Study (Fisher, Boroditsky, & Morris, 2004b). The survey asked women if they had experienced three types of sexual difficulty: low sexual desire, painful intercourse, and lack of orgasm during intercourse. About half of the women had experienced at least one of these problems. More married women reported sexual difficulties than single women did. The most common problem was diminished sexual desire (43%). Married women (57%) were twice as likely to report low desire as unmarried women (26%). The second most common problem was difficulty with orgasm; 24% of the women said they didn't usually have orgasms during intercourse. Painful intercourse was reported by 15% of the women. The percentages of Canadian women reporting these sexual problems was similar to the percentages of American women reporting the same problems (Laumann et al., 1994).

In a survey of 40- to 80-year-old Canadian men and women, Brock, Moreira, Glasser, and Gingell (2006) found that 23% of the men experienced rapid ejaculation, and 16% had problems with erection. Thirty percent of the women reported lack of interest in sex, and 24% reported difficulties with vaginal lubrication. Another survey looked at 40- to 88-year-old Canadian men, and found that 49% experienced some degree of erectile dysfunction (Grover et al., 2006).

The rates of sexual dysfunction reported in these and other studies depend on the measures used and the populations studied. The higher the average age of the participants, for example, the higher the percentage who will report erectile dysfunction. Nevertheless, it's clear from the available studies that sexual problems are common within the adult Canadian population. A national survey of people between the ages of 40 and 64 found that more than half were often too tired to have sex, 42% were too stressed, and 40% didn't have time (Reuters, 2006).

Unfortunately, many Canadians who experience difficulty with sexual functioning don't seek help. In the study by Brock and his colleagues (2006), 75% of those with sexual-function problems hadn't sought help from health professionals.

To what extent are people frustrated by their sexual problems? Traditionally, our society believed women didn't get sexually frustrated, because of the stereotype that sexual pleasure wasn't important to women. However, when Tanya Hill (2005) conducted an online survey of 236 17- to 24-year-old women at the University of Guelph, she found that three-quarters felt sexually frustrated at least some of the time, and 9% felt frustrated often. The most frustrating situations they reported were:

- Lack of orgasm during intercourse.
- Unaffectionate partners.
- Unavailability of partners.
- Refusal of partners to have sex.

CRITICAL THINKING QUESTIONS

Are you surprised at how high the rates of sexual dysfunction are in the Canadian population?

Types of Sexual Dysfunction

The most widely used system of classification for sexual dysfunction is based on the American Psychiatric Association's (2000) *Diagnostic and Statistical Manual of Mental Disorders* (DSM). It groups sexual dysfunctions into four categories:

- *Sexual-desire disorders*—These involve lack of interest in sex or aversion to sexual contact.
- *Sexual-arousal disorders*—In men, these involve persistent difficulty in obtaining or sustaining erections sufficient to engage in satisfactory sexual activity. In women, they typically involve insufficient lubrication.
- *Orgasmic disorders*—These involve persistent problems reaching orgasm, or reaching orgasm more quickly than the individuals would like. Women are more likely to encounter difficulties having orgasms, and men are more likely to reach orgasm too quickly (rapid ejaculation).
- *Sexual-pain disorders*—Both men and women may suffer from **dyspareunia** (pain during sex). Women may experience **vaginismus**, or involuntary contraction of the muscles that surround the vaginal barrel, preventing or making penetration painful.

Sexual dysfunctions are classified as lifelong or acquired (the latter follow periods of unproblematic functioning), and as generalized or situational. Generalized dysfunctions occur in all situations. Situational dysfunctions affect sexual functioning only in some situations, such as during partnered sexual activity but not with solo masturbation, or with one partner but not another. Thus, if a man has never been able to obtain an erection during sexual activity with a partner but can do so during masturbation, his dysfunction is lifelong and situational.

Dyspareunia A sexual dysfunction characterized by persistent or recurrent pain during sexual activity.

Vaginismus A sexual dysfunction characterized by involuntary contraction of the muscles surrounding the vaginal barrel, preventing or making penetration painful.

Sexual-Desire Disorders

Sexual-desire disorders involve lack of sexual desire or aversion to genital sexual activity. People with little or no sexual interest or desire are said to have hypoactive sexual-desire disorder. They often report an absence of sexual thoughts or fantasies. A recent survey of 2000 American women (West et al., 2008) found that the incidence of low sexual desire was 26.7% for premenopausal women and 52.4% for postmenopausal women. The problem is more common among women than men. Nevertheless, the belief that men are always eager for sex is a myth (Hackett, 2008).

CRITICAL THINKING QUESTIONS

To what extent do you think it's important for partners in a long-term relationship to have roughly equal levels of sexual desire?

Lack of sexual desire doesn't imply that a person is unable to get an erection, lubricate adequately, or reach orgasm. Some people with low sexual desire can become sexually aroused and reach orgasm when adequately stimulated. Many enjoy sexual activity, even if they're unlikely to initiate it. Many appreciate the affection and closeness of physical intimacy, but have no interest in genital stimulation.

Hypoactive sexual desire is one of the most commonly diagnosed sexual dysfunctions. Yet there's no clear consensus among clinicians and researchers about how to define "low sexual desire" (Heiman, 2008). How much sexual interest or desire is "normal"? There's no standard level of sexual desire, and instances of low desire often become apparent only when there's a discrepancy between levels of desire experienced by a couple.

Although many women have strong levels of sexual desire, the literature on gender differences suggests that men are generally more interested in sex than women are (Heiman, 2008; Peplau, 2003). As a result, when discrepancies in desire arise for heterosexual couples, the men are more likely than the women to have higher levels of desire. To the extent that gender differences in sexual interest levels exist, it's been speculated that gay and lesbian couples may have fewer discrepancy troubles than heterosexual couples. When one member of a couple is more interested in sex than the other, sex therapists often recommend that the couple try to compromise. They also attempt to uncover and resolve problems in the relationship that may be dampening sexual ardour (Aubin et al., 2009).

When is lack of sexual desire a dysfunction? Not everyone has the same level of sexual desire as other men and women in the same age group. A person with a lower level of desire doesn't necessarily have a sexual dysfunction. Remember, lack of desire should be classified as a dysfunction only when the person finds his or her level of sexual desire personally distressing. Basson (2010) suggests that many women can lead active, satisfying sex lives without ongoing or frequent feelings of desire between sexual engagements with their partners.

SEXUAL-AVERSION DISORDER People with low sexual desire may have little or no interest in sex, but they're not repelled by genital contact. Some people, however, find sex disgusting or aversive, and avoid genital contact.

Histories of erectile problems can cause sexual aversion in men. They may be overly anxious in sexual situations, because these situations trigger feelings of shame. Histories of sexual trauma, such as rape or childhood sexual abuse or incest, often figure prominently in cases of sexual aversion, especially among women (Najman et al., 2005).

Sexual-Arousal Disorders

When we're sexually stimulated, our bodies normally respond with **vasocongestion**, which produces erection in the male and vaginal lubrication in the female. People with sexual-arousal disorders, however, fail to achieve or sustain the erections or lubrication necessary to facilitate sexual activity (Rowland & Incrocci, 2008). Or they lack the subjective feelings of sexual pleasure or excitement that normally accompany sexual arousal.

In the past, problems with arousal were referred to as impotence in men and frigidity in women. These terms have come to be seen as unnecessarily negative, belittling, and unhelpful. Today health professionals use the less pejorative terms "erectile dysfunction" in men and "female sexual-arousal disorder" in women.

MALE ERECTILE DISORDER Sexual-arousal disorder in the male is called **male erectile disorder** or erectile dysfunction. It's characterized by persistent difficulty in achieving or maintaining an erection sufficient to allow completion of sexual activity. In most cases, the failure is limited to sexual activity with partners, or with some partners and not others. It can thus be classified as situational. In rare cases,

---

CRITICAL THINKING QUESTIONS

What myths or misinformation about sexuality have you heard that might contribute to the development of sexual problems?

Vasocongestion
Engorgement of blood vessels with blood, which swells the genitals and breasts during sexual arousal.

Male erectile disorder
Persistent difficulty getting or maintaining an erection sufficient to allow the man to engage in or complete sexual activity. Also termed *erectile dysfunction*.

the dysfunction is found during any sexual activity, including masturbation. In such cases, it's classified as generalized. Some men with erectile disorder are unable to attain erections with their partners, while others can achieve but not sustain erections.

The incidence of erectile dysfunction increases with age. The Grover et al. (2006) survey found that about 30% of men in their forties, a little over 40% in their fifties, and about 65% in their sixties have some degree of erectile dysfunction. Occasional problems in achieving or maintaining erection are quite common, happening to nearly all men. Fatigue, too much alcohol, anxiety over impressing a new partner, and other factors may cause occasional erectile difficulties. Even an isolated occurrence, however, can lead to a persistent problem if the man fears it will happen again. The more anxious and concerned he becomes about his ability to have an erection, the more likely he is to suffer with **performance anxiety**. This anxiety can contribute to repeated difficulty in gaining and maintaining an erection, resulting in a vicious circle of anxiety and erection problems.

Performance anxiety Anxiety concerning one's ability to perform behaviours, especially behaviours that may be evaluated by other people.

A man with erectile problems may try achieve an erection by force of will, which can compound the problem. Each time it happens, it's more demoralizing. He may ruminate about his sexual problem, setting the stage for yet more anxiety. His partner may try to comfort and support him by saying things like "It can happen to anyone," "Don't worry about it," or "It will get better in time." But attempts at reassurance may be to no avail. As one client put it in a private conversation with one of the authors:

> I always felt inferior, like I was on probation, having to prove myself. I felt like I was up against the wall. You can't imagine how embarrassing this [erectile failure] was. It's like you walk out [naked] in front of an audience that you think is a nudist convention, and it turns out to be a tuxedo convention.

The vicious circle of anxiety and erectile failure may be interrupted if the man recognizes that occasional problems are normal, and doesn't overreact. However, the emphasis on sexual prowess in our culture may spur him to view occasional erectile problems as catastrophes, rather than transient disappointments. Viewing occasional problems as inconveniences, rather than tragedies, may help avert the development of persistent erectile difficulty.

Performance anxiety is a prominent cause of erectile disorder. So are other psychological factors, including depression, lack of self-esteem, and problems with the relationship. Biological factors such diabetes and heart disease can also play causal roles. Especially among middle-aged and older men, in fact, medical conditions are frequently associated with erectile dysfunction (Grover et al., 2006).

It's a common belief that sexual arousal is much simpler for men than for women. However, a recent focus group study (Jansen et al., 2008) suggests that men's sexual arousal is also complex, and that there's considerable variation in what men find arousing. The older men in the study reported that emotional connections with their partners were now more important than physical attractiveness when it came to sexual arousal. Some men reported that they were less likely to be aroused by women with low self-esteem, even if they were physically attractive.

FEMALE SEXUAL-AROUSAL DISORDER Women may encounter persistent difficulties becoming sexually excited or sufficiently lubricated in response to sexual stimulation. In some cases, these difficulties are lifelong. In others, they develop after periods of normal functioning. In some cases, difficulties are pervasive and occur during both masturbation and sex with partners. More often, they occur in specific situations. For example, they may occur with some partners and not with others, or during vaginal penetration but not during oral–genital sex or masturbation.

According to Basson (2004), most women with arousal disorder experience little or no subjective arousal or sexual excitement. These women can be categorized into two groups. Those with combined-arousal disorder experience no subjective arousal and feel no genital response. Women with subjective-arousal disorder are aware that their genitals physically respond to stimulation, but feel no subjective arousal.

A minority of women can become aroused by many different kinds of stimuli, but don't find stimulation of their genitals arousing. These women have genital-arousal disorder. Women with this disorder can still be highly interested in sex, and become subjectively aroused as long as they experience non-genital stimulation (Basson, 2004).

Female sexual-arousal disorder, like its male counterpart, may have physical causes. A thorough evaluation by a medical specialist is recommended. Any neurological, vascular, or hormonal problem that interferes with the lubrication or swelling response of the vagina to sexual stimulation may contribute to female sexual-arousal disorder. For example, diabetes mellitus may lead to diminished sexual excitement, because the nerves that service the clitoris degenerate and the blood vessels become damaged. Reduced estrogen production can also result in vaginal dryness.

Another interesting line of research suggests that the skin of some women with sexual-arousal problems is less sensitive to touch than the skin of women who don't have such problems (Frohlich & Meston, 2005). Such women might seek to increase their sexual stimulation by psychological as well as physical means.

Female sexual-arousal disorder more often has psychological causes. In some cases, women may harbour deep-seated anger and resentment toward their partners (Moore & Heiman, 2006). Or they may fail to become aroused during sexual activity simply because they're no longer sexually attracted to their partners, or because they're experiencing nonsexual conflicts in their relationships. It would be incorrect to say these women have arousal disorders; rather than problems with sexual functioning, they have relationship difficulties.

Childhood sexual abuse is especially prevalent among women with sexual-arousal disorder (van der Made et al., 2008; van Lankveld, 2008). Survivors of sexual abuse often find it difficult to respond sexually to their partners. Feelings of helplessness, anger, or guilt—or even flashbacks of the abuse—may surface when these women begin sexual activity, undermining their ability to become aroused. Other psychosocial causes include anxiety and guilt about sex, and ineffective stimulation by the women's partners (Goldstein et al., 2006).

At the opposite end of the sexual-arousal continuum are women who experience persistent, intense genital sexual arousal (Leiblum & Chivers, 2007). This condition is extremely distressing to some who experience it. (We discussed this condition briefly in Chapter 4.)

Orgasmic Disorders

Orgasmic disorders include female orgasmic disorder, male orgasmic disorder, and premature or rapid ejaculation. In female or male orgasmic disorder, the individual is persistently delayed in reaching orgasm, or doesn't reach orgasm at all, despite achieving sexual stimulation that would normally be of sufficient intensity to result in orgasm. The problem is more common among women than men. In some cases, a person can reach orgasm without difficulty while engaging in sexual relations with one partner, but not with another.

FEMALE ORGASMIC DISORDER Women with female orgasmic disorder are unable to reach orgasm, or have difficulty reaching orgasm after what would usually be adequate sexual stimulation. Women who have never reached orgasm through any means are sometimes labelled **anorgasmic** or pre-orgasmic.

Anorgasmic Unable to reach orgasm, through any means.

A woman who reaches orgasm through masturbation or oral sex might not reach orgasm during intercourse with a male partner. Penile thrusting may not provide sufficient clitoral stimulation to facilitate orgasm. In other words, a woman who doesn't reach orgasm during intercourse but can reach orgasm through other types of sexual stimulation doesn't have an orgasmic disorder. University of Waterloo researcher B. J. Rye (2001) found that 93% of university women sometimes or usually needed direct clitoral stimulation during intercourse to reach orgasm. Only 46% of the women surveyed had orgasms during at least half of their intercourse experiences, and 49% said it often took them a long time to have orgasms.

MALE ORGASMIC DISORDER Male orgasmic disorder has also been called delayed ejaculation, retarded ejaculation, and ejaculatory incompetence. The problem may be lifelong or acquired, generalized or situational.

Very few men have never ejaculated. In most cases, the disorder is limited to intercourse. The men may be capable of ejaculating during masturbation or oral sex, but find it difficult or impossible to ejaculate during intercourse, despite high levels of sexual excitement. There's a myth that men with male orgasmic disorder and their partners enjoy this condition, because it enables them to "go on forever." Actually, the experience is frustrating for both partners (Richardson et al., 2006).

Male orgasmic disorder may be caused by physical problems, such as multiple sclerosis or neurological damage that interferes with neural control of ejaculation. It may also be a side effect of certain drugs. Various psychological factors may also play a role, including performance anxiety, sexual guilt, and hostility toward a partner.

RAPID EJACULATION Men with **rapid ejaculation (RE),** also referred to as premature ejaculation, ejaculate too quickly to permit their partners or themselves to fully enjoy sexual relations. The degree of rapidity varies. Some men ejaculate during foreplay, even at the sight of their partners disrobing. But most men with this condition ejaculate either just before or immediately after penetration, or after a few penile thrusts.

Guy Grenier and Sandra Byers (2001) at the University of New Brunswick studied the ejaculatory behaviour of a community sample of men. The men reported that intercourse typically lasted for about eight minutes before they ejaculated. They also reported that ejaculation happened more quickly than they wished in about one-third of their acts of sexual intercourse. They attempted to delay the timing of their ejaculations during about half of their intercourse experiences.

The percentage of men experiencing RE varies, depending on the criteria the researchers use. Twenty-three percent of the men in Grenier and Byers's (2001) study said they had problems with premature ejaculation. They ejaculated sooner than other men, perceived that they had less control over the timing of ejaculation, and were concerned about ejaculating sooner than they wished. Another Canadian study found a prevalence of RE ranging from 16% to 24%, depending on how RE was defined (Brock et al., 2009). The authors noted that 90% of the men with RE in their study had not discussed the problem with their doctors.

Just what constitutes "rapid"? There's no clear cutoff. Some scholars argue that the focus should be on whether the couple is satisfied with the duration of sexual activity, rather than on a specific time period.

In another study, involving 52 New Brunswick couples, Byers and Grenier (2003) compared the men's and women's reports of the men's ejaculatory behaviour. There was only moderate agreement. The women tended to underestimate how seriously their male partners viewed RE. However, both the men and the women reported lower sexual satisfaction as a result of the men's RE problems.

Helen Singer Kaplan (1974) suggested that the label "premature" be applied to cases in which men persistently or recurrently lack voluntary control over their

Rapid ejaculation (RE)
A sexual dysfunction in which ejaculation occurs with minimal sexual stimulation, and before the man desires it. It's also called premature ejaculation.

ejaculations. This may sound like a contradiction in terms, given that ejaculation is a reflex, and reflexes needn't involve thought or conscious control. Kaplan meant men might control their ejaculations by learning to regulate the amount of sexual stimulation they experienced, keeping it below the threshold at which the ejaculation reflex was triggered.

Sexual-Pain Disorders

For most of us, sexual activity is a source of pleasure. For some of us, however, it causes pain and discomfort.

DYSPAREUNIA   Traditionally, dyspareunia has been defined as painful intercourse. However, it also includes persistent pain associated with any stimulation of the vaginal area (Basson, 2004). According to Caroline Pukall of Queen's University, some therapists and researchers believe a more accurate term is "vulvodynia" (Pukall et al., 2003). Most of the discussion and research on dyspareunia, and on sexual dysfunction in general, has been focused on problems related to heterosexual intercourse. Obviously, women with female partners can also experience genital pain during sexual activities, especially during the insertion of fingers or a dildo into the vagina. Painful intercourse is less common in men, and then it's generally associated with genital infections that cause burning or painful ejaculation.

Dyspareunia is one of the most common sexual dysfunctions, and a common complaint of women seeking gynecological services. The location of the pain can vary. It can be at the entrance to the vagina, for example, in the vagina, or in the pelvic region (Pukall et al., 2003). Unfortunately, many women are too embarrassed to talk about genital pain, and they don't seek treatment. Few doctors and therapists are properly trained in the diagnosis of dyspareunia, so many women with this condition don't receive adequate care (Pukall et al., 2005). Researchers at Queen's University have developed a vulvalgesiometer, which can measure the severity of pain experienced by women (Pukall et al., 2007).

Pain is a sign that something is wrong—physically or psychologically. Dyspareunia may result from physical causes, emotional factors, or an interaction of the two (Binik, 2005). The most common cause of pain during intercourse is inadequate lubrication. In this case, additional foreplay or artificial lubrication may help. Vaginal infections and sexually transmitted infections (STIs) may also produce genital pain. Allergic reactions to spermicides, even the latex material in condoms, can give rise to genital irritation. Pain during deep penetration may be caused by endometriosis, pelvic inflammatory disease (PID), other diseases, or structural disorders of the reproductive organs.

Psychological factors such as unresolved guilt or anxiety about sex or the lingering effects of sexual trauma may also be involved. They may inhibit lubrication and cause involuntary contractions of the vaginal musculature, making penetration painful or uncomfortable.

Researchers in Montreal (Binik et al., 2002) have extensively studied dyspareunia in women and evaluated various treatment strategies. They've found that women with dyspareunia tend to have a lower tolerance for pain, not only in the vaginal area, but also on the upper arms, suggesting that a generalized hypersensitivity may contribute to this problem in some women (Pukall et al., 2002).

Based on these findings, Binik (2005) argues that dyspareunia should be categorized as a pain disorder, rather than a sexual dysfunction, as defined by the American Psychiatric Association's DSM-4, and should be assessed and treated like other pain disorders. Binik's recommendations have caused considerable controversy, with some experts maintaining that dyspareunia should continue to be classified as a specifically sexual dysfunction.

Binik (2005) believes every case of dyspareunia has both physiological and psychological components. Researchers have found that women who believe their pain is due to psychosocial factors report higher levels of pain and more sexual problems than women who believe their pain is due to physical causes. For many women, the pain of dyspareunia cannot be totally eliminated, but they can often be taught coping strategies for managing the pain.

VAGINISMUS Vaginismus involves an involuntary contraction of the pelvic muscles that surround the outer one-third of the vaginal barrel, resulting in pain. Avoidance of penetration seems to be the key factor differentiating vaginismus from dyspareunia (Bergeron & Lord, 2003). Vaginismus occurs reflexively during attempts at vaginal penetration, making entry by a penis, fingers, or a dildo painful or impossible. Some women with vaginismus are unable to tolerate penetration by any object, including a tampon or a physician's speculum.

Some experts believe vaginismus is usually caused by a fear of penetration, rather than by physical injury or defect (Brauer et al., 2009; ter Kuile et al., 2009). Women with vaginismus often have histories of sexual trauma, sexual assault, or botched abortions that have resulted in vaginal injury. They may desire sexual relations, and may be capable of becoming sexually aroused and achieving orgasm, but their fear of penetration triggers an involuntary spasm of the vaginal musculature at the point of insertion of an object into their vaginas. Vaginismus can also be a cause or an effect of dyspareunia. Women who experience painful penetration may develop a fear of it, which leads to involuntary vaginal contractions. Vaginismus and dyspareunia may also give rise to, or result from, erectile disorder in men, as feelings of failure and anxiety overwhelm both partners.

Some Canadian researchers (Reissing et al., 2004) disagree that vaginismus is easily diagnosed and easily treated. Instead, they propose that vaginismus be reconceptualized as either an aversion to vaginal penetration or a genital pain disorder. These distinctions are important in suggesting different courses of treatment.

VULVODYNIA

The pain has lasted for months. You're so uncomfortable you can hardly sit. Having sex is unthinkable. Nothing alleviates the pain, burning, and irritation, at least not for long. (Mayo Clinic Staff, 2006)

This is a description of vulvodynia posted online by the Mayo Clinic (2006). Vulvodynia is a gynecological condition characterized by vulval pain, particularly

Innovative Canadian Research

SEXUAL AROUSAL AND VULVAR VESTIBULITIS (VV)

Some therapists believe VV is associated with insufficient sexual arousal. To test this theory, researchers at McGill University conducted an experimental study.

They showed both an erotic film and a non-erotic film to two samples of women—a group with VV and a group who were healthy—and measured their genital arousal (specifically, of the labia minora) with a labial thermistor clip (Payne et al., 2007).

Both groups were sexually aroused in response to the erotic film. The group with VV did not report subjective arousal, but exhibited greater pain in both genital and non-genital areas than the control group did.

The findings indicate that women with VV are not incapable of physiological sexual arousal. However, lack of subjective feelings of arousal may contribute to their experience of vulvar pain during intercourse (Payne et al., 2007).

a chronic burning sensation, irritation, and soreness (Lotery et al., 2004; Masheb et al., 2004). Although vulvodynia and related conditions, such as vestibulitis, can give rise to pain during vaginal penetration, they're not in themselves considered sexual dysfunctions (Kaler, 2005).

Vulvar vestibulitis (VV) is pain that can be experienced through both sexual and nonsexual contact at the entrance of the vagina (i.e., at the vulvar vestibule, which is bordered by the inner vaginal lips). Women with VV usually seek treatment, because they experience pain when penetration is attempted. Unlike VV, vulvodynia does not require some kind of external contact for pain to be triggered (Pukall et al., 2005).

Vulvar vestibulitis may be caused by various factors, such as repeated yeast infections, hormonal changes, and genetics. Other possibilities are STIs, allergies, urinary infections, and sexual abuse. Psychological factors such as low sexual esteem, anxiety, and hyper-vigilance (obsessional focus on pain) may also contribute to VV (Pukall et al., 2005).

A World of Diversity

A NEW VIEW OF WOMEN'S SEXUAL DYSFUNCTIONS?

by Lori A. Brotto, PhD, Department of Obstetrics and Gynaecology, University of British Columbia

Classification of sexual dysfunction in the Diagnostic and Statistical Manual of Mental Disorders (American Psychiatric Association, 2000) is based on the human sexual response cycle model developed by Masters and Johnson (1966).

This classification has been criticized because of the specific wording used for the criteria for sexual dysfunction, and because of the overall taxonomic system used for classifying sexual dysfunction in women. These criticisms have resulted in attempts to establish new classification systems. Yet these revisions have continued to use the Masters and Johnson medical model, which is symptom-focused, for problems relating to desire, arousal, orgasm, and pain.

In 2000, Leonore Tiefer, a clinical psychologist and activist, convened a group of feminist social scientists to propose a new diagnostic system, free of the medical model and pharmaceutical conflicts of interest. Specifically, the group was concerned about the creation of a "female sexual dysfunction (FSD)" diagnosis by pharmaceutical companies, which would then be in a profitable position to develop and market drugs to treat this "disease." The New View Campaign was thereby formed.

The New View classification system is a radical departure from the American Psychiatric Association's DSM-4 taxonomic structure. It's based on feminist theories that attribute women's sexual problems to cultural and relational factors (Tiefer, 2001). The system deliberately avoids specifying any particular "normal" pattern of sexual response. Instead, the four-part classification system focuses on the causes of sexual problems, defined as "discontent or dissatisfaction with any emotional, physical, or relational aspect of sexual experience." It doesn't differentiate among the problematic symptoms of desire, arousal, orgasm, and other sexual complaints.

The New View system classifies women's sexual problems into four main groups, based on their causes (Tiefer, 2001):

- Sexual problems due to sociocultural, political, and economic factors.
- Sexual problems relating to partners and relationships.
- Sexual problems due to psychological factors.
- Sexual problems due to medical factors.

The New View classification is an improvement over the DSM-4 perspective of sexual response, which is based on a medical model of men's sexuality. However, empirical data hasn't been collected to support the usefulness and validity of the new classification system. Moreover, this radical departure from the DSM-4 system means there's no continuity of research between the two systems.

This leads to an overriding question: is it useful to diagnose sexual dysfunctions on the basis of causes, rather than symptoms? With a new system, we'd need to start all over again in determining the prevalence of sexual difficulty. This would mean losing what we already know about the rates of sexual desire, arousal and orgasm problems, and complaints of genital pain.

Origins of Sexual Dysfunction

Human beings are complex, with complex bodies and complex mental processes. We're reared in families, within cultural settings. For these reasons, we need to consider possible biological, psychological, and social factors in sexual dysfunction, which can interact in a number of ways (Brown & Haaser, 2005). For example, biological and psychosocial factors—hormonal deficiencies, depression, dissatisfaction with a relationship, and so on—can contribute to lack of desire. Researchers refer to an approach that considers the interactions of biological, psychological, and sociocultural factors as a **biopsychosocial model**.

Biopsychosocial model An approach to explaining dysfunction that looks at the interactions of biological, psychological, and sociocultural factors.

Biological Causes

Among the medical conditions that diminish sexual desire are testosterone deficiencies, thyroid overactivity, thyroid underactivity, and temporal lobe epilepsy.

Sexual desire is stoked by testosterone, which is produced by men in the testes and by both men and women in the adrenal glands (Heiman, 2008). Women may experience lower sexual desire when their adrenal glands are surgically removed. Low sexual interest, along with erectile difficulty, is also common among men with **hypogonadism**, which is treated with testosterone (Lue, 2000).

Hypogonadism An endocrine disorder that reduces the output of testosterone.

The reduction in testosterone levels that occurs in middle and later life may in part explain the gradual decline in male sexual desire (Hackett, 2008). Female sexual desire may also decline with age, however, because of physical and psychological changes (Goldstein et al., 2006). Some medications, especially those used to control anxiety or hypertension, may reduce desire. Changing medications or doses may increase a person's level of desire.

People with sexual dysfunctions are generally advised to undergo physical examinations, to determine whether their problems are biologically based. For example, men with erectile disorder may be evaluated in sleep centres, to determine whether they attain erections while they're asleep. The technique is termed nocturnal penile **tumescence** (NPT). Healthy men usually have erections during REM sleep, which occurs every 90 to 100 minutes. Men with biologically based erectile disorder often don't have nocturnal erections.

Tumescence Swelling; erection.

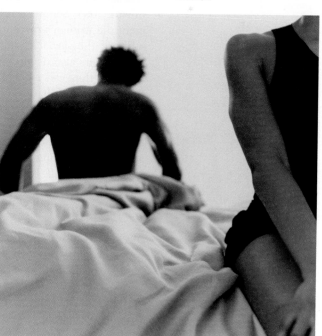

A physical examination, particularly in the pelvic area, and assessment of hormone levels can uncover the root causes of some cases of sexual dysfunction among women. Medical investigation of a sexual dysfunction can lead to the discovery of an underlying medical condition that might otherwise remain unknown to the patient and his or her doctor.

Fatigue may lead to erectile disorder and orgasmic disorder in men, and to inadequate lubrication and orgasmic disorder in women, but these remain isolated incidents unless the person attaches too much meaning to them and becomes concerned about future sexual activity.

HEALTH PROBLEMS Researchers find that health problems contribute to all kinds of sexual dysfunction in men, and particularly to sexual pain in women (Barsky et al., 2006; Binik, 2005; Schultz et al., 2005). Painful sex often reflects an underlying infection. Medical conditions that affect sexual response include

Too Tired for Sex.
They were tired, and it didn't happen. Should they keep trying, or wait until they've had a good night's sleep?

heart disease (Lane & Thayer, 2008), diabetes mellitus, multiple sclerosis, spinal-cord injury, complications from surgery (such as removal of the prostate in men), hormonal problems, and the use of some medicines, such as those that treat hypertension and psychiatric disorders (Byerly et al., 2006; Olfson et al., 2005; Wooten, 2008). Even when biological factors are involved in sexual dysfunctions, psychological factors such as anger and depression can prolong or worsen them (Laurent & Simons, 2009).

Cardiovascular problems can lead to erectile disorder by affecting the flow of blood to and through the penis, a problem that becomes more common as men age. Damage to the nerves involved in erection can also play a role (Goldstein, 1998). Erectile problems can arise when clogged or narrow arteries leading to the penis deprive it of oxygen (Thompson et al., 2005). For example, erectile disorder is common among men with diabetes mellitus, a disease that can damage blood vessels and nerves.

Rimm (2000) studied 2000 men and found that erectile dysfunction was connected with a large waist, physical inactivity, and too much alcohol consumption (or no alcohol consumption!). The common condition among these men may have been high cholesterol levels. Cholesterol can impede the flow of blood to the penis, just as it impedes the flow of blood to the heart. Another study connects erectile dysfunction with heart disease and hypertension (Johannes et al., 2000).

Sexual functioning in women seems to be less affected by cardiovascular disease. For both men and women, however, hypertension (high blood pressure) and the drugs used to treat it can negatively affect sexual functioning (Perez, Gadgil, & Dizon, 2009).

AGING Perimenopausal and post-menopausal women usually produce less vaginal lubrication than younger women, and their vaginal walls become thin—changes that can render sex painful (Dennerstein & Goldstein, 2005; Dennerstein & Hayes, 2005; Hayes & Dennerstein, 2005). These physical changes, along with negative stereotypes about older women and men, create performance anxiety and discourage both partners from initiating sexual activity (McCabe, 2005; McCarthy & Fucito, 2005; Schultz et al., 2005). In such cases, artificial lubrication can supplement the woman's own production, and estrogen replacement may halt or reverse some of the sexual changes of aging (Goldstein & Alexander, 2005). However, the partners also need to have realistic expectations and consider enjoyable sexual activities they can engage in without discomfort or high demands (McCarthy & Fucito, 2005; Mohan & Bhugra, 2005).

The findings of the Massachusetts Male Aging Study suggest that men who exercise regularly seem to ward off erectile dysfunction (Derby, 2000). Men who burned 200 calories or more a day in physical activity—an amount that can be achieved by walking briskly for three kilometres—cut their risk of erectile dysfunction almost in half. Exercise seems to prevent clogging of the arteries, keeping them clear for the flow of blood into the penis.

Nerve damage resulting from prostate surgery may impair erectile response. Erectile disorder may also result from multiple sclerosis (MS), a disease in which nerve cells lose the protective coatings that facilitate transmission of neural messages. MS has also been implicated in male orgasmic disorder.

Medical conditions associated with advancing age, such as chronic kidney disease, hypertension, cancer, emphysema, and heart disease, can all impair erectile response. So can endocrine disorders that impair testosterone production (Ralph & McNicholas, 2000). Women can also develop vascular and nervous disorders that impair genital blood flow, reducing lubrication and sexual excitement, rendering intercourse painful, and reducing their ability to reach orgasm. All of these problems become more likely as people age.

DRUGS Use of certain prescription and illicit drugs can contribute to sexual dysfunction in both women and men. Antidepressant medications and antipsychotic drugs can impair erectile functioning and cause orgasmic disorders (Olfson et al., 2005; Taylor et al., 2005). Tranquilizers such as Valium and Xanax may cause orgasmic disorder in either sex. Some drugs used to treat high blood pressure can impair erectile response. Switching to other blood-pressure drugs or adjusting dosages may help. Other drugs that can lead to erectile disorder include adrenergic blockers, diuretics, cholesterol-lowering drugs (statins), anticonvulsants, anti-Parkinson drugs, and dyspepsia- and ulcer-healing drugs (Do et al., 2009).

Central nervous system depressants such as alcohol, heroin, and methadone can reduce sexual desire and impair sexual arousal (Brown et al., 2005). Narcotics also depress testosterone production, thereby reducing sexual desire and leading to erectile dysfunction. Regular use of cocaine can cause erectile disorder or male orgasmic disorder, and may reduce sexual desire in both men and women (Rawson et al., 2002). While moderate alcohol consumption (one or two drinks per day) is unlikely to affect sexual functioning, long-term heavy drinking is clearly associated with sexual dysfunction among both women and men (McKay, 2005). (See Chapter 4 for further discussion of the effects of drugs on sexual response.)

SSRIS AND SEXUAL RESPONSE People—especially physicians—need to be aware of the sexual side effects of some drugs used to treat depression. Selective serotonin reuptake inhibitors (SSRIs) are widely prescribed not only for depression, but also for panic disorder, obsessive-compulsive disorder, anorexia nervosa, and other conditions. Most physicians are aware that these drugs have some sexual side effects in some patients. However, they almost completely impair sexual arousal in many patients, especially older patients (Heiman, 2008). Moreover, even when patients discontinue the drugs, sexual functioning doesn't necessarily bounce back (Bolton et al., 2006; Csoka & Shipko, 2006).

Some drugs that are helpful with depression may not impair sexual functioning—at least in the short run. Wellbutrin, for example, can improve sexual functioning, and is sometimes prescribed along with an SSRI to help prevent sexual side effects.

Psychosocial Causes

Abrupt changes in sexual desire are often explained by psychological and interpersonal factors such as depression, stress, and problems in the relationship (Aubin et al., 2009; Moore & Heiman, 2006). Anxiety is the most commonly reported factor. Sexual desire can be dampened by performance anxiety (anxiety over being evaluated negatively), anxiety involving fears of pleasure or loss of control, and deeper sources of anxiety relating to fear of injury (Janssen & Bancroft, 2006). Depression is also a common cause (Laurent & Simons, 2009), and a history of sexual assault has been linked to low sexual desire (McCarthy et al., 2006).

Psychosocial factors connected with sexual dysfunction include cultural influences, economic problems, psychosexual traumas, dissatisfaction with relationships, lack of sexual skills, irrational beliefs, and performance anxiety (Bancroft et al., 2005b; McCabe, 2005).

CULTURAL INFLUENCES Children reared in sexually repressive cultural or home environments may learn to respond to sex with feelings of anxiety and shame, rather than anticipation and pleasure (Nobre & Pinto-Gouveia, 2006). People whose parents instilled in them a sense of guilt over touching their genitals may find it difficult to accept their sex organs as sources of pleasure (McCarthy et al., 2006).

In most cultures, sexual pleasure has traditionally been a male preserve. Young women may be reared to believe sex is a duty they're to perform for their husbands, not a source of personal pleasure. Although the traditional double standard has diminished in developed countries (Fugl-Meyer et al., 2006), some girls are still exposed to repressive attitudes. Women are more likely than men to be taught to suppress sexual desires (Nobre & Pinto-Gouveia, 2006). Self-control and vigilance—not sexual awareness and acceptance—become identified as feminine virtues. Women reared with such attitudes may not learn about their sexual potential or express their erotic desires to their partners.

Many women who were exposed to negative attitudes about sex during childhood and adolescence find it difficult to suddenly view sex as a source of pleasure and satisfaction as adults. A lifetime of learning to turn themselves off sexually may impair sexual arousal and enjoyment when acceptable opportunities arise (Fishman & Mamo, 2001).

PSYCHOSEXUAL TRAUMA Women and men who were sexually victimized in childhood are more likely to have trouble becoming sexually aroused (Matthews et al., 2006; McCarthy et al., 2006; Mosher et al., 2005). Some learning theorists contend that conditioned anxiety explains many cases of sexual dysfunction. Sexual stimuli come to elicit anxiety when they've been paired with traumatic experiences, such as rape, incest, or sexual molestation. Unresolved anger, misplaced guilt, and feelings of disgust also make it difficult for victims of sexual trauma to respond sexually, even years later and with loving partners.

EMOTIONAL FACTORS Pleasurable, fulfilling sexual activity with a partner typically involves allowing yourself to let go emotionally, at least to some extent. Fear of losing control or of letting go may make it more difficult for you to let down your guard enough to become sexually aroused. Other emotional factors, especially depression, are often implicated in sexual dysfunction (Laurent & Simons, 2009). Prolonged and high levels of stress can also interfere with sexual interest and response.

MYTHS AND MISINFORMATION Although Western culture often seems to be saturated in superficial sexual imagery, many people grow up badly misinformed about sexuality. Sex-education programs in schools focus mainly on pregnancy and STI prevention, and rarely teach about sexual response. Some non-Western cultural traditions restrict and discourage learning about sexual pleasure, particularly for women. Since many, if not most, people have few credible and easily accessible sources of information about sexual functioning, it's not surprising that myths and misinformation often prevail. Myths and misinformation about sexuality are, in many cases, contributing factors in the development of sexual dysfunction, and providing corrective information is a key factor in overcoming them.

INEFFECTIVE SEXUAL TECHNIQUES People who lack information about sexuality, and particularly about sexual response, are more likely to be unaware of what techniques are sexually pleasurable for themselves and their partners. For example, a woman who remains ignorant about the erotic importance of her clitoris may be unlikely to seek direct clitoral stimulation. People often make assumptions about what's pleasurable for their partners on the basis of their own preferences and past experiences with previous partners. Based on his own preferences, for example, a man may assume he knows which techniques are pleasurable for his male partner, simply because they're both men.

As we'll see, effective sexual communication is an important factor in the prevention and resolution of sexual dysfunction.

BOREDOM AND ROUTINE It's common for couples to fall into narrow sexual routines, in which the timing and sequence of sexual activity follow constant, familiar patterns. A couple may have sex only once they've gone to bed for the night, for example, and may always use the same one or two favoured positions or techniques.

While some people remain sexually satisfied with standard routines, others find that, over time, their sexual relationships become monotonous. Once boredom and complacency about the sexual component of a relationship sets in, arousal often diminishes.

LACK OF SEXUAL COMMUNICATION Partners who don't communicate their sexual preferences or experiment with new techniques may find themselves losing interest.

Canadian researchers MacNeil and Byers (2009) have examined how communicating sexual likes and dislikes can affect sexual satisfaction within relationships. Their research indicates that, for both women and men, communicating sexual likes and dislikes contributes to greater sexual satisfaction within long-term relationships.

Holmberg and Blair (2009) compared heterosexual, gay, and lesbian couples' responses on a sexual communication scale (e.g., "My partner often complains that I am not very clear about what I want sexually"). They found that levels of sexual communication generally don't differ among lesbian, gay, and heterosexual couples. In all of these relationship types, clear communication about sexual likes and dislikes may improve sexual satisfaction, while lack of such communication may lead to or compound existing sexual problems.

RELATIONSHIP ISSUES Problems in a relationship are not easily left at the bedroom door (McCarthy et al., 2006; Moore & Heiman, 2006). Heterosexual and homosexual couples alike usually find that sex is no better than other facets of their relationships (Matthews et al., 2006). Partners who have trouble communicating in general may also be unable to communicate their sexual desires. Couples who harbour resentments may make sex one of their conflict areas. They may not allow themselves to become aroused by their partners, or they may withhold orgasm to express their resentment (Firestone et al., 2006b).

The following hypothetical cases highlight how sexual problems or dysfunctions can develop against the backdrops of troubled relationships.

Alia and Fernando met in university, when they were both in their early twenties. After graduation, they moved into an apartment together. At first, the sexual component of their relationship was characterized by passion and discovery. After a few years, however, tensions began to build in their relationship, as conflicts around finances, when and whether they'd have children, and other domestic issues began to emerge. For Fernando, having sex with Alia was a way to restore intimacy between them, and he frequently tried to initiate sex after they argued. Alia, on the other hand, was reluctant to have sex when she and Fernando had been arguing. Even when their relationship was going well, Alia was slower to respond to sexual stimulation than Fernando. Now, as conflict in their relationship has grown, Alia finds that she has difficulty becoming aroused when they do have sex, which Fernando finds both frustrating and hurtful. Alia feels under increasing pressure to respond sexually to Fernando, as she senses that her lack of arousal is making their relationship problems worse. Both Alia and Fernando are committed to making their relationship work. What began as a series of problems in other aspects of their relationship, however, has now spread to their sexual relationship.

A Vicious Cycle.
Conflict in a relationship may dampen sexual interest, and lack of sexual interest may further strain the relationship.

Kim and Lisa have been in a relationship for several years. Kim grew up in a family with a cultural tradition that didn't accept homosexuality. She only fully accepted that she was a lesbian in her mid-thirties. Lisa, on the other hand, readily embraced her lesbian identity, and proudly came out to her friends and family when she was 16. From the beginning, Lisa took a more assertive role in most aspects of the relationship. She feels very much in touch with her sexuality, and has a clear sense of what her turn-ons are. Although Kim has always been happy that Lisa seems to be so enthusiastic about their sex life, she's been less certain about her own likes and dislikes in the bedroom, and it seems to her that she may not enjoy exactly the same sexual activities as Lisa. Over time, Kim has begun to resent Lisa, complaining that their relationship is increasingly one-sided. Kim's growing sense of resentment has spilled over into their sex life, as she's increasingly unable to have an orgasm when they have sex.

Huang and Mila are a middle-income couple in their forties with three children. Like many couples, they struggle with the financial obligations of maintaining their household. Mila has enjoyed some degree of career success, and her income has gradually increased. Huang, on the other hand, has seen his career stall, and his income has failed to grow at the same pace as Mila's. Mila and Huang frequently argue about family finances. Huang's self-esteem has declined, and he feels that Mila's putting pressure on him to pull his weight financially. Mila and Huang's sexual relationship has been reasonably satisfying for both of them, though Huang has had occasional difficulties getting and maintaining an erection when he's having sex with Mila. Lately, however, as their arguments about money have become more intense, Huang finds that he's unable to achieve an erection with Mila.

PERFORMANCE ANXIETY Anxiety—especially performance anxiety—plays an important role in sexual dysfunction (Bancroft et al., 2005b; McCabe, 2005). Performance anxiety occurs when a person becomes overly concerned with how well he or she performs a certain act or task. Performance anxiety may place a dysfunctional individual in a spectator role, rather than a performer role. Rather than focusing on erotic sensations and allowing reflexes such as erection, lubrication, and orgasm to occur naturally, the person focuses on self-doubts and thinks, "Will I be able to do it this time? Will this be another failure?"

In men, performance anxiety can either inhibit erection or trigger rapid ejaculation (Bancroft et al., 2005b; Hellstrom et al., 2006; Janssen & Bancroft, 2006). Erection is mediated by the parasympathetic nervous system, and can be blocked when anxiety activates the sympathetic nervous system. Because ejaculation, like anxiety, is mediated by the sympathetic nervous system, arousal of this system can increase the level of stimulation and heighten the potential for rapid ejaculation.

Performance anxiety can reduce vaginal lubrication and contribute to female orgasmic disorder (Goldstein et al., 2006). Women with performance anxieties may try to force orgasm, only to find that the harder they try, the more elusive it becomes.

As its name suggests, performance anxiety often involves the thought that sexual activity with a partner is a "performance," similar to what an actor does on stage or screen. When we think of sex as a performance, we're more likely to judge ourselves as performing well or inadequately. When we're able to conceptualize sex as an undemanding exchange of pleasure, rather than as a performance, we may feel less anxiety.

OTHER FACTORS Using data from the Canadian Contraception Study, researchers at the University of Western Ontario found a number of factors related to common sexual concerns in women (Gruszecki et al., 2005).

A World of Diversity

CULTURAL COMPARISONS OF SEXUAL DYSFUNCTION

Researchers conducted an international survey to determine the prevalence of sexual dysfunction among adults who were 40 to 80 years of age (Nicolosi et al., 2004). They collected data from 27 500 men and women in 29 countries.

More than 80% of the men and 65% of the women reporting that they'd had sexual intercourse during the previous year.

The most common dysfunctions for men were early ejaculation (14%) and erectile difficulties (10%). The most frequent dysfunctions for women were lack of sexual interest (21%), inability to reach orgasm (16%), and lubrication difficulties (16%).

Overall, 28% of the men and 39% of the women said that they'd been affected by at least one sexual dysfunction. The prevalence of dysfunction increased with age.

Problems with early ejaculation were most common among men in the Asian and South and Central American countries, while erectile difficulties were highest in Asia. The prevalence of erectile difficulties greatly increased with age. The highest frequencies of sexual dysfunction among women were in Asia and the Middle East (Nicolosi et al., 2004).

Vancouver researchers Jane Woo and Lori Brotto (2008) surveyed a sample of university students in British Columbia. They found that Asian Canadians had more sexual problems, such as sexual avoidance and sexual dissatisfaction.

The Asian women experienced more vaginismus and orgasm difficulties than women from European backgrounds. Those who identified more with Western culture, with open attitudes toward sex, were less likely to have these sexual problems. They also could communicate more easily with their partners about sex.

These findings suggest that people's personal beliefs about sexuality can override the general cultural beliefs of their ethnic backgrounds.

Higher body weight was associated with low sexual desire and infrequent orgasm during intercourse. These sexual issues could be due to health issues, as well as to self-esteem issues connected with body weight. Married women, older women, and those with higher levels of education were also more likely to report low desire.

Treatments for Sexual Dysfunction

The most common models in **sex therapy** are cognitive and behavioural. Sex therapy aims to modify dysfunctional cognitions (beliefs and attitudes) and behaviours as directly and as quickly as possible. Sex therapists also recognize the roles of childhood conflicts and the quality of current relationships, so they draw on various forms of therapy, as needed (Adams, 2006; Annon, 1976; Kleinplatz, 2003; Corty, 2006). Sex therapy usually involves both partners, although individual therapy is preferred in some cases. Although the particular approaches vary, sex therapy generally aims to change self-defeating beliefs and attitudes, enhance sexual knowledge, improve sexual communication, teach sexual skills, and reduce performance anxiety.

Biological treatments are now emerging for various sexual dysfunctions. Most public attention has been focused on Viagra and similar drugs, which are helpful in most cases of erectile dysfunction. Biological treatments are also being developed for rapid ejaculation, female orgasmic dysfunction, and lack of sexual desire. Research findings indicate that psychotherapy combined

Sex therapy A collective term for behavioural models for treating sexual dysfunctions.

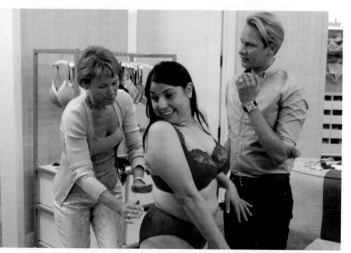

Feeling Good Naked.
Among women, higher body weight is associated with low sexual desire. The goal of the television show How to Look Good Naked *is to teach women to love their bodies, no matter what imperfections they believe they have. The show features overweight women who appear in bras and panties.*

with medical treatments such as drugs for erectile dysfunction can be more effective than medicine alone (Aubin et al., 2009).

An important issue in therapy is gender. Many therapists have adopted feminist perspectives in order to challenge sexist ways of thinking. Calgary therapists Mary Valentich and James Gripton (1992) have broadened this approach to encompass a gender-sensitive practise. This involves analyzing gender issues facing both women and men, and critiquing how traditional gender roles restrict sexual fulfillment for both genders. Such analysis encourages people to find their own ways of expressing love and sex, so they don't have to follow the traditional gender scripts.

Now let's explore the psychological and behavioural approaches to the treatment of sexual dysfunction.

The PLISSIT Model

Developed by Annon (1976), the PLISSIT model is used by many therapists to address the sexual concerns of their clients (Ohl, 2007; Timm, 2009). This model allows health professionals and their clients to differentiate between sexual problems that can be resolved through basic education and counselling and problems that require intensive or specialized sex therapy.

The PLISSIT model consists of four escalating levels:

- *Permission* (P)—At the first level, the therapist gives the client permission to talk about sexuality and personal concerns. The therapist often asks exploratory questions, to bring out the relevant issues and put the client at ease.
- *Limited information* (LI)—Some sexual problems may be rooted in myths and misinformation about sexuality. Providing a limited amount of correct information about sexual functioning is often a key step in resolving a problem.
- *Specific suggestions* (SS)—Once the basic nature of a sexual problem is identified, the therapist provides suggestions to help resolve it. The client may be encouraged to read books about sexual enhancement, for example, such as sex manuals, or to watch instructional sex videos. With a basic understanding of the client's sexual issues, the therapist may also make specific suggestions for incorporating specific sexual techniques, or suggest ways the couple can refocus their sexual interaction.
- *Intensive therapy* (IT)—If the first three levels of therapy are unsuccessful in solving the problem, a more intensive form of sex therapy may be required. At this point, a therapist who doesn't specialize in sex therapy will refer the client to someone with advanced training in treating sexual dysfunction.

The Masters and Johnson Approach

Masters and Johnson pioneered the use of direct behavioural approaches to treating sexual dysfunction (Masters & Johnson, 1970). A female-and-male therapy team focuses on the couple as the unit of treatment during a two-week residential program. Masters and Johnson considered the couple dysfunctional, not the individual. A couple may describe the male partner's erectile disorder as the problem, but it's likely to have led to other problems by the time the couple seeks therapy. Similarly, a man whose female partner has an orgasmic disorder is likely to be anxious about his ability to provide effective sexual stimulation.

Masters and Johnson developed their approach with heterosexual couples, so it's uncertain how well it applies to same-sex couples. There's no reason, however, to believe a focus on couple dynamics would be less effective with lesbian and gay couples than with heterosexuals.

In this approach, anxieties and resentments are aired, but the focus of treatment is behavioural change. A couple performs daily sexual homework assignments, such as **sensate-focus exercises**, in the privacy of their own room.

Sensate-focus exercises
Exercises in which sexual partners take turns giving and receiving pleasurable stimulation in non-genital areas.

Sensate-focus sessions are carried out in the nude. Partners take turns giving and receiving stimulation in non-genital areas. Without touching the breasts or genitals, the giver massages or fondles the receiving partner, to provide pleasure under relaxing, undemanding conditions. Because genital activity is restricted, there's no pressure to "perform." The giving partner is free to engage in trial-and-error learning about the receiving partner's sensate preferences. The receiving partner is free to enjoy the experience, without feeling rushed to reciprocate or obliged to respond by becoming sexually aroused. The receiving partner's only responsibility is to direct the giving partner, as needed.

In addition to these general sensate-focus exercises, Masters and Johnson used specific assignments to help couples overcome particular sexual dysfunctions.

Working with LGB Couples.
Therapists who work with LGB couples find many problems akin to those of heterosexual couples, but some problems reflect the couple's sexual orientation. Examples include LGB identity development and gay parenthood.

Integrating Sex Therapy and Psychotherapy

Sex therapy has cognitive components, such as the need to address self-defeating attitudes and expectations and to provide sex education. Because sexual activity is so often embedded in relationships, many therapists (e.g., Coyle, 2006;

Applied Knowledge

HOW DO YOU FIND A QUALIFIED SEX THERAPIST?

How do you locate a sex therapist, if you think you have a sexual dysfunction?

Since the provinces don't regulate use of the term "sex therapist," it's essential to determine that a sex therapist is a member of a recognized profession—such as psychology, social work, medicine, or marriage and family counseling—and has had training and supervision in sex therapy.

Professionals are usually licensed or certified by their provinces. All provinces require licensing of psychologists and physicians, but some don't license social workers or marriage counsellors. Only physicians are permitted to bill their provincial health plans for providing sex therapy.

If you're uncertain how to locate a qualified sex therapist in your area, contact your

university or college psychology department, health department, or counselling centre, a medical or psychological association, a marriage and family therapy association, or a family physician.

Relatively few people in Canada have been trained as specialists in sex therapy. The only Canadian organization that certifies sex therapists is the Board of Examiners in Sex Therapy and Counselling in Ontario (BESTCO), which includes professionals from diverse backgrounds with clinical expertise in human sexual concerns.

Some Canadian therapists are also certified by American-based organizations such as the American Association of Sex Educators, Counselors, and Therapists (AASECT) and the Society for Sex Therapy and Research (SSTAR).

It's a good idea to ask a therapist the following:

- What discipline(s) has s/he been educated in?
- Where did s/he earn degrees, and what are those degrees?
- Is s/he licensed or certified?
- What fees does s/he charge?
- What treatment plans does s/he use?
- What training has s/he received in human sexuality and sex therapy?

These questions are important because there's such a wide diversity in professional backgrounds and training for sex therapists. Accordingly, the types of treatments and services they offer vary enormously (Kleinplatz, 2003). If the therapist becomes uncomfortable, asks why you're asking such questions, or fails to provide a direct answer, beware.

Remember, under no circumstances is it ethical for a professional therapist to engage in any form of sexual activity with a client.

McCarthy et al., 2004, 2006) use psychotherapy and couples therapy to help couples learn how to share power, improve sexual communication, and negotiate differences. The combination of sex therapy and couples therapy appears to be a powerful tool for enhancing relationships as well as sex lives.

Helen Singer Kaplan (1974) combined sex therapy with psychoanalytic methods. She saw sexual dysfunctions as having immediate causes and remote causes (i.e., conflicts that dated to childhood). As a sex therapist, Kaplan focused on improving a couple's sexual communication, eliminating performance anxiety, and fostering sexual skills and knowledge. As a psychoanalyst, she used insight-oriented therapy when it appeared that remote issues impaired a client's response to sex therapy. By so doing, she aimed to bring to awareness unconscious conflicts that might have stifled the person's sexual desire or response.

Treatments for Sexual-Desire Disorders

Some sex therapists help kindle sexual appetites in people with hypoactive sexual desire by prescribing self-stimulation exercises combined with erotic fantasies. Sex therapists also assist dysfunctional couples by prescribing sensate-focus exercises, enhancing communication, and expanding the couples' repertoires of sexual skills. Sex therapists recognize that hypoactive sexual desire is often a complex problem that requires more intensive treatment than problems of the arousal or orgasm phases. Helen Singer Kaplan (1987) argued that insight-oriented approaches were especially helpful in treating hypoactive sexual desire and sexual aversion, by uncovering and resolving deep-seated psychological conflicts.

Some cases of hypoactive sexual desire in men involve hormonal deficiencies, especially deficiencies in testosterone. But testosterone replacement therapy works with only about half of men who have low testosterone levels (Rakic et al., 1997). Among women, as among men, lack of sexual desire can be connected with low levels of androgens. One study of post-menopausal women found that after using testosterone patches of various doses for 24 weeks, women taking 150 micrograms of testosterone had a mean increase of 1.2 satisfying sexual episodes per four-week period, whereas women taking 300 micrograms testosterone had a mean increase of 2.1 episodes over the same period (Davis et al., 2008). Those using the patch also experienced heightened sexual desire.

When lack of desire is connected with depression, sexual interest may rebound when the depression lifts. Treatment in such cases may involve psychotherapy, rather than sex therapy. When problems in the relationship are involved, couples therapy may be required, to improve the relationship. Once interpersonal problems are ironed out, sexual interest may return.

Treatment of sexual-aversion disorder may involve a multi-faceted approach, including biological treatment, such as a medication to reduce anxiety, and psychological treatment designed to help the individual overcome the underlying sexual phobia. Couples therapy may be used in cases where sexual aversions arise from relationship problems. Sensate-focus exercises may be used to lessen generalized anxiety about sexual contact. But fears of specific aspects of the sexual act may need to be overcome through behavioural exercises in which the clients learn to manage the stimuli that evoke fears of sexual contact.

Treatments for Sexual-Arousal Disorders

Men with chronic erectile disorder may believe they've "forgotten" how to have erections. Erection is an involuntary reflex, however, not a skill.

In sex therapy, women who have trouble becoming lubricated and men who have erectile problems learn that they needn't do anything to become sexually aroused. As long as their problems are psychologically and not organically based,

Figure 13.1 **A behavioural approach to treating erectile disorder.**
In one part of a program designed to overcome erectile disorder, a man's partner repeatedly teases him to erection and allows the erection to subside. This avoids the creation of performance anxiety that could lead to his losing the erection. Through repeatedly regaining his erection, the man loses his fear that losing an erection means it won't return.

they need only receive sexual stimulation under relaxed circumstances, so anxiety doesn't inhibit their natural reflexes.

To reduce performance anxiety, the partners engage in undemanding sexual contacts that don't demand lubrication or erection. They may start with non-genital sensate-focus exercises, in the style of Masters and Johnson. After a couple of sessions, sensate focus extends to the genitals. The position shown in Figure 13.1 allows the woman easy access to her partner's genitals. She repeatedly teases him to erection and allows the erection to subside. She thereby avoids creating performance anxiety that could lead to erection loss. By repeatedly regaining his erection, the man loses his fear that losing an erection means it won't return. He also learns to focus on erotic sensations for their own sake. He experiences no demand to perform, because the couple is instructed to refrain from intercourse.

Even when the dysfunctional partner can reliably become sexually excited (denoted by erection in the male and lubrication in the female), the couple doesn't immediately attempt intercourse; this might rekindle performance anxiety. Rather, they engage in a series of undemanding, pleasurable sexual activities, which eventually culminates in intercourse if that's what they desire.

With Masters and Johnson's approach, the couple begin intercourse after about 10 days of treatment. The woman teases the man to erection while she sits above him, straddling his thighs. When he's erect, she inserts the penis (to avoid fumbling attempts at entry) and moves slowly back and forth in an undemanding way. Neither attempts to reach orgasm. If the man loses his erection, the two repeat the teasing and intercourse. Once the partners become confident that the man can retain his erection—or reinstate it, if he loses it—they may gradually increase coital thrusting, to reach orgasm.

ERECTILE DISORDER The world's attention has recently been focused on biological approaches to treating erectile disorder. Biological or biomedical approaches can be helpful, especially when organic factors are involved.

Oral medications are by far the most popular biological treatment for erectile problems. Oral forms of several compounds—sildenafil (Viagra), vardenafil (Levitra), and tadalafil (Cialis)—relax the muscles that surround the small blood vessels in the penis, allowing them to dilate so blood can flow into them more freely. After taking the drug, a man must still be aroused through manual, oral, or other stimulation for an erection to occur. The amount of time it takes to become effective varies with the drug. Viagra can become effective within half an hour, and is effective for up to four hours. The oral form of tadalafil (Cialis) becomes effective in about half an hour and lasts for up to 36 hours. Users in France have dubbed it "the weekender."

The most common side effects of these drugs are facial flushing, stuffy nose, and headache, sometimes including migraine. These drugs shouldn't be used by individuals taking any type of nitrate drug, such as nitroglycerine, due to the risk of developing potentially life-threatening low blood pressure.

Viagra was hailed as an important new treatment for erectile dysfunction when it hit the market in early 1998. A study published in the *New England Journal of Medicine* tested the effects of Viagra on more than 800 men with erectile dysfunction caused by both psychological and organic factors (Goldstein et al., 1998). In one phase of the study, 69% of attempts to engage in intercourse were successful for men taking Viagra, compared to 22% for men taking a placebo. A Canadian study (Carrier et al., 2005) found that Viagra was still effective for men who had been taking it for three years. There's ample evidence that these oral medications are effective for most men (Hatzichristou et al., 2000, 2005).

Applied Knowledge

THINKING CRITICALLY ABOUT BUYING DRUGS ONLINE

Viagra, Levitra, and Cialis are prescription drugs. Many men who might otherwise use them are reluctant to discuss erectile dysfunction with their physicians. The anonymity of doing things on the internet is therefore a lure—you don't have to admit your personal worries to your doctor face to face, or feel embarrassment about asking for an erectile dysfunction drug. Some men don't even have regular physicians. What to do?

Many have discovered that by searching for Viagra on the internet, they can find many websites where they can "consult" with online physicians, obtain a prescription, and order the drug for home delivery. Easy! A few questions and a fee, and they've got it.

But is it wise?

Prescriptions are needed for various drugs because physicians are better equipped than lay people to diagnose individuals' health problems, understand the chemical natures and side effects of the drugs available for treatment, and predict how the drugs will affect individual patients. Physicians are also usually prepared to deal with the unexpected effects of the drugs—and there can be many.

Ask yourself what kind of physician will prescribe drugs online, without personally examining the patient to determine his health status and the appropriateness and safety of specific treatments for him. If you have a question about the drug once you use it, or if you experience side effects, will you be able to get back to the prescriber easily for an answer, or will you wind up making an embarrassed call to your own physician—or a trip to the emergency room?

There's also the possibility that when you buy prescription drugs online, you'll become the victim of a scam in which an unscrupulous website sells fake pills that may contain harmful substances.

While surfing the net, you may also come across sites that claim to have "natural"

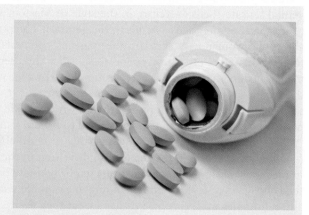

The Lure of Online Drugs.
You might like the idea of not having to talk to a physician face to face, but how trustworthy is an online source? Does the "expert" behind the website understand how it will affect you in light of your particular medical history? Is the drug even real? Is it safe?

preparations (including a variety of herbs) that are as effective as Viagra, but without the side effects and without the need for a prescription. Use some critical thinking: are you convinced of the effectiveness and safety of these preparations? Many of them escape the scrutiny of government regulators—the government isn't watching over them. Be warned.

Even if it's convenient to buy a drug online, you're well advised to get your prescription face to face from a doctor who knows your specific medical history.

In a study by the University of Western Ontario's Bill Fisher and his colleagues (2005), many women whose partners had erectile dysfunction reported that they experienced lower levels of sexual desire, arousal, orgasm, and sexual satisfaction. A significant proportion of the women whose partners used an erection drug experienced increased sexual desire, arousal, and orgasm.

Hormone treatments can also be effective in some cases. Testosterone helps restore the sex drive and erectile ability in many men who have abnormally low levels of testosterone (Lue, 2000; Rakic et al., 1997). There's no evidence that hormone therapy helps men who already have normal hormone levels.

Various other treatments are available, such as vascular surgery on the penis, penile implants (Figure 13.2), penile injections, penile suppositories, and a vacuum pump held over the penis to increase blood flow. Relatively few men use these techniques, however, because they're not very practical or comfortable to use.

FEMALE SEXUAL-AROUSAL DISORDER Psychological treatments for female sexual-arousal disorder typically parallel those for orgasmic disorder. They involve sex education (identifying the parts of the body involved in sexual response, discussing their functions, and explaining how to arouse them), searching out and coping with possible cognitive interference (such as negative sexual attitudes), creating undemanding situations in which sexual arousal may occur, and—when appropriate—working on problems in the relationship.

Yet many cases of female sexual-arousal disorder reflect impaired blood flow to the genitals, just as erectile disorder does. Female sexual arousal involves vaginal lubrication, which permits sexual activity without a great deal of painful friction. Lubrication is made possible by vasocongestion—the flow of blood into the genitals. Lack of lubrication can reflect the physical effects of aging, menopause, or surgically induced menopause.

Sometimes all that's necessary to deal with lack of lubrication is an artificial lubricant such as K-Y Jelly. But lessened blood flow to the genitals can also sap sexual pleasure, and thereby lessen a woman's desire for sex.

The development of effective biological treatments for female sexual dysfunction has lagged behind the development of treatments for men. Some have speculated that this is because female sexual response tends to be tied more directly

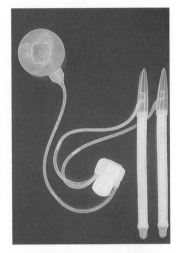

Figure 13.2 A penile implant.
A penile implant provides erection when a man's cardiovascular system doesn't do the job. Cylinders are implanted in the penis and a fluid reservoir (shown at top left) is placed near the bladder. A pump (shown in lower middle) is typically inserted in the scrotum. Squeezing the pump forces fluid into the cylinders, inflating the penis. Tripping a release valve later returns the fluid to the reservoir, deflating the penis.

Applied Knowledge

PROMOTING EROTICISM IN SEX THERAPY

Ottawa sex therapist Peggy Kleinplatz (2003) has developed an innovative approach to sex therapy. She argues that most sex therapy is too focused on treating symptoms and solving problems, and should focus instead on personal growth, which includes enhancing sexual relationships and erotic potential.

Kleinplatz is especially concerned about the focus on pills and devices. She argues that the medical model emphasizes performance measures such as frequency and firmness of erections, and ignores the quality of interactions (e.g., satisfaction, intimacy).

Kleinplatz presents a thorough critique of the field of sex therapy in her 2001 book *New Directions in Sex Therapy: Innovations and Alternatives*. She believes many therapists are personally uncomfortable with promoting eroticism, and attempt only to enable couples to engage in the mechanics of sexual intercourse, rather than helping them maximize sexual pleasure (Kleinplatz, 2001). This mechanical approach results in sexual boredom for many couples, who come to rely on specific routines for achieving orgasm and are then afraid to risk trying new, possibly more fulfilling approaches.

According to Kleinplatz (2003), many people want to excite their partners and establish deep, sensual connections that will bring more intense sexual ecstasy. Eroticism, in her view, is the key to maintaining sexual desire. The erotic encounter should focus on pleasure for its own sake, rather than on the tension release of orgasm (Kleinplatz, 2003).

Figure 13.3 A clitoral device for stimulating vasocongestion.
This device works by creating gentle suction over the clitoris, stimulating blood flow into the woman's genitals. This allows vaginal lubrication, which in turn facilitates sexual activity.

to psychosocial influences, such as relationship factors. Nevertheless, researchers continue to search for medical treatments to enhance female arousal. For example, researchers are investigating the use of alprostadil (a vasodilator) for use with women, in the form of a cream that's inserted into the vagina to enhance the flow of blood and hence lubrication. Other biological treatments for women include testosterone skin patches. There's even a device called Eros that creates gentle suction over the clitoris, increasing vasocongestion and sexual sensations. (See Figure 13.3.)

After Viagra was shown to be highly effective in treating erectile dysfunction in men, researchers began investigating the potential benefits of Viagra for women. Reviews of the research have not shown a consistent positive effect of Viagra in women with arousal disorders (Chivers & Rosen, 2010). However, the research does indicate that Viagra may be useful for women who experience arousal difficulties caused by antidepressant medications (Nurnberg et al., 2008).

Canadian sex therapists Peggy Kleinplatz (2003) and Rosemary Basson (2000) have been vocal in their opposition to what they view as the medicalization of female sexuality. Indeed, other factors are often involved in sexual dysfunction, including intimacy and relationship issues, and if these aren't addressed, the sexual problems will likely persist.

Orgasmic Disorders

FEMALE ORGASMIC DISORDER Women who have never experienced orgasm often harbour negative attitudes about sex that cause anxiety and inhibit sexual response. Treatment in such cases may first address these attitudes.

The Masters and Johnson method is a couples-oriented approach to treating anorgasmic women. It begins with sensate-focus exercises. Then, during genital massage and later during intercourse, the woman guides her partner in the caresses and movements she finds sexually exciting. Taking charge helps free the woman from the traditional stereotype of the passive, subordinate female role.

The Masters and Johnson approach recommends a training position (see Figure 13.4) that gives the man access to his partner's breasts and genitals. She can guide his hands, to show him the types of stimulation she enjoys. The genital play is *undemanding*. The goal is to learn to provide and enjoy effective sexual stimulation, not to reach orgasm. The clitoris is not stimulated early, because doing so may produce a high level of stimulation before the woman is prepared.

After a number of occasions of genital play, the couple has intercourse in the female-superior position. (See Figure 13.5.) This position allows the woman

Figure 13.4 The training position for undemanding stimulation of the female genitals.
This position gives the woman's partner access to her breasts and genitals. She can guide her partner's hands, to show him what types of stimulation she enjoys.

Figure 13.5 The female-superior position.
In treatment for female orgasmic disorder, the couple has intercourse in the female-superior position after a number of occasions of genital play. This position allows the woman freedom of movement and control over her genital sensations. She's told to regard the penis as her toy. She and her partner engage in several sessions of deliberately slow thrusting, to sensitize the woman to sensations produced by the penis and to break the common, counterproductive pattern of desperate, rapid thrusting.

freedom of movement and control over her genital sensations. She is told to regard the penis as her toy. She and her partner engage in several sessions of deliberately slow thrusting, to sensitize her to sensations produced by the penis and to break the common, counterproductive pattern of desperate, rapid thrusting.

Orgasm cannot be willed or forced. When a woman receives effective stimulation, feels free to focus on erotic sensations, and feels that nothing is being demanded of her, she will generally reach orgasm. Once she's able to attain orgasm in the female-superior position, she and her partner may extend their sexual repertoire to other positions.

Masters and Johnson preferred working with the couple in cases of anorgasmia. Other sex therapists prefer to begin working with the woman individually, and suggest masturbation as therapy. Masters and Johnson worked with heterosexual couples, but placing the focus on undemanding genital play may be equally applicable to lesbian couples in which one of the partners has difficulty reaching orgasm.

Masturbation allows individuals to get in touch with their sexual responses at their own pace. Many sex therapists recommend that women having difficulty with orgasm focus on masturbation. It frees them of the need to rely on or please a partner. The sexual pleasure they experience helps counter lingering sexual anxieties. Although there is some variation, the following elements are commonly found in directed masturbation programs for women:

- *Education*—The woman and her partner (if she has one) are educated about female sexuality.
- *Self-exploration*—Self-exploration is encouraged as a way of increasing the woman's sense of body awareness. She may hold a mirror between her legs to locate her sexual anatomic features.
- *Self-massage*—The woman creates a private, relaxing setting for self-massage. She begins to explore the sensitivity of her body to touch, discovering and repeating the caresses she finds pleasurable. She may use non-alcohol-based oils and lotions to enhance the sensuous quality of the massage and provide lubrication for the external genitalia. To prevent performance anxiety, the woman doesn't attempt to reach orgasm during the first few occasions.
- *Self-permission*—The woman may be advised to challenge lingering guilt and anxiety about sex in general and self-pleasuring in particular. For example, she might reassure herself that experiencing sexual pleasure is a natural and positive part of life, giving herself permission to enjoy it.

- *Fantasy*—Arousal is heightened through the use of sexual images, fantasies, and fantasy aids, such as erotic books or videos.
- *A vibrator*—Millions of women use vibrators, either during solo masturbation or with their partners. Because a vibrator may provide more intense stimulation, they can be useful for women seeking to have orgasms more easily.
- *Partner involvement*—After the woman is capable of regularly achieving orgasm through masturbation, the focus may shift to her sexual relationship with her partner. She can teach her partner how to stimulate her in ways that enable her to reach orgasm.

Our focus has been on sexual techniques, but a combination of approaches that focus on sexual techniques and underlying interpersonal problems may be more effective than focusing on sexual techniques alone, at least for couples whose relationships are troubled.

MALE ORGASMIC DISORDER Treatment of male orgasmic disorder generally focuses on increasing sexual stimulation and reducing performance anxiety. The Masters and Johnson approach has the couple practise sensate-focus exercises for several days, during which the man makes no attempt to ejaculate. The couple is then instructed to bring him to orgasm any way they can, usually by having the partner stroke the man's penis. Once he can ejaculate in his partner's presence, the partner brings him to the point at which he's about to ejaculate. Then, if the couple is heterosexual, they use the female-superior position, with the woman thrusting vigorously to bring him to orgasm.

RAPID EJACULATION In the Masters and Johnson approach, sensate-focus exercises are followed by practise in the training position shown in Figure 13.1. The partner teases the man to erection, and uses the **squeeze technique** when he indicates that he's about to ejaculate. The partner holds the penis between the thumb and the first two fingers of one hand. The thumb presses against the frenulum. The fingers straddle the coronal ridge on the other side of the penis. Squeezing the thumb and forefingers together fairly hard for about 20 seconds (or until the man's urge to ejaculate passes) prevents ejaculation. The erect penis can withstand fairly strong pressure without discomfort, but erection may be partially lost. The couple repeats this process three or four times in a 15- to 20-minute session before the man purposely ejaculates.

After two or three days of these sessions, the couple is instructed to begin intercourse in the female-superior position, because it creates less pressure to ejaculate. The woman inserts the penis. At first she contains it without thrusting, allowing the man to get used to intravaginal sensations. If he signals that he's about to ejaculate, she lifts off and squeezes his penis. After some repetitions, she begins slowly to move backward and forward, lifting off and squeezing as needed. The man gradually learns to tolerate higher levels of sexual stimulation without ejaculating.

The alternating stop-start method for treating premature ejaculation was introduced by urologist James Semans (1956). The method can be applied to manual stimulation or intercourse. For example, the partner can manually stimulate the penis until the man is about to ejaculate. He then signals his partner to suspend sexual stimulation, and allows his arousal to subside before stimulation is resumed. This process enables him to recognize the cues that precede his point of ejaculatory inevitability, or point of no return, and to tolerate longer periods of sexual stimulation.

When the stop-start technique is applied to intercourse, the partners begin with simple vaginal containment, with no pelvic thrusting, preferably in the female-superior position. The man withdraws if he feels he's about to ejaculate. As the man's sense of control increases, thrusting can begin, along with variations in intercourse positions. They again stop when the man signals that he's approaching ejaculatory inevitability.

Gay men sometimes face problems with premature ejaculation when engaging in anal sex. Their partners can also try either the squeeze technique or the stop-start method.

Squeeze technique A method for treating premature ejaculation. The tip of the penis is squeezed, to temporarily prevent ejaculation.

Although the squeeze and stop-start techniques have been widely recommended as methods to alleviate rapid ejaculation, there's little research showing that they're effective, particularly for men with severe or persistent cases (Sharlip, 2005). While these techniques may be more useful for men with mild cases of rapid ejaculation, emphasis is increasingly being placed on biological treatments.

BIOLOGICAL TREATMENTS FOR RAPID EJACULATION Some drugs that are usually used to treat psychological problems can be effective in treating premature ejaculation (Bancroft et al., 2005b, 2005c). Clomipramine, which is used to treat obsessive-compulsive disorder and schizophrenia, can impair erectile response at high doses. But in a study with 15 couples, low doses helped men engage in intercourse five times longer than usual without ejaculating (Althof, 1994). Antidepressant drugs have also been helpful in the treatment of rapid ejaculation (Waldinger et al., 2001, 2002; Meston & Frohlich, 2000).

Why do drugs used to treat psychological problems help with rapid ejaculation? The psychological problems are frequently connected with imbalances in body chemicals, such as neurotransmitters—the chemical messengers of the brain. Neurotransmitters are also involved in other bodily functions, including ejaculation. Anti-depressant drugs all work by increasing the action of the neurotransmitter serotonin. Serotonin, in turn, may inhibit the ejaculatory reflex (Meston & Frohlich, 2000; Shipko, 2000). But note the cautions about using SSRIs we discussed earlier in the chapter!

Treatments for Sexual-Pain Disorders

DYSPAREUNIA Dyspareunia, or painful intercourse, generally calls for medical intervention, to identify and treat any underlying physical problems that might cause pain, such as urinary-tract infections. When dyspareunia is caused by vaginismus, treatment through the behavioural approach we'll describe next may reduce pain.

VAGINISMUS Vaginismus is generally treated with behavioural exercises in which plastic vaginal dilators of increasing size are inserted to help relax the vaginal musculature. A gynecologist may first demonstrate insertion of the narrowest dilator. Later, the woman practises inserting wider dilators at home. She increases the size of the dilator as she becomes capable of tolerating insertion and containment for 10 or 15 minutes without discomfort or pain.

Innovative Canadian Research

TREATMENT FOR DYSPAREUNIA

A team of Canadian and American researchers led by Sophie Bergeron and Yitzchak Binik of McGill University (Bergeron et al., 2001) has conducted controlled studies of the effectiveness of three types of treatment programs for dyspareunia resulting from vulvar vestibulitis (a sharp, burning pain experienced when direct pressure is applied just inside the vaginal opening). The three approaches were cognitive-behavioural therapy, biofeedback, and surgery involving the excision of the vestibular area.

While each treatment resulted in pain reduction, the surgery had the highest success rate. The three treatment approaches were equally successful in improving psychological adjustment and sexual functioning. The researchers noted, however, that some of the women who were assigned to the surgical treatment refused to go ahead with that intervention.

The findings indicate that both psychological and surgical interventions can be useful in the treatment of dyspareunia.

Sophie Bergeron and others from the University of Quebec (Bergeron et al., 2008) did a follow-up study with participants from the original sample. Treatment gains were still maintained for each intervention.

Over this longer period, however, cognitive-behavioural therapy was found to be as effective as surgery in reducing levels of reported pain during intercourse. Women who held negative attitudes toward sex and sexual pleasure responded less favourably to the surgery.

The woman herself—not her partner or her therapist—controls the pace of treatment. The woman's or her partner's fingers (first the littlest finger, then two fingers, and so on) may be used in place of the plastic dilators, with the woman controlling the speed and depth of penetration. When the woman is able to tolerate dilators (or fingers) equivalent in thickness to a penis or dildo, the couple may attempt penetration. Still, the woman should control insertion. Circumstances should be relaxed and undemanding. The idea is to avoid re-sensitizing her to fears of penetration.

Because vaginismus often occurs among women with histories of sexual trauma, such as rape or incest, treatment may also be in order for the psychological effects of these experiences (Crowley et al., 2006).

Innovative Canadian Research

A PORTRAIT OF GREAT SEX

Most research on human sexuality focuses on sexual problems, rather than sexual pleasure. In contrast, Ottawa researcher Peggy Kleinplatz and her colleagues (2009) interviewed people who reported experiencing "great sex" with the objective of building a conceptual model that would outline the key characteristics of optimal sexuality.

Many of the people participating in the study were over the age of 60, and some had been in relationships for 25 years or longer. In describing great sex, many of them were drawing on several decades of experience with sex and relationships. Perhaps younger people have something to learn from the wisdom of those with more experience.

Eight major components of great sex emerged from the interviews.

- *Being present, focused, and embodied*—The most basic characteristic of great sex was being totally immersed in and intensely focused on the experience. This led to total surrender of the body to the experience, without any other distracting thoughts.
- *Connection, or being in sync*—A strong sense of connection and a feeling of synchronicity was an important component of great sex for many of the participants. As one woman said, it's a feeling of "two people being in the right head space at the right time together, being able to share that" (Kleinplatz et al., 2009, p. 6).
- *Deep sexual and erotic intimacy*—Regardless of whether the sexual encounters occurred in long-term or other kinds of relationships, there was a powerful sense of intimate engagement and trust in the relationships. As one participant suggested, "It's part of the way you act with each other long before you're actually engaged in any kind of, you know, technical sex" (Kleinplatz et al., 2009, p. 6).

- *Extraordinary communication and heightened empathy*—Being able to communicate, both verbally and nonverbally, and being tuned in to their partners' responses were seen by some as crucial to great sex.
- *Authenticity*—Participants felt they could be free to be themselves and open about their own desires. They spoke of feeling totally uninhibited and transparent.
- *Transcendence and transformation*—Some participants indicated that great sex was a "high" similar to what can be experienced through meditation. Others noted that great sex with a partner could be transformative, carrying over in a positive way to other aspects of life.
- *Exploration and interpersonal risk-taking*—Great sex was seen as an ongoing process of discovery, with the partners continuing to explore their sexuality over time. This required taking some personal risks in exploring new things. Many participants stressed that sexual exploration was done with a sense of fun and humour.
- *Vulnerability*—Freely allowing themselves to be vulnerable was, for some participants, an important aspect of great sex. An older male participant believed vulnerability was what distinguished good from great sex:

> In normal good sex or good relationships, I think there's always some maybe small but detectable barriers, some things held back. In great sex, I think those for me disappear, and so that one is quite transparent to the other person, and therefore quite vulnerable, but it feels, it goes with an intensely erotic and good feeling, rather than a scary feeling (Kleinplatz et al., 2009, p. 9).

The participants emphasized that they had developed their ability to experience great sex over time, in some cases many years. For many, their perceptions of great sex changed with their life experiences and personal growth.

A World of Diversity

AN ALTERNATIVE APPROACH TO ENHANCING FEMALE SEXUALITY

by Lori A. Brotto, PhD, Department of Obstetrics and Gynaecology, University of British Columbia

Treatment approaches designed to help women with sexual problems have generally focused on improving sexual response.

A healthy sexual response, however, doesn't necessarily signify overall sexual satisfaction or lack of sexual distress. Specifically, 5.5% of American women aged 30 to 79 report that sexual activity is unsatisfying (Lutfey et al., 2008), despite the fact that they experience no difficulties with desire, arousal, or orgasm.

In the Global Study of Sexual Attitudes and Behaviors (Laumann et al., 2005), 8% to 18% of the 40- to 80-year-old women reported not finding sex pleasurable. Some women therefore weren't sexually satisfied, even though the mechanics of sexual response were operating, and the women didn't meet the criteria for a sexual dysfunction as defined by DSM-4 (American Psychiatric Association, 2000).

These women (Ogden et al., 2007) described their sexual experiences as boring, dry, and unemotional. In response to this situation, Ogden and others (2007) have called for a non-goal-oriented, spiritual element to sexuality.

Eastern techniques, with their origins in the *Kama Sutra* of the fourth to sixth centuries, might provide some of the spiritual dimensions the traditional Western approaches lack. One Eastern technique that might improve women's sexuality is mindfulness.

Mindful Meditation

Mindfulness involves nonjudgmental, present-moment awareness. It has roots in Buddhist meditation. Although it's a non-religious practise, transcending all organized religions, it does have a spiritual component (Carmody et al., 2008).

Recently, mindfulness has been incorporated into a brief, psycho-educational treatment program for women with disorders of sexual desire and arousal, and found to be effective as part of a larger treatment program that includes education, cognitive and behavioural skills, and couples-therapy exercises. In the study, women who used a combination of in-session and at-home exercises evaluated the mindfulness component as the most valuable aspect of treatment (Brotto & Heiman, 2007).

Specifically, mindfulness was introduced to women by giving them instructions about how to be mindful in their nonsexual lives. They were introduced to the topic with the following:

Many of us go through life not living in the present moment. We fluctuate between thinking in the future (worrying, planning, thinking), and living in the past (reviewing past events, conversations, plans). We miss out on valuable and meaningful experiences in the present. We have evolved to multi-task, and this reinforces mindlessness. However, in instances when we wish to be present, such as the sexual scenario, it's difficult if not impossible for us to turn off the cerebral chatter. The net effect is a reduction in arousal, thereby making the sexual experience less rewarding and pleasurable.

The heart of mindfulness is practising the body scan exercise, which involves attending to the sensations in specific parts of the body. Women can practise the body scan a few times a week, in addition to practising mindfulness every day, usually for 10 minutes, during other activities (e.g., eating, driving, having a conversation, playing a sport or instrument).

They're also given a set of body-focused mindfulness exercises to practise at home.

The first is a focusing exercise. The women are asked to visually attend to their bodies during and after their baths or showers. They're encouraged to describe what they see in nonjudgmental ways, and given a list of possible statements to repeat during the exercise, such as "My body is my own," "My body is alive," and "I appreciate the following aspects of my body."

The self-observation exercise asks women to use hand-held mirrors to observe their genitals. They're reminded that this is a nonsexual exercise, with the goal of allowing them to remain in the present while letting any judgments about themselves, their bodies, or how they're struggling with the exercise to float away.

The self-observation and touch exercise asks women to gently touch their own genitals while repeating the self-observation exercise.

After some weeks of practise, a sexual goal is added. The woman is encouraged to repeat the self-observation-and-touch exercise while imagining herself as a competent sexual, feminine, sensual woman. There's then a discussion about incorporating mindfulness while being sexual, either alone or with a partner.

Two studies have tested the efficacy of a mindfulness-based sex therapy intervention for women with low desire and arousal. Both studies found a significant improvement in sexual response and a decrease in sexual distress (Brotto, Basson, & Luria, 2008; Brotto et al., 2008).

Mindfulness techniques therefore show great promise in treating women's sexual concerns, and may fill the spiritual gap for some women who have unsatisfying sexual experiences.

Summing Up

A sexual dysfunction is a difficulty with sexual desire, arousal, or orgasm.

Sexual-desire disorders involve dysfunctions in sexual desire, interest, or drive. The individuals experience a lack of sexual desire or an aversion to genital sexual contact.

In men, sexual-arousal disorders involve recurrent difficulty in getting or sustaining erections sufficient to successfully engage in sexual intercourse. In women, they typically involve failure to become sufficiently lubricated.

Women are more likely to encounter difficulties reaching orgasm, and men are more likely to have trouble with rapid ejaculation.

Sexual pain disorders include dyspareunia, vaginismus, and vulvodynia.

Many sexual dysfunctions involve the interaction of organic and psychological factors.

Fatigue may lead to erectile disorder in men, and to orgasmic disorder and dyspareunia in women. Dyspareunia often reflects vaginal infections and STIs. Organic factors are believed to be involved in the majority of cases of erectile disorder. Medications and other drugs may also impair sexual functioning.

Psychosocial factors connected with sexual dysfunction include cultural influences, psychosexual traumas, marital dissatisfaction, psychological conflicts, lack of sexual skills, irrational beliefs, and performance anxiety.

Performance anxiety may place a dysfunctional individual into a spectator role, rather than a performer role.

Sex therapy aims to modify behaviours directly by changing self-defeating beliefs and attitudes, fostering sexual skills and knowledge, enhancing sexual communication, and providing behavioural exercises to enhance sexual stimulation while reducing performance anxiety.

Masters and Johnson pioneered the direct, behavioural approach to treating sexual dysfunction.

Some sex therapists help kindle sexual appetites in people with inhibited sexual desire by prescribing self-stimulation exercises combined with erotic fantasies.

Men and women with impaired sexual arousal receive sexual stimulation from their partners under relaxed circumstances, so anxiety doesn't inhibit their natural reflexes. Biological treatments such as the drug Viagra are also used for male erectile disorder.

Masters and Johnson used a couples-oriented approach in treating anorgasmic women. Other sex therapists prefer a program of directed masturbation, to enable women to learn about their own bodies at their own pace and free them of the need to rely on partners or on pleasing partners.

Rapid ejaculation is usually treated with the squeeze technique, the stop-start method, or medical treatments.

Dyspareunia, or painful intercourse, is generally treated with medical interventions. Vaginismus is generally treated with plastic vaginal dilators of increasing size.

Test Yourself

Multiple-Choice Questions

1. The sexual problem most commonly reported by women in the 2002 Canadian Contraception Study was:
(a) Rapid ejaculation.
(b) Painful intercourse.
(c) Low sexual desire.
(d) Lack of orgasm.

2. According to the study of Canadian adults by Brock et al., what percentage of people with sexual-function problems sought help from health professionals?
(a) 0.
(b) 25.
(c) 50.
(d) 75.

3. Permission and specific suggestions are components of:
(a) An insight-oriented approach to treating low desire.
(b) The Masters and Johnson approach to sex therapy.
(c) The biological treatment of sexual dysfunction.
(d) The PLISSIT model.

4. According to the study by Kleinplatz, which of the following was not found to be a key component of great sex?
(a) Expertise in performing oral sex.
(b) Erotic intimacy.
(c) Communication.
(d) Exploration and interpersonal risk-taking.

5. _____ is a common cause of erectile difficulties.

(a) Orgasm anxiety

(b) Ejaculatory incompetence

(c) Performance anxiety

(d) Hyposensitivity of the penis

6. An involuntary contraction of the muscles that makes penetration painful or impossible is known as:

(a) Dyspareunia.

(b) Vaginismus.

(c) Phimosis.

(d) Anorgasmia.

7. A low level of _____ can lessen sexual desire.

(a) testosterone

(b) sildenafil

(c) Depo-Provera

(d) alprostadil

8. Which of the following is not one of the psychosocial factors associated with sexual dysfunction?

(a) Dissatisfaction with the relationship.

(b) Lack of sexual skills.

(c) Anxiety due to a previous negative experience.

(d) Side effects of prescription drugs.

9. A behavioural approach to treating sexual disorders might include all of the following except:

(a) Adjusting hormone balance to improve sexual functioning.

(b) Changing self-defeating beliefs and attitudes.

(c) Enhancing sexual knowledge.

(d) Improving communication skills.

10. Sex therapists are most likely to recommend masturbation as a treatment for:

(a) Rapid ejaculation.

(b) Female orgasmic disorder.

(c) Vaginismus.

(d) Retarded ejaculation.

You'll find answers to the "Test Yourself" questions on page 495.

Critical Thinking

1. It's been argued that the increasing emphasis on biological treatments for sexual dysfunction has resulted in over-medicalization of human sexuality. What's your opinion?

2. Why do you think so many people find it difficult to ask health-care providers such as doctors about sexual problems? Do you think men or women find it more difficult to talk about their sexual problems? Why?

3. Would you buy a drug such as Viagra over the internet? Why or why not?

MySearchLab

MySearchLab offers extensive help to students with their writing and research project and provides round-the-clock access to credible and reliable source material. Take a tour at www.mysearchlab.com.

CHAPTER FOURTEEN

Sexually Transmitted Infections

Harold and Carin, both 20, have been seeing each other for about a month. They feel strong sexual attraction toward each other, but haven't become sexually intimate, in part because of fears about sexually transmitted infections. Harold believes using condoms is no guarantee against infection, and wants the two of them to be tested for HIV and other **sexually transmitted infections**. Carin has resisted undergoing these tests, partly because she feels insulted that Harold fears that she may be infected, and frankly, partly in fear of the test results. She's heard that symptoms of many STIs may not be visible, or may not develop for years after infection. She wonders whether she might have been infected by one of the men she's had sex with in the past.

Keisha has genital herpes. A 19-year-old pre-law student, she's had no recurrences since her initial outbreak, two years ago. She knows herpes is a lifelong infection that may recur from time to time. She also knows she may inadvertently pass the herpes virus along to her sex partners. She's begun thinking seriously about Steve, a man she's been dating for the past month. She'd like to tell him she has herpes before they become sexually intimate, yet she fears that telling him might scare him off.

José, 21, is a math and computer science major. He lives off campus with several buddies, in a run-down house they've dubbed "the Nuclear Dumpsite." He's been seeing Bill, a history major, for several months. They've begun having sexual relations, and have practiced safer sex—at least, most of the time. During the past week José has noticed some odd-looking bumps around his penis that didn't seem to be there before. For now, he's adopting a wait-and-see attitude, hoping they'll go away, but in the back of his mind he wonders whether he should see a doctor.

Scenarios like these play out thousands of times each year on college and university campuses across Canada. If you have an STI, think you might have one, or are worried that you're at risk for infection, you're not alone. STIs are more common than most of us think. The World Health Organization estimates that at least 340 million people around the world are infected with STIs each year (World Health Organization, 2008). STIs are something many of us prefer not to think or talk about with friends and intimate partners, mainly because it would involve frank discussions about sexual behaviour, which Western culture has often discouraged. Many people—if not most—lack even a basic knowledge of STIs and their own personal risks for infection.

Although discussions about STIs often focus on their medical implications, when someone learns s/he has an STI, the emotional impact can be as great as—if not greater than—the medical consequences. There remains a stigma associated with STIs, rooted in the false belief that they only happen to certain types of people, especially those who some might call promiscuous. Many people with STIs worry about the implications of their infections for current and future relationships. The reality is that STIs can happen to anyone who's sexually active, and they're very common among Canadians. Becoming knowledgeable about STIs enables us to reduce our risk of infection and deal with any infections that may occur.

STIs in Canada

Canadian rates vary by STI type. Human papillomavirus (HPV) and genital herpes (herpes simplex virus, or HSV) are the most common. Unfortunately, we don't have national statistics on them, as physicians aren't required to report cases of these STIs. We'll discuss the prevalence of HIV/AIDS later in the chapter.

Of the STIs for which cases are reported, chlamydia is the most common. There were 82 919 reported cases of chlamydia in 2008, with more than twice as many women as men contracting the infection (Public Health Agency of Canada, 2009a). Teens and young adults have the highest rates of chlamydia.

MySearchLab

- Self-grading practice tests
- Media links
- Flashcards
- Access to thousands of fulltext articles from academic journals and help on the research and writing process

Sexually transmitted infection (STI) An infection that's passed from one person to another through sexual contact. (Some STIs, such as HIV, can also be transmitted in other ways.)

CRITICAL THINKING QUESTIONS

How knowledgeable are you about STIs? What questions do you have?

TABLE 14.1

Reported Cases and Rates[1] of Chlamydia by Age Group and Sex, 2008[2]

	Sex						Chlamydia						
		<1	1-4	5-9	10-14	15-19	20-24	25-29	30-39	40-59	60+	NS	Total
Cases	Male	13	0	1	43	4141	10368	6210	4682	2276	122	20	27876
	Female	12	1	4	472	18161	20281	8707	5487	1736	51	53	54967
	Unspecified[3]	0	0	0	0	16	23	12	6	5	0	14	76
	Total	25	1	5	515	22318	30672	14929	10175	4017	173	87	82919
Rates	Male	7.0	0.0	0.1	4.2	358.1	884.2	538.7	205.5	45.6	4.2		168.7
	Female	6.8	0.1	0.5	48.0	1651.9	1824.3	768.8	244.1	34.7	1.5		327.4
	Total	6.9	0.1	0.3	25.6	989.4	1342.7	653.3	224.8	40.2	2.7		248.9

[1] Rate per 100 000 population. Population estimates provided by Statistics Canada.

[2] 2008 data are preliminary and changes are anticipated. Data were verified with provinces and territories as of October 2009.

[3] Unspecified sex includes transgendered cases.

Note: Small variability may exist between data reported by the provinces/territories and the Public Health Agency of Canada. Should a discrepancy exist, provincial/territorial data are definitive.

Source: Public Health Agency of Canada. (2010). Reported cases and rates of chlamydia by age group and sex, 1991 to 2008. Hepatitis C and STI Surveillance and Epidemiology Section, Community Acquired Infections Division, Centre for Communicable Diseases and Infection Control, Public Health Agency of Canada. Retrieved from http://www.phac-aspc.gc.ca/std-mts/sti-its_tab/chlamydia1991-08-eng.php

(See Table 14.1.) Chlamydia declined between 1992 and 1997, but has since increased. Toronto researchers Alex McKay and Michael Barrett (2008) question whether recent reported rate increases may be attributed to more sensitive testing methods and increases in the number of people tested, as has happened in the United States.

Rates of chlamydia and other STIs vary across Canada. The highest STI rates occur in Canada's North, and the next highest in the western provinces, especially Saskatchewan. This trend is attributed to the higher rates among Canada's First Nations people. We'll discuss these differences in the section on social factors and STIs, near the end of the chapter.

Gonorrhea is less common than chlamydia. The rate of gonorrhea infection declined substantially from the mid-1980s through 1997, then in 2008 it increased from 16.1 to 38.2 per 100 000 people. In 2008, 12 723 cases of gonorrhea were reported (Public Health Agency of Canada, 2009a).

Compared with gonorrhea and chlamydia, the number of syphilis cases is relatively small. Syphilis infection rates decreased in Canada with the introduction of penicillin in the 1940s. In recent years it's been increasing, however, especially among men who have sex with men. In 2008, 1394 cases of syphilis were diagnosed in Canada, and 86% of those were in men. (Public Health Agency of Canada, 2009a). Most of the increase has been due to localized outbreaks in Vancouver, Yukon, Calgary, Edmonton, the Northwest Territories, Winnipeg, Toronto, Ottawa, Montreal, and Halifax.

Researchers at the Public Health Agency of Canada compared STI rates in different age groups between 1997 and 2007. They found that although rates were still highest among younger people, rates of chlamydia, gonorrhea, and syphilis were

Who's at Risk?
Adolescents and young adults tend to have shorter relationships than older adults, and therefore more sexual partners. This helps explain why STI rates are highest among young people.

increasing faster among 40- to 59-year-olds (Fang, Oliver, Jayaraman, & Fong, 2010). The researchers suggested that "There is a need for sexual-health information targeting Canada's middle-aged adults and their health-care providers" (Fang, Oliver, Jayaraman, & Fong, 2010, p. 18).

The actual prevalence of these STIs (in terms of percentage of the population) is much higher than the numbers that make up the reported rates. The reported rates represent only the cases that are officially diagnosed.

Bacterial Infections

Bacteria cause a range of diseases, such as pneumonia, tuberculosis, meningitis, and the STIs chlamydia, gonorrhea, and syphilis.

Chlamydia

Although some viral STIs are more common, chlamydia is the most common bacterial STI in Canada. Chlamydia infection is caused by the *Chlamydia trachomatis* bacterium, a parasitic organism that can survive only within cells. This bacterium can cause several types of infection, including non-gonococcal urethritis in men and women, epididymitis (infection of the epididymis) in men, and cervicitis (infection of the cervix), endometritis (infection of the endometrium), and pelvic inflammatory disease in women (Hatcher et al., 2008).

TRANSMISSION Chlamydia is usually transmitted through sexual intercourse—vaginal or anal. Chlamydia may also cause an eye infection if a person touches his or her eyes after handling the genitals of an infected partner. Oral sex with an infected partner can infect the throat.

SYMPTOMS Chlamydia usually produces symptoms similar to those of gonorrhea, but milder.

In men, chlamydia can lead to non-gonococcal urethritis (NGU), an inflammation of the urethra that's not caused by the gonococcus bacterium. NGU used

Bacteria A class of single-celled micro-organisms that have no chlorophyll and can give rise to many illnesses. The singular is "bacterium."

to be called non-specific urethritis, or NSU. Many organisms can cause NGU, but chlamydia accounts for about half of the cases among men (Hatcher et al., 2008). It causes a thin, whitish discharge from the penis, burning or other pain during urination, soreness in the scrotum, and feelings of heaviness in the testes. These symptoms contrast with the yellow-green discharge and more intense pain produced by gonorrhea. NGU is two to three times as prevalent among American men as gonorrhea (Hatcher et al., 2008).

In women, chlamydial infection usually gives rise to infections of the urethra or cervix. This inflammation of the urethra is called a chlamydia infection, or simply chlamydia. Women may experience burning when they urinate, genital irritation, and a mild vaginal discharge. Women are also likely to have pelvic pain and irregular menstrual cycles. The cervix may look swollen and inflamed.

Up to 50% of men and 70% of women infected with chlamydia show no symptoms (Hatcher et al., 2008). People without symptoms may go untreated, and unknowingly pass their infections to their partners. In women, an untreated chlamydial infection can spread throughout the reproductive system, leading to **Pelvic Inflammatory Disease (PID)** and scarring of the fallopian tubes, resulting in infertility (Public Health Agency of Canada, 2010). Untreated chlamydial infections can also damage the internal reproductive organs of men.

Chlamydial infections frequently occur together with other STIs, most often gonorrhea. Nearly half of all cases of gonorrhea involve coexisting chlamydial infections (Hatcher et al., 2006).

DIAGNOSIS AND TREATMENT Various tests can verify a diagnosis of chlamydia in women. Some tests analyze cervical or urethral smears, while others use self-obtained urine samples and vaginal swabs, which are also highly reliable and preferred by most women because they're less invasive (McKay, 2006b). To test men, swabs are inserted through the penile openings, and fluid is extracted for analysis.

Antibiotics other than penicillin are highly effective in eradicating chlamydia infections. Penicillin, which is effective in treating gonorrhea, is ineffective against chlamydia. Treatment of sex partners is critical to preventing the infection from bouncing back and forth (Hatcher et al., 2006).

Because of the risks posed by untreated chlamydia, especially for women, and the high rate of symptom-free infections, many physicians screen young women for chlamydia during regular checkups. Toronto researcher Alexander McKay (2006a) has found that many physicians still don't screen for chlamydia, and that male physicians are less likely than female physicians to do so. McKay argues that physicians need to be aware of the need for regular chlamydia screening, especially among sexually active young women.

Gonorrhea

Gonorrhea is the second most commonly reported bacterial STI in Canada. Caused by the *Neisseria gonorrhoeae* bacterium, it's characterized by a discharge and burning urination. Left untreated, gonorrhea can cause pelvic inflammatory disease and infertility.

TRANSMISSION The gonococcus bacterium requires a warm, moist environment like that found along the mucous membranes of the urinary tract in both genders and the cervix in women. Outside the body, they die in about a minute. There's no evidence that gonorrhea can be picked up from public toilet seats or by touching dry objects. In rare cases, gonorrhea can be contracted by contact with a moist, warm towel or sheet immediately after it's been used by an infected person. Gonorrhea is nearly always transmitted by unprotected vaginal, oral, or anal sexual activity, or from mother to newborn during delivery.

Pelvic inflammatory disease (PID) Inflammation of the pelvic region in women, possibly including the cervix, uterus, fallopian tubes, abdominal cavity, and ovaries. Its symptoms are abdominal pain, tenderness, nausea, fever, and irregular menstrual cycles. The condition may lead to infertility.

A person who performs fellatio on an infected partner may develop **pharyngeal gonorrhea**, which produces a throat infection. Mouth-to-mouth kissing and cunnilingus are less likely to spread gonorrhea.

A gonorrheal infection may also be spread from the penis to the partner's rectum during anal intercourse. Likewise, a cervical gonorrheal infection can be spread to the rectum if an infected woman and her partner follow vaginal intercourse with anal intercourse. Gonorrhea is less likely to be spread by vaginal discharge than by penile discharge.

Gonorrhea is highly contagious. Women stand nearly a 50% chance of contracting gonorrhea after one exposure. Men have a 25% risk of infection (Hatcher et al., 2008). The risks to women are apparently greater because women retain infected semen in the vagina. The risk of infection increases with repeated exposure.

SYMPTOMS Most men experience symptoms within two to five days of infection. Symptoms include a penile discharge that's clear at first (see Figure 14.1), and turns yellow to yellow-green, thickens, and becomes pus-like within a day or two. The urethra becomes inflamed, and urination is accompanied by a burning sensation. About 30% to 40% of males have swelling and tenderness in the lymph glands of the groin.

The initial symptoms usually abate within a few weeks without treatment, leading people to think gonorrhea is no worse than a bad cold. However, the gonococcus bacterium usually continues to damage the body even if the early symptoms fade. If left untreated, inflammation and other symptoms may become chronic.

The primary site of infection in women is the cervix, where gonorrhea causes **cervicitis**. This results in a yellowish to yellow-green, pus-like discharge that irritates the vulva. If the infection spreads to the urethra, women may also note burning urination. About 80% of women who contract gonorrhea have no symptoms during the early stages of the infection. Because many don't seek treatment until symptoms develop, they may unknowingly infect other sex partners.

When gonorrhea isn't treated early, it may spread through the urogenital systems in both men and women, striking the internal reproductive organs. In men, it can lead to **epididymitis**, which can cause fertility problems. Swelling and tenderness or pain in the scrotum are the principal symptoms of epididymitis. Fever may also be present. Occasionally the kidneys are affected.

In women, the bacterium can spread through the cervix to the uterus, fallopian tubes, ovaries, and other parts of the abdominal cavity, causing PID. PID symptoms include cramps, abdominal pain and tenderness, cervical tenderness and discharge, irregular menstrual cycles, pain during intercourse, fever, nausea, and vomiting. PID may also occur without symptoms. Whether or not there are symptoms, it can cause scarring that blocks the fallopian tubes, leading to infertility. PID is a serious illness that requires aggressive treatment with antibiotics. Surgery may be needed, to remove infected tissue. Unfortunately, many women become aware of gonococcal infections only when they develop PID.

These consequences are all the more unfortunate because gonorrhea, when diagnosed and treated early, clears up rapidly more than 90% of the time.

DIAGNOSIS AND TREATMENT Diagnosis of gonorrhea involves clinical inspection of the genitals by a physician, and culturing and examination of a sample of genital discharge.

Antibiotics are the standard treatment. Penicillin was once the favoured antibiotic, but the rise of penicillin-resistant strains of *Neisseria gonorrhoeae* has required the use of alternate antibiotics (Hatcher et al., 2008). An injection of the antibiotic ceftriaxone is often recommended. Other antibiotics used for treating gonorrhea include ciprofloxacin and ofloxacin.

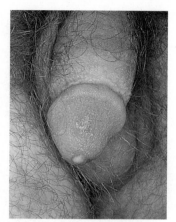

Figure 14.1 **A gonorrheal discharge.**
Gonorrhea in the male often causes a thick, yellowish, pus-like discharge from the penis.

Pharyngeal gonorrhea A gonorrheal infection of the pharynx, which is the cavity leading from the mouth and nasal passages to the larynx and esophagus. It's characterized by a sore throat.

Cervicitis Inflammation of the cervix.

Epididymitis Inflammation of the epididymis.

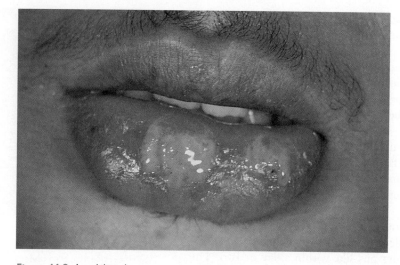

Figure 14.2 A syphilitic chancre.
The primary stage of a syphilis infection is marked by the appearance of a painless sore, or chancre, at the infection site.

Syphilis An STI caused by the *Treponema pallidum* bacterium. It may progress through several stages of development, often from a chancre to a skin rash to damage to the cardiovascular or central nervous system.

Chancre A sore or ulcer.

Congenital syphilis A syphilis infection that's present at birth.

Because gonorrhea and chlamydia often occur together, people who are infected with gonorrhea are usually also treated for chlamydia with another antibiotic (Hatcher et al., 2008). Sex partners of people with gonorrhea should be examined.

Syphilis

In 1905, the German scientists Fritz Schaudinn and Erich Hoffmann isolated *Treponema pallidum* (*T. pallidum*), the bacterium that causes **syphilis**. Although syphilis isn't as widespread as it used to be, its effects can be extremely harmful, including heart disease, blindness, gross confusion, and death.

TRANSMISSION Syphilis is most often transmitted by vaginal or anal intercourse or by oral–genital or oral–anal contact with an infected person. The spirochete (bacterium) is usually transmitted when an infected person's open lesions come into contact with the mucous membranes or skin abrasions of the partner's body during sexual activity. The chance of contracting syphilis from one sexual contact is estimated at one in three. Syphilis can also be contracted by touching an infectious **chancre**, but not by using the same toilet seat as an infected person.

Pregnant women can transmit syphilis to their fetuses, because the spirochete crosses the placental membrane. Miscarriage, stillbirth, or **congenital syphilis** may result. Congenital syphilis can impair vision and hearing and deform bones and teeth. Blood tests are administered routinely during pregnancy to diagnose syphilis in the mother, so congenital problems can be prevented in the baby.

SYMPTOMS Syphilis develops through several stages. In the first stage, or primary stage, two to four weeks after contact, a painless chancre—a hard, round, ulcer-like lesion with raised edges—appears at the infection site. When a woman is infected, the chancre usually forms on the vaginal walls or the cervix. It may also form on the external genitalia, most often on the labia. When a man is infected, the chancre usually forms on the penile glans. It may also form on the scrotum or the penile shaft. If the mode of transmission is oral sex, the chancre may appear on the lips or tongue (see Figure 14.2). If the infection is spread by anal sex, the chancre may appear in the rectum. The chancre disappears within a few weeks, but if the infection remains untreated, syphilis will continue to work within the body.

The secondary stage begins a few weeks to a few months later. A skin rash develops, consisting of painless, reddish, raised bumps that eventually darken and burst, oozing a discharge. Other symptoms include sores in the mouth, painful swelling in the joints, a sore throat, headaches, and fever. A person with syphilis may thus wrongly assume that s/he has the flu.

These symptoms also disappear. Syphilis then enters the latent stage, in which it may lie dormant for one to 40 years. But spirochetes continue to multiply and burrow into the circulatory system, central nervous system (brain and spinal cord), and bones. The person may no longer be contagious to sex partners after several years, but a pregnant woman can still transmit the infection to her newborn during delivery.

In many cases, the disease eventually progresses to the late stage, or tertiary stage. A large ulcer may form on the skin, muscle tissue, digestive organs, lungs, liver, and other organs. This destructive ulcer can often be successfully treated, but still more serious damage can occur as the infection attacks the central nervous system or the cardiovascular system (the heart and the major blood vessels). Either outcome can be fatal.

The primary and secondary symptoms of syphilis inevitably disappear. Infected people may therefore be tempted to believe they're no longer at risk, and fail to see their doctors. This is unfortunate, because failure to eradicate the infection through proper treatment can eventually lead to dire consequences.

DIAGNOSIS AND TREATMENT   Primary-stage syphilis is diagnosed by clinical examination. If a chancre is found, fluid drawn from it can be examined under a microscope. The spirochetes are usually quite visible. Blood tests are not definitive until the secondary stage begins.

Penicillin is the treatment of choice for syphilis, although people allergic to penicillin can use doxycycline and some other antibiotics (Hatcher et al., 2008). Sex partners of individuals infected with syphilis should be evaluated by physicians.

Vaginal Infections

Vaginitis is any kind of vaginal infection or inflammation. Women with vaginitis may encounter genital irritation or itching and burning during urination, but the most common symptom is an odorous discharge.

Most cases of vaginitis are caused by organisms that reside in the vagina or by sexually transmitted organisms. Organisms that reside in the vagina may overgrow and cause symptoms when the environmental balance of the vagina is upset by such factors as birth-control pills, antibiotics, dietary changes, excessive douching, nylon underwear, or pantyhose. (See Chapter 3 for suggestions about reducing the risk of vaginitis.) Other cases are caused by sensitivities or allergic reactions to various chemicals.

The great majority of vaginal infections involve bacterial vaginosis, candidiasis (commonly called a yeast infection), or trichomoniasis. The microbes that cause vaginal infections in women can also infect men's urethral tracts. A "vaginal infection" can therefore be passed back and forth between sex partners.

Vaginitis Any type of vaginal infection or inflammation.

Bacterial Vaginosis

Bacterial vaginosis (BV) is most often caused by overgrowth of the bacterium *Gardnerella vaginalis*. The bacterium is transmitted primarily through sexual contact. The most characteristic symptom is a thin, foul-smelling vaginal discharge, but infected women often have no symptoms. Diagnosis requires culturing the bacterium in the laboratory.

Besides causing troublesome symptoms in some cases, BV may increase the risk of various gynecological problems, including infections of the reproductive tract. Oral treatments are recommended, and effective in most cases. Topical treatments are also effective. Recurrences are common, however.

Questions remain about whether the male partner should also be treated. The bacterium can usually be found in the urethras of symptom-free males.

Bacterial vaginosis (BV) A form of vaginitis usually caused by the *Gardnerella vaginalis* bacterium.

Candidiasis

Also known as moniliasis, thrush, or (most often) a yeast infection, **candidiasis** is caused by a yeast-like fungus called *Candida albicans*. Candidiasis commonly produces soreness, inflammation, and intense (sometimes maddening!) itching around the vulva, accompanied by a thick, white, curd-like vaginal discharge (see Figure 14.3). Yeast infections can also occur in the mouth in both men and women and in the penis in men.

Candidiasis A form of vaginitis caused by a yeast-like fungus called *Candida albicans*.

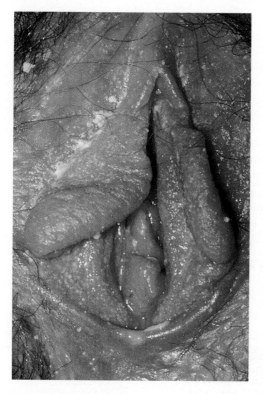

Figure 14.3 Candidiasis.
A yeast infection causes soreness, inflammation, and itching around the vulva that's accompanied by a thick, white vaginal discharge.

Yeast generally produces no symptoms when the vaginal environment is normal. Infections most often arise from changes in the vaginal environment that allow the fungus to overgrow. Antibiotics, birth-control pills, intrauterine devices, pregnancy, and diabetes may alter the vaginal balance, allowing the fungus that causes yeast infections to grow to infectious levels. Nylon underwear and tight, restrictive, poorly ventilated clothing may also set the stage for a yeast infection.

Although most cases aren't the results of sexual transmission, candidiasis can be passed back and forth between sex partners through vaginal intercourse. It can also be passed back and forth between the mouth and the genitals through oral–genital contact, and can infect the anus through anal intercourse. Most infections in women are believed to be caused by an overgrowth of the yeast normally found in the vagina. Still, it's advisable to evaluate both partners simultaneously. Whereas most men with *Candida* have no symptoms, some may develop NGU or a genital thrush accompanied by itching and burning during urination, or reddening of the penis. Candidiasis can also be transmitted by nonsexual means, such as between women who share a washcloth.

About 75% of women will experience at least one episode of candidiasis in their lifetimes (Public Health Agency of Canada, 2008). About 50% of women have recurrent infections. Recommended treatments include vaginal suppositories or creams (Hatcher et al., 2008), many of which are sold over the counter. Women with vaginal complaints should consult their physicians before taking any of these medications, to ensure that they receive the proper diagnosis and treatment.

Trichomoniasis

Trichomoniasis A form of vaginitis caused by the protozoan *Trichomonas vaginalis.*

Trichomoniasis ("trich") is caused by *Trichomonas vaginalis,* a single-celled parasite. It's the most common parasitic STI. Symptoms in women include burning or itching in the vulva, mild pain during urination or intercourse, and an odorous, foamy, whitish to yellowish-green discharge. Many women notice that symptoms appear or worsen during, or just after, their menstrual periods. Trichomoniasis facilitates the transmission of HIV and is linked to the development of tubal adhesions that can result in infertility. Women can be infected with trichomoniasis and have no symptoms.

Unlike candidiasis, trichomoniasis is nearly always sexually transmitted. Because the parasite can survive for several hours on moist surfaces outside the body, trich can be communicated via contact with infected semen or vaginal discharge on towels, washcloths, and bedclothes. This parasite is one of the few disease agents that can be picked up from a toilet seat, but the penis or vulva has to directly touch the seat.

Trichomonas vaginalis can cause NGU in men, and can cause a slight penile discharge that's usually noticeable before first urination in the morning. There may be tingling, itching, and other irritating sensations in the urethral tract. Yet most infected men are symptom-free. They can therefore unwittingly transfer the organism to their sex partners.

Diagnosis is frequently made by microscopic examination of a smear of vaginal fluid in a physician's office. Diagnosis based on examination of cultures grown from the vaginal smear is considered more reliable, however. When both partners are treated simultaneously, the success rate approaches 100% (Hatcher, 2008).

Viral Infections

Viruses are tiny particles of DNA surrounded by protein coatings. They're incapable of reproducing on their own. When they invade a body cell, however, they can direct the cell's own reproductive machinery to spin off new viral particles that spread to other cells, causing infection. In this section we'll discuss several viral STIs: HIV and AIDS, herpes, viral hepatitis, and genital warts.

HIV and AIDS

Human immunodeficiency virus (HIV) is the virus that causes **acquired immunodeficiency syndrome (AIDS)**. HIV attacks and disables the immune system, the body's natural line of defence, stripping it of its ability to fend off disease-causing organisms. AIDS is considered fatal, although many people now live with HIV/AIDS for many years, thanks to the development of powerful antiviral medications. For people in industrialized nations like Canada, HIV/AIDS may become a chronic but manageable condition, like diabetes. But for many millions in developing nations, where medications are expensive or difficult to deliver, HIV/AIDS may remain a death sentence.

Globally, about 33.4 million people were living with HIV in 2008, 2.7 million new infections occurred, and two million people died from AIDS-related causes (Henry J. Kaiser Family Foundation, 2009). More than 90% of those with HIV live in low- or middle-income countries, particularly in sub-Saharan Africa. In many parts of the world (e.g., Africa), most new HIV infections are transmitted through heterosexual sex, but in some countries, men having sex with men, injection drug use, and sex work are major risk factors.

CANADIAN HIV TRENDS According to the Public Health Agency of Canada, from 1985 (when HIV testing began) through December 2008, 67 422 people in Canada were diagnosed with HIV (including those with AIDS). The reported number of positive HIV tests decreased between 1995 and 2000, but has since increased. An estimated 2300 to 4300 new cases occurred in 2008. The number of people in Canada living with HIV (including AIDS) grew from an estimated 57 000 in 2005 to 65 000 in 2008. Of these 65 000, it's estimated that 16 900 (26%) were unaware that they were infected (Public Health Agency of Canada, 2009b). Table 14.2 gives the distribution of positive HIV tests by exposure category for 2008.

The proportion of new HIV test reports among women remained stable at 26% from 2005 to 2008. The number of aboriginal people living with HIV has increased in recent years. The HIV infection rate for aboriginal people is 3.6 times higher than for non-aboriginal populations. A significant proportion of the heterosexual HIV infections originate in countries with high HIV prevalence rates, such as those in Africa. The estimated infection rate for individuals who have immigrated from countries where HIV is endemic is 8.5 times higher than for other Canadians (Public Health Agency of Canada, 2009b).

Injection-drug users account for 14% of new HIV infections. First Nations people make up a growing percentage of people who test positive for HIV, and injection-drug use is the most common means of HIV transmission among this group. Rates of HIV infection are also much higher in Canadian prisons than in the general population (Public Health Agency of Canada, 2006).

Many people living with HIV are unaware that they're infected. These people are thus denied the option of beginning the viral therapy treatment that could fight the infection and prolong their lives.

Human immunodeficiency virus (HIV) A sexually transmitted virus that destroys white blood cells in the immune system, leaving the body vulnerable to life-threatening diseases.

Acquired immunodeficiency syndrome (AIDS) A condition caused by the human immunodeficiency virus (HIV) and characterized by destruction of the immune system, stripping the body of its ability to fend off life-threatening diseases.

TABLE 14.2
Distribution of HIV-Positive Test Reports by Exposure Category, 2008

Men who have sex with men (MSM)	45.1%
Heterosexual sex	30.8%
Injection drug use	19.1%
Men who have sex with men and injection drug use	3.2%

Source: Adapted from Public Health Agency of Canada. (2009a). HIV and AIDS in Canada: Surveillance Report to December 31, 2008. Ottawa: Surveillance and Risk Assessment Division, Centre for Communicable Diseases and Infection Control.

CANADIAN AIDS TRENDS Between 1979 until the end of 2008, a total of 21 300 cases of AIDS were reported in Canada (Public Health Agency of Canada, 2009). As Figure 14.4. shows, the number of new AIDS cases reported peaked in 1993, and then declined.

In 2008, women accounted for 24.4% of reported AIDS cases, a significant increase from the 7% of the pre-1997 period. Currently, men who have sex with men (MSM) account for 48.8% of new AIDS cases. This is a major decrease—prior to 1994, this group accounted for three-quarters of all AIDS cases. The development of antiviral drugs has significantly contributed to this decrease.

THE IMMUNE SYSTEM The **immune system** is the body's natural line of defense against disease-causing organisms. The immune system combats disease in a number of ways. It produces white blood cells that envelop and kill **pathogens** such as bacteria, viruses, and fungi, as well as worn-out body cells and cancer cells.

White blood cells are referred to as **leukocytes**. They engage in microscopic warfare, undertaking search-and-destroy missions to identify and eradicate foreign agents and debilitated cells. Leukocytes recognize foreign agents by their surface fragments, which are called **antigens** because the body reacts to their presence by developing specialized proteins, or **antibodies**. Antibodies attach themselves to the foreign agents, inactivate them, and mark them for destruction. HIV infection can therefore be determined by examining blood or saliva for the presence of antibodies to the virus.

Rather than destroying or marking pathogens for destruction, special memory lymphocytes are held in reserve. Memory lymphocytes can remain in the bloodstream for years, forming the basis for a quick immune response if an invader appears a second time.

Immune system The complex of mechanisms the body uses to protect itself from disease-causing agents such as pathogens.

Pathogen An agent, especially a micro-organism, that can cause disease.

Leukocytes White blood cells that are essential to the body's defences against infection.

Antigen A protein, toxin, or other substance to which the body reacts by producing antibodies. The word is formed from "antibody generator."

Antibody A specialized protein that attaches itself to a foreign body, inactivates it, and marks it for destruction.

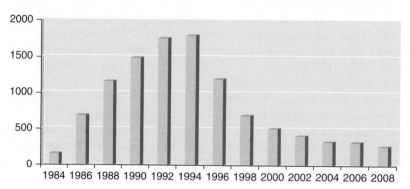

Figure 14.4 Number of AIDS cases by year of diagnosis, 1984 to 2008.

Source: Adapted from Public Health Agency of Canada. (2009). HIV and AIDS in Canada: Surveillance report to December 31, 2008. Ottawa: Surveillance and Risk Assessment Division, Centre for Communicable Diseases and Infection Control.

HIV INFECTION Spikes (technically known as gpl20 spikes) on the surface of HIV allow it to bind to sites on cells in the immune system (Sodroski et al., 1998). Like other viruses, HIV uses the cells it invades to spin off copies of itself. HIV uses an enzyme called reverse transcriptase to cause genes in the attacked cells to make proteins the virus needs for reproduction.

HIV directly attacks the immune system by invading and destroying a type of lymphocyte called the CD4 cell, or helper T cell (see Figure 14.5). The CD4 cell is the quarterback of the immune system. CD4 cells recognize invading pathogens, and signal B lymphocytes, or B cells (another kind of white blood cell), to produce antibodies that inactivate and mark the pathogens for annihilation. CD4 cells also signal another class of T cells, called killer T cells, to destroy infected cells. By attacking and destroying helper T cells, HIV disables the very cells which the body relies on for fighting off infections HIV and other diseases. As HIV cripples the body's defences, the individual is exposed to infections that wouldn't otherwise take hold. Cancer cells might also proliferate. Although the CD4 cells appear to be its main target, HIV also attacks other types of white blood cell.

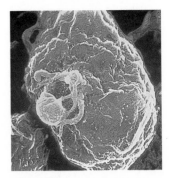

Figure 14.5 HIV (the AIDS virus) attacks a white blood cell.
HIV progressively weakens the immune system, leaving the body vulnerable to infections and diseases that would otherwise be fended off.

The blood normally contains about 1000 CD4 cells per cubic millimetre. The number of CD4 cells may remain at about this level for years following HIV infection. Many people show no symptoms, appearing healthy, while CD4 cells remain at this level. Then, for reasons that aren't clearly understood, the CD4 cell level begins to drop off, although symptoms may not appear for a decade or more. As the number of CD4 cells declines, symptoms generally increase, leaving the individual vulnerable to diseases the weakened immune system can't fight off. A person becomes most vulnerable to opportunistic infections when the level of CD4 cells falls below 200 per cubic millimetre.

Researchers in Vancouver have discovered that treatment for AIDS symptoms can be started later than previously thought, with no difference in health outcomes (Hogg et al., 2001). Specifically, patients can wait until their CD4 cell count drops to 300, instead of 500.

HIV/AIDS PROGRESSION HIV follows a complex course once it enters the body. Shortly after infection, the person may experience mild, flu-like symptoms—fatigue, fever, headaches, muscle pain, lack of appetite, nausea, swollen glands, and possibly a rash. These symptoms usually disappear within a few weeks, and the person may dismiss them as a passing case of flu. Once people enter this symptom-free or carrier state, they generally look and act well, and don't realize they're infectious, so they may unwittingly pass the virus to others.

Most people who are infected with HIV remain symptom-free for years. Some enter a symptomatic state that's typically marked by chronically swollen lymph nodes and intermittent weight loss, fever, fatigue, and diarrhea. This symptomatic state doesn't constitute full-blown AIDS, but it shows that HIV is undermining the integrity of the immune system.

The beginnings of full-blown AIDS are often marked by such symptoms as swollen lymph nodes, fatigue, fever, night sweats, diarrhea, and weight loss that can't be attributed to dieting or exercise.

AIDS is connected with the appearance of diseases such as pneumonia, Kaposi's sarcoma (a form of cancer), toxoplasmosis of the brain (an infection by parasites), and herpes simplex with chronic ulcers. These diseases are termed

Can Kissing Transmit HIV?
HIV is a blood-borne virus that's transmitted via various bodily fluids, including blood, semen, and vaginal fluids. The Centers for Disease Control and Prevention (CDC) has found that HIV does not occur in infectious quantities in saliva.

Opportunistic diseases
Diseases that take hold only when the immune system is weakened and unable to fend them off.

opportunistic diseases, because they're unlikely to emerge unless a disabled immune system provides the opportunity.

About 10% of people with AIDS have a wasting syndrome. Wasting, the unintentional loss of more than 10% of a person's body weight, is connected with AIDS, some other infections, and cancer. As AIDS progresses, the individual grows thinner and more fatigued. S/he becomes unable to perform ordinary life functions, and falls prey to opportunistic infections.

If left untreated, AIDS nearly always results in death within a few years.

TRANSMISSION HIV can be transmitted by certain contaminated bodily fluids—blood, semen, vaginal secretions, and breast milk. The first three of these may enter the body through vaginal, anal, or oral–genital intercourse with an infected partner. HIV can enter the body through tiny cuts or sores in the mucosal lining of the vagina, the rectum, and even the mouth. These cuts or sores can be so tiny that you're unaware of them. Transmission of HIV through kissing—even prolonged or French kissing—is unlikely.

Another avenue of infection is by sharing a hypodermic needle with an infected person. When someone injects drugs, a small amount of his or her blood remains inside the needle and syringe. If s/he's infected with HIV, the virus may be in the blood that remains in the needle and syringe. Others who use the needle inject the infected blood into their bloodstreams. HIV can also be spread by sharing needles used for other purposes, such as injecting steroids, piercing ears, or tattooing.

Seropositive Having a pathogen or antibodies to that pathogen in the bloodstream.

Seronegative Lacking a pathogen or antibodies to that pathogen in the bloodstream.

HIV can be transmitted from mother to fetus during pregnancy, or from mother to child through childbirth or breastfeeding. Transmission is most likely during childbirth. In Canada, the HIV prevalence rate among pregnant women is estimated to be three to five per 10 000 and it's recommended that all pregnant women be offered HIV testing and counselling (Public Health Agency of Canada, 2008).

Male-to-female transmission through vaginal intercourse is about twice as likely as female-to-male transmission, partly because more of the virus is found in ejaculate than in vaginal secretions. A man's ejaculate may also remain for many days in the vagina, providing greater opportunity for infection. Worldwide, male–female sexual intercourse accounts for most HIV/AIDS cases.

Male–female and male–male anal intercourse are especially risky, particularly to the recipient, because the rectal tissue often tears or abrades, facilitating the virus's entry into the bloodstream (UNAIDS, 2006).

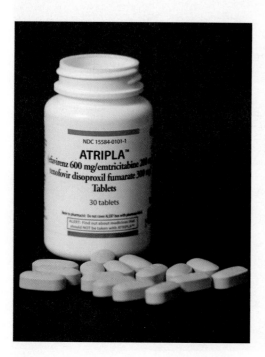

Atripla.
This new three-in-one pill makes it easy to manage the regimen of highly active antiretroviral therapy (HAART). Atripla contains a cocktail of antiviral drugs that have become the standard treatment for HIV/AIDS in developed countries.

DIAGNOSIS The most widely used test for HIV infection is the enzyme-linked immunosorbent assay (ELISA), which may take three weeks to yield results. ELISA doesn't directly detect HIV in the blood. Instead, it reveals HIV antibodies. People may show an antibody response to HIV long before they develop symptoms of infection. A positive (**seropositive**) test result means antibodies have been found, and usually indicates that the person is infected with HIV. A negative (**seronegative**) outcome means antibodies to HIV have not been detected.

ELISA can be performed on a sample of blood, saliva, or urine. A group of Ontario researchers has demonstrated that the less expensive saliva test is almost as accurate as the blood test (Major et al., 1991). A saliva test might encourage testing among people who avoid blood tests. Saliva is absorbed by a cotton pad on a stick that's placed between the lower gum and the cheek, then it's analyzed in a laboratory. Although HIV antibodies can be detected in saliva, HIV itself isn't found in measurable quantities. This is why kissing isn't considered an avenue of HIV transmission.

When these types of tests show evidence of HIV antibodies, the presence of the virus itself can be confirmed by more expensive tests, such as the Western blot test or the immunofluorescence assay. HIV tests are not considered accurate until three months have passed since the person's last exposure to the virus. This is how long the body generally takes to produce antibodies.

The most significant change in testing procedure has been the development of rapid testing technologies, which allow test results to be provided much sooner after testing than they used to be (though you still have to wait for three months after exposure to the virus before you can administer the tests). In 2007, Ontario became the first province to offer HIV tests that provide results within one minute of testing. The test is available at anonymous HIV- and STI-testing sites and clinics across the province.

Individuals can choose to be tested in doctors' offices or at anonymous testing sites. In a 2003 survey, one-quarter of Canadians reported that they'd been tested for HIV. Seventy-one percent of men who'd had sex with men said they'd been tested for HIV (Public Health Agency of Canada, 2007).

TREATMENT For many years, researchers were frustrated by their failure to develop effective vaccines and treatments for HIV and AIDS. Work continues on development of a vaccine for HIV, but to date there's still no safe, effective vaccine.

Many drugs are now used to combat HIV and AIDS. Drugs called protease inhibitors target the protease enzyme, blocking HIV replication. A combination of antiviral drugs has become the standard treatment for HIV and AIDS. This combination, referred to as **highly active antiretroviral therapy (HAART)**, decreases the likelihood that HIV will develop resistance to treatment. HAART has also created hope that AIDS will become increasingly manageable—a chronic health problem, as opposed to a terminal illness.

HAART therapies can have a number of negative side effects that make continually taking them difficult for HIV-positive people. These therapies can also accelerate problems such as depression, memory deficits, and liver and kidney disease. HAART is expensive, too, and many people who could benefit from it can't afford it. People in less-developed nations make do—or not—on less expensive medications or no medication.

HAART has worked wonders in reducing the death rate from AIDS. Yet even when HIV has been reduced to levels that are undetectable by ordinary means, scientists have been able to use methods of close scrutiny to locate it in resting (non-replicating) CD4 cells (Lederman & Valdez, 2000). HAART therefore doesn't appear to be a cure.

In Windsor, Ontario, researchers studied how the newer HAART therapies for HIV had affected the lives of 31 men and four women who are HIV-positive (Adams et al., 2001). While many reported substantial improvements in their health as a consequence of the therapies, some emphasized that their conditions were "tolerable." Those who'd been recently diagnosed with symptoms related to HIV were all responding well. Many felt they could lead more normal lives. Most reported that sexual desire decreased significantly at the time of HIV diagnosis, but that sexual desire and activity returned over time. Severity of illness, rather than

Highly Active Antiretroviral Therapy (HAART) A combination of drugs used to treat HIV and AIDS. It's a protease inhibitor combined with a couple of other antiretroviral agents.

Welcome to Condom Country.
Condom ads based on the ruggedly masculine Marlboro tobacco ads are used by the AIDS Committee of Toronto during Pride Week to encourage gay men to use condoms.

relationship status, was the strongest predictor of sexual activity. Most of those who didn't have physical symptoms were sexually active, whereas those who had the most severe physical symptoms weren't. Some avoided sexual activity, because they didn't want to put their partners at risk. For those who didn't feel comfortable disclosing their HIV status to others, the internet provided a source of information and friendship. Several were involved in HIV/AIDS support groups.

PREVENTION What can we do to curb the spread of HIV and AIDS? Given that we lack both a vaccine and a cure, prevention is our best hope. Our discussion of prevention will focus on sexual transmission, but other efforts have been made to prevent transmission via pregnancy, childbirth, and breastfeeding, shared needles, and blood transfusions. For example, HIV-infected women are advised to avoid breastfeeding. The drug zidovudine, Caesarian section, and other measures decrease the probability of transmission through childbirth (Ricci et al., 2000). And screening of potential blood donors has rendered the probability of transmission via blood transfusion almost negligible.

Canadian researchers have found evidence that HAART is effective in reducing HIV transmission (Montaner et al., 2010). Examining data from British Columbia, researchers have found that as the number of HIV-positive individuals taking HAART therapy increases, the number of new HIV infections decreases. This is because HAART reduces levels of HIV in the body, and as a result decreases the likelihood of virus transmission. The findings suggest that making HAART therapy easily accessible and affordable to HIV-positive people can be an important tool in HIV prevention.

There's evidence from Africa that male circumcision reduces the risk of HIV acquisition for men. Studies conducted in South Africa, Uganda, and Kenya have found that circumcision reduces HIV infection among heterosexual men by 38% to 66% (Siegfried, Muller, Deeks, & Volmink, 2009).

Most prevention efforts focus on education. According to the World Association for Sexual Health (2008), the success of HIV/AIDS-prevention education in the developing world depends on access to effective education interventions, access to condoms, and adequate funding for prevention programming. To some extent, these same factors apply to the developed world, including Canada. In Canada, HIV/AIDS prevention is often integrated into broader sexual-health education in the schools. (See Chapter 12.) Public-health units or agencies and community groups also conduct HIV/AIDS-prevention interventions aimed at higher-risk groups, including men who have sex with men and injection-drug users.

Herpes (HSV)

The annual incidence of genital herpes in Canada is unknown, but in the United States, it's estimated that about 1 640 000 new genital herpes infections occur each year. It's safe to assume a similar infection rate for Canada (Public Health Agency of Canada, 2008). Herpes is a chronic infection, which means the virus remains in the body for life.

Approximately 60% of genital herpes infections are asymptomatic—that is, they have no observable signs or symptoms (Public Health Agency of Canada, 2008). People with asymptomatic infections can transmit the virus to others.

People with symptoms experience recurrent outbreaks that often happen at the worst times, such as around final exams. This isn't just bad luck—stress can depress the immune system and heighten the likelihood of an outbreak. Outbreaks can continue to recur, sometimes with annoying frequency. On the other hand, some people have no recurrences. Still others have mild, brief recurrences that become less frequent over time.

Different types of herpes are caused by variants of the herpes simplex virus. The most common type, **herpes simplex virus, type 1 (HSV-1)**, causes oral herpes, which is characterized by cold sores (fever blisters) on the lips and in the mouth and throat. It can be transmitted to the genitals by the hands or by oral–genital contact. **Genital herpes** is caused by a related but distinct virus, the **herpes simplex virus, type 2 (HSV-2)**, which produces painful, shallow sores and blisters on the genitals. HSV-2 can be transferred to the mouth through oral–genital contact. Both types of herpes can be transmitted sexually.

TRANSMISSION Herpes can be transmitted through oral, anal, or vaginal sexual activity with an infected person. The herpes viruses can also survive for several hours on toilet seats and other objects, where they can be picked up by direct contact. Oral herpes is easily contracted by drinking from the same cup as an infected person, by kissing, and even by sharing towels. But genital herpes is generally spread by vaginal intercourse or by oral or anal sex.

Many people don't realize they're infected, so they unknowingly transmit the virus through sexual contact. Many of those who know they're infected don't realize they can pass the virus along even when they don't have noticeable outbreaks (Wald et al., 1995). Although genital herpes is most contagious during active flare-ups, it can also be transmitted when an infected partner has no symptoms (genital sores or feelings of burning or itching in the genitals). Any intimate contact with an infected person carries some risk of transmission, even if the infected person never has another outbreak. People may also be infected with the virus and have no outbreaks, yet pass the virus along to others.

Herpes can be spread from one part of the body to another by touching. One potentially serious result is a herpes infection of the eye, called **ocular herpes**. Thorough washing with soap and water after touching an infected area may reduce the risk of spreading the infection to other parts of the body.

Research has shown that consistent condom use reduces the risk of transmission of HSV-2 (Martin et al., 2009). However, herpes lesions can occur on skin that's not covered by condoms, so condom effectiveness is limited.

Women with genital herpes are more likely to have miscarriages than women in the general population. Passage through the birth canals of infected mothers can infect babies with genital herpes, damaging or killing them. Obstetricians thus often perform Caesarean sections if mothers have active lesions or **prodromal symptoms** at the time of delivery.

SYMPTOMS Genital lesions or sores appear about six to eight days after infection with genital herpes. At first they appear as reddish, painful bumps, or papules, along the penis or vulva. (See Figure 14.6.) They may also appear on the thighs or buttocks, in the vagina, or on the cervix.

These papules turn into groups of small blisters that are filled with fluid containing infectious viral particles. The blisters are attacked by the body's immune system (white blood cells). They fill with pus, burst, and become extremely painful, shallow sores (ulcers) surrounded by red rings. People are especially infectious during such outbreaks, because the ulcers shed millions of viral particles. Other symptoms may include headaches and muscle aches, swollen lymph glands, fever, burning urination, and vaginal discharge.

The blisters crust over and heal in one to three weeks. Internal sores in the vagina or on the cervix may take 10 days longer than external (labial) sores to heal. Physicians therefore advise infected women to avoid unprotected intercourse for at least 10 days after the external sores heal.

Although the symptoms disappear, the disease doesn't. The virus remains in the body permanently, burrowing into nerve cells in the base of the spine, where it may lie dormant for years or for a lifetime. The infected person is least contagious

Herpes simplex virus, type 1 (HSV-1) The virus that causes oral herpes, which is characterized by cold sores (fever blisters) on the lips and in the mouth and throat.

Genital herpes An STI caused by the herpes simplex virus, type 2. It's characterized by painful, shallow sores and blisters on the genitals.

Herpes simplex virus, type 2 (HSV-2) The virus that causes genital herpes.

Ocular herpes A herpes infection of the eye, usually caused by touching an infected area of the body and then touching the eye.

Prodromal symptoms Warning symptoms that signal the onset or flare-up of a disease.

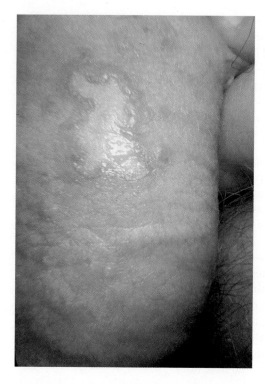

Figure 14.6 A herpes lesion on the male genitals.
Herpes lesions or sores can appear on the genitals in both men and women. In contrast to the syphilis chancre, they can be quite painful. Herpes is most likely to be transmitted during outbreaks of the disease (when the sores are present, that is), but it can also be transmitted at other times.

during this dormant stage. For reasons that remain unclear, in most cases the virus becomes reactivated and gives rise to recurrences.

Recurrences may be related to infections (such as a cold), stress, fatigue, depression, exposure to the sun, and hormonal changes such as those that occur during pregnancy or menstruation. Recurrences tend to occur within three to 12 months of the initial episode, and affect the same parts of the body.

The symptoms of oral herpes include sores and blisters on the lips, inside the mouth, on the tongue, and in the throat. The person may experience fever and feelings of illness, as well as swollen, reddened gums. The sores heal over in about two weeks, and the virus retreats into nerve cells at the base of the neck, where it lies dormant between flare-ups.

DIAGNOSIS AND TREATMENT Genital herpes is first diagnosed by clinical inspection of herpetic sores or ulcers in the mouth or on the genitals. A sample of fluid may be taken from the base of a genital sore, and cultured in the laboratory, to detect the growth of the virus.

Unlike the bacteria that cause gonorrhea and syphilis, viruses don't respond to antibiotics. Antiviral drugs, however, can relieve pain, speed healing, and reduce the duration of viral shedding (Hatcher et al., 2008). Oral administration of antiviral drugs may reduce the severity of the initial episode and—if taken regularly—the frequency and duration of recurrent outbreaks (Hatcher et al., 2008). Warm baths, loosely fitting clothing, aspirin, and cold, wet compresses may relieve pain during flare-ups. People with herpes are advised to maintain regular sleeping habits and learn to manage stress.

There's no safe, effective vaccine for genital herpes, but clinical trials of experimental vaccines are underway (National Institute of Allergy and Infectious Diseases, 2009).

COPING WITH GENITAL HERPES The psychological impact of herpes can be more distressing than its physical effects. The prospect of a lifetime of recurrences and concern about infecting sex partners exacerbate the emotional impact of herpes. However, most people with herpes learn to cope with the infection, and with adjustments, are able to establish and maintain satisfying intimate relationships. Some are helped by support groups that share ways to live with the infection. A caring, trusting partner is important.

The attitudes of people with herpes affect their success in adjusting to it. People who view herpes as a manageable condition, not as a medical disaster or a character deficit, find it easier to adjust.

Viral Hepatitis

Hepatitis An inflammation of the liver.

Jaundice A yellowish discoloration of the skin and the whites of the eyes.

Hepatitis is an inflammation of the liver that may be caused by such factors as chronic alcoholism and exposure to toxic substances. Viral hepatitis includes several types of hepatitis caused by related but distinct viruses. The major types are hepatitis A, hepatitis B, hepatitis C, and hepatitis D.

Most people with acute hepatitis have no symptoms. When symptoms do appear, they often include **jaundice**, feelings of weakness and nausea, loss of appetite, abdominal discomfort, whitish bowel movements, and brownish or tea-coloured urine. The symptoms of hepatitis B tend to be more severe and long-lasting than those of hepatitis A or C. In about 10% of cases, hepatitis B leads to chronic liver disease. Hepatitis C tends to have milder symptoms, but often leads to chronic liver diseases such as cirrhosis and cancer of the liver. Hepatitis D occurs only in the presence of hepatitis B. It has symptoms similar to those of hepatitis B, can produce severe liver damage, and often leads to death.

The hepatitis A virus is transmitted through contact with infected fecal matter in contaminated food or water, and by oral contact with fecal matter, such as through oral–anal sexual activity (licking or mouthing the partner's anus). It's largely because of the risk of hepatitis A that restaurant employees are required to wash their hands after using the toilet. Ingesting uncooked infested shellfish is also a frequent means of transmission for hepatitis A.

Hepatitis B can be transmitted through anal, vaginal, or oral intercourse with an infected partner, transfusion with contaminated blood supplies, sharing of contaminated needles or syringes, and contact with contaminated saliva, menstrual blood, nasal mucus, or semen. Sharing razors, toothbrushes, and other personal articles with an infected person can also transmit hepatitis B.

Hepatitis C and hepatitis D can be transmitted sexually or through contact with contaminated blood. Hepatitis D can occur only if hepatitis B is present (Hatcher et al., 2008). People can transmit the viruses that cause hepatitis even if they're unaware that they have the disease.

In Canada, infection rates for hepatitis A and B declined significantly during the 1990s. Today the incidence of hepatitis B is about 2.3 per 100 000, and twice as high in men as in women (Public Health Agency of Canada, 2008). The rate for hepatitis C has been increasing so that today its highest infection rate is by far the highest of the hepatitis viruses (Health Canada, 2001).

Hepatitis is usually diagnosed by testing blood samples for the presence of hepatitis antigens and antibodies. There's no cure for viral hepatitis. Bed rest and fluids are usually recommended until the acute stage of the infection subsides, generally in a few weeks. Full recovery may take months. A vaccine provides protection against hepatitis B and D (Hatcher et al, 2008).

Human Papillomavirus (HPV)

The human papillomavirus (HPV) is the most common STI. It's estimated that about 70% of adult Canadians will have at least one HPV infection in their lifetimes (Public Health Agency of Canada, 2008). One study of female university students in Canada has reported an HPV rate of 29% (Richardson et al., 2003).

Most HPV infections are asymptomatic and harmless. In up to 90% of cases, the body's immune system clears up the infection within two years (Centers for Disease Control and Prevention, 2007).

There are many different subtypes of HPV. Some, such as types 6 and 11, cause genital warts. Others, such as types 16 and 18, which don't cause **genital warts**, can eventually lead to cervical cancer if they persist undetected for a number of years. The Pap test is designed to detect abnormal changes in the cervix caused by HPV infection, so regular Pap tests reduce women's chances of developing cervical cancer (Public Health Agency of Canada, 2008). HPV is also associated with penile cancer in men, as well as some cases of oral cancer.

Genital warts An STI caused by the human papillomavirus. It takes the form of warts around the genitals and anus.

It bears repeating that HPV infection is extremely common, usually resolves on its own, and only in rare instances progresses to cancer. In most cases, the cancer can be effectively treated, especially if it's detected early (Barrett, 2006).

TRANSMISSION Vaginal and anal intercourse are the most common means of HPV transmission. Oral sex can also transmit HPV (Wright, 2009), and other types of skin-to-skin contact with infected areas can transmit HPV.

Because HPV is so common, reducing the risk of infection is difficult, especially for people who are sexually active. Abstaining from sexual activity is clearly one way a person can avoid HPV infection. Latex condoms reduce

Figure 14.7 Genital warts.
Genital warts are caused by the human papilloma virus (HPV) and may have a cauliflower-like appearance. Many cases occur where they remain visually undetected. HPV is implicated in cervical cancer.

the risk of contracting HPV if they're used consistently. One study found that women whose partners always used condoms were 70% less likely to be infected with HPV than women whose partners used condoms less than 5% of the time (Winer et al., 2006). Condoms don't eliminate the risk entirely, because the virus can be transmitted from unprotected areas of the skin, such as the scrotum.

Some types of HPV can result in genital warts, which vary in size and shape. Genital warts can be hard and yellow-grey when they form on dry skin, or they can take on a pink, soft, cauliflower appearance in moist areas such as the lower vagina. (See Figure 14.7.) In men, they appear on the penis, foreskin, and scrotum and in the urethra. In women, they appear on the vulva, along the vaginal wall, and on the cervix. They can also occur outside the genital area—for example, in the mouth, on the lips, eyelids, or nipples, around the anus, and in the rectum. The incubation period from time of infection to appearance of the warts can range from a few weeks to more than a year.

There are several treatments for genital warts. Cryotherapy, or freezing the warts with liquid nitrogen, is a preferred treatment. Another treatment involves painting or coating the warts over several days with an alcohol-based podophyllin solution, gel, or cream, which causes the warts to dry up and fall off (Hatcher et al., 2008). The warts can also be treated by a doctor, who may burn them off with electrodes or remove them by laser or conventional surgery. Unfortunately, removing the warts doesn't rid the body of the virus (Hatcher et al., 2008), and there may be recurrences. Eventually, the warts will clear up.

People with active warts should probably avoid sexual contact until the warts are removed and the area heals completely.

VACCINE The most recent advance in the fight against STIs has been the development of a vaccine that immunizes against HPV strains 6, 11, 16, and 18. These strains are responsible for 90% of genital warts and 70% of cases of cervical cancer. The vaccine Gardasil was approved in Canada for females between the ages of nine and 26 in 2006, and more recently for males of the same age (Public Health Agency of Canada, 2010). Another HPV vaccine called Cervarix has recently been approved for use in Canada. The main target for the vaccine are females who haven't yet been sexually active and thus have never had HPV infections. Three injections of the vaccine are required over a six-month period.

All provinces and territories in Canada have implemented publicly funded school vaccine programs to lower cervical risk for women, but acceptance of the HPV vaccine hasn't been universal. Some have questioned whether a large-scale HPV vaccination program is appropriate, given that cervical cancer is relatively rare in Canada and Pap tests are an effective method of screening (Lippman et al., 2007). Some parents and religious groups have opposed the vaccine, fearing that it might encourage promiscuity. Some health professionals are concerned that long-term data about potential side effects of the vaccine aren't yet available. There has been considerable media attention to these concerns. Accordingly, only 54% of Ontario parents whose daughters were in grade eight during the 2007–2008 school year gave permission for their daughters to receive the vaccine (Crawford, 2008).

Ectoparasitic Infestations

Ectoparasite A parasite that lives on the outer surface of an animal.

Ectoparasites live on the outer surfaces of animals. They're larger than the agents that cause other STIs. In this section, we'll consider two types of STIs caused by ectoparasites—pediculosis and scabies.

A World of Diversity

AN HIV INTERVENTION IN KENYA

Eleanor Maticka-Tyndale (2007) of the University of Windsor led an international group of researchers in developing and evaluating a primary-school-based HIV-prevention program in Kenya.

They used a quasi-experimental research procedure, along with both quantitative and qualitative research methods. They compared the effects in 40 schools that received the educational HIV-prevention program with the effects in 40 schools that didn't receive the program.

The research showed that the educational program had a significant impact on 11- to 16-year-olds. These students learned about HIV prevention and how to communicate more openly about HIV.

The effects on behaviour were gender-specific: the girls delayed engaging in sexual activities, and the boys used condoms more frequently.

The educational program had its greatest impact on youth who weren't yet sexually active. The researchers therefore concluded that it should be implemented with the youngest age groups possible (Maticka-Tyndale et al., 2007).

Pediculosis

Pediculosis is the name given to an infestation of a parasite whose proper Latin name, *Phthirus pubis*, sounds rather too dignified for these bothersome (dare we say ugly?) creatures. Their common name is pubic lice, but they're commonly called crabs, because that's what they look like under the microscope. (See Figure 14.8.)

In the adult stage, pubic lice are large enough to be seen with the naked eye. They're spread sexually, and can also be transmitted via contact with infested towels, sheets, and—yes—toilet seats. They can survive for only about 24 hours without a human host, but they may deposit eggs that can take up to seven days to hatch in bedding and towels. All bedding, towels, and clothes that have been used by an infested person must be dry cleaned or washed in hot water and dried on the hot cycle, to ensure that they're safe.

Fingers may also transmit the lice from the genitals to other hair-covered parts of the body, including the scalp and armpits. Sexual contact should be avoided until the infestation is eradicated.

Itching that ranges from mildly irritating to intolerable is the most prominent symptom of an infestation of pubic lice. The itching is caused by the crabs' attaching themselves to the pubic hair and piercing the skin to feed on the blood of their hosts. (Yech!) An infestation can be effectively treated with medication.

Figure 14.8 Pubic lice.
Pediculosis is an infestation by pubic lice (*Phthirus pubis*). Pubic lice are commonly called crabs, because of their appearance under a microscope.

Pediculosis An infestation of pubic lice.

Scabies

Scabies (*Sarcoptes scabiei*) is a parasitic infestation by a tiny mite that may be transmitted through sexual contact or contact with infested clothing, bed linens, towels, and other fabrics. The mites attach themselves to the base of the pubic hair and burrow into the skin, where they lay eggs and subsist for the duration of their 30-day life spans.

Like pubic lice, scabies are often found in the genital region, where they cause itching and discomfort. They're responsible for reddish lines (created by burrowing), sores, welts, and blisters on the skin. Unlike lice, they're too tiny to be seen with the naked eye. Diagnosis is made by detecting the mite or its by-products via microscopic examination of scrapings from suspicious-looking areas of skin. Scabies are most often found on the hands and wrists, but they may also appear on the genitals, buttocks, armpits, and feet. They don't appear above the neck, thankfully!

Scabies, like pubic lice, can be effectively treated with medication. To avoid reinfection, sex partners and others in close bodily contact with infected individuals

Scabies A parasitic infestation by a tiny mite that may be transmitted through sexual contact or contact with infested fabrics.

should also be treated. Clothing and bed linens used by an infested person must be dry cleaned or washed and dried on the hot cycle. Sexual contact should be avoided until the infestation is eliminated.

STI Epidemiology: Biological, Psychological, and Social Factors

Despite advances in medical knowledge about the biology of STIs and HIV/AIDS, and extensive research on how they spread through the population, these infections are still common in Canada and around the world. Why?

One obvious answer is that too many people are unaware of their own personal risks for STIs and HIV, and therefore engage in high-risk behaviours. At a basic level, this is undoubtedly true. Many people lack a basic knowledge of STIs and HIV, and are unaware that they're at risk. To fully understand why it's so difficult to eliminate these infections, however, we need to examine several important factors that drive the spread of STIs and HIV.

At the beginning of this book, we emphasized the importance of a multidisciplinary approach to understanding human sexuality. You may recall that we need to account for the biological, psychological, and social factors that shape our sexuality. This multidisciplinary approach helps us more fully understand how STIs and HIV spread within the population.

Biological Factors

MULTIPLE MEANS OF TRANSMISSION STIs and HIV can be transmitted in multiple ways. These include high-risk sexual behaviours, such as unprotected penile–vaginal and penile–anal intercourse. Oral sex is another form of potential transmission. For STIs such as herpes and the human papillomavirus, transmission can occur through skin-to-skin contact with an infected area. STIs and HIV can also be spread in nonsexual ways. Sharing contaminated needles for injecting drugs is one of the most common ways of transmitting HIV. Using contaminated needles for tattooing can also transmit HIV and hepatitis. Some infections, such as HIV and HSV, can be transmitted from an infected mother to her infant, in the womb or during birth.

LIFELONG INFECTIONS Among the most effective ways to reduce the spread of STIs and HIV are effective treatments and cures. Although medical science has made progress in developing treatments, some viral infections are lifelong. Once a person has been infected with HSV or HIV, for example, the virus will stay in the body for life.

There are now more effective treatments to manage the symptoms, and in some cases to reduce the chances of transmitting these infections. But because they can't be cured, it's more difficult to control the spread of these infections in the population.

ASYMPTOMATIC CASES Many people who become infected with STIs have no observable symptoms. These cases are referred to as asymptomatic. The symptoms may never show up, or there may be time lags between the infections and the appearance of symptoms.

Because many are asymptomatic, people with HIV, HSV, HPV, chlamydia, and other STIs often don't know they're infected. These people are unlikely to get treatment or take preventive measures, such as using condoms. This is a key biological factor that facilitates the spread of these infections.

INCREASED VULNERABILITY STIs that produce genital ulcers, such as syphilis and genital herpes, heighten vulnerability to HIV infection by allowing

CRITICAL THINKING QUESTIONS

Are you surprised to learn that so many cases of STI are asymptomatic? Does this change the way you think about how STIs spread?

other viruses to enter the circulatory system through the ulcers. Some STIs, such as gonorrhea, trichomoniasis, and chlamydia, can inflame the genital region, which heightens the risk of sexual transmission of other STIs.

GENDER Women are more susceptible to STI infection than men. The warm, moist environment of the vagina is more hospitable to bacteria, viruses, and fungi than is the exterior of the penis. The location of the urethra and bladder in women also makes them more susceptible to infection.

LACK OF VACCINES AND CURES It has been very difficult to develop vaccines to prevent STIs. The HIV virus has been especially resistant to vaccines. Fortunately, an effective vaccine has recently been developed that prevents many strains of HPV. There's also a vaccine being developed that appears to be successful in preventing herpes infections.

Psychological Factors

A number of psychological factors predict sexual risk-taking. These include perceived low risks of infection, the myth of personal invulnerability, lack of awareness of a partner's infection, negative attitudes toward condoms, drug and alcohol abuse, and difficulty discussing sexual-health issues.

PERCEIVED LOW RISK In a national survey, one-half of Canadians distanced themselves from HIV and AIDS. They perceived that only people other than themselves could become infected with HIV (Rattner et al., 2007).

One of the major stumbling blocks in promoting safer-sex practices such as condom use is the fact that many young heterosexuals perceive themselves at low risk for contracting STIs and HIV. McGill University researchers Rupert Klein and Bärbel Knäuper (2003) have found that some young people purposely avoid thinking about STIs, and are therefore less likely to discuss safer sex with their partners, and less likely to use condoms. Another study (Knäuper et al., 2005) has shown that university students feel they're less at risk if they have sex with appealing rather than unappealing partners, and therefore are less likely to use condoms with appealing partners.

Gay men may also operate under the "I'm not the type" fallacy, underestimating their personal risks. In a 2002 survey of gay and bisexual men in Ontario, half of the those who had never had an HIV test said it was because they believed they were at low risk of infection (Myers et al., 2004a).

LACK OF COMMUNICATION Many people are embarrassed about asking partners about their past risk behaviours and their STI or HIV status. And people who have engaged in high-risk behaviours or contracted STIs or HIV may be uncomfortable about revealing this information, because they fear their partners will refuse to have sex or end the relationships.

In a University of Guelph study of communication about sexual-health issues such as HIV and pregnancy prevention, female students typically reported that they didn't discuss these issues prior to engaging in sexual intercourse for the first time with new partners (Cleary et al., 2002). Generally, the women reported feeling uncomfortable about initiating discussions about sexual-health topics, and sensed that their partners were also uncomfortable. In the 2002 Ontario study of gay and bisexual men (Myers et al., 2004b), 45% of those with HIV said that in the three months previous to the study, they hadn't disclosed their conditions to casual sex partners, and another 30% said they only sometimes disclosed their status. Unfortunately, we don't have comparable data about disclosure among HIV-positive heterosexuals.

An emerging issue is the question of whether people with HIV have a legal obligation to inform their sexual partners of their status before having sex. Currently, in

Canada, HIV-positive individuals who are aware of their status and don't inform their partners or take measures to prevent infection are committing criminal acts. There have been more than 60 criminal convictions related to HIV transmission, including one for murder (Picard, 2010). There are different perspectives on this issue among HIV/AIDS specialists in Canada. Some argue that criminally prosecuting people who knowingly transmit HIV is a valid approach (Berger, 2009), while others argue that these types of laws discourage people from getting tested for HIV, because someone who doesn't know s/he's infected can't be prosecuted (Wainberg, 2009).

PSYCHOLOGICAL OBSTACLES TO CONDOM USE Effectively promoting the consistent use of latex condoms may be the most important factor in reducing the burden of STIs and HIV in Canada. Yet many Canadians who are at risk don't use condoms.

A recent national survey found that condoms are the most popular method of contraception among Canadian women, especially younger women (Black et al., 2009). When the survey was taken, 74.3% of 15- to 19-year-olds, 55.5% of 20- to 29-year-olds, 48.8% of 30- to 39-year-olds, and 42.5% of women over 40 who'd had vaginal intercourse in the previous six months said they'd used condoms for contraception. Notice that the percentage of people who use condoms declines with age; sexually active teens are those most likely to use condoms.

Analyzing data from the Canadian Community Health Survey, Rotermann and McKay (2009) found that among unmarried, non-cohabiting 20- to 34-year-old Canadians, 35.8% had had more than one intercourse partner during the previous 12 months, while about 30% of the males and nearly 40% of the females who'd had three or four partners during the previous year hadn't used condoms at last intercourse.

There are a number of explanations for why Canadians at risk for STIs and HIV don't use condoms. Some we've already discussed, such as perceived low risk for infection. As adolescents get older and form longer-term relationships, some switch from condoms to the pill. Although birth-control pills are reliable methods of contraception, they don't prevent STIs. After examining data from the Canadian Contraception Study, Fisher et al. (2004) concluded that many young women were using the condom first and foremost as a method of birth control, not as a method of STI/HIV prevention, and were therefore unconcerned about switching to the pill. In many cases, this also speaks to their low perceived risk for infection.

Researchers at Okanagan University College in British Columbia have found that young people in monogamous relationships don't use condoms because they're in love, and trust their partners to be faithful (Netting & Burnett, 2004). In the Canadian Contraception Study, 47% of the women who'd reduced or discontinued their condom use gave the reason "I have only one sexual partner," and 46% said "I know and trust my husband or partner" (Fisher et al., 2004). While many of these women may have been be correct in their assessments, if their known, trusted partners had unknown asymptomatic STI or HIV infections from previous relationships, their discontinuation of condom use resulted in high risks for infection.

It has also been found that the more in love a woman is with her partner, the more strongly she believes she's not at risk for getting an STI from him (Knäuper et al., 2002). Rupert Klein and Bärbel Knäuper (2002) at McGill University have found that female university students believe condom use signifies lack of commitment and trust in their relationships. These studies, and many others, indicate that one of the most significant obstacles to condom use involves the dynamics of a couple relationship.

Other obstacles to condom use are more practical. Some people feel embarrassed about buying them. Some feel that interrupting the sexual act to apply a condom reduces spontaneity. Some men and women say condoms reduce sexual

CRITICAL THINKING QUESTIONS

In your opinion, what's the most important obstacle to condom use among sexually active college and university students?

pleasure. In an Ontario study (Adam et al., 2005), gay and bisexual men gave the following reasons for not using condoms:

- Fear of erection loss.
- Urgency of passion overcoming fear of infection.
- Stress and depression overcoming rational prevention.
- Low self-esteem, leading to indifference about consequences.
- Reliance on intuition to determine whether a partner is HIV-negative.
- Development of a trusting relationship with a partner.

Unless such obstacles to using condoms are overcome, efforts to stem the tide of STI and HIV infection may be thwarted.

ALCOHOL AND DRUG ABUSE Drug and alcohol abuse are associated with increased risk for STIs. A study of heterosexuals has found that people who abuse drugs or alcohol are more likely than others to engage in risky sexual practices (Lowry et al., 1994). Moreover, certain forms of drug use, such as needle sharing, can directly transmit infectious organisms such as HIV.

University of Toronto researchers found that HIV-positive men who had sex with men were least likely to practice safer sex when they were drinking or doing drugs (Calzavara et al., 1992). In Toronto, some gay and bisexual men using crystal meth reported that it reduced sexual inhibitions and intensified the sexual experience (Myers et al., 2004b). North American AIDS organizations are concerned that

Innovative Canadian Research

ANATOMY OF A FORBIDDEN DESIRE

There's been extensive publicity surrounding the HIV risk of unprotected anal sex between men ("bareback sex"). Health educators are therefore puzzled about why some men purposely engage in anal sex without condoms.

To understand this practice, Dave Holmes at the University of Ottawa and Dan Warner at Duquesne University in Pittsburgh conducted interviews with gay men in Canada, the United States, and Europe (Holmes & Warner, 2005). Previous research on this topic had focused on variables such as HIV knowledge, drug use, and number of sexual partners. Holmes and Warner chose to focus on the issues of desire, transgression, and pleasure.

They found that semen exchange was an important part of bareback sexuality. Many of the respondents said semen exchange was essential to providing feelings of connectedness with their sexual partners. The giving of semen was seen as a gift. Other respondents felt that a sense of completion with the sex act couldn't occur without semen exchange. Some interviewees said they had to experience intense feelings of sexual arousal to engage in semen exchange, while others said it felt natural. In other words, sex felt more real when ejaculation took place in the anus.

Some of the respondents didn't feel semen exchange had any special meaning, however, and didn't allow it to happen.

Holmes and Warner concluded that to understand barebacking, we need to be aware of "the real world of sexual desire." Barebackers are aware of the sexual risks, but they prefer to focus on their sexual desire for semen exchange, so the sex act can satisfy their emotional needs for connectedness, naturalness, and sexual completion.

Barry Adam (2007) interviewed Toronto men who engaged in barebacking, and found that they'd adopted a different type of moral reasoning to explain why they weren't concerned about HIV infection. Their premise was that each individual was responsible for his own safety. If a potential partner was worried about HIV, it was up to him to take precautions. For this reason, those who engaged in barebacking didn't feel the need to disclose their HIV status to partners.

This practice is contrary to a Supreme Court of Canada decision that requires HIV-positive people to disclose their HIV status before engaging in sexual relations. Adam contends that most gay men consider barebacking irresponsible, and reject it.

Although Holmes and Warner focused on gay men, their findings may also be applicable to some heterosexuals. Some heterosexuals may feel they haven't really had sex unless the male ejaculates directly into the vagina. One of the authors of this textbook had a discussion about these issues with an African physician at an AIDS conference in Africa. The physician stated that for him, sex had to involve ejaculating into the woman's vagina. This was essential for him to enjoy sex, and outweighed any probability of HIV infection.

Obviously, an anecdotal example such as this is insufficient to answer the question of whether some heterosexuals have the same feelings about semen exchange as the men in the Holmes and Warner study. We hope researchers will examine this question with samples of heterosexual men and women.

the search for heightened sexual pleasure through crystal meth is contributing to an increase in HIV infections. The AIDS Committee of Toronto warns that taking crystal meth increases sexual risk-taking among gay and bisexual men. Of course, it can also increase risk-taking among heterosexuals.

Many other psychological factors can account for sexual risk-taking. Barry Adam (2006) at the University of Windsor has taken a broader perspective by critiquing some health educators' contention that rational decision-making should result in avoidance of risky sexual behaviours. He argues that the drive to satisfy certain emotional needs can often override longer-range safety concerns. For example, someone who is less attractive, less secure, or more needy than his or her partner may not insist on condom use, for fear of losing the partner. And someone who believes true sexual intimacy involves ejaculation without a condom may feel emotionally and sexually unfulfilled if a condom is used. (See "Innovative Canadian Research: Anatomy of a Forbidden Desire.")

Social Factors

STI rates vary by social factors such as gender, age, sexual orientation, group marginalization, province or territory of residence, and negative societal attitudes toward STI-infected people.

GENDER INEQUALITY Social factors make heterosexual females vulnerable to STIs and HIV. Women around the world are more likely than men to be infected, and the number of infected women in Canada may be catching up with the number of infected men. Violence—or the threat of violence—against women increases their vulnerability to HIV, reducing their ability to protect themselves against infection.

At the 2006 International AIDS Conference in Toronto, a key theme was how gender imbalance in many cultures is a key factor in the spread of HIV. Women are more likely than men to be in situations where they lack the right to refuse sex or to require that their partners wear condoms. A United States study of HIV-positive women found a strong relationship between having abusive sex partners and never using condoms (Lang, 2007). Research on youth in Canada found that girls—but not boys—who'd been pressured to have sex were less likely to use condoms than girls who'd had sex without being pressured (Gallupe, Boyce, & Fergus, 2009).

SEXUAL ORIENTATION Gay males have the highest STI rates, and lesbians have the lowest. One explanation is that gay men have more sexual partners than lesbians and heterosexuals. Rates of unprotected sex have been increasing among gay and bisexual men. In the 2002 Ontario Men's Survey (Myers et al., 2004a), 40% of the men reported engaging in unprotected anal sex during the previous year, compared with 20% of the men in a 1991 Canadian survey of gay and bisexual men (Myers, Godin, et al., 1993).

Men who have sex with men but identify themselves as heterosexual are less likely to use condoms than men who identify themselves as gay. However, they also have fewer partners (Patha et al., 2006).

An international study of adolescents in Canada, New Zealand, and the United States has revealed that lesbian, gay, and bisexual (LGB) youth are more likely than heterosexuals to engage in behaviours that pose high risk for HIV (Meininger et al., 2007). In all three countries, LGB youth experience more discrimination and stigmatization than heterosexual youth. In the Canadian and American samples, this stigmatization has a significant influence on risk-taking, regardless of sexual orientation. The researchers have concluded that reducing discrimination against LGB youth may reduce sexual risk-taking among this age group.

A study of adolescents in British Columbia and Seattle has found that LGB youth experience higher rates of sexual abuse and coercion than heterosexual youth (Saewyc, 2006). Those who have experienced sexual abuse are more likely to engage in HIV-risky behaviours.

Innovative Canadian Research

THE INFORMATION-MOTIVATION-BEHAVIOURAL SKILLS MODEL

Simply providing information about AIDS is not enough to decrease the incidence of HIV infection.

Bill Fisher of the University of Western Ontario has conducted research into factors affecting the use of safer-sex practices among various groups, including high school and university students, inner-city minority youth, and gay males.

He and his colleagues have developed the information-motivation-behavioural skills (IMB) theoretical model to explain what determines the behaviours that prevent STIs (Fisher & Fisher, 1992). The model has also been used to explain contraceptive use.

According to the IMB model, people need to be informed not only about the causes of STIs and HIV, but also about effective means of prevention, including how to use condoms correctly.

The model encourages the development of positive attitudes toward condoms and strong social support for their use.

Developing communication skills helps people become more assertive in insisting on condom use, especially with reluctant partners. Behavioural skills also include gaining experience in going to pharmacies or sexual health clinics, to overcome any embarrassment about obtaining condoms.

Based on this model, Fisher (2007) has developed and evaluated what he calls the Options Project. Clinicians are taught to briefly discuss HIV-prevention strategies when first meeting with HIV-positive patients.

Follow-up data with 500 patients, a control group, and a group participating in an intervention program show a dramatic drop in HIV-risky behaviours for the patients in the intervention program, and an increase in HIV-risky behaviours among the control group. This intervention program has been adopted in several clinics in North America and South Africa.

A common misperception is that STIs can't be transmitted between female sex partners. There's a high prevalence of bacterial vaginosis among lesbians. One study of lesbian and bisexual women found that even though one-half of those between the ages of 18 and 22 had histories of BV, they perceived little risk of STI infection from female partners (Marrazzo, 2005). The women took no precautions to prevent STIs. In particular, they didn't wash their hands before sexual activity, didn't use rubber gloves for vaginal or oral penetration, and shared sex toys without washing them or using them with condoms.

GROUP MARGINALIZATION The highest STI rates are among First Nations youth (Shields et al., 2004). According to the 2003 Canadian Community Health Survey, First Nations youth are two and a half times as likely as Canadian youth in general to have STIs (Rotermann, 2005). First Nations women are especially at risk. They're more likely to be poor than other Canadian women, and more likely to live in environments where substance abuse and spousal violence are common (Prentice, 2005).

Disproportionately high numbers of First Nations and black Canadians are living with HIV and AIDS. Before 1992, First Nations people accounted for 1.3% of AIDS cases; this increased to 15% in 2004 and 24.4% in 2006 (Public Health Agency of Canada, 2007). Among aboriginal youth, STI infection is associated with sexual abuse and substance abuse (Devries, Free, Morison, & Saewyc, 2009). Black Canadians accounted for 8% of AIDS cases before 1992, and 15.5% in 2004 (Public Agency of Canada, 2005).

A key explanation for higher levels among these racial minorities are the high levels of poverty and discrimination they often experience. In a Toronto study, STI rates were much higher in areas where people were more likely to be living at the poverty level (Hardwick & Patychuck, 1999). A study of the perceptions of HIV risk and prevention among black women in Toronto concluded that more attention needed to be given to structural factors that affect risk, including gender inequality, poverty, racial discrimination in health care, homophobia, and the need for female-controlled prevention methods (Williams et al., 2007).

CRITICAL THINKING QUESTIONS

Has any of the information in this chapter changed your attitudes toward STIs? If so, how have your attitudes changed?

Applied Knowledge

REDUCING YOUR RISKS FOR STIs AND HIV

STIs are very common, especially among young adults, and HIV/AIDS presents a significant threat to the health and well-being of Canadians. You can do a number of things to lower your risk for STI and HIV infection.

Be Knowledgeable

The first step in protecting yourself is to get the facts. In this chapter we've provided extensive information about STIs and HIV. You can use this information to make well-informed choices that will lower your risk of infection or of transmitting an infection to a sexual partner.

Abstinence

The most effective way to avoid the sexual transmission of STIs and HIV is abstinence.

For preventing infection, abstinence means not engaging in any sexual behaviours that carry a risk of transmission. This includes penile-vaginal and penile-anal intercourse, oral sex, skin-to-skin genital contact, and the exchange of body fluids such as semen, vaginal secretions, and blood.

Use Latex Condoms

Using latex condoms every time you have sex substantially reduces—but doesn't eliminate—the risk of contracting or transmitting STIs and HIV. Latex condoms have been shown to be highly effective in preventing HIV transmission, and studies indicate that they can significantly reduce the risk of

common STIs such as chlamydia, HPV, and HSV.

Remember, to be effective as an STI-prevention tool, condoms must be used properly every time you have sex, not just sometimes. Carry condoms with you, so you'll be prepared, and be clear in your mind about how and when you'll bring up the topic of condom use with a partner.

Limit Your Number of Sexual Partners

The fewer sexual partners you have in your lifetime, the lower your chances of coming into contact with STIs and HIV. Practicing monogamy (having only one sexual partner at a time) is one way to reduce your risk.

Most of us will be serially monogamous, however, having a series of monogamous relationships over our lifetimes. There's a tendency for some couples to use condoms at the beginnings of their relationships, but to stop using them as the relationships become serious. Heterosexual couples often stop using condoms when the female partners start using oral contraception, because their biggest concern is pregnancy, not STIs and HIV.

If you stop using condoms in each of a series of monogamous relationships over a number of years, you'll have unprotected sex with as many partners as you have relationships with, which will increase your chances of STI and HIV infection.

Get Tested for STIs and HIV

It's common for people to assume that if they and their partners have no STI

symptoms and have been selective in their partner choices, there's little or no chance that they have STIs. But remember, most cases of STI and HIV are asymptomatic, and STIs and HIV can happen to anybody.

You can significantly reduce your risk of contracting or transmitting STIs and HIV by agreeing with a new partner that you'll both be tested before having sex. If you regularly have new sexual partners, having equally regular STI and HIV testing is a good idea.

Most doctors and clinics offer routine testing for HIV and common STIs such as chlamydia, but you may need to ask your doctor or clinic to specifically arrange tests for HPV and HSV.

If you think you may have been exposed to an STI or HIV, consult a doctor as soon as possible. Early detection and treatment can make a big difference in reducing or eliminating the infection.

Avoid Nonsexual Risk Behaviours

Avoid contact with bodily substances from other people that can transmit infections—blood, semen, vaginal secretions, fecal matter, and so on.

Don't share hypodermic needles, razors, cuticle scissors, or other instruments that may have another person's blood on them. Be careful when handling wet towels, bed linens, and other materials that may contain bodily substances.

Get Regular Medical Checkups

As part of a regular medical checkup, your doctor will examine your genitals to see

Marginalization affects street youth, who have extremely high rates of STI infection. Their chlamydia rates are nine times greater than those of youth in general (Shields et al., 2004).

Female injection-drug users are another marginalized group (Open Society Institute, 2007). They're more likely to exchange sex for drugs and shelter. They experience high levels of violence from sexual partners, and are less able to insist on condom use. They're also subject to infection from contaminated needles.

if you have any visible symptoms of STI infection. More and more doctors are asking about their patients' sexual behaviours, to determine whether they're at high risk for STIs and HIV, and whether testing is needed.

If you're a woman, talk to your doctor about whether you should have a Pap test to check for abnormal changes to your cervix that may have resulted from HPV infection. A medical checkup is a great opportunity to ask any questions you may have about sexual health.

Engage in Lower-Risk Sexual Behaviours

Some sexual behaviours present higher risks for STIs and HIV than others. Unprotected penile-vaginal and penile-anal intercourse are high-risk behaviours. Although oral sex is less risky than intercourse for HIV and many STIs, it still carries some risk of transmission.

You can lower your risks when engaging in these behaviours by using condoms for vaginal and anal intercourse and fellatio. For cunnilingus, you can cover the genital area with a piece of latex.

Other risky behaviours include inserting a hand or fist into a person's rectum or vagina (fisting). Oral-anal sex (anilingus, or "rimming") is also risky, because of its potential for transmitting microbes between the mouth and the anus.

Mutual masturbation with your partner is a good way to exchange sexual pleasure and carries lower risks than intercourse and oral sex. Some couples find that watching each other masturbate can be a pleasurable means of sexual intimacy, with no risk of STI or HIV transmission.

Using sex toys such as vibrators and dildos—as long as you wash them with soap and water before and after you use them—is another lower-risk way to enjoy sexual activity.

Rubbing your bodies together is also a lower-risk activity, as long there's no genital-to-genital contact and semen and vaginal sections don't come into contact with the other person' genital area or with breaks in the skin.

Engage in **outercourse**, or forms of sexual expression that don't involve the exchange of body fluids. Examples include massage, hugging, caressing, mutual masturbation, and rubbing your bodies together.

Make Your Own Sexual-Health Plan

Many people make decisions about sexual behaviour spontaneously. These decisions are made in the heat of passion, sometimes under the influence of alcohol or drugs.

One way to avoid making snap sexual decisions that may put you at risk for STIs and HIV is to make your own sexual-health plan. In other words, make some of these decisions in advance.

Here are some questions you can ask yourself in making your sexual-health plan:

- At this point in my life, do I want to be sexually active?
- What types of sexual activities am I ready to engage in (e.g., intercourse, oral sex, genital touching)?
- Under what circumstances am I willing to have sex (e.g., hooking up, friends with benefits, dating relationships, committed relationships)?

- What steps will I take to avoid STIs and HIV (e.g., always use condoms, get tested for STIs and HIV, engage in lower-risk behaviours)?

Talk to Your Partners about Sexual Health

If you're comfortable enough to have sex with a partner, you should also be comfortable enough to talk about the importance of protecting your sexual health.

For example you can mention that you've read about how common STIs are, and that most cases don't have visible or obvious symptoms. This can open the way for you to bring up the topic of condom use, choosing to engage in lower-risk sexual behaviours, and getting tested for STI/HIV.

Consult Your Physician if You Suspect You've Been Exposed

If you think you may have been exposed to an STI or HIV, see a doctor as soon as possible.

Many STIs are detectable in the early stages, and can be successfully treated. If you're infected with HIV, early treatment may keep the virus levels low and prevent you from developing AIDS.

Early intervention may also prevent the dangers of an STI spreading to your vital organs.

Be sensitive to any physical changes that may be symptomatic of STIs. Talk to a health professional if you're in doubt.

Sex workers are also marginalized, and often blamed for the spread of STI infections.

PROVINCE OR TERRITORY Reported STI rates are far higher in Yukon, Nunavut, and the Northwest Territories than in the rest of Canada, reflecting the higher incidence among aboriginal people. However, more than 85% of HIV-positive test reports have occurred in Ontario, Quebec, and British Columbia (Public Health Agency of Canada, 2009).

Outercourse Forms of sexual expression, such as massage, hugging, caressing, mutual masturbation, and rubbing bodies together, that don't involve the exchange of body fluids.

Innovative Canadian Research

THE STIGMA OF HIV AND AIDS

HIV and AIDS seems to carry more stigma than any other disease. Heterosexuals appear to worry more about this than gay males.

In a Windsor study of HIV-positive people who were undergoing combination therapies, the heterosexuals were much more secretive about their HIV status, because they perceived that they'd receive little support from others (Adam et al., 2001). Gay males, on the other hand, felt accepted by their friends and social networks.

The researchers attributed this difference to the perception that HIV wasn't part of the heterosexual community. Whether gay or straight, however, almost all of the participants worried that disclosure in the workplace could lead to discrimination and job loss.

In 2006, the Public Health Agency of Canada conducted a national survey of Canadians to determine their attitudes and knowledge related to HIV and AIDS (Rattner et al., 2007). The majority of Canadians (59%) had only low or moderate knowledge about the disease.

Of even greater concern was the level of discriminatory attitudes toward those with HIV and AIDS. Only one-quarter had a high degree of comfort with people who were infected with HIV, and one-fifth didn't believe in supporting the rights of people living with HIV and AIDS.

CULTURE Canada is home to recent immigrants from around the world. Their native cultural traditions and customs related to sexuality are often quite different than those of Canada. In some cases, newcomers may come from countries where open discussion of sexuality, particularly with strangers, is taboo. As a result, some immigrants may be uncomfortable seeking sexual-health care (Shirpak, Maticka-Tyndale, & Chinichian, 2007). This can present an important obstacle to STI and HIV prevention, diagnosis, and treatment (Public Health Agency of Canada, 2008).

SOCIAL CAPITAL University of Windsor researchers (Smylie et al., 2006) have found that youth with strong social ties to family, peers, and community organizations are less likely to engage in risky sexual behaviours than youth without these strong ties. Their social networks provide intangible resources that enable them to make healthier decisions, resulting in fewer social problems for themselves and for society.

SOCIETAL ATTITUDES People equate STIs with immoral sexual behaviour, and therefore regard people with STI and HIV infections negatively. For people infected with STIs, fear of being judged often leads to guilt, which means they delay seeking treatment and are reluctant to tell others—including their partners—about their infections. (This is discussed in more detail in "Innovative Canadian Research: The Stigma of HIV and AIDS.")

Talking About Prevention.
Most people don't find it easy to talk frankly about preventing STIs, including HIV ... but what's the alternative?

Education and Prevention

A wide variety of groups in Canada provide STI- and HIV-prevention education and programming. These include the Public Health Agency of Canada, provincial ministries of health, universities, schools, and community groups. These programs are often integrated into broader sexual-health education programs.

The most effective programs go beyond simply providing information, and try to motivate people to reduce their risks and acquire specific behavioural skills (such as negotiating condom use) to enable them to put what they learn into practice. (See "Innovative Canadian Research: The Information-Motivation-Behavioural Skills Model.")

In Chapter 12, we discussed the status of Canadian sexual-health education, including STI and HIV prevention, and the ingredients of effective sexual-risk-reduction programming.

Summing Up

Although public attention has been riveted on AIDS for more than two decades, other STIs such as chlamydia and HPV are more common.

Chlamydia, gonorrhea, and syphilis are STIs caused by bacteria.

Human papillomavirus (HPV) and herpes simplex virus, type 2 (HSV-2), are two common STIs caused by viruses.

The highest rates of common STIs in Canada are among adolescents and young adults.

A large proportion of cases of common STIs such as chlamydia and HPV are asymptomatic (i.e., have no symptoms).

Chlamydia is the most common bacterial STI. In Canada, rates are highest among young women. Many cases have no symptoms. If untreated, chlamydia can damage a woman's reproductive tract.

Gonorrhea is a less-common bacterial STI that can also damage the reproductive system.

Syphilis undergoes several stages of development. Although it can lie dormant for many years, it can be lethal.

Vaginitis is usually characterized by a foul-smelling discharge, genital irritation, and burning during urination. Most cases involve bacterial vaginosis, candidiasis, or trichomoniasis.

AIDS is caused by HIV, a virus that attacks the body's immune system. As HIV disables the body's natural defences, the person becomes vulnerable to opportunistic diseases—such as serious infections and cancers—that are normally held in check. HIV is a blood-borne virus that's also found in semen, vaginal secretions, and breast milk.

The most common avenues of HIV transmission are vaginal and anal intercourse and shared hypodermic needles. There's no cure for AIDS, and an effective, safe vaccine hasn't been developed. Condoms are highly effective in preventing the sexual transmission of HIV.

Oral herpes is caused by the Herpes simplex virus, type 1 (HSV-1). Genital herpes is caused by the Herpes simplex virus, type 2 (HSV-2), which produces painful, shallow sores and blisters on the genitals. HSV-1 can also infect the genitals.

Several types of hepatitis are caused by different viruses. Most cases of hepatitis are transmitted sexually or through contact with contaminated blood or fecal matter.

Human papillomavirus (HPV) is the most common STI. HPV types 6 and 11 can cause genital warts. Types 16 and 18 can, if undetected, lead to cervical cancer. A vaccine is available to protect against these four types of HPV.

The spread of STIs and HIV is driven by a combination of factors that are biological (e.g., multiple means of transmission, lack of vaccines for HIV and most STIs), psychological (e.g., perceived low risk of infection, lack of communication about risk), and social (e.g., gender inequality, marginalization).

Consistent condom use, limiting your number of sexual partners, and getting tested for STIs and HIV are three important steps you can take to reduce your risk of infection.

Test Yourself

Multiple-Choice Questions

1. Many Canadian university students are unaware of HPV, which causes:
    (a) Genital herpes.
    (b) Hepatitis B.
    (c) Genital warts.
    (d) Molluscum contagiosum.

2. As many as _____ of men and _____ of women with chlamydia have no symptoms.
    (a) 50%; 75%
    (b) 75%; 50%
    (c) 35%; 10%
    (d) 25%; 70%

(continued)

3. Untreated chlamydia can lead to _____ in women.
   (a) yeast infections
   (b) wasting syndrome
   (c) cervical cancer
   (d) pelvic inflammatory disease

4. The vaccine Gardasil immunizes against:
   (a) Herpes.
   (b) HPV.
   (c) HIV.
   (d) None of the above.

5. About _____ of women will experience at least one yeast infection during their lifetimes.
   (a) 15%
   (b) 50%
   (c) 75%
   (d) 90%

6. HIV directly attacks the immune system by destroying:
   (a) Pathogenic cells.
   (b) CD4 cells.
   (c) Red blood cells.
   (d) Platelets.

7. All of the following have been shown to transmit HIV infection except:
   (a) Artificial insemination with infected semen.
   (b) Kissing.
   (c) Breastfeeding.
   (d) Unprotected sexual intercourse.

8. The current standard of treatment for HIV/AIDS, known as _____, consists of a mixture of antiretroviral drugs and protease inhibitors.
   (a) ELISA
   (b) AIDSBS
   (c) HAART
   (d) LSMFT

9. Which of the following is a social factor in the spread of STIs?
   (a) Group marginalization.
   (b) Lack of vaccines.
   (c) Perceived low risk of infection.
   (d) The fact that many STIs are asymptomatic.

10. Which of the following is not considered an effective prevention strategy for reducing your risk of STIs and HIV?
    (a) Going with your partner to a clinic so you can both be tested for STIs and HIV.
    (b) Using birth-control pills.
    (c) Engaging in mutual masturbation instead of vaginal or anal intercourse.
    (d) Using latex condoms.

You'll find answers to the "Test Yourself" questions on page 495.

Critical Thinking

1. How would you bring up the topic of condom use with a new sexual partner? What might stop you from bringing it up?

2. What are some of the steps society can take to reduce the number of STI and HIV cases in Canada?

3. You and some friends are sitting around having a drink. One of your friends is certain s/he can tell what sort of person is likely to have an STI, and would never have sex with "someone like that." How do you respond?

MySearchLab

MySearchLab offers extensive help to students with their writing and research project and provides round-the-clock access to credible and reliable source material. Take a tour at www.mysearchlab.com.

Sexual Variations

CRITICAL THINKING QUESTIONS

When you've heard someone call a sexual behaviour abnormal, what criteria for abnormality do you think s/he's used?

Paraphilia A diagnostic category used by the American Psychiatric Association to describe an atypical pattern of sexual arousal or behaviour that becomes problematic in the eyes of the individual or of society. Examples include fetishism and exhibitionism. The urges are recurrent, and either acted on or distressing to the individual who experiences them.

In Western society, there's a tendency to classify behaviour as "normal" or "abnormal," and this is often the case with sexual behaviours. People often wonder, "Am I normal?" In this chapter, we'll examine a number of sexual behaviours that deviate from the norm. First, however, it's important to clarify what we mean when we say a sexual behaviour is abnormal, or deviant.

Normal Versus Deviant Sexual Behaviour

One approach to defining normality versus deviance is statistical (Laws & O'Donohue, 2008). That is, something that falls outside a statistical norm can be considered abnormal. Put another way, something can be considered deviant because it deviates from the norm. So, for example, only a small percentage of people have naturally red hair. In statistical terms, we can say that, with respect to hair colour, red-haired people are abnormal. A sexual behaviour that's unusual is, by statistical definition, abnormal and deviant. But this statistical abnormality doesn't necessarily make an unusual sexual behaviour problematic or harmful.

A second approach to assessing whether a behaviour is normal is to determine how closely it adheres to the accepted norms of a society. For example, in Western culture, oral sex used to be thought of as immoral and "dirty." It violated societal norms for acceptable behaviour. Oral sex was, in other words, considered abnormal and deviant. Today, oral sex is considered a typical sexual behaviour. This example is instructive, because it demonstrates that societal standards for abnormality and deviance can change over time. Societal standards for sexuality can also vary considerably between cultures.

A third approach to determining whether a sexual behaviour is normal focuses on harm—for the individual(s) involved, for others, and for society. In this approach, a sexual behaviour is considered abnormal if it causes stress, anxiety, or unhappiness for the individual who engages in it, or if it's non-consensual or it harms someone else. The discipline of abnormal psychology, for example, focuses less on how statistically rare a specific behaviour is, and more on whether the behaviour causes problems in a person's life, or harms or disrupts the lives of others.

These differences in how the terms "abnormal" and "deviant" are used are extremely important. Some of the behaviours we'll discuss in this chapter may be unusual in a statistical sense, and may be contrary to the accepted norms of mainstream society, but they may also be quite harmless for the individuals in question. Other sexual variations can be quite destructive, both for the individuals who practise them and for others.

Because of the confusing array of meanings for "deviant" and "abnormal," we prefer to speak about unusual patterns of sexual arousal or behaviour as atypical variations in sexual behaviour, rather than as sexual deviations. Atypical patterns of sexual arousal or behaviour that become problematic in the eyes of the individual or of society are labelled as "paraphilias" in the American Psychiatric Association's catalogue of sexual disorders (DSM-IV-TR, 2000). Clinicians consider paraphilias to be mental disorders. But milder forms of these behaviours may be practised by many people and not considered harmful. According to Ottawa psychiatrist Paul Fedoroff, a major factor in delineating paraphilic disorders is that they "involve sex without the possibility of a consensual, mutually reciprocal relationship" (Fedoroff, 2003, p. 336).

The Paraphilias

Paraphilias involve sexual arousal in response to unusual stimuli such as children or other non-consenting individuals (e.g., watching unsuspecting people, or exposing his or her genitals to them), nonhuman objects (such as shoes, leather, rubber, or undergarments), or pain or humiliation (Barbaree & Blanchard, 2008; Laws & O'Donohue, 2008).

The psychiatric diagnosis of paraphilia requires that the person act on the urges in socially unacceptable or harmful ways, or be distinctly distressed by them.

People with paraphilias usually feel that their urges are insistent, demanding, or compulsive (Fedoroff, 2003; Lehne, 2009). They may describe themselves as overcome by them. People with paraphilias tend to experience their urges as uncontrollable, just as drug addicts and compulsive gamblers feel helpless to avert their irresistible urges. For these reasons, theorists have speculated that paraphilias may represent a type of sexual compulsion or addiction.

Paraphilias vary in severity. In some cases, people can function sexually in the absence of the unusual stimuli, seldom if ever acting on their deviant urges. In other cases, people resort to paraphilic behaviour only in times of stress. In more extreme forms, individuals repeatedly engage in paraphilic behaviour, and may become preoccupied with thoughts and fantasies about these experiences. People in this last category may be unable to become sexually aroused without either fantasizing about or being in the presence of the paraphilic stimuli. For them, paraphilic behaviour may be the only means of attaining sexual gratification (Lehne, 2009).

The person with a paraphilia typically replays the paraphilic act in sexual fantasies to stimulate arousal during masturbation or sexual relations. It's as though s/he mentally replays a videotape of the paraphilic scene. The scene grows stale after a while, and the individual feels the urge to perform another paraphilic act, to make a new "video."

Some paraphilias are generally harmless and victimless. Examples include fetishism and cross-dressing to achieve sexual arousal (transvestic fetishism). Indeed, because behaviours such as cross-dressing don't harm others, some experts, including San Francisco physician Charles Moser and Ottawa psychologist Peggy Kleinplatz, believe they shouldn't be categorized as sexual disorders (Moser & Kleinplatz, 2002). Michael Seto and Howard Barbaree of the Centre for Addiction and Mental Health in Toronto further argue that sexual preferences for particular types of people and activities are strongly influenced by cultural values (Seto & Barbaree, 2001). For example, until relatively recently in Western culture,

CRITICAL THINKING QUESTIONS

Can you think of examples from other chapters in this book that illustrate how standards for what's normal sexual behaviour vary across cultures?

From Paraphilic to Convicted Murderer.
The 2010 case of Colonel Russell Williams in Ontario illustrates an extreme form of paraphiliac behaviour in which the individual's urges become compulsive. Williams behaviour escalated from stealing and wearing women's underwear to sexual assault and murder.

Innovative Canadian Research

FEMALE PARAPHILIACS

Many people believe women don't engage in paraphilic activities, partly because so little research has been conducted in this area. One of the relatively few studies of female paraphiliacs was conducted by Paul Fedoroff, an Ottawa psychiatrist and one of Canada's leading experts on paraphilias, along with his colleagues Alicia Fishell and Beverly Fedoroff.

The study was based on 14 women who were referred to clinics in Canada, the United States, and Great Britain. Each had more than one paraphilic disorder. The most common were pedophilia, sexual sadism, and exhibitionism. Only three of the 14 women reported past sexual victimization.

One of the participants, a heterosexual woman, had referred herself to a clinic because of a tendency to exhibit:

She described a ritual of undressing herself and masturbating with the lights on in front of her apartment window, approximately five times a month. While she was aroused by the idea of being seen by male strangers, she denied any wish to engage in sex with anyone who saw her. Unless she was involved in "really bizarre situations," she had primary anorgasmia even when masturbating.

At one point she began driving her truck through unfamiliar neighbourhoods with pet food, in an attempt to befriend cats and dogs, which she would "abduct." She would coax the cats to lick her genitals by placing honey on her vaginal area. She would perform oral sex on male dogs whom she "abducted" in a similar manner. She also described sexual fantasies about having sex with boys and girls between the ages of eight and 10. On one occasion she had "punished" an eight-year-old

boy she was babysitting by squeezing his penis and "physically smacked him around." She was sexually aroused by this activity, and would often masturbate while recalling this episode.

Three years prior to assessment, she had become involved in a unique form of prostitution in which she would flag down taxis from her truck and then proceed to talk the taxi drivers into paying to have sex with her. She did the same thing with men she met on "phone sex lines." She did this for about a year, and then stopped because, she said, "It wasn't me." She had been engaged, but found she could not have sex with her male partner unless she acted out her paraphilic interests (activities that caused him to leave her). (p. 133)

Fedoroff and his colleagues offered these comments on the case:

This woman's presentation is typical of many self-referred men who are not facing charges, in that there are multiple highly idiosyncratic and obligatory sex "rituals" described. She was "obsessed" with sex, devoting the majority of her waking days to fulfilling her sexual desires. However, she also described high levels of sex guilt (a finding also characteristic of male sex offenders). Although she found these activities highly sexually arousing, they were at the same time highly aversive to her, particularly "because she was a Christian."

This case is also instructive because her partner (in this case, a male) was not supportive of her paraphilic activities. This woman found it impossible to forgo her paraphilic activities, even though she knew it spelled the end of the most important romantic relationship she had ever established. (p. 133)

Source: Adapted from Fedoroff, J. P., Fishell, A., & Fedoroff, B. (1999). A case series of women evaluated for paraphilic disorders. The Canadian Journal of Human Sexuality, 8, 127–140.

homosexuality was considered a mental pathology, whereas there's now a consensus among the mental-health community that it's not.

In another article, Moser and Kleinplatz (2005a) argue that paraphilias should be removed from DSM-IV. Their main concern is that the section is based not on current scientific findings, but on political values about what's considered acceptable behaviour. Moser and Kleinplatz argue that unusual sexual interests aren't signs of pathology, but variations on the continuum of sexual interest (Moser & Kleinplatz, 2005b).

Because of these concerns, Moser (2001) has proposed that the concept of sexual-interest disorder (SID) should be substituted for paraphilia. Here Moser calls for elimination of the naming of specific interests, because he argues that a behaviour by itself is not an indication of pathology. Rather, the key issue is whether the behaviour causes distress or dysfunction for the individual.

Moser (2001) also argues that therapists shouldn't always work toward eliminating particular sexual interests, but should offer clients the option of learning how to express these interests in healthier ways. He doesn't, however, propose that all sexual interests should be acceptable. Some paraphilic behaviours, such as exposing oneself in public or enticing children into sexual relations, do have victims, and may cause severe physical or psychological harm. They're also against the law. Sexual sadism, in which sexual arousal is connected to hurting or humiliating another person, can be very harmful when it's forced upon a non-consenting person. Some brutal rapes involve sexual sadism.

Paraphilias are more common among men than women (American Psychiatric Association, 2000). (See "Innovative Canadian Research: Female Paraphiliacs" to read about a Canadian study of female paraphiliacs.) Because people are generally unwilling to talk about them, the prevalence of paraphilias in the general population remains unknown. Much of what we've learned about paraphilias derives from the reported experiences of people who've been apprehended for performing illegal acts (such as exposing themselves in public), and from the few who have voluntarily sought help. The characteristics of people who haven't been identified or studied remain virtually unknown.

In this chapter, we'll discuss all of the major types of paraphilia except pedophilia, which we'll discuss in Chapter 16. In pedophilia, children become the objects of sexual arousal. It often involves sexual coercion, including incest and sexual molestation.

Fetishism

In **fetishism**, an inanimate object elicits sexual arousal. Articles of clothing (e.g., women's panties, bras, lingerie, stockings, gloves, shoes, or boots) and materials made of rubber, leather, silk, or fur are among the more common fetishistic objects. Leather boots and high-heeled shoes are especially popular.

The fetishist may act on the urges to engage in fetishistic behaviour, such as masturbating while stroking or fantasizing about an object, or he may be distressed about such urges or fantasies, and not act on them. In a related paraphilia, **partialism**, people are excessively aroused by a particular body part, such as the feet, breasts, or buttocks.

Most fetishes and partialisms are harmless. Fetishistic practises are nearly always private, involving masturbation, or are incorporated into intercourse with willing partners (Darcangelo, 2008). Only rarely have fetishists coerced others into paraphilic activities. Yet some partialists have touched parts of women's bodies in public. And some fetishists have committed burglaries to acquire fetishistic objects. In Calgary, a man was charged with stealing women's panties during real estate tours of houses that were for sale, then placing obscene phone calls to the occupants of the houses ("Man Accused . . . ," 2002).

Transvestism

Fetishism appears to include **transvestism**. Although other fetishists become sexually aroused by handling fetishistic objects while they masturbate, transvestites become excited by wearing articles of clothing—the fetishistic objects—of the other gender. A fetishist may find the object—or sex involving the object— erotically stimulating. The transvestite finds the

Fetishism A paraphilia in which an inanimate object, such as an article of clothing or items made of rubber, leather, or silk, elicits sexual arousal.

Partialism A festishism-related paraphilia in which sexual arousal is exaggeratedly associated with a particular body part, such as feet, breasts, or buttocks.

Transvestism A paraphilia in which a person repeatedly cross-dresses to achieve sexual arousal or gratification, or is troubled by persistent, recurring urges to cross-dress.

Fetishism.
In fetishism, inanimate objects such as leather shoes or boots, or parts of the body such as feet, elicit sexual arousal.

Transvestism.
Transvestites cross-dress for sexual arousal and gratification. Are women who wear jeans engaging in transvestic activity? (The answer is no. But as a critical thinker, explain why.)

object sexually alluring only by wearing it. Transvestites are mostly male (Långström & Zucker, 2005). Transvestism has been described among both heterosexual and gay males (Taylor & Rupp, 2004; Wheeler et al., 2008). Many are in committed male–female relationships and otherwise stereotypically masculine in behaviour.

Transvestism differs markedly from transsexualism. It's true that some transvestites and some transsexuals appear to be motived by autogynephilia, a condition in which an individual is sexually stimulated by fantasies that his own body is female (Bailey, 2003b; Lawrence, 2004), but transvestites are usually sexually gratified by cross-dressing and masturbating or by cross-dressing and having sex with others. They may also find it gratifying to masturbate while fantasizing about cross-dressing.

Many transvestites have masculine gender identities, and don't seek to change their anatomic sex. Transsexuals, on the other hand, usually cross-dress because they're uncomfortable with the attire associated with their anatomic sex, and truly wish to be members of the other sex. For this reason, many transsexuals seek sex reassignment.

Like fetishism in general, the origins of transvestism remain obscure. Evidence of hormonal and neurological abnormalities in transvestism is mixed (Bailey, 2003b). Långström and Zucker (2005) surveyed 2 450 Swedes and found transvestism in about 2.8% of the men and 0.4% of the women. They found that transvestism was associated with separation from parents, same-sex sexual experiences, use of pornography, high rates of masturbation, and paraphilias—namely, sexual masochism, exhibitionism, and voyeurism.

Some men cross-dress for reasons other than sexual arousal, and so aren't true transvestites. Some make their livings by impersonating women such as Marilyn Monroe and Madonna on stage, and are not motivated by sexual arousal. Among some segments of the gay community, it's fashionable to masquerade as a woman. Gay men don't usually cross-dress to become sexually stimulated.

Transvestic behaviours can range from wearing a single female garment when alone to sporting a dress, wig, makeup, and feminine mannerisms at a transvestite club. Some transvestites become sexually aroused by masquerading as women and attracting the interest of unsuspecting males. They sometimes entice these men, stringing them along until they find some excuse to back out before their anatomic sex is revealed. The great majority of transvestites don't engage in antisocial or illegal behaviour. Most practise their sexual predilections in private, and would be horrified to be discovered by associates while dressed in female attire.

Kathleen Cairns, a Calgary therapist, has found that wives of cross-dressers required several sessions with therapists to deal with the fear, betrayal, and grief they experience upon learning of their husbands' behaviour (Cairns, 1997). Wives were far more concerned than their husbands about their children's finding out about the cross-dressing.

Exhibitionism

Exhibitionists ("flashers") have persistent, powerful urges and sexual fantasies that involve exposing their genitals to unsuspecting strangers, to achieve sexual arousal or gratification (Murphy & Page, 2008). They either act on the urges or find them disturbing. Exhibitionists are almost always male, although there are some female exhibitionists (Hugh-Jones et al., 2005).

What we know of exhibitionists, like most people with paraphilias, is almost entirely derived from studies of men who've been apprehended or treated by mental-health professionals (Langevin, 2006). Such knowledge may yield a biased picture. Although about one in three arrests for sexual offences involve exhibitionism, relatively few reported incidents result in charges and convictions (Cox, 1988).

Based on the available information, the typical exhibitionist is thought to be young, lonely or in an unhappy male–female relationship, and sexually repressed. An exhibitionist may claim that sex with his regular partner is reasonably satisfactory, but that he also experiences the compulsion to expose himself to strangers. Many exhibitionists are single, however. They typically have difficulties relating to women and are unable to establish meaningful heterosexual relationships (Leue et al., 2004; Murphy & Page, 2008).

Exhibitionism usually begins before age 18 (American Psychiatric Association, 2000). The urge to "flash," if not the actual act, usually begins in early adolescence, generally between the ages of 13 and 16 (Freund et al., 1988). The frequency of exhibitionism declines markedly after age 40 (American Psychiatric Association, 2000). The typical exhibitionist doesn't attempt further sexual contact with the victim.

The police may sometimes trivialize exhibitionism as a nuisance crime, but the psychological consequences can be serious for victims, especially young children. Victims may feel violated, and may be bothered by recurrent images or nightmares. They may also develop fears of venturing out on their own.

An Ontario study of exhibitionists who were repeat offenders found that 12% were also convicted of other sexual offences, and 17% were convicted of violent crimes (Rabinowitz et al., 2002). Another Ontario study (Firestone et al., 2006) found that men who exhibit may be at high risk for engaging in more serious offences. About one-third of the sample in the second study went on to commit sexual or violent offences.

Some evidence suggests that exhibitionists may attempt to assert their masculinity by evoking responses from their victims, or that they exhibit themselves to express hostility toward women (Murphy & Page, 2008). A number of exhibitionists have reported that they've hoped the women would enjoy the experiences and be impressed with the sizes of their penises (Langevin et al., 1979).

Other studies show exhibitionists to be shy, dependent, passive, lacking in sexual and social skills, and even inhibited (Leue et al., 2004). Exhibitionists who are socially shy or inadequate may be using exhibitionism as a substitute for the intimate relationships they can't develop.

Exhibitionism A paraphilia characterized by persistent, powerful urges and sexual fantasies that involve exposing one's genitals to unsuspecting strangers. The exhibitionist achieves sexual arousal or gratification from this behaviour.

An Exhibitionist?
How do the motives of an exotic dancer differ from that of a paraphillic exhibitionist?

The preferred victims are typically girls or young women. The typical exhibitionist drives up to or walks in front of a stranger and exposes his penis. In one sample of 130 exhibitionists, about 50% reported that they always or nearly always had erections when they exposed themselves (Langevin et al., 1979). After his victim registers fear, disgust, confusion, or surprise, an exhibitionist typically covers himself and flees. He usually masturbates, either while exposing himself or shortly afterward while thinking about the act and the victim's response (American Psychiatric Association, 2000). Some exhibitionists ejaculate during the act. Most of the 238 exhibitionists in an Ontario study reported masturbating to orgasm while exposing themselves or while fantasizing about it later (Freund et al., 1988).

Sometimes a couple will engage in public exhibitionism. At a Toronto Blue Jays game, for example, a man and woman had sex by the window of their hotel room, which directly faced the playing field, and thousands of fans got to watch more than the baseball game.

Definitions of exhibitionism also bring into focus the boundaries between normal and abnormal behaviour (Hugh-Jones et al., 2005; Laws & O'Donohue, 2008). People in intimate relationships may enjoy and become sexually aroused by showing their bodies to their partners, especially if the displays also arouse the partners. The behaviour is exhibitionist in some respects—but is it appropriate to label it as abnormal or even paraphilic? If we assume both partners are consenting and the behaviour isn't motivated by a person's overwhelming, uncontrollable urge to expose his genitals, then we're likely to see the behaviour as harmless fun, rather than abnormal.

And we might ask whether exotic dancers (strippers) are exhibitionists. After all, aren't they exposing themselves to strangers? Yes, they are, but they are not exhibitionist in the paraphilic sense. They're more successful at their work if they sexually excite their audiences, but their audiences are not unsuspecting victims. They pay for the privilege of watching. The main motivation of exotic dancers is to earn a living, rather than their own sexual gratification (Philaretou, 2006).

Obscene Phone Calling (Telephone Scatologia)

Like exhibitionists, obscene phone callers (almost all of whom are male) seek to become sexually aroused by shocking their victims (Briken et al., 2005; Pakhomou, 2006). Whereas an exhibitionist exposes his genitals to produce the desired response, the obscene phone caller "exposes" himself verbally by uttering obscenities and sexual provocations to a non-consenting person. DSM-IV labels this type of paraphilia **telephone scatologia** (American Psychiatric Association, 2000). People practising chat scatologia are sexually aroused by sending obscene emails, instant messages, and chat-room messages (Abal et al., 2003; Quayle, 2008). These behaviours are sometimes considered a form of exhibitionism.

Relatively few obscene callers are women (Quayle, 2008). Women who are charged with such offences are generally motivated by rage for some actual or fantasized rejection, rather than the desire for sexual arousal. They use the phone to hurl sexual invectives against men who they feel have wronged them. By contrast, male obscene phone callers are generally motivated by a desire for sexual excitement, and usually choose their victims randomly from the phone book or by chance dialing. They typically masturbate during or shortly after the phone calls. Most obscene telephone callers also engage in other paraphilic acts, especially voyeurism and exhibitionism (Heil & Simons, 2008).

There are many patterns of obscene phone calling. Some callers limit themselves to obscenities. Others make sexual overtures. Some just breathe heavily into the receiver. Others describe their masturbatory activities to their victims. Some profess to have previously met the victims at social gatherings or through mutual acquaintances. Some even present themselves as "taking a sex survey," and ask a series of personally revealing questions.

Telephone scatologia A paraphilia characterized by the making of obscene telephone calls.

Applied Knowledge

RESPONDING TO EXHIBITIONISTS AND OBSCENE PHONE CALLERS

How to Respond to an Exhibitionist

It's understandable that if you're an unsuspecting woman who's confronted by an exhibitionist, you may react with shock, surprise, or fear. Unfortunately, your display of shock or fear may reinforce the flasher's tendency to expose himself.

You may fear that the flasher, who has already broken at least one social code, is likely to assault you physically, as well. Fortunately, most exhibitionists don't seek actual sexual contact with their victims, and run away before they can be apprehended by police or passersby.

When possible, showing no reaction or simply continuing on your way may be the best response. If you do want to respond to the flasher, you might calmly say something like "You really need professional help. You should see a professional to help you with this problem." You should then promptly report the incident to police, so authorities can apprehend the offender.

How to Respond to an Obscene Phone Caller

What should you do if you receive an obscene phone call? Advice generally parallels that given to women who are victimized by exhibitionists. Above all, remain calm, and don't reveal shock or fright, because such reactions tend to reinforce the caller's behaviour and increase the probability of repeat calls.

You may be best advised to say nothing at all and gently hang up the phone. Or you might offer a brief response that alludes to the caller's problems before hanging up. You might say in a calm but strong voice, "It's unfortunate that you have this problem. I think you should seek professional help."

If you receive repeated calls, you might request an unlisted number or contact the police about tracing the calls. Many women list themselves only by their initials in the phone directory, to disguise their gender. This practise is so widespread, however, that obscene callers may assume people listed by initials are women who live alone.

The typical obscene phone caller is a socially inadequate heterosexual male who has difficulty forming intimate relationships with women (Leue et al., 2004). The relative safety and anonymity of the telephone may shield him from the risk of rejection (Leue et al., 2004). Reactions of shock or fright from his victims may fill him with the feelings of power and control that are lacking in his life, especially in his relationships with women. The obscenities may vent rage that he holds against women who have rejected him.

Obscene phone calls are illegal, but it's been difficult for authorities to track down perpetrators. Call tracing can help police track offending phone callers. Call tracing works in different ways in different locales. Caller ID shows the caller's telephone number on a display panel on the receiving party's telephone. In some locales, people can program their telephone services, so callers from private or anonymous numbers (i.e., numbers that don't provide caller ID) receive messages stating that the recipients only accept calls from people who provide their phone numbers or names. These services may deter some obscene callers, but others may use public phones instead of their home phones.

Voyeurism A paraphilia characterized by strong, repetitive urges and sexual fantasies related to observing unsuspecting strangers who are naked, disrobing, or engaged in sexual relations.

Voyeurism

Voyeurism involves strong, repetitive urges to watch unsuspecting strangers who are naked, disrobing, or engaged in sexual activity (Lavin, 2008). The voyeur becomes sexually aroused by the act of watching, and typically doesn't seek sexual relations with the person he observes. Like fetishism and exhibitionism, voyeurism is more common among males than females. It usually begins before age 15 (APA, 2000). In Toronto, Kurt Freund and

Blurring Boundaries.
How would you describe this scene? Is it voyeurism? Exhibitionism? Or normal behaviour?

Innovative Canadian Research

NORMAL VOYEURISM

Waterloo researchers B. J. Rye and Glenn Meaney (2007) conducted a survey to determine whether university students would, hypothetically, watch an attractive person undressing or two attractive people having sex.

Most (84% the males and 74% of the females) said they'd watch an attractive person undressing if they wouldn't be caught

doing so. However, far fewer females (40%) than males (70%) said they'd watch a couple having sex if they wouldn't be caught.

For both situations, fewer said they'd watch if there was a chance of being caught.

The finding that fewer students would watch a couple having sex suggests that this voyeuristic behaviour is considered more invasive of people's privacy.

---

his colleagues found that 12% of university males and 23% of a sample of community males had masturbated while watching females who were unaware of their presence (Freund et al., 1997).

The voyeur may masturbate while peeping, or afterward while replaying the incident in his imagination or engaging in voyeuristic fantasies. The voyeur may fantasize about making love to the observed person, but have no intention of actually doing so.

Are people voyeurs if they become sexually aroused by the sight of their lovers undressing? What about people who enjoy watching pornographic films, or stripteases? No, no, and no. The people being observed are not unsuspecting strangers. The lover knows his or her partner is watching. Porn actors and strippers know others are viewing them. They wouldn't be performing if they didn't expect or have audiences.

It's perfectly normal for men and women to be sexually stimulated by the sight of other people who are nude, undressing, or engaged in sexual activity. Voyeurism is characterized by urges to spy on *unsuspecting* strangers.

A World of Diversity

IT SEEMS LIKE VOYEURS ARE EVERYWHERE!

Traditionally, the voyeur has been categorized as a "peeping Tom" who looks through windows in the hopes of seeing a woman undressing. In recent years, voyeurs have been caught in many other kinds of situations.

The development of small video cameras and lenses has made voyeurism easier. Consider the following examples:

■ In Toronto, a man secretly videotaped women using a washroom in a rooming house.

■ In Winnipeg, a restaurant owner installed a camera just above the toilet in the women's washroom.

■ In Edmonton, a landlord using a camera hooked up to his computer spied on a female tenant living in the basement apartment.

■ In Toronto, a man attached the lens of a video camera to his shoe, and used this to film under women's skirts in public locations. He posted these video shots for sale on the internet at an "Up-Skirt" website.

■ In Toronto, a medical technician used a video camera hidden in a medical laboratory's change room to film women undressing.

■ In Peterborough, a man used a two-way mirror in a KFC outlet to spy on women who were changing into their uniforms.

■ In Toronto, a man secretly videotaped his sexual behaviour with a teacher's aide, and blackmailed her into giving him money so he wouldn't show the tape to her parents and her employer.

Research with voyeurs and exhibitionists has usually been conducted with people who've been charged with crimes or seeing therapists. We lack research on general populations. A national survey conducted in Sweden did reveal, however, that 11.5% of men and 4% of women had been sexually aroused by spying on others having sex, and that 4% of men and 2% of women had been sexually aroused by exposing their genitals to strangers (Langstrom & Seto, 2006).

Although most voyeurs are nonviolent, some commit violent crimes such as assault and rape (Langevin, 2003). Voyeurs who break into and enter homes or buildings, or who tap at windows to gain the attention of victims, are among the more dangerous.

Sexual Masochism

As long as it occurs with mutual consent, it's considered normal to enjoy some mild forms of pain during sexual activity. Love bites, hair pulls, and minor scratches are examples that fall within normal limits (Laws & O'Donohue, 2008).

But people who prefer or need to have pain or humiliation inflicted on them by their sex partners are **sexual masochists**. A sexual masochist may act on or be distressed by persistent urges and sexual fantasies involving the desire to be bound, flogged, humiliated, or made to suffer in some way in order to achieve sexual excitement. In some cases, the sexual masochist can't become aroused unless s/he is bound, flogged, or humiliated by a sex partner. **Sexual masochism** is the most common paraphilia among women (Hucker, 2008; Logan, 2008).

The word "masochism" derives from the name of Austrian storyteller Leopold von Sacher-Masoch (1836–1895). He wrote tales of men who derived sexual satisfaction from having female partners inflict pain on them, typically by flagellation (beating or whipping).

Sexual masochists may derive pleasure from various types of punishing experiences, including being restrained (a practise known as **bondage**), blindfolded (sensory bondage), spanked, whipped, or made to perform humiliating acts, such as walking around on all fours and licking the boots or shoes of the partner, or being subjected to vulgar insults. Some masochists have their partners urinate or defecate on them. Some masochists prefer particular sources of pain; others seek an assortment. But we shouldn't think sexual masochists enjoy types of pain that

Sexual masochist A person who becomes sexually aroused by experiencing pain or humiliation inflicted by a sexual partner.

Sexual masochism A paraphilia characterized by the desire or need for pain or humiliation to enhance sexual arousal and attain gratification.

Bondage Ritual restraint (e.g., by shackles) practised by many sexual masochists.

In 2005, Parliament passed legislation that makes it a crime to secretly observe or record a person in situations where privacy is expected. This includes situations where someone is nude or engaged in sexual activity. It also includes situations where a person is fully clothed and someone observes or records him or her for sexual purposes.

In 2010, for example, an Ontario man was convicted of voyeurism for recording his friends and employees with a hidden camera in the bathroom of his house.

Because of concerns over the misuse of camera phones, some fitness centres and other organizations have banned them, especially in change rooms.

Shooting Private Parts in Public Places.
Police are beginning to catch people trying to shoot private parts in public places. The offenders aim compact camcorders up women's skirts in crowded stores, shopping malls, parks, and fairs. They sometimes post the pictures on the internet, where they often wind up for sale on sex sites.

don't involve sex. Sexual masochists are no more likely than anyone else to derive pleasure from the pain they experience when they stub their toes or touch hot stoves. Pain must be part of an elaborate sexual ritual, to provide erotic gratification (Hucker, 2008).

Sexual masochists and **sexual sadists** often form sexual relationships to meet one another's needs (Yates et al., 2008). Sexual sadism is a paraphilia characterized by the desire to inflict pain or humiliation on someone else in order to enhance sexual arousal and achieve gratification. Some sexual masochists enlist the services of prostitutes or their regular sexual partners to help them enact their masochistic fantasies.

It may seem contradictory for pain to become connected with sexual pleasure. The association of sexual arousal with mildly painful stimuli, however, is actually quite common. Kinsey and his colleagues (1953) reported that perhaps one person in four has experienced erotic sensations from being bitten during lovemaking. The eroticization of mild forms of pain (love bites, hair pulls, minor scratches) may fall within the normal range of sexual variation. Pain from these sources increases overall bodily arousal, which may enhance sexual excitement. Some of us become sexually excited when our partners "talk dirty" to us or call us vulgar names. When the urge for pain for purposes of sexual arousal becomes so persistent or strong that it overshadows other sources of sexual stimulation, or when the masochistic experience causes physical or psychological harm, we may say the boundary between normality and abnormality has been breached.

Sexual masochism can range from relatively benign to potentially lethal practises such as **hypoxyphilia** (also known as auto-erotic asphyxia). Hypoxyphiliacs put plastic bags over their heads, nooses around their necks, or pressure on their chests to temporarily deprive themselves of oxygen while engaging in some form of sexual stimulation, usually masturbation. They often fantasize that they're being strangled by a lover. They try to discontinue oxygen deprivation before they lose consciousness, but miscalculations result in death by suffocation or strangulation (Behrendt et al., 2002; Santtila et al., 2002).

Sexual Sadism

Sexual sadism is named after the infamous Marquis de Sade (1740–1814), a Frenchman who wrote tales of becoming sexually aroused by inflicting pain or humiliation on others. The virtuous Justine, heroine of his novel of the same name, endures terrible suffering at the hands of fiendish men.

Sexual sadism is characterized by persistent, powerful urges and sexual fantasies involving the inflicting of pain and suffering on others in order to achieve sexual excitement or gratification (Yates et al., 2008). The sexual sadist acts on his or her urges, or finds them distressing. Some sexual sadists cannot become sexually aroused unless they make their sex partners suffer. Others can become sexually excited without such acts.

Some sadists hurt or humiliate willing partners, such as prostitutes or sexual masochists. Others—a small minority—stalk and attack non-consenting victims (Yates et al., 2008).

SADO-MASOCHISM **Sado-masochism (S&M)** is a mutually gratifying sexual interaction involving power exchange between consenting partners. A variation is bondage and discipline (B&D), which involves restraining and punishing a submissive partner physically or verbally. Today the term "BDSM" is often used instead of "S&M."

Occasional S&M is quite common among the general population. Couples may incorporate light forms of S&M into their lovemaking now and then, in the form of mild dominance-and-submission games or gentle physical restraint. It's

Sexual sadist A person who becomes sexually aroused by inflicting pain or humiliation on a sexual partner.

Hypoxyphilia A practice in which a person seeks to enhance sexual arousal, usually during masturbation, by depriving himself of oxygen.

Sexual sadism A paraphilia characterized by the desire to inflict pain or humiliation on others in order to enhance sexual arousal and attain gratification.

Sado-masochism (S&M) A mutually gratifying sexual interaction between consenting partners, in which sexual arousal is associated with inflicting and receiving pain or humiliation. It's commonly known as S&M.

not uncommon for lovers to scratch or bite their partners, to heighten their mutual arousal during intercourse. They generally don't inflict severe pain or damage.

Most S&M encounters are time-limited. They're often built around particular themes involving role play, such as a schoolteacher and a naughty schoolboy. Both the dominant person and the submissive person agree ahead of time on the rules, and usually choose a safe word that the submissive person will say to stop a particular action if it exceeds his or her limits. Once the scene is over, the participants assume their regular relationship (Dancer et al., 2006).

In a small minority of relationships, referred to as "24/7 S&M slavery," the participants attempt to live full-time in owner–slave relationships. In one study, the participants were almost

S&M.
An S&M club patron pays money for the services of a dominatrix.

evenly divided between female and male, and ranged in age from 18 to 72. Of the 66 men, 51 were involved with other men and 15 were involved with women. Of the 80 women, 74 were involved with men and six were involved with other women. According to the study respondents, the majority of these relationships were long-lasting and satisfying. The individuals who adopted the slave roles did have the right to exercise their free will, and could therefore leave the relationships at any time (Dancer et al., 2006).

Although some forms of sado-masochism may fall within the boundaries of normal sexual variation, sado-masochism becomes pathological when the fantasies are acted on in ways that become destructive, dangerous, or distressing to either partner. How would you categorize the following example?

> A 25-year-old female graduate student described a range of masochistic experiences. She reported feelings of sexual excitement during arguments with her husband, when he'd scream at her or hit her in a rage. She would sometimes taunt him to make love to her in a brutal fashion, as though she were being raped. She found the brutality and the sense of being punished sexually stimulating. She had also begun having sex with strange men, and enjoyed being physically punished by them during sex more than any other type of sexual stimulus. Being beaten or whipped produced the most intense sexual experiences she'd ever had. Although she recognized the dangers posed by her sexual behavior, and felt somewhat ashamed about it, she wasn't sure she wanted treatment for it, because of the pleasure it provided her. (Adapted from Spitzer et al., 1989, pp. 87–88)

Some S&M practises can be dangerous. A married couple living near Rockwood, Ontario, played a sex game in their barn, taking turns hanging each other with a rope tied to their necks (Dharmajah, 2008). They engaged in this game numerous times, and videotaped themselves. The last time they played this game, the husband lost consciousness and died. The wife was charged with criminal negligence causing death, and sentenced to 12 months of home confinement. Her husband had been convicted of manslaughter in 1985, for the death of a 19-year-old woman who'd been found buried in handcuffs. The Crown's theory had been that the woman had died during a sex act, when the man had compressed a nerve in her neck and it had stopped her heart (Tracey, 2007).

There's a subculture in which sexual sadists and sexual masochists form liaisons to inflict and receive pain and humiliation during sexual activity. The S&M subculture is catered to by sex shops that sell S&M magazines and paraphernalia,

Innovative Canadian Research

WOMEN'S SUBMISSIVE DESIRES

Numerous websites deal with S&M behaviours. Amy Muise (2008), a researcher at the University of Guelph, conducted a study of anonymous women's blogs that focused on sexual desire.

On many of these blogs, the women wrote about their thoughts, experiences, and feelings about their submissive sexual desires. Because of the anonymity of the internet, they felt comfortable revealing personal aspects of their sexual desires that they usually kept hidden. One woman wrote:

I want to beg to be fucked and flogged. I know I look more innocent than sultry, but my inner slut is inside, just waiting to be set loose. I have kept her hidden all my life, and now that I've opened the door, my slut wants to share everything.

In analyzing these blogs, Muise (2008) found two main themes.

First, the women described in explicit detail the intense degrees of physical arousal they felt, especially in their genitals, in response to S&M fantasies and experiences. Describing these powerful physical reactions helped validate their submissive desires.

Second, several of the women put their experiences into the context of trusting love relationships with their partners. For some, this helped legitimize their desires (Muise, 2008).

including leather restraints and leather face masks that resemble the ancient masks of executioners. People in the subculture seek one another out through mutual contacts, S&M social organizations, and personal ads in S&M magazines.

Participants in sado-masochism often engage in highly elaborate rituals involving dominance and submission. They stage rituals as though they're scenes in a play (Gross, 2006). In the master-and-slave game, the sadist leads the masochist around by a leash, and the masochist performs degrading or menial acts. In bondage and discipline (B&D), the dominant partner restrains and flagellates (spanks or whips) or sexually stimulates the submissive partner. The erotic appeal of bondage seems to be connected with controlling or being controlled.

Various types of stimulation may be used to administer pain during S&M encounters, but pain isn't always used. When it is, it's usually mild or moderate. Psychological pain, or humiliation, is perhaps as common as physical pain. Pain may also be symbolic, such as when a sadist uses a harmless, soft rubber paddle to spank the masochist. The erotic appeal of pain for some S&M participants may therefore derive from the ritual of control, rather than from the pain itself (Gross, 2006).

Extreme forms of pain, involving torture and severe beatings, are rarely reported by sado-masochists. Masochists may seek pain, but they usually avoid serious injury and dangerous partners (Gross, 2006).

S&M participants may be heterosexual, gay, or bisexual (Gross, 2006). They may assume just the masochistic or just the sadistic role, or they may alternate roles, depending on the sexual script. People who seek sexual excitement by enacting both roles are known as sado-masochists. In heterosexual relationships, the partners may reverse traditional gender roles. The men may assume submissive or masochistic roles, and the women may take dominant or sadistic roles (Gross, 2006).

The causes of sexual masochism and sadism, like other paraphilias, are unclear. Pain may have direct biological links to pleasure. Natural chemicals called endorphins, similar to opiates, are released in the brain in response to pain, producing feelings of euphoria and general well-being. Perhaps pleasure is derived from pain because of endorphin release or augmentation.

In Canadian society, there's the negative stereotype that people who engage in S&M behaviours are mentally disturbed. Research doesn't support this view (Kleinplatz & Moser, 2005). There's no evidence that people involved in S&M have greater difficulty than other people in establishing intimate relationships. There's also no evidence that engaging in S&M is distressing or dysfunctional. Kleinplatz and Moser therefore conclude that S&M is not pathological.

Frotteurism

Frotteurism, also known as mashing or groping, is a paraphilia characterized by the desire to rub against or touch a non-consenting person in order to become sexually aroused. Like other paraphilias, a diagnosis of frotteurism requires that the person act on or be distressed by these urges. Mashing has been reported exclusively among males (American Psychiatric Association, 2000).

Most mashing takes place in crowded places, such as buses, subway cars, and elevators. The man is sexually stimulated by the rubbing or touching, not by the coercive nature of the act. While rubbing against a woman, he may fantasize a consensual, affectionate sexual relationship with her. Typically, he incorporates images of mashing within his masturbation fantasies (Lussier & Piche, 2008). Mashing also incorporates a related practise, **toucherism**, the fondling of non-consenting strangers.

Frotteurism.
Mashing or groping occurs most often in crowded places, such as subways. It's been reported exclusively among males.

Mashing may be so fleeting and furtive that the woman may not realize what's happened. Mashers therefore stand little chance of being caught.

Many mashers have difficulty forming relationships with women, and are handicapped by fears of rejection. Mashing provides sexual contact in a relatively nonthreatening context.

Other Paraphilias

Let's consider some less common paraphilias.

ZOOPHILIA One of the less common paraphilias, **zoophilia** is often associated with other disorders (Dittert et al., 2005). A person with zoophilia experiences repeated, intense urges and fantasies involving sexual contact with animals. Someone with zoophilia may act on or be distressed by these urges. Actual sexual contact with an animal is referred to as bestiality.

Although the prevalence of zoophilia in the general population is unknown, Kinsey and his colleagues (1948, 1953) found that about 8% of the men and 3% to 4% of the women they interviewed admitted to sexual contacts with animals. Men more often had sexual contact with farm animals, such as calves and sheep. Women more often reported sexual contacts with household pets. Men were more likely to masturbate or copulate with the animals. Women more often reported general body contact. People of both genders reported encouraging the animals to lick their genitals. A few women reported that they'd trained dogs to engage in intercourse with them.

Urban–rural differences also emerged. Kinsey found rates of bestiality higher among boys reared on farms. Compared with only a few city boys, 17% of farm boys had reached orgasm at some time through sexual contact with dogs, cows, and goats. These contacts were generally restricted to adolescence, when human outlets were unavailable. Still, adults sometimes engaged in sexual contact with animals.

Frotteurism A paraphilia characterized by recurrent, powerful sexual urges and fantasies that involve rubbing against or touching a non-consenting person.

Toucherism A practise related to frotteurism, characterized by the persistent urge to fondle non-consenting strangers.

Zoophilia A paraphilia involving persistent or repeated sexual urges and fantasies that involve sexual contact with animals.

Necrophilia A paraphilia characterized by a desire for sexual activity with corpses.

Klismaphilia A paraphilia in which sexual arousal is derived from the use of enemas.

Coprophilia A paraphilia in which sexual arousal is attained in connection with feces.

Urophilia A paraphilia in which sexual arousal is associated with urine.

In Canada, it's a criminal offence to have sex with an animal. In 2003, a 28-year-old Toronto man was charged with cruelty to animals after he was seen having sex with a pregnant Jersey cow. He refused to dismount from the animal even after farm employees repeatedly screamed at him (Godfrey, 2003).

NECROPHILIA In **necrophilia**, a rare paraphilia, a person desires sex with corpses.

Three types of necrophilia have been identified (Holmes & Holmes, 2002). In regular necrophilia, the person has sex with a deceased person. In necrophilic homicide, the person commits murder to obtain a corpse for sexual purposes. In necrophilic fantasy, the person fantasizes about sex with a corpse, but doesn't actually carry out necrophilic acts.

Necrophiliacs often get jobs that provide access to corpses, working in cemeteries, morgues, or funeral homes. The primary motivation for necrophilia appears to be the desire to sexually possess a completely unresisting and non-rejecting partner (Holmes & Holmes, 2002).

Many necrophiliacs have other serious psychological disorders.

OTHER LESS COMMON PARAPHILIAS In **klismaphilia**, sexual arousal is derived from the use of enemas. Klismaphiliacs generally prefer the receiving role to the giving role. They may have derived sexual pleasure in childhood from the anal stimulation provided when their parents gave them enemas.

In **coprophilia**, sexual arousal is connected with feces. The person may feel an urge to be defecated on or to defecate on a sex partner. The association of feces with sexual arousal may also be a throwback to childhood.

In **urophilia**, sexual arousal is associated with urine. Again, the person may feel an urge to be urinated on or to urinate on a sexual partner. Urophilia may also have childhood origins.

Theoretical Perspectives

The paraphilias are among the most fascinating and perplexing variations in sexual behaviour. People without paraphilic desires may find it difficult to understand why some people have sexual desires so different from their own. Let's consider explanations that have been advanced from the major theoretical perspectives.

Biological Perspectives

Researchers are investigating whether there are biological factors in the paraphilias. The biological perspective looks at the involvement of factors such as the endocrine (hormonal) and nervous systems in paraphilic behaviour.

Studies appear to confirm that many paraphiliacs have higher-than-normal sex drives (Haake et al., 2003; Kafka, 2003). A German study, for example, found that men with paraphilias had shorter refractory periods after orgasm by masturbation than most men, and experienced more frequent sexual fantasies and urges (Haake et al., 2003).

But these studies have addressed the strength of the sex drive, not the direction it takes. More recent studies have used the electroencephalograph (EEG) to investigate electrical responses in the brain among paraphiliacs and control subjects (e.g., Kirenskaya-Berus & Tkachenko, 2003).

Researchers measured what's called evoked electrical potentials to erotic stimuli in a sample of 62 right-handed men, half of whom were considered normal in terms of sexual fantasies and behaviours (the control subjects), and half of whom had been diagnosed as paraphilic (fetishistic and sado-masochistic) (Waismann et al., 2003).

The men were shown three sets of 57 slides in random order—57 paraphilic slides that portrayed fetishistic and sado-masochistic themes; 57 "normal" sexual slides that depicted nude women, intercourse, and oral sex; and 57 neutral slides of landscapes, street scenes, and the like. An electrical response labelled "P600" was determined as the best indicator of sexual arousal in men. The researchers found that the main site for evoking the P600 response to "normal" sexual stimuli was in the right side of the brain. The main site for paraphilic stimuli was in the left frontal part of the brain. The paraphilic men showed significantly greater P600 response in the left frontal part of the brain than the control subjects did. Moreover, control subjects were more likely to differentiate between paraphilic and normal stimuli in the right side of the brain.

Another neurological study may offer some insight into masochism. A research team at Massachusetts General Hospital found that the same neural circuits in the brain are often activated by painful and by pleasurable stimuli (Becerra et al., 2001). The researchers discovered that a painfully hot (46°C) stimulus to the hand activated areas of the brain believed to involve "reward" circuitry. The researchers had set out to find ways to help chronic pain patients, not to investigate sexual masochism, but their findings certainly have implications for masochism.

As time goes on, we may learn more about potential biological foundations of paraphilic behaviour. A better understanding of these atypical patterns of sexual behaviour may lead to development of more effective treatments.

Psychoanalytic Perspectives

Psychoanalytic theory suggests that paraphilias are psychological defences, usually against unresolved castration anxieties dating to the Oedipus complex (Friedman & Downey, 2008).

Perhaps the sight of a woman's vagina threatens to arouse castration anxiety in the transvestite, reminding him that women don't have penises and that he might suffer the same fate. Sequestering his penis beneath women's clothing symbolically asserts that women do have penises, providing unconscious reassurance against his own fears of castration.

By exposing his genitals, perhaps the exhibitionist unconsciously seeks reassurance that his penis is secure. It's as if he's asserting, "Look! I have a penis!" Shock or surprise on the victim's face confirms that his penis exists, temporarily relieving castration anxiety.

Perhaps masturbation with an object such as a shoe allows the fetishist to gratify his sexual desires while keeping a safe distance from the dangers he unconsciously associates with female sexual contact. Or he may unconsciously see the fetishistic object as a symbol of his penis.

Is a sadist attempting to defend him or herself against unconscious feelings of impotence by inflicting pain on others?

One psychoanalyst associates a type of male sexual masochism with a history of repressed feelings of sexual guilt and shame (Schrut, 2005). As an adult, the man wants to be punished for feelings of wrongdoing at the same time as he experiences sexual arousal. The pain or humiliation makes the experience okay.

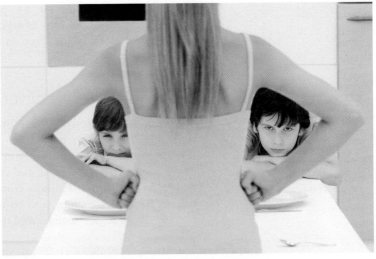

Psychoanalysts suggest that some cases of early punishment by the mother can lead to the development of aberrant sexual fantasies and deviant behaviour.

The paraphilias have provided a fertile ground for psychoanalytic theories. Whatever evidence there is, however, consists of case studies and anecdotes, which are open to interpretation.

Cognitive-Behavioural Perspectives

Cognitive-behavioural theorists generally believe fetishes and other paraphilias are learned. An object may acquire sexually arousing properties through association with sexual arousal or orgasm. Alfred Kinsey and his colleagues (1953) wrote:

> Even some of the most extremely variant types of human sexual behavior may need no more explanation than is provided by our understanding of the processes of learning and conditioning. Behavior which may appear bizarre, perverse, or unthinkably unacceptable to some persons, and even to most persons, may have significance for other individuals because of the way in which they have been conditioned. (pp. 645–646)

For example, a boy who glimpses his mother's stockings hanging on the towel rack while he's masturbating may develop a fetish for stockings. Orgasm in the presence of the object reinforces the erotic connection, especially if it's repeated.

Friedrich and Gerber (1994) studied five adolescent boys who engaged in hypoxyphilia, and found extensive early histories of choking in combination with physical or sexual abuse. The combination seems to have encouraged each boy to associate choking with sexual arousal.

Cognitive-behavioural explanations of sexual masochism focus on the pairing of sexual excitement with punishment. A child may be punished when discovered masturbating, for example, or a boy may reflexively experience an erection if his penis accidentally rubs against his parent's body while he's being spanked. With repeated encounters like these, pain and pleasure may become linked.

Many exhibitionists, voyeurs, frotteurs, and other people with paraphilias have poor interpersonal skills when it comes to women, and fear of rejection may cause them to avoid normal social interactions with women (Leue et al., 2004). Their furtive, paraphilic behaviours may provide sexual release without the risk of rejection.

Observational learning may also play a role. A parent, for example, may inadvertently model exhibitionistic behaviour to a young son, leading the son to eroticize the act of exposing himself. A young person may also read books or magazines or view films or TV programs with paraphilic content. Media may give young people the idea of trying paraphilic behaviour, and they may find it exciting, especially if acts such as exhibitionism or voyeurism provide rushes of adrenaline.

CRITICAL THINKING QUESTIONS

In your opinion, is it ethical for a health-care provider to work with paraphilic clients who don't want treatment?

Sociological Perspectives

Sociological perspectives focus on the effects of the group and of society on individual and group behaviour. Sexual masochists and sadists, for example, require partners. Most sado-masochists learn S&M rituals, make sexual contacts, acquire sexual paraphernalia, and confirm their sado-masochistic identities within an S&M subculture—a loosely connected network of S&M clubs, specialty shops, organizations, magazines, and so on. But the S&M subculture exists within the context of the larger society, and its rituals mirror widely based social and gender roles.

Martin Weinberg (1987) proposes a sociological model that focuses on the social context of sado-masochism. S&M rituals generally involve some form of dominance and submission. Weinberg (1987) attributes their erotic appeal to the opportunity to reverse the customary power relationships that exist between males and females and between social classes. Within the confines of the carefully scripted S&M encounter, the meek can be powerful, and the powerful can be meek. People from lower social classes or in menial jobs may be drawn to S&M so they can enact dominant roles. Dominance-and-submission games allow people to accentuate or reverse the gender stereotypes that identify masculinity with dominance and femininity with submissiveness. Interviews and observations involving sado-masochists suggest that most often, dominance-and-submission relationships tend to be consistent with traditional masculine and feminine gender roles in society (Damon, 2002; Santtila et al., 2002). Although there are many exceptions, in S&M rituals, men more often tend to be dominant, and women to be submissive.

An Integrated Perspective

Paraphilias may have complex biopsychosocial origins (Seligman & Hardenburg, 2000). Might our understanding of them therefore be best approached from a theoretical framework that incorporates multiple perspectives?

John Money (2003), for example, traces the origins of paraphilias to childhood. He believes every person has what he calls a lovemap, which forms in the brain during childhood. The lovemap contains the image of the person's ideal lover, and includes the types of stimuli and activities that become sexually arousing to the individual. In the case of paraphilias, lovemaps become distorted by early traumatic experiences such as incest, anti-sexual upbringings, and abuse or neglect.

Research suggests that voyeurs and exhibitionists have often been victims of childhood sexual abuse (Barbaree & Blanchard, 2008). Not all children exposed to such influences develop paraphilic compulsions, however. For reasons that remain unknown, some children exposed to these influences appear to be more likely to develop distorted lovemaps than others. Genetic predispositions, hormonal factors, brain abnormalities, or a combination of these and other factors may play a role in determining one's vulnerability to vandalized lovemaps (Lehne, 2009).

Treatment for Paraphilias

Treatment for the paraphilias raises a number of issues.

First, many people with paraphilias don't want or voluntarily seek treatment. Ontario criminologist Ron Langevin (2006) followed nearly 800 sex offenders from the 1960s through the first decade of the twenty-first century, and found that only about half wanted and completed courses of treatment. Many offenders are seen by health-care providers only when they come into conflict with the law, or at the urging of family members or partners.

Second, health-care providers may encounter ethical problems when asked to contribute to the judicial process by trying to persuade sex offenders (who are virtually all male) to change their behaviour. Health-care providers traditionally help clients clarify or meet their own goals; it's not their role to impose societal goals on individuals. Some health-care providers believe the criminal-justice system—not the health-care system—ought to enforce social standards.

Third, health-care providers realize that they're generally unsuccessful in treating resistant or recalcitrant clients. Unless the motivation to change is present, therapeutic efforts are often wasted.

And fourth, sex offenders typically claim that they can't control their impulses. Accepting personal responsibility for one's actions is a prelude to change. If therapy is to be constructive, then, it must break through the offender's personal mythology that s/he's powerless to control the criminal behaviour.

Despite these issues, many offenders are referred for treatment by the courts. Some seek therapy themselves, because they've come to see how their behaviour harms themselves and others (Langevin, 2006).

Psychotherapy

Psychoanalysis focuses on resolving unconscious conflicts that are believed to originate in childhood and to give rise to pathological problems such as paraphilias in adulthood. The aim of therapy is to help bring unconscious conflicts, principally Oedipal conflicts, into conscious awareness, so they can be worked through in light of the individual's adult personality (Laws & Marshall, 2003).

Psychoanalytic therapy for the paraphilias has not been subjected to experimental analysis. We therefore don't know whether successes are due to the psychoanalytic treatment itself or to other factors, such as spontaneous improvement or a client's willingness to change.

Cognitive-Behaviour Therapy

Cognitive-behaviour therapy
Systematic application of the principles of learning in order to modify a problem behaviour.

Systematic desensitization
A method for terminating the connection between a stimulus (such as a fetishistic object) and an inappropriate response (such as sexual arousal to the paraphilic stimulus). The individual practises muscle relaxation in the presence of a series of increasingly arousing stimuli, until s/he learns to remain relaxed (and not sexually aroused) in their presence.

Aversion therapy A method for terminating an undesirable sexual behaviour. The behaviour is repeatedly paired with an aversive stimulus, such as electric shock, until the person develops a conditioned aversion to the stimulus.

Covert sensitization A form of aversion therapy in which thoughts about engaging in undesirable behaviours are repeatedly paired with imagined aversive stimuli.

Pedophile A person with pedophilia, a paraphilia that involves sexual interest in children.

Social-skills training A method of behaviour therapy that relies on coaching and practise to build social skills.

Whereas psychoanalysis tends to entail a lengthy process of exploring the childhood origins of problem behaviours, **cognitive-behaviour therapy** is briefer and focuses on changing behaviour. Cognitive-behaviour therapy has spawned a number of techniques to help eliminate paraphilic behaviours and strengthen appropriate sexual behaviours. These techniques include systematic desensitization, aversion therapy, social skills training, covert sensitization, and orgasmic reconditioning.

Systematic desensitization attempts to break the link between the sexual stimulus (such as a fetishistic stimulus) and the inappropriate response (sexual arousal). The client is first taught to relax selected muscle groups in his or her body. Muscle relaxation is then repeatedly paired with a series of progressively more arousing paraphilic images or fantasies. Relaxation comes to replace sexual arousal in response to each stimulus, including the most provocative.

In **aversion therapy**, the undesirable sexual behaviour (e.g., masturbation to fetishistic fantasies) is repeatedly paired with an aversive stimulus (e.g., a harmless but painful electric shock or a nausea-inducing chemical), in the hope that the client will develop a conditioned aversion to the paraphilic behaviour.

Covert sensitization is a variation of aversion therapy in which paraphilic fantasies are paired with an aversive stimulus in the client's imagination. In a broad-scale application, 38 **pedophiles** and 62 exhibitionists, more than half of whom were court-referred, were treated by pairing imagined aversive images or odours with fantasies of the problem behaviours (Maletzky, 1980). Clients were instructed to fantasize pedophiliac or exhibitionistic scenes. Then:

> At a point when sexual pleasure is aroused, aversive images are presented. Examples might include a pedophiliac fellating a child, but discovering a festering sore on the boy's penis, an exhibitionist exposing to a woman, but suddenly being discovered by his wife or the police, or a pedophiliac laying a young boy down in a field, only to lie next to him in a pile of dog feces. (Maletzky, 1980, p. 308)

Maletzky used this treatment weekly for six months, then followed it with booster sessions every three months for three years. The procedure resulted in at least a 75% reduction in the deviant activities and fantasies for more than 80% of the study participants, at follow-up periods of up to 36 months.

Social-skills training focuses on helping the individual improve his ability to relate to the other gender. The therapist might first model a desired behaviour, such as asking a woman out on a date or handling a rejection. The client might then role-play the behaviour, with the therapist playing the part of the woman. Following the role-play enactment, the therapist provides feedback and additional guidance and modeling, to help the client improve his skills. This process is repeated until the client masters the skill.

Orgasmic reconditioning aims to increase sexual arousal to socially appropriate sexual stimuli, by pairing culturally appropriate imagery with orgasmic pleasure. The person is instructed to become sexually aroused by masturbating to paraphilic images or fantasies. But as he approaches the point of orgasm, he switches to appropriate imagery, and focuses on it during orgasm. These images and fantasies eventually acquire the capacity to elicit sexual arousal. Orgasmic reconditioning is often combined with other techniques, such as social-skills training, so desirable social behaviours can be strengthened.

Orgasmic reconditioning A method for strengthening the connection between sexual arousal and an appropriate sexual stimulus (such as a fantasy about an adult of the other gender). It involves repeatedly pairing the desired stimulus with orgasm.

Although behaviour-therapy techniques tend to have higher reported success rates than most other methods, our knowledge about their efficacy is limited by reliance on uncontrolled case studies. Without appropriate controls, we can't isolate the effective elements of therapy or determine whether the results are due merely to the passage of time or to other factors unrelated to treatment. It's possible that clients who are highly motivated to change may succeed in doing so with *any* systematic approach.

Medical Approaches

There may be no medical cures for the paraphilias. No drug or surgical technique eliminates paraphilic ideas while leaving other cognitive functions intact. But some progress has been reported in the use of selective serotonin reuptake inhibitors (SSRIs), which are mainly used as antidepressants, to treat exhibitionism, voyeurism, and fetishism (Grubin, 2008).

Why antidepressants? In addition to treating depression, SSRIs are often used to treat obsessive-compulsive disorder, a psychological disorder involving recurrent obsessions (intrusive ideas) and/or compulsions (urges to repeat certain behaviours or thoughts). Paraphilic behaviour has an obsessive-compulsive quality. People with paraphilias often experience intrusive, repetitive fantasies and urges (Saleh, 2009).

People who experience such intense urges that they risk committing sexual offenses may also be helped by drugs that reduce testosterone levels in the bloodstream (Grubin, 2008; Saleh, 2009). Testosterone is closely linked to sex drive and interest. In men, antiandrogen drugs reduce sexual desire and frequency of erection and ejaculation. Medroxyprogesterone acetate (MPA, sold as Depo-Provera), which is administered by weekly injection, is the antiandrogen most extensively used to treat sex offenders. It suppresses the male sexual appetite, lowering the intensity of the sex drive and erotic fantasies and urges, so the man may feel less compelled to act on them (Grubin, 2008; Saleh, 2009). Antiandrogens do not, however, eliminate all paraphilic urges or completely change a person's sexual behaviour.

Appropriate Behaviour?
Research indicates that parental nudity that isn't sexually suggestive isn't harmful to a child.

The use of antiandrogens is sometimes incorrectly referred to as chemical castration. Surgical castration, the surgical removal of the testes, has sometimes been performed on convicted rapists and violent sex offenders (Roesler & Witztum, 2000). Surgical castration eliminates testicular sources of testosterone. Antiandrogens suppress but do not eliminate testicular production of testosterone. Unlike surgical castration, antiandrogen effects can be reversed when the treatment is terminated.

Evidence suggests that antiandrogens in conjunction with psychological treatment can help some people (Roesler & Witztum, 2000). The value of antiandrogens has been limited by high refusal and dropout rates (Fedoroff, 1995; Roesler & Witztum, 2000). Questions about side effects also remain.

Ottawa psychiatrist John Bradford (2000) has suggested a six-level schema for treatment, based on the severity of the deviation. The first level for any type of paraphilia involves cognitive-behavioural treatment. The second level involves treatment for mild paraphilias, and begins with an SSRI such as Prozac. If the SSRI isn't effective within four to six weeks, a small dose of an antiandrogen is added as treatment moves to level three. For moderate and some severe cases, antiandrogen or hormonal treatment is given in level four. For more severe cases, at level five, this treatment is given by injection. For the most serious cases, especially those considered catastrophic, at level six, the therapist attempts to completely reduce androgens and the sex drive by administering high dosages of an antiandrogen or a luteinizing-hormone-releasing hormone (LHRH).

At all levels of treatment, the goal is to suppress deviant fantasies, urges, and behaviours. Treatment at levels four and five aims for a strong reduction in sex drive, and at level six for elimination or near-elimination of the sex drive (Bradford, 2000). The broader objective of these treatments is to reduce the possibility of recidivism and further victimization.

Sexual Addiction, Compulsive Sexual Behaviour, and Hypersexuality

Three terms have been used to describe a psychological disorder in which a person is unable to control an excessively frequent sexual behaviour: sexual addiction, sexually compulsive behaviour, and hypersexuality.

The terminology we use is important. While all three terms apply to out-of-control sexual behaviours, they each imply somewhat different conceptualizations of the factors underlying those behaviours, and therefore the most effective ways of addressing them.

SEXUAL ADDICTION Of these three terms, you're probably most familiar with "sexual addiction," which is frequently used in the media. The concept of sexual addiction as a clinically defined psychological disorder was articulated and popularized by the 1983 book *Out of the Shadows: Understanding Sexual Addiction*, by Patrick Carnes.

In this conceptualization, sexual addiction is similar to other addictions, such as alcohol, drug, and gambling addictions. A sex addict engages in sexual behaviour to relieve anxiety, but typically doesn't achieve a high level of gratification. The addict feels bad about the behaviour, but is unable to control or resist it. Attempts to stop lead to further anxiety (withdrawal symptoms), which fuels the person's preoccupation or craving to engage in this behaviour. The sex addict becomes caught in a spiral of anxiety and loss of control that often leads to risk-taking, inappropriate behaviours, and excessive levels of sexual activity that take over the addict's life.

Treatments are similar to the treatments for other addictions, including 12-step programs and group therapies such as Sexaholics Anonymous (Schneider & Irons, 2001).

COMPULSIVE SEXUAL BEHAVIOUR Although the term "sex addiction" is popular, some experts argue that excessively frequent, out-of-control sexual behaviour is not an indication that a person is addicted to sex. They reject the belief that a person can be addicted to a basic human function such as sex the same way s/he can be addicted to a substance such as alcohol or a drug. Rather, they argue that a sexual behaviour that's frequent enough to interfere with a person's ability to carry on with his or her daily life is best seen as an obsessive-compulsive disorder (Coleman, 2003).

Compulsive sexual behaviour is characterized by recurrent, sexually arousing fantasies that the individual is unable to get out of his or her mind, and intense sexual urges that, when acted upon, temporarily relieve anxiety. Psychotherapy similar to that used for other obsessive-compulsive behaviours is used to treat compulsive sexual behaviour. Medications such as certain types of antidepressants can also be helpful for obsessive-compulsive disorders (Ravindran & Stein, 2010).

HYPERSEXUALITY Neither sexual addiction nor compulsive sexual behaviour is listed as a specific diagnostic category in the fourth edition of the American Psychiatric Association's *Diagnostic and Statistical Manual of Mental Disorders* (DSM-IV-TR, 2000). Hypersexuality, however, is being considered for inclusion as a distinct clinical disorder in the fifth edition, due for release in May of 2013 (Marshall & Briken, 2010).

The proposed diagnostic criteria for hypersexuality are similar to those commonly described for sexual addiction and compulsive sexual behaviour (Kafka, 2010):

■ Time consumed by the sexual fantasies or behaviours interferes with other important activities and obligations.
■ The person repetitively engages the in sexual fantasies or behaviours in response to mood states such as anxiety or depression.
■ Frequency and intensity of the sexual fantasies or behaviours causes clinically significant personal distress.
■ The sexual fantasies or behaviours are not due to medication or drug abuse.
■ The person has been unable reduce the frequency of the sexual fantasies or behaviours.

Like sexual addiction and compulsive sexual behaviour, the concept of hypersexuality as a specific mental disorder is controversial, and some experts in the field oppose its proposed inclusion in DSM-V (e.g., Fedoroff, 2011). Paul Fedoroff at the Royal Ottawa Hospital fears that inclusion of hypersexuality in DSM-V will pathologize consensual sexual thoughts and behaviours by linking them with psychiatric problems such as addiction, anxiety, depression, and compulsions. He's concerned that people with mood disorders will instead be labelled hypersexual, and as a result will not receive appropriate treatment.

Although we've amassed a great deal of research on the paraphilias and other atypical sexual behaviours, our scientific understanding of them remains in its infancy.

Summing Up

Patterns of sexual arousal in response to atypical stimuli are called paraphilias. The psychiatric diagnosis of paraphilia requires that a person act on these persistent urges in socially unacceptable ways, or be distinctly distressed by them.

In fetishism, an inanimate object comes to elicit sexual arousal. A transvestite become excited by wearing articles of clothing—the fetishistic objects—of the other gender. An exhibitionist experiences the compulsion to expose himself to strangers. The obscene phone caller becomes sexually aroused by shocking his victim. A voyeur becomes sexually aroused by watching, and doesn't seek sexual relations with the target.

A sexual masochist associates the receiving of pain or humiliation with sexual arousal. Sexual sadism is characterized by persistent, powerful urges and sexual fantasies that involve inflicting pain and suffering on others in order to achieve sexual excitement or gratification.

Most frotteuristic acts—rubbing against nonconsenting persons—take place in crowded places such as buses, subway cars, and elevators. Frotteurism is also known as mashing.

Zoophiliacs desire sexual contact with animals. Necrophiliacs desire sexual contact with dead people.

The links between paraphilias and biological factors have yet to be fully explored.

Classical psychoanalytic theory suggests that paraphilias in males are psychological defenses against castration anxiety.

Some learning theorists argue that unusual stimuli may acquire sexually arousing properties through association with sexual arousal or orgasm. According to Weinberg's sociological model, the erotic appeal of S&M rituals may result from the opportunity to reverse the customary power relationships that exist between the genders and between social classes in society at large.

Money suggests that childhood experiences etch a pattern in the brain—a lovemap—that determines which stimuli and activities become sexually arousing. In paraphilias, these lovemaps become distorted by early traumatic experiences.

Psychoanalysis aims to bring unconscious Oedipal conflicts that prompt paraphilic behaviour into awareness, so they can be worked through in adulthood.

Cognitive-behaviour therapy attempts to eliminate paraphilic behaviours through such techniques as systematic desensitization, aversion therapy, social-skills training, covert sensitization, and orgasmic reconditioning.

SSRIs, which are usually used as antidepressants, tend to curb compulsive behaviour and depress sexual response. They've been used with some paraphilic individuals.

"Sexual addiction," "compulsive sexual behaviour," and "hypersexuality" are terms used to describe excessively frequent, out-of-control sexual behaviours.

Test Yourself

Multiple-Choice Questions

1. **Which of the following is not used to distinguish normal from abnormal sexual behaviour?**
   (a) Statistical norms.
   (b) Pain thresholds.
   (c) Social norms.
   (d) Personal distress and anxiety.

2. **Which of the following are most likely to need to risk capture, to heighten their sexual arousal?**
   (a) Sado-masochists.
   (b) Coprophiliacs.
   (c) Exhibitionists.
   (d) Mashers.

3. **People who become sexually aroused by experiencing pain inflicted by their sexual partners are:**
   (a) partialists
   (b) sexual masochists
   (c) sexual sadists
   (d) toucherists

4. **A man who dresses in women's clothing for the purposes of sexual gratification is labelled as a:**
   (a) Transsexual.
   (b) Partialist.
   (c) Frotteur.
   (d) Transvestite.

5. **All paraphilias:**
   (a) Pose physical threats to the victims.
   (b) Are evidence that the perpetrators are out of touch with reality.
   (c) Are more common among males than females.
   (d) Can be treated with psychoanalysis.

6. **Hypoxyphilia is related to:**
   (a) Sexual sadism.
   (b) Sexual masochism.
   (c) Fetishism.
   (d) Zoophilia.

7. **People who are excessively aroused by particular body parts, such as the feet, breasts, or buttocks, are said to exhibit:**
   (a) Partialism.
   (b) Frotteurism.
   (c) Voyeurism.
   (d) Transvestism.

8. **Which of the following has been proposed for inclusion in the forthcoming edition of the DSM?**
   (a) Hypersexuality.
   (b) Sexual addiction.
   (c) Internet voyeurism.
   (d) Compulsive sexual behaviour.

9. Which approach to the treatment of paraphilia uses social-skills training and systematic desensitization?

(a) Psychoanalysis.
(b) Antiandrogen therapy.
(c) Cognitive-behaviour therapy.
(d) Antidepressant therapy.

10. The image of an ideal lover and of the types of activities a person finds arousing that forms in the brain during childhood is known as a:

(a) Sexual script.
(b) Lovemap.
(c) Gender stereotype.
(d) Fantasy.

You'll find answers to the "Test Yourself" questions on page 495.

Critical Thinking

1. How do you decide whether a sexual behaviour is normal? Where do you draw the line for yourself? For others?

2. When is it okay to cross-dress? For a costume party? For a role in a play? At a viewing of *The Rocky Horror Picture* Show? In class? As you answered these questions, were you thinking of men or women?

3. Criminal behaviours such as flashing are sometimes referred to as nuisance offences, which implies that they're harmless. Do you agree with this representation? If you've ever experienced one of these offences, do you think your experience has affected your answer?

4. Can you think of explanations for the finding that nearly all people with paraphilias are male?

MySearchLab

MySearchLab offers extensive help to students with their writing and research project and provides round-the-clock access to credible and reliable source material. Take a tour at www.mysearchlab.com.

Sexual Coercion

This chapter is about sexual coercion. As well as actual force or threat, sexual coercion includes *any* sexual activity between an adult and a child. Even when they cooperate, sexual relations with children are considered coercive, because children are below the legal age of consent.

In this chapter, we'll look at diverse forms of sexual pressure and sexual harassment. As we'll see from the statistics, sexual coercion affects large numbers of Canadians.

Promoting sexual health and well-being in Canadian society requires that we not only emphasize and accentuate the positive, life-enhancing aspects of human sexuality, but also fully recognize and address sexual behaviour that violates the basic human rights of others.

Sexual Assault

Until 1983, the word "rape" was used in the Canadian Criminal Code to describe forced sexual intercourse. "**Sexual assault**" has replaced "rape" in the Canadian legal system. The American justice system still uses the term "rape," although its definition varies from state to state.

In Canada, there are three levels of sexual assault:

- **Level 1**—Any form of sexual activity forced on another person, or non-consensual bodily contact for a sexual purpose (e.g., kissing, touching, oral sex, vaginal or anal intercourse). Level 1 sexual assault involves minor physical injury or no injury to the victim. Conviction for a level 1 sexual assault is punishable by up to 10 years in prison.
- **Level 2**—A sexual assault in which the perpetrator uses or threatens to use a weapon, threatens the victim's friends or family members, causes bodily harm to a third party, or commits the assault with another person (multiple assailants). Conviction for a level 2 sexual assault is punishable by up to 14 years in prison.
- **Level 3**—A sexual assault that wounds, maims, or disfigures the victim, or endangers the victim's life. Conviction for a level 3 sexual assault is punishable by up to life in prison.

There's no statute of limitations for prosecution of sexual assault. This means a victim can go to police many years after a sexual assault has occurred, and criminal charges can still be laid.

A central issue in determining whether an assault has occurred, especially at level 1, is whether consent has been freely given. The person has to be capable of giving consent. Someone who's drunk, under the influence of drugs, unconscious, fearful, or under age is unable to give consent.

Underlying the 1983 changes to the Criminal Code was the perspective that sexual assault is an act of power and dominance, rather than an act of sex. The Canadian law regarding sexual assault is gender-neutral, recognizing that sexual assault can be committed by women against men, as well as by people against others of their own gender. The law also acknowledges that sexual assault can be committed by a victim's spouse.

It's important to understand that consent for one type of sexual behaviour doesn't mean consent for other behaviours. In one case, an Ontario man was convicted of sexual assault because he'd engaged in anal sex despite his partner's objections. After having sexual relations together for some months, the man had asked the woman about having anal sex, but she hadn't wanted to try it. A week later, during a sexual interaction that had included vaginal intercourse, he penetrated her anally, despite her resistance. The woman later went to the police, and the man was charged with sexual assault ("Sexual assault plea," 1994). In another case, a Toronto

MySearchLab

- Self-grading practice tests
- Media links
- Flashcards
- Access to thousands of full-text articles from academic journals and help on the research and writing process

Sexual assault Non-consensual bodily contact for a sexual purpose.

man received a jail sentence after he'd removed his condom during sexual intercourse. The victim had consented to having intercourse only if he'd wear a condom, but he continued having sex with her, nonetheless (Oakes, 1994).

In Canada, people who are infected with HIV can be charged with sexual assault if they don't disclose their HIV status to their partners before engaging in sexual behaviour. There have been several such convictions across Canada. (We discussed this topic in Chapter 14.)

Incidence in Canada

Statistics Canada relies on two data sources to track the incidence of sexual assault—the Uniform Crime Reporting Survey (UCR) and the General Social Survey (GSS), which includes data on victimization. The UCR tracks the number of substantiated sexual assaults reported to police, and the GSS asks Canadians whether they've been victims of sexual assault, including assaults they may not have reported to police.

These surveys use different methods to collect data. While the UCR is an important data source for tracking trends in sexual assaults, particularly those of a more violent nature, it doesn't capture the many sexual assaults that are never reported to police.

According to data from the UCR, almost 21 000 sexual assaults were reported to police in Canada in 2009 (Dauvergne & Turner, 2010). More than 95% of these sexual assaults were classified as level 1. The total number of sexual assaults reported to police peaked in 1993, and has been declining ever since, including a 4% decline from 2008 to 2009. This trend mostly reflects a decline in the number of level 1 sexual assaults reported to police, since rates of level 2 and 3 sexual assaults have remained relatively stable since 1993. For level 3 sexual assaults that are reported to police, victimization rates are four times greater for women than for men (Brennan & Taylor-Butts, 2008).

UCR data from 2007 shows that the highest rates (per 100 000 people) for sexual assaults reported to police occurred in Nunavut (746), Northwest Territories (518), and Yukon (203). Among the provinces, Saskatchewan (138) and Manitoba (113) had the highest rates, while Ontario (61) and Prince Edward Island (58) had the lowest (Brennan & Taylor-Butts, 2008).

The GSS uses a different method of data collection. It calculates self-reported crime rates by asking a nationally representative sample of 15-and-older Canadians whether they've been victims of various types of crime during the previous 12 months. Overall, the GSS results for sexual assault were similar in 1999, 2004, and 2009.

In 2009, the GSS revealed 677 000 incidents of sexual assault in Canada, or 24 incidents per 1000 people who were 15 and older (Perreault & Brennan, 2010). Most (81%) involved unwanted sexual touching, grabbing, kissing, or fondling, while about one in five involved more serious sexual attacks. In more than half of all the 2009 incidents, the perpetrators were friends, acquaintances, or neighbours of the victims (Perreault & Brennan, 2010). Seventy percent of the 2009 incidents involved female victims, and 87% involved male perpetrators (Perreault & Brennan, 2010). Sexual assault rates for 2009 were almost twice as high for 15- to 24-year-olds as for 25- to 34-year-olds, and many times higher than for people who were 35 and older (Perreault & Brennan, 2010).

As the URC and GSS statistics show, there's a large difference between the number of sexual assaults reported to police and the number that actually take place. Although the two surveys define sexual assault in slightly different ways, making direct comparisons difficult, researchers estimate that only about one in 10 sexual assaults in Canada is reported to the police (Brennan & Taylor-Butts, 2008).

In a survey at an Ontario university, 12% of female students reported that they'd been forced by physical threats to have sex, and 8% said they'd been forced by verbal threats to have sex (Rye, 2001). A study of street youth in Toronto found that young women who are homeless are at even greater risk of being sexually assaulted than the Ontario female students (Gaetz, 2004).

Occasionally, there have been documented cases of false reporting of sexual assaults. In Toronto, for example, a male elementary school teacher was found not guilty of sexually assaulting a 13-year-old student (Small, 2007). The student admitted that before making the allegations she'd had a crush on the teacher, and had left a phone message saying she loved him. The student was embarrassed when the man's wife phoned and said the message was inappropriate. After seeing a television show detailing a sexual assault, the student used the program's storyline to fabricate sexual-assault allegations against the teacher, in hopes that he'd be transferred to another school (Small, 2007).

It's important to put documented cases of false allegations of sexual assault into perspective. They're rare, and outnumbered by a wide margin by actual instances of assault that are never reported.

In Canada, there's a rising incidence of drug-facilitated sexual assault. A study in British Columbia concluded that in 2002, 27% of sexual assaults involved drugs such as GHB (gamma-hydroxybutyric acid) and Rohypnol (McGregor et al., 2004).

CRITICAL THINKING QUESTIONS

Sexual abuse of boys by women isn't always recognized as traumatizing, but sexual abuse of girls by men is almost universally condemned. Why does this double standard exist? How might it affect boys and their willingness to report abuse?

A World of Diversity

FEMALE SEX OFFENDERS

It's often assumed that women rarely commit sexual offences, if ever. Using police and court records and victim surveys from Canada and other Western countries, however, researchers estimate that women are responsible for 4% to 5% of all sexual offences (Cortoni, Hanson, & Coache, 2009).

Because there's been less research on female than on male sex offenders, we know relatively little about them. Studies have been limited by very small sample sizes and by the fact that most have included only women who have committed more serious sexual offences. Nevertheless, our knowledge of female sexual offending is growing as more research is done.

Although female sex offenders share some characteristics with male sex offenders (e.g., they're likely to have antisocial attitudes), they also tend to differ from male sex offenders in fundamental ways. In a review of the research, Jill Atkinson (1996) at Queen's University has found that female sex offenders are less likely than males to use violence and to deny their actions once they're caught.

Many female sex offenders have been physically or sexually abused as children, and are likely to have problems with alcohol or drugs. Their victims are likely to be relatives or acquaintances under 12 years of age (Vandiver, 2006).

One study found that about half of the women charged with sexual offences have acted in tandem with male co-offenders (Vandiver, 2006). In the majority of cases, the male co-offenders have been husbands or boyfriends.

A substantial number of women who have committed sex offences with male co-offenders have been coerced to do so by the males. They may have been persuaded through intimidation, or forced to participate in the sexual abuse of children. According to Atkinson (1996), "They usually resist at first, but eventually become passive partners in the abuse as a result of physical punishment or intimidation. These sex offenders tend to be of low intelligence, under-assertive, dependent on men, desperate to maintain a relationship, and willing to participate and even initiate sexual relationships to please a male partner" (p. 40).

One subtype of female sexual offender is the so-called teacher/lover. The teacher/lover uses a position of authority (e.g., as an older family member, teacher, or employer) to initiate sexual activity with an under-aged, usually male youth.

Cases of women charged with teacher/lover sexual offences tend to receive a high degree of media attention, especially if the women are deemed to be attractive. There have been several high-profile cases in Canada and the United States in which attractive female teachers have been prosecuted for having sex with their male students. In some instances, media stories have suggested that the boys in these cases have "gotten lucky."

David Finkelhor (2005a), director of the Crimes Against Children Research Center at the University of New Hampshire, notes that the bringing of these cases to court reflects a decline in the double standard that's applied to men and women. Finkelhor suggests that increasing numbers of female police officers and prosecutors are less likely to buy into the traditional idea that boys who have sex with older women have something to be thankful for (Zernicke, 2005).

A survey of 977 sexual-assault victims in Ontario found that 20.9% of the assaults were drug-facilitated (Du Mont et al., 2009). These drugs are typically mixed into drinks served to the victims. Odourless and tasteless, they loosen inhibitions and cause amnesia for up to 12 hours. Victims often have little or no memory of what's occurred after ingesting the drug, and are therefore unlikely to report the incidents.

In Toronto, a man put a drug into a drink and served it to a couple he was visiting. He then sexually assaulted both the man and the woman. In court, the two victims reported that for brief moments they'd observed the accused sexually assaulting one or both of them, but because of the drug's effects, they couldn't act to stop the assaults. The accused was found guilty of sexual assault and of administering a noxious substance (Small, 2004). More recently, a Toronto area husband and wife were convicted and sentenced to prison terms of six and four years, respectively, for drugging and sexually assaulting another couple they'd met at a bar (Mitchell, 2010).

Some pharmacies in Quebec have begun selling Drink Detective™ cards that people can use to test their drinks for GHB and several prescription sleep and anti-anxiety drugs (Chung, 2010).

Not all drug-facilitated sexual assaults involve GHB and Rohypnol. Researchers who used toxicology reports to look at suspected drug-facilitated sexual assaults in Ontario found that many of the victims had ingested cannabinoids such as marijuana (40.2%), cocaine (32.2%), or amphetamines (13.8%) (Du Mont et al., 2010). The researchers noted that they were unable to determine the extent to which these drugs were taken voluntarily by the victims, but the findings do suggest that a number of different substances can play a role in drug-facilitated sexual assault.

Types of Sexual Assault

One of the central myths in our culture is that most sexual assaults are perpetrated by strangers lurking in dark alleyways, or by intruders who climb through open windows in the middle of the night. In fact, most women are assaulted by men they know—and often by men they trust (Roberts, 1994).

STRANGER SEXUAL ASSAULT **Stranger sexual assault** is committed by an assailant (or assailants) previously unknown to the victim. The stranger often selects a target who seems vulnerable—a woman who lives alone, is older or mentally challenged, is walking down a deserted street, or is asleep or intoxicated. After choosing a target, the assailant may search for a safe time and place to commit the crime, such as a deserted, rundown part of town, a dark street, or a second-floor apartment without window bars or locks.

Sometimes an assailant will use a phony ploy to get a woman to lower her guard. In Toronto, a man posed as a photographer for a university, and asked women on campus if he could take their pictures for a project. After taking the women to a more secluded area, he assaulted them ("Women warned," 2008).

The police-reported data from the 2007 URC show that the victims and perpetrators were strangers in only 18% of the incidents reported in Canada that year (Brennan & Taylor-Butts, 2008).

ACQUAINTANCE SEXUAL ASSAULT Data from the 2007 URC indicates that 82% of sexual-assault victims in 2007 knew their perpetrators in some way (Brennan & Taylor-Butts, 2008). More detailed information from 2002 shows that 51% of victims of sexual offences were sexually assaulted by friends or acquaintances, while 28% were victimized by family members (Statistics Canada, 2003b).

Acquaintance sexual assaults are much less likely to be reported to police than assaults by strangers (Fisher et al., 2001), in part because victims may not perceive being forced into sexual activity by acquaintances as sexual assault.

Stranger sexual assault
A sexual assault committed by an assailant previously unknown to the victim.

Acquaintance sexual assault
A sexual assault committed by an acquaintance of the victim.

DATE SEXUAL ASSAULT One of the most common forms of acquaintance sexual assault occurs within the dating context. Date sexual assault (often called date rape) is more likely to occur when the couple has too much to drink and parks in the man's car or goes back to his residence (Cole, 2006). The man tends to perceive his partner's willingness to return home with him as a signal of sexual interest, even if she resists his advances.

Some men may assume that women who frequent places like singles bars are expressing tacit agreement to have sex with men who show interest in them. Some assailants believe a woman who resists advances is just "protesting too much," so she won't appear "easy." They interpret resistance as coyness—in other words, as a ploy in the cat-and-mouse game that to them typifies the "battle of the sexes." They may believe that when a woman says no she means maybe, and that when she says maybe she means yes. They may therefore not see themselves as committing sexual assaults—but of course they are.

It's important to acknowledge that most people won't force non-consenting individuals to have sex. For example, in a study of New Brunswick university students, Byers and Lewis (1988) found that most males accepted dating partners' refusals to have sex.

The issue of consent lies at the heart of whether a sexual act is an assault. Unlike stranger assault, date rape occurs within a context in which sexual relations could occur voluntarily. The issue of consent can become murky. The defendant may concede that sexual intercourse took place, but claim it was consensual. Judges and juries face the task of discerning shadings in the meaning of "consent." Lawyers on both sides vie to persuade judges and juries to see things their way.

A sexual-assault charge stemming from a dating situation often comes down to his word against hers. Her word often becomes less persuasive in the eyes of the

A Closer Look

ANATOMY OF A DATE RAPE

Her Story

I first met him at a party. He was really good-looking, and he had a great smile. I wanted to meet him, but I wasn't sure how. I didn't want to appear too forward.

Then he came over and introduced himself. We talked, and found we had a lot in common. I really liked him.

When he asked me over to his place for a drink, I thought it would be okay. He was such a good listener, and I wanted him to ask me out again.

When we got to his room, the only place to sit was on the bed. I didn't want him to get the wrong idea, but what else could I do? We talked for a while, and then he made his move. I was so startled. He started by kissing. I really liked him, so the kissing was nice.

But then he pushed me down on the bed. I tried to get up, and I told him to stop. He was so much bigger and stronger. I got scared, and I started to cry. I froze, and he sexually assaulted me.

It took only a couple of minutes, and it was terrible–he was so rough. When it was over, he kept asking me what was wrong, like he didn't know. He had just forced himself on me, and he thought that was okay.

He drove me home and said he wanted to see me again. I'm so afraid to see him. I never thought it would happen to me.

His Story

I first met her at a party. She looked really hot, wearing a sexy dress that showed off her great body. We started talking right away. I knew she liked me by the way she kept smiling and touching my arm while she was speaking.

She seemed pretty relaxed, so I asked her back to my place for a drink. When she said yes, I knew I was going to get lucky!

When we got to my place, we sat on the bed kissing. At first, everything was great. Then, when I started to lay her down on the bed, she started twisting and saying she didn't want to. Most women don't like to appear too easy, so I knew she was just going through the motions. When she stopped struggling, I knew she would have to throw in some tears before we did it.

She was still very upset afterward, and I just don't understand it! If she didn't want to have sex, why did she come back to the room with me? You could tell by the way she dressed and acted that she was no virgin, so why she had to put up such a big struggle, I don't know.

jury if it's clear that she consented to mutual activities before the incident, such as sharing dinner, attending a movie, accompanying her date to his home, sharing a drink, and perhaps kissing or petting.

But let's be clear: it doesn't matter whether a woman wears a sexy outfit, is on the pill, or shares a passionate kiss or embrace with a man. If the encounter ends with her being forcibly violated, a sexual assault has taken place. When a woman says no, a man must take no for an answer.

The problem of date rape has been subject to closer public scrutiny in recent years. Take Back the Night marches on university campuses have become a common form of protest against men's sexual misconduct. Many universities have mandated date-rate seminars and workshops.

GANG SEXUAL ASSAULT Exercise of power appears to be the major motive behind gang assaults, although some attackers may also be expressing anger against women. An American college survey showed that sexual assaults involving groups of assailants tend to be more vicious than individual assaults (Gidycz & Koss, 1990). Relatively few survivors of gang assaults reported the attacks to police or sought support from crisis centres.

SEXUAL ASSAULT AGAINST MALES Although rates of sexual assault against males are far lower than rates of sexual assault against females, sexual assault of men is more common than many people assume. According to GSS data, an estimated 204 000 incidents of sexual assault were committed against men in Canada in 2009 (Perreault & Brennan, 2010). In a study of university students in New Brunswick, about one-fifth of the men reported that they'd been coerced into having sex during the previous year (O'Sullivan et al., 1998).

This finding runs contrary to the stereotype that men are willing to have sex all the time. Many women believe this stereotype, as demonstrated by a study of women living in the Kitchener-Waterloo area of Ontario (Clements-Schreiber & Rempel, 1995). Eighty-five percent of the women believed it's easy for a woman to sexually arouse a man if she wants to, and 68% believed men enjoy sexual advances from women even when they don't respond positively. According to the researchers, such beliefs might make women think refusals shouldn't be taken seriously.

Sarrel and Masters (1982) reported 11 cases of men who'd been sexually assaulted by women, including a 37-year-old man who'd been coerced into sexual intercourse by two women who'd accosted him at gunpoint. In another case, a 27-year-old man had fallen asleep in his hotel room with a woman he'd just met in a bar, and awakened to find himself bound to the bed, gagged, and blindfolded. He'd then been forced into sexual intercourse with four different women, who threatened him with castration if he didn't perform satisfactorily.

Despite these examples, most sexual assaults against men are committed by other men. While they often occur in prison settings, some occur outside prison walls. It's not true that men who sexually assault other men are typically gay. Most are heterosexual. Their motives tend to include domination and control, revenge and retaliation, sadism and degradation, and—when the assaults are carried out by gang members—status and

\ (')no\ adv [ME, fr. OE na, fr. ne not + a always; akin to ON & OHG ne not, Lne-, Gk ne - More at AYE] 1 a:

NO means NO

Date rape drugs are illegal in Canada.

date rape is a serious crime

What part of no don't you understand?

To get involved in "No Means No" and other campaigns of the Canadian Federation of Students, contact your local students' union.

CUPE 1281

Canadian Federation of Students

Combatting Sexual Assault on Campus.
Many Canadian universities and colleges have instituted awareness programs to combat the problem of date rape and other types of sexual assault on campus.

affiliation (Krahe et al., 2003). In recent years the media have been full of stories about men in positions of authority, such as teachers and priests, assaulting boys.

Males can also be assaulted in college sports hazing rituals. A rookie football player withdrew from McGill University after his teammates forced him down onto all fours and prodded him anally with a broom handle. Other rookies were coerced into simulating oral sex on one another in their boxer shorts (Peritz, 2005).

Male survivors tend to suffer greater physical injury than female survivors (Kaufman et al., 1980). Males are more often attacked by multiple assailants, held captive longer, and more reluctant to report the assaults. After all, victimization doesn't fit the male stereotype of capacity for self-defence. Men are expected to be not only strong, but silent. Nevertheless, male survivors may suffer traumatic effects similar to those suffered by female survivors (Bogin, 2006).

SEXUAL ASSAULT AGAINST GAY AND BISEXUAL MALES There have been few studies of sexual assault against gay and bisexual men. Researchers in Vancouver (Ratner et al., 2003) asked 358 19- to 35-year-old gay and bisexual men if they'd ever been forced into unwanted sex. Fourteen percent reported that they'd been coerced or forced into sex before the age of 14. Half of the reported incidents involved forced receptive anal intercourse. Men who'd been sexually coerced had lower self-esteem and higher rates of depression. They were more likely to abuse alcohol and to have attempted suicide.

PARTNER OR MARITAL SEXUAL ASSAULT Although there are many countries where it's legal for a husband to sexually assault his wife, in Canada it's clearly illegal.

Partner sexual assault is probably more common than date rape, because a sexual relationship has already been established (Osman, 2003). A "traditional" man may believe it's his wife's duty to satisfy his sexual needs, even when she's not interested. Men who are better educated and less rigid regarding stereotypes about sexual relationships are less likely to sexually assault their partners (Basile, 2002).

Data from the United States suggests that partner sexual assault is more likely to go unreported—and, often, unrecognized by survivors as actually being sexual assault (Strebeigh, 2009). Women may also fail to report partner sexual assault because of fear that no one will believe them.

Motives for partner sexual assault vary. Some people use sex to dominate their partners. Others use it to degrade their partners, especially after arguments. Sexual coercion often occurs within a pattern of violence and physical intimidation (Johnson, 2003). In some cases, though, violence is limited to the sexual relationship. Some men see sex as the solution to disputes. They think that if they can force their partners into sex, "Everything will be okay."

Victims of partner sexual assault may fear serious injury or death just as much as victims of stranger sexual assault do. The long-term effects of partner sexual assault are also similar to those experienced by survivors of stranger sexual assault, including fear, depression, and sexual dysfunction (Kaczmarek et al., 2006; Polusny & Arbisi, 2006). Moreover, the woman who's sexually assaulted by her husband usually has to live with her assailant, and may fear repeated attacks.

The Complexity of Consent

A central issue in cases of sexual assault is that of sexual consent. As presented in "A Closer Look: Anatomy of a Date Rape," differing perceptions of sexual consent can be problematic in dating situations.

Melanie Beres (2007), a University of Alberta researcher, conducted a comprehensive review and analysis of the research on sexual consent. She found that sexual consent has been conceptualized and defined numerous ways. Many scholars have discussed sexual consent without defining the term at all, assuming that everyone shares the same understanding of its meaning. Following are some of Beres's key findings from the literature on sexual consent:

- Some researchers argue that a person who says yes to sexual advances is giving consent, even under coercion or force. Others disagree, and state that consent can be given only if there is no coercion.
- Researchers disagree over whether sexual consent must be given verbally. For example, does sexual consent mean a person must say yes to a sexual request, or is it sufficient for the person to refrain from stopping a partner's physical advances, or does sexual consent involve a combination of the two?
- Some scholars view sexual consent as an agent of moral transformation that turns an illegal, objectionable activity into a potentially pleasurable, morally permissible activity.
- Sexual consent is usually seen as overly simplistic, involving a yes or no response to a sexual request.
- Only a few researchers have studied the ways people actually ask for and give consent.
- Research on—and discussion of—sexual consent has mainly taken place in the context of a heterosexual bias. This perspective mistakenly assumes that sexual consent from men isn't needed, because of the stereotype that men are always willing to have sex.
- Researchers usually assume women seldom initiate sexual encounters.
- Sex educators provide female students with strategies for saying no to sex, but not for saying yes.
- Little research has been done on sexual consent involving gay men and lesbians.
- Most of the research on sexual consent has been related to violent sexual activity. Research about the more common, consensual sexual interactions is limited.

Beres (2007) believes it's essential for researchers to clearly define sexual consent. She also stresses the need to develop interactive models using qualitative research methods. This approach will help us better understand how sexual consent is perceived, and how it's actually communicated within sexual relationships. An example of such research is Beres's study of communicating sexual consent with casual sex partners, which we discussed in Chapter 7.

Terry Humphreys (2007) at Trent University in Peterborough has also researched the complexities of the sexual-consent process. He's especially critical of educational programs that assume simply saying no means no. Humphreys's own research indicates that the sexual-consent process involves many factors. One of his main findings is that most women and men have nonverbal means of asking for and giving sexual consent. Typically, people indirectly indicate consent in a number of ways, such as by *not* pulling away from their partners. Most people find it very awkward to make direct, verbal sexual requests. If a person does say no to a sexual request, most men and women believe s/he should give a reason for the refusal. Humphreys's research is discussed in more detail in Chapter 7.

Social Attitudes and Myths

Many people believe a number of myths about sexual assault, such as that women say no when they mean yes, that women like men who are pushy and forceful, and that women dress in a way that invites assault. Yet another myth is that deep down, women want to be assaulted (Osman, 2003).

Sexual-assault myths create a social climate that legitimizes sexual assault. Though both men and women may subscribe to sexual-assault myths, researchers at the University of British Columbia have found that male students are more accepting of these myths than female students are (Kennedy & Gorzalka, 2002). There are also ethnic differences; Asian students are more likely to accept these myths than students from Western backgrounds are. The longer the Asian students have been in Canada, the less likely they are to accept such myths.

Men also cling more stubbornly to myths about date sexual assault, even after taking classes designed to challenge these views (Maxwell et al., 2003). Such myths don't occur in a social vacuum. They're related to other social attitudes, including gender-role stereotyping, a perception of sex as adversarial, and acceptance of violence in relationships (Yost & Zurbriggen, 2006).

Many observers contend that our society encourages sexual assault by socializing males into socially and sexually dominant roles. Males are often conditioned from childhood to engage in aggressive and competitive behaviour.

Research with university students supports the connection between stereotypical masculine identification and tendencies to sexual assault. In New Brunswick, researchers compared students who believed in strictly traditional gender roles with students who held less rigid attitudes. Men who engaged in coercive sex were more likely to hold more traditional views of women's roles, and more likely to hold coercion-supportive beliefs (Byers & Eno, 1991). Men with traditional views were more likely to ignore partners who said they didn't want to have sex. The traditionalists express a greater likelihood of committing sexual assault, were more accepting of violence against women, were more likely to blame survivors for their assaults, and were more aroused by depictions of sexual assault than men who didn't hold traditional views (Raichle & Lambert, 2000).

Young men may come to view dates not as chances to get to know their partners, but as opportunities for sexual conquest, in which the object is to overcome their partners' resistance. Sexual behaviour and sports are linked in our culture through common idioms. A young man may be taunted by his friends after a date with such questions as "Did you score?" or, more bluntly, "Did you get in?"

CRITICAL THINKING QUESTIONS

Images of women and girls in popular media (music videos, advertising) have been said to perpetuate sexual-assault myths. Can you think of any images that might support this claim?

Applied Knowledge

THE DATE-RAPE DRUG

Rophies, roofies, R2, roofenol, roachies, la rocha, rope, or whatever you call it, the date-rape drug is easily slipped into the drinks of unsuspecting women. The drug has no taste or odour, so the victims don't realize anything has happened.

It lowers their inhibitions, lessens their ability to resist sexual assault, and, when mixed with alcohol, often causes blackouts that prevent victims from remembering what's happened to them. For this reason, Rohypnol has also been called the forget pill, trip-and-fall, and mind erasers.

Rohypnol is often used with other drugs, such as alcohol, to create a dramatic high. Rohypnol intoxication is generally associated with impaired judgment, memory, and motor skills, and can make a victim unable to resist or recall a sexual attack.

About 10 minutes after taking it, the victim may feel dizzy and disoriented, simultaneously too hot and too cold, or nauseated. She may have difficulty speaking and moving before she passes out, usually about 30 minutes after ingesting the drug. Effects peak within two hours, and can persist for eight to 24 hours. Once she awakens, the victim has little or no memory of what's happened.

Rohypnol is prescribed as a treatment for insomnia and a sedative hypnotic in other countries. It's in the same class of drugs as the tranquillizer Valium, but about 10 times stronger.

Here are some tips for avoiding problems with Rohypnol:

- Be wary about accepting drinks from anyone you don't know well or long enough to trust.
- Don't put your drink down and leave it unattended, even to go to the bathroom.
- If you think you've been a victim, notify authorities immediately.

Source: National Institute on Drug Abuse. (2010). Club drugs (GHB, ketamine, and Rohypnol). NIDA infofacts. United States Department of Health and Human Services. Retrieved from www.drugabuse.gov/Infofacts /RohypnolGHB.html

Some researchers, such as Queen's University psychologist Vernon Quinsey, hypothesize that evolutionary psychology can account for the role of male sexual competitiveness in sexual assault. According to this perspective, during the course of human evolution, the main constraint on male reproductive success was the limited number of potential mating partners, and as a result, males were obliged to compete with one another for mating opportunities. To increase their opportunities for successfully perpetuating their genes, some men engaged in sexual coercion (Quinsey, 2002).

Although the evolutionary perspective may view sexual aggressiveness in men, as expressed in the prehistoric environment, as "natural," sexual assault in contemporary society is inexcusable and criminal, and psychologists believe males can *choose* not to be aggressive (Koss, 2003). Perhaps men carry genes that now and then give rise to aggressive impulses, some of which involve sex, but men also carry other genes that enable them to picture themselves in the place of the victim and choose *not* to behave aggressively. Empathy—that is, experiencing the feelings of another person—appears to be more common in women than in men, but it's not absent in men, and it can be cultivated in men, as sexual-assault-prevention programs have shown (Foubert & Newberry, 2006).

Sexually Coercive Men

Although sexual aggressiveness may be woven into our social fabric, not all men are equally vulnerable to such cultural influences. Canadian researchers are playing a leading role in identifying factors that predict which men are more likely to be sexually coercive.

Some researchers argue that anger and power are the basic motivations for sexual assault (Groth & Birnbaum, 1979). Those who are motivated by power seek to control and dominate their victims (Mardorossian, 2002). From this perspective, a sexual assault is an attempt "to resolve disturbing doubts about [his] masculine identity and worth, [or] to combat deep-seated feelings of insecurity and vulnerability" (Groth & Hobson, 1983, p. 165). Other researchers believe sexual motivation is an element in at least some sexual assaults (Baumeister et al., 2002; Malamuth et al., 2005).

Much of our knowledge of the psychological characteristics of sexually coercive men derives from studies of incarcerated sex offenders. One conclusion that emerges is that no single type of man commits violent sexual assault. Perpetrators vary in psychological characteristics, family backgrounds, mental health, and criminal histories (Lalumière et al., 2005a). It also appears that most sexually coercive men aren't mentally ill, even though their crimes might strike us as "sick." Generally speaking, sexually coercive men are just as intelligent and just as mentally fit as other people. However, while they don't show deep psychological disturbance, many sexually coercive men do have anti-social personalities that enable them to violate their victims without guilt, shame, anxiety, or empathy (Lalumière et al., 2005a). Some anti-social sex offenders have long histories of violent behavior (Lalumière et al., 2005a, 2005b). Alcohol may also dampen their self-restraint and spur sexual aggressiveness.

For some sexually coercive men, violence and sexual arousal become enmeshed, so they seek to enhance their sexual arousal by combining sex and violence (Lalumière et al., 2005a). Lalumière and his colleagues have found that some sexually coercive men find verbal descriptions, films, and audiotapes that portray rape more sexually arousing (as measured by the sizes of their erections) than other men do (Lalumière et al., 2005a, 2005b, 2005c). Other researchers, however, have failed to find deviant patterns of arousal in sexually coercive men (Lalumière et al., 2005a, 2005b, 2005c).

Innovative Canadian Research

MALE VERSUS FEMALE VICTIMS OF SEXUAL COERCION

University of Guelph researchers (Hartwick et al., 2007) conducted a study of university students to compare the characteristics of male and female victims of sexual coercion.

More women (48%) than men (39%) in the study had experienced sexual coercion. The main difference between male and female victims was that more women (34%) than men (23%) had experienced coerced kissing and fondling. The rates of coerced sexual intercourse were almost the same (21% for females and 18% for males).

The most common coercive strategies involved getting the person intoxicated and inducing guilt. Men were more likely to be coerced through intoxication, while women were more likely to be pressured into feeling guilty for refusing sex. Strangers tended to use the intoxication strategy, whereas dating partners and friends tended to use the guilt strategy.

Both men and women who had more sex partners were more likely to have experienced coercive sexual intercourse.

A key finding was that both sexes were more likely to have experienced sexual coercion if they believed the stereotype of men's greater sexual accessibility—that is, that men always want sex. The researchers speculated that men who believe this feel guilty that they're not living up to this expectation if they refuse sex, while some women may feel that they should give in to men's greater sexual needs (Hartwick et al., 2007).

Toronto researchers (Langevin et al., 2006) have found that sex offenders tend to come from families with alcohol problems. The researchers have speculated that parental alcohol addiction has often been a factor in the sons' developmental and learning problems. Another Ontario study has found that sexual offenders have significantly greater problems with alcohol abuse than other violent offenders (Looman et al., 2004). The researchers have speculated that something about the combination of alcohol abuse and intimacy problems contributes specifically to sexual offending.

A survey of men from a Canadian city has found that belief in sexual-assault myths and hostility are *not* predictive of coercive male behaviour (Senn et al., 2000). The fact that this is one of the few studies on sexual coercion that has attempted to randomly sample men from the community may account for the differences between its findings and those of other studies. The survey did find that men who are sexually coercive are more likely to have experienced childhood abuse, had more sexual partners during adolescence, and lack the ability to express their emotions (Senn et al., 2000). In another study of male sexual aggressors, University of Montreal researchers have reported that male adult sexual aggressors are more likely to have experienced childhood sexual abuse, pornography during childhood or adolescence, and deviant sexual fantasies during childhood or adolescence (Beauregard et al., 2004).

Adjustment of Sexual Assault Survivors

Many people who survive sexual assault by strangers fear for their lives during the attacks (Polusny & Arbisi, 2006). Regardless of whether weapons or threats are used, the experience of being dominated by an unpredictable and threatening assailant is terrifying. The victim doesn't know whether she'll survive, and may feel helpless to do anything about it.

Many survivors are in crisis in the days and weeks after the sexual assault (Campbell, 2006; Macy et al., 2006). They have insomnia, and they cry frequently. They tend to report eating problems, cystitis, headaches, irritability, mood changes, anxiety and depression, and menstrual irregularity (Kaczmarek et al., 2006). They may become withdrawn, sullen, and mistrustful. Because some people tend to

Applied Knowledge

IF YOU'RE SEXUALLY ASSAULTED

Here are some suggestions for what to do if you're sexually assaulted.

- Don't change anything about your body—don't wash, don't even comb your hair. Leave your clothes as they are. Otherwise, you could destroy evidence.
- Strongly consider reporting the incident to police. You may prevent another woman from being assaulted, and you'll be taking charge, starting on the path from victim to survivor.

- Ask a relative or friend to take you to a hospital, if you can't get an ambulance or a police car. If you call the hospital, say why you're requesting an ambulance, in case they're able to send someone trained to deal with sexual-assault cases.
- Seek help in an assertive way. Seek medical help. A medical professional may detect injuries you're unaware of. Insist that a written or photographic record be made, to document your condition. If you decide to file charges, the prosecutor may need this evidence to obtain a conviction.

- Question health professionals. Ask about your biological risks. Ask what treatments are available. Ask about phylactic treatment against HIV infection. Ask for whatever will help make you comfortable. Call the shots. Demand confidentiality, if that's what you want. Refuse what you don't want.

You may also wish to call a sexual-assault hotline or sexual-assault crisis centre for advice, if one is available in your area. A sexual-assault crisis volunteer may be available to accompany you to the hospital and help you through the medical evaluation, and the police investigation, if you report the attack.

believe women who are sexually assaulted are at least partly to blame for the assaults (Boros et al., 2005), some survivors experience guilt and shame. Emotional distress tends to peak in severity about three weeks after the assault, and generally remains high for a month or two before it begins to abate (Duke et al., 2009; Littleton & Henderson, 2009).

Many survivors encounter more lasting problems. Their feelings of being powerless to affect their own fates can endure, and change their personalities (McEwan et al., 2005). Survivors may encounter problems at work, such as problems with co-workers or bosses, or difficulty concentrating. Relationships with spouses or partners may be impaired. Survivors often report a lack of sexual desire, fear of sex, and difficulty becoming sexually aroused (Beutal et al., 2008; Koss et al., 2003). Sexual-assault victims may also suffer physical injury and be exposed to sexually transmitted infections, including HIV.

Many women choose not to report sexual assaults to police. Why? Reasons include fear of retaliation, fear of social stigma, worry that others won't believe them, the feeling that it's hopeless to try to bring charges against the perpetrators, concern about negative publicity, and fear about the emotional distress they'll experience if their cases go to trial (Campbell, 2006; Logan et al., 2006). The GSS survey for 2004 reveals that Canadian sexual-assault victims do, however, turn to sources of support such as friends (72%), family (41%), co-workers (33%), and doctors or nurses (13%) (Brennan & Taylor-Butts, 2008).

PSYCHOLOGICAL DISORDERS RESULTING FROM SEXUAL ASSAULT Sexual-assault survivors are at higher than average risk for developing anxiety disorders and depression, and for abusing alcohol and other substances (Littleton & Henderson, 2009). Researchers at Carleton University have found that university women who've experienced sexual coercion in their dating relationships are more likely to have lower levels of self-esteem and sexual self-esteem than women who haven't experienced sexual coercion while dating. They're also more likely to experience depression (Offman & Matheson, 2004).

Survivors may experience **post-traumatic stress disorder (PTSD)** (Vickerman & Margolina, 2009), a disorder brought on by exposure to a traumatic event. It's often seen among soldiers who've been in combat (American Psychiatric Association, 2000). Someone with PTSD may have flashbacks to the traumatic experience, disturbing dreams, emotional numbing, and nervousness. PTSD may persist for years. The person may also develop a fear of situations connected with the traumatic event. A woman who's been sexually assaulted in an elevator, for example, may develop a fear of riding in elevators.

Researchers report that women who blame themselves for their sexual assaults tend to suffer more severe depression and adjustment problems, including sexual problems, than women who don't blame themselves (Kaczmarek et al., 2006; Vikerman & Margolina, 2009).

Treatment of Sexual Assault Survivors

Treatment of sexual-assault survivors typically involves a two-stage process—helping the victim through the crisis after the attack, then fostering long-term adjustment (Vickerman & Margolina, 2009). Crisis intervention typically provides survivors with support and information, to help them express their feelings and develop strategies for coping with the trauma.

Psychotherapy, involving a group or individual approach, can help the survivor cope with the emotional consequences of sexual assault, avoid self-blame, improve self-esteem, validate the welter of feelings surrounding the experience, and establish or maintain loving relationships. Therapists also recognize the importance of helping the sexual-assault survivor mobilize social support. In major cities and many towns, concerned men and women have formed sexual-assault crisis centres and hotlines, peer-counselling groups, and referral agencies geared to assessing and meeting survivors' needs. Some counsellors are specially trained to mediate between survivors and their loved ones. These counsellors help people discuss and work through the often complex emotional legacies of sexual assault. Phone numbers for these services are available from crisis centres, women's shelters, hospital emergency departments, police departments, and telephone directories.

A national survey of rape-crisis and sexual-assault centres in Canada has found that many face precarious financial situations because of insufficient government funding (Beres, Crow, & Gotell, 2009). These agencies rely heavily on the unpaid services of volunteers to provide adequate services to sexual-assault and -abuse survivors. Most of these agencies are also politically active, raising awareness of issues of violence and inequality experienced by Canadian women (Beres, Crow, & Gotell, 2009).

Preventing Sexual Assault

Eliminating sexual assault altogether would probably require massive changes in cultural attitudes and socialization processes. However, educational

Taking Back the Night.
Whose fault is it if a woman is sexually assaulted when she goes out alone at night? Many women—and men who care about women—have marched to demonstrate their disgust with the men who might assault them if they're out walking by themselves, and with a society that too often blames the victim for what happens to her.

intervention on a smaller scale may reduce its incidence. Many colleges and universities offer educational programs about date sexual assault that have apparently reduced its incidence (Foubert & Newberry, 2006; Potter et al., 2009).

Until the basic cultural attitudes that support sexual assault change, however, preventing sexual assault means women must take a number of precautions. Why should they be advised to do this? Isn't the very listing of such measures a subtle way of blaming women, should they fall prey to attackers? No! Providing information is not blaming the victims. The offenders are *always* responsible for the assaults.

Confronting an Attacker

What if you're accosted by a sexual assailant? Should you try to fight him off, flee, or plead with him to stop? Some women have thwarted attacks by pleading or crying. Screaming may ward off some attacks (Gidycz et al., 2006). Running away sometimes works. No single strategy is likely to be helpful in all cases of sexual assault.

Self-defence training may help you become better prepared to fend off an assailant (Gidycz et al., 2006). Yet physical resistance may spur some assailants to become more aggressive. Effective self-defence is built upon the use of multiple strategies, ranging from attempts to avoid dangerous situations (e.g., installing a home security system and walking only in well-lit areas) to acquiescence when active resistance seems too risky to more active verbal and physical forms of resistance in low-risk situations (Gidycz et al., 2006).

Applied Knowledge

LOWERING YOUR RISK OF SEXUAL ASSAULT

Taking precautions such as these, recommended by the Boston Women's Health Book Collective (2005), may lower your risk for being assaulted:

- Establish a set of signals with other women in the building or neighbourhood.
- List yourself in the phone directory and on the mailbox by your first initials only.
- Use deadbolt locks.
- Keep doorways and entries well lit.
- Keep your keys handy when approaching the car or the front door.
- Avoid deserted areas.
- Don't allow strange men into your house or apartment without first checking their credentials.
- Check out the back seat of your car before getting in.
- Don't give rides to hitchhikers (including female hitchhikers).

Here are some suggestions for avoiding sexual assault by a date:

- Tell your partner how far you're willing to go, so he knows your limits. For example, if your partner starts fondling you in ways that make you uncomfortable, you might say, "I'd prefer if you didn't touch me there. I really like you, but I prefer not getting so intimate at this point in our relationship."
- When meeting a new date, meet at a public place, and arrive and leave in your own car. Don't drive with a stranger or offer a ride to a stranger or a group of people you've just met.
- State your refusal definitively. Be firm in refusing a sexual overture. Look your partner straight in the eye. The more definite you are, the less likely your partner is to misinterpret your wishes.
- Become aware of your fears. Notice any fears about displeasing your partner that might stifle your assertiveness. If your date is truly respectful, you needn't fear an angry or demeaning response. If your date isn't respectful, it's best to become aware of the fact, and end the relationship right there.
- Pay attention to your vibes. Trust your gut-level feelings. Many victims of sexual assault by acquaintances have said they had strange feelings about the men, but failed to pay attention to their feelings.
- Be especially cautious if you're in a new environment, whether it's a university or a foreign country. You may be especially vulnerable to exploitation when you're becoming acquainted with a new environment, different people, and different customs.
- If you've broken off a relationship with someone you don't really like or feel good about, don't let him into your place. Many so-called date rapes are committed by ex-lovers and ex-boyfriends.

Coercive Verbal Pressure Tactics

Verbal sexual coercion is persistent verbal pressure or the use of seduction lines to manipulate a person into sexual activity. Verbal coercion is difficult to define precisely. People use a wide spectrum of persuasion, ranging from coaxing to outright bullying and threats. In the middle of the spectrum there's a grey area that might be considered coercive by some, but not by others.

Verbal coercion is used far more often than physical coercion. In a study involving students from more than 40 universities and community colleges across Canada, DeKeseredy and Kelly (1993) found that since beginning university, 32% of the women had given in to sex play (not involving intercourse) because they'd been overwhelmed by men's continual arguments and pressure, and 20% had given in to sexual intercourse because of this kind of verbal pressure. In a community survey of men from an Ontario city, 23% reported that they'd used arguments and verbal pressure to try to get women to engage in sex play, and 9% said they'd used this kind of pressure to have sexual intercourse (Senn et al., 2000).

Researchers in Toronto studied young adults who were involved in street life, to find out what strategies they used to coerce dating partners into having sex (Strike et al., 2001). The sample included heterosexuals, gays, lesbians, and bisexuals. Almost all of the men and women had experienced pressure to have sex, and 62% of the men and 42% of the women admitted having pressured dates to have sex. In the Strike et al. study, the tactics used to get sex included the following:

- Using alcohol and drugs to decrease a partner's reluctance to have sex. Some of those who'd been coerced said they'd used alcohol or drugs to loosen their own inhibitions.
- Using obligations, expectations, and guilt. Some coerced their partners by threatening to end the relationships or to get sex elsewhere. Another strategy involved saying how much they were looking forward to having sex. Some made their partners feel obliged to have sex, and tried to make them feel guilty for not having it. A commonly held belief was that if a partner paid for date-related expenses such as dinner and drinks, the person was obliged to have sex.
- Exploiting emotional and economic vulnerabilities. People with low self-esteem may be told they're worthless and should consider themselves lucky to be in relationships. Some of the men and women admitted that they'd manipulated people with few or no economic resources by providing food, housing, or money in return for sex. An extreme example of this exploitation occurred when a man provided a woman with shelter, and demanded that she provide sex—not only to him, but to his friends, as well.

A number of the study participants admitted that they'd developed sophisticated sets of strategies to obtain sex—strategies that included knowing when and how to use them. While some continued to pressure reluctant partners, others stopped trying to get sex when the partners were adamant in refusing it. Those who'd been coerced to have sex often resigned themselves to simply getting it over with, so their partners would stop bothering them (Strike et al., 2001).

In a community-based survey of men living in Windsor, Senn and her colleagues (2000) found that the most common strategy used to coerce reluctant partners into having sex involved continual arguments and verbal pressure. The second most common strategy involved providing women with alcohol or drugs.

A common sexual stereotype is that women never have to use pressure tactics to engage in sex with male partners. Researchers at the University of Guelph have found that some young women use a diversity of sexual pressure tactics to get reluctant male partners to engage in sex (Parr-LeFeuve & Desmarais, 2005).

Verbal coercion also occurs in same-sex relationships. In a study of these relationships in Canada and the United States, Melanie Beres (2002) has found that

23% of women in lesbian relationships have experienced sexual coercion from other women. The rates for men are somewhat higher; 35% have experienced sexual coercion from other men.

Sexual Abuse of Children

Many view sexual abuse of children as among the most heinous of crimes. Canadians are shocked and horrified when they find out about children being sexually abused. One of the most publicized cases was the sexual abuse of boys by priests at the Mount Cashel Orphanage in Newfoundland. Eleven priests were convicted of those offences, and the Newfoundland government paid $11 million to 40 abuse victims.

Children who are sexually assaulted often suffer social and emotional problems that impair their development and persist into adulthood, affecting their self-esteem and their ability to form intimate relationships.

Data from the 2007 UCR survey of sexual assaults reported to police in Canada show that more than half of all sexual-assault victims that year were under age 18, and 25% were under 12 (Brennan & Taylor-Butts, 2008). The UCR data also showed that the vast majority (81%) of sexual-assault victims under age 18 were female. In a sample of men from an Ontario city, 8% reported having been sexually abused in childhood (Senn et al., 2000). Since many cases are never reported, we don't know with certainty how many children have been sexually abused. An analysis of 65 studies in 22 countries has estimated that 7% to 8% of boys and 19% to 20% of girls have been sexually abused (Pereda et al., 2009).

Sexual abuse of children ranges from exhibitionism, kissing, fondling, and sexual touching to oral sex, anal intercourse, and vaginal intercourse. Sexual contact between an adult and a child is abusive, even if the child is willing, because children are legally incapable of consenting to sexual activity. (Acts such as touching children's sexual organs while changing or bathing them, sleeping with children, or appearing nude before them are not usually considered sexual contact. While they're open to interpretation, they're often innocent [Haugaard, 2000].)

Voluntary sexual activity *between children* of similar ages is not sexual abuse. Children often engage in consensual sex play with peers or siblings, playing doctor or engaging in mutual masturbation. Although such experiences may be recalled in adulthood with feelings of shame or guilt, they're not typically harmful. When an experience involves coercion, or when one child is significantly older or in a position of power over the younger child, the sexual contact may be considered sexual abuse.

The Mount Cashel Scandal.
One of the most publicized child sex-abuse cases in Canada involved Catholic priests at the Mount Cashel Orphanage in Newfoundland.

In Canada, it's against the law for an adult or a teenager to engage in any type of sexual activity, ranging from kissing to intercourse, with a child under the age of 14. The exception is for sexual activity between a child who's at least 12 years old and someone who's less than two years older.

In 1985, Parliament amended the Criminal Code to make it an offence for a person in a position of trust or authority to have any sexual contact, consensual or not, with a person under 18. There's been more controversy about this law when the accused has been a female, probably because of traditional stereotypes that young men who are involved sexually with older females are "lucky," rather than exploited. In recent years, there have been several cases across Canada in which female teachers have been charged with having sexual relationships with male students. For example, a 42-year-old grade-seven teacher in Ontario was found guilty of sexually assaulting one of her 13-year-old male students. She and the student had kissed and fondled one another in the basement of her home (Seymour, 2008). Female teachers have also been charged with sexual assault of female students. In Toronto, a female high-school teacher was charged with sexually assaulting a 17-year-old girl she taught. The teacher was accused of fondling the girl and exchanging sexually explicit emails with her (Mitchell, 2006).

To provide greater protection for 14- to 18-year-olds, 2002 legislation created a new category of sexual exploitation for any adult who, because of his or her age and/or position of authority, is able to coerce a young person into having sex. This legislation also makes it illegal for an adult to use the internet to lure a person s/he believes is under 18 for the purpose of committing a sexual assault, or to entice a child believed to be under 14 into sexual relations.

The first person charged under this law was a 33-year-old Toronto man who arranged a meeting with an 11-year-old girl he'd met on the internet. He was also charged with sexual assault after spending the night with the girl in a hotel room. The man was convicted of internet luring, abduction of a person under age 16, and sexual interference (Levy, 2004). Internet luring crosses national borders. A 32-year-old man from Belgium was arrested at a Montreal hotel and charged with sexual offences and internet luring, when he was found there with a missing 13-year-old girl. The pair had been chatting online for several months (Banerjee, 2008).

To combat internet luring, police have laid traps by posing as children in chat rooms. In 2005, a Toronto detective posed as a 12-year-old girl on the Yahoo chat room Teen Oh Canada Chat. A man entered the chat room and engaged in casual conversation with her. After a few months, they arranged to meet to have sex. At this meeting, the police arrested a 36-year-old pastor (Naili & Josey, 2005).

In 2008, the Canadian Parliament raised the legal age of consent from 14 to 16, to protect adolescents in that age group from adult sexual exploitation. The new law allowed a close-in-age provision of five years, so it would be legal for a 19-year-old to have sex with a 15-year-old. Gay-rights organizations claim that the age-of-consent law is discriminatory toward gay males, because it's illegal in Canada to engage in anal sex with someone who's under 18.

In Bountiful, British Columbia, a fundamentalist Mormon sect not only flouts Canadian law with its practice of polygamy, but also allegedly forces girls as young as 13 to marry much older men (Braham, 2008). Winston Blackmore, the bishop of the religious group, has admitted to having sex with minors. He argues that freedom of religion in Canada prohibits the justice system from interfering with the church's beliefs. In 2009, however, Blackmore and another sect leader were charged by the British Columbia government with engaging in polygamy. In the United States, Warren Jeffs, the leader of the American segment of this Mormon sect, was sentenced in 2011 to life in prison for sexually assaulting underage girls (Associated Press, 2011).

Pamela Rogers Turner.
A physical education teacher and coach in Tennessee, Pamela Rogers Turner was convicted in 2005 of having sex with one of her 13-year-old students. She was sentenced to nine months in prison. After violating the terms of her probation, she was sentence to another seven years in 2006, and then to another two years in 2007.

Patterns of Abuse

Children from stable, middle-class families appear to be generally at lower risk for sexual abuse than children from poorer, less cohesive families (Amodeo et al., 2006; Turner et al., 2006). In most cases, children who are sexually abused are not accosted by the proverbial stranger lurking in the schoolyard. According to Canadian police reports, in 2003 half of all victims under the age of six were sexually assaulted by family members, and only 4% were assaulted by strangers. Twenty percent of the 14- to 17-year-old victims were assaulted by family members, and 20% were assaulted by strangers (Statistics Canada, 2005g). In many cases, the molesters are people who are close to their victims—relatives, step-relatives, family friends, and neighbours (Edwards et al., 2003).

Parents who discover that their children have been abused by family members are often reluctant to notify authorities (Zerubavel, 2006). The decision to report the abuse to police depends largely on the relationship between the abuser and the person who discovers the abuse (Finkelhor, 2005a).

Typically, the child initially trusts the abuser. Physical force is seldom needed to gain compliance, largely because of the child's helplessness, gullibility, and submission to adult authority. Whereas most sexually abused children are abused only once, those who are abused by family members are more likely to suffer repeated acts of abuse than those who are abused by strangers.

Genital fondling is the most common type of abuse (Edwards et al., 2003). In one sample of women who'd been molested in childhood, most of the contacts involved genital fondling (38% of the cases) or exhibitionism (20% of the cases). Intercourse is rare. Repeated abuse by a family member, however, commonly follows a pattern that begins with affectionate fondling during the preschool years, and progresses to oral sex or mutual masturbation during the early school years, and then to sexual penetration (vaginal or anal intercourse) during preadolescence or adolescence.

Abused children rarely report the abuse, often because they fear retaliation from their abusers, or because they believe they'll be blamed for it. Adults may suspect abuse if a child shows sudden personality changes or develops fears, problems in school, or difficulty eating or sleeping. A pediatrician may discover physical signs of abuse during a medical exam. The average age at which most children are first sexually abused ranges from six to 12 years for girls and seven to 10 for boys (Finkelhor et al., 2005b).

ABUSER TYPES The overwhelming majority of people who sexually abuse children—both boys and girls—are male (Turner et al., 2006). Although most child abusers are adults, some are adolescents. Male adolescent sex offenders are more likely than other adolescents to have been molested themselves as boys. Some adolescent sex offenders may be imitating their own victimization. Adolescent child molesters also tend to feel socially inadequate, and to fear social interactions with same-aged peers.

Although the great majority of sexual abusers are male, the number of female sexual abusers may be greater than we've generally believed (Zernike, 2005). Many female sexual abusers may go undetected, because society accords women a much freer range of physical contact with children than it does men. A study of Canadian police officers and psychiatrists has found among these groups a culture of denial of women as potential sexual aggressors (Denov, 2001).

SEX TOURISM Some Canadians travel to developing countries to have sex with children, partly because there's less chance of being prosecuted there. In 1997, the Canadian government changed the Criminal Code to allow prosecution of Canadians who sexually abuse children while out of the country. A 2002 amendment allows prosecution in Canada even without the agreement of the country in which the offence occurs.

In 2005, the first conviction was obtained under this legislation when a British Columbia man was convicted of having sex with children under the age of 14 in Cambodia (Girard, 2005). In 2008, two Quebec men were charged with sexual abuse of children in an orphanage in Haiti.

Yet, because of lax enforcement, few Canadians who are charged in other countries with child sex abuse are ever prosecuted in Canada (Bains, 2008).

Pedophilia

Pedophilia is a paraphilia in which an adult finds children the preferred and sometimes the exclusive objects of sexual desire. According to the *Diagnostic and Statistical Manual of Mental Disorders* (American Psychiatric Association, 2000), pedophilia involves sexually arousing fantasies, urges, or behaviours that involve sexual activity with a prepubescent child. A clinical diagnosis is given when a person acts on or is distressed by these pedophilic urges.

Pedophilia A paraphilia that features sexual attraction to children.

Not all child molesters are necessarily pedophiles, and not all pedophiles, despite their fantasies and urges, necessarily molest children. The prevalence of pedophilia in the general population is unknown. Based on a few small-sample surveys, it's been estimated that up to 5% of men have sexual fantasies or sexual contact with prepubescent children (Seto, 2009).

Pedophiles are almost exclusively male, although some isolated cases of female pedophiles have been reported (Finkelhor, 2005b). Some pedophiles are sexually attracted only to children. Others are sexually attracted to both children and adults. Some pedophiles may never have any sexual contact with children (Seto, 2009). Some pedophiles limit their sexual interest in children to incestuous relationships with family members, while others abuse children they're not related to. Some pedophiles limit their sexual interest in children to looking at or undressing them, while others fondle them or masturbate in their presence. Some manipulate or coerce children into oral, anal, or vaginal intercourse.

Children tend not to be worldly-wise. They can often be taken in by pedophiles who say they want to show them something, teach them something, or do something with them that they'll like. Some pedophiles seek to gain children's affection, and, later, to discourage the children from disclosing the sexual activity by showering them with attention and gifts. Others threaten the children or their families, to prevent disclosure.

Although most pedophiles don't wear trench coats and hang around schoolyards, there's research evidence that many do have personality disorders (Madsen et al., 2006). Research finds them emotionally unstable, disagreeable, angry, impulsive, and mistrustful. A study by Toronto researchers has found that many offenders have grown up in families with insecure attachment experiences (Stripe et al., 2006).

Some pedophiles who lack social skills may turn to children after failing to establish gratifying relationships with adult women. Many pedophiles distort reality in ways that enable them to pursue sexual activity with children (Marziano et al., 2006). Pedophiles often:

- See children as sexual beings who want to have sex with adults.
- Believe sex doesn't harm children, and that it may be beneficial.
- Think themselves so important that they're entitled to have sex with whomever they want.

Ray Blanchard and his colleagues at the Centre for Addiction and Mental Health in Toronto are exploring how disturbances in early neurodevelopment are related to pedophilia. They find that pedophiles are more likely to have experienced

There Really Was a Monster in Her Bedroom.
Not all monsters are make-believe. Some, such as perpetrators of incest, are family members.

serious head injuries before age six, and that these injuries are associated with memory loss and lower levels of intelligence. Pedophilia is somewhat related to left-handedness, which may be attributable to altered fetal development (Blanchard et al., 2007; Cantor et al., 2004, 2005a).

A group of Ontario researchers has also found that men with older brothers are more prone to sexually coercing both children and adults, and that male perpetrators with older brothers are more likely to choose male than female victims (Lalumière et al., 1998). In another Ontario study (Cantor et al., 2006), pedophilia has been associated with school failure by one or more years and subsequent enrolment in special education. In a separate study, Cantor et al. (2005b) has found that pedophiles have lower intelligence levels as measured by IQ (intelligence quotient) tests.

In a groundbreaking study, Cantor and his colleagues (2008) have found significant brain differences between pedophiles and other men—differences that may exist at birth. By using magnetic resonance imaging, the researchers have discovered that the wiring that connects the brain regions responsible for sexual response is thinner in pedophiles. This indicates that the part of the brain related to identifying sexual partners may not develop normally in pedophiles.

Using penile tests of sexual arousal, Toronto researchers (Seto et al., 2006) have found that men charged with child pornography offences are highly likely to be aroused by sexual images of children. The researchers have concluded that child-pornography offences are stronger than child sexual offences in indicating pedophilia. The researchers have speculated that some men who sexually assault young victims are attracted to those who show some signs of sexual development, rather than to their victims' youth (Seto et al., 2006).

What's the relationship between committing child-porn offences and other sexual offences? In a sample of adult males convicted of child-porn offences, Michael Seto and Angela Eke (2005) found that 24% had committed previous sexual offences involving contact. Child-pornography offenders who had committed prior or concurrent contact offences were most likely to offend again.

Incest

Incest Sexual relations between individuals who are so closely related that sexual relations are prohibited and punishable by law.

Incest involves people who are consanguineous, or related by blood. The law may also proscribe intercourse between, say, a stepfather and a stepdaughter. Although a few societies have permitted incestuous pairings among royalty, all known cultures have some sort of incest taboo. Most of our knowledge of incestuous relationships concerns father–daughter incest. Why? Most identified cases involve fathers who were eventually incarcerated.

About 1% of a sample of women in five American cities reported sexual encounters with fathers or stepfathers (Anderson, 2006). But brother–sister incest, not parent–child incest, is the most common type (Caffaro & Conn-Caffaro, 2005). Brother–sister incest is also believed to be greatly under-reported, possibly because it tends to be transient, and because it appears to be less harmful than parent–child incest. Finkelhor (1990) found that 21% of the college men in his sample, and 39% of the college women, reported incestuous relationships with siblings of the other sex. Only 4% reported incestuous relationships with their fathers. Mother–daughter incest is the least common form of incest, but it does occur (Bartolo, 2005; Turton, 2005).

FATHER-DAUGHTER INCEST Father–daughter incest often begins with affectionate cuddling or embraces, and progresses to teasing sexual play, lengthy caresses, hugs, kisses, and genital contact—even penetration. In some cases, genital contact occurs more abruptly, usually when the father has been drinking or arguing with his wife. Force isn't typically used to gain compliance, but daughters are sometimes physically overcome and injured by their fathers.

BROTHER-SISTER INCEST In sibling incest, the brother usually initiates the sexual activity and assumes the dominant role. Some brothers and sisters may view their sexual activity as natural, and not know it's taboo.

Evidence on the effects of incest between brothers and sisters is mixed. In one study of university undergraduates, those who reported childhood incest with siblings showed no greater evidence of sexual-adjustment problems than those who didn't report incest experiences (Greenwald & Leitenberg, 1989). Sibling incest is most likely to be harmful when it's recurrent or forced, or when parental response is harsh (Adams, 2007).

MOTHER-SON INCEST Mother–son incest occurs far less frequently than father–daughter incest. However, it may be that boys who are sexually abused by their mothers are less likely to report it. Nevertheless, these cases do occur.

In an unusual case in Cambridge, Ontario, a mother and her son had three children together. The son was 16 years old when he fathered the first child. In an attempt to cover up the incestuous relationship, the son fabricated identity documents. Both mother and son were found guilty of incest (Wood, 2005).

FAMILY FACTORS Incest frequently occurs within the context of general family disruption. There may also be spousal abuse, a dysfunctional marriage, or alcoholic or physically abusive parents. Stressful events in the father's life, such as a job loss or work problems, often precede the initiation of incest (Welldon, 2005).

Fathers who abuse their daughters when they're older tend to be domineering and authoritarian with their families (Waterman, 1986). Fathers who abuse preschool daughters are more likely to be passive, dependent, and low in self-esteem.

Marriages in incestuous families tend to be characterized by uneven power relationships between the spouses. Abusive fathers are usually dominant. Another thread that frequently runs through incestuous families is troubled sexual relationships between the spouses. The wives often rejects the husbands sexually (Waterman, 1986).

Gebhard and his colleagues (1965) found that many fathers who committed incest with their daughters were religiously devout, fundamentalist, and moralistic. Perhaps such men, when sexually frustrated, are less likely to seek extramarital and extra-familial sexual outlets or to turn to masturbation for sexual release. In many cases, the father is under stress, but doesn't find adequate emotional and sexual support from his wife (Gagnon, 1977). He turns to a daughter as a wife surrogate, often when he's been drinking alcohol (Gebhard et al., 1965). The daughter may become, in her father's fantasies, the "woman of the house." This fantasy may become his justification for continuing the incestuous relationship. In some incestuous families, a role reversal occurs—the abused daughter assumes many of the mother's responsibilities for managing the household and caring for the younger children.

Incestuous abuse is often repeated from generation to generation. One study found that in 154 cases of sexual abuse within families, more than one-third of the male offenders and about one-half of the mothers had either been abused themselves or been exposed to abuse as children (Faller, 1989).

Australian and Canadian researchers (Greenberg et al., 2005) compared the characteristics of male incest offenders who were biological fathers with those who were stepfathers. Both groups reported serious problems in their own childhoods, including sexual and physical abuse and placement outside of their homes. Their current problems involved alcohol abuse and deviant sexual arousal. Of all the variables analyzed, biological fathers and stepfathers differed statistically only in their sexual arousal to children—biological fathers were less aroused by sexual abuse of children than stepfathers were.

Effects of Sexual Abuse on Children

The effects of sexual abuse are varied, and no single identifiable syndrome emerges from it (Anderson, 2006; Resick, 2003). Children who are sexually abused may suffer from a litany of short- and long-term psychological complaints, including anger, depression, anxiety, eating disorders, inappropriate sexual behaviour, aggressive behaviour, self-destructive behaviour, sexual promiscuity, drug abuse, suicide attempts, post-traumatic stress disorder, low self-esteem, sexual dysfunction, mistrust of others, and feelings of detachment (Edwards et al., 2003). Sexual abuse may also have physical effects, such as genital injuries, and may cause stress-related problems such as stomach aches and headaches.

Abused children often act out. Younger children may have tantrums or display aggressive or antisocial behaviour, while older children may turn to substance abuse (Anderson, 2006). Some abused children become withdrawn, retreating into fantasy or refusing to leave the house. Regressive behaviours, such as thumb-sucking, fear of the dark, and fear of strangers, are also common among sexually abused children. On the heels of the assault and in the ensuing years, many survivors of childhood sexual abuse—like many sexual-assault survivors—show signs of post-traumatic

Applied Knowledge

HELPING CHILDREN AVOID SEXUAL ABUSE

Many of us were taught never to accept a ride or an offer of candy from a stranger. However, many instances of sexual abuse are perpetrated by familiar adults—often family members or friends (Zielbauer, 2000).

Prevention programs help children understand what sexual abuse is and how they can avoid it. In addition to learning to avoid strangers, children need to recognize the differences between acceptable touching, such as an affectionate embrace or pat on the head, and unacceptable or "bad" touching. Even children of elementary school age can learn the distinction between "good touching" and "bad touching."

Good school-based programs are generally helpful in preparing children to handle actual encounters with potential

molesters. Children who receive comprehensive training are more likely to use strategies such as running away, yelling, and saying no when they're threatened by abusers. They're also more likely to report such incidents to adults.

Researchers recognize that children can be easily intimidated and overpowered by adults and older children (Miller, 2005). They may be unable to say no in sexually abusive situations, even though they want to and know it's the right thing to do.

Although children may not always be able to prevent abuse, they can be encouraged to tell someone about it. Most prevention programs emphasize such as "It's not your fault," "Never keep a bad or scary secret," and "Always tell your parents about this, especially if someone says you *shouldn't* tell them."

Children also need to be alerted to the types of threats they might receive for

disclosing the abuse. They're more likely to resist threats if they're reassured that they'll be believed if they disclose the abuse, that their parents will continue to love them, and that they and their families will be protected from the molesters.

School-based prevention programs focus on protecting children. In Canada, teachers and helping professionals are required to report suspected abuse to authorities. Tighter controls and better screening are needed to monitor the hiring of daycare employees. Administrators and teachers in preschool and daycare facilities need to be taught to recognize the signs of sexual abuse, and to report suspected cases.

Treatment programs to help people who are sexually attracted to children *before* they commit abusive acts would also be beneficial.

stress disorder. They suffer flashbacks, nightmares, numbing of emotions, and feelings of estrangement from others (Herrera & McCloskey, 2003).

The sexual development of abused children may also be adversely affected. A survivor may, for example, become prematurely sexually active or promiscuous in adolescence and adulthood (Herrera & McCloskey, 2003). Researchers find that adolescent girls who are sexually abused tend to engage in consensual sex at earlier ages than their peers who are not abused (Herrera & McCloskey, 2003).

Researchers generally find more similarities than differences between the sexes with respect to the effects of sexual abuse in childhood (Edwards et al., 2003). Both boys and girls tend to experience fears and sleep disturbances. There are some sex differences, however. The most consistent is that boys are more likely to externalize their problems (e.g., become more physically aggressive), while girls are more likely to internalize their difficulties (e.g., become depressed) (Anderson, 2006).

Late adolescence and early adulthood seem to be especially difficult for survivors of childhood sexual abuse. Studies of women in these age groups reveal more psychological and social problems in abused than in non-abused women (Anderson, 2006).

Treatment of Childhood Sexual Abuse Survivors

Psychotherapy in adulthood often becomes the first opportunity for survivors to confront residual pain, anger, and misplaced guilt. Group and individual therapy can help improve survivors' self-esteem and ability to develop intimate relationships.

Many therapists recommend a multi-component treatment approach, which may involve individual therapy for the child, mother, and father group therapy for the adolescent or even the preadolescent survivor art therapy or play therapy for the younger child (e.g., using drawings or puppets to express feelings), marital counselling for the parents, and family therapy for the entire family.

In 2011, the Ontario government announced $2.2 million in funding to 45 agencies to provide individual and group counselling for male victims of sexual abuse (Wood, 2011).

Treatment of Perpetrators

What does "treatment" mean? When a helping professional treats someone, the goal is usually to help that individual. When we speak of treating a sex offender, the goal is just as likely—or more likely—to be to help society by eliminating the problem behaviour.

A group of Canadian and American researchers has conducted an extensive review of the effectiveness of psychological treatment programs for sex offenders. They've found that treatment programs before 1980 had little effect, but that current treatments are somewhat effective in reducing rates of recidivism (Hanson et al., 2002). More recently, Ontario researchers have developed treatment programs that have resulted in reoffences by only 3% of sex offenders (Marshall et al., 2006).

Marshall and his colleagues (2007) emphasize the importance of having offenders take responsibility for their offences. They also teach offenders more effective coping skills for dealing with their relationship problems. With offenders who continue to have deviant patterns of sexual arousal, Marshall and his colleagues use reconditioning strategies to enhance appropriate sexual interests and reduce deviant ones.

Some Canadian communities, including Victoria, Winnipeg, and Kitchener, have volunteer groups known as Circles of Support and Accountability (COSA), which have the twin goals of community protection and offender rehabilitation. These trained volunteer groups help integrate sexual offenders into the community, and help them avoid reoffending by meeting their intimacy and relationship needs.

A World of Diversity

SHAME ON EGYPT'S SEXIST BULLIES

by Mona Eltahawy

When I was only four years old, and still living in Cairo, a man exposed himself to me as I stood on a balcony at my family's home, and gestured for me to come down.

At 15, I was groped as I was performing the rites of the hajj pilgrimage at Mecca, the holiest site for Muslims. Every part of my body was covered except for my face and hands. I'd never been groped before, and burst into tears, but I was too ashamed to explain to my family what had happened.

During my twenties, when I had returned to Cairo and wore the hijab, a way of dressing that again covers everything but the face and the hands, I was groped so many times that whenever I passed a group of men, I'd place my bag between myself and them. Headphones helped block out the disgusting things men—and even boys barely in their teens—hissed at me.

So it was no surprise to learn that 98% of foreign women visiting Egypt and 83% of native Egyptian women who were recently surveyed said they, too, had been sexually harassed, and they've recounted a catalogue of horrors similar to mine. What an awful time to be a woman in Egypt.

When the Egyptian Centre for Women's Rights reported that 62%

of Egyptian men admitted to harassing women, I could only shudder at what sexist bullies so many of my countrymen are.

Even worse, when I read that the majority of the more than 2000 Egyptian men and women that Centre surveyed blamed women for bringing on the harassment because of the way they dressed, I honestly thought my countrymen and women had lost their minds.

In Egypt today, up to 80% of women wear one form of veil or another—be it a head scarf or a full-body veil that covers the face, too—so you'd think it was obvious that sexual harassment had nothing to do with the way a woman dresses. So, what is it that drives such a stubborn wish to fault women?

The answer lies in perhaps the saddest of all the Centre's findings. Unlike foreign women, most Egyptian women said women should keep their harassment to themselves, because they were ashamed or feared it could ruin their reputations. This shame is fuelled by religious and political messages that bombard Egyptian public life, turning women into sexual objects and giving men free rein to women's bodies.

In 2006, it was the well-publicized episode of the Australian mufti's comparing women who didn't wear the hijab to uncovered meat left out for wild cats. He was educated at Al-Azhar, the religious institution in Egypt that trains clerics from

all over the Sunni Muslim world. He was suspended, but his reprehensible views are very much at work among many other clerics.

There is no law criminalizing sexual harassment in Egypt, and police often refuse to report women's complaints. And when it is the police themselves who are harassing women, then clearly women's safety is far from a priority in Egypt.

The state itself taught Egyptians a most spectacular lesson in institutionalized patriarchy when security forces and government-hired thugs sexually assaulted demonstrators, especially women, during an anti-regime protest in 2005, giving a green light to harassers.

At a demonstration against sexual harassment that I attended in Cairo a year later, there were nearly more riot police than protesters. My sister Nora was 20 at the time, and she, with several of her friends, joined the protest. We swapped our sexual-harassment stories like veterans comparing war wounds, and we unravelled a taboo that shelters the real criminals of sexual harassment and has kept us hiding in shame.

And that's why I began here with my own stories—to free myself of the tentacles of that shame.

Source: Eltahawy, M. (2008, August 5). Shame on Egypt's sexist bullies. The Globe and Mail, p. A11.

This process assumes that offenders needn't be isolated to protect the community (Petrunik, 2003). An evaluation project in Ontario has found that involvement in a COSA can reduce further sexual offending by more than 60% (Wilson, 2005).

In the past, some programs have used extreme measures such as surgical castration to lower offenders' sex drives. Surgical castration raises ethical concerns, because it's invasive and irreversible. Anti-androgen drugs such as Depo-Provera chemically reduce testosterone and sex drive levels, but are reversible (Roesler & Witztum, 2000).

Pedophilia appears to be linked to prenatal neurological factors. It's therefore unlikely that a sexual preference for children can be changed (Seto, 2009). Psychological and medical interventions are intended to reduce sexual responsiveness to children and increase self-management skills. One study has shown that anti-androgen drugs can decrease pedophilic fantasies and masturbation to pedo-philic fantasies in incarcerated sex offenders (Schober et al., 2005). In reviewing the literature, Ontario researcher Michael Seto (2009) has concluded that the effec-tiveness of psychological interventions to reduce recidivism among pedophilic sex offenders has not been scientifically demonstrated. Nevertheless, he suggests that "learning to control their sexual arousal to children may help motivated individuals to refrain from sexually offending" (Seto, 2009, p. 402).

In 2004, the Canadian federal government responded to pressure from com-munity groups, some provincial governments, and police forces by establishing a national sex-offender registry. Convicted sex offenders must register within 15 days of being released from prison, and must reregister annually and within two weeks of moving. Police agencies from across Canada have access to this database, which they believe will help them investigate cases of sexual assault.

By 2010, more than 24 000 names were included in the Canadian sex offender registry. However, an investigation discovered that many offenders were not regis-tered, and that the list of offenders wasn't up to date (Friscolanti, 2008). Judges have the discretion to decide whether individuals convicted of sexual offences must be included in the sex-offender registry. In some cases, particularly when the offences are nonviolent and the judges believe the offenders aren't dangerous to the commu-nity, the offenders aren't placed on the registry. However, a series of legal reforms introduced to the Canadian Parliament in 2011 will likely result in automatic reg-istration of anyone convicted of a sex crime.

Marshall and his colleagues (2006) have criticized public-notification approaches, in the belief that they're likely to cause stress in offenders that will increase the recidivism rate. The researchers therefore suggest that public notifica-tion should be used only in extremely dangerous cases, when alternative contain-ment strategies are unavailable.

Some legal experts have argued that the registry violates the human rights of offenders, who can never have their names removed from the list even after living for many years as model citizens. No other category of offender is required to register with police after being released from prison and no longer on parole (Ward et al., 2007).

CRITICAL THINKING QUESTIONS

Should judges have some level of discretion in decid-ing whether individuals convicted of sexual offenses should be listed in a sex-offender registry?

Sexual Harassment

For legal purposes, **sexual harassment** in the workplace is usually defined as deliberate or repeated unwanted comments, gestures, or physical contact (Craig, 2005; Finkelman, 2005). It's forbidden by both federal and provincial human-rights legislation. Sexual harassment makes the workplace and other settings hostile. Examples range from unwelcome sexual jokes and sexual innuendos to outright sexual assaults. Sexual harassment may include such behaviours as the following:

Sexual harassment
Deliberate or repeated unsolicited and unwelcome comments, gestures, or physical contact of a sexual nature.

- Verbal harassment.
- Verbal abuse.
- Subtle pressure for sexual activity.
- Remarks about a person's clothing, body, or sexual activities.
- Leering at or ogling of a person's body.
- Unwelcome touching, patting, or pinching.
- Brushing against a person's body.
- Demands for sexual favours, accompanied by implied or overt threats about a person's job or student status.
- Physical assault.

In a national survey of about 2000 Canadian working women, 56% reported that they'd experienced sexual harassment during the previous year, and 77% said they'd experienced sexual harassment during their lifetimes (Crocker & Kalemba, 1999).

Sexual Harassment.
Many victims of sexual harassment keep the incidents to themselves, for fear that they'll be blamed for their own victimization, or that their supervisors will fire them for complaining. Perpetrators can claim that they've been misunderstood or that the victims are exaggerating.

The three most common types of incidents included staring, jokes, and remarks about women or about the respondents themselves. The least common incidents included physical force, threats, and bribery.

Evidence shows that people subjected to sexual harassment do suffer from it. In a survey of Canadian women in the workforce, 30% of those who'd been sexually harassed reported that their jobs were affected, and 14% of those who'd been sexually harassed reported personal difficulties as a result (Crocker & Kalemba, 1999). Some find harassment on the job so unbearable that they resign.

Sexual harassment may have more to do with abuse of power than with sexual desire (Chaiyavej & Morash, 2009). Relatively few cases of sexual harassment involve outright requests for sexual favours. The harasser is usually in a dominant position, and abuses that position by exploiting the victim's vulnerability. Sexual harassment may also occur between doctors and patients, and between therapists and clients. Therapists may use their power and influence to pressure clients into sexual relations. In Canada, professional organizations for teachers, doctors, and therapists have strict ethical guidelines that forbid sexual contact between doctors and patients, therapists and clients, and teachers and students.

Minority Groups

A Canadian study has shed light on various experiences of harassment (Berdahl & Moore, 2006). It compared the experiences of white women, black women, and Filipina women. White women with full rights as citizens felt most free to report the harassment to authorities. Black women and Filipinas felt that the term "sexual harassment" didn't fully capture their experience—that their treatment also had to do with the power white men could exercise over blacks and, especially, live-in Filipina caregivers. The study also found that women experienced more sexual harassment than men, and in what the authors call double jeopardy, minority women encountered more harassment than white women.

Innovative Canadian Research

GENDER, ETHNICITY, AND PERCEPTIONS OF SEXUAL HARASSMENT

The genders often differ in their perceptions of sexual harassment.

University of Windsor researchers Pek Ne Knoo and Charlene Senn (2004) asked students to rate the offensiveness of 10 types of email.

Messages containing sexual content were rated as more offensive by women than by men. In particular, women found sexual propositions from strangers extremely offensive, while the men found them enjoyable.

Researchers at the University of British Columbia found that male students were more tolerant of behaviours indicative of sexual harassment than female students were, and that students from Asian backgrounds were more tolerant of these behaviours than students from Western backgrounds (Kennedy & Gorzalka, 2002).

The longer the Asian students had been in Canada, the less accepting they were of these behaviours. This trend indicates that over time, Asian Canadians tend to become acculturated to the views of other Canadians regarding sexual harassment (Kennedy & Gorzalka, 2002).

Robin Milhausen (2000) of the University of Guelph surveyed 413 young adults at university and in the community about workplace behaviours and perceptions.

The majority of both men and women believed men have to be more careful than women in the workplace when it comes to making sexual jokes, sexual comments, comments about the physical appearances of co-workers, and any kind of sexual contact with co-workers. For example, 80% of the men and 68% of the women said men have to be more careful than women about making sexual comments.

Only a minority (15% of the men and 29% of the women) said both genders have to be careful, while hardly any (4% of men and 2% of women) said women have to be more careful.

Workplaces

Harassers in the workplace can be employers, supervisors, co-workers, or clients. If a worker asks a co-worker for a date and is refused, it's not sexual harassment. If the co-worker persists with unwelcome advances and doesn't take no for an answer, the behaviour crosses the line and becomes harassment.

Perhaps the most severe form of sexual harassment, short of outright assault, involves an employer or supervisor who demands sexual favours as a condition of employment or advancement. In Canada, human rights commissions have expanded the definition of sexual harassment in the workplace to include any behaviour of a sexual nature that interferes with an individual's work performance or creates a hostile, intimidating, or offensive work environment. Canadian legislation recognizes sexual harassment as a form of sex discrimination.

Some organizations have gone a step further, banning their employees from having any sexual contact with other employees, even if it's consensual. A Canadian Forces ban on all forms of sexual activity—including flirting and holding hands—at an overseas peacekeeping base led to a 2001 court challenge. The military judge upheld the ban, arguing that sexual activity "could lead to feelings of jealousy, even violence, feelings of favouritism, and disrupting the feelings of cohesion and morale" (Weber, 2001, p. A3). In 2011, a general in the Canadian armed forces was demoted and fined $7,000 for having an affair with a female soldier (Peritz, 2011).

In a widely publicized 2005 case, the City of Toronto suspended a female senior manager and her (married) male second-in-command, who admitted that they'd had an affair. Concerns were raised that the male assistant's rapid promotion—from temporary employee to a senior position in only 10 months—resulted from favouritism on the part of his boss, who was also his lover.

Despite prohibitions against intimate relationships in the workplace, many people do get involved with their fellow workers. In a recent national survey, about one-third of both men and women said they'd had sex with someone they'd worked with, and more than half said they had crushes on co-workers (van der Voort, 2008).

Employers can be held responsible not only for their own actions, but also for sexual harassment by their employees, when they've either known or *should have known* harassment was taking place and failed to eliminate it promptly. To protect themselves, many companies and universities have developed programs to educate workers about sexual harassment, established mechanisms for dealing with complaints, and imposed sanctions against harassers.

Relatively few people who encounter sexual harassment in the workplace file formal complaints or seek legal remedies. Among Canadian women, the most common responses to sexual harassment are either confronting the harassers (38%) or ignoring the incidents (20%). Relatively few (5%) report them. One percent of women have quit their jobs because of harassment. Like people subjected to other forms of sexual coercion, those experiencing sexual harassment often don't report the offences for fear that they won't be believed or that they'll be subjected to retaliation. Some fear they'll be branded as troublemakers, or that they'll lose their jobs (Goleman, 1991).

Campuses

Kathleen Cairns and Doyle Hatt (1995) of the University of Calgary have found that 9% of the female graduate students and 2% of the male graduate students at a large Canadian university have experienced sexual harassment. The most common form has involved sexist remarks and sexual comments. Very few of the students have experienced sexual coercion. The female students have been harassed mainly by male professors and instructors, but also by other students. The male students have been harassed mainly by female students.

Researchers at the Ontario Institute for Studies in Education surveyed psychologists in Ontario about their sexual-harassment experiences while they were in graduate school (Schneider et al., 2002). The reported incidence of harassment was much higher than that found by Cairns and Hatt, most likely because the Ontario researchers measured a wider scope of harassment experiences. Sixty percent of the psychologists reported that by far the most common type of harassment was suggestive jokes or stories told by professors. Very few reported sexual coercion by their professors.

Harassers are typically—but not always—male. Most students who encounter sexual harassment don't report it. If they do, they usually tell friends, and not people in authority.

Most forms of harassment involve unequal power relationships between the harassers and their targets. Peer harassment involves people who are equal in power, and includes sexual taunts from fellow employees, students, or colleagues. In some cases, the harassers may have less formal power than the individuals they're harassing. Both female and male professors, for example, have been sexually harassed by students.

University faculty associations in Canada support policies on sexual harassment. Still, the associations are concerned that their policies may in some instances limit academic freedom, especially the ability to have open discussions of controversial topics. Consider the case of an Ontario law professor. In teaching his students about the arguments for and against an anti-pornography law, he asked them to adopt a perspective that was contrary to their own. Some of the students, upset at having to argue against their own beliefs, complained to the university's sexual harassment officer. The official warned the instructor that repeating the class exercise could lead to a sexual-harassment investigation (Fekete, 1994).

CRITICAL THINKING QUESTIONS

Are you aware of any sexual-harassment policies at your school?

Schools

Playful sexual antics are common during adolescence. Unwelcome sexual advances and lewd comments go beyond playfulness, however, and have become a concern for many of Canada's teens.

A research team consisting of Loren McMaster, Jennifer Connolly, and Debra Pepler of York University and Wendy McCraig of Queen's University conducted a study of peer-to-peer sexual harassment among 1213 students in grades six to eight in a large Canadian city (McMaster et al., 2002). The study defined sexual harassment as unwanted sexual attention, and asked students whether they'd perpetrated or experienced any of 10 types of sexual harassment. Boys were significantly more likely (36%) than girls (21%) to report perpetration, while both genders were equally likely (42% of boys and 38% of girls) to report victimization. The three behaviours both boys and girls most often experienced were homophobic name-calling, sexual comments or jokes or looks, and flashing or mooning. The boys perpetrated more same-sex harassment, while the girls perpetrated more cross-sex harassment. The most common form of same-sex harassment among boys was homophobic name-calling.

The researchers found that students who were at more advanced stages of pubertal development both perpetrated and experienced sexual harassment more than other students. McMaster et al. (2002) concluded that for some youth, harassment is a phase of development, while for others it's part of a developmental pattern that includes other forms of aggression, such as bullying, and is a predictor of aggression in future dating relationships.

Higher levels of harassment were found in a study of 565 older adolescents in British Columbia and New Brunswick (Dahinten, 2003). The picture that emerges from this poll of teenagers in grades nine to 11 indicates that sexual taunts and advances have become part of an unwelcome ritual for many students, especially girls, as they try to make their way through high school hallways and stairwells. Almost all of the students reported that they'd experienced at least one form of sexual harassment during the preceding two months, while about two-thirds of the girls and half of the boys reported five or more forms of harassment. The most common forms of harassment for two-thirds of the girls were sexual comments, whistles, sexual gestures, stares, and derogatory comments about females.

The students didn't label most of the behaviours as sexual harassment. Of those who'd experienced at least one of the 19 items measuring sexual harassment, only 35% of the girls and 14% of the boys replied yes to the general question of whether they'd been sexually harassed. This discrepancy in labelling clearly illustrates how the type of measurement a researcher chooses can influence the incidence of harassment reported in the literature. It also raises the important question of whether it's legitimate for researchers to categorize behaviours as harassment when the people experiencing them don't consider them harassment.

Girls in the study were more likely than boys to report that they'd been upset by the sexual harassment behaviours. For boys, the most upsetting experiences were being targets of sexual rumours and graffiti, and being followed or pestered for dates. For girls, the most upsetting experiences were being forced to do something other than kissing or hugging, and being targets of sexual rumours. Most of the students responded passively to the harassment. Hardly any complained to a teacher or made a complaint through the school system (Dahinten, 2003).

In a more recent survey of Ontario high school students conducted by the Centre for Addiction and Mental Health, one-third of the students said they'd at times felt unsafe at school. About half of the girls said they'd been subjected to sexual comments or gestures at school, and one-third said they'd been touched in a sexual manner (Rushowy, 2008).

Large-scale studies of youth in both Canada and the United States have found that gays, lesbians, and bisexuals experience more physical and sexual abuse than heterosexuals do (Saewyc et al., 2006). The researchers attribute this to the stigma that's often attached to LGB orientations. They also note that most LGB youth aren't physically or sexually abused.

Applied Knowledge

RESISTING SEXUAL HARASSMENT

What would you do if you were sexually harassed by an employer or a professor? How would you handle it? Would you try to ignore it, and hope it would stop? What actions might you take?

We offer some suggestions you may find helpful. Recognize, however, that responsibility for sexual harassment always lies squarely with the perpetrator and with the organization that permits sexual harassment to take place, not with you.

- *Convey a professional attitude.* Harassment may be stopped cold if you respond to the harasser with a businesslike, professional attitude.

- *Discourage harassing behaviour, and encourage appropriate behaviour.* Harassment may also be stopped cold if you shape the harasser's behaviour. Your reactions may encourage businesslike behaviour and discourage flirtatious or suggestive behaviour. If a harassing professor suggests that you come back after school to review your term paper, so the two of you won't be disturbed, set limits assertively. Tell the professor you'd feel more comfortable discussing the paper during regular office hours. Remain task-oriented. Stick to business. The harasser should quickly get the message that you insist on maintaining a strictly professional relationship. If the harasser persists, don't blame yourself—you're responsible only for your own actions. When the harasser persists, a more direct response may be appropriate (e.g., "Dr. Jones, I'd like to keep our relationship on a purely professional basis").

- *Avoid being alone with the harasser.* If you're being harassed by your professor but need advice about your term paper, approach him or her after class, when other students are milling about, not privately, during office hours. Or bring a friend to wait outside the office while you consult the professor.

- *Maintain a record.* Keep a record of all incidents of harassment, to use as documentation in the event that you decide to lodge an official complaint. The record should include where each incident took place, the date and time, what happened (including the exact words used, if you can recall them), how you felt, and the names of witnesses.

- *Talk with the harasser.* It may be uncomfortable to address the issue directly with a harasser, but doing so puts the offender on notice that you're aware of the harassment and want it to stop. It may be helpful to describe the specific offending actions (e.g., "When we were alone in the office, you repeatedly attempted to touch me or brush up against me"), your feelings about the offending behaviour (e.g., "It made me feel like my privacy was being violated"), and what you'd like the offender to do (e.g., "So I'd like you to agree never to attempt to touch me again. Okay?"). Having a talk with the harasser may stop the harassment. If the harasser denies the accusations, you may have to take further action.

- *Write a letter to the harasser.* Set down on paper a record of the offending behaviour, and put the harasser on notice that the harassment must stop. Your letter might describe what happened (e.g., "Several times you've made sexist comments about my body"), describe how you felt (e.g., "It made me feel like a sexual object when you talked to me that way"), and describe what you'd like the harasser to do (e.g., "I want you to stop making sexist comments to me").

- *Seek support.* Support from people you trust can help you through the often trying process of resisting sexual harassment. Talking with others enables you to express your feelings and receive emotional support, encouragement, and advice. It may also strengthen your case if you have opportunities to identify and talk with other people who've been harassed by the offender.

- *File a complaint.* Organizations are required by law to respond reasonably to complaints of sexual harassment. In large organizations, a designated official (e.g., a human-rights officer) is usually charged with handling such complaints. Set up an appointment with this official to discuss your experiences. The major government agencies that handle charges of sexual harassment are the provincial human-rights offices. Look in the government section of your phone book for the number of the nearest office.

- *Seek legal remedies.* Sexual harassment is illegal and actionable. If you're considering legal action, consult a lawyer familiar with this area of law.

The question isn't what victims of sexual assault, incest, and sexual harassment will do to redress the harm that's been done to them. The question is what we'll all do to reshape society so sex can no longer be used as an instrument of power, coercion, and violence.

Today, there's considerable concern in Canadian high schools about websites that spread sexual rumours about students. The most typical rumours are about boys being gay and girls being promiscuous. These websites can be extremely nasty and hateful, and can demoralize the students they discuss. An even more hurtful form of harassment is posting nude photos of a current or former romantic partner on a website without the person's consent. (See "Applied Knowledge: Sexting and Canadian Youth" in Chapter 7.)

Teachers are also being sexually harassed on websites. A 14-year-old grade eight student in Toronto was banned from an end-of-school-year class trip to Montreal after he made sexual comments about a teacher on Facebook. He said he thought he'd seen the female science teacher masturbating at the back of a class-room (Boyle, 2007).

In 2008, at its annual meeting in Moncton, the Canadian Teachers' Federation unanimously voted that cyber-bullying should be a criminal offence. The teachers said they would lobby members of Parliament to have this offence included in the Criminal Code (Canadian Press, 2008).

Summing Up

The definition of sexual assault involves more than just sexual intercourse.

Types of sexual assault include stranger sexual assault, acquaintance sexual assault, date sexual assault, and partner sexual assault.

Social attitudes such as gender-role stereotyping, seeing sex as adversarial, and acceptance of violence in interpersonal relationships all help create a climate that encourages sexual assault.

Some sexually coercive men feel socially inadequate, lack social skills, and avoid social interactions with women. Others are basically anti-social, and have long histories of violent behaviour.

Sexual-assault survivors often experience post-traumatic stress disorder (PTSD).

Treatment of sexual-assault survivors typically involves helping them through the crisis period following the attack, and then fostering long-term adjustment.

Sexual-assault prevention involves educating society at large, and familiarizing women with a number of precautions they can take.

Verbal sexual coercion involves the use of verbal pressure or seduction lines to manipulate a person into having sexual relations.

Any form of sexual contact between an adult and a child is abusive, even if force or physical threat isn't used, because a child is legally incapable of consenting to sexual activity with an adult.

In most cases of child sexual abuse, the molesters are close to the children they abuse—relatives, step-relatives, family friends, and neighbours.

Pedophilia is a type of paraphilia in which adults are sexually attracted to children.

Incest is sexual relations between people who are closely related.

Children who are sexually abused often suffer social and emotional problems that impair their development and persist into adulthood, affecting their self-esteem and their formation of intimate relationships.

Psychotherapy may help adult survivors of sexual abuse improve their self-esteem and their ability to develop intimate relationships.

The effectiveness of prison-based rehabilitation programs and anti-androgen drugs in curbing repeat offences requires further empirical support.

The definition of sexual harassment in the workplace has been expanded to include any behaviour of a sexual nature that interferes with an individual's work performance or creates a hostile, intimidating, or offensive work environment.

Most incidents of sexual harassment on campus take the form of sexist comments.

Sexual harassment at school has become an unwelcome ritual that many junior and senior high school students are forced to endure.

Test Yourself

Multiple-Choice Questions

1. A sexual assault causing significant physical injury to the victim would be categorized as _____ under the Criminal Code of Canada.
   - (a) level 1
   - (b) level 2
   - (c) level 3
   - (d) level 4

2. Sexual assaults are most often committed by:
   - (a) Strangers.
   - (b) Family members.
   - (c) Gangs.
   - (d) Acquaintances.

3. According to the General Social Survey—Victimization, a person is most likely to be sexually assaulted at age:
   - (a) 15 to 24.
   - (b) 25 to 34.
   - (c) 35 to 44.
   - (d) 45 to 54.

4. Which of the following is not a myth that encourages sexual assault?
   - (a) In general, women like men to be aggressive, even forceful, when it comes to sex.
   - (b) When women dress in revealing clothing, they're asking to be sexually assaulted.
   - (c) Women who say no to sex really mean no.
   - (d) Women say no to sex when they really mean yes.

5. Which of the following is not a suggestion about what to do if you're sexually assaulted?
   - (a) Don't wash, change your clothes, or comb your hair.
   - (b) Seek medical help, and make sure any injuries are documented.
   - (c) Think about reporting the assault to police.
   - (d) Don't talk to anyone about the assault.

6. Rohypnol is used as a date-rape drug because it:
   - (a) Impairs memory.
   - (b) Enhances sexual response.
   - (c) Multiplies the effects of testosterone.
   - (d) Encourages women to recall consensual sex as assaults.

7. Which of the following statements about pedophilia is false?
   - (a) Many pedophiles have personality disorders.
   - (b) With proper treatment, it's likely that a sexual preference for children can be changed.
   - (c) Many pedophiles believe sex with a child isn't harmful.
   - (d) Researchers have found brain differences that are likely prenatal between pedophiles and other men.

8. The most common type of child sexual abuse is:
   - (a) Genital fondling.
   - (b) Vaginal intercourse.
   - (c) Oral sex.
   - (d) Exhibitionism.

9. The most common type of incest is:
   - (a) Father-daughter incest.
   - (b) Stepfather-stepdaughter incest.
   - (c) Brother-sister incest.
   - (d) Mother-son incest.

10. When it comes to assessing behaviours as sexual harassment:
   - (a) Men find more behaviours offensive than women do.
   - (b) Men and women have similar perceptions.
   - (c) Women find more behaviours offensive than men do.
   - (d) Women find all sexual behaviour in the workplace offensive.

You'll find answers to the "Test Yourself" questions on page 495.

Critical Thinking

1. Have you ever tried to convince someone to engage in sexual activity even after they've said no? What eventually happened? How do you feel about it now?

2. Has anyone ever tried to convince you to engage in sexual activity even when you haven't wanted to? What happened? How do you feel about it now? How do you feel about the other person? About yourself?

3. A woman goes to a bar, has a few too many drinks, dances suggestively with several men, and goes home with one of them. If she later reports that she's been sexually assaulted, do you think she's to blame? If she'd been assaulted on the street while waiting for a bus at the same time of night, would she be less to blame?

4. Imagine that you are sexually harassed and are considering reporting it to authorities, but a friend advises, "Why make such a fuss? Is it really worth it? After all, complaining could backfire." How would you respond?

MySearchLab

MySearchLab offers extensive help to students with their writing and research project and provides round-the-clock access to credible and reliable source material. Take a tour at www.mysearchlab.com.

Commercial Sex

Sex as commerce runs the gamut from street-based sex work, sexually explicit video, and adult magazines to strip shows, sex-toy shops, escort or outcall services, massage parlours, 1-900 telephone services, cybersex (sex over the internet), and sexually oriented messages and images in advertisements for a wide range of products. The types of sexual commerce seem unlimited. The annual Everything To Do With Sex Show held in a number of Canadian cities has hundreds of exhibitors, selling all kinds of products and services related to sex. Many thousands of people attend these events.

Let it all hang out.

THE EVERYTHING TO DO WITH
SEX SHOW

October 21 to 23, Metro Toronto Convention Centre

The Everything to Do With Sex Show.
This trade show, held in various cities across Canada, attracts many thousands of people. The exhibitors sell all kinds of erotic products, including toys and videos. The business of sex is booming in Canada.

Prostitution

Prostitution is often called the world's oldest profession—for good reason. It can be traced at least to ancient Mesopotamia, where temple prostitution flourished. Prostitution also thrived in medieval Europe and during the sexually repressive Victorian period.

Then, as now, the major motive for becoming a prostitute was economic. Many poor women were drawn to prostitution as a means of survival. In Victorian England, prostitution was widely regarded as a necessary outlet for men's sexual appetites. It was widely held that women didn't enjoy sex, so it was better for a man to visit a prostitute than to "soil" his wife with his carnal passions.

In recent years, "sex worker" has increasingly replaced "prostitute" as the preferred term for a person who engages in sexual activity in exchange for monetary compensation.

Prostitution Law in Canada

Canadian laws governing prostitution are confusing. While prostitution itself is legal, almost all of the activities involved with it are illegal. The Criminal Code prohibits a number of activities related to prostitution, including the following:

- Transporting or directing, or offering to transport or direct, another person to a common bawdy house (establishment within which acts of sex for payment occur).
- Keeping, being an inmate of, being found without lawful excuse in, or allowing a place to be used for the purpose of a common bawdy house.
- Procuring and living off the avails of prostitution.

In other words, it's against the law to engage in activities that facilitate prostitution, or to be in a house of prostitution.

Some Canadian cities, such as Edmonton, Vancouver, Calgary, Winnipeg, and Windsor, have attempted to regulate prostitution by licensing escorts and escort agencies. Owners of escort agencies and the escorts themselves are required to register with local police, pay licensing fees, and keep records of clients' names and addresses. Obtaining a city licence, however, is no guarantee that these escort services won't face prosecution for engaging in prostitution-related activities.

University of Windsor researchers Eleanor Maticka-Tyndale, Jacqueline Lewis, and Megan Street (2005) have analyzed the process of licensing escorts in

MySearchLab

- Self-grading practice tests
- Media links
- Flashcards
- Access to thousands of full-text articles from academic journals and help on the research and writing process

Prostitution The sale of sexual activity for money or goods of value, such as drugs.

A World of Diversity

"PROSTITUTION" OR "SEX WORK"?

Many prostitutes have redefined themselves as sex workers, and prostitution as sex work (Lucas, 2005).

The new terms underscore the economic aspects of the work, and are less laden with a history of lewdness and depravity. They've also caught on in the research literature.

The Commercial Sex Information Service (CSIS) in Vancouver explains the shift this way:

The terms "sex work" and "sex worker" have been coined by sex workers themselves to redefine commercial sex, not as the social or psychological characteristic of a class of women, but as an income-generating activity or form of employment for women and men. As such, it can be considered along with other forms of economic activity. An employment or labour perspective is a necessary, if not sufficient, condition for making sex work a part of the mainstream debate on human, women's, and workers' rights at local, national, and international levels.

The lack of international and local protection renders sex workers vulnerable to exploitation in the workplace, and to harassment or violence at the hands of employers, law enforcement officials, clients, and the public.

The need for worker protection, including occupational health and safety provisions, is of particular relevance in the current context of HIV and AIDS.

Source: Bindman, J. (1997). Redefining prostitution as sex work on the international agenda. *Vancouver: Commercial Sex Information Service. Retrieved from http://www.walnet.org/csis/paper/redefining.html*

Windsor. When escorts and agencies were first given licences, there was a feeling that they'd be treated as legitimate businesses. The city bylaws purposely didn't use the word "sex"in descriptions of the escort business. After obtaining their licences, however, the escorts felt the police treated their businesses as undesirable. They felt victimized when the police used entrapment techniques, such as encouraging escorts to negotiate fees for sexual services and then charging them for engaging in illegal activities.

In 1983, the Canadian minister of justice appointed a special committee (the Fraser Committee) to study pornography and prostitution and make recommendations to Parliament. Although the committee recommended that prostitution offences be removed from the Criminal Code, the federal government instead brought in more restrictive legislation, with the aim of decreasing street prostitution. To make it easier for police to prosecute prostitutes as well as their clients, the Criminal Code was changed to make it illegal to communicate with or stop a person in a public place (including a motor vehicle) to negotiate sexual services for payment.

The new legislation was soon challenged as being inconsistent with the Canadian Charter of Rights and Freedoms. In 1990, however, the Supreme Court ruled that freedom of expression as granted by the Charter could be limited, because street solicitation caused too great a social nuisance. Nonetheless, while the new legislation did facilitate prosecution of both prostitutes and clients, it did not decrease street prostitution (Gemme, 1993).

Police and politicians have been particularly concerned about teen prostitution. Parliament significantly increased penalties for clients who attempt to obtain the sexual services of a person under the age of 18. And in 1999, Alberta passed the Protection of Children Involved in Prostitution Act, allowing police or social workers to apprehend and detain under-18 prostitutes in safe houses for up to 72 hours.

Police in Canada often use the strategy of entrapment to obtain convictions against prostitutes and their clients. Male plainclothes officers pretend they're clients wanting sex (e.g., obtaining topless body rubs at massage studios), to determine whether sex is being sold on the premises. Female police officers act as decoys by standing in locations frequented by street prostitutes. When men approach and suggests having sex for money, the decoy officers immediately arrest and charge them with communicating for the purposes of prostitution.

In 2007, a court judge in Newmarket, Ontario, chastised a police officer who'd posed as a client at a massage parlour. The officer stripped naked and obtained a body massage from a female attendant, but stopped her when she went to put her hand on his penis to provide a manual release. The judge stated that the actions of the police officer were unnecessary and "outside a protocol of investigative techniques." The judge also dismissed charges against the massage parlour, because he believed Canadians wouldn't consider masturbation to be sexual (Pron, 2007).

As this case demonstrates, there are a number of grey areas when it comes to interpreting laws about prostitution. The laws—and their interpretation—are continually changing. There are also wide variations across the country in the degree to which prostitution laws are enforced by police.

Police are less likely to entrap those who engage in homosexual prostitution (Gemme, 1993), possibly because male police officers are reluctant to act as decoys for potential male clients. However, the gay and lesbian communities face the possibility of arrest for other kinds of activities. For example, while investigating Sperm Attack Mondays, when male dancers at a gay strip club would ejaculate on stage, Toronto police laid bawdy-house charges against 11 dancers and four customers. Although these were later dropped, the club and its owners were still charged. The police also raided a Toronto gay pornography bar and laid public-indecency charges against men who were engaged in consensual sex in cubicles (Woods, 2000).

In recent years, politicians and police forces have targeted the customers of prostitutes. In 2005, for example, the Manitoba government introduced legislation to suspend the drivers' licences of men convicted of soliciting prostitutes.

LEGAL CHALLENGES Attempts over the years to legalize prostitution in Canada have been resisted by government leaders. Because of concern over a high number of deaths among prostitutes in Vancouver and Edmonton, Parliament voted in 2003 to establish a Subcommittee on Solicitation Laws, with a mandate to review and recommend changes to prostitution laws in order to improve the safety of sex workers.

The subcommittee heard from academic researchers, legal experts, and sex workers who presented well-documented examples of how Canadian laws promote unsafe working conditions for sex workers. These delegations proposed several

CRITICAL THINKING QUESTIONS

Should prostitution be decriminalized? What points would you use to support your answer?

Amsterdam's Red-Light District.
It's one of the city's tourist attractions, where prostitution is legal and regulated. Condoms are a must. Tourists and locals stroll by the canals and window-shop.

changes to the Criminal Code that would give sex workers safer work environments. The subcommittee presented its report, *The Challenge of Change: A Study of Canada's Criminal Prostitution Laws*, in December of 2006. The report acknowledged the analysis of, and recommendations for, greater safety for sex workers presented by numerous witnesses. The subcommittee recommended that the federal government reform the laws so consensual sexual relations between adults, including sex for money, wouldn't be criminalized. However, it didn't offer specific recommendations to promote the safety of sex workers. Instead, the subcommittee focused mainly on the sexual exploitation of children and human trafficking.

The Conservative members of the subcommittee disagreed with the idea that prostitution should be decriminalized. Rather, they viewed prostitution as a degrading activity that no one would willingly consent to be involved in. This view suggests that while the Conservative party forms the federal government, efforts to decriminalize prostitution will be resisted.

In 2007, frustrated with federal government inaction, a small group of lawyers in collaboration with sex workers launched constitutional challenges to the prostitution laws. In Ontario, a legal team led by Osgoode Hall Law School professor Alan Young worked with the Toronto-based Sex Professionals of Canada, and in British Columbia, a legal team led by Katrina Pacey of the Pivot Legal Society collaborated with the Downtown Eastside Sex Workers United Against Violence Society. The underlying principle of the constitutional challenge is that Canadian prostitution laws contribute to violence against street-based sex workers, and the resulting harm outweighs the laws' benefits to society. Three main sections of the laws are challenged:

■ The provision against communication for the purpose of prostitution, because it prevents sex workers from screening potentially violent clients.
■ The provision against bawdy houses, because it prohibits sex workers from working in an indoor environment, which is safer than working on the streets.
■ The provision against living off the avails of prostitution, because it's too broad, and it prevents sex workers from hiring security personnel. (The constitutional challenge does not, however, aim to stop prosecution of pimps who exploit sex workers.)

As a result of the challenge, in 2010 both the Ontario Superior Court and the British Columbia Court of Appeal issued rulings that effectively struck down Canada's prostitution laws. In response to an application by the Attorney General, the Supreme Court of Canada announced in March of 2011 that it would consider the challenge brought by the Downtown Eastside Sex Workers United Against Violence Society (Canadian Press, 2011). The Supreme Court ruling, which will shape Canadian prostitution law, is expected in late 2011 or 2012.

Canadian Attitudes

A 2009 Angus Reid poll found that most Canadians would like to see Canada's prostitution laws modified, though there was considerable disagreement about how. Half (50%) of the poll respondents preferred that some aspects of prostitution that are currently illegal should be decriminalized and that adults should be allowed to engage in consensual prostitution. Twenty-five percent believed prostitution should be prohibited entirely, 16% believed the laws should remain as they were, and 8% weren't sure what they thought (Angus Reid Public Opinion, 2009).

In a 1998 Compas poll, church attendance was one of the strongest predictors of attitudes toward prostitution. Twice as many of those who attended once a week or more (52%) believed prostitution should be kept completely against the law, compared with 26% of those who didn't attend church once a week or more.

People in their twenties and younger were less accepting of prostitution than older Canadians (Compas, 1998), perhaps because they tended to be more idealistic about relationships.

Female Sex Workers

Female sex workers—commonly called hookers, whores, working girls, and escorts—are usually classified according to the settings in which they work. The major types today are street-based sex workers, brothel or house workers (many of whom work in massage parlours), and escorts or call girls.

STREET-BASED SEX WORKERS **Street-based sex workers** occupy the bottom rung in the hierarchy of sex workers. Although street-based sex workers are most visible to the public, most sex work in Canada takes place off-street (O'Doherty, 2011).

In Canada, about 20% of commercial sex workers negotiate their transactions on the streets (Lowman & Atchison, 2006). They typically earn less than off-street sex workers such as escorts and brothel workers. They also incur a high risk of abuse by customers and **pimps**. Studies of street-based sex workers on Vancouver's Downtown Eastside indicate that up to 98% have experienced violence from clients, pimps, and other sex workers (O'Doherty, 2011). Homeless youth living on the streets are often forced to trade sex for money, food, or shelter, an activity known as survival sex.

Between 1991 and 2004, 171 female sex workers in Canada were murdered, and almost all were streetwalkers. Serial murderers have targeted street-based sex workers. One of the most publicized was British Columbia pig farmer Robert Pickton, who was convicted in 2007 of murdering six streetwalkers and charged with killing 20 more. In Edmonton, where the bodies of 20 sex workers have been found since 1983, police suspect a serial killer is the culprit.

Street-based sex workers tend to operate in the open. This makes them more likely than other sex workers to draw attention to themselves and risk arrest (Shaver, 2005). To avoid arrest, street-based sex workers may be indirect about their services. They may ask passersby if they're interested in a good time or some fun, rather than offering sex per se.

In most locales, penalties for prostitution involve small fines or short jail terms. Many police departments, besieged by drug peddling and violent crime, consider prostitution a minor or nuisance crime. For many sex workers, the criminal-justice system is a revolving door. They pay the fine, they spend a night or two in jail, and they return to the streets.

Some sex workers support pimps, especially those who are younger and have less than high-school educations (Shaver, 2005). A pimp acts as lover, father, companion, and master. He provides protection, bail, and sometimes room and board, in exchange for a high percentage of a sex worker's earnings—often more than 90%. Sex workers are often physically abused by their pimps, who may use threats and beatings as a means of control (Norton-Hawk, 2004).

For many street-based sex workers, life is a round of sex, violence, disease, and substance abuse (Degenhardt et al., 2006; Romero-Daza et al., 2005). Many feel powerless to control their own fates, and are often talked or coerced into oral or vaginal sex without protection. Many die young from drug abuse, disease, suicide, and physical abuse from pimps and customers. Those who survive become less marketable with age. Researchers find high levels of psychological disturbance among street-based sex workers (Brown, 2005; Farley, 2005), often related to the physical and sexual abuse they've experienced.

Sex workers who work hotels and conventions generally hold a higher status than those who work the streets or bars. Clients are typically conventioneers

Street-based sex workers Sex workers who solicit customers on the street.

Pimps Men who serve as agents for sex workers and live off their earnings.

Sex Workers in Mexico City.
Street-based sex workers are most visible to the public, because they work in the open, in diverse places.

or businessmen travelling away from home. Hotel sex workers must be skilled in conveying subtle messages to potential clients without attracting the attention of hotel management or security. They usually provide sexual services in the clients' hotel rooms. Some hotel managers tolerate known sex workers (usually for a payoff under the table), so long as the women conduct themselves discreetly.

BROTHEL WORKERS Brothel workers occupy a middle position in the hierarchy of sex work, between street-based sex workers and call girls. They work in brothels or—more commonly, today—massage parlours.

MASSAGE-PARLOUR WORKERS Many massage parlours provide massage—and only massage—to customers. Masseuses and masseurs are licensed by provincial governments, and laws prohibit them from offering sexual services. Many localities require that masseuses and masseurs keep certain parts of their bodies clothed, and refrain from touching clients' genitals.

Many massage parlours, however, serve as fronts for sex work. In these establishments, clients typically pay fees for standard massages and tip the workers for sexual extras.

To avoid massage-parlour regulations, some owners have obtained licenses by claiming they were holistic health centres or aromatherapy centres. In May of 2005, *The Toronto Star* ran front-page exposés of the holistic health centre industry, with headlines such as "What Can Toronto Do About Sex Dens?" At one of the centres the reporters visited, the manager outlined the additional options available beyond the $40 entrance fee: $20 for a topless massage, $40 for a nude massage, and $60 for a body slide (the nude masseuse slides herself over the naked body of the client). Many places also offer a nude reverse, in which clients can massage the naked masseuse (Cribb & Brazao, 2005). The articles created a furor at City Hall, and Toronto City Council instructed its licensing staff and police to clamp down on agencies that weren't legitimate health centres.

Massage parlours that do offer sexual services generally limited them to masturbation of the client (hence the term "rub and tug"). Most don't offer oral sex or penetration ("full service"), in the sometimes mistaken belief that this will protect them from prosecution.

ESCORTS Conventioneers and businessmen are more likely to check the listings for massage and escort services in telephone directories and newspaper personals columns than to seek hotel prostitutes. Services that provide outcalls send masseuses (or masseurs) or escorts to hotel rooms.

Escort services typically (but not always) offer sexual services. Escort services are found in every major Canadian city, where they present themselves as legitimate businesses that provide escorts for men. Indeed, unattached men travelling away from home and to corporate functions can find female companionship under "escort services." Many escort services provide only sexual services, however, and others negotiate sexual services after formal escort duties are completed—or in their stead.

Sex workers who work for escort services often come from middle-class backgrounds and are well educated—the better to hold their own in social conversation. Escort services may make arrangements with legitimate companies to provide escorts for visiting customers or potential clients.

CALL GIRLS So-called **call girls** occupy the highest rungs on the social ladder of female sex work. Many of them overlap with escorts. Call girls tend to be the most attractive and best educated sex workers, and tend to charge more for their services. Many come from middle-class backgrounds. Unlike other types of sex worker, call girls usually work on their own. Because they don't split their incomes with pimps, escort services, or massage parlours, they can earn substantial amounts and can be more selective about the customers they accept.

Call girls may escort their clients to dinners and social functions, providing not only sex, but also charming, gracious conversation (Sanders, 2005). They give clients the feeling that they're important and attractive. They may simulate sexual pleasure and create the illusion that time doesn't matter. It does, of course. To the call girl, as to other entrepreneurs, time is money.

Call girls may receive clients in their apartments (incalls), or make outcalls to clients' homes and hotels. To protect themselves from police and abusive clients, they may insist on seeing a client's business card or learning his home telephone number before making personal contact. They may investigate whether the customer is in fact the person he purports to be.

Advocacy for Sex Workers

Sex work can be a dangerous, highly stigmatized occupation. Although the exchange of sex for money doesn't violate the Criminal Code, various aspects of Canadian law related to prostitution (e.g., keeping or being found in a common bawdy house) push sex workers further to the margins of society. These conditions make it difficult for many sex workers to do their work in a safe, secure manner (Young, 2008).

Meaningful progress toward improving safety and working conditions will likely depend on the direction set by the Supreme Court of Canada's decision on the constitutional challenge against existing laws. Francis Shaver of Concordia University and Jacqueline Lewis and Eleanor Maticka-Tyndale of the University of Windsor have conducted studies with sex workers across Canada. They argue that, beyond decriminalization, the safety and well-being of sex workers can be enhanced through policies that focus on occupational health and safety, access to essential services, and rights. They propose an approach to sex work similar to that adopted in New Zealand, which places sex work in a harm-reduction and labour-rights framework (Shaver, Lewis & Maticka-Tyndale, 2011).

A number of organizations provide support services to sex workers across Canada, such as legal aid offered by the Pivot Legal Society in Vancouver. A major Canadian resource is Maggie's & the Prostitutes' Safe Sex Project of Toronto, the first education project in Canada run by sex workers. The project provides information about health promotion, HIV and STI prevention, Canadian law, and dangerous clients. Maggie's has been a model for international sex-worker peer-education projects.

International Human Trafficking

Human trafficking is a major global enterprise that generates $5 to 7 billion US each year, and the trafficking of girls and women for sexual exploitation is the industry's major component (Stewart & Gajie-Veljanoski, 2005). Because it's illegal and underground, accurate information about the numbers of girls and women trafficked to Canada is difficult to obtain. It's estimated that 800 to 16 000 people

Call girls Sex workers who arrange for their sexual contacts by telephone. "Call" refers both to telephone calls and to being on call.

may be trafficked into Canada each year (Stewart & Gajie-Veljanoski, 2005). The Royal Canadian Mounted Police (RCMP, 2011) has documented cases of girls and women from Eastern Europe, Asia, and Africa being trafficked into Canada, usually by organized-crime groups.

Asian and Eastern European women are lured to big cities in developing countries and to the West by promises of the good life (Rubenson et al., 2005). Upon arrival, they find themselves enslaved in brothels—working for tips and not allowed to leave. In a typical scenario, a woman comes to Canada after false promises of a high-paying job as a nanny, housekeeper, or exotic dancer. Upon her arrival in Canada, she's coerced into sex work, to repay the trafficker for her travel costs. The trafficker keeps her working in the sex trade by withholding her passport, isolating her from the wider community, confining her with force, and threatening her with violence (RCMP, 2011). In 2008, six people were arrested in Toronto for trafficking after police were informed that women from Eastern Europe had been lured to Canada with the promise of modelling jobs. Instead, their passports were taken away from them and they were confined and forced to work in the sex trade (Piercy, 2008).

Entry into Sex Work

No single factor explains women's entry into sex work. Yet poverty and sexual and/or physical abuse figure prominently in the backgrounds of a sizable percentage of sex workers (Carter & Dalla, 2006).

In some developing nations, such as Thailand, some rural, impoverished parents sell their daughters to recruiters, who place them in city brothels (Kristof, 2006). Many of the women send home whatever money they can, and work hard to try to pay off their procurers and break free of their financial bonds.

In Canada and the United States, many street-based sex workers are teen runaways. While some come from middle-class or affluent homes, others have been reared in poverty. Family discord and dysfunction frequently set the stage for their entry into street life and sex work (Carter & Dalla, 2006). Many teen runaways perceive life on the street—despite its dangers—as the only possible escape from family strife and conflict, or from the physical, emotional, or sexual abuse they suffer at home. Teen runaways with marginal skills and limited means of support may find few alternatives to sex work.

The great majority of studies of sex workers have focused on those who work on the street. Their findings may not reflect the characteristics of other categories of sex worker, such as those employed by escort services. Shaver (2002) has conducted several field studies of sex workers in Canada, and believes much of the material on them overstates the disadvantaged backgrounds they may come from. For example, some university students may engage in some form of sex work, such as stripping, because the pay is better than for many other jobs (Lewis, 1998).

Shaver (1996a) argues that researchers who study sex workers from a deviance perspective typically ignore the fact that some of them voluntarily enter this business and don't see themselves as victims. According to Shaver, they feel they have a lot of control over their work, in that "the prostitute sets the price, chooses the client, and has the last say as to when, how, and even if sex takes place" (p. 219). Shaver believes many of the problems associated with sex work would diminish if it were recognized as a legitimate profession.

Male Customers of Female Sex Workers

Many sex workers refer to customers as johns or tricks. Men who pay female sex workers for their services come from all walks of life and represent all socioeconomic and racial groups. One of the most publicized was Eliot Spitzer, former governor of the State of New York, who was forced to resign in 2008 when it became public knowledge that he was spending of thousands of dollars on high-priced call girls.

A Vancouver survey of 500 men arrested for soliciting found that in many respects they were similar to other Canadian men (Kennedy et al., 2003). They ranged in age from 18 to 92, with an average age of 38. More than half were married or in serious relationships. Their incomes, education levels, and ethnic backgrounds were similar to those of the Vancouver population. On average, the men had used the services of sex workers 19 times. Seventy percent reported that no one close to them knew they visited sex workers. They didn't differ from a comparison group of university men in sexual attitudes and sex drive (Kennedy et al., 2003).

Most Canadian studies of clients of sex workers have used samples from john schools. These samples are biased, since they consist of men arrested for soliciting streetwalkers. Vancouver researchers John Lowman and Chris Atchison (2006) obtained a broader range of sex workers' clients. One-half had regular sex partners or spouses, and two-thirds of these men said they were either satisfied or very happy with their relationships. The most common reason they gave for their first visits to sex workers was availability and visibility. The second reason they gave was that their decisions were spontaneous.

Most patrons are occasional johns. Examples include travelling salesmen and military personnel who stop in town without their regular sex partners. Many men

Innovative Canadian Research

MEDIA STEREOTYPES

University of Victoria researchers Helga Hallgrimsdottir, Rachel Phillips, and Cecilia Benoit (2006) compared media portrayals of sex workers with sex workers' accounts of their personal backgrounds and experiences.

The researchers wanted to demonstrate how media portrayals are often inaccurate, presenting stereotypes that encourage stigmatization of sex workers. They analyzed articles about sex workers in Victoria's *Times Colonist* newspaper for the years 1980 to 2004, to illustrate how media portrayals of sex workers have changed.

In general, the newspaper negatively described sex workers as criminals who were morally lost and the source of major social problems such as drug addiction and violence. They were seen as a bad influence on morality, and as a source of sexually transmitted diseases. Most of the articles focused on streetwalkers, ignoring male sex workers.

There was a change in blame attribution over that time. Whereas sex workers were seen in the early 1980s as wicked women who should be punished for their sexual transgressions, they were presented in 2004 as victims who'd been trapped into sex work by pimps or international sex-slave traders, and who were at the mercy of their clients. In the latter years, the newspaper included more stories about child and adolescent prostitution. For the entire period of the survey, sex workers were presented as emotionally damaged.

The researchers (Hallgrimsdottir et al., 2006) compared a sample of sex workers with these representations. Contrary to media stereotypes of young girls brought to Canada by international traffickers, the sex workers in the survey averaged 32 years of age, and the great majority were born in Canada. One-quarter were caring for dependent children, a fact not commonly noted in the media. However, many did come from unstable family backgrounds, which does coincide with the media reports.

There were also media distortions about why women entered sex work. The articles said sex workers were either forced into sex work or turned to it to finance drug addictions. Hardly any of the sex workers surveyed said they'd been forced into the occupation, and only a minority said they'd entered it to pay for drug addictions. The majority said they'd voluntarily chosen to become sex workers, for economic reasons and because they'd had the opportunity to do so.

Although the newspaper articles didn't portray sex work as a career choice, most of the workers saw it that way. Like other jobs, it elicited a diversity of feelings among the workers, yet most of those surveyed felt the benefits of sex work outweighed the costs.

Research with sex workers in three Maritime cities (Jeffrey & MacDonald, 2006) supports the findings of Hallgrimsdottir and her colleagues (2006). Most of the Maritime sex workers said they'd carefully decided which economic choices were available, and voluntarily decided sex work was a better choice than such alternatives as living on welfare or working at minimum-wage jobs.

are interested in sexual novelty or variety, which may be a major motive for occasional johns.

Habitual johns use sex workers as their major or exclusive sexual outlets. Some habitual johns have never established intimate sexual relationships. Some wealthy men who wish to avoid intimate relationships habitually patronize call girls.

Some johns employ sex workers to meet psychological or sexual needs they're unable to meet otherwise. Some want to engage in acts of fetishism or transvestism that they're unable to engage in with their wives and girlfriends. Others may have a **whore–madonna complex**. They see women as either sinners or saints. They can permit themselves to enjoy sex only with sex workers, or ask only sex workers to engage in acts such as fellatio. When they have sex with wives and girlfriends (the "saints"), they engage only in conventional sexual activities such as vaginal intercourse.

In Canada, there's a stigma attached to paying for the services of a sex worker. Negative publicity from doing so can result in job loss and marriage breakup.

Vancouver researchers John Lowman and Chris Atchison (2006) found that two-thirds of a sample of male clients of sex workers had been victimized on at least one occasion. The most common types of victimization were robbery of possessions or money and assault by sex workers or their accomplices.

MOTIVES FOR BUYING SEX There appear to be six common motives for hiring a sex worker:

- Sex without negotiation—By turning to a sex worker, a man needn't spend the time, effort, and money involved in dating and getting to know someone for the sake of sexual activity.
- Sex without emotional commitment—A sex worker requires no emotional commitment from the man, other than payment for services rendered. The sex worker won't call him at home or expect to be called in return.
- Sex for eroticism and variety—Many sex workers offer "something extra" in the way of novel or kinky sex, such as oral sex, costumes (e.g., leather attire), and S&M rituals (e.g., bondage and discipline or spanking). A man may desire such activity, but be unable to obtain it with his regular partner. He may even be afraid to mention the idea.
- Prostitution as a social outlet—In the nineteenth and early twentieth centuries, the brothel served not only as a place to obtain sex, but also as a kind of stopping-off place between home and work. Sex was secondary to the companionship and amiable conversation men found in brothels. Similarly, women who attend male strip clubs enjoy bonding with their friends, as well as the stripping itself (Montemurro et al., 2003).
- Sex away from home—Among the most common contemporary reasons is that a man is away from home, such as at a convention or an out-of-town sporting event.
- Difficulty attracting a partner—A man with a physical disability or a disfiguring condition may seek the services of a sex worker because of difficulty attracting other partners, or because of fear of rejection. A lonely man who lacks sex partners may seek sex workers as a substitute.

JOHN SCHOOLS Some Canadian cities have established john schools for men with no previous criminal records who are charged with communicating for the purpose of prostitution. In return for attending the day-long school, charges against the client are erased from the official court record. Typically, the men listen to presentations from street-based sex workers about the sex trade's negative effects on them. They also receive lectures on sexually transmitted infections, and in some instances they hear community representatives talk about the impact of street prostitution on their communities. The men are expected to provide donations to help support the programs (Fischer et al., 2002).

Whore–madonna complex
A rigid stereotyping of women as either sinners or saints.

CRITICAL THINKING QUESTIONS

Why are men so much more likely than women to pay for sex?

Male Sex Workers

Male sex work includes both male–male and male–female activities. Male sex workers who service female clients—gigolos—are rare. Gigolos' clients are typically older, relatively wealthy, unattached women. Gigolos may serve as escorts or as surrogate sons for the women, and they may or may not offer sexual services.

An interesting variation of male sex work involves female tourists from developed countries who have sex with local men in the developing countries they travel to. Unlike female sex workers, the beach boys who make money from their relations with female tourists don't openly demand fixed sums of money. Rather, they make requests for money and other goods in a disguised, subtle manner.

The overwhelming majority of male sex workers service gay men. Men who engage in sex work are sometimes called **hustlers**. Their patrons are typically called **scores**. Many male sex workers, like their female counterparts, come from families troubled by conflict, alcoholism, and physical and sexual abuse (Bimbi, 2007).

Hustlers may be gay, bisexual, or heterosexual in orientation. In a large-scale Australian survey, half of the male sex workers described themselves as gay, about one-third (31%) said they were bisexual, and 5.5% considered themselves straight (Minichiello et al., 2001).

Frances Shaver (1996a) compared male and female street-based sex workers in Montreal. Half of the women worked for pimps, but none of the men did. More women than men indicated that sex work was their only source of income. The women serviced twice as many (28.5) clients per week as the men (14.5). However, the men typically spent about twice as long with each client (40 minutes for the men versus 20 minutes for the women), and were more likely to include non-genital touching and kissing in their services. The women were much more likely than the men to experience sexual and physical assault and robbery. That female sex workers face greater danger than males do is also reflected in murder statistics. Between 1991 and 1995, for example, of the 63 reported murders of sex workers in Canada, 60 were women (Allman, 1999).

Hustlers typically aren't attached to pimps. They generally make contact with clients in gay bars and social clubs, or by working the streets in areas frequented by gay men. They typically learn to hustle from watching other hustlers ply their trade.

Various kinds of male sex worker have been identified (Minichiello et al., 2001):

- Strippers—These males dance and strip. Female and male patrons fondle them and sometimes have sex with them.
- Kept boys—These males have relationships with older, economically secure men who keep them in affluent lifestyles. The older males, or "sugar daddies," often assume parental roles.
- Call boys—Like call girls, call boys may work on their own or through agencies or escort services.
- Punks—These are prison inmates who are used sexually by other inmates, in return for protection or goods such as cigarettes and drugs.
- Drag prostitutes—These are transvestites or pre-surgical male-to-female transsexuals who impersonate female prostitutes and have sex with men, who are frequently unaware of their gender. Some drag prostitutes limit themselves to fellatio on their customers, to conceal their gender. Others take the passive role in anal sex.
- Brothel prostitutes—Because fewer houses of male prostitution exist, male brothel prostitutes are rarer than their female counterparts.
- Bar hustlers and street hustlers—Like their female counterparts, these males have the lowest status, and ply their trade in gay bars or on streets frequented by gay passersby. Street hustlers are the most common and typically the youngest subtype. They're also the most visible, and consequently the ones most likely to draw police attention.

Hustler A man who engages in sex work with male customers.

Score A customer of a hustler.

By and large, male sex work tends to be an adolescent enterprise. The younger the hustler, the higher the fee he can command, and the more tricks he can turn. By the time he reaches his mid-twenties, he may be forced to engage in sexual activities he might have rejected when he was younger, or seek clients in sleazier places.

Why do men purchase the services of male sex workers? In a British Columbia study, clients of male sex workers generally fell into three categories: men who kept their desire to have sex with other men hidden from others, men who wanted to have sex with younger men, and men who couldn't attract regular male sex partners (Allman, 1999).

STIs and Sex Work

In a Montreal study in the mid-1990s, about one-third of both male and female sex workers reported that they'd had STIs within the previous two years (Shaver, 1996b). All of the women said they always used condoms when engaging in vaginal or anal sex with clients, and 97% always used condoms with oral sex. Ninety percent of the male sex workers reported using condoms with clients during anal sex,

A World of Diversity

THE WEST GETS WILDER—A BROTHEL FOR WOMEN
by Mireya Navarro

Picture a pleasure oasis in the Nevada desert: a collection of luxurious bungalows featuring bedrooms with fireplaces, where sexual fantasies and desires are catered to. Starting at $250 an hour.

But at this house, Heidi's Stud Farm, the prostitutes are hunky men and the patrons are women.

Heidi Fleiss, a former Hollywood madam, is planning the all-male brothel on 60 acres in Nevada, where prostitution is often legal.

"The times have changed so much, with women in control," Fleiss, 40, said in a telephone interview from Nevada on Thursday. "Women make more money. They're more powerful. And it's a lonely world."

Is that possible? Are American women really ready for what will be among the first brothels of its kind? Will they pay for sex as a no-fuss transaction?

Women have become major consumers of pornographic films and websites in recent years, largely because of the privacy afforded by the internet. But women are also openly displaying interest in all things sexual, from the groups that gather for sex-toy parties in private homes to the ritual of celebrating birthdays, bachelorette parties, and even divorces at male strip clubs.

Though some of these sexual outlets are just erotic entertainment, some women seek more.

"We get offered all the time, 'How much for this guy?'" said Dan Remington, an owner of *The Hollywood Men*, a show of male strippers in Hollywood. "We don't do that."

On a recent Saturday night, more than 100 women screamed, hollered, and gawked at a performance of *The Hollywood Men*, as well-toned guys peeled down to their G-strings. The crowd included both young and older women. Would they drive or fly to Heidi's Stud Farm in Crystal, Nevada, near Pahrump, about 88 miles northwest of Las Vegas, to indulge their wild side in a brothel?

"I would do it just for the experience," said Mayra Barreras, 20, a customer service representative for a mortgage company who came to the club with three friends.

"Let's face it," said Bianca Nichole, 19, a college student majoring in computer science, "there's a lot of unhappy women out there. If I were in a bad relationship, and I felt I needed something, I would go, too."

Gina Pinon, a college student who was celebrating her birthday at the strip club, said she didn't believe she would ever pay for sex, "because I could go out and get it for free." Then she added: "But some women would pay for it—women who are in unhappy situations, or who are into fantasies. I'd say, 'Go for it. Have your fun.' If men can do it, women can do it, too."

Some sex experts and psychologists said a brothel for women is overdue. Many more women would avail themselves of professionals if it were legal, some experts argue, for reasons not unlike those of men who frequent prostitutes. A regulated business that does criminal and medical screening of its workers would find a market in women, said Patti Britton, president-elect of the American Association of Sexuality Educators, Counselors, and Therapists.

Source: Navarro, M. (2006, January 8). The west gets wilder—A brothel for women. The New York Times. Retrieved from http://www.nytimes.com/2006/01/08/fashion/sundaystyles/01HEIDI.html

but only 50% used condoms during oral sex. Both men and women used condoms far less often with men who weren't clients. A study of Montreal male street youth involved in sex work about 10 years later had similar findings—many didn't use condoms, especially when having oral sex (Haley et al., 2004).

In a Vancouver study of female sex workers in massage parlours, 5% reported having had STIs within the previous six months (Johnson et al., 2007). Nine percent of the sex workers reported inconsistent condom use. A key reason was a financial incentive—some clients offered more money to have sex without condoms. Some sex workers gave in to persistent verbal pressure not to use condoms. Some sex workers of Asian background lacked knowledge of proper condom use.

The sex workers were at greater risk of STI transmission from having sex with people who weren't clients; 63% reported inconsistent condom use with their lovers. With non-clients, the sex workers believed they were protected, because they felt that their partners were monogamous. Another reason they gave for not using condoms was the feeling that condoms belonged at work, and not in a relationship.

Female street youth in Montreal who engaged in sex work were twice as likely to have experienced anal intercourse as those who didn't engage in prostitution, and many were inconsistent about using condoms during anal intercourse (Weber et al., 2002).

Sex with sex workers is an important factor in the male–female transmission of HIV in Africa, where the infection is spread predominantly via male–female sexual intercourse.

STRIPPING Stripping is a type of sex work, though women and men who dance in strip clubs typically refer to themselves as dancers. Many sex workers in strip clubs limit their activity to dancing and doffing their clothes. Others do lap dances or table dances, making contact with customers as they dance. Customers buy the dances from the club and are expected to tip the strippers (Frank, 2002, 2003). Some strip clubs have private shows, VIP rooms, and the like, where strippers can be alone with their customers. What happens in these private shows may be tightly regulated by the clubs, or may depend on the sizes of the tips.

Many sex workers engage in this work only on a part-time or temporary basis. In a study of female strippers, Jacqueline Lewis of the University of Windsor (1998) distinguished between career and short-term, goal-oriented dancers. The latter group included several university students:

> And I looked at the salaries these people were making, and it was, you know, a thousand dollars a night, some nights, and it was really, really substantially helping with their tuition. And these were people working on master's degrees and doctorates and all kinds of things, and I thought, "Wow, if they can do this, hey, maybe I can." (Lewis, 1998, p. 59)

A recent Canadian trend is for women to take striptease lessons from professional instructors. Striptease has become so mainstream that many fitness centres offer classes in erotic dancing, pole dancing, and belly dancing.

Sexually Explicit Material (SEM)

Sexually explicit material (SEM) is found nearly everywhere. In addition to adult magazines and DVD rentals, millions of people use Google and Yahoo to search for pornography on the internet, and cable and satellite dishes to rent pornographic films. People also download pornography onto their camera cellphones and video MP3 players.

SEM is typically used to elicit or enhance sexual arousal, often as a masturbation aid (Boies, 2002; Strager, 2003). SEM may also be used by couples to enhance sexual arousal during lovemaking. Some sex therapists recommend that couples who are bored with their sexual routines, or experiencing other difficulties with the sexual aspects of their relationships, experiment with SEM, to help them become aroused. Many couples find that sexy videos, DVDs, and cable television movies enliven their sexual appetites and suggest novel techniques.

What's Pornographic?

Pornography Written, visual, or audiotaped material that's sexually explicit and produced to elicit or enhance sexual arousal. It has a negative connotation today, and is typically associated with SEM that's violent and/or degrading.

Prurient Tending to excite lust; lewd.

Sexually explicit material (SEM) Written, visual, or audiotaped material that's graphic and produced to elicit or enhance sexual arousal.

Erotica SEM that doesn't involve violence or degradation of women. It may be as sexually explicit as pornography.

Obscenity SEM that offends community standards.

Webster's Deluxe Unabridged Dictionary defines **pornography** as "writing, pictures, etc., intended to arouse sexual desire." Inclusion of the word "intended" places the determination of what's pornographic in the mind of the person composing the work. Applying this definition makes it all but impossible to determine what's pornographic. If a filmmaker admits that s/he wants to arouse the audience sexually, we may judge the work to be pornographic even if no naked bodies or explicit sex scenes are shown. On the other hand, explicit representations of people engaged in sexual activity would not be pornographic if the work is intended as an artistic expression, rather than created for its **prurient** value.

Many works that were once prohibited in Canada because of explicit sexual content, such as the novels *Tropic of Cancer* by Henry Miller and *Lady Chatterley's Lover* by D. H. Lawrence, are now generally considered literary works, rather than excursions into pornography.

Let's define **sexually explicit material (SEM)** as written, visual, or audiotaped material that's graphic and produced to elicit or enhance sexual arousal. This has been the traditional definition of pornography.

In the 1980s, feminist groups began to differentiate two types of SEM—pornography and erotica. Pornography was defined as SEM that involves violence and/or degradation of women. **Erotica** was defined as SEM that doesn't involve violence or degradation of women. Erotica may be as sexually explicit as pornography.

SEM is often classified as either hard-core or soft-core. Hard-core SEM includes graphic and sexually explicit depictions of sex organs and sexual acts. Soft-core material, as represented by R-rated films and *Playboy* photo spreads, features more stylized nude photos and suggested (or simulated) rather than explicit sexual acts.

Art or Obscenity?
Eric Fischl is a mainstream artist, yet some of his subject matter has been labelled obscene by some critics.

Perspectives on Pornography

As "A World of Diversity: Should this Photo be Censored?" shows, there are many different opinions of SEM. These differences of opinion are often characterized as the pornography debates. Let's briefly look at some of the schools of thought that have been advanced in the discussion. Watson (2010) identifies five basic approaches: obscenity-based, conservative, liberal, anti-pornography feminist, and pro-pornography feminist.

THE OBSCENITY-BASED APPROACH

Lawmakers in the United States and Canada often consider legal regulation of SEM on the basis of whether certain types of material can be judged obscene. That is, legislative bodies usually write laws about **obscenity**, rather than about pornography.

A World of Diversity

SHOULD THIS PHOTO BE CENSORED?

In the spring of 2005, a group of feminists in Guelph, Ontario, were disturbed when *Echo* magazine placed a close-up picture of a woman diving into a pool on the cover of its *Hot Summer Guide* issue. *Echo* is a Guelph publication that advertises local events.

The woman diving into the pool is Melanie Gillis, wife of the magazine's publisher, who took the picture. Gillis is a Guelph photographer who specializes in maternity and family photography. She also does nude photography.

The feminist group upset by the photo removed several copies of the magazine from downtown display boxes and destroyed them. They also removed the cover from several other copies. One of the women left a phone message at the *Echo* office explaining that the photo objectified women and thereby contributed to misogyny. They found the photo "horribly offensive" and "disgusting" (Gillis, 2005).

Following the incident, a number of *Echo* readers wrote letters to the editor deploring the censorship actions. Here are two excerpts from these letters:

It looks more like you oppressed *Echo*.

Not only did you oppress *Echo*, but

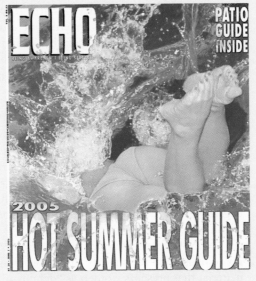

Should this Photo be Censored? In 2005, a group of feminists took action when Echo magazine, which advertises local events, placed a close-up of a woman diving into a pool on the cover of its **Hot Summer Guide** issue. Some readers were displeased by the feminists' actions.

you oppressed everyone in downtown Guelph who relies on the publication for info on coming events and local news. Ever heard of having fun? I hate you feminist types who assume that every pretty woman out there who doesn't trash men all the time is dumb, and allowing herself to be objectified. . . . You do not have the right to censor what other people read. . . . People like you are anti-feminist, because you remove choice and ridicule women for choosing a path that you would not have taken.

What do you think about the reasons given for censoring the photo? Do you feel the actions of the feminist group were justified?

This story of censorship is not an isolated one. Almost every day in Canada, people are making decisions about what is or isn't appropriate for us to see and read.

Sources: Freeman, N. (2005, June 16). Blatant objectification: Echo's Hot Summer Issue crossed the line. Echo, pp. 10–11. Gillis, M. (2005, June 16). It's my ass. Echo, p. 11.

However, obscenity is difficult to define. In general, an obscenity is something that offends community standards—but determining exactly what the community standards are or should be with respect to SEM is notoriously difficult. United States Supreme Court judge Potter Stewart famously quipped that he couldn't define obscenity or pornography precisely, but "I know it when I see it." The Supreme Court of Canada has also had a difficult time defining obscenity and determining where, if anywhere, laws against obscenity run afoul of the Canadian Charter of Rights and Freedoms.

THE CONSERVATIVE POSITION The conservative position on pornography holds that SEM is a threat to the "traditional values" of society. The proliferation of pornography is seen as encouraging immoral promiscuity and deemphasizing the importance of confining sexual behaviour to monogamous marriage.

This approach is often taken by conservative religious institutions. In their view, the increasing access to SEM in contemporary society reflects " . . . a declining public morality, a decline which conservatives argue seriously threatens the overall stability of civil society" (Watson, 2010, p. 538).

THE LIBERAL POSITION The liberal approach to pornography argues that in the absence of clear evidence of harm to others or to the community as a result of SEM consumption, the government shouldn't restrict people's right to access it. Philosopher Ronald Dworkin has championed this point of view, arguing that access to SEM is a matter of individual liberty and free expression (McGlynn & Ward, 2009). In one variant of the liberal approach, legal regulation of SEM is seen as a violation of free speech.

THE ANTI-PORNOGRAPHY FEMINIST APPROACH As SEM became much more widespread in the United States and Canada during the 1960s and '70s, some feminists began to object to pornography that portrayed women simply as objects intended to provide sexual pleasure for men. They noted that the vast majority of commercially available pornographic material was produced by men, for men, and claimed that such material often presented women in dehumanized, degrading ways. As a result, they argued, pornography promoted gender inequality and sexual violence against women.

In 1980, feminist activists Catherine MacKinnon and Andrea Dworkin proposed legislation for the city of Minneapolis that defined pornography, in part, as material that presents women as "dehumanized sexual objects," material that presents "women's body parts such that women are reduced to those parts," or material that presents women "in scenarios that are degrading" (MacKinnon, 2007). The legislation, which didn't pass, would have allowed women who were victimized as a result of pornography to sue the producers, distributors, and sellers of pornography.

Nevertheless, some feminists continue to argue that many contemporary forms of pornography promote gender inequality and harm women.

THE PRO-PORNOGRAPHY FEMINIST APPROACH Pro-pornography feminists believe SEM can promote gender equality. According to this view, pornography can be summarized as " . . . a source of freedom and liberation from dominant and patriarchal notions of sexuality for women (as well as other marginalized groups, including gays, lesbians, and transgendered persons)" (Watson, 2010, p. 540–541).

The pro-pornography feminist approach is exemplified by Candida Royalle and Tristan Taormino, who make sexually explicit films from a woman's point of view, promoting women's exploration of sexual pleasure on their own terms. Since 2006, the Toronto sex store Good for Her has sponsored the Feminist Porn Awards, celebrating SEM that depicts genuine female sexual pleasure and challenges the sexual and gender stereotypes so often portrayed in many forms of pornography (Walker, 2008).

Canadian Law and SEM

Laws against obscenity provide the legal framework for outlawing the dissemination of pornography. Because the definition of obscenity relies on offending people or running afoul of community standards, what's deemed obscene may vary from person to person and from culture to culture.

The Supreme Court of Canada has been strongly influenced by the feminist argument that pornography exploits and degrades women. For example, the Women's Legal Education and Action Fund has argued that pornography causes violence against women, a view that was used by the Supreme Court to uphold the right of censorship in *Regina v. Butler* (1992). This case concerned the police raid of a Winnipeg store that sold sexually explicit videos. In his appeal to the Supreme

---

CRITICAL THINKING QUESTIONS

Which of the five perspectives on pornography described here best matches your own perspective?

Feminist Porn Awards.
The Toronto women's sex shop Good for Her sponsors an annual event that recognizes the work of Canadian and international pornography producers and actors. One of the event's objectives is to show that pornography and feminism are not mutually exclusive categories. At the sixth annual Feminist Porn Awards show, actor Bobbi Starr accepted the award for Steamiest Romantic Movie for A Little Part of Me.

Court, store owner Donald Butler argued that according to the Canadian Charter of Rights and Freedoms, he had a right to freedom of expression.

In upholding the constitutionality of the federal obscenity law, the Supreme Court argued that for a work to be considered obscene, there must be "undue" exploitation of sex. A "community-standard-of-tolerance" test must be applied, to determine whether undue exploitation has occurred. The courts must consider whether a community is likely to accept or tolerate the exposure of others to these materials, taking into consideration the possibility of harm that may result from such exposure. A key factor is whether the exploitation of sex is seen a degrading or dehumanizing to society in general, and to women in particular.

In *Regina v. Butler*, the Supreme Court devised three categories of obscenity. The first category involves material that mixes sex with violence and/or includes children. The second category includes material that involves sex and degradation, and is therefore seen as encouraging violence or harm to women. Materials that fall into either of these categories are deemed obscene. The third category involves material that's considered nonviolent and not degrading to women, and that doesn't involve children. Materials that fall into the third category are not seen as involving undue exploitation of sex, and are therefore considered acceptable to Canadian society.

Civil libertarians were strongly opposed to legal changes resulting from the *Butler* decision, and felt the new interpretations were too restrictive. They were also concerned about the potential subjectivity involved in trying to determine which materials are degrading. In some respects, however, the new interpretation of obscenity allowed for greater permissiveness in legalizing previously banned explicit materials.

The Supreme Court decision had a monumental effect on changing the guidelines used by provincial censorship boards. In Canada, censorship and classification of films is a provincial responsibility. Until the 1992 *Butler* decision, some provincial censorship boards, particularly in Ontario, had banned any scenes of hard-core or penetrative sex. The Ontario Film Review Board revised its guidelines after 1992, which resulted in the legitimizing of sexually explicit films and videos and an increase in the number of adult video stores.

All materials such as books and videos that come into Canada can be confiscated by the Canada Border Services Agency if they're deemed to violate Canada's obscenity laws, and video stores can still be charged by police for selling materials that are defined as obscene under the Criminal Code (Benzie, 2004).

In many respects, legal efforts to regulate the distribution of obscene SEM in Canada have been thwarted by the fact that an increasing proportion of SEM is accessed from websites in the borderless world of cyberspace. It's difficult, if not impossible, for Canadian law enforcement to regulate obscene material at its source if the material originates outside of Canada.

In recent years, Canadian law enforcement has increasingly focused on identifying and prosecuting Canadians who use the internet to distribute or download child pornography onto their computers. In 2002, the Canadian child pornography law was amended to include such language as "transmission," "making available," and "accessing," to target the online distribution of child pornography (Casavant & Robertson, 2007). Since 2005, police departments in Canada have begun using Microsoft's Child Exploitation Tracking System, software that enables them to detect computers in Canada that are accessing child pornography (Wilkes, 2011).

Child Pornography

Although many people don't find depictions of consensual sexual activity between adults—however explicit—obscene, Canadians almost universally regard child pornography as obscene and harmful. Canada's first Criminal Code law specifically directed toward child pornography was enacted in 1993. It makes it illegal to sell child pornography, as well as to possess anything that depicts people under the age of 18 engaging in real or simulated sexual behaviour. It also forbids visual representations (intended for sexual purposes) of the sex organs of people who are under 18, as well as written materials and pictures that advocate having sex with underaged individuals. The law does allow for exemption from prosecution if the material has artistic merit or an educational, scientific, or medical purpose.

One of the most controversial legal decisions regarding pornography occurred in 1999, when a British Columbia Supreme Court judge ruled that the Criminal Code section prohibiting simple possession of child pornographic materials violated a Vancouver man's right to freedom of expression, because his stories about young boys had artistic merit. Many members of Parliament were so incensed by the ruling that they wanted the government to override the Constitution, to ensure that the child-porn law would be upheld.

In 2001, the Supreme Court of Canada did uphold the law, although it allowed for minor exceptions. These include private materials, such as drawings and personal journals, that are intended only for the eyes of the individuals who create them, and SEM created by children and adolescents, such as photos of themselves that are meant to be kept strictly private and only for personal use.

CRITICAL THINKING QUESTIONS

What potentially positive and negative effects on society result from the proliferation of SEM on television and the internet?

Legislation passed in 2005 narrowed the defence allowed individuals accused of possessing child pornography. The accused must prove that s/he was using the material for a legitimate purpose related to the administration of justice, science, medicine, education, or art, and that this purpose doesn't pose undue risk of harm to a child.

To avoid police detection, some people who access child pornography use their laptop computers to tap into other people's wireless networks without their knowledge or permission. This practice is called "war driving." Many people don't turn on the security features of their wireless networks, leaving themselves vulnerable to war drivers who can access their computers and files and do whatever they want online—such as access sexually explicit websites (Millar, 2003).

Convicted users of internet child porn come from all social classes and are of all ages. In a series of raids in January of 2008, the Ontario Provincial Police arrested 23 people for possession of child pornography. The offenders were from 16 communities, and included a woman and a young offender. The oldest was 65.

Because of societal concerns about child pornography, parents may wonder whether they're allowed to take nude photos of their young children. In 2006, a California man who was applying for landed immigrant status in Canada was turned back at the Canadian border because he had pictures of his unclothed toddler son on his cellphone. Charges of attempting to smuggle child pornography into Canada were later dropped, when police decided the photos hadn't been taken for sexual gratification.

Television and SEM

Prior to the 1990s, SEM and nudity were rarely found on broadcast television. With the advent of videocassette recorders in the 1980s, people were able to watch hard-core SEM in the privacy of their own homes. SEM on video proved to be highly popular, and by the 1990s, cable television companies in Canada started offering sexually explicit pay-per-view movies, which have since become a highly profitable aspect of the cable television business. Canadian satellite companies also offer channels that show hard-core material. In 2010, Canada's first adult-oriented television channel, offering locally produced, hard-core SEM, went on air in Quebec (Chung, 2011). Soft-core SEM is readily available on television. Cable television shows such as *Californication* and *Entourage* regularly feature nudity and simulated sexual activity.

The availability and apparent popularity of SEM on television likely reflects a significant change in Canadian attitudes toward SEM, and perhaps toward aspects of sexuality. Some have referred to the increasing consumption of SEM on television and the internet as the "mainstreaming of porn."

Employers and SEM

Many Canadian employers have policies that forbid the viewing of SEM in the workplace. Some use filtering software to prevent employees from visiting certain websites, and screen email messages for offensive content. Some employees have lost their jobs for looking at internet SEM at work. In 2003, six employees of the Catholic Children's Aid Society of Toronto were fired after they were discovered exchanging SEM via office email. Contrary to the stereotype that only males engage in this behaviour, four of the six fired employees were women (Brennan, 2004).

The Internet and SEM

Canadians increasingly use the internet to view SEM. In a survey of university students in British Columbia, 42% reported having viewed sexually explicit materials while online (75% of males and 27% of females), and about half had begun doing so before the age of 17 (Boies, 2002). Those who'd viewed SEM had found it sexually arousing (82%), and learned new sexual techniques from it (63%), while 40% had masturbated while online. Yet 57% had been disturbed by what they'd seen. There were notable gender differences, especially with regard to masturbating while online (70% of males and 22% of females). Nine percent of both men and women had entered sexually focused chat rooms, and 8% had met sexual partners online. Finding online SEM sexually arousing was one of the best predictors of online SEM experience, especially for masturbating while online (Boies, 2002).

Another survey of Canadian university students found higher rates of exposure to online SEM (Byers, 2005). Almost all of the men (95%) and half of the women (53%) had accessed nude pictures online, and three-quarters of the men and half of the women had accessed sexually explicit movies. The men spent more time per week viewing and sending SEM than the women did (2.8 hours for men versus 0.2 hours for women). Yet about the same proportion of women (64%) as men (60%) had sent sexually explicit emails. Another major gender difference was that 69% of the men but only 18% of the women had saved SEM on their computer (Byers, 2005).

Many Canadians are exposed to unsolicited SEM through email messages and pop-ups. Researchers at Wilfrid Laurier University and the University of Guelph studied student reactions to this type of advertising (Nosko, Wood, & Desmarais, 2007). Males were more likely than females to have positive attitudes about these messages, and to follow up by searching online for the explicitly promoted websites. Students who spent more time with computers were more likely to follow through with searches in response to these email messages and pop-ups, and so were students who were more curious about online sexual material.

One of the newer forms of cybersex is virtual sex. On the website "SecondLife. com," the avatars (animated, cartoon-like figures) of residents (players) can engage in any activity they want to, including virtual sex with the avatars of other residents.

Gender Differences in Response to SEM

Researchers have found that both men and women are physiologically aroused by SEM. In one study, both men and women were more aroused by depictions of oral sex and intercourse than of petting (Harte et al., 2007). However, the women were more aroused by depictions of oral sex than of intercourse. The women's responses varied more than the men's. Although both men and women responded physically to sexually explicit stimuli, women were more likely to express negative feelings about SEM.

In practice, sexually explicit visual material (pictures and films) is largely a male preserve (Boies, 2002; Goodson et al., 2001). Most erotic visual materials are produced by men, for men. Anthony Bogaert (2001) at Brock University found that the type of film most preferred by men showed women with insatiable sexual desires. Many women may find SEM a "turn-off" or disgusting, especially when it portrays women in unflattering roles (e.g., as "whorish" and subservient to men's desires).

Could a basic evolutionary process be at work? Did ancestral men who were more sexually aroused by the sight of passing females have reproductive advantages over their less-aroused peers? Women had fewer mating opportunities than men, and had to make the most of any reproductive opportunities, by selecting the best possible mates and providers. Becoming sexually aroused by the sight of male

Innovative Canadian Research

WOMEN WHO VISIT SEX SHOPS

Increasing acceptance of SEM by Canadian women is illustrated by the increasing number of female-friendly sex shops.

Stacey Jacobs (2007), a graduate student at the University of Guelph, conducted a survey of women who visited female-friendly sex shops in Ontario. Most were single and had higher education. Only 15% had children.

The women were most likely to visit sex shops with their partners and by themselves. The most important reason they gave for making purchases was to increase their own sexual pleasure, and the second most important reason was to increase their partners' pleasure.

The items they most often purchased were (in order of frequency) sex toys, lubricants, novelty items, massage oils, lingerie, condoms, sex manuals, BDSM (bondage, domination, and sado-masochism) equipment, and SEM. Only 19% purchased sex DVDs and videos in the stores, but almost one-half purchased them online.

Although most of the women were comfortable in the sex shops, one-third said they'd at some time wanted to ask the employees questions, but had been too embarrassed or frightened to do so. They asked questions mainly about sex toys such as vibrators and lubricants. Two-thirds were more comfortable asking questions when talking to female than to male employees.

genitalia might have encouraged random matings, which would have undermined women's reproductive success.

Are women really uninterested in viewing SEM? A study of women in Sweden found that almost all (85%) had been exposed to SEM (Rogala & Tydén, 2003). Of those who had viewed the materials, 65% believed the experience had been positive (e.g., making them feel sexy or encouraging them to try new things), while 27% had reacted negatively (e.g., some felt their partners would want to make them engage in sexual behaviours they didn't want to be involved with). And a large-scale study of 18- to 30-year-olds in Denmark found that both men and women reported generally positive effects from viewing hard-core SEM, and few if any negative effects. Men tended to report higher levels of positive effects than women did. Those who reported higher rates of SEM viewing and masturbating saw more positive effects of viewing SEM (Hald & Malmuth, 2008).

More Canadian women are comfortable today than in the past with posing in such SEM as topless and nude photos. Members of the Canadian women's Nordic ski team and the Canadian women's rugby team have posed nude or semi-nude for fundraising calendars. Women of varying ages from across Canada also posed topless in the *Breast of Canada* calendar, which raised awareness of breast health and cancer prevention from 2002 to 2008.

Also on the rise is boudoir photography, in which women have themselves photographed in sexually provocative poses, for their own enjoyment or as gifts for boyfriends and husbands. Photographer Mark Laurie in Calgary has taken pictures of more than 4000 women over 25 years, ranging from seductive poses to completely nude images (Mark, 2003).

Many Canadian couples of all sexual orientations use modern technology such as digital cameras to produce homemade SEM for private consumption. This involves taking nude photographs and videos of their partners or of both of them having sex together. Some couples post these photos on the internet.

Some young women in North America voluntarily pose for revealing photos for the websites GirlsGoneWild.com and CanadianWildGirls.com. The photos are typically taken at bars and special events, such as spring break in Florida. The women receive hats or T-shirts for this, instead of cash. It seems that posing topless in certain contexts has become more acceptable in Canadian society. The media

Boudoir Photography.
As this photo by Melanie Gillis shows, many Canadian women have seductive pictures of themselves taken by professional photographers as gifts for their boyfriends and husbands.

Innovative Canadian Research

AN EDUCATIONAL PROGRAM TO COUNTERACT THE EFFECTS OF INTERNET PORN

University of Western Ontario researchers Corey Isaacs and William Fisher (2008) developed and tested an educational program to counteract the potentially negative effects of watching internet pornography.

They assigned male participants to three groups. Group 1 viewed violent and degrading pornography accompanied by an educational intervention. Group 2 viewed the same pornography accompanied with a fake intervention that lacked the educational content given to group 1. Group 3 neither viewed pornography nor received an intervention.

The intervention consisted of an interactive computer program designed to sensitize participants to the negative messages portrayed in violent and degrading pornography. Viewers were presented with examples of pornography that had negative messages, as well as the reality of the issue of sexual violence. They were encouraged to evaluate the content of sexual media more critically.

The dependent measures were acceptance of rape myths, attraction to sexual aggression, and opinions of SEM.

Contrary to their expectations, the researchers did not observe any negative effects of viewing pornography for any of the dependent measures. However, the educational intervention did diminish positive reactions to sexual aggression, and encouraged participants to become more sensitive to—and to reject—violence in pornography.

seem to support this trend, as evidenced by the film *Calendar Girls*, in which a group of older women posed nude for a charity fundraising calendar.

Cybersex Addiction

It appears that at least one-third of internet visits involve sexually oriented websites, chat rooms, and news groups (Cooper et al., 2000, 2004). For most people, these ventures into cybersex are harmless enough, but the accessibility and anonymity of sex on the internet are fuelling what some health professionals call cybersex addiction, which is believed to be spreading rapidly and bringing turmoil to the lives of the afflicted (Ayres & Haddock, 2009).

Surveys show that many people, mostly men, now spend dozens of hours each week surfing pornographic and other sex-related websites (Cooper et al., 2000, 2004; Daneback et al., 2006). Those most strongly hooked on online sex may spend hours a day masturbating to pornographic images or—less often—having "online sex" with people they contact via chat rooms or webcams (Daneback et al., 2005, 2006).

Cybersex compulsives are like drug addicts (Cooper et al., 2004; Schneider, 2005). They "use the Internet as an important part of their sexual acting out, much like a drug addict who has a drug of choice. Especially vulnerable are those whose sexuality may have been suppressed and limited all their lives, who suddenly find an infinite supply of sexual opportunities" online (Cooper, cited in Brody, 2000). Although some studies find that men who become addicted to online sex have ample sexual opportunities in the real world, other studies find them to be lonelier than men with those opportunities (Yoder et al., 2005).

Online viewing that begins as a harmless recreation can become all-consuming, and can even lead to real sexual encounters with people the individual meets online. Cybersex compulsives sometimes ignore their partners and children and risk their jobs. Schneider (2005) reports other adverse consequences, including broken relationships. Partners often report feeling betrayed, ignored, and unable to compete with the online fantasies.

Sex in Cyberspace.
One-third of Internet visits are thought to involve sexually oriented websites. Many people, mostly men, spend dozens of hours each week surfing porn sites. Some even have "online sex" with people they contact via chat rooms or webcams.

A 34-year-old woman who was married for 14 years to a minister told a researcher, "How can I compete with hundreds of anonymous others who are now in our bed, in his head? Our bed is crowded with countless faceless strangers, where once we were intimate" (Schneider, cited in Brody, 2000).

Sexual Coercion and SEM

Is SEM a harmless diversion, or an inducement to commit sexual violence and other antisocial acts? Let's consider sources of evidence for this highly charged issue, beginning with the findings of a 1985 federal committee.

THE FRASER COMMITTEE REPORT In 1983, the Canadian government appointed a special committee to study the issues of prostitution and pornography and to make policy recommendations based on its findings. This committee's report became known as the Fraser Committee Report (1985). Despite hearing from numerous individuals and groups that pornography is harmful to society, the Fraser Committee concluded that the available evidence didn't support the belief that pornography leads to such antisocial behaviour as violent crime, sexual abuse of children, and disintegration of communities and society.

SEM AND SEX OFFENDERS Another approach to examining the role of SEM in crimes of sexual violence involves comparing sex offenders' and non-sex offenders' experiences with sexually explicit materials.

In a review of the research literature, Marshall (1989) found little or no difference in levels of SEM exposure between incarcerated sex offenders and comparison groups of felons incarcerated for nonsexual crimes. More recent research, however, has found that sexually aggressive individuals are more likely than others to use pornography (Alexy et al., 2009).

These studies are correlational, not experimental. It may be that a desire to use pornography and to commit sexually aggressive acts are both related to other factors, such as a general tendency to seek out sexual images and experiences that humiliate women.

VIOLENT SEM Research suggests that it's the violence in violent SEM—not the sexual explicitness—that potentially affects or reinforces the attitudes and behaviours of sex offenders.

In an Ontario study, Kingston and his colleagues (2008) studied the use of pornography among convicted child molesters. Those who viewed deviant (including violent) pornography were more likely to reoffend. Higher frequency of porn use was predictive of recidivism among those who were already considered to be at high risk for reoffending. The researchers speculate that more aggressive men are drawn to images of violent pornography, which reinforces negative attitudes such as hostility toward women. They note that use of deviant pornography is more predictive of violent sexual reoffending than of sexual offending in general.

Research on the effects of SEM should be interpreted with caution. We still lack evidence that normal men are spurred to sexually assault women because of exposure to violent SEM or other depictions of violence.

NONVIOLENT SEM Nonviolent SEM may not contain scenes of sexual violence, but it typically portrays women as sexually promiscuous, insatiable, and subservient. Might such portrayals of women reinforce traditional stereotypes of women as sex objects? Might they lead viewers to condone sexual assault by suggesting that women are essentially promiscuous? Might the depiction of women as readily sexually accessible inspire men to refuse to "take no for an answer" on dates?

Michael Seto, Alexandra Maric, and Howard Barbaree (2001) at the Centre for Addiction and Mental Health in Toronto conducted an extensive review of the research, and concluded that there's little empirical support for the idea that SEM causes sexual aggression. Rather, they believe men who are predisposed to sexual aggression are more likely to view violent SEM, and therefore likely to show the strongest effects. Men who are not predisposed to sexual violence are unlikely to show any effects.

William Fisher, a psychology professor at the University of Western Ontario, has conducted several experimental studies to measure the effects of SEM. In one study (Barak and Fisher, 1997), he and a colleague explored the effects of computer-based, interactive erotic stimuli on men's attitudes and behaviours toward women. University men who were exposed to computer-based erotic stimuli showed significant increases in sexual arousal, but didn't show negative changes in attitude or behaviour toward women when compared to men who were exposed to control stimuli. Specifically, exposure to interactive erotic stimulation neither resulted in aggressive behaviour toward women nor affected men's attitudes toward women's rights and roles in society. This exposure also didn't change men's perceptions of sexual assault myths.

Another concern is the potential effect of nonviolent SEM on a viewer's sexual values. Nonviolent SEM typically features impromptu sexual encounters between new acquaintances. Might repeated exposure to such material alter viewers' attitudes toward traditional sexual values? Brown (2003) reports intriguing evidence that repeated exposure to this type of nonviolent SEM loosens traditional sexual and family values. When compared with people who viewed nonsexual films, men and women who were exposed to six weekly, hour-long sessions involving scenes of explicit sexual encounters between new acquaintances showed attitudinal changes, including greater acceptance of premarital and extramarital sex and simultaneous sexual relationships with multiple partners. Prolonged exposure to such SEM may also foster dissatisfaction with the physical appearance and sexual performance of one's intimate partners (Brown, 2003).

Another concern is that SEM doesn't offer realistic presentations of how most people function sexually. While many people in real life experience sexual problems, the people portrayed in the sexual media never have sexual problems. The actors are always able to have sex, any time and any place, for hours at a time. Penises are always erect, vaginas are continuously lubricated, and the women have insatiable desires for sex, as well as orgasms that occur with little effort. Most of the actors don't use condoms, and sexually transmitted infections are never discussed.

In sum, research on the effects of nonviolent SEM is so far inconclusive. Its effects may be more closely connected with whether women are presented in a dehumanizing manner than with sexual explicitness per se. No research has yet linked sexual explicitness itself with undesirable effects.

A group of researchers in Ireland and western Canada (Morrison et al., 2004) criticizes most previous research for being narrowly focused on a harm-based approach to the study of SEM's effects. They're also concerned that almost all of the research has surveyed only men and viewed women as victims.

Morrison and his colleagues (2004) argue that researchers have generally ignored the fact that an increasing amount of sexually explicit material is produced by women, for women and couples, which indicates that many women are willing consumers of these materials. To gain a broader perspective, these researchers surveyed 382 females and 202 males attending a university in western Canada. Among both genders, those with higher sexual self-esteem and lower sexual anxiety had higher levels of exposure to SEM on television and DVDs. Females with more recent experience with vaginal and anal intercourse were also more likely to have seen SEM. Safer sex practices were not related to degree of SEM exposure. Based on these findings, the researchers concluded that exposure to SEM is not related to many of the types of harm that are often discussed in the literature.

Summing Up

Commercial sex runs the gamut from street-based sex work and sexually explicit videos to strip shows, sex-toy shops, brothels, escort services, massage parlours, and "1-900" telephone services.

One view is that prostitution is immoral and exploits women. A contrasting view is that prostitution is a legitimate occupation that should be legalized.

The laws governing prostitution (the exchange of sex for money) in Canada are confusing, because prostitution itself is legal, but almost all of the activities that involve prostitution are illegal.

In 2011, the Supreme Court of Canada agreed to consider a challenge to Canada's prostitution laws.

The major types of female sex worker are street-based sex workers, brothel workers (many of whom work in massage parlours), escorts, and call girls. No single factor explains entry into female sex work.

Those who pay sex workers for their services are often referred to as "johns" or "tricks." Most patrons are "occasional johns" who have regular sex partners.

Most male sex workers are "hustlers," who service male clients. Hustlers typically begin selling sex in their teens, and may be gay or heterosexual.

The majority of sex workers consistently use condoms with clients. Some are pressured by clients and offered more money to have sex without condoms.

Pornography is "writing, pictures, etc., intended to arouse sexual desire." The judgment of what's pornographic or obscene varies from person to person and from culture to culture.

The feminist movement has had a strong influence on federal laws governing SEM in Canada.

Accessing SEM on the internet is increasingly common.

Although both genders can become physiologically aroused by erotic materials, men are generally more interested than women in sexually explicit pictures and films.

Some researchers argue that it's the violence in violent SEM, and not the sexual explicitness, that promotes violence against women. The effects of nonviolent SEM on normal populations remain unclear.

Test Yourself

Multiple-Choice Questions

1. In a 2009 Angus Reid poll, _____ of Canadians said it should be legal for adults to "engage in consensual prostitution."
    (a) 30%
    (b) 40%
    (c) 50%
    (d) 60%

2. Among sex workers, _____ have the lowest status and earn the lowest wages.
    (a) street-based workers
    (b) brothel workers
    (c) call girls
    (d) massage-parlour workers

3. Among sex workers, _____ have the highest status and earn the highest wages.
    (a) street-based workers
    (b) brothel workers
    (c) call girls
    (d) massage-parlour workers

4. All of the following are important factors in the backgrounds of many young sex workers except:
    (a) Poverty.
    (b) Sexual addiction.
    (c) Physical abuse.
    (d) Sexual abuse.

5. Shaver, Lewis, and Maticka-Tyndale propose an approach to sex work that emphasizes:
    (a) Penalizing johns rather than sex workers for acts of prostitution.
    (b) Increasing the legal penalties for sex work.
    (c) Financial incentives for sex workers to seek other types of employment.
    (d) Harm reduction and labour rights.

6. Men who engage in sex work with male customers are commonly known as:
    (a) Pimps.
    (b) Gigolos.
    (c) Hustlers.
    (d) Johns.

(continued)

7. **A photograph or video is considered hard-core SEM if it contains:**
   (a) Hints or suggestions of sexual acts.
   (b) Explicit depictions of sexual acts.
   (c) Stylized nude photos.
   (d) Non-consensual sexual behaviour.

8. **The work of Tristan Taormino reflects which of the following perspectives on pornography?**
   (a) The conservative position.
   (b) The liberal position.
   (c) The anti-pornography feminist approach.
   (d) The pro-pornography feminist approach.

9. **Most research on the effects of exposure to sexually explicit materials has focused on:**
   (a) Violence.
   (b) Orgasm.
   (c) Relationship enhancement.
   (d) Sexual orientation.

10. **Which of the following groups was not included in the study that included the educational intervention to reduce the potential negative effects of pornography?**
   (a) A group that viewed violent pornography and received an educational intervention.
   (b) A group that viewed violent pornography and received a fake intervention.
   (c) A group that viewed nonviolent pornography and received an educational intervention.
   (d) A group that neither viewed pornography nor received an educational intervention.

You'll find answers to the "Test Yourself" questions on page 495.

Critical Thinking

1. Should all aspects of prostitution be legal in Canada? Why or why not?

2. Look at one of your favourite magazines. Do you see advertisers using sex to sell their products? If these images were shown just as pictures, rather than as ads, would you see them as art or as pornography? Explain.

3. Have you ever used sexually explicit material with a sex partner? Has this helped or hurt your relationship?

4. You're having a late-night discussion about sexually explicit material over a few beers with some friends. One of them says that since most sex offenders drank milk as children, we should ban milk, along with sexually explicit material. How do you respond?

MySearchLab

MySearchLab offers extensive help to students with their writing and research project and provides round-the-clock access to credible and reliable source material. Take a tour at **www.mysearchlab.com.**

Answer Key

Chapter 1	Chapter 2	Chapter 3	Chapter 4	Chapter 5	Chapter 6
1. b	1. a	1. c	1. a	1. c	1. b
2. a	2. c	2. b	2. c	2. b	2. b
3. b	3. d	3. b	3. b	3. d	3. d
4. a	4. b	4. c	4. c	4. a	4. b
5. c	5. c	5. d	5. a	5. d	5. d
6. d	6. b	6. c	6. a	6. b	6. c
7. c	7. b	7. c	7. d	7. d	7. b
8. a	8. d	8. d	8. a	8. c	8. c
9. b	9. a	9. c	9. c	9. b	9. c
10. d	10. c	10. a	10. a	10. d	10. a

Chapter 7	Chapter 8	Chapter 9	Chapter 10	Chapter 11	Chapter 12
1. c	1. c	1. d	1. c	1. d	1. b
2. b	2. c	2. b	2. a	2. b	2. d
3. d	3. d	3. b	3. c	3. a	3. d
4. d	4. d	4. c	4. d	4. b	4. b
5. a	5. b	5. a	5. b	5. b	5. b
6. a	6. a	6. c	6. d	6. c	6. c
7. b	7. b	7. b	7. c	7. a	7. a
8. b	8. a	8. b	8. b	8. c	8. c
9. d	9. c	9. a	9. d	9. c	9. c
10. d	10. d	10. a	10. d	10. d	10. a

Chapter 13	Chapter 14	Chapter 15	Chapter 16	Chapter 17
1. c	1. c	1. b	1. c	1. c
2. b	2. a	2. c	2. d	2. a
3. d	3. d	3. b	3. a	3. c
4. a	4. b	4. d	4. c	4. b
5. c	5. d	5. c	5. d	5. d
6. b	6. b	6. b	6. a	6. c
7. a	7. b	7. a	7. b	7. b
8. d	8. c	8. a	8. a	8. d
9. a	9. a	9. c	9. c	9. a
10. b	10. b	10. b	10. c	10. c

References

Aarts, H., & van Honk, J. (2009). Testosterone and unconscious positive priming increase hu man motivation separately. *NeuroReport, 20*(14), 1300–1303.

Abal, Y. N., Maríín, J. A. L., & Sánchez, S. R. (2003). A new paraphilia of the XXI century: Chat-scatophilia. *Archivos Hispanoamericanos de Sexologíía, 9*(1), 81–104.

ABC News. (2004). *The American Sex Survey: A Peek Beneath the Sheets*. ABC News Primetime Live Poll. http://abcnews.com/pollvault.html

Abell, J., Locke, A., Condor, S., Gibson, S., & Stevenson, C. (2006). Trying similarity, doing difference: The role of interviewer self-disclosure in interview talk with young people. *Qualitative Research, 6*(2), 221–244.

Abraham, C. (2006, December 23). Critics troubled by new fertility panel. *The Globe and Mail*, pp. A1, A8.

Adam, B. (2006a.) New gay relations: Relationship innovation in male relationships? *Sexualities, 9*(1), 5–26.

Adam, B. (2006b). Infectious behaviour: Imputing subjectivity to HIV behaviour. *Social Theory and Health, 4*, 168–179.

Adam, B. (2007). Cultural trends in safe and unsafe sex. Paper presented at the annual meeting of the International Academy of Sex Research, Vancouver, BC.

Adam, B., Husbands, W., Murray, J., & Maxwell, J. (2005). AIDS optimism, condom fatigue, or self-esteem? Explaining unsafe sex among gay and bisexual men. *Journal of Sex Research, 42*(3), 238–248.

Adam, B. D. (2000a). Age preferences among gay and bisexual men. *GLQ, 6*(3), 413–414.

Adam, B. D. (2000b). Love and sex in constructing identity among men who have sex with men. *International Journal of Sexuality and Gender Studies, 5*(5), 325–339.

Adam, B. D., Maticka-Tyndale, E., & Cohen, J. J. (2001). *Living with combination therapies*. A report to the Ontario HIV Treatment Network.

Adams, H. E., Wright, L. W., Jr., & Lohr, B. A. (1996). Is homophobia associated with homosexual arousal? *Journal of Abnormal Psychology, 105*, 440–445.

Adams, N. (2006). Systemic therapy techniques for sexual difficulties. In Hiller, J., et al. (Eds.). *Sex, mind, and emotion: Innovation in psychological theory and practice* (pp. 209–227). London, UK: Karnac Books.

Agrawal, A. (1997). Gendered bodies: The case of the "third gender" in India. *Contributions to Indian Sociology, 31*, 273–297.

Ah Shene, D. (2003). Crystal meth. *Developments, 23*(2). Alberta Alcohol and Drug Abuse Commission. [Online]. Available: http://corp.aadac.com/services/developments_newsletter/dev_news_vol23_issue2.asp

Ahrols, T. K., & Meston, C. M. (2010). Ethnic differences in sexual attitudes of U.S. college students: gender, acculturation, and religiosity factors. *Archives of Sexual Behavior, 39*(1), 190–202

Albarracin, D. et al. (2005). A test of the major assumptions about behavior change: A comprehensive look at the effects of passive and active HIV-prevention interventions since the beginning of the epidemic. *Psychological Bulletin, 31*, 856–897

Alcoba, N. (2009). Should the state be funding in vitro fertilization? *National Post*, August 21st, 2009.

Alderson, K. (2007). "What's love got to do with it?" Defining and measuring sexual orientation. Paper presented at the Annual Meeting of the Canadian Sex Research Forum, Banff, Alberta.

Alderson, K. G. (2003). The ecological model of gay male identity. *Canadian Journal of Human Sexuality, 12*, 75–85.

Alderson, K. G., & Jevne, R. F. J. (2003). Yin and yang in mortal combat: The psychic conflict beneath the coming out process for gay males. *Guidance and Counselling, 18*, 128–141.

Alexander, G. M., Wilcox, T., & Woods, R. (2009). Sex differences in infants' visual interest in toys. *Archives of Sexual Behavior, 38*(3), 427–433.

Alexander, J. (2006). An introduction to queer theory. *Sexualities, 9*(1), 115–117.

Alexy, E. M., Burgess, A. W., & Prentky, R. A. (2009). Pornography use as a risk marker for an aggressive pattern of behavior among sexually reactive children and adolescents. *Journal of the American Psychiatric Nurses Association, 14*(6), 442–453.

Allen, E. S., & Atkins, D. C. (2005). The multidimensional and developmental nature of infidelity: Practical applications. *Journal of Clinical Psychology, 61*(11), 1371–1382.

Allman, D. (1999). *M is for mutual: A is for acts*. Ottawa: Health Canada.

Altemeyer, B. (2001). Changes in attitudes toward homosexuals. *Journal of Homosexuality, 42*(2), 63–75.

Althof, S. E. (1994). Paper presented at the annual meeting of the American Urological Association, San Francisco, CA.

Alzate, H., & Hoch, Z. (1986). The "G spot" and "female ejaculation": A current appraisal. *Journal of Sex and Marital Therapy, 12*(3), 211–220.

Amankwah, E., Ngwakongnwi, E., & Quan, H. (2009). Why visible minority women in Canada do not participate in cervical cancer screening. *Ethnicity and Health, 14*(4), 337–349.

American Academy of Family Physicians. (2006). *Depo-Provera: An injectable contraceptive*. Retrieved from http://familydoctor.org/043.xml?printxml

American Academy of Pediatrics. (2005). Breastfeeding and the use of human milk. *Pediatrics, 115*, 496–506.

American Cancer Society. (2009). Cancer facts & figures 2009. http://www.cancer.org/downloads/STT/500809web.pdf.

American Fertility Association. (2006, February). [Online]. www.theafa.org

American Psychiatric Association. (2000). *Diagnostic and statistical manual of mental disorders* (4th ed.). Washington, DC: Author.

Amodeo, M., Griffin, M. K., Fassler, I. R., Clay, C. M., & Ellis, M. A. (2006). Childhood sexual abuse among black women and white women from two-parent families. *Child Maltreatment, 11*(3), 237–246.

Amodio, D. M., & Showers, C. J. (2005). "Similarity breeds liking" revisited: The moderating role of commitment. *Journal of Social and Personal Relationships, 22*(6), 817–836.

Andersen, M. L., Bignotto, M., & Tufik, S. (2003). The effect of apomorphine on genital reflexes in male rats deprived of paradoxical sleep. *Physiology & Behavior, 80*(2–3), 211–215.

Andersen, M. L., & Tufik, S. (2005). Effects of progesterone blockade over cocaine-induced genital reflexes of paradoxical sleep-deprived male rats. *Hormones and Behavior, 47*(4), 477–484.

Anderson, K. M. (2006). Surviving incest: The art of resistance. *Families in Society, 87*(3), 409–416.

Anderson Moore, K. (2008). *Teen Births: Examining the Recent Increase.* Washington, D.C.: The National Campaign to Prevent Teen and Unplanned Pregnancy.

Andriole, G. L., et al. (2009). Mortality results from a randomized prostate-cancer screening trial. *New England Journal of Medicine, 360,* 1310–1319.

Angus Reid Public Opinion. (2009). *Canadians reject status quo on prostitution.* Angus Reid Public Opinion. www.angus-reid/polls

Angus Reid. (2010a). Canadians and Britons are More Open on Same-Sex Relations Than Americans. July 26th, 2010. Angus Reid Public Opinion.

Angus Reid. (2010b). Canadians endorse multiculturalism, but pick melting pot over mosaic. http://angus-reid.com

Anderson, S. E., et al. (2003). Relative weight and race influence average age at menarche: Results from two nationally representative surveys of U.S. girls studied 25 years apart. *Pediatrics, 111,* 844–850

Ann Johnston Health Station. (Online). People with physical disabilities – SexAbility. www.ajhs.ca

Annon, J.S. (1976). *Behavioral treatment of sexual problems.* New York, NY: Harper & Row.

Aron, A., et al. (2008). Falling in love. In S. Sprecher, A. Wenzel, & J. Harvey (Eds.), *Handbook of relationship initiation* (pp. 315–336). New York: CRC Press.

Associated Press (2008, April 10). Five homosexuals jailed for "debauchery." *Toronto Star,* p. AA2.

Associated Press. (2011). Polygamist leader Warren Jeffs convicted of child sex abuse in Texas. *Globe and Mail,* Aug., 4th.

Associated Press/MTV. (2009). A Thin Line: 2009 AP-MTV Digital Abuse Study. http://www.athinline.org

Astley, S. J., & Clarren, S. K. (2001). Measuring the facial phenotype of individuals with prenatal alcohol exposure: Correlations with brain dysfunction. *Alcohol & Alcoholism, 36*(2), 147–159.

Atkinson, J. L. (1996). Female sex offenders: A literature review. *Forum on Corrections Research, 8*(2), 39–42.

Aubin, S., Heiman, J. R., Berger, R. E., Murallo, A. V., & Yung-Wen, L. (2009). Comparing sildenafil alone vs. sildenafil plus brief couple sex therapy on erectile dysfunction and couples' sexual and marital quality of life. *Journal of Sex and Marital Therapy, 35*(2), 122–143.

Ayres, M. M., & Haddock, S. A. (2009). Therapists' approaches in working with heterosexual couples struggling with male partners' online *sexual behavior. Sexual Addiction & Compulsivity, 16*(1), 55–78.

Bagley, C., & D'Augelli, A. R. (2000). Suicidal behaviour in gay, lesbian, and bisexual youth. *British Medical Journal, 320,* 1617–1618.

Bailey, I. (2000, April 26). They are a couple and proud of it. *National Post,* pp. A1, A2.

Bailey, J. M. (1999). Homosexuality and mental illness. *Archives of General Psychiatry, 56*(10), 883–884.

Bailey, J. M. (2003a). Personal communication.

Bailey, J. M. (2003b). *The man who would be queen: The science of gender-bending and transsexualism.* Washington, DC: Joseph Henry Press.

Bailey, S. (2008, January 15). Native population growing. *The Canadian Press.*

Bains, C. (2008, April 2). Canada has global sex abuse problem, expert finds. *Waterloo Region Record,* p. Z5.

Baker, J. L., et al. (2008). Breastfeeding reduces postpartum weight retention. *American Journal of Clinical Nutrition, 88,* 1553–1551.

Baldwin, J. D., & Baldwin, J. I. (1989). The socialization of homosexuality and heterosexuality in a non-Western society. *Archives of Sexual Behavior, 18,* 13–29.

Bancroft, J., Carnes, L., Janssen, E., Goodrich, D., & Long, J. S. (2005b). Erectile and ejaculatory problems in gay and heterosexual men. *Archives of Sexual Behavior, 34*(3), 285–297.

Bancroft, J., et al. (2005c). The relevance of the dual control model to male sexual dysfunction: The Kinsey Institute/BASRT collaborative project. *Sexual & Relationship Therapy, 20,* 13–30.

Banerjee, S. (2008, June 17). Belgian faces sex-related charges. *Toronto Star,* p. A14.

Barak, A., & Fisher, W. A. (1997). Effects of interactive computer erotica on men's attitudes and behavior toward women: An experimental study. *Computers in Human Behavior, 13,* 353–369.

Barbaree, H. E., & Blanchard, R. (2008). Sexual deviance over the lifespan. In D. R. Laws and W. T. O'Donohue (Eds.), *Sexual deviance: Theory, assessment, and treatment* (2nd ed., pp. 27–60). New York: Guilford Press.

Barnard, N. D., Scialli, A. R., Hurlock, D., & Bertron, P. (2000). Diet and sex-hormone binding globulin, dysmenorrhea, and premenstrual symptoms. *Obstetrics & Gynecology, 95,* 245–250.

Barnes, M. L., & Sternberg, R. J. (1997). A hierarchical model of love and its prediction of satisfaction in close relationships. In Sternberg, R. J., & Hojjat, M. (Eds.), *Satisfaction in close relationships* (pp. 79–101). New York: Guilford Press.

Barrett, M. (2006). What everyone should know about human papilomavirus (HPV): Questions and answers. *The Canadian Journal of Human Sexuality, 15*(3–4), 171–174.

Barrett, M. B. (1990). *Invisible lives: The truth about millions of women-loving women.* New York: Harper & Row (Perennial Library).

Barsky, J. L., Friedman, M. A., & Rosen, R. C. (2006). Sexual dysfunction and chronic illness: The role of flexibility in coping. *Journal of Sex & Marital Therapy, 32*(3), 235–253.

Bartolo, K. C. (2005). Mother–daughter incest: A guide for helping professionals. *Journal of Family Studies, 11*(2), 328–329.

Bartoshuk, L. M., & Beauchamp, G. K. (1994). Chemical senses. *Annual Review of Psychology, 45,* 419–449.

Basile, K. C. (2002). Attitudes toward wife rape: Effects of social background and victim status. *Violence & Victims, 17*(3), 341–354.

Basow, S. A., & Rubenfeld, K. (2003). "Troubles talk": Effects of gender and gender-typing. *Sex Roles, 48*(3–4), 183–187.

Basson, R. (2000, May). Paper presented at the annual meeting of the American College of Obstetricians and Gynecologists, San Francisco, CA.

Basson, R. (2002). A model of women's sexual arousal. *Journal of Sex and Marital Therapy, 28,* 1–10.

Basson, B., Davis, S. R., & Rodenberg, C. (2009). Testosterone for low libido. *New England Journal of Medicine, 360*(7), 728–729.

Basson, R. (2004). Recent advances in women's sexual function and dysfunction. *Menopause, 11*(6 Pt 2), 714–725.

Basson, R. (2008). Women's sexual function and dysfunction: current uncertainties, future directions. *International Journal of Impotence Research, 20*, 466–478.

Basson, R. (2010). Is it time to move on from "hypoactive sexual desire disorder?" *Menopause, 17*(6), 1097–1098.

Bastian, L. A., Smith, C. M., & Nanda, K. (2003). Is this woman perimenopausal? *Journal of the American Medical Association, 289*, 895–902.

Bauerle, S. Y., Amirkhan J. H., & Hupka, R. B. (2002). An attribution theory analysis of romantic jealousy. *Motivation & Emotion, 26*(4), 297–319.

Baumeister, R. F., Catanese, K. R., & Wallace, H. M. (2002). Conquest by force: A narcissistic reactance theory of rape and sexual coercion. *Review of General Psychology, 6*(1), 92–135.

Baute, N. (2010). "Sexting" nude photos a teen concern. *The Toronto Star*, January 7, 2010.

Beauregard, E., Lussier, P., & Proulx, J. (2004). An exploration of developmental factors related to deviant sexual preferences among adult rapists. *Sexual Abuse: A Journal of Research and Treatment, 16*(2), 151–161.

Behrendt, N., Buhl, N., & Seidl, S. (2002). The lethal paraphiliac syndrome: Accidental auto-erotic deaths in four women and a review of the literature. *International Journal of Legal Medicine, 116*(3), 148–152.

Bell, A. P., & Weinberg, M. S. (1978). *Homosexualities: A study of diversity among men and women.* New York: Simon & Schuster.

Bem, S. L. (1975). Sex role adaptability: One consequence of psychological androgyny. *Journal of Personality and Social Psychology, 31*, 634–643.

Bem, S. L. (1993). *The lenses of gender.* New Haven, CT: Yale University Press.

Bem, S. L., Martyna, W., & Watson, C. (1976). Sex typing and androgyny: Further explorations of the expressive domain. *Journal of Personality and Social Psychology, 34*, 1016–1023.

Bennett, S., & Assefi, N. (2005). School-based pregnancy prevention programs: A systematic review of randomized controlled studies. *Journal of Adolescent Health, 36*, 72–81.

Benzie, R. (2004, December 10). Film board cut out as censor. *The Toronto Star*, p. A4.

Berdahl, J. L., & Moore, C. (2006). Workplace harassment: Double jeopardy for minority women. *Journal of Applied Psychology, 91*(2), 426–436.

Bereket, T., & Adam, B. (2006). The emergence of gay identities in contemporary Turkey. *Sexualities, 9*(2), 131–151.

Beres, M. (2006). Sexual miscommunication? Untangling communication between casual sex partners. Doctorate thesis, University of Alberta.

Beres, M., Crow, B., & Gotell, L. (2009). The perils of institutionalization in neoliberal times: results of a national survey of Canadian sexual assault and rape crisis centres. *Canadian Journal of Sociology, 34*, (1), 135–164.

Beres, M. A. (2002). *Sexual consent behaviors in same sex relationships.* Unpublished master's thesis, University of Guelph.

Beres, M. A. (2007). "Spontaneous" sexual consent: An analysis of sexual consent literature. *Feminism & Psychology, 17*(1), 93–108.

Berger, P. B. (2009). Prosecuting for knowingly transmitting HIV is warranted. *Canadian Medical Association Journal, 180*(13), 1368

Berger, L. (2000, June 25). A racial gap in infant deaths, and a search for reasons. *The New York Times*, p. WH13.

Bergeron, S., Binik, Y. M., Khalife, S., Pagidas, K., Glazer, H. I., Meana, M., & Amsel, R. (2001). A randomized comparison of group cognitive-behavioral therapy, surface electromyographic biofeedback, and vestibulectomy in the treatment of dyspareunia resulting from vulvar vestibulitis. *Pain, 91*, 297–306.

Bergeron, S., Khalifé, S., Glazer, H. I., & Binik, Y. M. (2008). Surgical and behavioral treatments for vestibulodynia: Two-and-one-half-year follow-up and predictors and outcome. *Obstetrics & Gynecology, 111*(1), 159–166.

Bergeron, S., & Lord, M. (2003). The integration of pelvi-perineal re-education and cognitive-behavioural therapy in the multidisciplinary treatment of the sexual pain disorders. *Sexual & Relationship Therapy, 18*(2), 135–141.

Bergner, D. (2009, January 22). What do women want? *The New York Times*.

Bernstein, I. M., et al. (2005). Maternal smoking and its association with birth weight. *Obstetrics & Gynecology, 106*, 986–991.

Berscheid, E. (2003). On stepping on land mines. In Sternberg, R. J. (Ed.), *Psychologists defying the crowd: Stories of those who battled the establishment and won* (pp. 33–44). Washington, DC: American Psychological Association.

Berscheid, E., & Reis, H. T. (1998). Attraction and close relationships. In D. T. Gilbert, S. T. Fiske, et al. (Eds.), *The handbook of social psychology*, (Vol. 2, 4th ed., pp. 193–281). New York: McGraw-Hill.

Best Start. (2007). *Update Report on Teen Pregnancy Prevention.* Toronto, ON: Best Start: Ontario's Maternal, Newborn and Early Child Development Resource Centre.

Best Start. (2008). *Teen Pregnancy Prevention: Exploring Out-Of-School Approaches.* Toronto, ON: Best Start: Ontario's Maternal, Newborn and Early Child Development Resource Centre.

Beutel, M. E., Stöbel-Richter, Y., & Brähler, E. (2008). Sexual desire and sexual activity of men and women across their lifespans: Results from a representative German community survey. *BJU International, 101*(1), 76–82.

Bhugra, D. (2005). Queer theory. *Sexual and Relationship Therapy, 20*(4), 476.

Bibby, R. (2006). *The boomer factor: What Canada's most famous generation is leaving behind.* Bastian Books.

Bibby, R. W. (2001). *Canada's teens: Today, yesterday and tomorrow.* Toronto: Stoddart.

Bielay, B., & Herold, E. S. (1995). Popular magazines as a source of sexuality information for university women. *Journal of Canadian Sexuality, 4*, 247–261.

Bimbi, D. S. (2007). Male prostitution: Pathology, paradigms and progress in research. *Journal of Homosexuality, 53*(1-2), 7–35.

Binik, Y. M. (2005). Should dyspareunia be retained as a sexual dysfunction in *DSM-V*? A painful classification decision. *Archives of Sexual Behavior, 34*(1), 11–21.

Binik, Y. M., Reissing, E., Pukall, C., Flory, N., Payne, K. A., & Khalife, S. (2002). The female sexual pain disorders: Genital pain or sexual dysfunction? *Archives of Sexual Behavior, 31*, 425–429.

Bisson, M. A., & Levin, T. R. (2009). Negotiating a friends with benefits relationship. *Archives of Sexual Behavior, 38*, 66–73

Black, A. et al. (2009). Contraceptive use among Canadian women of reproductive age: results of a national survey. *Journal of Obstetrics and Gynecology Canada, 31*(7), 627–40.

Blais, K., Collin-Vezina, D., Marcellin, K., & Picard, A. (2004). Current reality of homosexual couples: Clinical implications in the context of partnership counseling. *Canadian Psychology, 45*(2), 174–186.

Blanchard, R. (1988). Nonhomosexual gender dysphoria. *Journal of Sex Research, 24*, 188–193.

Blanchard, R. (1989). The concept of autogynephilia and the typology of male gender dysphoria. *Journal of Nervous & Mental Disease, 177*(10), 616–623.

Blanchard, R., Cantor, J. M., Bogaert, A. F., Breedlove, S. M., & Ellis, L. (2006). Interaction of fraternal birth order and handedness in the development of male homosexuality. *Hormones and Behavior, 49*, 405–414.

Blanchard, R., Christensen, B. K., Strong, S. M., Cantor, J. M., Kuban, M. E., Klassen, P., Dickey, R., & Blak, T. (2002). Retrospective self-reports of childhood accidents causing unconsciousness in phallometrically diagnosed pedophiles. *Archives of Sexual Behaviour, 31*(6), 511–526.

Blanchard, R., & Lippa, R. A. (2007). Birth order, sibling sex ratio, handedness, and sexual orientation of male and female participants in a BBC internet research project. *Archives of Sexual Behaviour, 36*, 163–176.

Blanchard, R., Steiner, B. W., & Clemmensen, L. H. (1985). Gender dysphoria, gender reorientation, and the clinical management of transsexualism. *Journal of Consulting and Clinical Psychology, 53*, 295–304.

Bloch, M., Rotenberg, N., Koren, D., & Ehud, K. (2006). Risk factors for early postpartum depressive symptoms. *General Hospital Psychiatry, 28*(1), 3–8.

Bockting, W. O., & Fung, L. C. T. (2006). Genital reconstruction and gender identity disorders. In D. B. Sarwer et al. (Eds.), *Psychological aspects of reconstructive and cosmetic plastic surgery: Clinical, empirical, and ethical perspectives* (pp. 207–229). New York: Lippincott Williams & Wilkins.

Bogaert, A. F. (1996). Volunteer bias in human sexuality research: Evidence for both sexuality and personality differences in males. *Archives of Sexual Behavior, 25*(2) 125–140.

Bogaert, A. F. (2004). Asexuality: Prevalence and associated factors in a national probability sample. *Journal of Sex Research, 41*, 279–287.

Bogaert, A. F. (2005). Sibling sex ratio and sexual orientation in men and women: New tests in two national probability samples. *Archives of Sexual Behavior, 34*(1), 111–116.

Bogaert, A. F. (2006a). Toward a conceptual understanding of asexuality. *Review of General Psychology, 10*(3), 241–250.

Bogaert, A. F. (2006b). Biological versus nonbiological older brothers and men's sexual orientation. *Proceedings of the National Academy of Sciences of the United States of America, 103*(28), 10771–10774.

Bogaert, A. F., & Jamieson, L. (2008). Justice beliefs and other predictors of the timing of "coming out" in gay and bisexual men. Paper presented at the Guelph Sexuality Conference, Guelph, ON.

Bogin, G. Y. (2006). Out of the darkness: Male adolescents and the experience of sexual victimization. *School Social Work Journal, 30*(2), 1–21.

Boies, S. C. (2002). University students' uses of and reactions to online sexual information and entertainment: Links to online and offline sexual behavior. *Canadian Journal of Human Sexuality, 11*(2), 77–89.

Bolton, J. M., Sareen, J., & Reiss, J. P. (2006). Genital anaesthesia persisting six years after sertraline discontinuation. *Journal of Sex & Marital Therapy, 32*(4), 327–330.

Bonoguore, T. (2007, July 18). Still Single? Time to move west. *Toronto Star*.

Borisoff, J. J., Elliot, S. L., Hocalski, S., & Birch, G.. E. (2010). The development of a sensory substitution system for the sexual rehabilitation of men with chronic spinal cord injury. *Journal of Sexual Medicine, 7*, 3647–3658.

Born, L., Soares, C. N., Phillips, S., Jung, M., & Steiner, M. (2006). Women and reproductive-related trauma. In Yehuda, R. (Ed.). (2006). *Psychobiology of posttraumatic stress disorders: A decade of progress* (pp. 491–494). Vol. 1071. New York: Blackwell Publishing.

Boros, S., Mateuca, A., & Matus, M. (2005). The role of social identity in attributions—Evaluating the guilt in rape assault. *Cognitie Creier Comportament, 9*(1), 35–57.

Boston Women's Health Book Collective. (2005). *Our bodies, ourselves: A new edition for a new era.* New York: Touchstone.

Boyce, W. et al. (2006). Sexual health of Canadian youth: Findings from the Canadian Youth, Sexual health and HIV AIDS Study. *The Canadian Journal of Human Sexuality, 15*(2), 59–68.

Boyce, W., Craig, W., & Elgar, F., et al. (2008). *Healthy settings for young people in Canada.* Ottawa: Public Health Agency of Canada.

Boyce, W., Doherty, M., & MacKinnon, D. (2003). *Canadian youth, sexual health and HIV/AIDS study.* Council of Ministers of Education, Canada.

Boyle, T. (2007, April 30). Pupils punished over Facebook comments. *Toronto Star*, p. E5.

Bradford, J. M. W. (1998). Treatment of men with paraphilia. *The New England Journal of Medicine, 338*, 464–465.

Bradford, J. M. W. (2000). The treatment of sexual deviation using a pharmacological approach. *Journal of Sex Research, 37*, 248–257.

Bradford, J. M. W., & Pawlak, A. (1993). Double-blind placebo crossover study of cyproterone acetate in the treatment of the paraphilias. *Archives of Sexual Behavior, 22*(5), 383–402.

Bradley, S. J., Oliver, G. D., Chernick, A. B., & Zucker, K. J. (1998). Experiment of nurture: Ablatio penis at 2 months, sex reassignment at 7 months, and a psychosexual follow-up in young adulthood. *Pediatrics, 102*(1), e9.

Brauer, M., ter Kuile, M. M., Laan, E., & Trimbos, B. (2009). Cognitive-affective correlates and predictors of superficial dyspareunia. *Journal of Sex & Marital Therapy, 35*(1), 1–24.

Brean, J. (2008, May 21). Campus abortion debate reaches compromise. *National Post*, p. A6.

Brennan, R. (2004, July 13). Ontario rehires "smut" traders. *The Toronto Star*.

Brennan, S., & Taylor-Butts, A. (2008). *Sexual assaults in Canada 2004 and 2007.* Canadian Centre for Justice Statistics Profile Series. Statistics Canada.

Briken, P., Hill, A., Nika, E., & Berner, W. (2005). Obscene telephone calls—Relations to paraphilias, paraphilia related disorders and stalking. *Psychiatrische Praxis, 32*(6), 304–307.

Brock, G., Moreira, E.D., Glasser, D.B. & Gingell, C. (2006). Sexual disorders and associated help-seeking behaviours in Canada. *The Canadian Journal of Urology, 3, (1)*, 2953–2961.

Brock, G. et al. (2009). Canadian male sexual health council survey to assess the prevalence and treatment of premature ejaculation in Canada. *The Journal of Sexual Medicine, 6(8)*, 2115–2123.

Broder, M. S., Kanouse, D. E., Mittman, B. S., & Bernstein, S. J. (2000). The appropriateness of recommendations for hysterectomy. *Obstetrics & Gynecology, 95*, 199–206.

Brody, J. E. (2000, May 16). Cybersex gives birth to a psychological disorder. *The New York Times*, pp. F7, F12.

Brodzinsky, D. M., & Palacios, J. (2005). *Psychological issues in adoption: Research and practice.* Westport, CT: Praeger Publishers/Greenwood Publishing Group.

Bronner, E. (1998, February 1). "Just say maybe. No sexology, please. We're Americans." *The New York Times*, p. WK6.

Brotman, S., Ryan, B., & Cormier, R. (2003). The health and social service needs of gay and lesbian elders and their families in Canada. *The Gerontologist, 43*(2), 192–202.

Brotto, L., Heiman, J., Goff, B., Greer, B., Lentz, G., Swisher, E., et al. (2008). A psychoeducational intervention for sexual dysfunction in women with gynecologic cancer. *Archives of Sexual Behavior, 37*(2), 317–329.

Brotto, L. A. (2010). Asexuality: A mixed methods approach. *Archives of Sexual Behavior, 39*, 599–618).

Brotto, L. A., Basson, R., & Luria, M. (2008). A mindfulness-based group psychoeducational intervention targeting sexual arousal disorder in women. *Journal of Sexual Medicine, 5*(7), 1646–1659.

Brotto, L. A., Chik, H. M., Ryder, A. G., Gorzalka, B. B., & Seal, B. N. (2005). Acculturation and sexual function in Asian women. *Archives of Sexual Behaviour, 34*(6), 613–626.

Brotto, L. A., Chou, A. Y., Singh, T., & Woo, J. S. (2008). Reproductive health practices among Indian, Indo-Canadian, Canadian East Asian, and Euro-Canadian women: the role of acculturation. *Journal of Obstetrics and Gynaecology Canada: JOGC, 30*(3), 229–256.

Brotto, L. A., & Gorzalka, B. B. (2002). Genital and subjective sexual arousal in postmenopausal women: Influence of laboratory-induced hyperventilation. *Journal of Sex & Marital Therapy, 28*(Suppl1), 39–53.

Brotto, L. A., & Heiman, J. R. (2007). Mindfulness in sex therapy: Applications for women with sexual difficulties following gynecologic cancer. *Sex and Marital Therapy, 22*(1), 3–11.

Brotto, L. A., Woo, J. S., & Ryder, A. G. (2007). Acculturation and sexual function in Canadian East Asian men. *Journal of Sexual Medicine, 4*(1), 72–82

Brotto, L. A., & Yule, M. A. (2011). Physiological and subjective sexual arousal in self-identified asexual women. *Archives of Sexual Behavior, 40*, 699–712.

Brown, D. (2003). Pornography and erotica. In Bryant, J., Roskos–Ewoldsen, D., & Cantor, J. (Eds.). *Communication and emotion: Essays in honor of Dolf Zillmann* (pp. 221–253). LEA's communication series. Hillsdale, NJ: Lawrence Erlbaum Associates.

Brown, G. R., & Haaser, R. C. (2005). Sexual disorders. In Levenson, J. L. (Ed.), *The American psychiatric publishing textbook of psychosomatic medicine* (pp. 359–386). Washington, DC: American Psychiatric Publishing.

Brown, L. M., McNatt, P. S., & Cooper, G. D. (2003). Ingroup romantic preferences among Jewish and non-Jewish white undergraduates. *International Journal of Intercultural Relations, 27*(3), 335–354.

Brown, L. S. (2005). Prostitution, trafficking and traumatic stress. *Journal of Trauma & Dissociation, 6(3)*, 143–145. Canadian Press. (2011). Top court will hear prostitution law challenge. www.cbc.ca. March 31st, 2011.

Brown, R., Balousek, S., Mundt, M., & Fleming, M. (2005). Methadone maintenance and male sexual dysfunction. *Journal of Addictive Diseases, 24*(2), 91–106.

Brown, T. (2002). A proposed model of bisexual identity development that elaborates on experiential differences of women and men. *Journal of Bisexuality, 2*(4), 67–91.

Browning, D. S., et al. (2006). *Sex, marriage, and family in world religions.* New York: Columbia University Press.

Brunet, P. M., & Schmidt, L. A. (2008). Are shy adults really bolder online? It depends on the context. *CyberPsychology & Behavior, 11*(6), 707–709.

Bryant, C. (2010). Adolescence, pornography and harm. *Youth Studies Australia, 29*(1), 18–26

Bullough, V. L. (2002). Masturbation: A historical overview. *Journal of Psychology & Human Sexuality, 14*(2–3), 17–33.

Bumpass, L. (1995, July 6). Cited in J. Steinhauer. No marriage, no apologies. *The New York Times*, pp. C1, C7.

Buss, D. M., & Schmitt, D. P. (1993). Sexual strategies theory: An evolutionary perspective on human mating. *Psychological Review, 100*(2), 204–232.

Buss, D. M. (1994). *The evolution of desire: Strategies of human mating.* New York: Basic Books.

Buss, D. M. (Ed.). (2005). *The handbook of evolutionary psychology.* Hoboken, NJ: John Wiley & Sons.

Buss, D. M. (2009). An evolutionary formulation of person–situation interactions. *Journal of Research in Personality, 43*(2), 241–242.

Buss, D. M. (2009). The great struggles of life: Darwin and the emergence of evolutionary psychology. *American Psychologist, 64*(2), 140–148.

Butler, J. (1993). *Bodies that matter: On the discursive limits of sex.* New York: Routledge.

Butler, J. (2003). *Kritik der ethischenGewalt.* Adorno lectures. 2002. Frankfurt am Main: Institut fur Sozialforschung an der Johann Wolfgang Goethe-Universitat.

Byerly, M. J., et al. (2006). Sexual dysfunction associated with second-generation antipsychotics in outpatients with schizophrenia or schizoaffective disorder: An empirical evaluation of olanzapine, risperidone, and quetiapine. *Schizophrenia Research, 86*(1–3), 244–250.

Byers, E. S. (2011). Beyond the birds and the bees and was it good for you?: Thirty years of research on sexual communication. *Canadian Psychology, 52*(1), 20–28.

Byers, E. S., & Demmons, S. (1999). Sexual satisfaction and sexual self-disclosure within dating relationships. *Journal of Sex Research, 36*, 180–189.

Byers, E. S., & Eno, R. (1991). Predicting men's sexual coercion and aggression from attitudes, dating history and sexual response. *Journal of Psychology and Human Sexuality, 4*, 55–69.

Byers, E. S., & Grenier, G. (2003). Premature or rapid ejaculation: Heterosexual couples' perceptions of men's ejaculatory behavior. *Archives of Sexual Behavior, 32*(3), 261–270.

Byers, E. S., & Heinlein, L. (1989). Predicting initiations and refusals of sexual activities in married and cohabiting heterosexual couples. *Journal of Sex Research, 26*, 210–231.

Byers, E. S., & Lewis, K. (1988). Dating couples' disagreements over the desired level of sexual intimacy. *Journal of Sex Research, 24*, 15–29.

Byers, L. (2005). *Gendered use of and exposure to SEMI.* Paper presented at the 2005 Canadian Sociology Association Annual Meeting, London, ON.

Cado, S., & Leitenberg, H. (1990). Guilt reactions to sexual fantasies during intercourse. *Archives of Sexual Behavior, 19*, 49–64.

Caffaro, J. V., & Conn-Caffaro, A. (2005). Treating sibling abuse families. *Aggression and Violent Behavior, 10*(5), 604–623.

Cai, R., Alexander, M., & Marson, L. (2008). Activation of somatosensory afferents elicit changes in vaginal blood flow and the urethrogenital reflex via autonomic efferents. *The Journal of Urology, 180*(3), 1167–1172.

Cairns, K. V. (1997). Counseling the partners of heterosexual male cross-dressers. *Canadian Journal of Human Sexuality, 6*, 297–306.

Cairns, K. V., & Hatt, D. G. (1995). Discrimination and sexual harassment in a graduate student sample. *Canadian Journal of Human Sexuality, 4*, 169–176.

Calzavara, L. M., Bullock, S. L., Myers, T., Marshall, V. W., & Cockerill, R. (1999). Sexual partnering and risk of HIV/STD among Aboriginals. *Canadian Journal of Public Health, 90*(3), 186–191.

Calzavara, L. M., Coates, R., Raboud, J., Farewell, V., Read, S., Shepherd, F., Fanning, M., & MacFadden, D. (1992). Association between alcohol and drug use prior to sex and high risk sexual behavior in the Toronto sexual contact study cohort. *Canadian Journal of Infectious Diseases, 3*, 45A.

Campbell, R. (2006). Rape survivors' experiences with the legal and medical systems: Do rape victim advocates make a difference? *Violence Against Women, 12*(1), 30–45.

Canadian Cancer society. (2009). Hormone replacement therapy. http://www.cancer.ca

Canadian Cancer society. (2009). Hormone replacement therapy. http://www.cancer.ca

Canadian Cancer Society. (2010a). Statistics for cervical cancer. http://www.cancer.ca

Canadian Cancer Society. (2010b). Statistics for uterine cancer. http://www.cancer.ca

Canadian Cancer Society. (2010c). Statistics for ovarian cancer. http://www.cancer.ca

Canadian Cancer Society. (2010d). Statistics for breast cancer. http://www.cancer.ca

Canadian Cancer society. (2010e). Statistics for testicular cancer. http://www.cancer.ca

Canadian Cancer society. (2010f). Prostate cancer overview. http://www.cancer.ca

Canadian Institute for Health Information. (2004). *Giving birth in Canada: A regional profile.*

Canadian Institute for Health Information. (2007a). *Giving birth in Canada: Regional trends from 2001–2002 to 2005–2006.* Available: http://secure.cihi.ca/cihiweb/en/downloads/Childbirth _AiB_FINAL_E.pdf

Canadian Institute for Health Information. (2007b). Therapeutic abortions data. www.cihi.ca

Canadian Institute for Health Information. (2008). Therapeutic abortions data. www.cihi.ca

Canadian Institute for Health Information. (2010). Health Indicators, 2010. http://www.cihi.ca

Canadian Liver Foundation. (2010). *A Survey of Boomers' Sexual Behaviours and Attitudes: Summary of Findings.* Leger Marketing.

Canadian Press. (2007, September 10). Importance of marriage strong for individuals. *Toronto Star*, p. A6.

Canadian Press. (2008, July 14). Teachers vote in favour of criminalizing cyberbullying. *Toronto Star*, p. A5.

Canadian Press. (2010, May 17). Poll finds unease at tory tack on G8 health plan. *Toronto Star*, May 17, 2010, p. A6.

Canadian Press. (2011). Top court will hear prostitution law challenge. www.cbc.ca. March 31st, 2011.

Canadian Women's Health Network. (2010). Too many women getting hysterectomies when less invasive methods exist. http://www.cwhn.ca

Cantor, J. M., Blanchard, R., Christensen, B. K., Dickey, R., Klassen, P. E., Beckstead, A. L., et al. (2004). Intelligence, memory, and handedness in pedophilia. *Neuropsychology, 18*(1), 3–14.

Cantor, J. M., Blanchard, R., Robichaud, L. K., & Christensen, B. K. (2005b). Quantitative reanalysis of aggregate data on IQ in sexual offenders. *Psychological Bulletin, 131*(4), 555–568.

Cantor, J. M., Kabani, N., Christensen, B. K., Zipursky, R. B., Barbaree, H. E., Dickey, R., Klassen, P. E., Mikulis, D. J., Kuban, M. E., Blak, T., Richards, B. A., Hanratty, M. K., & Blanchard, R. (2008). Cerebral white matter deficiencies in pedophilic men. *Journal of Psychiatric Research, 42*, 167–183.

Cantor, J. M., Klassen, P. E., Dickey, R., Christensen, B. K., Kuban, M. E., Blak, T., et al. (2005a). Handedness in pedophilia and hebephillia. *Archives of Sexual Behaviour, 34*(4), 447–459.

Cantor, J. M., Kuban, M. E., Blak, T., Klassen, P. E., Dickey, R., & Blanchard, R. (2006). Grade failure and special education placement in sexual offenders' educational histories. *Archives of Sexual Behaviour, 35*(6), 743–751.

Carey, B. (2005, May 31). Watching new love as it sears the brain. *The New York Times.*

Carmody, J., Reed, G., Kristeller, J., & Merriam, P. (2008). Mindfulness, spirituality, and health-related symptoms. *Journal of Psychosomatic Research, 64*(4), 393–403.

Carrère, S., Buehlman, K. T., Gottman, J. M., Coan, J. A., & Ruckstuhl, L. (2000). Predicting marital stability and divorce in newlywed couples. *Journal of Family Psychology, 14*(1), 42–58.

Carrier, S., Morales, A., & Defoy, I. (2005). Viagra long-term efficacy and quality of life: Results of Canadian long-term study. Paper presented to World Congress of Sexology, Montreal.

Carter, D. J., & Dalla, R. L. (2006). Transactional analysis case report: Street-level prostituted women as mental health care clients. *Sexual Addiction & Compulsivity, 13*(1), 95–119.

Casavant, L. & Robertson, J.R. (2007). *Evolution of pornography law in Canada. Current Issue Review 84-3E.* Library of Parliament. Ottawa, ON: Government of Canada.

Centers for Disease Control and Prevention. (2007). *Human papillomavirus: HPV information for clinicians.* Atlanta, GA: Department of Health and Human Services

Chae, D. H., & Ayala, G. (2010). Sexual orientation and sexual behavior among Latino and Asian Americans: Implications for unfair treatment and psychological distress. *Journal of Sex Research, 47*(5), 451–459.

Chaiyavej, S., & Morash, M. (2009). Reasons for policewomen's assertive and passive reactions to sexual harassment. *Police Quarterly, 12*(1), 63–85.

Chandra, A., et al. (2008). Does watching sex on television predict teen pregnancy? Findings from a national longitudinal survey of youth. *Pediatrics, 122*(5), 1047–1054.

Chavez, M. L., & Spitzer, M. F. (2002). Herbals and other dietary supplements for premenstrual syndrome and menopause. *Psychiatric Annals, 32*(1), 61–71.

Chesler, P. (2006, February 24). The failure of feminism. *Chronicle of Higher Education, 52*(25).

Child, T. J., Henderson, A. M., & Tan, S. L. (2004). The desire for multiple pregnancy in male and female infertility patients. *Human Reproduction, 19*(3), 558–561.

Chiose, S. (2001). *Good girls do: Sex chronicles of a shameless generation.* Toronto: ECW Press.

Chivers, M., & Bailey, J. M. (2005). A sex difference in features that elicit genital response. *Biological Psychology, 70*(2), 115–120.

Chivers, M., Seto, M., & Blanchard, R. (2007). Gender and sexual orientation differences in sexual response to sexual activities versus gender of actors in sexual films. *Journal of Personality and Social Psychology, 93*(6), 1108–1121.

Chivers, M. L., & Bailey, J. M. (2007). The sexual physiology of sexual orientation. In E. Janssen (Ed.), *The psychophysiology of sex.* The Kinsey Institute series (pp. 458–474). Bloomington: Indiana University Press.

Chivers, M.L. & Rosen, R.C. (2010). Phosphodiestrase type 5 inhibitors and female sexual response: faulty protocols or paradigms? *Journal of Sexual Medicine, 7,* 858–872.

Cho, S., Park, E. S., Park, C. I., & Na, S. (2004). Characteristics of psychosexual functioning in adults with cerebral palsy. *Clinical Rehabilitation, 18*(4), 423–429.

Christin-Maitre, S., Bouchard, P., & Spitz, I. M. (2000). Drug therapy: Medical termination of pregnancy. *The New England Journal of Medicine* online, *342*(13).

Chung, A. (2010). Simple card detects date-rape drugs. *Toronto Star,* July 21, A6.

Chung, A. (2011). The profits of porn. *Toronto Star,* March 2, 2011.

Cleary, J., Barhman, R., MacCormack, T., & Herold, E. (2002). Discussing sexual health with a partner: A qualitative study with young women. *Canadian Journal of Human Sexuality, 11*(3–4), 117–132.

Clements-Schreiber, M. E., & Rempel, J. K. (1995). Women's acceptance of stereotypes about male sexuality: Correlations with strategies to influence reluctant partners. *Canadian Journal of Human Sexuality, 4*(4), 223–236.

Cnattingius, S. (2004). The epidemiology of smoking during pregnancy: Smoking prevalence, maternal characteristics, and pregnancy outcomes. *Nicotine & Tobacco Research, 6*(Suppl. 2), S125–S140.

Cnattingius, S., Bergstrom, R., Lipworth, L., & Kramer, M. S. (1998). Prepregnancy weight and the risk of adverse pregnancy outcomes. *The New England Journal of Medicine, 338,* 147–152

Coates, R. A., Soskolne, C. L., Calzavara, L., et al. (1986). The reliability of sexual histories in AIDS-related research: Evaluation of an interview administered questionnaire. *Canadian Journal of Public Health, 77,* 343–348.

Cochran, W. G., Mosteller, F., & Tukey, J. W. (1953). Statistical problems of the Kinsey Report. *Journal of the American Statistical Association, 48,* 673–716.

Cohen, A. B., & Tannenbaum, I. J. (2001). Lesbian and bisexual women's judgments of the attractiveness of different body types. *Journal of Sex Research, 38*(3), 226–232.

Cohen, J. N., Byers, E. S., Sears, H. A., & Weaver, A. D. (2004). Sexual health education: Attitudes, knowledge, and comfort of teachers in New Brunswick schools. *Canadian Journal of Human Sexuality, 13*(1), 1–15.

Cohen, L. S., et al. (2006). Relapse of major depression during pregnancy in women who maintain or discontinue antidepressant treatment. *Journal of the American Medical Association, 295*(5), 499–507.

Cohen–Bendahan, C. C. C., van de Beek, C., & Berenbaum, S. A. (2005). Prenatal sex hormone effects on child and adult sex-typed behavior: Methods and findings. *Neuroscience & Biobehavioral Reviews, 29*(2), 353–384.

Cohen-Kettenis, P. T., Owen, A., Kaijser, V. G., Bradley, S. J., & Zucker, K. J. (2003). Demographic characteristics, social competence, and behavior problems in children with gender identity disorder: A cross-national, cross-clinic comparative analysis. *Journal of Abnormal Child Psychology, 31*(1), 41–53.

Colapinto, J. (2000). *As nature made him: The boy who was raised as a girl.* New York: HarperCollins.

Colapinto, J. (2004, June 3). Gender gap: What were the real reasons behind David Reimer's suicide? [Online]. www.slate.com/id/2101678

Colditz, G. A., & Rosner, B. A. (2000). Cumulative risk for breast cancer to age 70 years according to risk factor status. Data from the Nurses' Health Study. *American Journal of Epidemiology, 152*(10), 950–964.

Colditz, G. A., et al. (2004). Risk factors for breast cancer according to estrogen and progesterone receptor status. *Journal of the National Cancer Institute, 96,* 218–228.

Cole, S. S. (1988). Women's sexuality, and disabilities. *Women and Therapy, 7,* 277–294.

Cole, F. S. (2000). Extremely preterm birth—Defining the limits of hope. *The New England Journal of Medicine, 343*(6).

Cole, T. B. (2006). Rape at US colleges often fueled by alcohol. *Journal of the American Medical Association, 296*(5), 504–505.

Coleman, E. (2002). Masturbation as a means of achieving sexual health. *Journal of Psychology and Human Sexuality, 14*(1-2), 5–16.

Coleman, E. (2003). Compulsive sexual behavior: what to call it, how to treat it. *SIECUS Report, 31*(5), 12–16.

Collins, R. L., et al. (2004). Watching sex on television predicts adolescent initiation of sexual behavior. *Pediatrics, 114*(3), e280–e289.

Compas Inc. (1998). *Modern life survey of the Canadian adult population.* Unpublished raw data. Toronto: Compas Inc.

Connell, E., & Hunt, A. (2006). Sexual ideology and sexual physiology in the discourses of sex advice literature. *The Canadian Journal of Human Sexuality, 15*(1), 23–45.

Connolly, J., Pepler, D., Craig, W., & Taradash, A. (2000). Dating experiences of bullies in early adolescence. *Child Maltreatment, 5*(4), 299–310.

Connor, P. D., Sampson, P. D., Streissguth, A. P., Bookstein, F. L., & Barr, H. M. (2006). Effects of prenatal alcohol exposure on fine motor coordination and balance: A study of two adult samples. Neuropsychologia, 44(5), 744–751.

Cooper, A., Delmonico, D. L., & Burg, R. (2000). Cybersex users, abusers, and compulsives: New findings and implications. *Sexual Addiction & Compulsivity, 7*(1–2), 5–29.

Cooper, A., Delmonico, D. L., Griffin–Shelley, E., & Mathy, R. M. (2004). Online sexual activity: An examination of potentially problematic behaviors. *Sexual Addiction & Compulsivity, 11*(3), 129–143.

Cortoni, F., Hanson, R. K., & Coache, M. E. (2009). Les delinquantes sexuelles: Prevalence et recidive [Female sexual offenders: Prevalence and recidivism]. *Revue internationale de criminolgie et de police technique et scientifique, LXII,* 319–336.

Cotton-Huston, A. L. & Waite, B. M. (2000). Anti-homosexual attitudes in college students: predictors and classroom interventions. *Journal of Homosexuality, 38,* 117–133.

Courtois, F. J., Charvier, K. F., Leriche, A., Vézina, J.-G., Côté, M., & Bélanger, M. (2007). Blood pressure changes during sexual stimulation, ejaculation and midodrine treatment in men with spinal cord injury. *British Journal of Urology, 101,* 331–337.

Cox, C. L., Wexler, M. O., Rusbult, C. E., & Gaines, S. O., Jr. (1997). Prescriptive support and commitment processes in close relationships. *Social Psychology Quarterly, 60*(1), 79–90.

Cox, D. J. (1988). Incidence and nature of male genital exposure behavior as reported by college women. *Journal of Sex Research, 24*, 227–234.

Coyle, J. P. (2006). Treating difficult couples: Helping clients with coexisting mental and relationship disorders. *Family Relations: Interdisciplinary Journal of Applied Family Studies, 55*(1), 146–147.

Crabtree, S., & Pelham, B. (2009). What Alabamians and Iranians Have in Common. Gallup Poll. http://www.gallup.com

Craig, R. J. (2005). Harassment. In R. J. Craig (Ed.), *Personality-guided forensic psychology. Personality-guided psychology* (pp. 155–167). Washington, DC: American Psychological Association.

Crawford, T. (2008, May 27). Giving it another shot. *Toronto Star*, p. L1.

Cribb, R., & Brazao, D. (2005, May 10). What can Toronto do about sex dens? Holistic centres "a never-ending mess" for city "Holistic" spas upset nearby residents Police not enforcing "moral offences." *Toronto Star*, p. A01.

Critelli, J. W., & Bivona, J. M. (2008). Women's erotic rape fantasies: An evaluation of theory and research. *Journal of Sex Research, 45*(1), 57–70.

Crocker, D., & Kalemba, V. (1999). The incidence and impact of women's experiences of sexual harassment in Canadian workplaces. *The Canadian Review of Sociology and Anthropology, 36*(4), 541–558.

Crosby, R. A., Sanders, S. A., Yarber, W. L., Graham, C. A., & Dodge, B. (2002). Condom use errors and problems among college men. *Sexually Transmitted Diseases, 29*, 552–557.

Crowley, T., Richardson, D., Goldmeier, D., & BASHH Special Interest Group for Sexual Dysfunction. (2006). Recommendations for the management of vaginismus: BASHH Special Interest Group for Sexual Dysfunction. *International Journal of STD & AIDS, 17*(1), 14–18.

Csoka, A. B., & Shipko, S. (2006). Persistent sexual side effects after SSRI discontinuation. *Psychotherapy and Psychosomatics, 75*(3), 187–188.

Cummings, A., & Leschied, W. (Eds.) (2002). *Violence in the lives of adolescent girls: Implications for educators and counsellors*. New York: Edwin Mellen Press.

Cummings, S. R., et al. (1999). The effect of raloxifene on risk of breast cancer in postmenopausal women: Results from the MORE randomized trial. *Journal of the American Medical Association, 281*, 2189–2197.

Cunningham, M. R., & Barbee, A. P. (2008). Prelude to a kiss: Nonverbal flirting, opening gambits, and other communication dynamics in the initiation of romantic relationships. In S. Sprecher, A. Wenzel, & J. Harvey (Eds.), *Handbook of relationship initiation* (pp. 97–120). New York: CRC Press.

Cunningham, M. R., et al. (1995). "Their ideas of beauty are, on the whole, the same as ours": Consistency and variability in the cross-cultural perception of female physical attractiveness. *Journal of Personality and Social Psychology, 68*(2), 261–279.

Curnoe, S., & Langevin, R. (2002). Personality and deviant sexual fantasies: An examination of the MMPIs. *Journal of Clinical Psychology, 58*(7), 803–815.

Cutler, W. B. (1999). Human sex-attractant hormones: Discovery, research, development, and application in sex therapy. *Psychiatric Annals, 29*(1), 54–59.

D'Amico, A. V. et al. (2000). Biochemical outcome following external beam radiation therapy with or without androgen suppression therapy for clinically localized prostate cancer. *Journal of the American Medical Association, 284*(10), 1280–1283.

Dabbs, J. M., Jr., & Morris, R. (1990). Testosterone, social class, and antisocial behavior in a sample of 4,462 men. *Psychological Science, 1*, 1–3.

Dahan, R., Feldman, R., & Harmoni, D. (2008). Is patients' sexual orientation a blind spot of family physicians? *Journal of Homosexuality, 55*(3), 524–532

Dahinten, V. S. (2003). Peer sexual harassment in adolescence: The function of gender. *The Canadian Journal of Nursing Research, 35*(2), 56–73.

Dalby, P. (2007, September 17). Cancer's on hold so life can go on. *Toronto Star*, p. X7.

Daley, A. (2009). Exercise and premenstrual symptomatology: A comprehensive review. *Journal of Women's Health, 18*(6), 895–899.

Daly, K. J., & Sobol, M. P. (1994). Public and private adoption: A comparison of service and accessibility. *Family Relations, 43*, 86–93.

Damon, W. (2002). Dominance, sexism, and inadequacy: Testing a compensatory conceptualization in a sample of heterosexual men involved in SM. *Journal of Psychology & Human Sexuality, 14*(4), 25–45.

Dancer, P. L., Kleinplatz, P. J., & Moser, C. (2006). 24/7 SM slavery. *Journal of Homosexuality, 50*(2–3), 81–101.

Daneback, K., Cooper, A., & Månsoon, S. (2005). An internet study of cybersex participants. *Archives of Sexual Behavior, 34*(3), 321–328.

Daneback, K., Ross, M. W., & Månsson, S. (2006). Characteristics and behaviors of sexual compulsives who use the internet for sexual purposes. *Sexual Addition & Compulsivity, 13*(1), 53–67.

Darcangelo, S. (2008). Fetishism: Psychopathology and theory. In D. R. Laws and W. T. O'Donohue (Eds.), *Sexual deviance: Theory, assessment, and treatment* (2nd ed., pp. 76–107). New York: Guilford Press.

Darling, C. A., Davidson, J. K., & Jennings, D. A. (1991). The female sexual response revisited: Understanding the multiorgasmic experience in women. *Archives of Sexual Behavior, 20*, 527–540.

Dauvergne, M., & Turner, J. (2010). Police-reported crime statistics in Canada, 2009. *Juristat, 30*(2).

Davidson, J. K. (2004). *Fearless sex: A babe's guide to overcoming your romantic obsessions and getting the sex life you deserve* (2nd ed.). Gloucester, MA: Fair Winds Press.

Davidson-Harden, J., Fisher, W. A., & Davidson, P. R. (2000). Attitudes toward people in exclusive dating relationships who initiate condom use. *Canadian Journal of Human Sexuality, 9*, 1–14.

Davies, M. (2004). Correlates of negative attitudes toward gay men: Sexism, male role norms, and male sexuality. *Journal of Sex Research, 41*(3), 259–266.

Davis, D., Shaver, P. R., & Vernon, M. L. (2003). Physical, emotional, and behavioral reactions to breaking up: The roles of gender, age, emotional involvement, and attachment style. *Personality & Social Psychology Bulletin, 29*(7), 871–884.

Davis, K. E., & Frieze, I. H., & Maiuro, R. D. (Eds.). (2002). *Stalking: Perspectives on victims and perpetrators* (pp. 212–236). New York: Springer.

Davis, S. R., et al. (2008). Testosterone for low libido in postmenopausal women not taking estrogen. *New England Journal of Medicine, 359*, 2005.

Dawood, K., Bailey, J. M., & Martin, N. G. (2009). Genetic and environmental influences on sexual orientation. In Y-K. Kim (Ed.), *Handbook of behavior genetics* (pp. 269–279). New York: Springer.

Decaire, B & Foster, D. (2010). Is being a lesbian a queer thing to do? In L. R. Ross (Ed). *Feminist Counselling: Theory, Issues, and Practice*. Toronto, ON: Canadian Scholars Press.

Degenhardt, L., Day, C., Conroy, E., & Gilmour, S. (2006). Examining links between cocaine use and street-based sex work in New South Wales, Australia. *Journal of Sex Research, 43(2)*, 107–114.

Dekeseredy, W., & Kelly, K. (1993). The incidence and prevalence of woman abuse in Canadian university and college dating relationships. *Canadian Journal of Sociology, 18*, 137–159.

Delamater, J., & Karraker, A. (2009). Sexual functioning in older adults. *Current Psychiatry Reports, 11*, 6–11

Delamater, J., & Moorman, S. M. (2007). Sexual behavior in later life. *Journal of Aging and Health, 19(6)*, 921–945

DeLuzio Chasin, C. J. (2011). Theoretical issues in the study of asexuality. *Archives of Sexual Behavior, 40*, 713–723.

den Tonkelaar, I., & Oddens, B. J. (2000). Determinants of long-term hormone replacement therapy and reasons for early discontinuation. *Obstetrics & Gynecology, 95(4)*, 507–512.

Denmark, F., Paludi, M. A., & Lott, B. (2008). *Psychology of women: A handbook of issues and theories.* Santa Barbara, CA: Greenwood Press.

Dennerstein, L., & Goldstein, I. (2005). Postmenopausal female sexual dysfunction: At a crossroads. *Journal of Sexual Medicine, 2*(Suppl. 3), 116–117.

Dennerstein, L., & Hayes, R. D. (2005). Confronting the challenges: Epidemiological study of female sexual dysfunction and the menopause. *Journal of Sexual Medicine, 2*(Suppl. 3), 118–132.

Dennis, W. (1992). *Hot and bothered: Men and women, sex and love in the nineties.* Toronto: Key Porter Books.

Denov, M. S. (2001). A culture of denial: Exploring professional perspectives on female sex offending. *Canadian Journal of Criminology, 43(3)*, 303–329.

Denzin, N. K., & Lincoln, Y. S. (Eds.). (2005). *The Sage handbook of qualitative research* (3rd ed.). Thousand Oaks, CA: Sage Publications.

Derby, C. A. (2000, October 2). Cited in Study finds exercise reduces the risk of impotence. The Associated Press.

Derlega, V. J., Winstead, B. A., & Greene, K. (2008). Self-disclosure and starting a close relationship. In S. Sprecher, A. Wenzel, & J. Harvey (Eds.), *Handbook of relationship initiation* (pp. 153–174). New York: CRC Press.

Devor, H. (1997). *FTM: Female-to-male transsexuals.* Bloomington, IN: Indiana University Press.

Devor, H. (2002). Who are "we"? Where sexual orientation meets gender identity. *Journal of Gay & Lesbian Psychotherapy, 6(2)*, 5–21.

De Vries, G. J., et al. (2002). A model system for study of sex chromosome effects on sexually dimorphic neural and behavioral traits. *Journal of Neuroscience, 22(20)*, 9005–9014.

Devries, K., Free, C., Morison, L., & Saewyc, E. (2009). Factors associated with pregnancy and STI among aboriginal students in British Columbia. *Canadian Journal of Public Health, 100(3)*, 226–230

Dharmajah, T. (2008, July 17). No jail after sex-game death. *Guelph Mercury*, p. A1.

Diamond, L. M. (2003a). Was it a phase? Young women's relinquishment of lesbian/bisexual identities over a 5-year period. *Journal of Personality & Social Psychology, 84(2)*, 352–364.

Diamond, L. M. (2003b). What does sexual orientation orient? A biobehavioral model distinguishing romantic love and sexual desire. *Psychological Review, 110(1)*, 173–192.

Diamond, M. (1996). Prenatal predisposition and the clinical management of some pediatric conditions. *Journal of Sex & Marital Therapy, 22(3)*, 139–147.

DiGiulio, G. (2003). Sexuality and people living with physical or developmental disabilities: A review of key issues. *The Canadian Journal of Human Sexuality, 12*, 53–68

Dijkstra, P., & Buunk, B. P. (2002). Sex differences in the jealousy-evoking effect of rival characteristics. *European Journal of Social Psychology, 32(6)*, 829–852.

Dindia, K., & Timmermann, L. (2003). Accomplishing romantic relationships. In J. O. Greene & B. R. Burleson (Eds.), *Handbook of communication and social interaction skills* (pp. 685–721). Mahwah, NJ: Erlbaum.

Dion, K., Berscheid, E., & Walster, E. (1972). What is beautiful is good. *Journal of Personality and Social Psychology, 24(3)*, 285–290.

Do, C., et al. (2009). Statins and erectile dysfunction: Results of a case/non-case study using the French Pharmacovigilance System Database. *Drug Safety, 32(7)*, 591–597.

Downs, M., & Nazario, B. (2003, February 11). *Aphrodisiacs through the ages.* WebMD Features. [Online].

Disney, E. R., Iacono, W., McGue, M., Tully, E., & Legrand, L. (2008). Strengthening the case: Prenatal alcohol exposure is associated with increased risk for conduct disorder. Pediatrics, 122(6), e1225–e1230

Dittert, S., Seidl, O., & Soyka, M. (2005). Zoophilia as a special case of paraphilia. Presentation of three case reports and an Internet survey. *Nervenarzt, 76(1)*, 61–67.

Dredger, A. (2008). The controversy surrounding *The Man Who Would be Queen: A Case History of the Politics of Science, Identity, and Sex in the Internet Age. Archives of Sexual Behavior, 37*, 366–421.

Drigotas, S. M., Rusbult, C. E., & Verette, J. (1999). Level of commitment, mutuality of commitment, and couple well-being. *Personal Relationships, 6(3)*, 389–409.

Driver, J., Tabares, A., Shapiro, A., Nahm, E. Y., & Gottman, J. M. (2003). Interactional patterns in marital success and failure: Gottman laboratory studies. In F. Walsh (Ed.). *Normal family processes: Growing diversity and complexity* (3rd ed.) (pp. 493–513). New York: Guilford Press.

Duenwald, M. (2002, July 16). Hormone therapy: One size, clearly, no longer fits all. *The New York Times.*

Duggavathi, R., Volle, D., Mataki, C., Antal, M., Messaddeq, N., Auwerx, J., Murphy, B., & Schoonjans, K. (2008). Liver receptor homolog 1 is essential for ovulation. *Genes & Development, 22*, 1871–1876.

Duke, L. A., Allen, D. N., Rozee, P. D., & Bommaritto, M. (2008). The sensitivity and specificity of flashbacks and nightmares to trauma. *Journal of Anxiety Disorders, 22(2)*, 319–327.

Du Mont, J. (2009). Factors associated with suspected drug-facilitated sexual assault. *Canadian Medical Association Journal, 180(5)*, 513–519.

Du Mont, J. et al., (2010). Drug-facilitated sexual assault in Ontario, Canada: Toxicological and DNA findings. *Journal of Forensic and Legal Medicine, 17*, 333–338.

Dye, M. L., & Davis, K. E. (2003). Stalking and psychological abuse: Common factors and relationship-specific characteristics. *Violence & Victims, 18(2)*, 163–180.

Eason, E., & Feldman, P. (2000). Much ado about a little cut: Is episiotomy worthwhile? *Obstetrics & Gynecology, 95(4)*, 616–618.

Edgley, K. (2002). Condom use among heterosexual couples. Unpublished doctoral dissertation, University of Ottawa.

Edser, S. J., & Shea, J. D. (2002). An exploratory investigation of bisexual men in monogamous, heterosexual marriages. *Journal of Bisexuality, 2(4)*, 5–29.

Edwards, V. J., Holden, G. W., Felitti, V. J., & Anda, R. F. (2003). Relationship between multiple forms of childhood maltreatment and adult mental health in community respondents: Results from the Adverse Childhood Experiences study. *American Journal of Psychiatry, 160*(8), 1453–1460.

Egale Canada. (2009). Youth speak up about homophobia and transphobia. http://egale.ca/extra/CG_Taylor_Climate_Survey_Phase_One_Report.pdf

EKOS Research Associates. (2010). Canadians decisively pro-choice on abortion. www.ekospolitics.ca

El-Defrawi, M. H., Lotfy, G., Dandash, K. F., Refaat, A. H., & Eyada, M. (2001). Female genital mutilation and its psychosexual impact. *Journal of Sex & Marital Therapy, 27*(5), 465–473.

Elliot, A. J., & Niesta, D. (2008). Romantic red: Red enhances men's attraction to women. *Journal of Personality and Social Psychology, 95*(5), 1150–1164.

Ellis, L., Robb, B., & Burke, D. (2005). Sexual orientation in the United States and Canadian college students. *Archives of Sexual Behavior, 34*(5), 569–581.

Eltahawy, M. (2003, January 9). *Young Africans reject female genital mutilation.* www.feminist.com/news/news141.html.

Eltahawy, M. (2008, August 5). Shame on Egypt's sexist bullies. *The Toronto Globe and Mail*, p. A11.

Epstein, R. (2008). *The Assisted Human Reproduction Act and LGBTQ communities.* A paper submitted by the AHRA/LGBTQ Working Group. Toronto: Sherbourne Health Centre.

Esmail, S., Darry, K., Walter, A., & Knupp, H. (2010). Attitudes and perceptions towards disability and sexuality. *Disability and Rehabilitation, 32*(14), 1148–1155.

Esmail, S., Munro, B., & Gibson, N. (2007). Couple's experience with multiple sclerosis in the context of their sexual relationship. *Sexuality and Disability, 25*(4), 163–177.

Esmail, S., Selman, J., Munro, B., Heather, J., Ponsetti, J., & Knupp, H. (2007). Using theatre to achieve student-centered sexual education. Paper presented at the Annual Conference of the Canadian Sex Research Forum. Banff, AB.

Faller, K. C. (1989). Why sexual abuse? An exploration of the intergenerational hypothesis. *Child Abuse and Neglect, 13*, 543–548.

Fang, L., Oliver, A., Jayaraman, G. C., & Wong, T. (2010). Trends in age disparities between younger and middle-age adults among reported rates of Chlamydia, gonorrhea, and infectious syphilis infections in Canada: findings from 1997 to 2007. Sexually *Transmitted Infections, 37*, 18–25

Farley, M., Lynne, J., & Cotton, A. J. (2005). Prostitution in Vancouver: Violence and the colonization of First Nations Women. *Transcultural Psychiatry, 42(2)*, 242–271.

Fausto-Sterling, A. (May/April 1993). The five sexes: Why male and female are not enough. *The Sciences*, 20–25.

Federoff, J. P. (1995). Antiandrogens vs. serotonergic medications in the treatment of sex offenders: A preliminary compliance study. *Canadian Journal of Human Sexuality, 4*, 111–123.

Federoff, J.P. (2011). Forensic and diagnostic concerns arising from proposed DSM-5 criteria for sexual paraphilic disorder. *The Journal of the American Academy of Psychiatry and the Law*, 39, 238–241.

Fedoroff, J. P., Fishell, A., & Fedoroff, B. (1999). A case series of women evaluated for paraphilic disorders. *The Canadian Journal of Human Sexuality, 8*, 127–140.

Fedoroff, P. (2003). The paraphilic world. In S. B. Levine, C. R. Risen, & S. E. Althof (Eds.), *Handbook of clinical sexuality for mental health professionals* (pp. 333–355). New York: Brunner-Routledge.

Feinberg, D. R., et al. (2006). Menstrual cycle, trait estrogen level, and masculinity preferences in the human voice. *Hormones and Behavior, 49*(2), 215–222.

Fekete, J. (1994*). Moral panic: Biopolitics rising.* Montreal: Robert Davies Publishing.

Felson, R. B. (2002). *Violence and gender reexamined.* Washington, DC: American Psychological Association.

Ferraro, G. (2004). *Cultural anthropology—An applied perspective* (5th ed.). Belmont, CA: Wadsworth.

Festa, E. D., et al. (2004). Sex differences in cocaine-induced behavioral responses, pharmacokinetics, and monoamine levels. *Neuropharmacology, 46*(5), 672–687.

Finkelhor, D. (1990). Early and long-term effects of child sexual abuse: An update. *Professional Psychology: Research and Practice, 21*, 325–330.

Finkelhor, D., Cross, T. P., & Cantor, E. N. (2005a). The justice system for juvenile victims: A comprehensive model of case flow. *Trauma, Violence, & Abuse, 6*(2), 83–102.

Finkelhor, D., Ormrod, R., Turner, H., & Hamby, S. L. (2005b). The victimization of children and youth: A comprehensive, national survey. *Child Maltreatment: Journal of the American Professional Society on the Abuse of Children, 10*(1), 5–25.

Finkelman, J. M. (2005). Sexual harassment: The organizational perspective. In Barnes, A. (Ed.). *The handbook of women, psychology, and the law* (pp. 64–78). New York: John Wiley & Sons.

Firestone, P., Kingston, D. A., Wexler, A., & Bradford, J. M. (2006). Long-term follow-up of exhibitionists: Psychological, phallometric, and offense characteristics. *The Journal of the American Academy of Psychiatry and the Law, 34*, 349–359.

Firestone, R. W., Firestone, L. A., & Catlett, J. (2006a). *Sex and love in intimate relationships.* Washington, DC: American Psychological Association.

Firestone, R. W., Firestone, L. A., & Catlett, J. (2006b). Sexual withholding. In R. W. Firestone, L. A. Firestone, & J. Catlett (Eds.), *Sex and love in intimate relationships* (pp. 171–195). Washington, DC: American Psychological Association.

Fischer, B., Wortley, S., Webster, C., & Kirst, M. (2002). The socio-legal dynamics and implications of "diversion": The case study of the Toronto "john school" diversion programme for prostitution offenders. *Criminal Justice, 2*(4), 385–410.

Fichner-Rathus, L. (2010). *Understanding art* (9th ed.). Belmont, CA: Thomson Learning/Wadsworth.

Fischtein, D. S., & Herold, E. S. (2002, June). *Gender differences in sexual attitudes and behaviours among Canadian adults: A national survey.* Poster session presented at the annual meeting of the International Academy of Sex Research, Hamburg, Germany.

Fisher, B. S., Daigle, L. E., Cullen, F. T., & Turner, M. G. (2003). Reporting sexual victimization to the police and others: Results from a national-level study of college women. *Criminal Justice & Behavior, 30*(1), 6–38.

Fisher, H. E. (2000). Brains do it: Lust, attraction and attachment. *Cerebrum, 2*, 23–42.

Fisher, J. D., & Fisher, W. A. (1992). Changing AIDS-risk behavior. *Psychological Bulletin, 111*, 455–474.

Fisher, W. (2007). Prevention for positives: Development, implementation and evaluation of a clinician-delivered intervention to promote safer sexual behavior among HIV+ patients in clinical care. Paper presented at the Annual Meeting of the Canadian Sex Research Forum, Banff, Alberta.

Fisher, W., Boroditsky, R., & Morris, B. (2004a). The 2002 Canadian contraception study: Part 1. *Journal of Obstetrics and Gynaecology Canada, 26*(6), 580–590.

Fisher, W., Boroditsky, R., & Morris, B. (2004b). The 2002 Canadian contraception study: Part 2. *Journal of Obstetrics and Gynaecology Canada, 26*(7), 646–656.

Fisher, W., et al. (2005). Association of PDE-5 inhibitor use in men with ED and sexual function of partners. Paper presented at the World Congress of Sexology, Montreal.

Fisher, W. A., & Black, A. (2007). Contraception in Canada: A review of method choices, characteristics, adherence and approaches to counselling. *Canadian Medical Association Journal, 176*(7), 953–961.

Fisher, W. A., & Fisher, J. D. (1998). Understanding and promoting sexual and reproductive health behavior: Theory and method. *Annual Review of Sex Research, 9*, 39–76

Fishman, J. R., & Mamo, L. (2001). What's in a disorder: A cultural analysis of medical and pharmaceutical constructions of male and female sexual dysfunction. *Women & Therapy, 24*(1–2), 179–193.

Flicker, S., et al. (2009). *Sexpress: The Toronto Teen Survey Report.* Toronto, ON: Planned Parenthood of Toronto

Fitzpatrick, M. (2010). Future of federal agency uncertain after supreme court fertility ruling. *Post Media News.* December 22, 2010.

Flaxman, S. M., & Sherman, P. W. (2000). Morning sickness: A mechanism for protecting mother and embryo. *The Quarterly Review of Biology, 5*(2), 113–148.

Forbes, A., While, A., Mathes, L., & Griffiths, P. (2006). Health problems and health-related quality of life in people with multiple sclerosis. *Clinical Rehabilitation, 20*(1), 67–78.

Ford, C. S., & Beach, F. A. (1951). *Patterns of sexual behavior.* New York: Harper & Row.

Foubert, J. D., & Newberry, J. T. (2006). Effects of two versions of an empathy-based rape prevention program on fraternity men's survivor empathy, attitudes, and behavioral intent to commit rape or sexual assault. *Journal of College Student Development, 47*(2), 133–148.

Fox, N. S., et al. (2008). Physical and sexual activity during pregnancy and near delivery. *Journal of Women's Health, 17*, 1431.

Franco, E. L., Schlecht, N. F., & Saslow, D. (2003). The epidemiology of cervical cancer. *Cancer Journal, 9*(5), 348–359.

Frank, K. (2002). *G-strings and sympathy: Strip club regulars and male desire.* Raleigh, NC: Duke University Press.

Frank, K. (2003). Just trying to relax: Masculinity, masculinizing practices, and strip club regulars. *The Journal of Sex Research, 40*(1), 61–75.

Frappier, J-Y., et al. (2008). Sex and sexual health: A survey of Canadian youth and mothers. *Pediatric and Child Health, 13*(1), 25–30.

Frayser, S. (1985). *Varieties of sexual experience: An anthropological perspective on human sexuality.* New Haven, CT: Human Relations Area Files Press.

Freeman, N. (2005, June 16). Blatant objectification: Echo's Hot Summer Issue crossed the line. *Echo*, pp. 10–11.

Freud, S. (1922/1959). Analysis of a phobia in a 5-year-old boy. In A. J. Strachey (Ed. & Trans.). *Collected papers* (Vol. 3). New York: Basic Books. (Original work published 1909.)

Freund, K., Watson, R., & Rienzo, D. (1988). The value of self-reports in the study of voyeurism and exhibitionism. *Annals of Sex Research 1*, 243–262.

Fried, P. A., & Smith, A. M. (2001) A literature review of the consequences of prenatal marihuana exposure: An emerging theme of a deficiency in aspects of executive function. Neurotoxicology & Teratology, 23(1), 1–11.

Friedman, R. C., & Downey, J. I. (2001). The Oedipus complex and male homosexuality. In P. Hartocollis (Ed.), *Mankind's Oedipal destiny: Libidinal and aggressive aspects of sexuality* (pp. 113–138). Madison, CT: International Universities Press.

Friedman, R. C., & Downey, J. I. (2008). Sexual differentiation of behavior: The foundation of a developmental model of psychosexuality. *Journal of the American Psychoanalytic Association, 56*(1), 147–175

Friedrich, W. N., & Gerber, P. N. (1994). Autoerotic asphyxia: The development of a paraphilia. *Journal of the American Academy of Child and Adolescent Psychiatry, 33*(7), 970–974.

Frisch, R. E. (2002). Female fertility and the body fat connection. Chicago: University of Chicago Press

Friscolanti, M. (2008, July 29). Taking the handcuffs off to keep track of sex offender. *Maclean's*, 18–21.

Frohlich, P. F., & Meston, C. M. (2005). Tactile sensitivity in women with sexual arousal disorder. *Archives of Sexual Behavior, 34*(2), 207–217.

Frohmader, K. S., Pitchers, K. K. Balfour, M. E., & Coolen, L. M. (2010). Mixing pleasures: review of the effects of drugs on sex behavior in humans and animal models. *Hormones and Behavior, 58*, (1), 149–162.

Fugl–Meyer, K. S., Öberg, K., Lundberg, P. O., Lewin, B., & Fugl–Meyer, A. (2006). On orgasm, sexual techniques, and erotic perceptions in 18- to 74-year-old Swedish women. *Journal of Sexual Medicine, 3*(1), 56–68.

Furnham, A. (2009). Sex differences in mate selection preferences. *Personality and Individual Differences, 47*(4), 262–267.

Gaetz, S. (2004). Safe streets for whom? Homeless youth, social exclusion, and criminal victimization. *Canadian Journal of Criminology & Criminal Justice, 46*(4), 423–455.

Gagnon, J. H. (1977). *Human sexualities.* Glenview, IL: Scott, Foresman.

Gallo, M. F., Grimes, D. A., Lopez, L. M., & Schulz, K. F. (2006). Non-latex versus latex male condoms for contraception. Cochrane Database system Reviews, Jan 25: (1) cd003550

Gallup, O., Boyce, W. F., & Fergus, S. (2009). Non-use of condoms at last sexual intercourse among Canadian youth: influences of sexual partners and social expectations. *The Canadian Journal of Human Sexuality, 18*(1&2), 27–34

Gavin, N. I., et al. (2005). Perinatal depression: A systematic review of prevalence and incidence. *Obstetrics & Gynecology, 106*, 1071–1083.

Gay, P. (1984). *The bourgeois experience: Victoria to Freud.* New York: Oxford University Press.

Gebhard, P. H. (1976). The institute. In M. S. Weinberg (Ed.), *Sex research: Studies from the Kinsey Institute.* New York: Oxford University Press.

Gebhard, P. H., et al. (1965). *Sex offenders: An analysis of types.* New York: Harper & Row.

Geddes, L. (2008). Ultrasound nails location of the elusive G spot. *The New Scientist, 197*(2644), 6–7.

Gemme, R. (1993). Prostitution: A legal, criminological and sexological perspective. *The Canadian Journal of Human Sexuality, 4*, 227–238.

George, W. H., Stoner, S. A., Norris, J., Lopez, P. A., & Lehman, G. L. (2000). Alcohol expectancies and sexuality: A self-fulfilling prophecy analysis of dyadic perceptions and behavior. *Journal of Studies on Alcohol, 61*(1), 168–176.

Gerressu, M., Mercer, C., Graham, C., Wellings, K., & Johnson, M. (2008). Prevalence of masturbation and associated factors in a British National Probability Survey. *Archives of Sexual Behavior, 37,* 266–278.

Gibbons, L., & Waters, C. (2003). Prostate cancer testing. (Statistics Canada Catalogue 82-003). *Health Reports,* 14, 3.

Gibson, V. (2002). *Cougar: A guide for older women dating younger men.* Toronto: Key Porter.

Gidycz, C. A., & Koss, M. P. (1990). A comparison of group and individual sexual assault victims. *Psychology of Women Quarterly, 14,* 325–342.

Gidycz, C. A., Rich, C. L., Orchowski, L., King, C., & Miller, A. K. (2006). The evaluation of a sexual assault self-defense and risk-reduction program for college women: A prospective study. *Psychology of Women Quarterly, 30*(2), 173–186.

Giguere, B., Lalonde, R., & Lou, E. (2010). *Living at the crossroads of cultural worlds:* The experience of normative conflicts by second generation immigrant youth. *Social and Personality Psychology Compass, 4,* 14–49.

Gillis, J. S., & Avis, W. E. (1980). The male-taller norm in mate selection. *Personality and Social Psychology Bulletin, 6,* 396–401.

Gillis, M. (2005, June 16). It's my ass. *Echo,* p. 11.

Gilmore, K. (2008). Birth mother, adoptive mother, dying mother, dead mother. In E. L. Jurist et al. (Eds.), *Mind to mind: Infant research, neuroscience, and psychoanalysis* (pp. 373–397). New York: Other Press.

Girard, D. (2005, June 2). First conviction in sex tourism case. *The Toronto Star.*

Glass, S. P., & Wright, T. L. (1992). Justifications of extramarital relationships: The association between attitudes, behaviors, and gender. *Journal of Sex Research, 29,* 361–387.

Glasser, C., Robnett, B., & Feliciano, C. (2009). Internet daters' body type preferences: Race-ethnic and gender differences. *Sex Roles, 61*(1), 14–33.

Globe & Mail Editorial Board. (2011). The UN coaxes the world toward universal gay rights. *The Globe & Mail,* June 20, 2011.

Godfrey, T. (2003, December 19). Drifter arrested after cow assault. *The Toronto Sun.*

Goldschmidt, L., Day, N. L., & Richardson, G. A. (2000). Effects of prenatal marijuana exposure on child behavior problems at age 10. *Neurotoxicology & Teratology, 22*(3), 325–336.

Goldstein, I. (1998). Cited in Kolata, G. (1998, April 4). Impotence pill: Would it also help women? *The New York Times,* pp. A1, A6.

Goldstein, I., et al. (1998). Oral sildenafil in the treatment of erectile dysfunction. *New England Journal of Medicine, 338,* 1397–1404.

Goldstein, I., & Alexander, J. L. (2005). Practical aspects in the management of vaginal atrophy and sexual dysfunction in perimenopausal and postmenopausal women. *Journal of Sexual Medicine, 2*(Suppl. 3), 154–165.

Goldstein, I., Meston, C., Davis, S., & Traish, A. (Eds.). (2006). *Female sexual dysfunction.* New York: Parthenon.

Golombok, S., et al. (2008). Developmental trajectories of sex-typed behavior in boys and girls: A longitudinal general population study of children aged 2.5–8 Years. *Child Development, 79*(5), 1583–1593.

Goodson, P., McCormick, D., & Evans, A. (2001). Searching for sexually explicit materials on the internet: An exploratory study of college students' behavior and attitudes. *Archives of Sexual Behavior, 30*(2), 101–118.

Goodwin, R. D., Canino, G., Ortega, A. N., & Bird, H. R. (2009). Maternal mental health and childhood asthma among Puerto Rican youth: The role of prenatal smoking. *Journal of Asthma, 46*(7), 726–730.

Gordon, A. E., et al. (2002). Why is smoking a risk factor for sudden infant death syndrome? *Child: Care, Health & Development, 28*(Suppl. 1), 23–25.

Goulet, J. (2006). The "berdache"/"two-spirit": A comparison of anthropological and native constructions of gendered identities among the Northern Athapaskans. *Journal of the Royal Anthropological Institute, 683*(19).

Gouveia, V. V., et al. (2009). Versão abreviada da Escala Triangular do Amor: Evidências de validade fatorial e consistência interna. *Estudos de Psicologia, 14*(1), 31–39.

Gower, P., & Philp, M. (2002a, November 24). Two dads and a family. *The Toronto Star,* pp. A1, A16–A17.

Gower, P., & Philp, M. (2002b, November 27). The curse of alcohol and pregnancy. *The Toronto Star,* pp. A1, A16–A17.

Gray, R., et al. (2009). The role of genital ulcer disease in the efficacy of male circumcision for HIV prevention. Sixteenth Conference on Retroviruses and Opportunistic Diseases. http://www.retroconference.org/2009/PDFs/1063.pdf.

Gray, R. E. et al. (2000). Managing the impact of illness: the experiences of men with prostate cancer and their spouses. *Journal of Health Psychology, 5*(4), 531–548.

Graziano, W. G., & Bruce, J. W. (2008). Attraction and the initiation of relationships. In S. Sprecher, A. Wenzel, & J. Harvey (Eds.), *Handbook of relationship initiation* (pp. 269–296). New York: CRC Press.

Green, R. (2008). Childhood cross-gender behavior and adult homosexuality: Why the link? *Journal of Gay & Lesbian Mental Health, 12*(1), 17–28.

Greenberg, D. M., Firestone, P., Nunes, K. L., Bradford, J. M., & Curry, S. (2005). Biological fathers and stepfathers who molest their daughters: Psychological, phallometric and criminal features. *Sexual Abuse: A Journal of Research and Treatment, 17*(1), 39–46.

Greenwald, E., & Leitenberg, H. (1989). Long-term effects of sexual experiences with siblings and non-siblings during childhood. *Archives of Sexual Behavior, 18,* 389–399.

Grenier, G. (2007). *The 10 conversations you must have before you get married (And how to have them).* Toronto: Key Porter.

Grenier, G., & Byers, E. S. (2001). Operationalizing premature or rapid ejaculation. *Journal of Sex Research, 38,* 369–378.

Griffith, K. H., & Hebl, M. R. (2002). The disclosure dilemma for gay men and lesbians: "Coming out" at work. *Journal of Applied Psychology, 87*(6), 1191–1199.

Gross, B. (2006). The pleasure of pain. *Forensic Examiner, 15*(1), 57–61.

Gross, J. (2006, April 20). Learning to savor a full life, love life included. *The New York Times.*

Groth, A. N., & Birnbaum, H. J. (1979). *Men who rape: The psychology of the offender.* New York: Plenum Press.

Groth, A. W., & Hobson, W. (1983). The dynamics of sexual assault. In L. Schlesinger & E. Revitch. (Eds.). *Sexual dynamics of antisocial behavior.* Springfield, IL: Thomas.

Grov, C., Bimbi, D. S., Nanin, J. E., & Parsons, J. T. (2006). Race, ethnicity, gender, and generational factors associated with the coming-out process among gay, lesbian, and bisexual individuals. *The Journal of Sex Research, 43*(2), 115–121.

Grover, S. et al. (2006). The prevalence of erectile dysfunction in the primary care setting. *Archives of Internal Medicine, 166*, 213–219.

Grubin, D. (2008). Medical models and interventions in sexual deviance. In D. R. Laws and W. T. O'Donohue (Eds.), *Sexual deviance: Theory, assessment, and treatment* (2nd ed., pp. 594–610). New York: Guilford Press.

Gruszecki, L., Forchuk, C., & Fisher, W. A. (2005). Factors associated with common sexual concerns in women: New findings from the Canadian Contraception Study. *The Canadian Journal of Human Sexuality, 14*(1–2), 1–13.

Gutmann, P. (2006). About confusions of the mind due to abnormal conditions of the sexual organs. *History of Psychiatry, 17*(1), 107–111.

Guttmacher Institute. (2009). Various fact sheets. (Accessed November 1, 2009). http://www.guttmacher.org/sections/adolescents.php.

Guzick, D. S., & Hoeger, K. (2000). Sex, hormones, and hysterectomies. *The New England Journal of Medicine* online, *343*(10).

Haake, P., et al. (2003). Acute neuroendocrine response to sexual stimulation in sexual offenders. *Canadian Journal of Psychiatry, 48*(4), 265–271.

Hackett, G. I. (2008). Disorders of male sexual desire. In D. L. Rowland & L. Incrocci (Eds.), *Handbook of sexual and gender identity disorders.* Hoboken, NJ: Wiley.

Hald, G., & Malmuth, N. (2008). Self-perceived effects of pornography consumption. *Archives of Sexual Behavior. 37*, 614–625.

Haley, N., Roy, E., Leclerc, P., Boudreau, J. F., & Boivin, J. F. (2004). HIV risk profile of male street youth involved in survival sex. *Sexually Transmitted Infections, 80*(6), 526–530.

Hallgrimsdottir, H. K., Phillips, R., & Benoit, C. (2006). Fallen women and rescued girls: Social stigma and media narratives of the sex industry in Victoria, B. C., from 1980–2005. *The Canadian Review of Sociology and Anthropology, 43*(3), 265–280.

Halpern, D. F. (2003). Sex differences in cognitive abilities. *Applied Cognitive Psychology, 17*(3), 375–376.

Hamann, S., Herman, R. A., Nolan, C. L., & Wallen, K. (2004). Men and women differ in amygdala response to visual sexual stimuli. *Nature Neuroscience, 7*(4), 411–416.

Hamer, D. H., et al. (1993, July 16). A linkage between DNA markers on the X chromosome and male sexual orientation. *Science, 261*, 321–327.

Hammack, P. L., & Cohler, B. J. (2009). *The story of sexual identity.* New York: Oxford University Press.

Hampton, M. R., Jeffery, B., McWatters, B., & Smith, P. (2005). Influence of teens' perceptions of parental disapproval and peer behaviour on their initiation of sexual intercourse. *The Canadian Journal of Human Sexuality, 14*(3–4), 105–121.

Hanson, R. K., Gordon, A., Harris, A. J. R., et al. (2002). First report of the collaborative outcome data project on the effectiveness of psychological treatment for sex offenders. *Sexual Abuse, 14*, 155–168.

Hardwick, D., & Patchuck, D. (1999). Geographic mapping demonstrates the association between social inequality, teen births, and STDs among youth. *Canadian Journal of Human Sexuality, 8*, 77–89.

Harris, M. & Johnson, O. (2000). *Cultural Anthropology.* Needham Heights, MA: Allyn & Bacon.

Harte, C. B., Rand, M., Adkins, R., & Meston, C. (2007). Gender-differential subjective sexual arousal patterns to diverse sexual stimuli. Paper presented at the annual meeting of the International Academy of Sex Research, Vancouver, British Columbia.

Hartwick, C., Desmarais, S., & Hennig, K. (2007). Characteristics of male and female victims of sexual coercion. *The Canadian Journal of Human Sexuality, 16*(1–2), 31–44.

Haselton, M. G., Mortezaie, M., Pillsworth, E. G., Bleske-Rechek, A., & Frederick, D. A. (2007). Ovulatory shifts in human female ornamentation: Near ovulation, women dress to impress. *Hormones and Behavior, 51*(1), 40–45.

Hatcher, R. (2006). *Contraceptive Technology Update.* 18th Ed. New York: Ardent Media.

Hatcher, R. A., Trussell, J., Nelson, A. L., Cates, W., Stewart, F., & Kowal, D. (Eds.) (2007). *Contraceptive technology,* 19th rev. ed. New York: Ardent Media.

Hatcher, R. A., et al. (2008). *Contraceptive technology* (19th ed.). New York: Ardent Media.

Hatfield, E. (1988). Passionate and companionate love. In R. J. Sternberg & M. L. Barnes (eds.), *The psychology of love* (pp. 191–217). New Haven, CT: Yale University Press.

Hatfield, E., Pillemer, J. T., O'Brien, M. U., & Le, Y-C. L. (2008). The endurance of love: Passionate and companionate love in newlywed and long-term marriages. Interpersona 2(1), 35–64.

Hatfield, E., & Rapson, R. L. (2002). Passionate love and sexual desire: Cultural and historical perspectives. In A. L. Vangelisti, H. T. Reis, et al. (Eds.), *Stability and change in relationships: Advances in personal relationships* (pp. 306–324). New York: Cambridge University Press.

Hatzichristou, D. G., et al. (2000). Sildenafil versus intracavernous injection therapy: Efficacy and preference in patients on intracaverous injection for more than 1 year. *The Journal of Urology, 164*, 1197–1200.

Hatzichristou, D. G., et al. (2005). Vardenafil improves satisfaction rates, depressive symptomatology, and self-confidence in a broad population of men with erectile dysfunction. *Journal of Sexual Medicine, 2*(1), 109–116.

Haubrich, D. J., Myers, T., Calzavara, L., Ryder, K., & Medved, W. (2004). Gay and bisexual men's experiences of bathhouse culture and sex: "Looking for love in all the wrong places." *Culture, Health & Sexuality, 6*(1), 19–29.

Haugaard, J. J. (2000). The challenge of defining child sexual abuse. *American Psychologist, 55*(9), 1036–1039.

Hayes, R., & Dennerstein, L. (2005). The impact of aging on sexual function and sexual dysfunction in women: A review of population-based studies. *Journal of Sexual Medicine, 2*(3), 317–330.

Health Canada. (2001). Sexually transmitted diseases data tables. Division of Sexual Health Promotion and STD Prevention and Control, Bureau of HIV/AIDS, STD & TB. Ottawa: Health Canada.

Health24.com. (2006, February 10). *The girl child.* [Online]. www.health24.com/sex/sexuality_throughout_life

Heil, P., & Simons, D. (2008). Multiple paraphilias: Prevalence, etiology, assessment, and treatment. In D. R. Laws and W. T. O'Donohue (Eds.), *Sexual deviance: Theory, assessment, and treatment* (2nd ed., pp. 527–556). New York: Guilford Press.

Heiman, J. R. (2008). Treating low sexual desire—New findings for testosterone in women. *New England Journal of Medicine, 359*(19), 2047–2049.

Hellstrom, W. J. G., Nehra, A., Shabsigh, R., & Sharlip, I. D. (2006). Premature ejaculation: The most common male sexual dysfunction. *Journal of Sexual Medicine, 3*(Suppl. 1), 1–3.

Henderson, A. W., Lehavot, K., & Simoni, J. M. (2009). Ecological models of sexual satisfaction among lesbian/bisexual and heterosexual women. *Archives of Sexual Behavior, 38*(1), 50–65.

Hendrick, C., & Hendrick, S. (1986). A theory and method of love. *Journal of Personality and Social Psychology, 50,* 392–402.

Hendrick, C., & Hendrick, S. (2003). Romantic love: Measuring Cupid's arrow. In S. Lopez & C. R. Snyder (Eds.), *Positive psychological assessment: A handbook of models and measures* (pp. 235–249). Washington, DC: American Psychological Association.

Hendrick, C., & Hendrick, S. (Eds.) (2000). *Close relationships: A sourcebook.* Thousand Oaks, CA: Sage.

Hendrick, S. S., & Hendrick, C. (2002). Love. In C. R. Snyder & S. J. Lopez (Eds.). *Handbook of positive psychology* (pp. 472–484). London: Oxford University Press.

Henry J. Kaiser Family Foundation. (2009). The global HIV/AIDS epidemic. www.kff.org/hivaids/3030.cfm

Herbenick, D., et al. (2010). Sexual behavior in the United States: results from a national probability sample of men and women ages 14–94. *Journal of Sexual Medicine,* 7(Suppl 5), 255–265.

Herold, E. S. (1984). *Sexual behaviour of Canadian young people.* Markham, ON: Fitzhenry & Whiteside.

Herold, E. S., Corbesi, B., & Collins, J. (1994). Psychosocial aspects of female topless behavior on Australian beaches. *Journal of Sex Research, 31,* 133–142.

Herold, E. S., & Way, L. (1988). Sexual self-disclosure among university women. *Journal of Sex Research, 24,* 1–14.

Herrera, V. M., & McCloskey, L. A. (2003). Sexual abuse, family violence, and female delinquency: Findings from a longitudinal study. *Violence & Victims,* 18(3), 319–334.

Hester, J. D. (2005). Eunuchs and the postgender Jesus: Matthew 19:12 and transgressive sexualities. *Journal for the Study of the New Testament,* 28(1), 13–40.

Hill, R. A., Donovan, S., & Koyama, N. F. (2005). Female sexual advertisement reflects resource availability in twentieth-century UK society. *Human Nature,* 16(3), 266–277.

Hill, T. (2005). Female sexual frustration. Unpublished M.A. thesis, University of Guelph.

Hines, D. A., & Saudino, K. J. (2003). Gender differences in psychological, physical, and sexual aggression among college students using the Revised Conflict Tactics Scales. *Violence & Victims,* 18(2), 197–217.

Hines, T. M. (2001). The G-spot: A modern gynecological myth. *American Journal of Obstetrics and Gynecology,* 185(2), 359–362.

Hird, M. J. (2004). Naturally queer. *Feminist Theory,* 5(1), 85–89.

Hird, M. J. (2006). Sex diversity and evolutionary psychology. *The Psychologist,* 19(1), 30–32.

Hogg, R. S., Yip, B., Chan, K. J., Wood, E., Craib, K. J., O'Shaughnessy, M. V., & Montaner, J. S. (2001). Rates of disease progression by baseline CD4 cell count and viral load after initiating triple-drug therapy. *Journal of the American Medical Association,* 286(20), 2568–2577.

Holmberg, D. Blair, K.L. (2009). Sexual desire, communication, satisfaction, and preferences of men and women in same-sex relationships. *Journal of Sex Research, 46,* 57–66.

Holmberg, D., Blair, K. L., & Phillips, M. (2009). Women's sexual satisfaction as a predictor of well-being in same-sex versus mixed-sex relationships. *Journal of Sex Research,* 1559–8519.

Holmes, D., O'Byrne, P. & Gastaldo, D. (2007). Setting the space: architecture, desire and health issues in gay bathhouses. *International Journal of Nursing Studies, 44,* 273–284.

Holmes, D., & Warner, D. (2005). The anatomy of a forbidden desire: Men, penetration and semen exchange. *Nursing Inquiry,* 12(1), 10–20.

Holmes, S. T., & Holmes, R. M. (2002). *Sex crimes.* Thousand Oaks, CA: Sage Publications.

Holmstrom, A. J. (2009). Sex and gender similarities and differences in communication values in same-sex and cross-sex friendships. *Communication Quarterly,* 57(2), 224–238.

Honeycutt, J. M., & Cantrill, G. (2001). *Cognition, communication, and romantic relationships.* Mahwah, NJ: Erlbaum.

Horowitz, H. L. (2002). Rereading sex: Battles over sexual knowledge and suppression in nineteenth-century America. New York: Knopf.

Howard-Hassmann, R. E. (2001). The gay cousin: Learning to accept gay rights. *Journal of Homosexuality,* 42(1), 127–149.

Huber, J. D., & Herold, E. (2006). Sexually overt approaches in singles bars. *Canadian Journal of Human Sexuality,* 15(3–4), 233–146.

Hucker, S. J. (2008). Sexual masochism: Psychopathology and theory. In D. R. Laws and W. T. O'Donohue (Eds.), *Sexual deviance: Theory, assessment, and treatment* (2nd ed., pp. 250–263). New York: Guilford Press.

Humphreys, T. (2007a). The complexity of sexual consent negotiations. Paper presented at the Annual Guelph Conference on Human Sexuality, Guelph, Ontario.

Hugh-Jones, S., Gough, B., & Littlewood, A. (2005). Sexual exhibitionism as "sexuality and individuality": A critique of psycho-medical discourse from the perspectives of women who exhibit. *Sexualities,* 8(3), 259–281.

Humphreys, T., DeCicco, T., King, D., & Kartes, K. (2007). Sex dreams & waking sexual activity: Is there a connection? Poster session presented at the Annual Meeting of the Society for the Scientific Study of Sexuality. Indianapolis, IN.

Humphreys, T., & Herold, E. (2003). Should universities and colleges mandate sexual behavior: Student perceptions of Antioch college's consent policy. *Journal of Psychology and Human Sexuality, 15,* 35–52.

Humphreys, T., & Herold, E. (2007). Sexual consent in heterosexual relationships: Development of a new measure. *Sex Roles, 57,* 305–315.

Humphreys, T., & Newby, J. (2007). Initiating new sexual behaviours in heterosexual relationships. *The Canadian Journal of Human Sexuality,* 16(3–4), 77–88.

Humphreys, T. P. (2004). Understanding sexual consent: An empirical investigation of the normative script for young heterosexual adults. In M. Cowling & P. Reynolds (Eds.), *Making sense of sexual consent.* Aldershot, UK: Ashgate.

Hussain, A. (2002, June 26). It's official: Men really are afraid of commitment. Reuters.

Imperato-McGinley, J., et al. (1974). Steroid 5 reductase deficiency in man: An inherited form of male pseudohermaphroditism. *Science, 186,* 1213–1215.

Intersex Society of North America. Accessed August 22, 2006. www.isna.org.

Info Reports. (2005). *World health organization updates guidance on how to use contraceptives,* 4.

Ipsos. (2010). Ipsos Global@dvisory: *Is Religion a Force for Good in the World?* Combined Population of 23 Major Nations Evenly Divided in Advance of Blair, Hitchens. http://www.ip505-na.com

Isaacs, C. R., & Fisher, W. A. (2008). A computer-based educational intervention to address potential negative effects of internet pornography. *Communication Studies,* 59(1), 1–18.

Jacobs, S. (2007). The characteristics and perceptions of women who visit adult retail stores. Unpublished master's thesis, University of Guelph.

Jamison, P. L., & Gebhard, P. H. (1988). Penis size increase between flaccid and erect states: An analysis of the Kinsey data. *Journal of Sex Research, 24,* 177–183.

Jannini, E., G. Gravina 1, F. Brandetti 1, P. Martini 1, E. Carosa, et al. (2008). In vivo measurement of the human G-spot. *Sexologies, 17*(S1), S52–S53.

Jansen, E., McBride, K., & Yarber, W. (2008). Factors that influence sexual arousal in men: A focus group study. *Journal of Sex Research, 37,* 252–265.

Janssen, E. (Ed.). (2006). *The psychophysiology of sex.* Bloomington, IN: Indiana University Press.

Janssen, E., & Bancroft, J. (2006). The dual-control model: The role of sexual inhibition & excitation in sexual arousal and behavior. In Janssen, E. (Ed.), *The psychophysiology of sex.* Bloomington, IN: Indiana University Press.

Javed, N. (2008, May 24). GTA's secret world of polygamy. *Toronto Star,* p. A10.

Jeffrey, L. A., & MacDonald, G. (2006). "It's the money, honey": The economy of sex work in the Maritimes. *Canadian Review of Sociology & Anthropology, 43*(3), 113–327.

Johannes, C. B., et al. (2000). Incidence of erectile dysfunction in men 40 to 69 years old: Longitudinal results from the Massachusetts male aging study. *The Journal of Urology, 163,* 460.

Johns, A., & Lush, G. (2004). *Adolescent sexual decision-making in Newfoundland and Labrador.* St. Johns, NF: Planned Parenthood Newfoundland and Labrador.

Johnson, C., Remple, V., & Bungay, V. (2007). Inconsistent condom use by indoor commercial sex workers (CSW) in Vancouver, British Columbia: A quantitative and qualitative study. Paper presented at the CAHR Conference, Toronto, Ontario.

Johnson, H. (2003). The cessation of assaults on wives. *Journal of Comparative Family Studies, 34*(1), 75–91.

Johnstone, S. J., et al. (2001). Obstetric risk factors for postnatal depression in urban and rural community samples. *Australian & New Zealand Journal of Psychiatry, 35*(1), 69–74.

Jonason, P. K., Li, N. P., Webster, G. D., & Schmitt, D. P. (2009). The dark triad: Facilitating a short-term mating strategy in men. *European Journal of Personality, 23*(1), 5–18.

Kaczmarek, P., LeVine, E., & Segal, A. F. (2006). Section 6. Civil and criminal trial matters. In P. Kaczmarek, E. LeVine, & A. F. Segal (Eds.) *Law & mental health professionals: New Mexico* (pp. 269–296). Washington, DC: American Psychological Association.

Kaestle, C. (2007). Sexual behaviors of opposite sex couples through emerging adulthood. *Perspectives on Sexual and Reproductive Health, 39,* 134–140.

Kafka, M. P. (2003). Sex offending and sexual appetite: The clinical and theoretical relevance of hypersexual desire. *International Journal of Offender Therapy & Comparative Criminology, 47*(4), 439–451.

Kafka, M.P. (2010). Hypersexual disorder: a proposed diagnosis for DSM-V. *Archives of Sexual Behavior, 39,* 377–400.

Kaler, A. (2005). Peer commentaries on Binik (2005): Classifying pain: What's at stake for women with dyspareunia. *Archives of Sexual Behavior, 34*(1), 34–36.

Kaplan, H. S. (1974). *The new sex therapy: Active treatment of sexual dysfunctions.* New York: Brunner/Mazel.

Kaplan, H. S. (1987). *Sexual aversion, sexual phobias, and panic disorder.* New York: Brunner/Mazel.

Karakiewicz, P. I., Tanguay, S., Kattan, M. W., Elhilali, M. M., & Aprikian, A. G. (2004). Erectile and urinary dysfunction after radical prostatectomy for prostate cancer in Quebec: A population-based study of 2415 men. *European Urology, 46*(2), 188–194.

Katzman, D. K., & Taddeo, D. (2010). Emergency contraception. *Pediatrics and Child Health, 15* (6), 363–367.

Kaufman, A., et al. (1980). Male rape victims: Noninstitutionalized assault. *American Journal of Psychiatry, 137,* 221–223.

Kaufman, M., Silverberg, C., & Odette, F. (2007). *The ultimate guide to sex and disability.* San Francisco, CA: Cleis Press.

Kellogg, J. H. (1881). *Plain facts for old and young.* Burlington, IA: Segner and Condit.

Kennedy, M. A., & Gorzalka, B. B. (2002). Asian and non-Asian attitudes toward rape, sexual harassment, and sexuality. *Sex Roles, 46*(7–8), 227–238.

Kennedy, M. A., Gorzalka, B. B., & Yuille, J. C. (2003). Prostitution myths held by consumers of the sex trade. Paper presented at annual meeting of American Psychological Association, Toronto.

Kennedy, S. H., & Rizvi, S. (2009). Sexual dysfunction, depression, and the impact of antidepressants. *Journal of Clinical Psychopharmacology, 29*(2), 157–164.

Kimble, D. P. (1992). *Biological psychology* (2nd ed.). Fort Worth, TX: Harcourt.

King, A. J. C., Beazley, R. P., Warren, W. K., Hankins, C. A., Robertson, A. S., & Radford, J. L. (1989). Highlights from the Canada youth and AIDS study. *Journal of School Health, 59*(4), 139–145.

King, D. B., DeCicco, T. L., & Humphreys, T. P. (2009). Investigating sexual dream imagery in relation to daytime sexual behaviours and fantasies among Canadian university students. *The Canadian Journal of Human Sexuality, 18*(3), 135–146.

King, M. (2008). A systematic review of mental disorder, suicide, and deliberate self harm in lesbian, gay and bisexual people. *BMC Psychiatry,* 8. http://www. biomedcentral. com/1471244X/8/70. (Accessed October 15, 2009).

King, R., Belsky, J., Mah, K., & Binik, Y. (2010). Are there different types of female orgasm? *Archives of Sexual Behavior,* [E-pub ahead of print].

Kingston, A. (2009). The sexting scare. *Macleans,* March 12, 2009.

Kingston, D. A., Fedoroff, P., Firestone, P., Curry, S., & Bradford, J. M. (2008). Pornography use and sexual aggression: The impact of frequency and type of pornography use on recidivism among sexual offenders. *Aggressive Behavior, 34*(4), 341–351.

Kinsey, A. C., Pomeroy, W. B., & Martin, C. E. (1948). *Sexual behavior in the human male.* Philadelphia: W. B. Saunders.

Kinsey, A. C., Pomeroy, W. B., Martin, C. E., & Gebhard, P. H. (1953). *Sexual behavior in the human female.* Philadelphia: W. B. Saunders.

Kinsman, G. (1996). *The regulation of desire: Sexuality in Canada.* Montreal: Black Rose Books.

Kippax, S., & Smith, G. (2001). Anal intercourse and power in sex between men. *Sexualities, 4*(4), 413–434.

Kirby, D., Laris, B. A., & Rolleri, L. (2007). Sex and HIV education programs: Their impact on sexual behaviors of young people throughout the world. *Journal of Adolescent Health, 40,* 206–217

Kirenskaya–Berus, A. V., & Tkachenko, A. A. (2003). Characteristic features of EEG spectral characteristics in persons with deviant sexual behavior. *Human Physiology, 29*(3), 278–287.

Kirkpatrick, R. C. (2000). The evolution of human homosexual behavior. *Current Anthropology, 41*(3), 385–413.

Kito, M. (2005). Self-disclosure in romantic relationships and friendships among American and Japanese college students. *Journal of Social Psychology, 145*(2), 127–140.

Kjerulff, K. H., et al. (2000). Effectiveness of hysterectomy. *Obstetrics & Gynecology, 95*, 319–326.

Klein, R., & Knäuper, B. (2002). The role of suppression, inquiry, and mental representations of condoms in condom discontinuation. Paper presented at the annual meeting of the Canadian Sex Research Forum, Toronto.

Klein, R., & Knäuper, B. (2003). The role of cognitive avoidance of STIs for discussing safer sex practices and for condom use consistency. *Canadian Journal of Human Sexuality, 12*(3–4), 137.

Kleinplatz, P. et al. (2009). The components of optimal sexuality: A portrait of "great sex". *The Canadian Journal of Human Sexuality, 18*(1-2), 1–13

Kleinplatz, P. J. (2003). What's new in sex therapy? From stagnation to fragmentation. *Sexual & Relationship Therapy, 18*(1), 95–106.

Kleinplatz, P. J. (Ed.) (2001). *New directions in sex therapy: Innovations and alternatives.* New York: Brunner-Routledge.

Kleinplatz, P. J., & Krippner, S. (2007). Spirituality and sexuality: Celebrating erotic transcendence and spiritual embodiment. In Kleinplatz, P. J., & Moser, C. (2005). Is SM pathological? *Lesbian & Gay Psychology Review, 6*(3), 255–260.

Kleinplatz, P.J. et al. (2009). The components of optimal sexuality: a portrait of "great sex." *The Canadian Journal of Human Sexuality, 18(1-2),* 1–13.

Kline, D., Gold, F., Canso, D., Winsor, Y., Stevenson, J., Taylor, D., Ogilvie, G., & Rekart, M. (2007). *Feasibility and acceptability of conducting research with male patrons of female sex workers.* Vancouver: BC Centre for Disease Control.

Klusmann, D. (2002). Sexual motivation and the duration of partnership. *Archives of Sexual Behavior, 31*, 275–287.

Klüver, H., & Bucy, P. C. (1939). Preliminary analysis of functions of the temporal lobes in monkeys. *Archives of Neurology and Psychiatry, 42*, 979.

Knaak, S. (2005). Breast-feeding, bottle-feeding and Dr. Spock: The shifting context of choice. *Canadian Review of Sociology and Anthropology, 42*(2), 197–216.

Knapp, M. L., & Vangelisti, A. L. (2000). *Interpersonal communication and human relationships* (4th ed.). Boston: Allyn & Bacon.

Knäuper, B., Aydin, C., Atkinson, K., Guberman, C., & Kornik, R. (2002). Paper presented at the annual meeting of the Canadian Sex Research Forum, Toronto.

Knäuper, B., Kornik, R., Atkinson, K., Guberman, C., & Aydin, C. (2005). Motivation influences the underestimation of cumulative risk. *Personality and Social Psychology Bulletin, 31*(11), 1511–1523.

Kniffin, K. M., & Wilson, D. S. (2004). The effect of nonphysical traits on the perception of physical attractiveness: Three naturalistic studies. *Evolution and Human Behavior, 25*(2), 88–101.

Knox, D., Schacht, C., & Zusman, M. E. (1999). Love relationships among college students. *College Student Journal, 31*(4), 445–448.

Koch, P. B., Mansfield, P. K., Thurau, D., & Carey, M. (2005). "Feeling frumpy": The relationships between body image and sexual response changes in midlife women. *The Journal of Sex Research, 42*(3), 215–224.

Kohlberg, L. (1966). A cognitive-developmental analysis of children's sex-role concepts and attitudes. In E. E. Maccoby (Ed.), *The development of sex differences.* Stanford, CA: Stanford University Press.

Kohler, R. K., Manhart, L. E., & Lafferty, W. E. (2008). Abstinence-only and comprehensive sex education and the initiation of sexual activity and teen pregnancy. *Journal of Adolescent Health, 42*, 344–351

Komisaruk, B. R., & Whipple, B. (2005). Brain activity imaging during sexual response in women with spinal cord injury. In Hyde, J. S. (Ed.), *Biological substrates of human sexuality* (pp. 109–145). Washington, DC: American Psychological Association.

Koo, M. M., Rohan, T. E., Jain, M., McLaughlin, J. R., & Corey, P. N. (2002). A cohort study of dietary fibre intake and menarche. *Public Health Nutrition, 5*(2), 353–360.

Koren, G., Pastuszak, A., & Ito, S. (1998). Drug therapy: Drugs in pregnancy. *New England Journal of Medicine, 338*, 1128–1137.

Korobov, N., & Thorne, A. (2006). Intimacy and distancing: Young men's conversations about romantic relationships. *Journal of Adolescent Research, 21*(1), 27–55.

Koss, M. P. (2003). Evolutionary models of why men rape: Acknowledging the complexities. In Travis, C. B. (Ed.), *Evolution, gender, and rape* (pp. 191–205). Cambridge, MA: MIT Press.

Koss, M. P., Bailey, J. A., Yuan, N. P., Herrera, V. M., & Lichter, E. L. (2003). Depression and PTSD in survivors of male violence: Research and training initiatives to facilitate recovery. *Psychology of Women Quarterly, 27*(2), 130–142.

Krahe, B., Waizenhofer, E., & Moller, I. (2003). Women's sexual aggression against men: Prevalence and predictors. *Sex Roles, 49*(5–6), 219–232.

Kramer, M. S., et al. (2000). The contribution of mild and moderate preterm birth to infant mortality. *Journal of the American Medical Association, 284*, 843–849.

Kristof, N. D. (2006, January 22). Slavery in our time. *The New York Times*, Section 4, p. 17.

Kuhnle, U., Krob, G., & Maier, E. (2003). True hermaphroditism: Presentation, management, outcomes. *Endocrinologist, 13*(3), 214–218.

Kuiper, B., & Cohen–Kettenis, P. (1988). Sex reassignment surgery: A study of 141 Dutch transsexuals. *Archives of Sexual Behavior, 17*, 439–457.

Kukkonen, T. M., Binik, Y. M., Amsel, R., & Carrier, S. (2007). Thermography as a physiological measure of sexual arousal in both men and women. *Journal of Sexual Medicine, 4*, 93–105.

Kulik, L. (2000). Gender identity, sex typing of occupations, and gender role ideology among adolescents: Are they related? *International Journal for the Advancement of Counselling, 22*(1), 43–56.

Kurdek, L. A. (2005). What do we know about gay and lesbian couples? *Current Directions in Psychological Science, 14*(5), 251–254.

Kurdek, L. A. (2006). Differences between partners from heterosexual, gay, and lesbian cohabiting couples. *Journal of Marriage and Family, 68*(2), 509–528.

Kurzban, R., & Weeden, J. (2005). HurryDate: Mate preferences in action. *Evolution and Human Behavior, 26*(3), 227–244.

Lamanna, M. A. & Riedmann. (2005). *Marriages and Families: Making choices in a diverse society.* Wadsworth Publishing.

LaMarre, A. K., Paterson, L. Q., & Gorzalka, B. B. (2003). Breastfeeding and postpartum maternal sexual functioning: A review. *Canadian Journal of Human Sexuality, 12*(3–4), 151–168.

Lamaze, F. (1981). *Painless childbirth.* New York: Simon & Schuster.

Lalonde, R. N., Hynie, M., Pannu, M., & Tatla, S. (2004). The role of culture in interpersonal relationships: Do second generation South Asian Canadians want a traditional partner? *Journal of Cross-Cultural Psychology, 35*(5), 503–524.

Lalumière, M. L., Blanchard, R., & Zucker, K. J. (2000). Sexual orientation and handedness in men and women: A meta-analysis. *Psychological Bulletin 126*(4), 575–592.

Lalumière, M. L., Harris, G. T., Quinsey, V. L., & Rice, M. E. (1998). Sexual deviance and number of older brothers among sex offenders. *Sexual Abuse, 10,* 5–15.

Lalumière, M. L., Harris, G. T., Quinsey, V. L., & Rice, M. E. (2005a). Introduction. In M. L. Lalumière, G. T. Harris, V. L. Quinsey, & M. E. Rice (Eds.), *The causes of rape: Understanding individual differences in male propensity for sexual aggression* (pp. 3–6). Washington, DC: American Psychological Association.

Lalumière, M. L., Harris, G. T., Quinsey, V. L., & Rice, M. E. (2005b). Antisociality and mating effort. In M. L. Lalumière, G. T. Harris, V. L. Quinsey, & M. E. Rice (Eds.), *The causes of rape: Understanding individual differences in male propensity for sexual aggression* (pp. 61–103). Washington, DC: American Psychological Association.

Landolt, M. A., Bartholomew, K., Saffrey, C., Oram, D., & Perlman, D. (2004). Gender nonconformity, childhood rejection, and adult attachment: A study of gay men. *Archives of Sexual Behavior, 33*(2), 117–128.

Lane, R., & Thayer, J. (2008). Sexual dysfunction and coronary artery disease. *The American Journal of Medicine, 121(4),* 256–257.

Lang, D. (2007). Association between recent gender-based violence and pregnancy, sexually transmitted infections, condom use and negotiation of safe sex practices among HIV+ women. *Journal of Acquired Immune Deficiency Syndrome, 46,* 216–221.

Langevin, R. (2003). A study of the psychosexual characteristics of sex killers: Can we identify them before it is too late? *International Journal of Offender Therapy & Comparative Criminology, 47*(4), 366–382.

Langevin, R. (2006). Acceptance and completion of treatment among sex offenders. *International Journal of Offender Therapy and Comparative Criminology, 50*(4), 402–417.

Langevin, R., Langevin, M., Curnoe, S., & Bain, J. (2006). Generational substance abuse among male sexual offenders and paraphilics. *Victims & Offenders, 1*(4), 395–409.

Langevin, R., et al. (1979). Experimental studies of the etiology of genital exhibitionism. *Archives of Sexual Behavior, 8,* 307–332.

Langhinrichsen–Rohling, J., Palarea, R. E., Cohen, J., & Rohlin, M. L. (2002). Breaking up is hard to do: Unwanted pursuit behaviors following the dissolution of a romantic relationship. In K. E. Davis, & I. H. Frieze, et al. (Eds.), *Stalking: Perspectives on victims and perpetrators* (pp. 212–236). New York: Springer.

Langlois, J. H., et al. (2000). Maxims or myths of beauty? A meta-analytic and theoretical review. *Psychological Bulletin, 126*(3), 390–423.

Laqueur, T. W. (2003). Solitary sex: A cultural history of masturbation. Zone Books. www.newzonebooks.com.

Långström, N., & Seto, M. (2006). Exhibitionistic and voyeuristic behavior in a Swedish national population survey. *Archives of Sexual Behavior, 35,* 427–435.

Långström, N., & Zucker, K. J. (2005). Transvestic fetishism in the general population: Prevalence and correlates. *Journal of Sex & Marital Therapy, 31*(2), 87–95.

La Rose, L. (2008, February 13). Most believe in love at first sight, survey suggests. *Toronto Star.*

Larsson, I., & Svedin, C. (2002). Experiences in childhood: Young adults' recollections. *Archives of Sexual Behavior, 31*(3), 263–273.

Laumann, E. O., et al. (2006). A cross-national study of subjective sexual well-being among older women and men: Findings from the global study of sexual attitudes and behaviors. *Archives of Sexual Behavior, 35*(2), 145–161.

Laumann, E. O., Gagnon, J. H., Michael, R. T., & Michaels, S. (1994). *The social organization of sexuality: Sexual practices in the United States.* Chicago: University of Chicago Press.

Laumann, E. O., Nicolosi, A., Glasser, D. B., Paik, A., Gingell, C., Moreira, E., et al. (2005). Sexual problems among women and men aged 40–80: Prevalence and correlates identified in the global study of sexual attitudes and behaviors. *International Journal of Impotence Research, 17*(1), 39.

Laurent, S. M., & Simons, A. D. (2009). Sexual dysfunction in depression and anxiety: Conceptualizing sexual dysfunction as part of an internalizing dimension. *Clinical Psychology Review.*

Lavin, M. (2008). Voyeurism: Psychopathology and theory. In D. R. Laws and W. T. O'Donohue (Eds.), *Sexual deviance: Theory, assessment, and treatment* (2nd ed., pp. 305–319). New York: Guilford Press.

Lawrence, A. (2007). Cultural differences in individualism predict prevalence of non-homosexual male-to-female transsexualism. Paper presented at the Annual Meeting of the International Academy of Sex Research. Vancouver.

Lawrence, A., Latty, E., Chivers, M., & Bailey, J. M. (2005). Measurement of sexual arousal in postoperative male-to-female transsexuals using vaginal photoplethysmography. *Archives of Sexual Behavior, 34*(2), 135–145.

Lawrence, A. A. (2004). Autogynephilia: A paraphilic model of gender identity disorder. *Journal of Gay & Lesbian Psychotherapy, 8*(1–2), 69–87.

Lawrence, K., & Byers, E. S. (1995). Sexual satisfaction in long-term heterosexual relationships: The interpersonal exchange model of sexual satisfaction. *Personal Relationships, 2,* 267–285.

Laws, D. R., & Marshall, W. L. (2003). A brief history of behavioral and cognitive behavioral approaches to sexual offenders: Part 1. Early developments. *Sexual Abuse: Journal of Research & Treatment, 15*(2), 75–92.

Laws, D. R., & O'Donohue, W. T. (2008). Introduction. *Sexual deviance: Theory, assessment, and treatment* (2nd ed., pp. 1–20). New York: Guilford Press.

Lederman, M. M., & Valdez, H. (2000). Immune restoration with antiretroviral therapies: Implications for clinical management. *Journal of the American Medical Association, 284,* 223–228.

Leger Marketing. (2010). Cialis on Demand Study. www.legermarketing.com

Leiblum, S., & Chivers, M. (2007). Normal and persistent genital arousal in women: New perspectives. *Journal of Sex & Marital Therapy, 33*(4), 357–373.

Lehne, G. K. (2009). Phenomenology of paraphilia: Lovemap theory. In F. M. Saleh et al. (Eds.), *Sex offenders: Identification, risk assessment, treatment, and legal issue* (pp. 12–26). New York: Oxford University Press.

Leinders–Zufall, T., et al. (2000). Ultrasensitive pheromone detection by mammalian vomeronasal neurons. *Nature, 405,* 792–796.

Leitenberg, H., Detzer, M. J., & Srebnik, D. (1993). Gender differences in masturbation and the relation of masturbation experience in preadolescence and/or early adolescence to sexual behavior and sexual adjustment in young adulthood. *Archives of Sexual Behavior, 22,* 87–98

Iemmola, F., & Ciani, A. C. (2009). New evidence of genetic factors influencing sexual orientation in men: Female fecundity increase in the maternal line. *Archives of Sexual Behavior, 38*(3), 393–399.

Lepischak, B. (2004). Building community for Toronto's lesbian, gay, bisexual, transsexual and transgender youth. *Journal of Gay & Lesbian Social Services: Issues in Practice, Policy & Research, 16*(3–4), 81–98.

Leue, A., Borchard, B., & Hoyer, J. (2004). Mental disorders in a forensic sample of sexual offenders. *European Psychiatry, 19*(3), 123–130.

LeVay, S. (1991). A difference in hypothalamic structure between heterosexual and homosexual men. *Science, 253,* 1034–1037.

Levin, R. J. (2003a). The G-spot: Reality or illusion? *Sexual and Relationship Therapy, 18*(1), 117–119.

Levine, D. (2000). Virtual attraction: What rocks your boat. *CyberPsychology & Behavior 3*(4), 565–573.

Levy, H. (2004, November 25). Internet luring sentence sparks outrage. *Toronto Star.*

Lewis, J. (1998). Learning to strip: The socialization experiences of exotic dancers. *The Canadian Journal of Human Sexuality, 7,* 51–66.

Lewis, A. L., & White, J. (2009). The defense mechanisms of homophobia adolescent males. *Journal of Adolescence, 31*(2).

Lindberg, L. D., Jones, R., & Santelli, J. S. (2008). Non-coital sexual activities among adolescents. *Journal of Adolescent Health, 43,* 231–238.

Lippa, R. (2008). The relation between childhood gender nonconformity and adult masculinity–femininity and anxiety in heterosexual and homosexual men and women. *Sex Roles, 59,* 684–693.

Lippman, A., Melnychuck, R., Shimanin, C., & Boscoe, M. (2007). Human papillomavirus vaccines and women's health: questions and cautions. *Canadian Medical Association Journal, 177*(5), 484–487

Littleton, H., & Henderson, C. E. (2009). If she is not a victim, does that mean she was not traumatized? Evaluation of predictors of PTSD symptomatology among college rape victims. *Violence Against Women, 15*(2), 148–167.

Liu, K. E., & Fisher, W. A. (2002). Canadian physicians' role in contraception from the 19th century to now. *Journal of Obstetrics and Gynaecology Canada, 24*(3), 239–244.

Loder, N. (2000). US science shocked by revelations of sexual discrimination. *Nature, 405,* 713–714.

Logan, C. (2008). Sexual deviance in females. In D. R. Laws and W. T. O'Donohue (Eds.), *Sexual deviance: Theory, assessment, and treatment* (2nd ed., pp. 486–507). New York: Guilford Press.

Logan, T. K., Walker, R., Jordan, C. E., & Leukefeld, C. G. (2006). Justice system options and responses. In T. K. Logan, R. Walker, C. E. Jordan, & C. G. Leukefeld (Eds.), *Women and victimization: Contributing factors, interventions, and implications* (pp. 161–194). Washington, DC: American Psychological Association.

Looman, J., Abracen, J., DiFazio, R., & Maillet, G. (2004). Alcohol and drug abuse among sexual and nonsexual offenders: Relationship to intimacy deficits and coping strategy. *Sexual Abuse: A Journal of Research and Treatment, 16*(3), 177–189.

Lotery, H. E., McClure, N., & Galask, R. P. (2004). Vulvodynia. *Lancet, 363*(9414), 1058–1060.

Lowman, J., & Atchison, C. (2006). Men who buy sex: A survey in the greater Vancouver regional district. *The Canadian Review of Sociology and Anthropology, 43*(3), 281–296.

Lowry, R., et al. (1994). Substance use and HIV-related sexual behaviors among U.S. high school students: Are they related? *American Journal of Public Health, 84*(7), 1116–1120.

Lucas, A. M. (2005). The work of sex work: Elite prostitutes' vocational orientations and experiences. *Deviant Behavior, 26*(6), 513–546.

Lue, T. F. (2000). Drug therapy: Erectile dysfunction. *The New England Journal of Medicine, 342*(24).

Lussier, P., & Piché, L. (2008). Frotteurism: Psychopathology and theory. In D. R. Laws and W. T. O'Donohue (Eds.), *Sexual deviance: Theory, assessment, and treatment* (2nd ed., pp. 131–149). New York: Guilford Press.

Lutfey, K., Link, C., Rosen, R., Wiegel, M., & McKinlay, J. (2008). Prevalence and correlates of sexual activity and function in women: Results from the Boston area community health (BACH) survey. *Archives of Sexual Behavior, 37,* 51–66.

Maaita, M. J., Bhaumik, J., & Davies, A. E. (2002). Sexual function after using tension-free vaginal tape for the surgical treatment of genuine stress incontinence. *British Journal of Urology International, 90*(6), 540.

MacDonald, T. K., MacDonald, G., Zanna, M. P., & Fong, G. T. (2000). Alcohol, sexual arousal, and intentions to use condoms in young men: Applying alcohol myopia theory to risky sexual behavior. *Health Psychology, 19,* 290–298.

MacGregor, E. (2009). Estrogen replacement and migraine. *Maturitas, 63*(1), 51–55.

MacIntosh, H., Reissing, E. D., & Andruff, H. (2010). Same sex marriage in Canada: The impact of legal marriage on the first cohort of gay and lesbians to wed. *The Canadian Journal of Human Sexuality, 19*(3), 79–90

Mackie, M. (1991). *Gender relations in Canada: Further explorations.* Markham, ON: Butterworths Canada Ltd.

Mackinnon, C. A. (2007). Women's lives, men's laws. Cambridge, MA: Harvard University Press.

Maclean's magazine (1998, July 20). Findings from the GoldParlo Poll. *Maclean's,* 10.

MacNeil, S. (2004). It takes two: Modeling the role of sexual self-disclosure in sexual satisfaction. (Doctoral dissertation, www.il.proquest.com/umi/). *Dissertation Abstracts International: Section B: The Sciences & Engineering, 65* (1-B), 481. (UMI Dissertation Order Number AAINQ87631; Print).

MacNeil, S., & Byers, E. S. (1997). The relationships between sexual problems, communication and sexual satisfaction. *Canadian Journal of Human Sexuality, 6*(4), 277–283.

MacNeil, S., & Byers, E. S. (2005). Dyadic assessment of sexual self-disclosure and sexual satisfaction in heterosexual dating couples. *Journal of Social and Personal Relationships, 22,* 169–181.

MacNeil, S., & Byers, E. S. (2009). Role of sexual self-disclosure in the sexual satisfaction of long-term heterosexual couples. *Journal of Sex Research, 46,* 1–12.

MacQueen, K. (2003, May 26). Boy vs. girl. *Maclean's,* 26–32.

Macy, R. J., Nurius, P. S., & Norris, J. (2006). Responding in their best interests: Contextualizing women's coping with acquaintance sexual aggression. *Violence Against Women, 12*(5), 478–500.

Madsen, L., Parsons, S., & Grubin, D. (2006). The relationship between the five-factor model and DSM personality disorder in a sample of child molesters. *Personality and Individual Differences, 40*(2), 227–236.

Mah, K., & Binik, Y. (2002). Do all orgasms feel alike? Evaluating a two-dimensional model of the orgasm experience across gender and sexual context. *The Journal of Sex Research, 39,* 104–114.

Mah, K., & Binik, Y. (2005). Are orgasms in the mind or the body? Psychosocial versus physiological correlates or orgasmic pleasure and satisfaction. *Journal of Sex & Marital Therapy*, *31*(3), 187–200.

Mahoney, D. (1994). *Staying connected: The coming out stories of parents with a lesbian daughter or gay son.* Unpublished master's thesis, University of Guelph.

Mahoney, A. R., & Knudson-Martin, C. (2009). *Couples, gender, and power.* New York: Springer

Maisel, L., & Meggars, H. (2007). Now and then: Females learning and practicing masturbation. Poster session presented at the Annual Meeting of the Society for the Scientific Study of Sexuality, Indianapolis, IN.

Major, B., Cozzarelli, C., Cooper, M. L., Zubek, J., Richards, C., et al. (2000). Psychological responses of women after first-trimester abortion. *Archives of General Psychiatry, 57,* 777–784.

Major, B., Kaiser, C. R., & McCoy, S. K. (2003). It's not my fault: When and why attributions to prejudice protect self-esteem. *Personality & Social Psychology Bulletin, 29*(6), 772–781.

Major, C. J., Read, S. E., Coates, R. A., et al. (1991). Comparison of saliva and blood for human immunodeficiency virus prevalence testing. *Journal of Infectious Diseases, 163*(4), 699–702.

Malamuth, N. M., Huppin, M., & Paul, B. (2005). Sexual coercion. In D. M. Buss (Ed.), *The handbook of evolutionary psychology* (pp. 394–418). Hoboken, NJ: Wiley.

Maletzky, B. M. (1980). Self-referred vs. court-referred sexually deviant patients: Success with assisted covert sensitization. *Behavior Therapy, 11,* 306–314.

Man accused of stealing panties agrees to counselling. (2002, April 28). *National Post,* p. A6.

Mantovani, F. (2001). Cyber-attraction: The emergence of computer-mediated communication in the development of interpersonal relationships. In L. Anolli, R. Cieri, & G. Riva (eds.), *Say not to say: New perspectives on miscommunication* (pp. 236–252). Amsterdam, Holland: IOS Press.

Maranda, M. J., Han, C., & Rainone, G. A. (2004). Crack cocaine and sex. *Journal of Psychoactive Drugs, 36*(3), 315–322.

Marazziti, D. (2005). The neurobiology of love. *Current Psychiatry Reviews, 1*(3), 331–335.

Marchbanks, P. A., et al. (2002). Oral contraceptives and the risk of breast cancer. *New England Journal of Medicine, 346,* 2025–2032

Marcus, D. K., & Miller, R. S. (2003). Sex differences in judgments of physical attractiveness: A social relations analysis. *Personality & Social Psychology Bulletin, 29*(3), 325–335.

Mardorossian, C. M. (2002). Toward a new feminist theory of rape. *Signs, 27*(3), 743–775

Mark, M. (2003, October 1). Consenting adults: A look behind closed doors in Calgary. *The Calgary Sun.*

Markman, H. J. (2005). The prevention of extramarital involvement: Steps toward "affair proofing" marriage. *Clinical Psychology: Science and Practice, 12*(2), 134–138

Marrazzo, J. M. (2005). Sexual practices, risk perception and knowledge of sexually transmitted disease risk among lesbian and bisexual women. *Perspectives on Sexual and Reproductive Health, 37,* 6–12.

Marshall, L.E. & Briken, P. (2010). Assessment, diagnosis, and management of hypersexual disorders. *Current Opinion in Psychiatry, 23,* 570–573.

Marshall, W. L. (1989). Pornography and sex offenders. In D. Zillmann & J. Bryant (Eds.), *Pornography: Research advances and policy considerations* (pp. 185–214). Hillsdale, NJ: Lawrence Erlbaum Associates.

Marshall, W. L., Marshall, L. E., & Serran, G. A. (2007). Strategies in the treatment of paraphilias: A critical review. *Annual Review of Sex Research, 17,* 162–182.

Marshall, W. L., Marshall, L. E., Serran, G. A., & Fernandez, Y. M. (2006). *Treating sexual offenders: An integrated approach.* New York: Routledge.

Martin, E. T. et al. (2009). A pooled analysis of the effect of condoms in preventing HSV-2 acquisition. *Archives of Internal Medicine, 163* (13), 1233–40

Martins, Y., Preti, G., Crabtree, C. R., Runyan, T., Vainius, A. A., & Wysocki, C. J. (2005). Preference for human body odors is influenced by gender and sexual orientation. *Psychological Science, 16*(9), 694.

Marziano, V., Ward, T., Beech, A. R., & Pattison, P. (2006). Identification of five fundamental implicit theories underlying cognitive distortions in child abusers: A preliminary study. *Psychology, Crime & Law, 12*(1), 97–105.

Masheb, R. M., Lozano–Blanco, C., Kohorn, E. I., Minkin, M. J., & Kerns, R. D. (2004). Assessing sexual function and dyspareunia with the female sexual function index (FSFI) in women with vulvodynia. *Journal of Sex & Marital Therapy, 30*(5), 315–324.

Masters, W. H., & Johnson, V. E. (1966). *Human sexual response.* Boston: Little, Brown.

Masters, W. H., & Johnson, V. E. (1970). *Human sexual inadequacy.* Boston: Little, Brown.

Maticka-Tyndale, E. (2001). Sexual health and Canadian youth: How do we measure up? *Canadian Journal of Human Sexuality, 10,* 1–17.

Maticka-Tyndale, E., Lewis, J., & Street, M. (2005). Making a place for escort work: A case study. *The Journal of Sex Research, 42*(1), 46–53.

Maticka-Tyndale, E., Shirpak, K. R., & Chinichian, M. (2007). Providing for the sexual health needs of Canadian immigrants. *Canadian Journal of Public Health, 98*(3), 183–186.

Maticka-Tyndale, E., & Smylie, L. (2008). Sexual rights: Striking a Balance. *International Journal of Sexual Health, 20* (1 + 2), 7–24.

Maticka-Tyndale, E., Wildish, J., & Gichuru, M. (2007). Quasi-experimental evaluation of a national primary school HIV intervention in Kenya. *Evaluation and Program Planning, 30,* 172–186.

Matthews, A. K., Hughes, T. L., & Tartaro, J. (2006). Sexual behavior and sexual dysfunction in a community sample of lesbian and heterosexual women. In A. M. Omoto & H. S. Kurtzman (Eds.), *Sexual orientation and mental health: Examining identity and development in lesbian, gay, and bisexual people, Contemporary perspectives on lesbian, gay, and bisexual psychology* (pp. 185–205). Washington, DC: American Psychological Association.

Maxwell, C. D., Robinson, A. L., & Post, L. A. (2003). The nature and predictors of sexual victimization and offending among adolescents. *Journal of Youth & Adolescence, 32*(6), 465–477.

Maybach, K. L., & Gold, S. R. (1994). Hyperfemininity and attraction to macho and non-macho men. *Journal of Sex Research, 31*(2), 91–98.

Mayo Clinic Staff. (2006, October 10). Vulvodynia. *MayoClinic.com.* Retrieved from http://www.mayoclinic.com/health/vulvodynia/DS00159

Mazur, T. *The infant's developing sexuality.* Accessed February 10, 2006. [Online]. www2.huberlin.de/sexology/gesund/archiv/sen/ch07.htm#b11-children%20and%20sex.

McCabe, M. P. (2004). Exacerbation of symptoms among people with multiple sclerosis: Impact on sexuality and relationships over time. *Archives of Sexual Behavior, 33*(6), 593–601.

McCabe, M. P. (2005). The role of performance anxiety in the development and maintenance of sexual dysfunction in men and women. *International Journal of Stress Management, 12*(4), 379–388.

McCabe, S. E., et al. (2005). Selection and socialization effects of fraternities and sororities on US college student substance use: A multi-cohort national longitudinal study. *Addiction, 100*(4), 512–524.

McCall, D., et al. (1999). *Schools, Public Health, sexuality and HIV: A status report.* Toronto, ON: Council of Ministers of Education.

McCarthy, B. W., Bodnar, L. E., & Handal, M. (2004). Integrating sex therapy and couple therapy. In Harvey, J. H., Wenzel, A., & Sprecher, S. (Eds.). *The handbook of sexuality in close relationships* (pp. 573–593). Philadelphia, PA: Lawrence Erlbaum Associates.

McCarthy, B. W., & Fucito, L. M. (2005). Integrating medication, realistic expectations, and therapeutic interventions in the treatment of male sexual dysfunction. *Journal of Sex & Marital Therapy, 31*(4), 319–328.

McCarthy, B. W., Ginsberg, R. L., & Fucito, L. M. (2006). Resilient sexual desire in heterosexual couples. *Family Journal: Counseling and Therapy for Couples and Families, 14*(1), 59–64.

McCoy, N. L., & Pitino, L. (2002). Pheromonal influences on sociosexual behavior in young women. *Physiology & Behavior, 75*(3), 367–375.

McCreary Centre Society. (2007). Not yet equal: The health of lesbian, gay, & bisexual youth in BC. Vancouver: Author.

McElduff, A., & Beange, H. (2003). Men's health and well-being: Testosterone deficiency. *Journal of Intellectual & Developmental Disability, 28*(2), 211–213.

McEwan, S. L., de Man, A. F., & Simpson-Housley, P. (2005). Acquaintance rape, ego-identity achievement, and locus of control. *Social Behavior and Personality, 33*(6), 587–592.

McGlynn, C & Ward, I. (2009). Pornography, pragmatism, and proscription. *Journal of Law and Society, 36*, (3), 327–251.

McGregor, M. J., Ericksen, J., Ronald, L. A., Janssen, P. A., Van Vliet, A., & Schulzer, M. (2004). Rising incidence of hospital-reported drug-facilitated sexual assault in a large urban community in Canada. *Canadian Journal of Public Health, 95*(6), 441–445.

McKay, A. (2005). Sexuality and substance use: The impact of tobacco, alcohol, and selected recreational drugs on sexual function. *Canadian Journal of Human Sexuality, 14*(1–2), 47–56.

McKay, A. (2006a). Chlamydia screening programs: A review of the literature. Part 2: Testing procedures and educational interventions for primary care physicians. *The Canadian Journal of Human Sexuality, 15*(1), 13–22.

McKay, A. (2006b). Chlamydia screening programs: A review of the literature. Part 1: Issues in the promotion of chlamydia testing of youth by primary care physicians. *The Canadian Journal of Human Sexuality, 15*(1), 1–11.

McKay, A. (2006c). Trends in teen pregnancy in Canada with comparisons to U.S.A. and England/Wales. *The Canadian Journal of Human Sexuality, 15*, (3 & 4), 157–162.

McKay, A. (2007). The effectiveness of latex condoms for prevention of STI/HIV. *The Canadian Journal of Human Sexuality, 16*(1–2), 57–61.

McKay, A. & Barrett, M. (1999). Pre-service sexual health education training of elementary, secondary, and physical education teachers in Canadian faculties of education. *The Canadian Journal of Human Sexuality, 7,* 139–145.

McKay, A., & Barrett, B. (2008). Rising reported rates of chlamydia among young women in Canada: What do they tell us about trends in the actual prevalence of the infection? *The Canadian Journal of Human Sexuality, 17*(1), 61–69.

McKay, A., & Barrett, M. (2010). Trends in teen pregnancy rates from 1996–-2006: A comparison of Canada, Sweden, U.S.A., and England/Wales. *The Canadian Journal of Human Sexuality, 19*(1-&2), 43–512.

McKay, A & Holowaty, P. (1997). Sexual health education: A study of adolescents' opinions, self-perceived needs, and current and preferred sources of information. *The Canadian Journal of Human Sexuality, 6,* 29–38

McMaster, L. E., Connolly, J., Pepler, D., & Craig, W. M. (2002). Peer to peer sexual harassment in early adolescence: A developmental perspective. *Development and Psycho-pathology, 14,* 91–105.

Meaney, G. J., Rye, B. J., Wood, E., Solovieva, E. (2009). Satisfaction with school-based sexual health education in a sample of university students recently graduated from Ontario high schools. *The Canadian Journal of Human Sexuality, 18*(3), 107–125

Meaney, G., & Rye, B. (2007). Sex, sexuality and leisure. In R. McCarville & K. MacKay (Eds.), *Leisure for Canadians.* State College, PA: Venture Publishing.

Meaney, G., & Rye, B. J. (2008). Portrayals of homosexuality in introductory human sexuality textbooks. Paper presented at the Guelph Sexuality Conference, Guelph, ON.

Meininger, E., Saewyc, E. M., Skay, C., Clark, T., Poon, C., Robinson, E., Pettingell, S., & Homma, Y. (2007). Enacted sigma and HIV risk behaviors in sexual minority youth of European heritage across three countries. [abstract]. *Journal of Adolescent Health, 40,* S27.

Mercury Staff. (2007, December 21). Dance floor incident leads to assault charges. *Guelph Mercury.*

Meston, C. M., & Frohlich, P. F. (2000). The neurobiology of sexual function. *Archives of General Psychiatry, 57*(11), 1012–1030.

Meston, C. M., Heiman, J. R., Trapnell, P., & Paulhus, D. (1998). Socially desirable responding and sexuality self-reports. *The Journal of Sex Research, 35,* 148–157.

Meston, C. M., Trapnell, P. D., & Gorzalka, B. B. (1996). Ethnic and gender differences in sexuality: Variations in sexual behavior between Asian and non-Asian university students. *Archives of Sexual Behavior, 25,* 33–72.

Metwally, M. & Ledger, W.L. (2011). Long-term complications of assisted reproductive technologies. *Human Fertility, 14*(2), 77–87.

Meyer-Bahlburg, H., Dolezal, C., & Schober, J. (2007). Self-ratings of genital anatomy and sexual function by women using the Sagasf-F. Paper presented at the annual conference of the International Academy of Sex Research, Vancouver, BC.

Michel, A., & Pédinielli, J.-L. (2005). Vers une conceptualisation du transsexualisme. *Annales Médico-Psychologiques, 163*(5), 379–386.

Migliardi, P. (2007). *Unheard voices of ethno-racial minority youth.* Winnipeg: Sexuality Education Resource Centre.

Mikach, S. M., & Bailey, J. M. (1999). What distinguishes women with unusually high numbers of sex partners? *Evolution & Human Behavior, 20*(3), 141–150.

Milhausen, R. (2004). Factors that inhibit and enhance sexual arousal in college men and women. Unpublished doctoral dissertation, Indiana University, Indianapolis, Indiana.

Milhausen, R. R. (2000). Double standard or reverse double standard: A comparative analysis of male and female perspectives. Unpublished master's thesis, University of Guelph.

Milhausen, R. R., & Herold, E. S. (1999). Does the sexual double standard still exist? Perceptions of university women. *Journal of Sex Research, 36*(4), 361–368.

Milhausen, R. R., & Herold, E. S. (2001). Reconceptualizing the sexual double standard. *Journal of Psychology and Human Sexuality, 13,* 63–83.

Millar, C. (2003, November 22). Web porn accessed from car. *The Toronto Star.*

Miller, R. (2005). Overcoming violence against women and girls: The international campaign to eradicate a worldwide problem. *Culture, Health & Sexuality, 7*(5), 519–521.

Minichiello, V., et al. (2001). Male sex workers in three Australian cities: Socio-demographic and sex work characteristics. *Journal of Homosexuality, 42*(1), 29–51.

Missailidis, K., & Gebre-Medhin, M. (2000). Female genital mutilation in eastern Ethiopia. *The Lancet, 356,* 137–138.

Mitchell, B. (2006, October 16). Sex assault charge for Peel teacher. *Toronto Star,* p. C4.

Mitchell, B. (2010). Mississauga couple sentenced for sex assault. *Toronto Star,* August 26, P. GT2.

Mohan, R., & Bhugra, D. (2005). Literature update: A critical review. *Sexual and Relationship Therapy, 20*(1), 115–122.

Molloy, G. L., & Herold, E. S. (1985). Sexual counseling for the physically disabled: A comparison of health care professionals' attitudes and practices. *Canadian Family Physician, 31,* 2277–2285.

Money, J. (1994). The concept of gender identity disorder in childhood and adolescence after 39 years. *Journal of Sex and Marital Therapy, 20*(3), 163–177.

Money, J. (2003). History, causality, and sexology. *Journal of Sex Research, 40*(3), 237–239.

Montaner, J. S., et al. (2010). Association of highly active antiretroviral therapy coverage, population viral load, and yearly new HIV diagnosis in British Columbia, Canada: a population-based study. *The Lancet,* Early online publication July 18, 2010

Montemurro, B., Bloom, C., & Madell, K. (2003). Ladies night out: A typology of women patrons of a male strip club. *Deviant Behavior, 24*(4), 333–352.

Montoya, R. M., Horton, R. S., & Kirchner, J. (2008). Is actual similarity necessary for attraction? A meta-analysis of actual and perceived similarity. *Journal of Social and Personal Relationships, 25*(6), 889–922.

Moore, D. R., & Heiman, J. R. (2006). Women's sexuality in context: Relationship factors and female sexual functioning. In I. Goldstein, C. Meston, S. Davis, & A. Traish (Eds.), *Female sexual dysfunction.* New York: Parthenon.

Moore, S. M., & Rosenthal, D. (1993). *Sexuality in Adolescence.* New York, NY: Routledge

Morley, J. E., & Perry, H. M., III. (2003). Androgens and women at the menopause and beyond. *Journals of Gerontology: Series A: Biological Sciences & Medical Sciences, 58A*(5), 409–416.

Morrison, G. G., Harriman, R., Morrison, M. A., Bearden, A., & Ellis, S. (2004). Correlates of exposure to sexually explicit material among Canadian post-secondary students. *The Canadian Journal of Human Sexuality, 13*(3–4), 143–157.

Morris, L. B. (2000, June 25). For the partum blues, a question of whether to medicate. *The New York Times.* [Online].

Morrison, E. S., et al. (1980). *Growing up sexual.* New York: Van Nostrand Reinhold.

Morry, M. M., & Gaines, S. O. (2005). Relationship satisfaction as a predictor of similarity ratings: A test of the attraction–similarity hypothesis. *Journal of Social and Personal Relationships, 22*(4), 561–584.

Moser, C. (2001). Paraphilia: A critique of a confused concept. In P. Kleinplatz (Ed.), *New directions in sex therapy: Innovations and alternatives* (pp. 91–108). New York: Brunner-Routledge.

Moser, C., & Kleinplatz, P. J. (2002, Spring). Transvestic fetishism: Psychopathology or iatrogenic artifact? *New Jersey Psychologist,* pp. 16–17.

Moser, C., & Kleinplatz, P. J. (2005a). DSM-IV-TR and the paraphilias: An argument for removal. *Journal of Psychology & Human Sexuality, 17*(3–4), 91–109.

Moser, C., & Kleinplatz, P. J. (2005b). Does heterosexuality belong in the DSM? *Lesbian & Gay Psychology Review, 6*(3), 261–267

Mosher, W. D., Chandra, A., & Jones, J. (2005). *Sexual behavior and selected health measures: Men and women 15–44 years of age, United States, 2002. Advance data from vital and health statistics.* Centers for Disease Control and Prevention. National Center for Health Statistics, No. 362.

Muehlenhard, C. L. (2000). Categories and sexuality. *The Journal of Sex Research, 37*(2), 101–107.

Muise, A. (2006). A discourse analytic study of the discursive management of female sexual desire in online weblogs. Poster session presented at the Annual Guelph Sexuality Conference, Guelph, Ontario.

Muise, A. (2008, September). The discursive management of female sexual desire in online weblogs. Paper presented at the 32nd Annual Meeting of the Canadian Sex Research Forum, Ottawa, Ontario.

Muise, A., Christofides, E., & Desmarais, S. (2008). Who are you "poking"?: Students' experience of jealousy on Facebook. Poster session presented at the Annual Guelph Conference on Human Sexuality, Guelph, Ontario.

Muise, A., Preyde, M., Maitland, S. B., & Milhausen, R. (2010). Sexual identity and sexual well-being in female heterosexual university students. *Archives of Sexual Behavior, 39,* 915–925

Mukherjee, S., et al. (2009). What is the effect of circumcision on risk of urinary tract infection in boys with posterior urethral valves? *Journal of Pediatric Surgery, 44*(2), 417–421.

Mulick, P. S., & Wright, L. W., Jr. (2002). Examining the existence of biphobia in the heterosexual and homosexual populations. *Journal of Bisexuality, 2*(4), 45–64.

Murphy, N., & Young, P. C. (2005). Sexuality in children and adolescents with disabilities. *Developmental Medicine & Child Neurology, 47,* 640–644

Murphy, W. D., & Page, I. J. (2008). Exhibitionism: Psychopathology and theory. In D. R. Laws and W. T. O'Donohue (Eds.), *Sexual deviance: Theory, assessment, and treatment* (2nd ed., pp. 61–75). New York: Guilford Press.

Murray, J. & Adam, B. (2001). Aging, sexuality, and HIV issues among gay and bisexual men. *Canadian Journal of Human Sexuality, 10*(3/4), 75–90.

Murray, S. O., & Roscoe, W. (1997). *Islamic homosexualities: Culture, history, and literature.* New York: New York University Press.

Mustanski, B., Chivers, M., & Bailey, M. (2003). A critical review of recent biological research on human sexual orientation. *Annual Review of Sex Research, 13,* 89–140.

Myers, T., Aguinaldo, J. P., Dakers, D., et al. (2004). How drug using men who have sex with men account for substance use during sexual behaviours: Questioning assumptions of HIV prevention and research. *Addiction Research and Theory, 12*(3), 213–229.

Myers, T., & Allman, D. 2004. *Ontario Men's Survey.* Ottawa: Canadian Public Health Association.

Myers, T., Allman, D., Calzavara, L., et al. (2004). *Ontario men's survey.* Toronto: University of Toronto, HIV Social, Behavioural and Epidemiological Studies Unit.

Myers, T., Allman, D., Calzavara, L., Maxwell, J., Remis, R., Swantee, C., & Travers, R. (2004a). Ontario men's survey. Library and Archives Canada Cataloguing in Publication. Available: cbr.cbrc.net/files/1126039797/Ontario%20Mens%20Survey%20Final%20Report.pdf

Myers, T., Bullock, S. L., Calzavara, L. M., Cockerill, R., & Marshall, V. W. (1997). Differences in sexual risk-taking behaviour with state of inebriation in an Aboriginal population in Ontario, Canada. *Journal of Studies in Alcohol, 58,* 312–322.

Myers, T., Calzavara, L. M., Cockerill, R., Marshall, V. W., & Bullock, S. L. (1993). *The Ontario First Nations AIDS and healthy lifestyle survey.* Ottawa, ON: Canadian Public Health Association.

Myers, T., Godin, G., Lambert, J., Calzavara, L., & Locker, D. (1996). Sexual risk and HIV-testing behaviour by gay and bisexual men in Canada. *AIDS Care, 8*(3), 297–309.

Myers, T., Orr, K. W., Locker, D., & Jackson, E. A. (1993). Factors affecting gay and bisexual men's decisions and intentions to seek HIV testing. *American Journal of Public Health, 83,* 701–704.

Naili, H., & Josey, S. (2005, August 11). Pastor faces sex charges. *The Toronto Star.*

Najman, J. M., Dunne, M. P., Purdie, D. M., Boyle, F. M., & Coxeter, P. D. (2005). Sexual abuse in childhood and sexual dysfunction in adulthood: An Australian population-based study. *Archives of Sexual Behavior, 34(5),* 517–526.

Nakhaie, R., & Arnold, R. (2010). A four year (1996 – 2000) analysis of social capital and health status of Canadians: The difference love makes. *Social Science and Medicine, 71,* 1037–1044.

Nanda, S., & Warms, R. L. (2004). *Cultural anthropology* (8th ed.). Belmont, CA: Wadsworth

Nappi, R. E., Wawra, K., & Schmitt, S. (2006). Hypoactive sexual desire disorder in postmenopausal women. *Gynecological Endocrinology, 22*(6), 318–323.

Narchi, H. (2003). Infantile masturbation mimicking paroxysmal disorders. *Journal of Pediatric Neurology, 1*(1), 43–45.

National Center for Biotechnology Information (NCBI). (2006, February 1). National Institute of Health. [Online]. www.ncbi.nlm.nih.gov/entrez/query.fcgi?=CMD=Search&db=homologene&term=SRY.

NCPTUP/Cosmogirl.com. (2008). Sex and Tech: Results From a Survey of Teens and Young Adults. http://www.thenationalcampaign.org

National Institute of Allergy and Infectious Diseases. (2009). Herpevac trial for women. http://www3.niad.nih.gov/topics/genitalHerpes/research/herpevac/default.htm

Netting, N. S., & Burnett, M. L. (2004). Twenty years of student sexual behavior: Subcultural adaptations to a changing health environment. *Adolescence, 39*(153), 19–38.

Newman, G. A. (2006). Woman's place or women's spaces: Intertwining history, herstory, and Christianity. In C. K. Robertson (Ed.), *Religion & sexuality: Passionate debates* (pp. 65–76). New York: Peter Lang Publishing.

Nickel, J. C., Elhilali, M., Vallancien, G., & ALF-ONE Study Group. (2005). Benign prostatic hyperplasia (BPH) and prostatitis: Prevalence of painful ejaculation in men with clinical BPH. *BJU International, 95*(4), 571–574.

Nicolosi, A., Laumann, E., Glasser, D., Moreira, E., & Paik, A. (2004). Sexual behavior and sexual dysfunctions after age 40: The global study of sexual attitudes and behaviors. *Urology, 64,* 991–997.

Ninomiya, M. M. (2010). Sexual health education in Newfoundland and Labrador schools: Junior high school teachers' experiences, coverage of topics, comfort levels and views about professional practice. *The Canadian Journal of Human Sexuality, 19*(1–2), 15–26.

Nobre, P. J., & Pinto-Gouveia, J. (2006). Dysfunctional sexual beliefs as vulnerability factors for sexual dysfunction. *Journal of Sex Research, 43*(1), 68–75.

Norris, S. (2001). *Reproductive infertility: Prevalence, causes, trends and treatments.* In Brief. Ottawa, ON: Parliamentary Research Branch, Library of Parliament.

Norton-Hawk, M. (2004). A comparison of pimp- and non-pimp-controlled women. *Violence Against Women, 10(2),* 189–194.

Nosek, M. A., et al. (2004). The meaning of health for women with physical disabilities: A qualitative analysis. *Family & Community Health, 27*(1), 6–21.

Nosko, A., Wood, E., & Desmarais, S. (2007). Unsolicited online sexual material: What affects our attitudes and likelihood to search for more? *The Canadian Journal of Human Sexuality, 16*(1–2), 1–10.

Nour, N. W. (2000). Cited in Dreifus, C. (2000, July 11). A conversation with Dr. Nawal M. Nour: A life devoted to stopping the suffering of mutilation. *The New York Times* online.

Nurnberg, G., Hensley, P., & Heiman, J. (2008). Sildenafil treatment of women with antidepressant-associated sexual dysfunction: A randomized controlled trial. *Journal of the American Medical Association, 300*(4), 395–404.

O'Doherty, T.O. (2011). Victimization on off-street sex industry workers. *Violence Against Women, 17*(7), 944–963.

Ogilvie, M. (2008, June 19). New egg-freezing technique gives women more options. *Toronto Star,* p. A20.

Ohl, L.E. (2007). Essentials of female sexual dysfunctions from a sex therapy perspective. *Urologic Nursing, 27(1),* 57–63.

Options for Sexual Health. (2004). *An assessment of the effectiveness of sexual health education in B.C. schools.* Vancouver, BC: Options for Sexual Health

O'Sullivan, L. F. (2003). The development of romantic relationships in adolescence. *Archives of Sexual Behavior, 32*(3), 292–294.

O'Sullivan, L. F., Byers, E. S., & Finkelman, L. (1998). A comparison of male and female college students' experiences of sexual coercion. *Psychology of Women Quarterly, 22,* 177–195.

O'Sullivan, L. F., & Majerovich, J. (2008). Difficulties with sexual functioning in a sample of male and female late adolescent and young adult university students. *The Canadian Journal of Human Sexuality, 17*(3), 109–121.

Oakes, G. (1994, February 4). Lover who removed his condom jailed 45 days for sexual assault. *The Toronto Star.*

Ochs, E. P., & Binik, Y. M. (1999). The use of couple data to determine reliability of self-reported sexual behavior. *Journal of Sex Research, 36*(4), 1–11.

Offman, A., & Matheson, K. (2005). Sexual compatibility and sexual function in intimate relationships. *The Canadian Journal of Human Sexuality, 14*(1–2), 31–39.

Ogden, G., et al. (2007). Spiritual dimensions of sexual health: Broadening clinical perspectives of women's desire. In A. F. Owens & M. S. Tepper (Eds.), *Sexual health, 4* (pp. 131–152). Westport, CT: Praeger.

O'Keeffe, M. J., et al. (2003). Learning, cognitive, and attentional problems in adolescents born small for gestational age. *Pediatrics, 112*(2), 301–307.

Olfson, M., Uttaro, T., Carson, W. H., & Tafesse, E. (2005). Male sexual dysfunction and quality of life in schizophrenia. *Journal of Clinical Psychiatry, 66*(3), 331–338.

Open Society Institute. (2007). Women, harm reduction, and HIV. New York: Author.

Ortega, V., Ojeda, P., Sutil, F., & Sierra, J. C. (2005). Culpabilidad sexual en adolescentes: Estudio de algunos factores relacionados. *Anales de Psicología, 21*(2), 268–275.

Osman, S. L. (2003). Predicting men's rape perceptions based on the belief that "No" really means "Yes." *Journal of Applied Social Psychology, 33*(4), 683–692.

Ott, M.A., & Santelli, J. S. (2007) Abstinence and abstinence-only education. *Current Opinion in Obstetrics & Gynecology, 19*, 446–452

Pakhomou, S. M. (2006). Methodological aspects of telephone scatologia: A case study. *International Journal of Law and Psychiatry, 29*(3), 178–185.

Palace, E. M. (1995). Modification of dysfunctional patterns of sexual arousal through autonomic arousal and false physiological feedback. *Journal of Consulting and Clinical Psychology, 63*, 604–615.

Parker-Pope, T. (2008, February 5). No answers for men with prostate cancer. *The New York Times.*

Parr-LeFeuve, R., & Desmarais, S. (2005). Do young women use sexual pressure to initiate sex? Unpublished paper. University of Guelph, Dept. of Psychology.

Parrott, D., Zeichner, A., & Hoover, R. (2006). Sexual prejudice and anger network activation: Mediating role of negative affect. *Aggressive Behavior, 32*(1), 7–16.

Pasupathy, D., & Smith, G. C. (2005). The analysis of factors predicting antepartum stillbirth. *Minerva Ginecology, 57*(4), 397–410.

Patel, D., Gillespie, B., & Foxman, B. (2003). Sexual behavior of older women: results of a random-digit-dialing survey of 2000 women in the United States. *Sexually Transmitted Diseases, 30*, 216–220

Patha, P., et al. (2006). Discordance between sexual behavior and self-reported sexual identity: A population–based survey of New York City men. *Annals of Internal Medicine, 145*, 416–425.

Patriquin, M. (2007, October 22). Canada: A nation of bigots? *Maclean's*, 17–22.

Payne, K. A., Binik, Y. M., Pukall, C. F., Thaler, L., Amsel, R., & Khalifé, S. (2007). Effects of sexual arousal on genital and non–genital sensation: A comparison of women with vulvar vestibulitis syndrome and healthy controls. *Archives of Sexual Behaviour, 36*, 289–300.

Payne, K. A., Thaler, K., Kukkonen, T. M., Carrier, S., & Binik, Y. M. (2007). Sensation and sexual arousal in circumcised and uncircumcised men. *Journal of Sexual Medicine, 4*(3), 667–674.

Peluso, P. R. (Ed.). (2008). *Infidelity.* Danvers, MA: CRC Press.

Pek, N. K., & Senn, C. Y. (2004). Not wanted in the inbox! Evaluations of unsolicited and harassing e-mail. *Psychology of Women Quarterly, 28*, 204–214.

Peplau, L. A. (2003). Human sexuality: How do men and women differ? *Current Directions in Psychological Science, 12*(2), 37–40.

Pereda, N., Guilera, G., Forns, M., & Gómez-Benito, J. (2009). The prevalence of child sexual abuse in community and student samples: A meta-analysis. *Clinical Psychology Review, 29*, 328–338.

Perez, K., Gadgil, M., & Dizon, D.S. (2009). Sexual ramifications of medical illness. *Clinical Obstetrics and Gynaecology, 52*(4), 691–701.

Peritz, I. (2005, September 23). Student leaves McGill over sports hazing ritual. *The Globe and Mail.*

Peritz, I. (2011). Former Canadian general fined, demoted for affair. *Global and Mail*, July 21.

Perreault, H. S., & Brennan, S. (2010). Criminal victimization in Canada 2009. *Juristat, 30*(2).

Perry, P. J., et al. (2001). Bioavailable testosterone as a correlate of cognition, psychological status, quality of life, and sexual function in aging males: Implications for testosterone replacement therapy. *Annals of Clinical Psychiatry, 13*(2), 75–80.

Petersen, J. L., & Shibley Hyde, J. (2011). Gender differences in sexual attitudes and behaviors: A review of meta-analytic results and large datasets. *Journal of Sex Research, 48*(2-3), 149–165.

Petrunik, M. (2003). The hare and the tortoise: Dangerousness and sex offender policy in the United States and Canada. *Canadian Journal of Criminology & Criminal Justice, 45*(1), 43–72.

Pew Research Center. (2009). Teens and Sexting: How and Why Minor Teens are Sending Sexually Suggestive Nude or Nearly Nude Images Via Text Messaging. Http://www.pewinternet.org

Pfaus, J. G., Kippin, T. E., & Coria-Avila, G. (2003).What can animal models tell us about human sexual response? *Annual Review of Sex Research, 14*, 1–63.

Philaretou, A. G. (2006). Female exotic dancers: Intrapersonal and interpersonal perspectives. *Sexual Addiction & Compulsivity, 13*(1), 41–52.

Picard, A. (2010). U.S., Canada lead world in prosecuting those who transmit AIDS virus. *Globe and Mail*, July 20, 2010

Piercy, J. (2008, January 12). Six charged in human trafficking ring. *Toronto Star.*

Pike, L. B. (2005, July 1). *Sexuality and your child.* MU Extension, University of Missouri–Columbia.

Pillard, R. C., & Weinrich, J. D. (1986). Evidence of familial nature of male homosexuality. *Archives of Sexual Behavior, 43*, 808–812.

Pinkerton, S. D., Bogart, L. M., Cecil, H., & Abramson, P. R. (2002). Factors associated with masturbation in collegiate sample. *Journal of Psychology & Human Sexuality, 14*(2–3), 103–121.

Planned Parenthood Federation of America Inc.. (2006). *Planned parenthood.* Retrieved from http://www.plannedparenthood.org/pp2/portal

Planned Parenthood Federation of Canada. (1999). *A history of birth control in Canada.* Brochure. Ottawa: Planned Parenthood Federation of Canada.

Planned Parenthood Federation of Canada. (2002). Emergency contraception: Get the facts! Retrieved from http://www.ppfc.ca/faqs/access.htm

Plant, E. A., Hyde, J. S., Keltner, D., &Devine, P. G. (2000). The gender stereotyping of emotions. *Psychology of Women Quarterly, 24*(1), 81–92.

Plaut, S. M. (2006). Consent to sexual relations. *Archives of Sexual Behavior, 35*(1), 101–103.

Plomin, R., & Asbury, K. (2005). Nature and nurture: Genetic and environmental influences on behavior. *Annals of the Amercian Academy of Political and Social Science, 600*, 86–98.

Polansky, D. C. (2006). The big book of masturbation: From angst to zeal. *Journal of Sex & Marital Therapy, 32*(1), 75–78.

Pollack, H. A. (2001). Sudden infant death syndrome, maternal smoking during pregnancy, and the cost-effectiveness of smoking cessation intervention. *American Journal of Public Health, 91*(3), 432–436.

Pollard, J. (2006). Ontario women and breast health. *Institute for Social Resarch Newsletter, 21*(1). Toronto: York University.

Polusny, M. A., & Arbisi, P. A. (2006). Assessment of psychological distress and disability after sexual assault in adults. In G. Young, et al. (Eds.), *Psychological knowledge in court: PTSD, pain, and TBI* (pp. 97–125). Berlin, Germany: Springer Science + Business Media.

Potosky, A. L., et al. (2000). Health outcomes after prostatectomy or radiotherapy for prostate cancer: Results from the Prostate Cancer Outcomes Study. *Journal of the National Cancer Institute, 92*, 1582–1592.

Potter, S. J., et al. (2009). Empowering bystanders to prevent campus violence against women. *Violence Against Women, 15*(1), 106–121.

Pound, N., Javed, M., Ruberto, C., Shaikh, M., & Del Vaille, A. P. (2002). Duration of sexual arousal predicts semen parameters for masturbatory ejaculates. *Physiology & Behavior, 76*(4), 685–689.

Prentice, R. L., et al. (2006). Low-fat dietary pattern and risk of invasive breast cancer: The Women's Health Initiative Randomized Controlled Dietary Modification Trial. *Journal of the American Medical Association, 295*, 629–642.

Prentice, T. (2005). Alarming rates of HIV/AIDS for Canada's Aboriginal women. *The Canadian Women's Health Network Magazine, 8*, 1–4.

Preti, G., et al. (1986). Human axillary secretions influence women's menstrual cycles: The role of donor extract of females. *Hormones and Behavior, 20*, 474–482.

Preti, G., Wysocki, C. J., Barnhart, K. T., Sondheimer, S. J., & Leyden, J. J. (2003). Male axillary extracts contain pheromones that affect pulsatile secretion of luteinizing hormone and mood in women recipients. *Biology of Reproduction, 68*(6), 2107–2113.

Pron, N. (2007, September 11). Parlour's "manual release" ruled legal; Charges thrown out in masturbation case. *Toronto Star*, p. A2.

Provost, M. P., Kormos, C., Kosakoski, G., & Quinsey, V. L. (2006). Sociosexuality in women and preference for facial masculinization and somatotype in men. *Archives of Sexual Behaviour, 35*(3), 305–312.

Provost, M. P., Quinsey, V. L., & Troje, N. F. (2008). Differences in gait across the menstrual cycle and their attractiveness to men. *Archives of Sexual Behavior, 37*(4), 598–604.

Psychology Today. (2006, July 25.) www.psychologytoday.com/images/.PT_MediaKit_Health_2006.pdf.

Public Health Agency of Canada. (2008a). Canadian Guidelines for Sexual Health Education. Ottawa: Government of Canada

Public Health Agency of Canada. (2008b). Canadian Guidelines for Sexual Health Education. Ottawa, ON: Public health Agency of Canada

Public Health Agency of Canada. (2008c). Hepatitis B fact sheet. Available: www.phac-aspc.gc.ca/hcai-iamss/bbp-pts/hepatitis/hep_b_e.html

Public Health Agency of Canada. (2008d). Genital human papillomavirus (HPV) infections. Canadian guidelines for sexually tranmitted infections. Ottawa, ON: Public Health Agency of Canada.

Public Health Agency of Canada. (2008e). Genital herpes simplex virus (HSV) infections. Canadian guidelines on sexually transmitted infections. Ottawa, ON: Public Health Agency of Canada.

Public Health Agency of Canada. (2008f). Immigrants and refugees. Canadian Guidelines on Sexually Transmitted Infections. Ottawa, ON: Public Health Agency of Canada.

Public Health Agency of Canada. (2008g). Vaginal Discharge (Bacterial vaginosis, Vulvovaginal Candidiasis, Trichomoniasis). Canadian Guidelines on Sexually Transmitted Infections. Ottawa, ON: Public Health Agency of Canada.

Public Health Agency of Canada. (2009a). STI data tables. Hepatitis C and STI Surveillance and Epidemiology Section, Acquired Infections Division, Centre for Communicable Diseases and Infection Control.

Public Health Agency of Canada. (2009b). HIV and AIDS in Canada:. Surveillance Rreport to December 31, 2008. Ottawa: Surveillance and Risk Assessment Division, Centre for Communicable Diseases and Infection Control.

Public Health Agency of Canada. (2010). *Questions & Answers: Gender Identity in Schools*. Ottawa, ON: Public Health Agency of Canada.

Public Health Agency of Canada. (2010). *Questions & Answers: Sexual Orientation in Schools*. Ottawa, ON: Public Health Agency of Canada.

Public Health Agency of Canada. (2010a). Pelvic inflammatory disease. Canadian guidelines on sexually transmitted infections. Ottawa, ON: Public Health Agency of Canada. www.publichealth.gc.ca/sti

Public Health Agency of Canada. (2010b). Primary care and sexually transmitted infection. Canadian Guidelines for Sexually Transmitted Infection. Ottawa, ON: Public Health Agency of Canada

Public Health Agency of Canada. (2010c). The facts on the safety and effectiveness of HPV vaccine. http://www.phac-aspc.gc.ca/std-mts/hpv-uph/fact-faits-vacc-eng-php

Puente, S., & Cohen, D. (2003). Jealousy and the meaning (or nonmeaning) of violence. *Personality & Social Psychology Bulletin, 29*(4), 449–460.

Pukall, C., Young, R., Roberts, M., Sutton, K., & Smith K. (2007). The vulvalgesiometer as a device to measure genital pressure-pain threshold. *Physiological Measurement, 28*, 1–8.

Pukall, C. F., Payne, K. A., Binik, Y. M., & Khalife, S. (2003). Pain measurement in vulvodynia. *Journal of Sex & Marital Therapy, 29*(s), 111–120.

Punyanunt-Carter, N. M. (2006). An analysis of college students' self-disclosure behaviors on the internet. *College Student Journal, 40*(2), 329–331.

Quayle, E. (2008). Online sex offending: Psychopathology and theory. In D. R. Laws and W. T. O'Donohue (Eds.), *Sexual deviance: Theory, assessment, and treatment* (2nd ed., pp. 439–458). New York: Guilford Press.

Quinsey, V. L. (2002). Evolutionary theory and animal behavior. *Legal and Criminological Psychology, 7*, 1–13.

Rabinowitz, S. R., Firestone, P., Bradford, J. M., & Greenberg, D. M. (2002). Prediction of recidivism in exhibitionists: Psychological, phallometric, and offense factors. *Sexual Abuse: Journal of Research & Treatment, 14*(4), 329–347.

Radlove, S. (1983). Sexual response and gender roles. In E. R. Allgeier & N. B. McCormick (Eds.), *Changing boundaries: Gender roles and sexual behavior*. Palo Alto, CA: Mayfield.

Raichle, K., & Lambert, A. J. (2000). The role of political ideology in mediating judgments of blame in rape victims and their assailants: A test of the just world, personal responsibility, and legitimization hypotheses. *Personality & Social Psychology Bulletin, 26*(7), 853–863.

Rakic, Z., Starcevic, V., Starcevic, V. P., & Marinkovic, J. (1997). Testosterone treatment in men with erectile disorder and low levels of total testosterone in serum. *Archives of Sexual Behavior, 26*(5), 495–504.

Rako, S. (2003). *No more periods? The risks of menstrual suppression and other cutting-edge issues about hormones and women's health.* New York: Crown.

Ralph, D., & McNicholas, T. (2000). UK management guidelines for erectile dysfunction. *British Medical Journal, 321,* 499–503.

Randall, H., & Byers, S. (2003). What is sex? Students' definitions of having sex, sexual partner, and unfaithful sexual behaviour. *The Canadian Journal of Human Sexuality, 12,* 87–96.

Rasmussen, P. R., & Kilborne, K. J. (2008). Sex in intimate relationships: Variations and challenges. In P. Peluso (Ed.), *Infidelity: A Practitioners Guide to Working With Couples in Crisis.* New York: Routledge.

Rathus, S. A. (2006). *Childhood and adolescence: Voyages in development,* 2nd ed. Belmont, CA: Thomson Learning/Wadsworth.

Rathus, S. A. (2011). *Childhood and adolescence: Voyages in development* (4th ed.) Belmont, CA: Cengage.

Ratner, P. A., Johnson, J. L., Shoveller, J. A., Chan, K., Martindale, S. L., Schilder, A. J., et al. (2003). Non-consensual sex experienced by men who have sex with men: Prevalence and association with mental health. *Patient Education and Counseling, 49*(1), 67–74.

Rattner, M., Choudhri, Y., Murphy, P., Goneau-Lessard, K., & Burke, N. (2007). Survey says! Results from the HIV/AIDS Attitudinal Tracking Survey 2006. Paper presented at the annual conference of the Canadian Association of HIV Research, Toronto, Ontario.

Ravindran, L.N. & Stein, M.B. (2010). The pharmacologic treatment of anxiety disorders: a review of progress. *Journal of Clinical Psychiatry, 71,* (7), 839–854.

Rawson, R. A., Washton, A., Domier, C. P., & Reiber, C. (2002). Drugs and sexual effects: Role of drug type and gender. *Journal of Substance Abuse Treatment, 22*(2), 103–108.

RCMP. (2011). *Human trafficking in Canada. RCMP Criminal Intelligence.* Ottawa, ON: royal Canadian Mounted Police.

Reback, C.J., & Larkins, S. (2010). Maintaining a heterosexual identity: sexual meaning among a sample of heterosexually identified men who have sex with men. *Archives of Sexual Behavior, 39,* 766–773.

Reinisch, J. M. (1990). *The Kinsey Institute new report on sex: What you must know to be sexually literate.* New York: St. Martin's Press.

Reissing, E. K., Binik, Y. M., Khalife, S., Cohen, D., & Amsel, R. (2004). Vaginal spasm, pain, and behavior: An empirical investigation of the diagnosis of vaginismus. *Archives of Sexual Behavior, 33*(1), 5–17.

Rempel, J. K., & Baumgartner, B. (2003). The relationship between attitudes towards menstruation and sexual attitudes, desires, and behavior in women. *Archives of Sexual Behavior, 32*(2), 155–163.

Resick, P. A. (2003). Post hoc reasoning in possible cases of child sexual abuse: Just say no. *Clinical Psychology: Science & Practice, 10*(3), 349–351.

Reuters. (2006, March 17). When it comes to sex and romance. *National Post,* p. A6.

Ribner, D. S., & Kleinplatz, P. J. (2007). The hole in the sheet and other myths about sexuality and Judaism. *Sexual and Relationship Therapy, 22*(4), 445–456.

Ricci, E., Parazzini, F., & Pardi, G. (2000). Caesarean section and antiretroviral treatment. *The Lancet, 355*(9202), 496–502.

Richardson, H. et al. (2003). The natural history of type specific human papillomavirus infections in female university students. *Cancer Epidemiology, Biomarkers and Prevention, 12,* 485–90

Richters, J. (2007). Researching sex between women. Paper presented at the Proceedings of the World Association of Sexual Health XVIII Congress, Sydney, Australia.

Richardson, D., Nalabunda, A. & Goldmeier, D. (2006). Retarded ejaculation—A review. *International Journal of STD and AIDS, 17*(3), 143–150.

Richters, J., deVisser, R., Rissel, C., & Smith, A. (2006). Sexual practices at last sexual encounter and occurrence of orgasm in a national survey. *The Journal of Sex Research, 43*(3), 217–226.

Richters, J., Hendry, O. L., & Kippax, S. (2003). When safe sex isn't safe. *Culture, Health & Sexuality, 5*(1), 37–52.

Richters, J., Smith, A., de Visser, R., Grulich, A., & Rissle, C. (2006). Circumcision in Australia: Prevalence and effects on sexual health. *International Journal of STD, 17,* 547–554.

Rickwood, A. M. K., Kenny, S. E., & Donnell, S. C. (2000). Towards evidence based circumcision of English boys: Survey of trends in practice. *British Medical Journal, 321,* 792–793.

Riddell, L., Varto, H., & Hodgson, Z. G. (2010). Smooth talking: the phenomenon of pubic hair removal in women. *The Canadian Journal of Human Sexuality, 19*(3), 121–130.

Riedmann, A., Lamanna, M., & Nelson, A. (2003). *Marriages and families* (1st Canadian ed.). Toronto: Thomson Canada.

Rieger, G., Linsenmeier, J. A. W., Gygax, L., & Bailey, J. M. (2008). Sexual orientation and childhood gender nonconformity: Evidence from home videos. *Developmental Psychology, 44*(1), 46–58.

Riggio, R. E., & Woll, S. B. (1984). The role of nonverbal cues and physical attractiveness in the selection of dating partners. *Journal of Social and Personal Relationships, 1,* 347–357.

Rimm, E. (May 2000). *Lifestyle may play role in potential for impotence.* Presented at the annual meeting of the American Urological Association, Atlanta, GA.

Robert-McComb, J. J. (2008). The female athletic triad: Disordered eating, amenorrhea, and osteoporosis. In Robert-McComb, J. J., Norman, R., & Zumwalt, M. (Eds.), The active female: Health issues throughout the lifespan (pp. 81–92). Totowa, NJ: Humana Press

Rodriguez, I., Greer, C. A., Mok, M. Y., & Mombaerts, P. (2000). A putative pheromone receptor gene expressed in human olfactory mucosa. *Nature Genetics, 26*(1), 18–19.

Roesler, A., & Witztum, E. (2000). Pharmacotherapy of paraphilias in the next millennium. *Behavioral Sciences & the Law, 18*(1), 43–56.

Rogala, C., & Tydén, T. (2003). Does pornography influence young women's sexual behavior? *Women's Health Issues, 13*(1), 39–43.

Romero-Daza, N., Weeks, M., & Singer, M. (2005). Conceptualizing the impact of indirect violence on HIV risk among women involved in street-level prostitution. *Aggression and Violent Behavior, 10*(2), 153–170.

Rosario, M., Schrimshaw, E. W., & Hunter, J. (2011). Different patterns of sexual identity development over time: implications for the psychological adjustment of lesbian, gay, and bisexual youth. *Journal of Sex Research, 48* (1), 3–15

Roscoe, W. (2000). *Changing ones: Third and fourth genders in native North America*. New York: Palgrave Macmillan.

Rosky, C. J. (2009). Like father, like son: Homosexuality, parenthood, and the gender of homophobia. *Yale Journal of Law & Feminism, 20*, 257.

Ross, L. E. (2005). Perinatal mental health in lesbian mothers: A review of potential risk and protective factors. *Women & Health, 41*(3).

Rotermann, M. (2005). Sex, condoms, and STDs among young people. *Health Reports, 16*(3). Statistics Canada: Analytical Studies and Reports. Available: www.statcan.ca/english/ads/82-003-XPE/pdf/16-3-04.pdf

Rotermann, M. (2009). Trends in teen sexual behaviour and condom use. *Health Reports, 19*(3), 1–5.

Rotermann, M., & McKay, A. (2009). Condom use at last sexual intercourse among unmarried, not living common-law 20-to-34 year-old Canadian young adults. *The Canadian Journal of Human Sexuality, 18*(3), 75–88

Roughgarden, J. (2004). *Evolution's rainbow: Diversity, gender, and sexuality in nature and people*. Berkeley: University of California Press.

Rowland, D. L., & Incrocci, L. (2008). *Handbook of sexual and gender identity disorders*. Hoboken, NJ: Wiley.

Rubenson, B., Hanh, L. T., Höjer, B., & Johansson, E. (2005). Young sex-workers in Ho Chi Minh City telling their life stories. *Childhood: A Global Journal of Child Research, 12*(3), 391–411.

Rupp, H. A., & Wallen, K. (2009). Sex-specific content preferences for visual sexual stimuli. *Archives of Sexual Behavior, 38*(3), 417–426.

Rusbult, C. E., & Van Lange, P. A. M. (2003). Interdependence, interaction and relationships. *Annual Review of Psychology, 54*, 351–375.

Rushowy, K. (2008, February 22). Safe Schools Action Team to advise education ministry. *Toronto Star*.

Russell, S. T., Clarke, T. J., & Clary, J. (2009). Are teens "post gay"? Contemporary adolescents' sexual identity labels. *Journal of Youth and Adolescence, 38*, 884–890.

Rye, B. J. (2001, June). Sex differences in sexual attitudes and sexual behaviours of a sample of university students. Poster session presented at the annual Guelph Sexuality Conference, Guelph, ON.

Rye, B. J., Elmslie, P., & Chalmers, A. (2007). Meeting a transsexual person: Experiences within a classroom setting. *Canadian Online Journal of Queer Studies in Education, 3*(1), https://jps.library.utoronto.ca/index.php/jqstudies/article/viewFile/3269/1444

Rye, B. J., & Meaney, G. (2007). Voyeurism: It is good as long as we do not get caught. *International Journal of Sexual Health, 19*(1), 47–56.

Rye, B. J., & Meaney, G. (2008). Self-defence, sexism, and etiological beliefs: Predictors of attitudes toward gay and lesbian adoption.

Rye, B. J., Yessis, J., Brunk, T., McKay, A., Morris, S., & Meaney, G. (2008). Outcome evaluation of Girl Time: Grade 7/8 Healthy Sexuality Program. *The Canadian Journal of Human Sexuality, 17*(1–2), 15–36.

Sadalla, E. K., Kenrick, D. T., & Vershure, B. (1987). Dominance and heterosexual attraction. *Journal of Personality and Social Psychology, 52*, 730–738.

Saewyc, E., et al. (2009). Protective factors in the lives of bisexual adolescents in North America. *American Journal of Public Health, 94*, 110–117

Saewyc, E. M., Poon, C., Wang, N., Homma, Y., Smith, A., & The McCreary Centre Society. (2007). *Not yet equal: The health of lesbian, gay, & bisexual youth in BC*. Vancouver, BC: The McCreary Centre Society.

Saewyc, E. M., Skay, C. L., Pettingell, S. L., Reis, E. A., Bearinger, L., Resnick, M., et al. (2006a). Hazards of stigma: The sexual and physical abuse of gay, lesbian, and bisexual adolescents in the United States and Canada. *Child Welfare, 85*(2), 195–213.

Saewyc, E. M., Skay, C., Richens, K., Reis, E., Poon, C., & Murphy, A. (2006b). Sexual orientation, sexual abuse, and HIV-risk behaviors among adolescents in the Pacific Northwest. *American Journal of Public Health, 96*(6), 1104–1110.

Saewyc, E. M., Taylor, D., Homma, Y., & Ogilvie, G. (2008). Trends in sexual health and risk behaviours among adolescent students in British Columbia. *The Canadian Journal of Human Sexuality, 17*(1-2), 1–13.

Sagan, C., & Dryan, A. (1990, April 22). The question of abortion: A search for answers. *Parade Magazine*, 4–8.

Sagarin, B. J., Becker, D. V., Guadagno, R. E., Nicastle, D., & Millevoi, A. (2003). Sex differences (and similarities) in jealousy. The moderating influence of infidelity experience and sexual orientation of the infidelity. *Evolution & Human Behavior, 24*(1), 17–23.

Saleh, F. M. (2009). Pharmacological treatment of paraphilic sex offenders. In F. M. Saleh et al. (Eds.), *Sex offenders: Identification, risk assessment, treatment, and legal issue* (pp. 189–210). New York: Oxford University Press.

Salska, I., et al. (2008). Conditional mate preferences: Factors influencing preferences for height. *Personality and Individual Differences, 44*(1), 203–215.

Sand, M., & Fisher, W. A. (2007). Women's endorsement of models of female sexual response: the nurse's sexuality study. *Journal of Sexual Medicine, 4*, 708–719.

Sand, M., Fisher, W., Rosen, R., Heiman., J., & Eardley, I. (2008). Erectile dysfunction and constructs of masculinity and quality of life in the multinational men's attitudes to life events and sexuality (MALES) study. *Journal of Sexual Medicine, 5*(3), 583–594.

Sanders, T. (2005). "It's just acting": Sex workers' strategies for capitalizing on sexuality. *Gender, Work & Organization, 12*(4), 319–342.

Sangrador, J. L., & Yela, C. (2000). "What is beautiful is loved": Physical attractiveness in love relationships in a representative sample. *Social Behavior & Personality, 28*(3), 207–218.

Santtila, P., Sandnabba, N. K., Alison, L., & Nordling, N. (2002). Investigating the underlying structure in sadomasochistically oriented behavior. *Archives of Sexual Behavior, 31*(2), 185–196.

Saks, B. R. (2008). Common issues in female sexual dysfunction. *Psychiatric Times, 25*(5), 2.

Sarrel, P., & Masters, W. (1982). Sexual molestation of men by women. *Archives of Sexual Behavior, 11*, 117–131.

Savage, L. (2008, August 4). Stifling free speech globally. *Maclean's*, 26–29.

Save the Children. (2008). State of the world's mothers 2008. www.savethechildren.org/publications/mothers/2008/SOWM-2008-full-report.pdf

Savic, I., & Lindstrom, P. (2008). PET and MRI show differences in cerebral asymmetry and functional connectivity between homo- and heterosexual subjects. *Proceedings of the National Academy of Sciences, 105*(27), 9403–9408.

Savin-Williams, R. C. (2005). *The new gay teenager*. Cambridge, MA: Harvard University Press.

Savin-Williams, R. C. (2006). Who's gay? Does it matter? *Current Directions in Psychological Science, 15*(1), 40–44.

Savin-Williams, R. C., & Diamond, L. M. (2000). Sexual identity trajectories among sexual-minority youths: Gender comparisons. *Archives of Sexual Behavior, 29*(6), 607–627.

Sax, L. (2002). How common is intersex? A response to Anne Fausto-Sterling. *Journal of Sex Research, 39*, 174–179.

Schaller, S., & Træen, B. (2008). Attitudes toward pornography, self-esteem and feelings about sex in a longitudinal sample of Norwegian adolescents. *Sexologies, 17*(Suppl. 1), S148.

Schlichter, A. (2004). *Contesting "straights," "lesbians," "queer heterosexuals," and the critique of heteronormativity.* Binghamton, NY: The Haworth Press.

Schmitt, D., Shackelford, T., Duntley, J., et al. (2002). Is there an early-30s peak in female sexual desire? Cross-sectional evidence from the United States and Canada. *The Canadian Journal of Human Sexuality, 11*, 1–18.

Schmitt, D. P. (2003). Universal sex differences in the desire for sexual variety: Tests from 52 nations, 6 continents, and 13 islands. *Journal of Personality and Social Psychology, 85*(1), 85–104.

Schneider, J. P. (2005). Addiction is addiction is addiction. *Sexual Addiction & Compulsivity, 12*(2/3), 75–77.

Schneider, J.P. & Irons, R.R. (2001). Assessment and treatment of addictive sexual disorders: relevance of chemical dependency relapse. *Substance Use and Misuse, 36*, 1795–1820.

Schneider, M., Baker, S., & Stermac, L. (2002). Sexual harassment experiences of psychologists and psychological associates during their graduate school training. *The Canadian Journal of Human Sexuality, 11*, 159–170.

Schneidewind-Skibbe, A., Hayes, R. D., Koochaki, P. E., Meyer, J., & Dennerstein, L. (2007). The frequency of sexual intercourse reported by women: A Review of community-based studies and factors limiting their conclusions. *Journal of Sexual Medicine, 5*(2), 301–335.

Schmitt, M. T., Branscombe, N. R., & Postmes, T. (2003). Women's emotional responses to the pervasiveness of gender discrimination. *European Journal of Social Psychology, 33*(3), 297–312.

Schover, L. R., Fouladi, R. T., Warneke, C. L., Neese, L., Klein, E. A., Zippe, C., et al. (2004). Seeking help for erectile dysfunction after treatment for prostate cancer. *Archives of Sexual Behavior, 33*(5), 443–454.

Schrader, A. M., & Wells, K. (2007). *Challenging silence, challenging censorship: Inclusive resources, strategies and policy directives for addressing bisexual, gay, lesbian, trans-identified, and two-spirited realities in school and public libraries.* Ottawa: Canadian Teachers' Federation

Schrut, A. (2005). A psychodynamic (nonoedipal) and brain function hypothesis regarding a type of male sexual masochism. *Journal of the American Academy of Psychoanalysis and Dynamic Psychiatry, 33*(2), 333–349.

Schulheiss, D. Glina, S. (2010). Highlights from the history of sexual medicine. *Journal of Sexual Medicine, 7*(6), 2031–2043

Schultz, W. W., et al. (2005). Women's sexual pain and its management. *Journal of Sexual Medicine, 2*(3), 301–316.

Schröder, F. H., et al. (2009). Screening and prostate-cancer mortality in a randomized European study. *New England Journal of Medicine, 360*, 1320–328.

Schwartz, P., & Young, L. (2009). Sexuality Sexual satisfaction in committed relationships. Research and Social Policy: *Journal of NSRC, 6*(1), 1–17.

Sciolino, E., & Mekhennet, S. (2008, June 11). In Europe, debate over Islam and virginity. *The New York Times.*

Scott, J., & Humphreys, T. P. (2007, June). Parents as a source of sexual education for their physically disabled children. Poster presentation at the annual Guelph Sexuality Conference, Guelph, Ontario.

Secker-Walker, R. H., & Vacek, P. M. (2003). Relationships between cigarette smoking during pregnancy, gestational age, maternal weight gain, and infant birthweight. *Addictive Behaviors, 28*(1), 55–66.

Seidman, S. M. (2003). The aging male: Androgens, erectile dysfunction, and depression. *Journal of Clinical Psychiatry, 64*(Suppl. 10), 31–37.

Seligman, L., & Hardenburg, S. A. (2000). Assessment and treatment of paraphilias. *Journal of Counseling & Development, 78*(1), 107–113.

Semans, J. (1956). Premature ejaculation: A new approach. *Southern Medical Journal, 49*, 353–358.

Senn, C. Y., & Desmarais, S. (2001). Are our recruitment practices for sex studies working across gender? The effect of topic and gender of recruiter on participation rates of university men and women. *Journal of Sex Research, 38*(2), 111–117.

Senn, C. Y., & Desmarais, S. (2006). A new wrinkle on an old concern: Are the new ethics review requirements for explicit warnings in consent forms affecting the results of sexuality research? *The Canadian Journal of Human Sexuality, 15*(3–4), 123–132.

Senn, C. Y., Desmarais, S., Verberg, N., & Wood, E. (2000). Predicting coercive sexual behavior across the lifespan in a random sample of Canadian men. *Journal of Social & Personal Relationships, 17*, 93–115.

Servais, L. (2006). Sexual health care in persons with intellectual disabilities. *Mental Retardation and Developmental Disabilities Research Reviews, 12*(1), 48–56.

Servin, A., Nordenström, A., Larsson, A., & Bohlin, G. (2003). Prenatal androgens and gender-typed behavior: A study of girls with mild and severe forms of congenital adrenal hyperplasia. *Developmental Psychology, 39*(3), 440–450.

Seto, M. C. (2009). Pedophilia. *The Annual Review of Clinical Psychology, 5*, 391–407.

Seto, M. C., & Barbaree, H. E. (2001). Paraphilias. In V. B. Van Hasseit & M. Hersen (Eds.), *Aggression & violence: An introductory text* (pp. 198–213). New York: Allyn & Bacon.

Seto, M. C., Cantor, J. M., & Blanchard, R. (2006). Child pornography offenses are a valid diagnostic indicator of pedophilia. *Journal of Abnormal Psychology, 115*(3), 610–615.

Seto, M. C., & Eke, A. W. (2005). The criminal histories and later offending of child pornography offenders. *Sexual Abuse: A Journal of Research and Treatment, 17*(2), 201–210.

Seto, M. C., Maric, A., & Barbaree, H. E. (2000). The role of pornography in the etiology of sexual aggression. *Aggression and Violent Behavior, 6*, 35–53.

Seto, M. C., Maric, A., & Barbaree, H. E. (2001). The role of pornography in the etiology of sexual aggression. *Aggression and Violent Behavior, 6*, 35–53.

Sex Information and Education Council of Canada. (2010). *Sexual health education in the schools: Questions and answers.* Toronto: SIECCAN.

Sexual assault plea shortens sentence. (1994, June 1). *The Guelph Mercury.*

Seymour, A. (2008, August 29). Teacher found guilty of sexual assault low risk to re-offend, psychiatrist says. *The Ottawa Citizen.*

Shakespeare, T. (2000). Disabled sexuality: towards rights and recognition. *Sexuality and Disability, 18*, 159–166.

Shamloul, R. (2010). Natural aphrodisiacs. *Journal of Sexual Medicine, 7*, 39–49

Sharlip, I. (2005). Diagnosis and treatment of premature ejaculation: the physician's perspective. *Journal of Sexual Medicine, Supple. 2*, 103–109.

Shaughnessy, K., Byers, E.S. & Walsh, L. (2011). Online sexual activity experiences of heterosexual students: gender similarities and differences. *Archives of Sexual Behavior, 40*, 419–427.

Shaver, F. M. (1996a). Prostitution: On the dark side of the service industry. In T. Fleming (Ed.), *Post critical criminology* (pp. 42–45). Scarborough, ON: Prentice Hall.

Shaver, F. M. (1996b). The regulation of prostitution: Setting the morality trap. In B. Schissel & L. Mahood, *Social control in Canada* (pp. 204–226). Toronto: Oxford University Press.

Shaver, F. M. (2002, November). Prostitution portraits: A cautionary tale. Paper presented at the Annual Meeting of the Society for the Scientific Study of Sexuality, Montreal.

Shaver, F. M. (2005). Sex work research: Methodological and ethical challenges. *Journal of Interpersonal Violence, 20*(3), 296–319.

Shaver, F.M., Lewis, J. & Maticka-Tyndale, E. (2011). Rising to the challenge: Addressing the concerns of people working in the sex industry. *Canadian Review of Sociology, 48*(1), 47–65.

Shaw, J. (2007). Look in the phonebook under "A": Women's experiences in attempting to access abortion services in Canadian hospitals. Paper presented at the Guelph Sexuality Conference, Guelph, Ontario.

Shercliffe, R. J., Hamton, M., McKay-McNabb, K., Jeffery, B., Beattie, P., & McWatters, B. (2007). Cognitive and demographic factors that predict self-efficacy to use condoms in vulnerable and marginalized aboriginal youth. *The Canadian Journal of Human Sexuality, 16*(1–2), 45–56.

Sherwin, B. B., Gelfand, M. M., & Brender, W. (1985). Androgen enhances sexual motivation in females: A prospective, crossover study of sex steroid administration in the surgical menopause. *Psychosomatic Medicine, 47*, 339–351.

Shevell, T., et al. (2005). Assisted reproductive technology and pregnancy outcome. *Obstetrics & Gynecology, 106*, 1039–1045.

Shibley-Hyde, J., & Durik, A. M. (2000). Gender differences in erotic plasticity—Evolutionary or sociocultural forces? Comment on Baumeister (2000). *Psychological Bulletin, 126*, 375–379.

Shields, S. A., Wong, T., Mann, J., et al. (2004). Prevalence and correlates of chlamydia infection in Canadian street youth. *Journal of Adolescent Health, 34*(5), 384–390.

Shipko, S. (2000, February 7). Antidepressants linked to sexual side effects. WebMD/Healtheon. (Online).

Shirpak, K. R., Maticka-Tyndale, E., & Chinichian. (2007). Iranian immigrants' perceptions of sexuality in Canada: A symbolic interactionist approach. *The Canadian Journal of Human Sexuality, 16*, 113–128

Shorter, E. (2005). *Written in the flesh: A history of desire.* Toronto: University of Toronto Press.

Shoveller, J. A., Johnson, J. L., Langille, D. B., & Mitchell, T. (2004). Socio-cultural influences on young people's sexual development. *Social Science & Medicine, 59*(3), 473–487.

Siegfried, N., Muller, M., Deeks, J., Volmink, T. (2009). Male circumcision for prevention of heterosexual acquisition in men. *Cochrane Database System Review.* April 15; (2): cdoo3362

Silverthorne, Z. A., & Quinsey, V. L. (2000). Sexual partner age preferences of homosexual and heterosexual men and women. *Archives of Sexual Behavior, 29*, 67–76.

Singer, J., & Singer, I. (1972). Types of female orgasm. *Journal of Sex Research, 8*, 255–267.

Singh, D., Vidaurri, M., Zambarano, R. J., & Dabbs, J. M., Jr. (1999). Lesbian erotic role identification: Behavioral, morphological, and hormonal correlates. *Journal of Personality and Social Psychology, 76*(6), 1035–1049.

Sipski, M. L., Alexander, C. J., & Rosen, R. (2001). Sexual arousal and orgasm in women. *Annals of Neurology, 49*(1), 35–44.

Slane, A. (2009). Sexting, teens, and a proposed offense of invasion of privacy. Iposgoode: Intellectual Property Law and Technology Program. http://www.iposgoode.ca

Small, P. (2004, June 30). Used drug for sex assault. *The Toronto Star.*

Small, P. (2007, December 28). Teacher scarred by charges. *Toronto Star*, p. A10.

Smith, A., Saewyc, E., Albert, M., MacKay, L., Northcott, M., and The McCreary Centre Society. (2007). *Against the odds: A profile of marginalized and street-involved youth in BC.* Vancouver, BC: The McCreary Centre Society.

Smith, T. W. (1992). Discrepancies between men and women in reporting number of sexual partners: A summary from four countries. *Social Biology, 26*, 203–211.

Smith, Y. L. S., Van Goozen, S. H. M., Kuiper, A. J., & Cohen-Kettenis, P. T. (2005). Sex reassignment: Outcomes and predictors of treatment for adolescent and adult transsexuals. *Psychological Medicine, 35*(1), 89–99.

Smylie, L., Medaglia, S., & Maticka-Tyndale, E. (2006). The effect of social capital and socio-demographics on adolescent risk and sexual health behaviours. *The Canadian Journal of Human Sexuality, 15*(2), 95–112.

Smylie, L., et al. (2011). Pilot-test and validation of a set of indicators of sexual health among young people in Canada. Abstract presented at the 20th World Congress of Sexual Health, Glasgow, United Kingdom, June 12–16, 2011.

Soble, A. (2009). A history of erotic philosophy. *Journal of Sex Research, 46*(2), 104–120.

Society of Obstetricians and Gynaecologists of Canada. (2006). Sexuality and child development. SexualityAndU.ca. Ottawa: Society of Obstetricians and Gynaecologists of Canada. Retrieved from http://www.sexualityandu.ca/health-care-professionals/sexuality-and-child-development

Society of Obstetricians and Gynaecologists of Canada. (2008, June 25). Media advisories: Rising C-section rates add risks during childbirth and place excess strain on the healthcare system, warn. *Canadian obstetricians.* Available: www.sogc.org/media/advisories-20080625_e.asp

Sodroski, J., et al. (1998). *Nature.* Cited in Scientists uncover "key" to AIDS virus. (1998, June 18). The Associated Press CNN.

SOGC. (2006). Canadian consensus conference on menopause, 2006 update. *Journal of Obstetrics and Gynaecology Canada: JOGC, 171*, 57–59.

Solursh, D. S., et al. (2003). The human sexuality education of physicians in North American medical schools. *Journal of Impotence Research, 15*(suppl), 541–545

Sommerfeld, J. (2000, April 18). Lifting the curse: Should monthly periods be optional? MSNBC online.

Spark, R. F. (1991). *Male sexual health: A couple's guide.* Mount Vernon, NY: Consumer Reports Books.

Spitzer, R. L., et al. (1989). *DSM-III-R casebook.* Washington, DC: American Psychiatric Press.

Spencer, N. (2006). Explaining the social gradient in smoking in pregnancy: Early life course accumulation and cross-sectional clustering of social risk exposures in the 1958 British national cohort. *Social Science & Medicine, 62(5),* 1250–1259.

Sprecher, S. (2009). Relationship initiation and formation on the internet. *Marriage and Family Review, 45,* 761–782

Sprecher, S., Sullivan, Q., & Hatfield, E. (1994). Mate selection preferences: Gender differences examined in a national sample. *Journal of Personality and Social Psychology, 66(6),* 1074–1080.

Squier, S., & Littlefield, M. M. (2004). Feminist theory and/of science: Feminist Theory special issue. *Feminist Theory, 5(2),* 123–126.

Statistics Canada. (2002c). General social survey—Cycle 15: Changing conjugal life in Canada. [Catalogue No. 89-576-XIE].

Statistics Canada (2002d). Crime statistics in Canada, 2001. *Juristat, 22*(b). [Catalogue. No. 85-002XIE].

Statistics Canada (2003a). Sexual offences. *The Daily,* July 25. [online]. Available: www.statcan.ca/daily/English/050420/d050420a.htm

Statistics Canada. (2004a). *The Daily,* June 15. Canadian Community Health Survey. [online]. Available: www.statcan.ca/Daily/English/040615/d040615b.htm

Statistics Canada. (2004b). *Spotlight: Mixed unions.* [online]. Available: www.statcan.ca/english/freepub/11-002-XIE/2004/06/17404/17404_04p.htm

Statistics Canada. (2005g). Children and youth as victims of violent crime. *The Daily,* April 20. [online]. Available: www.statcan.ca/daily/English/050420/d050420a.htm

Statistics Canada. (2006b). Cervical cancer screening. (Catalogue No 89-503-XIE). Available: www.statcan.ca/english/freepub/89-503-XIE/0010589-503-XIE.pdf www.statcan.ca/Daily/English/071204/d071204a.htm

Statistics Canada. (2007b). Births and birth rate by province and territory. (Catalogue No. 91-213-X.). [online]. Available: www40.statcan.ca/l01/cst01/demo04b.htm

Statistics Canada. (2007c). Maternal employment, breastfeeding and health. Available: www.statcan.ca/Daily/English/070619/d070619d.htm

Statistics Canada. (2007g). Table 106-9002 – Pregnancy outcomes by age group, Canada, Provinces and Territories, annual, CANSIM (database).

Statistics Canada. (2008a, April). 2006 Census: Ethnic origin and visible minorities. [Catalogue No. 97-562-XCB2006004].

Statistics Canada. (2008d). Teen sexual behaviour and condom use 1996/1997 to 2005. *The Daily,* August 20. [online]. Available: www.statisticscanada.com/Daily/English/080820/d080820c.htm

Statistics Canada. (2009a). 2006 Census Analysis Series. http://www.statscan.ca

Statistics Canada. (2009b). Visible Minority Population by Age Group. (2006 Census). http://www.statscan.ca

Statistics Canada. (2010). Breast Feeding, 2009. http://www.statscan.gc.ca

Statistics Canada. (2010). University enrolment. *The Daily,* July, 14. www.statscan.gc.ca

Statistics Canada. (2011). 2006 Census: Portrait of the Canadian Population in 2006. http://www.statscan.ca

Stearns, V., Beebe, K. L., Iyengar, M., & Dube, E. (2003). Paroxetine controlled release in the treatment of menopausal hot flashes. *Journal of the American Medical Association, 289,* 2827–2834.

Stein, C. J., & Colditz, G. A. (2004). Modifiable risk factors for cancer. *Journal of Breast Cancer, 90(2),* 299–303.

Steinemann, S., & Steinemann, M. (2005). Retroelements: Tools for sex chromosome evolution. *Cytogenetic and Genome Research, 110,* 134–143.

Stephenson, K. R., & Sullivan, K. T. (2009). Social norms and general sexual satisfaction: the cost of misperceived descriptive norms. *The Canadian Journal of Human Sexuality, 18* (3), 89–105.

Sternberg, R. J. (1986). A triangular theory of love. *Psychological Review, 93,* 119–135.

Sternberg, R. J. (1988). *The triangle of love: Intimacy, passion, commitment.* New York: Basic Books.

Stewart, D.F. & Gajic-Veljanoski, O. (2005). Trafficking in women: The Canadian perspective. *Canadian medical Association Journal, 173(1),* 25–26.

Stockett, M. K. (2005). On the importance of difference: Re-envisioning sex and gender in ancient Mesoamerica. *World Archaeology, 37(4),* 566–578.

Storms, M. D. (1980). Theories of sexual orientation. *Journal of Personality and Social Psychology, 38,* 783–792.

Strager, S. (2003). What men watch when they watch pornography. *Sexuality & Culture: An Interdisciplinary Quarterly, 7(1),* 50–61.

Strassberg, D. S., & Holty, S. (2003). An experimental study of women's internet personal ads. *Archives of Sexual Behavior, 32(3),* 253–260.

Strebeigh, F. (2009). *Equal: Women reshape American law.* New York: Norton.

Strike, C., Myers, T., Calzavara, L., & Haubrich, D. (2001). Sexual coercion among young street involved adults: Perpetrators and victims' perspectives. *Violence and Victims, 16,* 537–551.

Symons, D. (1995, Cited in Goleman, D., June 14). Sex fantasy research said to neglect women. *The New York Times,* p. C14.

Stripe, T., Abracen, J., Stermac, L., & Wilson, R. (2006). Sexual offenders' state-of-mind regarding childhood attachment: A controlled investigation. *Sexual Abuse: A Journal of Research and Treatment, 18,* 289–302.

Sulak, P. J., et al., (2000). Hormone withdrawal symptoms in oral contraceptive users. *Obstetrics & Gynecology, 95,* 261–266.

Tafoya, T. (1997). Native gay and lesbian issues: The two-spirited. In B. Green (Ed.), *Ethnic and Cultural Diversity Among Lesbian and Gay Men. Psychological Perspectives on Lesbian and Gay Issues.* Thousand Oaks, CA: Sage Publications, (pp. 1–10).

Tamini, R. M., Hankinson, S. E., Chen, W. Y., Rosner, B., & Colditz, G. A. (2006). Combined estrogen and testosterone use and risk of breast cancer in postmenopausal women. *Archives of Internal Medicine, 166,* 1483–1489.

Tarone, R. E., Cho, K. C., & Brawley, O. W. (2000). Implications of stage-specific survival rates in assessing recent declines in prostate cancer mortality rates. *Epidemiology, 11(2),* 167–170.

Taylor, C. et al. (2011). *Every Class in Every School. The First National Climate Survey on Homophobia, Biphobia, and Transphobia in Canadian Schools. Final Report.* Toronto, ON: Egale Canada Human Rights Trust.

Taylor, M. J., Rudkin, L., & Hawton, K. (2005). Strategies for managing antidepressant-induced sexual dysfunction: Systematic review of randomised controlled trials. *Journal of Affective Disorders, 88(3),* 241–254.

Taylor, V., & Rupp, L. J. (2004). Chicks with dicks, men in dresses: What it means to be a drag queen. *Journal of Homosexuality, 46*(3–4), 113–133.

Ter Kuile, M. M., et al. (2009). Therapist-aided exposure for women with lifelong vaginismus: A replicated single-case design. *Journal of Consulting and Clinical Psychology, 77*, 149–159.

Tessler Lindau, S., Schumm, L., Laumann, E., & Levinson, W. (2007). A study of sexuality and health among older adults in the United States. *New England Journal of Medicine, 357*(8), 51–67.

Thigpen, T. W. (2009). Early sexual behavior in a sample of low income, African American children. *Journal of Sex Research, 46* (1), 67–79.

Thomas, R. M., & Murray, T. R. (2009). Sex and the American teenager: Seeing through the myths and confronting the issues. Lanham, MD: L & R Publishers.

Thompson, E. M., & Morgan, E. M. (2008). "Mostly straight" young women: Variations in sexual behavior and identity. *Developmental Psychology, 44*(1), 15–21.

Thompson, I. M., et al. (2005). Erectile dysfunction and subsequent cardiovascular disease. *Journal of the American Medical Association, 294*(23), 2996–3002.

Thompson, J. K., & Tantleff, S. (1992). Female and male ratings of upper torso: Actual, ideal, and stereotypical conceptions. *Journal of Social Behavior and Personality, 7*, 345–354.

Tiefer, L. (1996). The medicalization of sexuality: conceptual, normative, and professional issues. Annual Review of Sex Research, Vol. 7, 252–282

Tiefer, L. (2001). A new view of women's sexual problems: Why new? Why now? *The Journal of Sex Research, 38*, 89–96.

Timm, T.M. (2009). "Do I really have to talk about sex?" Encouraging beginning therapists to integrate sexuality into couples therapy. *Journal of Couple and Relationship Therapy, 8*, 15–33.

Tobian, A. A. R, et al. (2009). Male circumcision for the prevention of HSV-2 and HPV infections and syphilis. *New England Journal of Medicine, 360*, 1298–1309.

Totman, R. (2004). *The third sex: Kathoey: Thailand's ladyboys.* London: Souvenir Press.

Tracey, S. (2007, September 12). Man died during sex act. *Guelph Mercury*, p. A1.

Traish, A. M., Goldstein, I., Munarriz, R., & Guay, A. (2006). Roles of androgens in women's sexual function & dysfunction: What have we learned in sex decades? *Current Women's Health Reviews, 2*(1), 75–86.

Trenholm, C. et al. (2007). *Impact of Four Title V, Section 510 Abstinence Education Programs, Final Report.* Mathematica Policy Research Inc. Submitted to: U.S. Department of Health and Human Services

Trotter, E. C., & Alderson, K. G. (2007). University students' definitions of having sex, sexual partner, and virginity loss: The influence of participant gender, sexual experience, and contextual factors. *The Canadian Journal of Human Sexuality, 16*(1–2), 11–29.

Trudel, G., Turgeon, L., & Piche, L. (2000). Marital and sexual aspects of old age. *Sexual & Relationship Therapy, 15*(4), 381–406

Trulsson, O., & Rådestad, I. (2004). The silent child—Mothers' experiences before, during, and after stillbirth. *Birth: Issues in Perinatal Care, 31*(3), 189–195.

Trussler, T. et al. (2010). *MaCount Sizes-up the Gaps: A Sexual Health Survey of Gay Men in Vacouver.* Vancouver Coastal Health: Vancouver, B.C.

Tuomikoski, P., et al. (2009). Evidence for a role for hot flushes in vascular function in recently postmenopausal women. *Obstetrics and Gynecology, 113*(4), 902–908.

Tunariu, A. D., & Reavey, R. (2003). Men in love: Living with sexual boredom. *Sexual and Relationship Therapy, 13*(1), 63–94.

Turner, H. A., Finkelhor, D., & Ormrod, R. (2006). The effect of lifetime victimization on the mental health of children and adolescents. *Social Science & Medicine, 62*(1), 13–27.

Turton, J. (2005). Perspectives on female sex offending: A culture of denial. *Sexualities, 8*(5), 632–633.

Twist, M. (2005). Relationship therapy with same-sex couples. *Journal of Marital & Family Therapy, 31*(4), 413.

Udry, J. R. (2001). Feminist critics uncover determinism, positivism, and antiquated theory. *American Sociological Review, 66*(4), 611–618.

UNAIDS. (2006). Report on the global AIDS epidemic: executive summary. Joint United nations Programme on HIV/AIDS (UNAIDS). Geneva: UNAIDS

UNICEF. (2007). Child Poverty in Perspective: An Overview of Child Well-being in Rich Countries. *Innocenti Report Card 7.* Florence: Innocenti Research Centre.

U.S. National Library of Medicine. (2006). Androgen insensitivity syndrome. National Institutes of Health. http://ghr.nlm.nih.gov/condition-androgeninsensitivitysyndrome.

Vaculík, M., & Hudecek, T. (2005). Development of close relationships in the internet environment. *Ceskoslovenská Psychologie, 49*(2), 157–174.

Valentich, M., & Gripton, J. (1992). Gender-sensitive practice in sexual problems. *Canadian Journal of Human Sexuality, 1*, 11–18.

Valocchi, S. (2005). Not yet queer enough: The lessons of queer theory for the sociology of gender and sexuality. *Gender & Society, 19*(6), 750–770.

van Anders, S. M., & Hampson, E. (2005). Testing the prenatal androgen hypothesis: Measuring digit ratios, sexual orientation, and spatial abilities in adults. *Hormones and Behavior, 47*, 92–98.

van der Made, F., et al. (2008). Childhood sexual abuse, selective attention for sexual cues and the effects of testosterone with or without vardenafil on physiological sexual arousal in women with sexual dysfunction: A pilot study. *Journal of Sexual Medicine, 6*(2), 429–439.

van Lankveld, J. (2008). Problems with sexual interest and desire in women. In D. L. Rowland & L. Incrocci (Eds.), *Handbook of sexual and gender identity disorders.* Hoboken, NJ: Wiley.

VanderLaan, D. P., & Vasey, P. L. (2008). Mate retention behavior of men and women in heterosexual and homosexual relationships. *Archives of Sexual Behavior, 37*, 572–585.

van der Made, F., et al. (2008). Childhood sexual abuse, selective attention for sexual cues and the effects of testosterone with or without vardenafil on physiological sexual arousal in women with sexual dysfunction: A pilot study. *Journal of Sexual Medicine, 6*(2), 429–439.

Vandiver, D. M. (2006). Female sex offenders: A comparison of solo offenders and co-offenders. *Violence and Victims, 21*(3), 339–354.

Vanier Institute of the Family. (2010). *Families Count: Profiling Canada's Families.* Ottawa, ON: Vanier Institute of the Family.

Vannier, S. A., & O'Sullivan, L. F. (2010). Communicating interest in sex: Verbal and non-verbal initiation of sexual activity in young adults romantic dating relationships. Archives of Sexual Behavior, doi 10.1007/s/0508-010-9663-7.

van Straaten, I., Engels, R. C. M. E., Finkenauer, C., & Holland, R. W. (2009). Meeting your match: How attractiveness similarity affects approach behavior in mixed-sex dyads. *Personality and Social Psychology Bulletin, 35*(6), 685–697.

Vasey, P. L. (2002). Sexual partner preference in female Japanese macaques. *Archives of Sexual Behavior, 31*(1), 51–62.

Vasey, P. L., & Bartlett, N. H. (2007). What can the Samoan "faf'afafine" teach us about the Western concept of gender identity disorder in childhood. *Perspectives in Biology and Medicine, 50*(4), 481–490.

Vasey, P. L., Foroud, A., Duckworth, N., & Kovacovsky, S. D. (2006). Male-female and female-female mounting in Japanese macaques: A comparative study of posture and movement. *Archives of Sexual Behavior, 35*(2), 117–129.

Vervoort, D. (1999). Gay fathers coming out to their children: Reaching for integrity. Unpublished master's thesis, University of Guelph.

Vickerman, K. A., & Margolina, G. (2009). Rape treatment outcome research: Empirical findings and state of the literature. *Clinical Psychology Review, 29*, 431–448.

Villar, F., Villamizar, D. J., & López– Chivrall, S. (2005). Components of loving experience in old age: Older people and long-term relationships. *Revista Espanola de Geriatria y Gerontologia, 40*(3), 166–177.

Vo, C. (2001). Vietnamese immigrant gay men: Cultural and personal influences on sexual health. Unpublished master's thesis, University of Guelph.

Voeller, B. (1991). AIDS and heterosexual anal intercourse. *Archives of Sexual Behavior, 20*, 233–276.

Wade, T. J., Butrie, L. K., & Hoffman, K. M. (2009). Women's direct opening lines are perceived as most effective. *Personality and Individual Differences, 47*(2), 145–149.

Wainberg, M. A. (2009). Criminalizing HIV transmission may be a mistake. *Canadian Medical Association Journal, 180*, (6), 688

Waismann, R., Fenwick, P. B. C., Wilson, G. D., Hewett, T. D., & Lumsden, J. (2003). EEG responses to visual erotic stimuli in men with normal and paraphilic interests. *Archives of Sexual Behavior, 32*(2), 135–144.

Waldinger, M. D., Zwinderman, A. H., & Olivier, B. (2001). Antidepressants and ejaculation: A double-blind, randomized, placebo-controlled, fixed-dose study with paroxetine, sertraline and nefazodone. *Journal of Clinical Psychopharmacology, 21*(3), 293–297.

Walfish, S., & Mayerson, M. (1980). Sex role identity and attitudes toward sexuality. *Archives of Sexual Behavior, 9*, 199–204.

Walker, S. (2008). Women behind the camera for new breed of adult film. *Toronto Star*, April 4, 2008.

Ward, T., Gannon, T. A., & Birgden, A. (2007). Human rights and the treatment of sex offenders. *Sexual Abuse, 19*, 195–216.

Warren, W. K., & King, A. J. (1994). Development and Evaluation of an AIDS/STD/Sexuality Program for Grade Nine Students. Kingston, ON: Social Program Evaluation Group, Queens University

Waterman, J. (1986). Overview of treatment issues. In K. McFarlane et al. (Eds.), *Sexual abuse of young children: Evaluation and treatment* (pp. 197–203). New York: Guilford.

Watson, L. (2010). *Pornography. Philosophy Compass*, 5/7, 535–550.

Weaver, S. J., & Herold, E. S (2000). Casual sex and women: Measurement and motivations issues. *Journal of Psychology and Human Sexuality, 12*, 23–41.

Weber, B. (2001, January 10). No sex please, we're in the army. *The Toronto Star*, p. A3.

Weinberg, T. S. (1987). Sadomasochism in the United States: A review of recent sociological literature. *Journal of Sex Research, 23*, 50–69.

Weinrich, J. D., & Klein, F. (2002). Bi-gay, bi-straight, and bi-bi: Three bisexual subgroups identified using cluster analysis of the Klein Sexual Orientation Grid. *Journal of Bisexuality, 2*(4), 109–139.

Welldon, E. V. (2005). Incest: A therapeutic challenge. In Ambrosio, G. (Ed.), *On incest: Psychoanalytic perspectives* (pp. 81–100). London: Karnac Books.

Wells, C. (2009). Research exploring the health, wellness, and safety concerns of sexual minority youth. *The Canadian Journal of Human Sexuality, 18*(4), 221–229.

Wells, K. (2008). Generation queer: Sexual minority youth and Canadian schools. *Education Canada, 48*(1), 18–23.

Wente, M. (2005). What are kids up to? Don't ask? *The Globe & Mail.* Sept 20, 2005.

Wentland, J. (2006). Sexual pleasure orientation in heterosexual women. Unpublished master's thesis, University of Guelph.

Wentland, J. J., Herold, E. S., Desmarais, S., & Milhausen, R. R. (2009). Differentiating highly sexual women from less sexual women. *The Canadian Journal of Human Sexuality, 18*(4), 169–182.

Wentland, L., Muise, A., & Desmarais, S. (2010). Out with the old, in with the new: The new technologized dating script. Poster Presented at the 53rd annual Meeting of the Society for the Scientific Study of Sexuality, Las Vegas Nevada.

West, S. L., et al. (2008). Prevalence of low sexual desire and hypoactive sexual desire disorder in a nationally representative sample of US women. *Archives of Internal Medicine, 168*(13), 1441–1449.

Wheeler, B. (2006, December 23). Top 10 of 2006 Nelly Furtado. *The Globe and Mail*, p. R2.

Wheeler, J., Newring, K. A. B., & Draper, C. (2008). Transvestic fetishism: Psychopathology and theory. In D. R. Laws and W. T. O'Donohue (Eds.), *Sexual deviance: Theory, assessment, and treatment* (2nd ed., pp. 272–284). New York: Guilford Press.

White, R. G., et al. (2008). Male circumcision for HIV prevention in sub-Saharan Africa: Who, what and when? *AIDS, 22*(14), 1841–1850.

Widman, L., Welsh, D. P., McNulty, J. K., & Little, K. C. (2006). Sexual communication and contraceptive use in adolescent dating couples. *Journal of Adolescent Health, 39*, 893–899.

Wieselquist, J., Rusbult, C. E., Foster, C. A., & Agnew, C. R. (1999). Commitment, pro-relationship behavior, and trust in close relationships. *Journal of Personality & Social Psychology, 77*(5), 942–966.

Wilcox, A. J., Dunson, D., & Baird, D. D. (2000). The timing of the "fertile window" in the menstrual cycle: Day-specific estimates from a prospective study. *British Medical Journal, 321*, 1259–1262.

Wilkes, J. (2011). Police can detect computers accessing child porn. *Toronto Star*, March 9, 2011.

Williams, C. (2010). Economic well-being. *Women in Canada: A Gender-Based Statistical Report*. (6th ed.). www.statcan.gc.ca

Williams, C., Newman, P., Massaquoi, N., Brown, M., and Logie, C. (2007). Sisters, mothers, daughters and aunties: Structural barriers and opportunities for HIV prevention among Black women. Paper presented at the annual conference of the Canadian Association of HIV Research, Toronto, Ontario.

Williams, M. E. (Ed.). (2001). *Abortion: Opposing viewpoints.* Farmington Hills, MI: Greenhaven Press.

Wilson, J. M. B., Tripp, D. A., & Boland, F. J. (2005). The relative contributions of waist-to-hip ratio and body mass index to judgments of attractiveness. *Sexualities, Evolution & Gender, 7*(3), 245–267.

Wilson, R. J. (2005). Circles of support and accountability: 10 years and counting. Paper presented at World Congress of Sexology, Montreal.

Wilbur, C. J., & Campbell, L. (2010). What do women want? An interactionist account of women's mate preferences. *Personality and Individual Differences, 49*, 749–754.

Winer, R., Hughes, J., Feng, Q., O'Reilly, S., Kiviat, N., Holmes, K., & Koutsky, L. (2006). Condom use and the risk of genital human papillomavirus infection in young women. *New England Journal of Medicine, 354*, 2645–2654.

Winter, S. (2003). Research and discussion paper: Language and identity in transgender: Gender wars and the case of the Thai kathoey. Paper presented at the Hawaii conference on Social Sciences, Waikiki, HI.

Wittenberg, A., & Gerber, J. (2009). Recommendations for improving sexual health curricula in medical schools: Results from a two-arm study collecting data from patients and medical students. *Journal of Sexual Medicine, 6*, 362–368

Women warned about potential sex offender. (2008, August 3). *Toronto Star*, p. A3.

Woo, J. S. T., & Brotto, L. A. (2008). Age of first intercourse and acculturation: effects on adult sexual responding. *Journal of Sexual Medicine, 5* (3), p. 571–582.

Wood, D. (2005, August 18). Cambridge mother and son guilty of incest. *The Record*.

Wood, E. (2011). Government funds services for male victims of sexual abuse. *Guelph Mercury*, April 16, A6.

Wood, J. T. (2005). *Gendered lives: Communication, gender, and culture* (6th ed.). Belmont, CA: Wadsworth.

Woods, A. (2000, October 7). Lesbian bathhouse organizers charged. *The Toronto Star*, p. B1.

Wooten, J. M. (2008). Drug-induced sexual problems. *Southern Medical Journal, 101*(11), 1092–1093.

World Association for Sexual Health. (2008). *Sexual Health for the Millennium: A Declaration and Technical Document.* Minneapolis, MN: World Association for Sexual Health http://www.worldsexology.org/sites/default/files/Millennium%20Declaration%20(English).pdf

World Health Organization. (2008) Epidemiological fact sheets.

Wright, T. C. (2009). Natural history of HPV infections. *The Journal of Family Practice, 58*(9), 53–57

Wylie, K., & Eardley, I. (2007). Penile size and the small penis syndrome. *BJU International, 99* (6), 1449–1455.

Yates, P. M., Hucker, S. J., & Kingston, D. A. (2008). Sexual sadism: Psychopathology and theory. In D. R. Laws and W. T. O'Donohue (Eds.), *Sexual deviance: Theory, assessment, and treatment* (2nd ed., pp. 213–230). New York: Guilford Press.

Yeh, K-Y., Pu, H-F., Wu, C-H., Tai, M-Y., & Tsai, Y-F. (2009). Different subregions of the medial preoptic area are separately involved in the regulation of copulation and sexual incentive motivation in male rats: A behavioral and morphological study. *Behavioural Brain Research, 205*(1), 219–225.

Yela, C. (2006). The evaluation of love: Simplified version of the scales for Yela's tetrangular model based on Sternberg's model. *European Journal of Psychological Assessment, 22*(1), 21–27.

Yoder, V. C., Virden, T. B., III, & Amin, K. (2005). Internet pornography and loneliness: An association? *Sexual Addiction & Compulsivity, 12*(1), 19–44.

Yost, M. R., & Zurbriggen, E. L. (2006). Gender differences in the enactment of sociosexuality: An examination of implicit social motives, sexual fantasies, coercive sexual attitudes, and aggressive sexual behavior. *The Journal of Sex Research, 43*(2), 163–173.

Young, A. (2008). The state is still in the bedrooms of the nation. *The Canadian Journal of Human Sexuality, 17(4)*, 203–209.

Youthography Ping Survey. (February 2004). Canadian Youth (13–29). 1358 respondents.

Zaviacic, M., & Whipple, B. (1993). Update on the female prostate and the phenomenon of female ejaculation. *Journal of Sex Research, 30*, 148–151.

Zaviacic, M., et al. (1988a). Concentrations of fructose in female ejaculate and urine: A comparative biochemical study. *Journal of Sex Research, 24*, 319–325.

Zaviacic, M., et al. (1988b). Female urethral expulsions evoked by local digital stimulation of the G-spot: Differences in the response patterns. *Journal of Sex Research, 24*, 311–318.

Zeichner, A., Parrott, D. J., & Frey, F. C. (2003). Gender differences in laboratory aggression under response choice conditions. *Aggressive Behavior, 29*(2), 95–106.

Zernike, K. (2005, December 11). The siren song of sex with boys. *The New York Times.* [Online].

Zerubavel, E. (2006). *The elephant in the room: Silence and denial in everyday life.* New York: Oxford University Press.

Zielbauer, P. (2000, May 22). Sex offender listings on Web set off debate. *The New York Times* online.

Zosuls, K. M., et al. (2009). The acquisition of gender labels in infancy: Implications for gender-typed play. *Developmental Psychology, 45*(3), 688–701

Zucker, K. J. (2002). Intersexuality and gender identity differentiation. *Journal of Pediatric and Adolescent Gynecology, 15*(3), 3–13.

Zucker, K. J. (2005a). Gender identity disorder in children and adolescents. *Annual Review of Clinical Psychology, 1*(1), 467–492.

Zucker, K. J. (2005b). Gender identity disorder in girls. In D. J. Bell, S. L. Foster, & E. J. Mash (Eds.). *Handbook of behavioral and emotional problems in girls. Issues in clinical child psychology* (pp. 285–319). Kluwer Academic/Plenum Publishers.

Zucker, K. J., Beaulieu, N., Bradley, S. J., Grimshaw, G. M., & Wilcox, A. (2001). Handedness in boys with gender identity disorder. *Journal of Child Psychology and Psychiatry, 42*(6), 767–776.

Zucker, K. J., Bradley, S. J., & Sanikhani, M. (1997). Sex differences in referral rates of children with gender identity disorder: Some hypotheses. *Journal of Abnormal Child Psychology, 25*(3), 217–227.

Name Index

Subject Index

Photo Credits

Notes

Notes